Table entry for z is the area under the standard normal curve to the left of z.

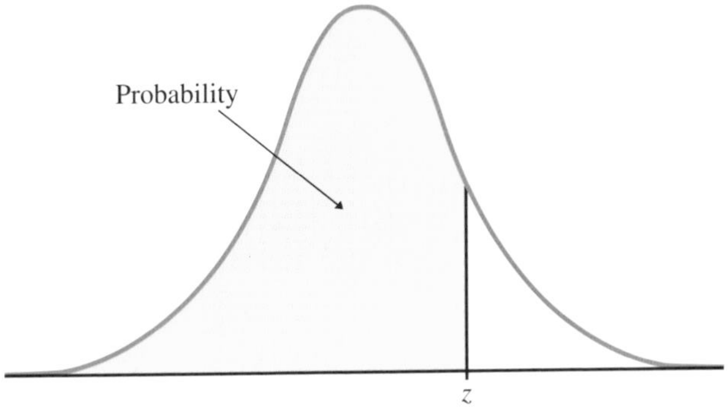

TABLE A **Standard normal probabilities** ***(continued)***

z	.00	.01	.02	.03	.04	.05	.06	.07	.08	.09
0.0	.5000	.5040	.5080	.5120	.5160	.5199	.5239	.5279	.5319	.5359
0.1	.5398	.5438	.5478	.5517	.5557	.5596	.5636	.5675	.5714	.5753
0.2	.5793	.5832	.5871	.5910	.5948	.5987	.6026	.6064	.6103	.6141
0.3	.6179	.6217	.6255	.6293	.6331	.6368	.6406	.6443	.6480	.6517
0.4	.6554	.6591	.6628	.6664	.6700	.6736	.6772	.6808	.6844	.6879
0.5	.6915	.6950	.6985	.7019	.7054	.7088	.7123	.7157	.7190	.7224
0.6	.7257	.7291	.7324	.7357	.7389	.7422	.7454	.7486	.7517	.7549
0.7	.7580	.7611	.7642	.7673	.7704	.7734	.7764	.7794	.7823	.7852
0.8	.7881	.7910	.7939	.7967	.7995	.8023	.8051	.8078	.8106	.8133
0.9	.8159	.8186	.8212	.8238	.8264	.8289	.8315	.8340	.8365	.8389
1.0	.8413	.8438	.8461	.8485	.8508	.8531	.8554	.8577	.8599	.8621
1.1	.8643	.8665	.8686	.8708	.8729	.8749	.8770	.8790	.8810	.8830
1.2	.8849	.8869	.8888	.8907	.8925	.8944	.8962	.8980	.8997	.9015
1.3	.9032	.9049	.9066	.9082	.9099	.9115	.9131	.9147	.9162	.9177
1.4	.9192	.9207	.9222	.9236	.9251	.9265	.9279	.9292	.9306	.9319
1.5	.9332	.9345	.9357	.9370	.9382	.9394	.9406	.9418	.9429	.9441
1.6	.9452	.9463	.9474	.9484	.9495	.9505	.9515	.9525	.9535	.9545
1.7	.9554	.9564	.9573	.9582	.9591	.9599	.9608	.9616	.9625	.9633
1.8	.9641	.9649	.9656	.9664	.9671	.9678	.9686	.9693	.9699	.9706
1.9	.9713	.9719	.9726	.9732	.9738	.9744	.9750	.9756	.9761	.9767
2.0	.9772	.9778	.9783	.9788	.9793	.9798	.9803	.9808	.9812	.9817
2.1	.9821	.9826	.9830	.9834	.9838	.9842	.9846	.9850	.9854	.9857
2.2	.9861	.9864	.9868	.9871	.9875	.9878	.9881	.9884	.9887	.9890
2.3	.9893	.9896	.9898	.9901	.9904	.9906	.9909	.9911	.9913	.9916
2.4	.9918	.9920	.9922	.9925	.9927	.9929	.9931	.9932	.9934	.9936
2.5	.9938	.9940	.9941	.9943	.9945	.9946	.9948	.9949	.9951	.9952
2.6	.9953	.9955	.9956	.9957	.9959	.9960	.9961	.9962	.9963	.9964
2.7	.9965	.9966	.9967	.9968	.9969	.9970	.9971	.9972	.9973	.9974
2.8	.9974	.9975	.9976	.9977	.9977	.9978	.9979	.9979	.9980	.9981
2.9	.9981	.9982	.9982	.9983	.9984	.9984	.9985	.9985	.9986	.9986
3.0	.9987	.9987	.9987	.9988	.9988	.9989	.9989	.9989	.9990	.9990
3.1	.9990	.9991	.9991	.9991	.9992	.9992	.9992	.9992	.9993	.9993
3.2	.9993	.9993	.9994	.9994	.9994	.9994	.9994	.9995	.9995	.9995
3.3	.9995	.9995	.9995	.9996	.9996	.9996	.9996	.9996	.9996	.9997
3.4	.9997	.9997	.9997	.9997	.9997	.9997	.9997	.9997	.9997	.9998

THE PRACTICE OF BUSINESS STATISTICS

THE PRACTICE OF BUSINESS STATISTICS

USING DATA FOR DECISIONS

SECOND EDITION

David S. Moore
Purdue University

George P. McCabe
Purdue University

William M. Duckworth
Creighton University

Layth C. Alwan
University of Wisconsin, Milwaukee

W. H. Freeman and Company
New York

Senior Publisher:	CRAIG BLEYER
Publisher:	RUTH BARUTH
Senior Acquisitions Editor:	TERRI WARD
Senior Developmental Editor:	BRUCE KAPLAN
Associate Editor:	LAURA CAPUANO
Media Editor:	ROLAND CHEYNEY
Assistant Media Editor:	BRIAN TEDESCO
Head of Strategic Market Development:	STEVE RIGOLOSI
Supplements Editor:	JULIE LINDSTROM
Photo Editor:	BIANCA MOSCATELLI
Senior Project Editor:	MARY LOUISE BYRD
Design Manager:	BLAKE LOGAN
Cover Designer:	BRIAN SHERIDAN
Text Designer:	LISA DOUGLIS
Production Coordinator:	PAUL W. ROHLOFF
Composition:	ICC MACMILLAN INC.
Printing and Binding:	RR DONNELLEY

Library of Congress Control Number: 2007938574

ISBN-13: 978-0-7167-8825-6
ISBN-10: 0-7167-8825-X

Printed in the United States of America

First printing

W. H. Freeman and Company
41 Madison Avenue, New York, NY 10010
Houndmills, Basingstoke RG21 6XS, England
www.whfreeman.com

BRIEF TABLE OF CONTENTS

The Core book includes Chapters 1–14. Chapters 15–18 are individual optional Companion Chapters.

TABLE OF CONTENTS

TO INSTRUCTORS: *About This Book*

Statistics is the science of data. ***The Practice of Business Statistics (PBS),*** second edition, is an introduction to statistics for students of business and economics that is based on that simple principle. Business statistics texts have tended to emphasize probability and inference. ***PBS*** reflects the current consensus among statisticians, in which data analysis and the design of data production join probability-based inference as major content areas.[1*] As the joint curriculum committee of the American Statistical Association and the Mathematical Association of America said, "Almost any course in statistics can be improved by more emphasis on data and concepts, at the expense of less theory and fewer recipes."

There are good reasons for giving more attention to data analysis and data production, along with a full treatment of inference. Data relevant to business decisions often represent complete populations for which data analysis rather than inference from sample to population is appropriate. Demographic data from the census for comparing several potential retail outlet locations have this nature, and the personnel files of a company include records for all employees. The currently hot topic of "data mining" combines the data analysis way of thinking with algorithmic advances that make exploration of immense data sets feasible. Moreover, because real data are often messy and inference requires clean data, data analysis is an essential preliminary to inference.

THEMES OF THIS BOOK

Look at your data is a consistent theme in ***PBS.*** Rushing to inference—often automated by software—without first exploring the data is the most common source of statistical errors that we see in working with users from many fields. A second theme is that *where the data come from matters.* When we do statistical inference, we are acting as if the data come from properly randomized sample or experimental designs. A basic understanding of these designs helps students grasp how inference works. The distinction between observational and experimental data helps students understand the truth of the mantra that "association does not imply causation." Moreover, managers need to understand the use of sample surveys for market research and customer satisfaction and of statistically designed experiments for product development, as in clinical trials of pharmaceuticals. Another strand that runs through ***PBS*** is that *data lead to decisions* in a specific setting. A calculation or graph or "reject H_0" is not the conclusion of an exercise in statistics. We encourage students to state a conclusion in the specific problem context, even though quite simple, and we hope that you will require them to do so. Finally, we think that a first course in any discipline should *focus on the essentials.* We have not tried to write an encyclopedia, but to equip students to use statistics (and learn more statistics as needed) by presenting the major concepts and most-used tools of the discipline. Longer lists of procedures "covered" tend to reduce student understanding and ability to use any procedures to deal with real problems.

---

[*] All notes are collected in the Notes and Data Sources section at the end of the book.

WHAT'S NEW IN THE SECOND EDITION

- **Co-author** We are delighted to welcome Professor Layth C. Alwan to *The Practice of Business Statistics* author team. Layth is currently Associate Professor in the Sheldon B. Lubar School of Business at the University of Wisconsin, Milwaukee. He specializes in Production and Operations Management and Quantitative Methods. An outstanding teacher, he received the EMBA Outstanding Teacher of the Year Award in 2003. With his research, teaching, and consulting experiences, he brings a valuable perspective to the team.
- **Exercises** The number of exercises has increased by 30 percent and many of the old exercises have been revised.
- **Ethics** Chapter 3 now contains a new section (Section 3.4) on ethics. We believe that this topic is a very important part of the undergraduate curriculum and that a course in statistics is an ideal forum to stimulate thought and discussion about ethical issues.
- **Regression and Statistics for Quality** Chapters 10, 11, and 12 have been substantially revised. New examples and exercises have been added. In response to reviewer comments, we have revised the exposition. We believe that the new versions of these chapters will be much more appealing to the students who use our text.
- **Software Appendices** Appendices have been added to each chapter giving detailed instructions on how to use Minitab and Excel to do the computing needed for the exercises.
- **Core Chapters** The new core text includes chapters 12 (Statistics for Quality), Chapter 13 (Time Series Analysis) and Chapter 14 (One-Way Analysis of Variance). This change has been made in response to reviewer comments.

CONTENT AND STYLE

PBS adapts to the business statistics setting the approach to introductory instruction that was inaugurated and proved successful in the best-selling general statistics texts *Introduction to the Practice of Statistics* (sixth edition, Freeman 2009) and *The Basic Practice of Statistics* (fourth edition, Freeman, 2007). Like these books, ***PBS*** features use of real data in examples and exercises and emphasizes statistical thinking as well as mastery of techniques. As the continuing revolution in computing automates most tiresome details, an emphasis on statistical concepts and on insight from data becomes both more practical for students and teachers and more important for users who must supply what is not automated.

Chapters 1 and 2 present the methods and unifying ideas of *data analysis.* Students appreciate the usefulness of data analysis, and that they can actually do it relieves a bit of their anxiety about statistics. We hope that they will grow accustomed to examining data and will continue to do so even when formal inference to answer a specific question is the ultimate goal. Note in particular that Chapter 2 gives an extended treatment of *correlation and regression* as descriptive tools, with attention to issues such as influential observations and the dangers posed by lurking variables. These ideas and tools have wider scope than an emphasis on inference (Chapters 10 and 11) allows. We think that a full discussion of data analysis for both one and several variables before students meet inference in these settings both reflects statistical practice and is pedagogically helpful.

Teachers will notice some nonstandard ideas in these chapters, particularly regarding the *Normal distributions*—we capitalize "Normal" to avoid suggesting that these distributions are "normal" in the usual sense of the word. We introduce density curves and Normal distributions in Chapter 1 as models for the overall pattern of some sets of data. Only later (Chapter 4) do we see that the same tools can describe probability distributions. Although unusual, this presentation reflects the historical origin of Normal distributions and also helps break up the mass of probability that is so often a barrier students fail to surmount. We use the notation $N(\mu, \sigma)$ rather than $N(\mu, \sigma^2)$ for Normal distributions. The traditional notation is in fact indefensible other than as inherited tradition. The standard deviation, not the variance, is the natural measure of scale in Normal distributions, visible on the density curve, used in standardization, and so on. We want students to think in terms of mean and standard deviation, so we talk in these terms.

In Chapter 3, we discuss *random sampling* and *randomized comparative experiments*. The exposition pays attention to practical difficulties, such as nonresponse in sample surveys, that can greatly reduce the value of data. We think that an understanding of such broader issues is particularly important for managers who must use data but do not themselves produce data. Discussion of statistics in practice alongside more technical material is part of our emphasis on data leading to practical decisions. In this second edition, we have added a section on data ethics, a topic of increasing importance for business manager.

Chapter 3 also uses the idea of random sampling to motivate the need for statistical inference (sample results vary) and probability (patterns of random variation) as the foundation for inference. Chapters 4 and 5 then present *probability*. We have chosen an unusual approach: Chapter 4 contains only the probability material that is needed to understand statistical inference, and this material is presented quite informally. Chapter 5 presents additional probability in a more traditional manner. *Chapter 4 is required to read the rest of the book, but Chapter 5 is optional.* We suggest that you consider omitting Chapter 5 unless your students are well prepared or have some need to know probability beyond an understanding of basic statistics. One reason is to maintain content balance—less time spent on formal probability allows full attention to data analysis without reducing coverage of inference. Pedagogical concerns are more compelling. Experienced teachers recognize that students find probability difficult. Research on learning confirms our experience. Even students who can do formally posed probability problems often have a very fragile conceptual grasp of probability ideas.[2] Formal probability does not help students master the ideas of inference (at least not as much as we teachers imagine), and it depletes reserves of mental energy that might better be applied to essentially statistical ideas.

The remaining chapters present *statistical inference,* still encouraging students to ask where the data come from and to look at the data rather than quickly choosing a statistical test from an Excel menu. Chapter 6, which describes the *reasoning of inference,* is the cornerstone. Chapters 7 and 8 discuss *one-sample and two-sample procedures,* which almost any first course will cover. We take the opportunity in these core "statistical practice" chapters to discuss practical aspects of inference in the context of specific examples. Chapters 9, 10, and 11 present selected more advanced topics in inference: *two-way tables* and *simple and multiple regression.* Chapter 12, 13, and 14 present additional advanced topics in inference: *quality control, time series forecasting, and one-way analysis of variance.*

Instructors who wish to customize a single-semester course or to add a second semester will find a wide choice of additional topics in the *Companion Chapters* that extend ***PBS.*** These chapters are:

Chapter 15 Two-Way Analysis of Variance

Chapter 16 Nonparametric Tests

Chapter 17 Logistic Regression

Chapter 18 Bootstrap Methods and Permutation Tests

Companion Chapters can be found on the book's companion web site: `www.whfreeman.com/pbs2e`.

One last comment on the style and content of ***PBS.*** We hope that the book presents an up-to-date picture of statistical practice, at least as far as such a picture is within the reach of beginners. Thus, for example, we encourage use of the version of the two-sample t procedures that does not assume equal population variances. We present the modified ("add two successes and two failures") confidence intervals for proportions that are now supported both by extensive simulation and by theory. We point out that p charts for process control are unsuitable for the high quality levels typical of modern manufacturing, but remain useful for many business processes. We include brief optional "Beyond the Basics" overviews of newer methods, such as density estimation, scatterplot smoothers, capture-recapture sampling, data mining, and the bootstrap.

ACCESSIBLE TECHNOLOGY

Any mention of the current state of statistical practice reminds us that quick, cheap, and easy computation has changed the field. Procedures such as our recommended two-sample t and logistic regression, not to mention the bootstrap and data mining, depend on software. Even the mantra "look at your data" depends in practice on software, as making multiple plots by hand is too tedious when quick decisions are required. What is more, automating calculations and graphs increases students' ability to complete problems, reduces their frustration, and helps them concentrate on ideas and problem recognition rather than mechanics.

*We therefore strongly recommend that a course based on **PBS** be accompanied by software of your choice.* Instructors will find using software easier because all data sets for ***PBS*** can be found in several common formats both on the Web (`www.whfreeman.com/pbs2e`) and on the CD-ROM that accompanies each copy of the book.

The Microsoft Excel spreadsheet is by far the most common program used for statistical analysis in business. Our displays of output therefore emphasize Excel, though output from several other programs also appears. ***PBS*** is not tied to specific software. However, appendices found at the end of most chapters provide general instructions for doing statistical procedures in Excel and Minitab. Even so, one of our emphases is that a student who has mastered the basics of, say, regression can interpret and use regression output from almost any software. Figure 2.14 (page 122) displays regression output from Excel, the Minitab statistical software, and the TI-83 graphing calculator to illustrate this point. Similar displays appear elsewhere in the book.

We are well aware that Excel lacks many advanced statistical procedures. More seriously, Excel's statistical procedures have been found to be inaccurate, and they lack adequate warnings for users when they encounter data for which they may give incorrect answers.[3] There is good reason for people whose profession requires continual use of statistical analysis to avoid Excel. But there are also good practical reasons why managers whose life is not statistical prefer a program that they regularly use for other purposes. Excel appears to be adequate for simpler analyses of the kind that occur most often in business applications.

Some statistical work, both in practice and in ***PBS,*** can be done with a calculator rather than software. *Students should have at least a "two-variable statistics" calculator* with functions for correlation and the least-squares regression line as well as for the mean and standard deviation. Graphing calculators offer considerably more capability. Because students have calculators, the text doesn't discuss "computing formulas" for the sample standard deviation or the least-squares regression line.

Technology can be used to assist *learning* statistics as well as *doing* statistics. The design of good software for learning is often quite different from that of software for doing. We want to call particular attention to the set of statistical applets available on the ***PBS*** Web site: `www.whfreeman.com/pbs2e`. These interactive graphical programs are by far the most effective way to help students grasp the sensitivity of correlation and regression to outliers, the idea of a confidence interval, the way ANOVA responds to both within-group and among-group variation, and many other statistical fundamentals. Exercises using these applets appear throughout the text, marked by a distinctive icon. We urge you to assign some of these, and we suggest that if your classroom is suitably equipped, the applets are very helpful tools for classroom presentation as well.

applet

CAREFULLY STRUCTURED PEDAGOGY

Few students find statistics easy. An emphasis on real data and real problems helps maintain motivation, and there is no substitute for clear writing. Beginning with data analysis builds confidence and gives students a chance to become familiar with your chosen software before the statistical content becomes intimidating. We have adopted several structural devices to aid students. Major settings that drive the exposition are presented as *cases* with more background information than other examples. (But we avoid the temptation to give so much information that the case obscures the statistics.) A distinctive icon ties together examples and exercises based on a case.

The *exercises* are structured with particular care. Short "Apply Your Knowledge" sections pose straightforward problems immediately after each major new idea. These give students stopping points (in itself a great help to beginners) and also tell them that "you should be able to do these things right now." Each numbered section in the text ends with a substantial set of exercises, and more appear as review exercises at the end of each chapter. Finally, each chapter ends with a few "Case Study Exercises" that are suitable for individual or group projects. Case Study Exercises are more ambitious, offer less explicit guidance, and often use large data sets.

DATA FILE NAMING CONVENTIONS

We use the following data file naming conventions throughout the text, CD-ROM, and website: 'ex' indicates exercise, 'eg' indicates example, 'ta' indicates table, 'ca' indicates case, 'cse' indicates case study exercise, and 'fg' indicates figure. Thus,

ex07_005	corresponds to	Exercise 7.5
ex07_002	corresponds to	Example 7.2
ta02_012	corresponds to	Table 2.12
ca02_001	corresponds to	Case 2.1
cse17_001	corresponds to	Case Study Exercise 17.1
fg02_006	corresponds to	Figure 2.6

ACKNOWLEDGMENTS

We are grateful to the many colleagues and students who have provided helpful comments about *Introduction to the Practice of Statistics* and *The Basic Practice of Statistics.* They have contributed to improving ***PBS*** as well. In particular, we would like to thank the following colleagues who, as reviewers, offered specific comments on ***PBS,*** second edition:

Radha Bose,
Florida State University
Bruce C. Brown,
Cal State Polytechnic Univ., Pomona
Howard R. Clayton,
University of Georgia
James Czachor,
Fordham University–Lincoln Center
Nicholas E. Flores,
University of Colorado
Dr. Guldem Gokcek,
New York University
Dr. Michael W. Hero,
University of Wisconsin–Milwaukee
Marlynne Beth Ingram,
The University of Iowa
Morgan Jones,
Kenan-Flagler Business School, UNC–Chapel Hill
Elias T. Kirche,
Florida Gulf Coast University
Paul Daniel Martin,
Pasadena City College
Elaine McGivern,
University of Pittsburgh
Scott Nicholson,
Stanford University
Thomas J. Page, Jr.,
Ohio State University
Dr. Dawn C. Porter,
Georgetown University
Krishan C. Rana,
Virginia State University
Deborah Rumsey-Johnson,
The Ohio State University
Lori E. Seward,
University of Colorado at Boulder
Paul Shaman,
The University of Pennsylvania, The Wharton School
Xiaofeng (Charlie) Shi,
Diablo Valley College
Alexandre Borges Sugiyama,
University of Arizona
Mark Tendall,
Stanford University
Elwin Tobing,
The University of Iowa
James S. Weber,
University of Illinois at Chicago

We also would like to thank the participants in an extremely useful focus group held at the University of Tennessee, Knoxville, and offer a special note of thanks to William Seaver for spearheading this focus group:

Kimberly Dawn Cooper,
University of Tennessee
Charles Cweik,
University of Tennessee
Jennifer Golek,
University of Tennessee
James Michael Lanning,
University of Tennessee
Derek M. Norton,
University of Tennessee
William L. Seaver,
University of Tennessee
Janna L. Young,
University of Tennessee
Russell Zaretzki,
University of Tennessee

We also want to thank the following colleagues who reviewed or class-tested the first edition of ***PBS:***

Mohamed H. Albohali,
Indiana University of Pennsylvania
Mary Alguire,
University of Arkansas
Andrew T. Allen,
University of San Diego
Djeto Assane,
University of Nevada–Las Vegas
Lynda L. Ballou,
Kansas State University
Ronald Barnes,
University of Houston–Downtown
Paul Baum,
California State University–Northridge
Vanessa Beddo,
University of California–Los Angeles
Dan Brick,
University of St. Thomas, St. Paul–Minnesota
Alan S. Chesen,
Wright State University

Siddhartha Chib,
Washington University
Judith Clarke,
California State University–Stanislaus
Lewis Coopersmith,
Rider University
Jose Luis Guerrero Cusumano,
Georgetown University
Frederick W. Derrick,
Loyola College, Maryland
Zvi Drezner,
California State University–Fullerton
Abdul Fazal,
California State University–Stanislaus
Yue Feng,
University of Oregon
Paul W. Guy,
California State University–Chico
Robert Hannum,
University of Denver
Erin M. Hodgess,
University of Houston–Downtown
J. D. Jobson,
University of Alberta
Howard S. Kaplon,
Towson University
Mohyeddin Kassar,
University of Illinois–Chicago
Michael L. Kazlow,
Pace University
Nathan R. Keith,
Devry University
John F. Kottas,
College of William and Mary
Linda S. Leighton,
Fordham University
Ramon V. Leon,
University of Tennessee–Knoxville
Ben Lev,
University of Michigan–Dearborn
Vivian Lew,
University of California–Los Angeles
Gene Lindsay,
St. Charles Community College
Richard N. Madsen,
University of Utah
Roberto S. Mariano,
University of Pennsylvania
David Mathiason,
Rochester Institute of Technology
B. D. McCullough,
Drexel University
John D. McKenzie, Jr.,
Babson College
Tim Novotny,
Mesa State College
Tom Obremski,
University of Denver
J. B. Orris,
Butler University
Steve Ramsier,
Florida State University
Stephen Reid,
BC Institute of Technology
Ralph Russo,
University of Iowa
Neil C. Schwertman,
California State University–Chico
Carlton Scott,
University of California–Irvine
Thomas R. Sexton,
SUNY–Stony Brook
Tayyeb Shabbir,
University of Pennsylvania
Anthony B. Sindone,
University of Notre Dame
John Sparks,
University of Illinois–Chicago
Michael Speed,
Texas A&M University
Debra Stiver,
University of Nevada–Reno
Sandra Strasser,
Valparaiso University
David Thiel,
University of Nevada–Las Vegas
Stephen Vardeman,
Iowa State University
Milan Velebit,
University of Illinois–Chicago
Raja Velu,
Syracuse University
Robert J. Vokurka,
Texas A&M University–Corpus Christi
Art Warburton,
Simon Fraser University
Jay Weber,
University of Illinois–Chicago
Rodney M. Wong,
University of California–Davis
Elaine Zanutto,
University of Pennsylvania
Zhe George Zhang,
Western Washington University

While she was a graduate student at Purdue, Betsy Hughes helped us by finding many interesting data sets used in the text. Thanks, Betsy.

The professionals at W. H. Freeman and Company, in particular Mary Louise Byrd, Bruce Kaplan, Terri Ward, Laura Capuano, and Katrina Wilhelm, have contributed greatly to the success of ***PBS.*** Most of all, we are grateful to the many people in varied disciplines and occupations with whom we have worked to gain understanding from data. They have provided both material for this book and the experience that enabled us to write it. What the eminent statistician John Tukey called "the real problems experience and the real data experience" has shaped our view of statistics. It has convinced us of the need for beginning instruction to focus on data and concepts, building intellectual skills that transfer to more elaborate settings and remain essential when all details are automated. We hope that users and potential users of statistical techniques will find this emphasis helpful.

David S. Moore
George P. McCabe
William M. Duckworth
Layth C. Alwan

MEDIA AND SUPPLEMENTS

FOR STUDENTS

NEW!

portals.bfwpub.com/pbs2e (Access code required. Available packaged with *The Practice of Business Statistics,* second edition, or for purchase online.) StatsPortal is the digital gateway to *PBS* second edition, designed to enrich the course and enhance students' study skills through a collection of Web-based tools. StatsPortal integrates a rich suite of diagnostic, assessment, tutorial, and enrichment features, enabling students to master statistics at their own pace. Organized around three main teaching and learning components:

- **Interactive eBook** offers a complete and customizable online version of the text, fully integrated with all of the media resources available with *PBS* 2e. The eBook allows students to quickly search the text, highlight key areas, and add notes about what they're reading. Similarly, instructors can customize the eBook to add, hide, and reorder content, add their own material, and highlight key text for students.
- **Resources** organizes all of the resources for *PBS* 2e into one location for the student's ease of use. Includes:
    - **StatTutor Tutorials** offer over 100 audio-multimedia tutorials tied directly to the textbook, containing videos, applets, and animations.
    - **Statistical Applets** offer 16 interactive applets to help students master key statistical concepts.
    - **CrunchIt! Statistical Software** allows users to analyze data from any Internet location. Designed with the novice user in mind, the software is not only easily accessible but also easy to use. CrunchIt! offers all the basic statistical routines covered in the introductory statistics courses and more. CrunchIt! is available via an access-code protected Web site. Access codes are available in every new copy of *PBS* 2e or can be purchased online.
    - **Stats@Work Simulations** put the students in the role of the statistical consultants, helping them better understand statistics interactively within the context of real-life scenarios. Students are asked to interpret and analyze data presented to them in report form, as well as to interpret current event news stories. All tutorials are graded and offer helpful hints and feedback.
    - **EESEE Case Studies** developed by The Ohio State University Statistics Department provide students with a wide variety of timely, real examples with real data. Each case study is built around several thought-provoking questions that make students think carefully about the statistical issues raised by the stories. **EESEE** Case Studies are available via an access-code-protected Web site. Access codes are available in every new copy of *PBS* or can be purchased online.
    - **Podcast Chapter Summary** provides students with an audio version of chapter summaries to download and review on their mp3 player.

- **Datasets** are available in ASCII, Excel, JMP, Minitab, TI, SPSS, and S-Plus formats.
- **Online Tutoring with SmarThinking** is available for homework help from specially trained, professional educators.
- **Student Solutions to Odd-Numbered Exercises** includes explanations of crucial concepts and detailed solutions to odd-numbered problems with step-by-step models of important statistical techniques.
- **Statistical Software Manuals** for TI-83/84, Minitab, Excel, JMP, and SPSS provide instruction, examples, and exercises using specific statistical software packages.
- **Interactive Table Reader** allows students to use statistical tables interactively to seek the information they need.

Resources (instructors only)

- **Instructor's Guide with Full Solutions** includes worked-out solutions to all exercises, teaching suggestions, and chapter comments.
- **Test Bank** contains hundreds of multiple choice questions.
- **Lecture PowerPoint slides** offering a detailed lecture presentation of statistical concepts covered in each chapter of *PBS*.

- **Assignment Center** organizes assignments and guides instructors through an easy-to-create assignment process providing access to questions from the Test Bank, Web Quizzes, and Exercises from *PBS* 2e. The Assignment Center enables instructors to create their own assignments from a variety of question-types for self-graded assignments. This powerful assignment manager allows instructors to select their preferred policies in regard to scheduling, maximum attempts, time limitations, feedback, and more!

Online Study Center: www.whfreeman.com/osc/pbs2e (Access code required. Available for purchase online.) The OSC includes all of the resources listed above, except for the Assignment Center.

Companion Web site: www.whfreeman.com/pbs2e Seamlessly integrates topics from the text. On this open-access Web site, students can find:

- **Interactive Statistical Applets** that allow students to manipulate data and see the corresponding results graphically.
- **Datasets** in ASCII, Excel, JMP, Minitab, TI, SPSS, and S-Plus formats.
- **Interactive exercises and self-quizzes** to help students prepare for tests.
- **Optional Companion Chapters 15, 16, 17, and 18** covering two-way analysis of variance, nonparametric tests, logistic regression, bootstrap methods and permutation tests.
- **Supplementary Exercises** for every chapter.
- **CrunchIt!** statistical software is available via an access-code protected Web site. Access codes are available in every new text or can be purchased online.

- **EESEE** case studies are available via an access-code-protected Web site. Access codes are available in every new text or can be purchased online.

Interactive Student CD-ROM: Included with every new copy of *PBS,* the CD contains access to all the content available on the Companion Web site, except for the optional Companion Chapters. CrunchIt! statistical software and EESEE case studies are available via an access-code-protected Web site. (Access code is included with every new text.)

Special Software Packages: Student versions of JMP, Minitab, S-PLUS, and SPSS are available on a CD-ROM packaged with the textbook. This software is not sold separately and must be packaged with a text or a manual. Contact your W. H. Freeman representative for information or visit `www.whfreeman.com`.

NEW! SMARTHINKING Online Tutoring: (Access code required.) W. H. Freeman and Company is partnering with SMARTHINKING to provide students with free online tutoring and homework help from specially trained, professional educators. Twelve-month subscriptions are available to be packaged with *PBS*.

Printed Student Solutions to Odd-Numbered Exercises prepared by Ellen Gundlach, Purdue University, offers students explanations of crucial concepts in each section of *PBS,* plus detailed solutions to key text problems and stepped-through models of important statistical techniques. ISBN: 0716728931

FOR INSTRUCTORS

The **Instructor's Web site** `www.whfreeman.com/pbs2e` requires user registration as an instructor and features all of the student Web materials plus:

- Instructor version of **EESEE** (Electronic Encyclopedia of Statistical Examples and Exercises), with solutions to the exercises in the student version, and CrunchIt! Statistical Software.
- The **Instructor's Guide,** including full solutions to all exercises in .pdf format.
- **PowerPoint slides** containing all textbook figures and tables.
- **Lecture PowerPoint slides** offering a detailed lecture presentation of statistical concepts covered in each chapter of *PBS*.
- **Full answers** to the **Supplementary Exercises** supplement on the student Web site.

Printed Instructor's Guide with Solutions

This printed guide includes full solutions to all exercises and provides additional examples and data sets for class use, Internet resources, and sample examinations. It also contains brief discussions of the *PBS* approach for each chapter.
ISBN: 0716730103

Test Bank

The test bank contains hundreds of multiple-choice questions to generate quizzes and tests. Available in print as well as electronically on CD-ROM (for Windows and Mac), where questions can be downloaded, edited, and resequenced to suit each instructor's needs.

Printed Version, ISBN: 0716728842
Computerized (CD) Version, ISBN: 0716728850

Enhanced Instructor's Resource CD-ROM: allows instructors to **search** and **export** (by key term or chapter) all the material from the student CD, plus:

- All text images and tables
- Statistical applets and data sets
- Instructor's Guide with full solutions
- PowerPoint files and lecture slides
- Test bank files

ISBN: 0716730316

Course Management Systems: W. H. Freeman and Company provides courses for Blackboard, WebCT (Campus Edition and Vista), and Angel course management systems. These are completely integrated solutions that you can easily customize and adapt to meet your teaching goals and course objectives. Upon request, we also provide courses for users of Desire2Learn and Moodle. Visit www.bfwpub.com/lmc for more information.

i-clicker is a new 2-way radio-frequency classroom response solution developed by educators for educators. University of Illinois physicists Tim Stelzer, Gary Gladding, Mats Selen, and Benny Brown created the i-clicker system after using competing classroom response solutions and discovering they were neither classroom-appropriate nor student-friendly. Each step of i-clicker's development has been informed by teaching and learning. i-clicker is superior to other systems from both a pedagogical and technical standpoint. To learn more about packaging i-clicker with this textbook, please contact your local sales rep or visit www.iclicker.com.

TO STUDENTS: *What Is Statistics?*

Statistics is the science of collecting, organizing, and interpreting numerical facts, which we call *data.*

We are bombarded by data in our everyday life. The news mentions imported car sales, the latest poll of the president's popularity, and the average high temperature for today's date. Advertisements claim that data show the superiority of the advertiser's product. All sides in public debates about economics, education, and social policy argue from data. A knowledge of statistics helps separate sense from nonsense in the flood of data.

An understanding of data is also a key skill for business managers. Market research that reveals consumer tastes guides development of products and services. Data from retail outlets, if looked at with understanding, can suggest better ways to position products in diverse markets. The success of new product lines or new advertising campaigns is assessed from data. Manufacturers improve their products and processes by using data on their quality and reliability. Monthly government data on unemployment, inflation, and economic growth influence strategic business decisions. The study of investment portfolios has become so heavily statistical that standard deviations and correlations appear even in mutual fund reports. If your company's personnel data appear to show that women or minorities are not fairly treated, you can expect a lawsuit that will require very thorough study of employee data. And don't forget that firms from General Motors to some of the world's largest banks have suffered losses of millions of dollars from fraud or unauthorized transactions that would have been obvious if managers (now former managers) had looked at the data presented to them.

UNDERSTANDING FROM DATA

The goal of statistics is to gain understanding from data. To gain understanding, we often operate on a set of numbers—we average or graph them, for example. But we must do more, because data are not just numbers; they are *numbers with a context* that helps us understand them. You hear that this month's unemployment rate is 6%. What does this number mean? Will it pose political problems for the party in power? Is it likely to reduce consumer spending and so reduce sales of your firm's products or services?

Much of the context rests on comparing this number with past data. An unemployment rate of 6% is somewhat high for the United States, where unemployment averaged 5.4% in the decade from 1993 to 2002. But 6% is low for Spain, where unemployment rates during the same decade ranged from over 10% to more than 22%. The president must worry about 6% unemployment in the United States, but a Spanish prime minister could win reelection for so low a rate.

The way variables are measured is also part of the context. A nation's unemployment rate is not a percent of all working-age people, but of the labor force—people who are available for work and looking for work. If public policy shrinks the labor force by offering early retirement pensions or making disability payments easily available, the unemployment rate will go down. Some European nations have done this. The context of a number also includes the methods used to produce it. Unemployment data in developed nations come from national sample surveys of households. That is, many households chosen by chance are asked about the employment status of all adults living there. This is superior to the older method of counting only people who signed up for unemployment benefits, which missed all those who were not eligible or didn't trouble to sign up.

When you do statistical problems—even simple textbook problems—don't just graph or calculate. Think about the context and state your conclusions in the specific setting of the problem. As you are learning how to do statistical calculations and graphs, remember that the goal of statistics is not calculation for its own sake but gaining understanding from numbers. The calculations and graphs can be automated by a calculator or software, but you must supply the understanding. This book presents only the most common specific procedures for statistical analysis. A thorough grasp of the principles of statistics will enable you to quickly learn more advanced methods as needed. On the other hand, a fancy computer analysis carried out without attention to basic principles will often produce elaborate nonsense. As you read, seek to understand the principles as well as the necessary details of methods and recipes.

THE RISE OF STATISTICS

Historically, the ideas and methods of statistics developed gradually as society grew interested in collecting and using data for a variety of applications. The earliest origins of statistics lie in the desire of rulers to count the number of inhabitants or measure the value of taxable land in their domains. As the physical sciences developed in the seventeenth and eighteenth centuries, the importance of careful measurements of weights, distances, and other physical quantities grew. Astronomers and surveyors striving for exactness had to deal with variation in their measurements. Many measurements should be better than a single measurement, even though they vary among themselves. How can we best combine many varying observations? Statistical methods that are still important were invented in order to analyze scientific measurements.

By the nineteenth century, the agricultural, life, and behavioral sciences also began to rely on data to answer fundamental questions. How are the heights of parents and children related? Does a new variety of wheat produce higher yields than the old, and under what conditions of rainfall and fertilizer? Can a person's mental ability and behavior be measured just as we measure height and reaction time? Effective methods for dealing with such questions developed slowly and with much debate.[1]

In the twentieth century, economics, finance, and the analysis of business decisions became heavily quantitative. Ideas and techniques that originated in the collection of government data, in the study of astronomical or biological measurements, and in the attempt to understand heredity or intelligence were used to describe national economies and to study investment portfolios. By this time, these ideas and techniques had come together to form a unified "science of data." That science of data—statistics—is the topic of this book.

THE ORGANIZATION OF THIS BOOK

Part I of this book, called simply "Data," concerns data analysis and data production. The first two chapters deal with statistical methods for organizing and describing data. These chapters progress from simpler to more complex data. Chapter 1 examines data on a single variable; Chapter 2 is devoted to relationships among two or more variables. You will learn both how to examine data produced by others and how to organize and summarize your own data. These summaries will be first graphical, then numerical, then, when appropriate, in the form of a mathematical model that gives a compact description of the overall pattern of the data. Chapter 3 outlines arrangements (called designs) for producing data that answer specific questions. The principles presented in this chapter will help you to design proper samples and experiments and to evaluate such investigations when you are presented with their results.

Part II, consisting of Chapters 4 to 8, introduces statistical inference—formal methods for drawing conclusions from properly produced data. Statistical inference uses the language of probability to describe how reliable its conclusions are, so some basic facts about probability are needed to understand inference. Probability is the subject of Chapter 4 and the optional Chapter 5. Chapter 6, perhaps the most important chapter in the text, introduces the reasoning of statistical inference. Effective inference is based on good procedures for producing data (Chapter 3), careful examination of the data (Chapters 1 and 2), and an understanding of the nature of statistical inference as discussed in Chapter 6. Chapters 7 and 8 describe some of the most common specific methods of inference, for drawing conclusions about means and proportions from one and two samples.

The six shorter chapters in Part III introduce somewhat more advanced methods of inference, dealing with relations in categorical data and regression and correlation. Your instructor may also choose to have you study one or more of the Companion Chapters found on the book's companion web site: `www.whfreeman.com/pbs2e`.

WHAT LIES AHEAD

The Practice of Business Statistics, second edition, is full of data. Many exercises ask you to express briefly some understanding gained from the data. In practice, you would know much more about the background of the data you work with and about the questions you hope the data will answer. No textbook can be fully realistic. But it is important to form the habit of asking, "What do the data tell me?" rather than just concentrating on making graphs and doing calculations.

You should have some help in automating many of the graphs and calculations. You should certainly have a calculator with basic statistical functions. Look for keywords such as "two-variable statistics" or "regression" when you shop for a calculator. More advanced (and more expensive) calculators will do much more, including some statistical graphs. You may be asked to use software as well. There are many kinds of statistical software, from spreadsheets to large programs for advanced users of statistics. The kind of computing available to learners varies a great deal from place to place—but the big ideas of statistics don't depend on any particular level of access to computing.

Because graphing and calculating are automated in statistical practice, the most important assets you can gain from the study of statistics are an understanding of the big ideas and the beginnings of good judgment in working with data. Ideas and judgment can't (at least yet) be automated. They guide you in telling the computer what to do and in interpreting its output. This book tries to explain the most important ideas of statistics, not just teach methods. Some examples of big ideas that you will meet are "always plot your data," "randomized comparative experiments," and "statistical significance."

You learn statistics by doing statistical problems. "Practice, practice, practice." Be prepared to work problems. The basic principle of learning is persistence. Being organized and persistent is more helpful in reading this book than knowing lots of math. The main ideas of statistics, like the main ideas of any important subject, took a long time to discover and take some time to master. The gain will be worth the pain.

INDEX OF CASES

INDEX OF DATA TABLES

BEYOND THE BASICS INDEX

ABOUT THE AUTHORS

David S. Moore is Shanti S. Gupta Distinguished Professor of Statistics, Emeritus, at Purdue University and was 1998 president of the American Statistical Association. He received his A.B. from Princeton and his Ph.D. from Cornell, both in mathematics. He has written many research papers in statistical theory and served on the editorial boards of several major journals. Professor Moore is an elected fellow of the American Statistical Association and of the Institute of Mathematical Statistics and an elected member of the International Statistical Institute. He has served as program director for statistics and probability at the National Science Foundation.

In recent years, Professor Moore has devoted his attention to the teaching of statistics. He was the content developer for the Annenberg/Corporation for Public Broadcasting college-level telecourse *Against All Odds: Inside Statistics* and for the series of video modules *Statistics: Decisions through Data,* intended to aid the teaching of statistics in schools. He is the author of influential articles on statistics education and of several leading texts. Professor Moore has served as president of the International Association for Statistical Education and has received the Mathematical Association of America's national award for distinguished college or university teaching of mathematics.

George P. McCabe is the Associate Dean for Academic Affairs and a Professor of Statistics at Purdue University. In 1966 he received a B.S. degree in mathematics from Providence College and in 1970 a Ph.D. in mathematical statistics from Columbia University. His entire professional career has been spent at Purdue with sabbaticals at Princeton, the Commonwealth Scientific and Industrial Research Organization (CSIRO in Melbourne (Australia), the University of Berne (Switzerland), the National Institute of Standards and Technology (NIST) in Boulder, Colorado, and the National University of Ireland in Galway. Professor McCabe is an elected fellow of the American Statistical Association and was 1998 Chair of its section on Statistical Consulting. He has served on the editorial boards of several statistics journals. He has consulted with many major corporations and has testified as an expert witness on the use of statistics in several cases.

Professor McCabe's research interests have focused on applications of statistics. Much of his recent work has been focused on problems in nutrition, including nutrient requirements, calcium metabolism, and bone health. He is author or coauthor of over 150 publications in many different journals.

William M. Duckworth specializes in statistics education, business applications of statistics, and design of experiments. He holds a B.S. and an M.S. from Miami University (Ohio) in mathematics and statistics and a Ph.D. in statistics from the University of North Carolina at Chapel Hill. His professional affiliations include the American Statistical Association (ASA), the International Association for Statistical Education (IASE), and the Decision Sciences Institute (DSI). He currently serves on the editorial board of the *Journal of Statistics Education* and has served as the ASA Editor for Statistics Education Web Content. Professor Duckworth was also a member of the Undergraduate Statistics Education Initiative (USEI) which developed curriculum guidelines for undergraduate programs in statistical science that were officially adopted by the ASA.

Professor Duckworth has published research papers and been invited to speak at professional meetings and at company training workshops. During his tenure in the Statistics Department at Iowa State University his main responsibility was coordinating, teaching, and improving introductory business statistics courses for over 1000 business students a year. He received the Iowa State University Foundation Award for Early Achievement in Teaching, based in part on his improvements to introductory business statistics. Professor Duckworth now teaches business statistics in the College of Business Administration at Creighton University.

Layth C. Alwan is an Associate Professor of Production/Operations Management and Quantitative Methods, Sheldon B. Lubar School of Business, University of Wisconsin-Milwaukee. He received a B.A. in mathematics, B.S. in statistics, M.B.A., and Ph.D. in business statistics/operations management, all from the University of Chicago, and an M.S. in computer science from DePaul University.

Professor Alwan is an author of many research articles related to statistical process control and business forecasting. He has consulted for many leading companies on statistical issues related to quality, forecasting, and operations/supply chain management applications. On the teaching front, he is focused on engaging and motivating business students on how statistical thinking and data analysis methods have practical importance in business. He is the recipient of several teaching awards, including Business School Teacher of the Year and Executive MBA Outstanding Teacher of the Year.

1.4 Occupational deaths. In 2004 there were 5703 job-related deaths in the United States. Among these were 659 deaths in agriculture-related jobs (including forestry, fishing, and hunting), 152 in mining, 1224 in construction, 459 in manufacturing, 880 in transportation and public utilities, 203 in wholesale trade, 372 in retail trade, 115 in finance-related jobs (including insurance and real estate), 1054 in service-related jobs, and 526 in government jobs.[5]

(a) Find the percent of occupational deaths for each of these job categories, rounded to the nearest whole percent. What percent of job-related deaths were in categories not listed above?

(b) Make a well-labeled bar graph of the distribution of occupational deaths. Be sure to include an "other occupations" bar.

(c) Make a well-labeled Pareto chart of these data. What percent of all occupational deaths are accounted for by the first three categories in your Pareto chart?

(d) Would it also be correct to use a pie chart to display these data? Explain your answer.

Quantitative variables: histograms

histogram

Quantitative variables often take many values. A graph of the distribution is clearer if nearby values are grouped together. The most common graph of the distribution of a single quantitative variable is a **histogram.**

CASE 1.1  **STATE UNEMPLOYMENT RATES**

Each month the Bureau of Labor Statistics (BLS) announces the *unemployment rate* for the previous month. Unemployment rates are economically important and politically sensitive. Unemployment may of course differ greatly among the states because types of work are unevenly distributed across the country. Table 1.1 presents the unemployment rates for each of the 50 states and Puerto Rico in December 2004. We will examine these data in detail, starting with the nature of the variable recorded.

What does it mean to be "unemployed" in the eyes of the government? People who are not available for work (retired people, for example, or students who do not want to work while in school) should not be counted as unemployed just because they don't have a job. To be unemployed, a person must first be in the *labor force*. That is, she must be available for work and looking for work. The unemployment rate is

$$\text{unemployment rate} = \frac{\text{number of people unemployed}}{\text{number of people in the labor force}}$$

To complete the exact definition of the unemployment rate, the BLS has very detailed descriptions of what it means to be "in the labor force" and what it means to be "employed." For example, if you are on strike but expect to return to the same job, you count as employed. If you are not working and did not look for work in the last two weeks, you are not in the labor force. So people who say they want to work but are too discouraged to keep looking for a job don't count as unemployed. The details matter. The official unemployment rate would be different if the government used a different definition of unemployment.

To understand the unemployment situation in December 2004, we begin with a graph.

TABLE 1.1 Unemployment rates by state, December 2004

State	Percent	State	Percent	State	Percent
Alabama	5.4	Louisiana	5.6	Ohio	5.9
Alaska	7.3	Maine	4.7	Oklahoma	4.2
Arizona	4.2	Maryland	4.0	Oregon	6.8
Arkansas	5.6	Massachusetts	4.6	Pennsylvania	5.6
California	5.8	Michigan	7.3	Puerto Rico	11.2
Colorado	5.1	Minnesota	4.4	Rhode Island	4.6
Connecticut	4.3	Mississippi	6.4	South Carolina	6.7
Delaware	4.1	Missouri	5.5	South Dakota	3.3
Florida	4.5	Montana	3.7	Tennessee	5.2
Georgia	4.4	Nebraska	3.6	Texas	5.8
Hawaii	3.0	Nevada	3.8	Utah	4.4
Idaho	4.0	New Hampshire	3.3	Vermont	3.4
Illinois	5.8	New Jersey	4.2	Virginia	3.3
Indiana	5.1	New Mexico	5.2	Washington	5.8
Iowa	4.7	New York	5.3	West Virginia	4.9
Kansas	4.6	North Carolina	5.2	Wisconsin	4.6
Kentucky	4.5	North Dakota	3.2	Wyoming	3.3

EXAMPLE 1.3 A Histogram of State Unemployment Rates

CASE 1.1

To make a histogram of the data in Table 1.1, proceed as follows.

Step 1. Divide the range of the data into classes of equal width. The unemployment rates range from 3.0% to 11.2%, so we choose as our classes

$$3.0 \le \text{unemployment rate} < 4.0$$
$$4.0 \le \text{unemployment rate} < 5.0$$
$$\vdots$$
$$11.0 \le \text{unemployment rate} < 12.0$$

Be sure to specify the classes precisely so that each individual falls into exactly one class. An unemployment rate of 3.9% would fall into the first class, but 4.0% falls into the second.

Step 2. Count the number of individuals in each class. Here are the counts:

Class	Count	Class	Count
3.0 to 4.0	10	8.0 to 9.0	0
4.0 to 5.0	19	9.0 to 10.0	0
5.0 to 6.0	16	10.0 to 11.0	0
6.0 to 7.0	3	11.0 to 12.0	1
7.0 to 8.0	2		

Step 3. Draw the histogram. Mark on the horizontal axis the scale for the variable whose distribution you are displaying. The variable is "unemployment rate" in this example. The scale runs from 3 to 12 to span the data. The vertical axis contains the scale of counts. Each bar represents a class. The base of the bar covers the class, and the bar height is the class count. Notice that the scale on the vertical axis runs from 0 to 20 to accommodate the tallest bar, which has a height of 19. There is no horizontal space between the bars unless a class is empty, so that its bar has height zero. Figure 1.2(a) is our histogram.

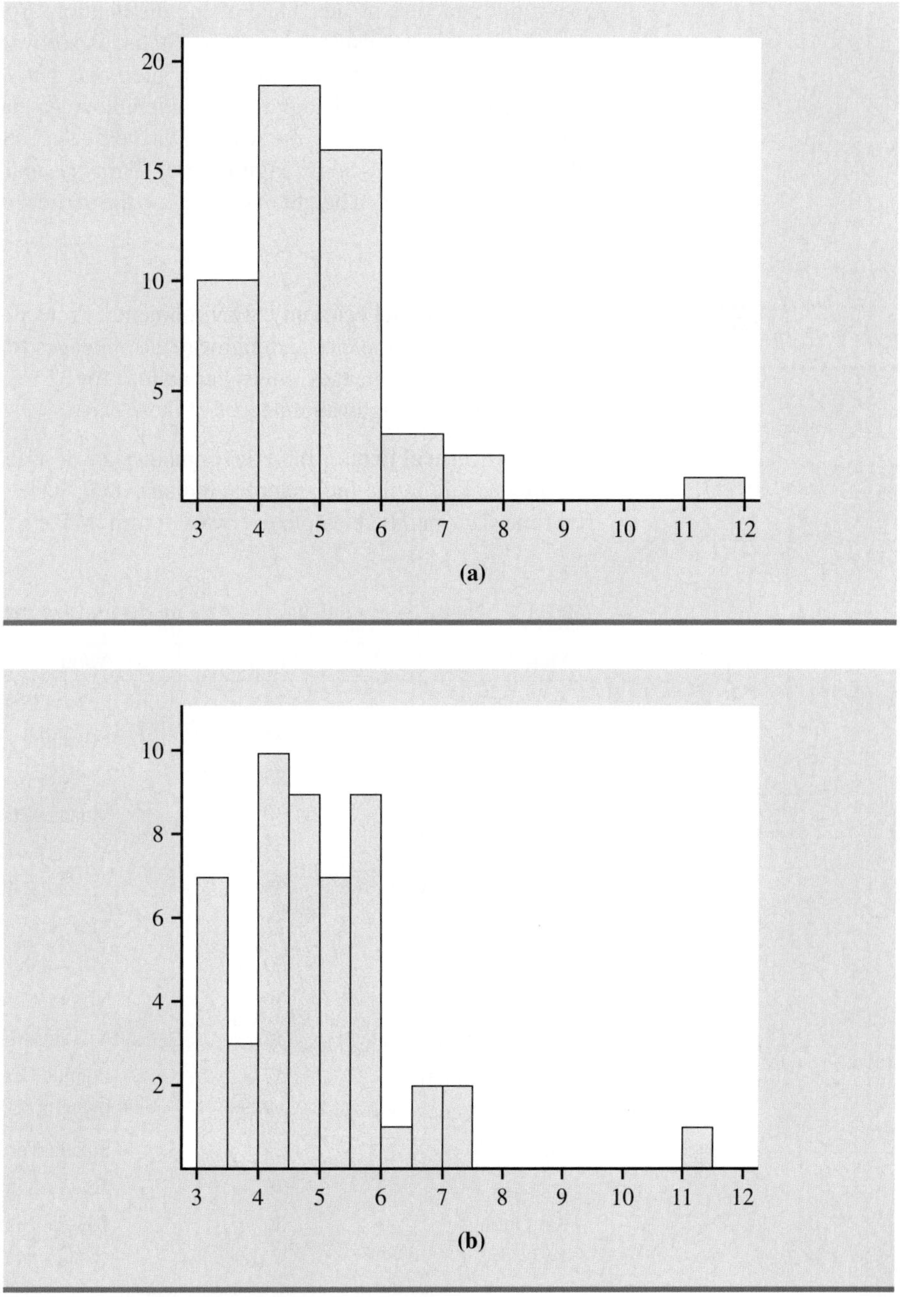

FIGURE 1.2 Histograms of the December 2004 unemployment rates in the 50 states and Puerto Rico, from Table 1.1. The two graphs differ only in the number of classes used.

The bars of a histogram should cover the entire range of values of a variable, with no space between bars unless a class is empty. When the possible values of a variable have gaps between them, extend the bases of the bars to meet halfway between two adjacent possible values. For example, in a histogram of the ages in years of university faculty, the bars representing 25 to 29 years and 30 to 34 years would meet at 29.5.

Our eyes respond to the *area* of the bars in a histogram.[6] Because the classes are all the same width, area is determined by height and all classes are fairly represented. There is no one right choice of the classes in a histogram. Too few classes will give a "skyscraper" graph, with all values in a few classes with tall bars. Too many will produce a "pancake" graph, with most classes having one or no observations. Neither choice will give a good picture of the shape of the distribution. You must use your judgment in choosing classes to display the shape. Statistics software will choose the classes for you. The computer's choice is usually a good one, but you can change it if you want. Figure 1.2(b) is another histogram of the unemployment data, with classes half as wide as in Figure 1.2(a). Notice that the scale on the vertical axis in Figure 1.2(b) runs from 0 to 10, unlike the vertical scale in Figure 1.2(a). With the smaller class sizes in Figure 1.2(b), the tallest bar now has a height of only 10, so the vertical axis need not extend to 20 as in Figure 1.2(a).

APPLY YOUR KNOWLEDGE

1.5 Automobile fuel economy. Environmental Protection Agency regulations require automakers to give the city and highway gas mileages for each model of car. Table 1.2 gives the highway mileages (miles per gallon) for 32 midsize 2006 model cars.[7] Make a histogram of the highway mileages of these cars.

1.6 Architectural firms. Table 1.3 contains data describing firms engaged in commercial architecture in the Indianapolis, Indiana, area.[8] One of the variables is the count of full-time staff members employed by each firm. Make a histogram of the staff counts.

TABLE 1.2 Highway gas mileage for 2006 model midsize cars

Model	MPG	Model	MPG
Acura 3.5RL	26	Lexus GS300	30
Audi A6 Quattro	27	Lincoln-Mercury LS	25
BMW 550I	23	Lincoln-Mercury Milan	32
Buick Allure	30	Mazda 626	32
Cadillac CTS	27	Mercedes-Benz E320	37
Cadillac STS AWD	25	Mercedes-Benz E350	27
Chevrolet Malibu	32	Mercedes-Benz E55 AMG	21
Chrysler Sebring	30	Mitsubishi Galant	30
Dodge Stratus	30	Nissan Altima	29
Honda Accord	34	Nissan Maxima	28
Hyundai Elantra	32	Pontiac Grand Prix	28
Jaguar S	28	Rolls-Royce Phantom	19
Jaguar S/R	23	Suzuki Verona	27
Jaguar X	26	Toyota Camry	34
Kia Optima	30	Toyota Prius	51
Kia Spectra	34	Volvo S80	30

TABLE 1.3 Indianapolis architectural firms

Name	1998 Total billings ($ millions)	1998 Arch. billings ($ millions)	1997 Arch. billings ($ millions)	Architects	Engineers	Staff
Schmidt Associates	11.5	11.5	5.0	19	7	111
CSO Architects	12.6	9.3	8.8	29	12	126
BSA Design	13.8	9.0	7.5	31	21	155
InterDesign Group	6.4	6.4	4.7	19	3	57
Browning Day Mullins	8.5	6.2	3.9	24	0	70
Ratio Architects	7.8	6.2	5.6	21	0	68
Odle McGuire	8.3	4.2	4.1	9	2	62
Gibraltar	5.8	3.6	4.2	12	4	52
American Consulting	12.0	3.5	3.3	5	23	131
Fanning/Howey	5.3	3.5	3.8	12	4	61
HNTB Corporation	15.0	3.4	3.0	10	35	110
SchenkelSchultz	2.7	2.7	2.5	5	0	22
Simmons & Associates	2.2	2.2	2.4	2	1	13
Paul I. Cripe	7.5	2.1	1.7	5	13	115
Plus4 Architects	2.7	2.1	2.0	5	0	15
Architectural Alliance	2.0	2.0	1.2	4	0	14
Blackburn Architects	2.6	1.8	1.5	8	1	24
Snapp & Associates	1.8	1.8	1.4	3	1	7
Sebree & Associates	1.7	1.7	1.0	3	0	15
Armstrong & Associates	9.1	1.6	2.4	3	23	96
Lamson & Condon	1.6	1.6	2.0	4	0	17
RQAW	6.3	1.6	2.3	6	14	72
Woollen Molzan	1.6	1.6	1.3	5	0	15
United Consulting	7.0	1.3	0.7	2	12	70
URS Greiner Woodward	1.7	1.3	0.9	5	1	17

Interpreting histograms

Making a statistical graph is not an end in itself. The purpose of the graph is to help us understand the data. After you make a graph, always ask, "What do I see?" Once you have displayed a distribution, you can see its important features as follows.

Examining a Distribution

In any graph of data, look for the **overall pattern** and for striking **deviations** from that pattern.

You can describe the overall pattern of a histogram by its **shape, center,** and **spread.**

An important kind of deviation is an **outlier,** an individual value that falls outside the overall pattern.

We will learn how to describe center and spread numerically in Section 1.2. For now, we can describe the center of a distribution by its *midpoint,* the value with roughly half the observations taking smaller values and half taking larger values. We can describe the spread of a distribution by giving the *smallest and largest values.*

EXAMPLE 1.4 The Distribution of Unemployment Rates

CASE 1.1

Look again at the histogram in Figure 1.2(a). The first feature we notice is an *outlier.* Puerto Rico has much higher unemployment (11.2%) than any of the 50 states. Some outliers are due to mistakes, such as typing 1.2 as 11.2. Other outliers point to the special nature of some observations. Although Puerto Rico is included in the government report from which we took the unemployment data, it is not a state and we should omit it when thinking about domestic unemployment.

Shape: The distribution has a *single peak.* Even omitting the outlier, the histogram is somewhat *right-skewed*—that is, the right tail extends farther from the peak than does the left tail. The states with unemployment rates at or higher than 6% are Alaska, Michigan, Mississippi, Oregon, and South Carolina. Some of these states are often near the top in unemployment due to generally weak job opportunities. Note that winter weather does not explain high unemployment in Alaska, Michigan, and Oregon—the data are *seasonally adjusted* to compensate for regular changes such as job losses in the winter months in northern states. **Center:** The midpoint of the 51 observations is near the center of the single peak, at about 4.6%.

Spread: The spread is 3.0% to 7.3% if we ignore Puerto Rico.

When you describe a distribution, concentrate on the main features. Look for major peaks, not for minor ups and downs in the bars of the histogram. Look for clear outliers, not just for the smallest and largest observations. Look for rough *symmetry* or clear *skewness.*

Symmetric and Skewed Distributions

A distribution is **symmetric** if the right and left sides of the histogram are approximately mirror images of each other.

A distribution is **skewed to the right** if the right side of the histogram (containing the half of the observations with larger values) extends much farther out than the left side. It is **skewed to the left** if the left side of the histogram extends much farther out than the right side.

EXAMPLE 1.5 Major League Baseball Salaries

Figure 1.3 displays a histogram of the average salaries (in millions of dollars) for players on the 30 Major League Baseball teams as of opening day of the 2000 season. The distribution has a single peak between 2.0 and 2.5 million dollars and falls off on either side of this peak. The two sides of the histogram are roughly the same shape, so we call the distribution *symmetric.*

In mathematics, symmetry means that the two sides of a figure like a histogram are exact mirror images of each other. Data are almost never exactly symmetric, but we are willing to call histograms like that in Figure 1.3 "approximately symmetric" as an overall description.

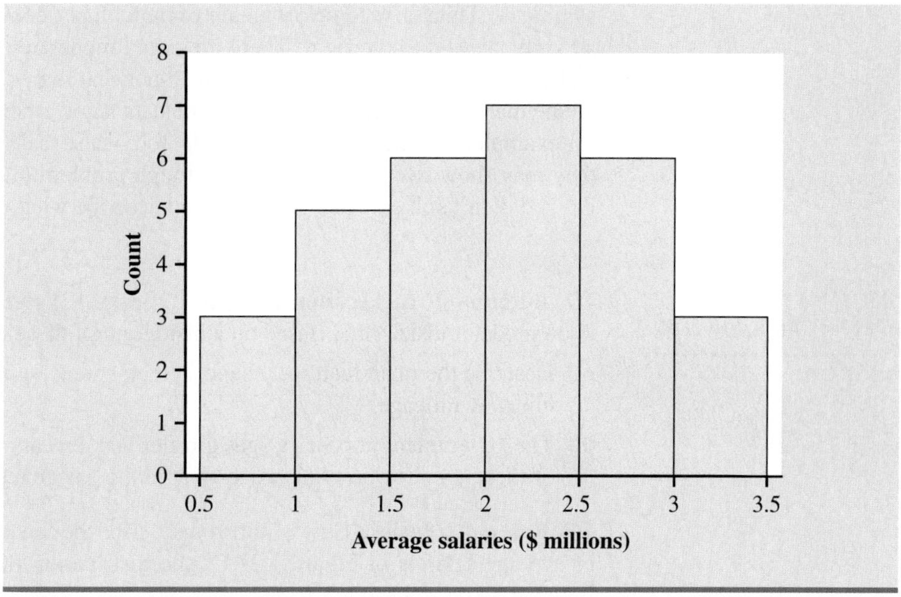

FIGURE 1.3 The distribution of the average salaries for the 30 Major League Baseball teams on opening day of the 2000 season, for Example 1.5.

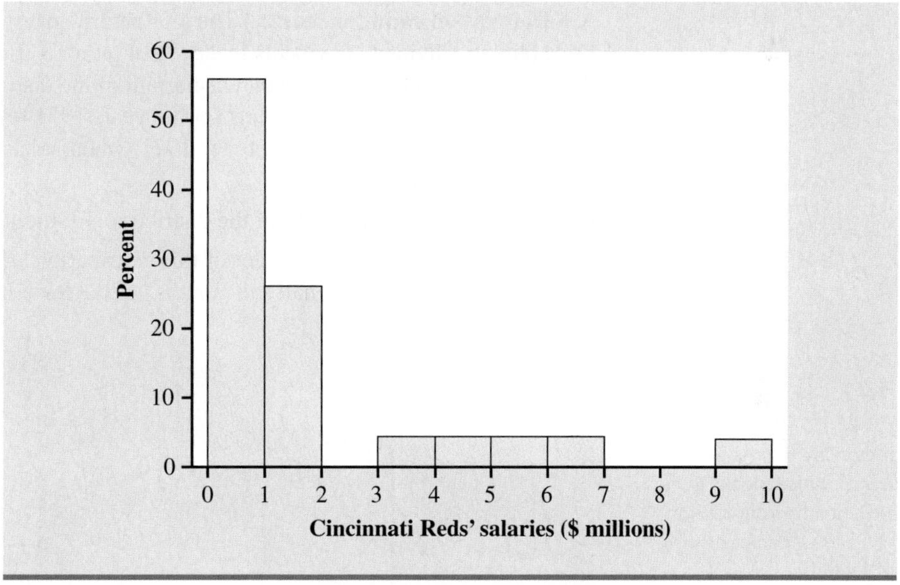

FIGURE 1.4 The distribution of the individual salaries of Cincinnati Reds players on opening day of the 2000 season, for Example 1.5.

For comparison, Figure 1.4 shows the distribution of salaries for the players on one team, the Cincinnati Reds. This distribution also has a single peak but is *skewed to the right*. Many of the players receive relatively small salaries (less than one million dollars), but a few earn large salaries (more than three million dollars). These large salaries form the long right tail of the histogram.

Notice that the vertical scale in Figure 1.4 is not the *count* of salaries but the *percent* of salaries in each class. A histogram of percents rather than counts is convenient when the counts are very large or when we want to compare several distributions.

The overall shape of a distribution is important information about a variable. Some types of data regularly produce distributions that are symmetric or skewed. For example, data on the diameters of ball bearings produced by a manufacturing process tend to be symmetric. Data on incomes (whether of individuals, companies, or nations) are usually strongly skewed to the right. There are many moderate incomes, some large incomes, and a few very large incomes. Do remember that many distributions have shapes that are neither symmetric nor skewed. Some data show other patterns. Scores on an exam, for example, may have a cluster near the top of the scale if many students did well. Or they may show two distinct peaks if a tough problem divided the class into those who did and didn't solve it. Use your eyes and describe what you see.

APPLY YOUR KNOWLEDGE

1.7 Automobile fuel economy. Table 1.2 (page 12) gives data on the fuel economy of 2006 model midsize cars. Based on a histogram of these data:

(a) Describe the main features (shape, center, spread, outliers) of the distribution of highway mileage.

(b) The government imposes a "gas guzzler" tax on cars with low gas mileage. Which of these cars do you think are subject to the gas guzzler tax?

1.8 Baseball salaries. How would you describe the center and spread of the distribution of average salaries in Figure 1.3? Of the distribution of Cincinnati Reds' salaries in Figure 1.4?

1.9 Returns on common stocks. The total return on a stock is the change in its market price plus any dividend payments made. Total return is usually expressed as a percent of the beginning price. Figure 1.5 is a histogram of the distribution of the monthly returns for all stocks listed on U.S. markets for the years 1951 to 2004 (648 months).[9] The low outlier is the market crash of October 1987, when stocks lost more than 22% of their value in one month.

(a) Describe the overall shape of the distribution of monthly returns.

(b) What is the approximate center of this distribution? (For now, take the center to be the value with roughly half the months having lower returns and half having higher returns.)

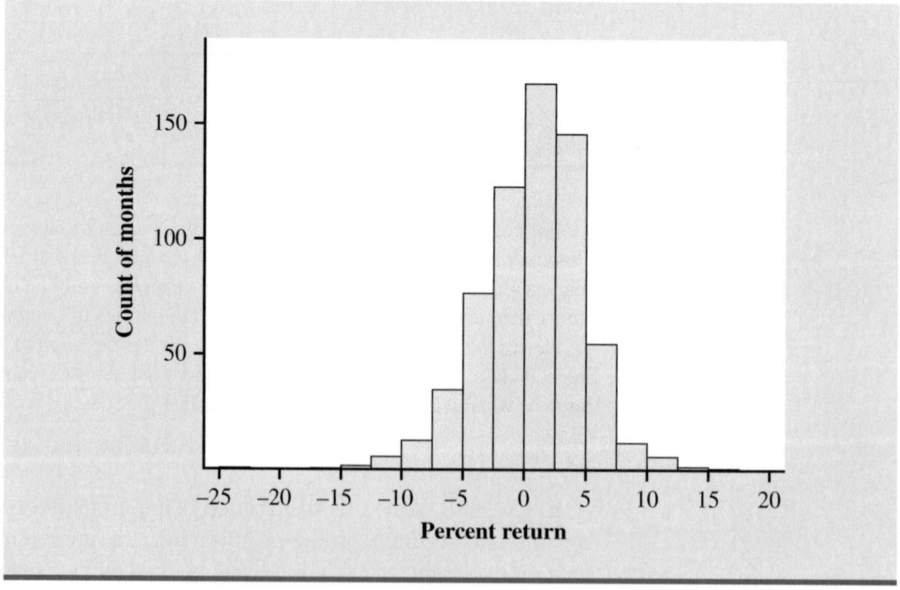

FIGURE 1.5 The distribution of monthly returns for all U.S. common stocks in the 648 months from January 1951 to December 2004, for Exercise 1.9.

(c) Approximately what were the smallest and largest total returns, leaving out the outlier? (This describes the spread of the distribution.)

(d) A return less than zero means that stocks lost value in that month. About what percent of all months had returns less than zero?

Quantitative variables: stemplots

Histograms are not the only graphical display of distributions of quantitative variables. For small data sets, a *stemplot* is quicker to make and presents more detailed information.

Stemplot

To make a **stemplot:**

1. Separate each observation into a **stem** consisting of all but the final (rightmost) digit and a **leaf,** the final digit. Stems may have as many digits as needed, but each leaf contains only a single digit.
2. Write the stems in a vertical column with the smallest at the top, and draw a vertical line at the right of this column.
3. Write each leaf in the row to the right of its stem, in increasing order out from the stem.

EXAMPLE 1.6 A Stemplot of State Unemployment Rates

CASE 1.1

The state unemployment rates in Table 1.1 (page 10) have only two digits (with the exception of Puerto Rico), so the whole-number part of the observation is the stem and the second digit (tenths) is the leaf. For example, Alabama's 5.4% appears as a leaf 4 on the 5 stem. California's 5.8% adds a leaf 8 on the same stem. After placing each state as a leaf on the proper stem, rearrange the leaves in order from left to right. Figure 1.6(a) is our stemplot for the 50 states (omitting Puerto Rico).

A stemplot looks like a histogram turned on end. The stemplot in Figure 1.6(a) resembles the histogram in Figure 1.2(a). The stemplot, unlike the histogram, preserves the actual value of each observation. We interpret stemplots like histograms, looking for the overall pattern and for any outliers.

rounding

You can choose the classes in a histogram. The classes (the stems) of a stemplot are given to you. When the observed values have many digits, it is often best to **round** the numbers to just a few digits before making a stemplot. For example, a stemplot of data like

3.468 2.137 2.981 1.095 ...

would have very many stems and no leaves or just one leaf on most stems. You can round these data to

3.5 2.1 3.0 1.1 ...

before making a stemplot.

FIGURE 1.6 Stemplots of the December 2004 unemployment rates in the 50 states, for Example 1.6. Figure 1.6(b) uses split stems. Compare the histograms of these data in Figure 1.2.

```
3 | 0233334678
4 | 00122234445566667779
5 | 1122234566688889
6 | 478
7 | 33
```

(a)

```
3 | 0233334
3 | 678
4 | 0012223444
4 | 556666779
5 | 1122234
5 | 566688889
6 | 4
6 | 78
7 | 33
```

(b)

splitting stems

You can also **split stems** to double the number of stems when all the leaves would otherwise fall on just a few stems. Each stem then appears twice. Leaves 0 to 4 go on the upper stem and leaves 5 to 9 go on the lower stem. Splitting the stems in Figure 1.6(a), for example, produces the new stemplot in Figure 1.6(b). The greater number of stems gives a clearer picture of the distribution. Rounding and splitting stems are matters for judgment, like choosing the classes in a histogram. Stemplots work well for small sets of data. When there are more than 100 observations, a histogram is almost always a better choice.

APPLY YOUR KNOWLEDGE

1.10 Architectural firms. Table 1.3 (page 13) gives the number of full-time staff employed by Indianapolis architectural firms. Make a stemplot of the staff counts. What are the main features of the shape of this distribution?

1.11 Supermarket shoppers. A marketing consultant observed 50 consecutive shoppers at a supermarket. One variable of interest was how much each shopper spent in the store. Here are the data (in dollars), arranged from smallest to largest:

3.11	8.88	9.26	10.81	12.69	13.78	15.23	15.62	17.00	17.39
18.36	18.43	19.27	19.50	19.54	20.16	20.59	22.22	23.04	24.47
24.58	25.13	26.24	26.26	27.65	28.06	28.08	28.38	32.03	34.98
36.37	38.64	39.16	41.02	42.97	44.08	44.67	45.40	46.69	48.65
50.39	52.75	54.80	59.07	61.22	70.32	82.70	85.76	86.37	93.34

Round these amounts to the nearest dollar and then make a stemplot of these data. About where is the center of the distribution? Are there any outliers? What is the spread of the values (ignoring any outliers)? Is the distribution symmetric, skewed left, or skewed right? Make a second stemplot of the data by splitting the stems as described in this section.

Time plots

Many variables are measured at intervals over time. We might, for example, measure the cost of raw materials for a manufacturing process each month or the price of a stock at the end of each day. In these examples, our main interest is change over time. To display change over time, make a *time plot*.

Time Plot

A **time plot** of a variable plots each observation against the time at which it was measured. Always put time on the horizontal scale of your plot and the variable you are measuring on the vertical scale. Connecting the data points by lines helps emphasize any change over time.

time series

Measurements of a variable taken at regular intervals over time form a **time series.** Plots against time can reveal the main features of a time series. As with distributions, look first for overall patterns and then for striking deviations from those patterns. Here are some types of overall patterns to look for in a time series.

Trend and Seasonal Variation

A **trend** in a time series is a persistent, long-term rise or fall.

A pattern in a time series that repeats itself at known regular intervals of time is called **seasonal variation.**

EXAMPLE 1.7 The Price of Oranges

Figure 1.7 is a time plot of the average price of fresh oranges over the decade from 1991 to 2000.[10] This information is collected each month as part of the government's reporting of retail prices. The monthly Consumer Price Index is the most publicized product of this effort. The price is presented as an **index number.** That is, the price scale gives the price as a percent of the average price of oranges in the years 1982 to 1984, indicated by "1982–84 = 100." The first value is 205.7 for January 1991, so at that time oranges cost about 206% of their 1982 to 1984 average price. The index number is based on the retail price of oranges at many stores in all parts of the country. The price of oranges at a single store will drop when the manager decides to advertise a sale on oranges, and it will rise when the sale ends. The index number is a nationwide average price that is less variable than the price at one store.

index number

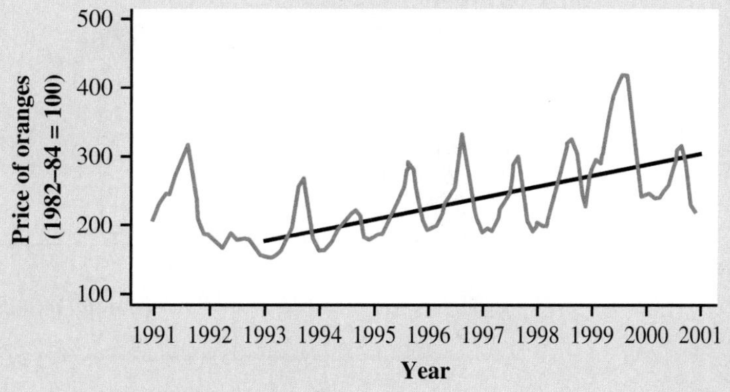

FIGURE 1.7 Time plot of an index number (1982–84 = 100) for the average retail price of oranges each month from 1991 through 2000, for Example 1.7.

Figure 1.7 shows an upward *trend* in the price of oranges starting in 1993. Statistical software can draw a line on the time plot that represents the trend. Such a line appears in Figure 1.7. Superimposed on this trend is a strong *seasonal variation,* a regular rise and fall that recurs each year. Orange prices are usually highest in August or September, when the supply is lowest. Prices then fall in anticipation of the harvest and are lowest in January or February, when the harvest is complete and oranges are plentiful. The large spikes in 1991 and 1999 may be deviations from the overall trend and seasonal variation, perhaps due to poor harvests.

seasonally adjusted

Because many economic time series show strong seasonal variation, government agencies often adjust for this variation before releasing economic data. The data are then said to be **seasonally adjusted.** Seasonal adjustment helps avoid misinterpretation. A rise in the unemployment rate from December to January, for example, does not mean that the economy is slipping. Unemployment almost always rises in January as temporary holiday help is laid off and outdoor employment in the North drops because of bad weather. The seasonally adjusted unemployment rate reports an increase only if unemployment rises more than normal from December to January.

EXAMPLE 1.8 Unemployment Rates

cross-sectional data

CASE 1.1

We have looked at the distribution of state unemployment rates for December 2004. These are called **cross-sectional data** because they concern a group of individuals (the states) at one time. Time series data can put cross-sectional data such as the December 2004 unemployment rates into a context. Figure 1.8 is a time plot of the monthly national unemployment rate from January 1990 to October 2005. The data are seasonally adjusted, so that long-term trends are easy to see.

We now see that December 2004 (marked by the broken vertical line) is in the middle of a steady decline in the unemployment rate that began in July 2003 (the 163rd month in this data set).

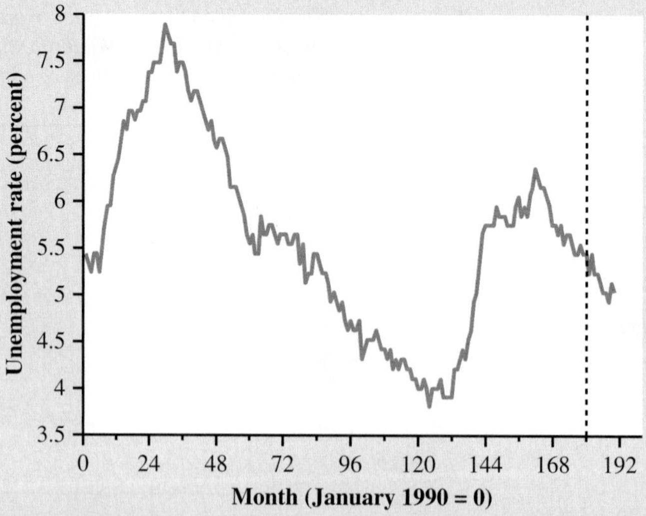

FIGURE 1.8 Time plot of the monthly national unemployment rate from January 1990 to October 2005, for Example 1.8.

APPLY YOUR KNOWLEDGE

1.12 Yields of Treasury bills. Treasury bills are short-term borrowing by the U.S. government. They are important in financial theory because the interest rate for Treasury bills is a "risk-free rate" that says what return investors can get while taking (almost) no risk. More risky investments should in theory offer higher returns in the long run. Here are the annual returns on Treasury bills from 1970 to 2004:[11]

Year	Rate	Year	Rate	Year	Rate	Year	Rate
1970	6.52	1979	10.38	1988	6.36	1997	5.25
1971	4.39	1980	11.26	1989	8.38	1998	4.85
1972	3.84	1981	14.72	1990	7.84	1999	4.69
1973	6.93	1982	10.53	1991	5.60	2000	5.88
1974	8.01	1983	8.80	1992	3.50	2001	3.86
1975	5.80	1984	9.84	1993	2.90	2002	1.63
1976	5.08	1985	7.72	1994	3.91	2003	1.02
1977	5.13	1986	6.16	1995	5.60	2004	1.19
1978	7.19	1987	5.47	1996	5.20		

(a) Make a time plot of the returns paid by Treasury bills in these years.

cycles

(b) Interest rates, like many economic variables, show **cycles,** clear but irregular up-and-down movements. In which years did the interest rate cycle reach temporary peaks?

(c) A time plot may show a consistent trend underneath cycles. When did interest rates reach their overall peak during these years? Has there been a general trend downward since that year?

SECTION 1.1 SUMMARY

- A data set contains information on a number of **individuals.** Individuals may be people, animals, or things. For each individual, the data give values for one or more **variables.** A variable describes some characteristic of an individual, such as a person's height, gender, or salary.
- Some variables are **categorical** and others are **quantitative.** A categorical variable places each individual into a category, like male or female. A quantitative variable has numerical values that measure some characteristic of each individual, like height in centimeters or salary in dollars per year.
- **Exploratory data analysis** uses graphs and numerical summaries to describe the variables in a data set and the relations among them.
- The **distribution** of a variable describes what values the variable takes and how often it takes these values.
- To describe a distribution, begin with a graph. **Bar graphs** and **pie charts** describe the distribution of a categorical variable, and **Pareto charts** identify the most important few categories for a categorical variable. **Histograms** and **stemplots** graph the distributions of quantitative variables.
- When examining any graph, look for an **overall pattern** and for notable **deviations** from the pattern.

- **Shape, center,** and **spread** describe the overall pattern of a distribution. Some distributions have simple shapes, such as **symmetric** and **skewed.** Not all distributions have a simple overall shape, especially when there are few observations.
- **Outliers** are observations that lie outside the overall pattern of a distribution. Always look for outliers and try to explain them.
- When observations on a variable are taken over time, make a **time plot** that graphs time horizontally and the values of the **time series** vertically. A time plot can reveal **trends, seasonal variation,** or other changes over time.

SECTION 1.1 Exercises

For Exercises 1.1 and 1.2, see page 5; for 1.3 and 1.4, see pages 8–9; for 1.5 and 1.6, see pages 12–13; for 1.7 to 1.9, see pages 16–17; for 1.10 and 1.11, see page 18; and for 1.12, see page 21.

1.13 Vehicle colors. Favorite vehicle colors differ among types of vehicle. Here are data on the most popular colors in 2003 for luxury cars and for SUVs, trucks, and vans.[12] The entry "—" means "less than 1%."

Color	Luxury car percent	SUV/truck/ van percent
Black	10.9	11.6
Light brown	—	6.3
Medium/dark blue	3.8	9.3
Medium/dark gray	23.3	8.8
Medium/dark green	—	7.0
Medium red	3.9	6.2
White	30.4	22.3
Silver	18.8	17.0

(a) Make a bar graph for the luxury car percents.

(b) Make a bar graph for the SUV/truck/van percents.

(c) Now, be creative: make *one* bar graph that compares the two vehicle types as well as comparing colors. Arrange your graph so that it is easy to compare the two types of vehicle.

1.14 Types of email spam. Email spam is the curse of the Internet. Here is a compilation of the most common types of spam:[13]

Type of spam	Percent	Type of spam	Percent
Adult	14.5	Leisure	7.8
Financial	16.2	Products	21.0
Health	7.3	Scams	14.2

(a) Make a bar graph of these percents with the bars ordered alphabetically (as in the table).

(b) Make another bar graph of these percents with the bars ordered from tallest to shortest.

(c) What is the name given to the bar graph in part (b)? What is the advantage of this type of bar graph?

1.15 Property damage by tornadoes. The states differ greatly in the kinds of severe weather that afflict them. Table 1.4 shows the average property damage caused by tornadoes per year over the period from 1950 to 1999 in each of the 50 states and Puerto Rico.[14] (To adjust for the changing buying power of the dollar over time, all damages were restated in 1999 dollars.)

(a) What are the top five states for tornado damage? The bottom five? (Include Puerto Rico, though it is not a state.)

(b) Make a histogram of the data, by hand or using software, with classes "$0 \le$ damage < 10," "$10 \le$ damage < 20," and so on. Describe the shape, center, and spread of the distribution. Which states may be outliers? (To understand the outliers, note that most tornadoes in largely rural states such as Kansas cause little property damage. Damage to crops is not counted as property damage.)

(c) If you are using software, also display the "default" histogram that your software makes when you give it no instructions. How does this compare with your graph in (b)?

1.16 Carbon dioxide emissions. Burning fuels in power plants or motor vehicles emits carbon dioxide (CO_2), which contributes to global warming. Table 1.5 displays CO_2 emissions per person from countries with populations of at least 20 million.[15]

(a) Why do you think we choose to measure emissions per person rather than total CO_2 emissions for each country?

TABLE 1.4 Average property damage per year due to tornadoes

State	Damage ($ millions)	State	Damage ($ millions)	State	Damage ($ millions)
Alabama	51.88	Louisiana	27.75	Ohio	44.36
Alaska	0.00	Maine	0.53	Oklahoma	81.94
Arizona	3.47	Maryland	2.33	Oregon	5.52
Arkansas	40.96	Massachusetts	4.42	Pennsylvania	17.11
California	3.68	Michigan	29.88	Puerto Rico	0.05
Colorado	4.62	Minnesota	84.84	Rhode Island	0.09
Connecticut	2.26	Mississippi	43.62	South Carolina	17.19
Delaware	0.27	Missouri	68.93	South Dakota	10.64
Florida	37.32	Montana	2.27	Tennessee	23.47
Georgia	51.68	Nebraska	30.26	Texas	88.60
Hawaii	0.34	Nevada	0.10	Utah	3.57
Idaho	0.26	New Hampshire	0.66	Vermont	0.24
Illinois	62.94	New Jersey	2.94	Virginia	7.42
Indiana	53.13	New Mexico	1.49	Washington	2.37
Iowa	49.51	New York	15.73	West Virginia	2.14
Kansas	49.28	North Carolina	14.90	Wisconsin	31.33
Kentucky	24.84	North Dakota	14.69	Wyoming	1.78

TABLE 1.5 Carbon dioxide emissions (metric tons per person)

Country	CO_2	Country	CO_2	Country	CO_2
Algeria	2.3	Iran	3.8	Poland	8.0
Argentina	3.9	Iraq	3.6	Romania	3.9
Australia	17.0	Italy	7.3	Russia	10.2
Bangladesh	0.2	Japan	9.1	Saudi Arabia	11.0
Brazil	1.8	Kenya	0.3	South Africa	8.1
Canada	16.0	Korea, North	9.7	Spain	6.8
China	2.5	Korea, South	8.8	Sudan	0.2
Colombia	1.4	Malaysia	4.6	Tanzania	0.1
Congo	0.0	Mexico	3.7	Thailand	2.5
Egypt	1.7	Morocco	1.0	Turkey	2.8
Ethiopia	0.0	Myanmar	0.2	Ukraine	7.6
France	6.1	Nepal	0.1	United Kingdom	9.0
Germany	10.0	Nigeria	0.3	United States	19.9
Ghana	0.2	Pakistan	0.7	Uzbekistan	4.8
India	0.9	Peru	0.8	Venezuela	5.1
Indonesia	1.2	Philippines	0.9	Vietnam	0.5

(b) Display the data of Table 1.5 in a graph. Describe the shape, center, and spread of the distribution. Which countries are outliers?

1.17 Demographics: 65 and older. The population of the United States is aging, though less rapidly than in other developed countries. Here is a stemplot of the percents of residents aged 65 and older in the 50 states, according to the 2000 census. The stems are whole percents and the leaves are tenths of a percent.

5	7
6	
7	
8	5
9	679
10	6
11	02233677
12	0011113445789
13	00012233345568
14	034579
15	36
16	
17	6

(a) There are two outliers: Alaska has the lowest percent of older residents, and Florida has the highest. What are the percents for these two states?

(b) Ignoring Alaska and Florida, describe the shape, center, and spread of this distribution.

1.18 Demographics: 65 and older. Make another stemplot of the percent of residents aged 65 and older in the states other than Alaska and Florida by splitting stems 8 to 15 in the plot from the previous exercise. Which plot do you prefer? Why?

1.19 Tracking quality. The J. D. Power Initial Quality Study polls more than 50,000 buyers of new motor vehicles 90 days after their purchase. A two-page questionnaire asks about "things gone wrong." Here are data on problems per 100 vehicles for vehicles made by Toyota and by General Motors in recent years. Toyota has been the industry leader in quality. Make two time plots in the same graph to compare Toyota and GM. What are the most important conclusions you can draw from your graph?

Year:	1998	1999	2000	2001	2002	2003	2004
GM	187	179	164	147	130	134	120
Toyota	156	134	116	115	107	115	101

1.20 Mass layoffs. The Bureau of Labor Statistics says that a "mass layoff" occurs when 50 or more people from the same employer file initial claims for unemployment insurance in a five-week period. The table at the bottom of the page gives data on the number of mass layoffs in the United States over an almost 10-year period.[16]

(a) Make a time plot of these data.

(b) There is strong seasonal variation, regular up-and-down movements that occur at about the same time each year. At what time of year are mass layoffs most common? Least common?

(c) Is there also a long-term trend in the number of mass layoffs? Explain your conclusion.

1.21 Motor vehicle fuel economy. The top of the next page shows a small part of a data set that describes the fuel economy (in miles per gallon) of 2001 model motor vehicles:

(a) What are the individuals in this data set?

(b) For each individual, what variables are given? Which of these variables are categorical and which are quantitative?

Year	Jan.	Feb.	Mar.	Apr.	May	June	July	Aug.	Sept.	Oct.	Nov.	Dec.
1995				1431	1194	1512	1502	680	706	1070	1282	2058
1996	1763	947	994	1030	942	924	1534	918	513	1289	1433	1824
1997	2139	755	783	1269	1152	1238	1899	973	548	1414	1156	1634
1998	2360	970	762	1253	1180	1208	2220	617	637	1553	1368	1776
1999	2421	1067	880	1270	1032	1140	1741	698	717	1098	1336	1509
2000	1934	1045	986	924	984	1597	1333	751	936	874	1697	2677
2001	1522	1501	1527	1450	1434	2107	2117	1490	1327	1831	2721	2440
2002	2146	1382	1460	1506	1723	1584	2042	1248	1062	1497	2153	2474
2003	2315	1363	1207	1581	1703	1691	2087	1258	868	1523	1438	1929
2004	2428	941	920	1458	988	1379	2094	809				

Make and model	Vehicle type	Transmission type	Number of cylinders	City MPG	Highway MPG
⋮					
BMW 330CI	Subcompact	Automatic	6	19	27
BMW 330CI	Subcompact	Manual	6	21	30
Buick Century	Midsize	Automatic	6	20	29
Chevrolet Blazer	Four-wheel drive	Automatic	6	15	20
⋮					

1.22 Pharmaceutical study. Data from a pharmaceutical company medical study contain values of many variables for each of the people who were the subjects of the study. Which of the following variables are categorical and which are quantitative?

(a) Gender (female or male)

(b) Age (years)

(c) Race (Asian, black, white, or other)

(d) Smoker (yes or no)

(e) Systolic blood pressure (millimeters of mercury)

(f) Level of calcium in the blood (micrograms per milliliter)

1.23 Mutual funds. The table at the bottom of the page is a small part of a data set that describes mutual funds available to the public:

(a) What individuals does this data set describe?

(b) In addition to the fund's name, how many variables does the data set contain? Which of these variables are categorical and which are quantitative?

(c) What are the units of measurement for each of the quantitative variables?

1.24 Insurance: cause of death. Cause of death is an important issue for life insurance companies—especially identifying the most likely causes of death for various demographic subgroups of the population. The number of deaths among persons aged 15 to 24 years in the United States in 1997 due to the seven leading causes of death for this age group were accidents, 12,958; homicide, 5793; suicide, 4146; cancer, 1583; heart disease, 1013; congenital defects, 383; AIDS, 276.[17]

(a) Make a bar graph to display these data.

(b) What additional information do you need to make a pie chart?

1.25 Location of a new facility. A company deciding where to build a new facility will rank potential locations in terms of how desirable it is to operate a business in each location. Describe five variables that you would measure for each location if you were designing a study to help your company rank locations. Give reasons for each of your choices.

1.26 Hurricanes. Hurricanes cause a great deal of property damage and personal injury when they hit populated landmasses. A substantial portion of hurricane loss is paid for by insurance companies in the form of paying for lost property and medical bills. For this reason, insurance companies study the number and severity of the hurricanes that can potentially cause them loss. The histogram in Figure 1.9 shows the number of hurricanes reaching the east coast of the United States each year over a 70-year period.[18] Give a brief description of the

Mutual Fund	Category	Net assets ($ millions)	Year-to-date return	Largest holding
⋮				
Fidelity Low-Priced Stock	Small value	6,189	4.56%	Dallas Semiconductor
Price International Stock	International stock	9,745	−0.45%	Vodafone
Vanguard 500 Index	Large blend	89,394	3.45%	General Electric
⋮				

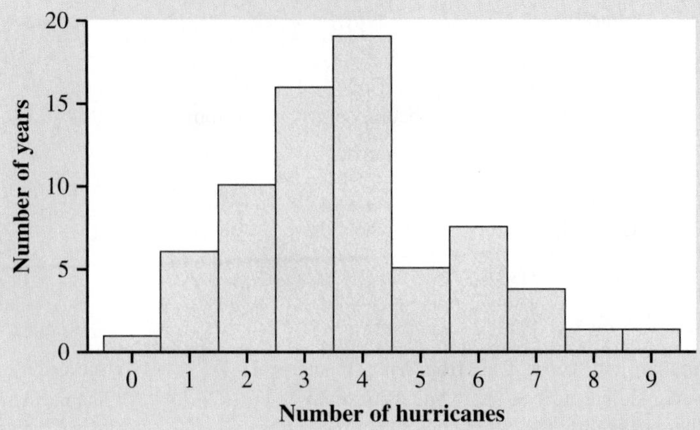

FIGURE 1.9 The distribution of the annual number of hurricanes reaching the U.S. east coast over a 70-year period, for Exercise 1.26.

overall shape of this distribution. About where does the center of the distribution lie?

1.27 **Left-skew.** Sketch a histogram for a distribution that is skewed to the left. Suppose that you and your friends emptied your pockets of coins and recorded the year marked on each coin. The distribution of dates would be skewed to the left. Explain why.

1.28 **The changing age distribution of the United States.** The distribution of the ages of a nation's population has a strong influence on economic and social conditions. Table 1.6 shows the age distribution of U.S. residents in 1950 and 2075, in millions of people. The 1950 data come from that year's census, while the 2075 data are projections made by the Census Bureau.

TABLE 1.6 **Age distribution in the United States, 1950 and 2075 (in millions of persons)**

Age group	1950	2075
Under 10 years	29.3	53.3
10–19 years	21.8	53.2
20–29 years	24.0	51.2
30–39 years	22.8	50.5
40–49 years	19.3	47.5
50–59 years	15.5	44.8
60–69 years	11.0	40.7
70–79 years	5.5	30.9
80–89 years	1.6	21.7
90–99 years	0.1	8.8
100–109 years	—	1.1
Total	151.1	403.7

(a) Because the total population in 2075 is much larger than the 1950 population, comparing percents in each age group is clearer than comparing counts. Make a table of the percent of the total population in each age group for both 1950 and 2075.

(b) Make a histogram with vertical scale in percents of the 1950 age distribution. Describe the main features of the distribution. In particular, look at the percent of children relative to the rest of the population.

(c) Make a histogram with vertical scale in percents of the projected age distribution for the year 2075. Use the same scales as in (b) for easy comparison. What are the most important changes in the U.S. age distribution projected for the years between 1950 and 2075?

1.29 **Reliability of household appliances.** Always ask whether a particular variable is really a suitable measure for your purpose. You are writing an article for a consumer magazine based on a survey of the magazine's readers on the reliability of their household appliances. Of 13,376 readers who reported owning Brand A dishwashers, 2942 required a service call during the past year. Only 192 service calls were reported by the 480 readers who owned Brand B dishwashers.

(a) Why is the count of service calls (2942 versus 192) not a good measure of the reliability of these two brands of dishwashers?

(b) Use the information given to calculate a suitable measure of reliability. What do you conclude about the reliability of Brand A and Brand B?

1.30 **Bear markets.** Investors speak of a "bear market" when stock prices drop substantially. Table 1.7 gives data on all declines of at least 10% in the Standard &

TABLE 1.7 Size and length of bear markets

Year	Decline (percent)	Duration (months)	Year	Decline (percent)	Duration (months)
1940–1942	42	28	1968–1970	36	18
1946	27	5	1973–1974	48	21
1950	14	1	1981–1982	26	19
1953	15	8	1983–1984	14	10
1955	10	1	1987	34	3
1956–1957	22	15	1990	20	3
1959–1960	14	15	1998	19	3
1962	26	6	2000–2002	47	26
1966	22	8			

Poor's 500 stock index between 1940 and 2002. The data show how far the index fell from its peak and how long the decline in stock prices lasted.

(a) Make a stemplot of the percent declines in stock prices during these bear markets. Make a second stemplot, splitting the stems. Which graph do you prefer? Why?

(b) The shape of this distribution is irregular, but we could describe it as somewhat skewed. Is the distribution skewed to the right or to the left?

(c) Describe the center and spread of the data. What would you tell an investor about how far stocks fall in a bear market?

TABLE 1.8 Salary distributions of female and male workers in a large factory

Salary ($1000)	Women Number	Women %	Men Number	Men %
10–15	89	11.8	26	1.1
15–20	192	25.4	221	9.0
20–25	236	31.2	677	27.9
25–30	111	14.7	823	33.6
30–35	86	11.4	365	14.9
35–40	25	3.3	182	7.4
40–45	11	1.5	91	3.7
45–50	3	0.4	33	1.4
50–55	2	0.3	19	0.8
55–60	0	0.0	11	0.4
60–65	0	0.0	0	0.0
65–70	1	0.1	3	0.1
Total	756	100.1	2451	100.0

1.31 "The Fortune 500." Each year *Fortune* magazine lists the top 500 companies in the United States, ranked according to their total annual sales in dollars. Describe three other variables that could reasonably be used to measure the "size" of a company.

1.32 Salary distributions in a factory. A manufacturing company is reviewing the salaries of its full-time employees below the executive level at a large plant. The clerical staff is almost entirely female, while a majority of the production workers and technical staff is male. As a result, the distributions of salaries for male and female employees may be quite different. Table 1.8 gives the counts and percents of women and men in each salary class. Make histograms from these data, choosing the type that is most appropriate for comparing the two distributions. Then describe the overall shape of each salary distribution and the chief differences between them.

1.33 The cost of Internet access. How much do users pay for Internet service? Here are the monthly fees (in dollars) paid by a random sample of 50 users of commercial Internet service providers in August 2000:[19]

20	40	22	22	21	21	20	10	20	20
20	13	18	50	20	18	15	8	22	25
22	10	20	22	22	21	15	23	30	12
9	20	40	22	29	19	15	20	20	20
20	15	19	21	14	22	21	35	20	22

Make a stemplot of these data. Briefly describe the pattern you see. About how much do you think America Online and its larger competitors were charging in August 2000? Which members of the

TABLE 1.9 Data for the states

State	2000 census population	Mean personal income	Median household income	Percent poverty	MDs per 100,000	Violent crimes per 100,000
Alabama	4,447,100	22,104	36,266	14.5	194	565
Alaska	626,932	26,468	50,692	9.4	160	701
Arizona	5,130,632	23,772	37,090	16.6	200	624
Arkansas	2,673,400	20,974	27,665	14.8	185	527
California	33,871,648	28,352	40,934	15.4	244	798
Colorado	4,301,261	29,542	46,599	9.2	234	363
Connecticut	3,405,565	38,759	46,508	9.5	344	391
Delaware	783,600	30,734	41,458	10.3	230	678
District of Columbia	572,059	38,429	33,433	22.3	702	2024
Florida	15,982,378	26,650	34,909	13.1	232	1024
Georgia	8,186,453	25,793	38,665	13.6	204	607
Hawaii	1,211,537	26,944	40,827	10.9	252	278
Idaho	1,293,953	21,731	36,680	13.0	150	257
Illinois	12,419,293	29,764	43,178	10.1	253	861
Indiana	6,080,485	24,967	39,731	9.4	192	515
Iowa	2,926,324	24,664	37,019	9.1	171	310
Kansas	2,688,418	25,752	36,711	9.6	202	409
Kentucky	4,041,769	22,171	36,252	13.5	205	317
Louisiana	4,468,976	22,006	31,735	19.1	239	856
Maine	1,274,923	23,661	35,640	10.4	214	121
Maryland	5,296,486	30,868	50,016	7.2	362	847
Massachusetts	6,349,097	33,809	42,345	8.7	402	644
Michigan	9,938,444	26,655	41,821	11.0	218	590
Minnesota	4,919,479	28,359	47,926	10.4	247	338
Mississippi	2,844,658	19,544	29,120	17.6	156	469
Missouri	5,595,211	25,181	40,201	9.8	225	577
Montana	902,195	20,795	31,577	16.6	188	132
Nebraska	1,711,263	25,519	36,413	12.3	213	438
Nevada	1,998,257	28,040	39,756	10.6	169	799
New Hampshire	1,235,786	29,919	44,958	9.8	230	113
New Jersey	8,414,350	34,985	49,826	8.6	287	493
New Mexico	1,819,046	20,551	31,543	20.4	209	853
New York	18,976,457	32,714	37,394	16.7	375	689
North Carolina	8,049,313	24,778	35,838	14.0	225	607
North Dakota	642,200	22,344	30,304	15.1	219	87
Ohio	11,353,140	25,910	38,925	11.2	230	435
Oklahoma	3,450,654	21,722	33,727	14.1	166	560
Oregon	3,421,399	25,530	39,067	15.0	221	444
Pennsylvania	12,281,054	27,619	39,015	11.2	282	442
Rhode Island	1,048,319	27,624	40,686	11.6	324	334
South Carolina	4,012,012	21,967	33,267	13.7	201	990

TABLE 1.9 Data for the states (*continued*)

State	2000 census population	Mean personal income	Median household income	Percent poverty	MDs per 100,000	Violent crimes per 100,000
South Dakota	754,844	22,797	32,786	10.8	177	197
Tennessee	5,689,283	24,286	34,091	13.4	242	790
Texas	20,851,820	25,728	35,783	15.0	196	603
Utah	2,233,169	21,667	44,299	9.0	197	334
Vermont	608,827	24,922	39,372	9.9	288	120
Virginia	7,078,515	28,230	43,354	8.8	233	345
Washington	5,894,121	28,824	47,421	8.9	229	441
West Virginia	1,808,344	19,960	26,704	17.8	210	219
Wisconsin	5,363,675	25,853	41,327	8.8	224	271
Wyoming	493,782	23,882	35,250	10.6	167	255

sample may have been early adopters of fast access via cable modems or DSL lines?

1.34 Architects and engineers. Table 1.3 (page 13) gives the numbers of architects and engineers employed by Indianapolis architectural firms. A ***back-to-back stemplot*** helps us compare these two distributions. Write the stems as usual, but with a vertical line both to their left and to their right. On the right, put leaves for architects. On the left, put the leaves for engineers. Arrange the leaves on each stem in increasing order out from the stem. Now write a brief comparison of the distributions.

1.35 Watch those scales! The impression that a time plot gives depends on the scales you use on the two axes. If you stretch the vertical axis and compress the time axis, change appears to be more rapid. Compressing the vertical axis and stretching the time axis make change appear slower. Make two time plots of the first 12 years of data in Exercise 1.12 (page 21), one that makes rates appear to increase very rapidly and one that suggests only a modest increase. The moral of this exercise is: pay close attention to the scales when you look at a time plot.

Table 1.9 presents government data that describe some aspects of the prosperity and quality of life in the 50 states and the District of Columbia. Study of a data set with many variables begins by examining each variable by itself. Exercises 1.36 to 1.38 concern the data in Table 1.9.

1.36 Population of the states. Make a stemplot of the population of the states. Briefly describe the shape, center, and spread of the distribution of population. Explain why the shape of the distribution is not surprising. Are there any states that you consider outliers?

1.37 Income in the states. Table 1.9 contains two measures of "average income." Mean personal income is the total income of all people living in a state divided by the state's population. Median household income is the midpoint of the distribution of incomes of all households in the state. (A household consists of all people living at the same address, whether or not they are related to each other.)

(a) Explain why you expect household income to be larger than personal income.

(b) Round the income data to the nearest hundred dollars and write them in units of thousands of dollars. For example, Alabama's mean personal income $22,104 becomes 22.1 and Alaska's mean personal income becomes 26.5. Make a back-to-back stemplot (see Exercise 1.34) of personal and household income.

(c) Write a brief description of the shape of each distribution and also a brief comparison of the two distributions.

1.38 Where are the doctors? Table 1.9 gives the number of medical doctors per 100,000 people in each state.

(a) Why is the number of doctors per 100,000 people a better measure of the availability of health care than a simple count of the number of doctors in a state?

(b) Make a graph that displays the distribution of doctors per 100,000 people. Write a brief description of the distribution. Are there any outliers? If so, can you explain them?

1.2 Describing Distributions with Numbers

CASE 1.2 EARNINGS OF HOURLY BANK WORKERS

Banks employ many workers paid by the hour, such as tellers and data clerks. A large bank, which we will call simply National Bank to preserve confidentiality, has been accused of discrimination in paying its hourly workers. In the course of an internal investigation into the charges, the bank collected data on all 1745 hourly workers listed in its personnel records. The data set is named HOURLY and is included on the book's CD and described in detail in the Data Appendix at the back of the book. Because the data set is so large, we will use randomly selected samples of full-time hourly workers in four race-and-gender groups to illustrate statistical analysis before applying the methods we develop to the complete data set. Table 1.10 presents the annual earnings for the workers in our samples.

The stemplot in Figure 1.10 shows us the *shape, center,* and *spread* of the earnings of the 15 black females in Table 1.10. The stems are thousands of dollars and the leaves are hundreds, rounded to the nearest hundred. As is often the case when there are few observations, the shape of the distribution is irregular. The earnings are quite tightly clustered except for one low outlier. The midpoint of the earnings is roughly \$17,500. The spread, omitting the outlier, is from about \$16,000 to about \$20,800. Shape, center, and spread provide a good description of the overall pattern of any distribution for a quantitative variable. In this section, we will learn specific ways to use numbers to measure the center and the spread of a distribution. The numbers, like the graphs of Section 1.1, are aids to understanding the data, not "the answer" in themselves.

Measuring center: the mean

A description of a distribution almost always includes a measure of its center or average. The most common measure of center is the ordinary arithmetic average, or *mean.*

TABLE 1.10 Annual earnings of hourly workers at National Bank

Black females	Black males	White females	White males	Black females	Black males	White females	White males
\$16,015	\$18,365	\$25,249	\$15,100	\$17,813	\$29,347	\$18,002	\$17,194
17,516	17,755	19,029	22,346	18,206	19,028	21,596	30,383
17,274	16,890	17,233	22,049	19,338		26,885	18,364
16,555	17,147	26,606	26,970	15,953		24,780	18,245
20,788	18,402	28,346	16,411	16,904		14,698	23,531
19,312	20,972	31,176	19,268			19,308	
17,124	24,750	18,863	28,336			17,576	
18,405	16,576	15,904	19,007			24,497	
19,090	16,853	22,477	22,078			20,612	
12,641	21,565	19,102	19,977			17,757	

FIGURE 1.10 Stemplot of the annual earnings of 15 black female hourly workers at National Bank.

12	6
13	
14	
15	
16	0069
17	1358
18	24
19	133
20	8

The Mean $\bar{x}$

To find the **mean** of a set of observations, add their values and divide by the number of observations. If the n observations are $x_1, x_2, \ldots, x_n$, their mean is

$$\bar{x} = \frac{x_1 + x_2 + \cdots + x_n}{n}$$

or, in more compact notation,

$$\bar{x} = \frac{1}{n}\sum x_i$$

The $\sum$ (capital Greek sigma) in the formula for the mean is short for "add them all up." The subscripts on the observations x_i are just a way of keeping the n observations distinct. They do not necessarily indicate order or any other special facts about the data. The bar over the x indicates the mean of all the x-values. Pronounce the mean $\bar{x}$ as "x-bar." This notation is very common. When writers who are discussing data use $\bar{x}$ or $\bar{y}$, they are talking about a mean.

EXAMPLE 1.9 Mean Earnings of Black Female Workers

CASE 1.2

The mean amount earned by the 15 black female bank workers in Table 1.10 is

$$\begin{aligned}\bar{x} &= \frac{x_1 + x_2 + \cdots + x_n}{n}\\ &= \frac{16{,}015 + 17{,}516 + \cdots + 16{,}904}{15}\\ &= \frac{262{,}934}{15} = \$17{,}528.93\end{aligned}$$

In practice, you can key the data into your calculator and hit the mean key. You don't have to actually add and divide. But you should know that this is what the calculator is doing.

The lowest-paid worker earned \$12,641. Use your calculator to check that the mean income of the other 14 workers *excluding this outlier* is $\bar{x}$ = \$17,878.07. The single outlier reduces the mean by almost \$350.

Example 1.9 illustrates an important fact about the mean as a measure of center: it is sensitive to the influence of one or more extreme observations. These may be outliers, but a skewed distribution that has no outliers will also pull the mean toward its long tail. Because the mean cannot resist the influence of extreme observations, we say that it is *not* a **resistant measure** of center.

resistant measure

APPLY YOUR KNOWLEDGE

1.39 Bank workers. Find the mean earnings of the remaining three groups in Table 1.10. Does comparing the four means suggest that National Bank pays male hourly workers more than females, or white workers more than blacks? (Of course, detailed investigation of such things as job type and seniority is needed before we claim discrimination.)

1.40 Supermarket shoppers. Here are the amounts spent (in dollars) by 50 consecutive shoppers at a supermarket, arranged in increasing order:

3.11	8.88	9.26	10.81	12.69	13.78	15.23	15.62	17.00	17.39
18.36	18.43	19.27	19.50	19.54	20.16	20.59	22.22	23.04	24.47
24.58	25.13	26.24	26.26	27.65	28.06	28.08	28.38	32.03	34.98
36.37	38.64	39.16	41.02	42.97	44.08	44.67	45.40	46.69	48.65
50.39	52.75	54.80	59.07	61.22	70.32	82.70	85.76	86.37	93.34

(a) Find the mean amount spent from the formula for the mean. Then enter the data into your calculator or software and use the mean function to obtain the mean. Verify that you get the same result.

(b) A stemplot (Exercise 1.11) suggests that the largest four values may be a cluster of outliers. Find the mean for the 46 observations that remain when you drop these outliers. How do the outliers change the mean?

Measuring center: the median

In Section 1.1, we used the midpoint of a distribution as an informal measure of center. The *median* is the formal version of the midpoint, with a specific rule for calculation.

The Median M

The **median** M is the midpoint of a distribution, the number such that half the observations are smaller and the other half are larger. To find the median of a distribution:

1. Arrange all observations in order of size, from smallest to largest.
2. If the number of observations n is odd, the median M is the center observation in the ordered list. Find the location of the median by counting $(n + 1)/2$ observations up from the bottom of the list.
3. If the number of observations n is even, the median M is the mean of the two center observations in the ordered list. The location of the median is again $(n + 1)/2$ from the bottom of the list.

Note that the formula $(n + 1)/2$ does *not* give the median, just the location of the median in the ordered list. Medians require little arithmetic, so they are easy to find by hand for small sets of data. Arranging even a moderate number of observations in order is very tedious, however, so that finding the median by hand for larger sets of data is unpleasant. Even simple calculators have an $\bar{x}$ button, but you will need software or a graphing calculator to automate finding the median.

EXAMPLE 1.10 Median Earnings of Black Female Workers

CASE 1.2 

To find the median earnings of our 15 black female bank workers, first arrange the data in order from smallest to largest:

12,641 15,953 16,015 16,555 16,904 17,124 17,274 **17,516** 17,813
18,206 18,405 19,090 19,312 19,338 20,788

The count of observations $n = 15$ is odd. The median, then, is the center observation in the ordered list. The center observation is the 8th observation as given by our formula for locating the median,

$$\text{location of } M = \frac{n+1}{2} = \frac{16}{2} = 8$$

The median is the bold \$17,516 in the list. This number has 7 observations to its left and 7 observations to its right.

How much does the outlier \$12,641 affect the median? Drop it from the list and find the median for the remaining $n = 14$ black females. The rule for locating the median in the list gives

$$\text{location of } M = \frac{n+1}{2} = \frac{15}{2} = 7.5$$

The location 7.5 means "halfway between the 7th and 8th observations in the ordered list."

15,953 16,015 16,555 16,904 17,124 17,274 **17,516** **17,813** 18,206 18,405
19,090 19,312 19,338 20,788

With an even number of observations, there is no center observation. The bold 7th and 8th observations are the middle pair in the list. There are 6 observations on either side of this pair. The median is halfway between \$17,516 and \$17,813. So

$$M = \frac{17{,}516 + 17{,}813}{2} = 17{,}664.50$$

Comparing the mean and the median

Examples 1.9 and 1.10 illustrate an important difference between the mean and the median. The low outlier pulls the mean earnings down by \$350. The median drops by only \$148 when we add the low outlier to our list. The median is more *resistant* than the mean. If the lowest-paid worker had earned nothing, the median for all 15 workers would remain \$17,516. The smallest observation just counts as one observation below the center, no matter how far below the center it lies. The mean uses the actual value of each observation and so will chase a single small observation downward.

The best way to compare the response of the mean and median to extreme observations is to use an interactive applet that allows you to place points on a line and then drag them with your computer's mouse. Exercises 1.62 to 1.64 use the *Mean and Median* applet on the Web site for this book, `www.whfreeman.com/pbs`, to compare mean and median.

applet

The mean and median of a symmetric distribution are close together. If the distribution is exactly symmetric, the mean and median are exactly the same. In a skewed distribution, the mean is farther out in the long tail than is the median. For example, the distribution of house prices is strongly skewed to the right. There are many moderately priced houses and a few very expensive mansions. The few expensive houses pull the mean up but do not affect the median. The mean price of existing houses sold in 2000 was $176,200, but the median price for these same houses was only $139,000. Reports about house prices, incomes, and other strongly skewed distributions usually give the median ("midpoint") rather than the mean ("arithmetic average"). However, if you are a tax assessor interested in the total value of houses in your area, use the mean. The total is the mean times the number of houses, but it has no connection with the median. The mean and median measure center in different ways, and both are useful.

APPLY YOUR KNOWLEDGE

1.41 Bank workers. Find the median earnings of the remaining three groups of workers in Table 1.10. Do your preliminary conclusions from comparing the medians differ from the results of comparing the mean earnings in Exercise 1.39? (Because the median is not distorted by outliers, we might prefer to base an initial look at possible inequity on the median rather than the mean.)

1.42 Gross domestic product. The success of companies expanding to developing regions of the world depends in part on the prosperity of the countries in those regions. Here are World Bank data on the growth of gross domestic product (percent per year) for the period 2000 to 2004 in countries in Asia (not including Japan):

Country	Growth	Country	Growth
Bangladesh	5.2	Malaysia	4.4
China	9.4	Pakistan	4.1
Hong Kong	3.2	Philippines	3.9
India	6.2	Singapore	2.9
Indonesia	4.6	Thailand	5.4
Korea (South)	4.7	Vietnam	7.2

(a) Make a stemplot of the data. Note the high outlier.

(b) Find the mean and median growth rates. How does the outlier explain the difference between your two results?

(c) Find the mean and median growth rates without the outlier. How does comparing your results in (b) and (c) illustrate the resistance of the median and the lack of resistance of the mean?

1.43 The richest 1%. The distribution of individual incomes in the United States is strongly skewed to the right. In 1997, the mean and median incomes of the top 1% of Americans were $330,000 and $675,000. Which of these numbers is the mean and which is the median? Explain your reasoning.

Measuring spread: the quartiles

A measure of center alone can be misleading. Two nations with the same median household income are very different if one has extremes of wealth and poverty and the other has little variation among households. A drug with the correct mean concentration of active ingredient is dangerous if some batches are much too high and others much too low. We are interested in the *spread* or *variability* of incomes and drug potencies as well as their centers. **The simplest useful numerical description of a distribution consists of both a measure of center and a measure of spread.**

One way to measure spread is to give the smallest and largest observations. For example, the earnings of the black female bank workers in Table 1.10 range from \$12,641 to \$20,788. These single observations show the full spread of the data, but they may be outliers. We can improve our description of spread by also giving several percentiles. The

percentile

***p*th percentile** of a distribution is the value such that p percent of the observations fall at or below it. The median is just the 50th percentile, so the use of percentiles to report spread is particularly appropriate when the median is our measure of center. The most commonly used percentiles other than the median are the *quartiles*. The first quartile is the 25th percentile, and the third quartile is the 75th percentile. That is, the first and third quartiles show the spread of the middle half of the data. (The second quartile is the median itself.) To calculate a percentile, arrange the observations in increasing order and count up the required percent from the bottom of the list. Our definition of percentiles is a bit inexact because there is not always a value with exactly p percent of the data at or below it. We will be content to take the nearest observation for most percentiles, but the quartiles are important enough to require an exact recipe. The rule for calculating the quartiles uses the rule for the median.

The Quartiles Q_1 and Q_3

To calculate the **quartiles:**

1. Arrange the observations in increasing order and locate the median M in the ordered list of observations.
2. The **first quartile** Q_1 is the median of the observations whose position in the ordered list is to the left of the location of the overall median.
3. The **third quartile** Q_3 is the median of the observations whose position in the ordered list is to the right of the location of the overall median.

Here is an example that shows how the rules for the quartiles work for both odd and even numbers of observations.

EXAMPLE 1.11 Finding the Quartiles

CASE 1.2

The earnings of the 15 black female bank workers in our sample of National Bank hourly employees (arranged from smallest to largest) are

12,641 15,953 16,015 16,555 16,904 17,124 17,274 **17,516** 17,813
18,206 18,405 19,090 19,312 19,338 20,788

The count of observations $n = 15$ is odd, so the median is the 8th observation in the list, the bold 17,516. This number has 7 observations to its left and 7 observations to its right. The first quartile is the median of the first 7 observations, and the third quartile is the median of the last 7 observations. Check that $Q_1 = 16{,}555$ and $Q_3 = 19{,}090$.

Notice that the quartiles are resistant. For example, Q_1 would have the same value if the low outlier 12,641 were 1000.

Table 1.10 also reports the annual earnings of 12 black male hourly workers. Here they are, arranged from smallest to largest:

16,576 16,853 16,890 17,147 17,755 18,365 | 18,402 19,028 20,972
21,565 24,750 29,347

The median is halfway between the 6th and 7th entries in the ordered list. We have marked its location by |. The value of the median is

$$M = \frac{18{,}365 + 18{,}402}{2} = 18{,}383.5$$

The first quartile is the median of the 6 observations to the left of the | in the list, and the third quartile is the median of the 6 observations to the right. Check that $Q_1 = 17{,}018.5$ and $Q_3 = 21{,}268.5$.

We find other percentiles more informally. For example, we take the 90th percentile of the earnings of the 12 black male workers to be the 11th in the ordered list, because $0.90 \times 12 = 10.8$, which we round to 11. The 90th percentile is therefore \$24,750.

Be careful when several observations take the same numerical value. Write down all of the observations and apply the rules just as if they all had distinct values.

Some software packages use a slightly different rule to find the quartiles, so computer results may differ a bit from your own work. Don't worry about this. The differences will always be too small to be important.

The five-number summary and boxplots

The smallest and largest observations tell us little about the distribution as a whole, but they give information about the tails of the distribution that is missing if we know only Q_1, M, and Q_3. To get a quick summary of both center and spread, combine all five numbers. The result is the *five-number summary* and a graph based on it.

The Five-Number Summary and Boxplots

The **five-number summary** of a distribution consists of the smallest observation, the first quartile, the median, the third quartile, and the largest observation, written in order from smallest to largest. In symbols, the five-number summary is

$$\text{Minimum} \quad Q_1 \quad M \quad Q_3 \quad \text{Maximum}$$

A **boxplot** is a graph of the five-number summary.

- A central box spans the quartiles.
- A line in the box marks the median.
- Lines extend from the box out to the smallest and largest observations.

Boxplots are most useful for side-by-side comparison of several distributions.

You can draw boxplots either horizontally or vertically. Be sure to include a numerical scale in the graph. When you look at a boxplot, first locate the median, which marks the center of the distribution. Then look at the spread. The quartiles show the spread of the middle half of the data, and the extremes (the smallest and largest observations) show the spread of the entire data set. We now have the tools for a preliminary examination of the National Bank earnings data.

EXAMPLE 1.12 Adverse Impact at National Bank

CASE 1.2

The complete data set HOURLY contains information about 1276 full-time hourly workers at National Bank. Among these workers are 315 black females, 697 white females, 81 black males, and 162 white males. Statistical software gives us the five-number summaries for the earnings of each group:

	A	B	C	D	E	F	G	H
1	Earnings	N	Min	25%	Median	75%	Max	
2	Black female	315	12641	17145.5	18354	20363	33703	
3	White female	697	12641	18492	21492	25583	37513	
4	Black male	81	14731	17155	18400	20972	32678	
5	White male	162	12605	18343.25	22029.5	25302	36608	
6								

The boxplots in Figure 1.11 compare the four distributions of earnings. Concentrate on the box spanning the quartiles, because the extremes in a large data set are often outliers. We see at once that whites, both female and male, tend to earn more than blacks. The median income of white hourly workers is greater than the third quartile of black income. There are only minor differences between females and males within each race. In legal terms, the data demonstrate that National Bank's pay policies have an *adverse impact* on blacks. The bank must now investigate whether there is a legitimate reason for the black/white earnings difference, such as hours worked, seniority, or job classification.

Figure 1.11 illustrates the power of simple statistical descriptions to make sense of a large amount of information. Although of less interest in this case, boxplots also suggest the symmetry or skewness of a distribution. In a symmetric distribution, the first and third quartiles are equally distant from the median. In most distributions that are skewed to the right, on the other hand, the third quartile will be farther above the median than the first quartile is below it. The extremes behave the same way, but remember that they are just single observations and may say little about the distribution as a whole, especially if either is an outlier. Figure 1.11 suggests that the earnings distributions are somewhat right-skewed.

APPLY YOUR KNOWLEDGE

1.44 Bank workers. Complete the calculation of the five-number summaries of earnings for the four sample groups of workers in Table 1.10. Make side-by-side boxplots to compare the groups. Do these small samples faithfully reflect the nature of the complete data set as shown in Figure 1.11?

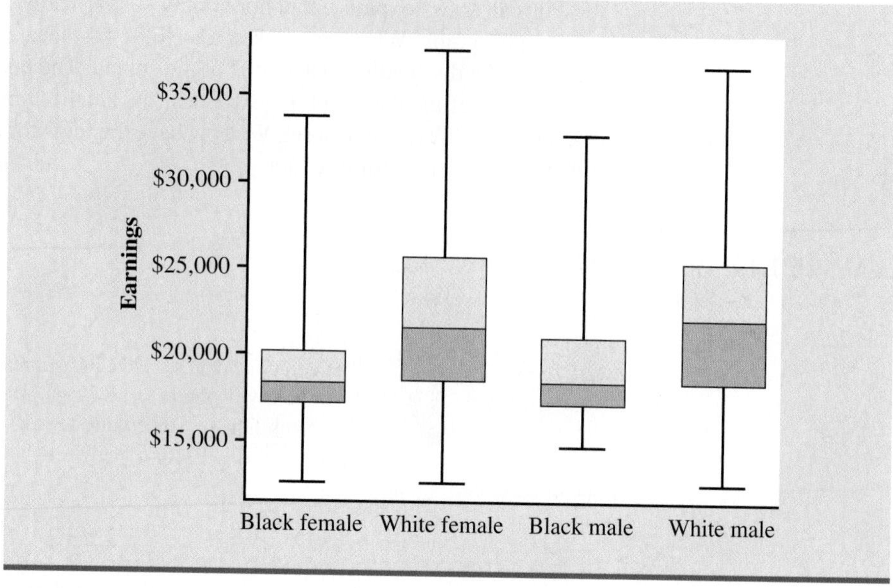

FIGURE 1.11 Side-by-side boxplots comparing the earnings of four groups of hourly workers at National Bank, for Example 1.12.

1.45 Gross domestic product. Exercise 1.42 (page 34) gives the growth of gross domestic product for 12 Asian countries. The World Bank data also looked at 13 Eastern European countries. Here is the growth of gross domestic product for each of these countries:

Country	Growth	Country	Growth
Albania	6.0	Latvia	1.0
Belarus	−5.2	Poland	4.9
Bulgaria	−1.0	Romania	1.4
Croatia	3.5	Russian Federation	7.0
Czech Republic	3.2	Slovenia	3.7
Estonia	−1.7	Ukraine	−12.1
Hungary	−1.5		

(a) Find the five-number summary for each group of countries (Asian and Eastern European).

(b) Make side-by-side boxplots to compare the growth of gross domestic product for the two groups of countries. What do you conclude?

1.46 Managerial employment. The Bureau of Labor Statistics collects data on employment and wages for various occupations in the United States. One major division of occupations is Management Occupations (OCC Code 11-0000). Table 1.11 displays the annual wage averages (rounded to the nearest thousand) for this occupational category.[20]

(a) Make a stemplot of the distribution of wages for these management occupations.

TABLE 1.12 Monthly percent returns on Philip Morris stock from June 1990 to July 2001

3.0	−5.7	1.2	4.1	3.2	7.3	7.5	18.7	3.7	−1.8
2.4	−6.5	6.7	9.4	−2.0	−2.8	−3.4	19.2	−4.8	0.5
−0.6	2.8	−0.5	−4.5	8.7	2.7	4.1	−10.3	4.8	−2.3
−3.1	−10.2	−3.7	−26.6	7.2	−2.4	−2.8	3.4	−4.6	17.2
4.2	0.5	8.3	−7.1	−8.4	7.7	−9.6	6.0	6.8	10.9
1.6	0.2	−2.4	−2.4	3.9	1.7	9.0	3.6	7.6	3.2
−3.7	4.2	13.2	0.9	4.2	4.0	2.8	6.7	−10.4	2.7
10.3	5.7	0.6	−14.2	1.3	2.9	11.8	10.6	5.2	13.8
−14.7	3.5	11.7	1.5	2.0	−3.2	−3.9	−4.7	9.8	4.9
−8.3	4.8	−3.2	−10.9	0.7	6.4	11.3	−5.1	12.3	10.5
9.4	−3.6	−12.4	−16.5	−8.9	−0.4	10.0	5.4	−7.3	0.5
−7.4	−22.9	−0.5	−10.6	−9.2	−3.3	5.2	5.4	19.4	3.5
−4.9	17.8	0.7	24.4	4.3	16.6	0.0	9.5	−0.4	5.6
2.6	−2.7	−8.1	4.2						

The quartiles? How do you know, without actual calculation? (Returns over longer periods of time, or returns on portfolios containing several investments, tend to follow a Normal distribution more closely than these monthly returns do. So use of the mean and standard deviation is better justified for such data.)

1.74 Initial public offerings. During the stock market boom of the 1990s, initial public offerings (IPOs) of the stock of new companies often produced enormous gains for people who bought the stocks when they first became available. At least that's what legend says. A study of all 4567 companies that went public in the years 1990 to 2000 (excluding very small IPOs) found that on the average their stock prices had either *risen* 111% or *declined* 31% by the end of the year 2000.[25] One of these numbers is the mean change in price and one is the median change. Which is which, and how can you tell?

1.75 Highly paid athletes. A news article reports that of the 411 players on National Basketball Association rosters in February 1998, only 139 "made more than the league average salary" of \$2.36 million. Is \$2.36 million the mean or median salary for NBA players? How do you know?

1.76 Mean or median? Which measure of center, the mean or the median, should you use in each of the following situations?

(a) Middletown is considering imposing an income tax on citizens. The city government wants to know the average income of citizens so that it can estimate the total tax base.

(b) In a study of the standard of living of typical families in Middletown, a sociologist estimates the average family income in that city.

1.77 A standard deviation contest. You must choose four numbers from the whole numbers 0 to 10, with repeats allowed.

(a) Choose four numbers that have the smallest possible standard deviation.

(b) Choose four numbers that have the largest possible standard deviation.

(c) Is more than one choice possible in either (a) or (b)? Explain.

1.78 Outliers in earnings data. The **1.5 × IQR rule** was defined in Exercise 1.51 (page 45). Use this rule to answer the following questions.

(a) Confirm that the low outlier in the earnings of black female bank workers (Table 1.10, page 30) lies more than $1.5 \times IQR$ below Q_1. That is, the $1.5 \times IQR$ rule fingers this observation as a suspected outlier.

(b) Does the rule point out any suspected outliers among the black male workers in Table 1.10?

1.3 The Normal Distributions

We now have a kit of graphical and numerical tools for describing distributions. What is more, we have a clear strategy for exploring data on a single quantitative variable:

1. Always plot your data: make a graph, usually a histogram or a stemplot.
2. Look for the overall pattern (shape, center, spread) and for striking deviations such as outliers.
3. Calculate a numerical summary to briefly describe center and spread.

Here is one more step to add to this strategy:

4. Sometimes the overall pattern of a large number of observations is so regular that we can describe it by a smooth curve.

Density curves

Figure 1.15 is a histogram of the city gas mileage achieved by all 856 motor vehicles (2001 model year) listed in the government's annual fuel economy report.[26] The distribution is quite regular. With the exception of a few high outliers, the histogram is roughly symmetric, and both tails fall off quite smoothly from a single center peak located at approximately 20 miles per gallon. The smooth curve overlying the histogram bars in Figure 1.15 is an approximate description of the overall pattern of the data. The curve is a **mathematical model** for the distribution. A mathematical model is an idealized description. It gives a compact picture of the overall pattern of the data but ignores minor irregularities as well as any outliers.

mathematical model

We will see that it is easier to work with the smooth curve in Figure 1.15 than with the histogram. The reason is that the histogram depends on our choice of classes, while with a little care we can use a curve that does not depend on any choices we make. Here's how we do it.

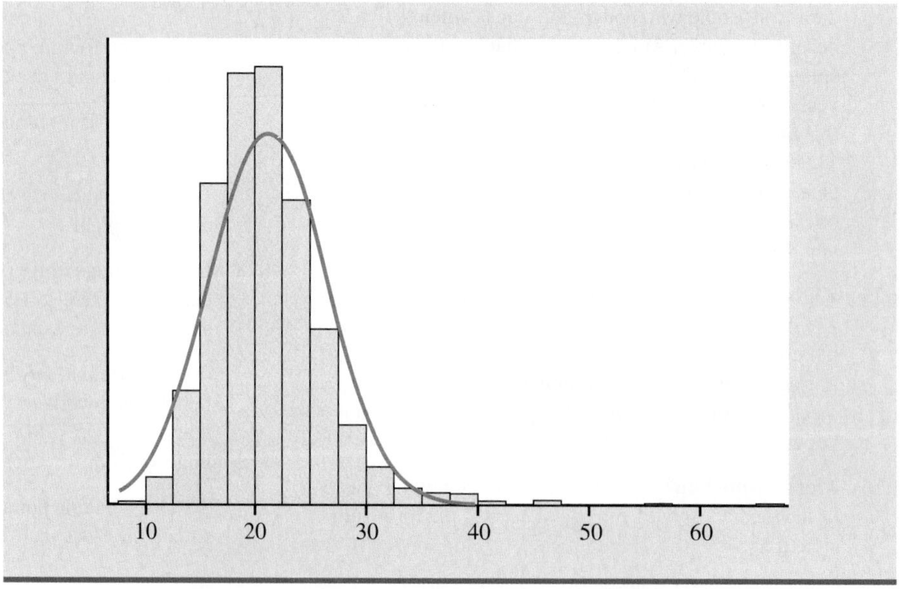

FIGURE 1.15 Histogram of the city gas mileage (miles per gallon) of 856 motor vehicles. The smooth curve shows the overall shape of the distribution.

EXAMPLE 1.15 From Histogram to Density Curve

Our eyes respond to the *areas* of the bars in a histogram. The bar areas represent proportions of the observations. Figure 1.16(a) is a copy of Figure 1.15 with the leftmost bars shaded. The area of the shaded bars in Figure 1.16(a) represents the proportion of 2001 model vehicles with miles per gallon ratings of less than 20. There are 384 such vehicles, which represent $384/856 = 0.449 = 44.9\%$ of all 2001 model vehicles.

Now concentrate on the curve drawn through the bars. In Figure 1.16(b), the area under the curve to the left of 20 is shaded. Adjust the scale of the graph so that *the total area under the curve is exactly 1*. This area represents the proportion 1, that is, all the observations. Areas under the curve then represent proportions of the observations. The curve is now a *density curve*. The shaded area under the density curve in Figure 1.16(b) represents the proportion of 2001 model

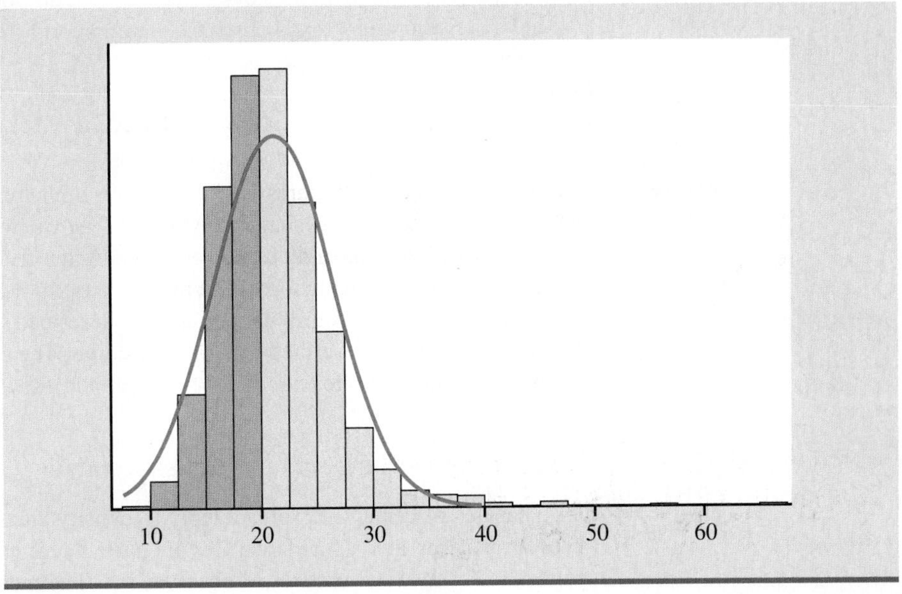

FIGURE 1.16(a) The proportion of gas mileages less than 20.0 from the histogram is 0.449, for Example 1.15.

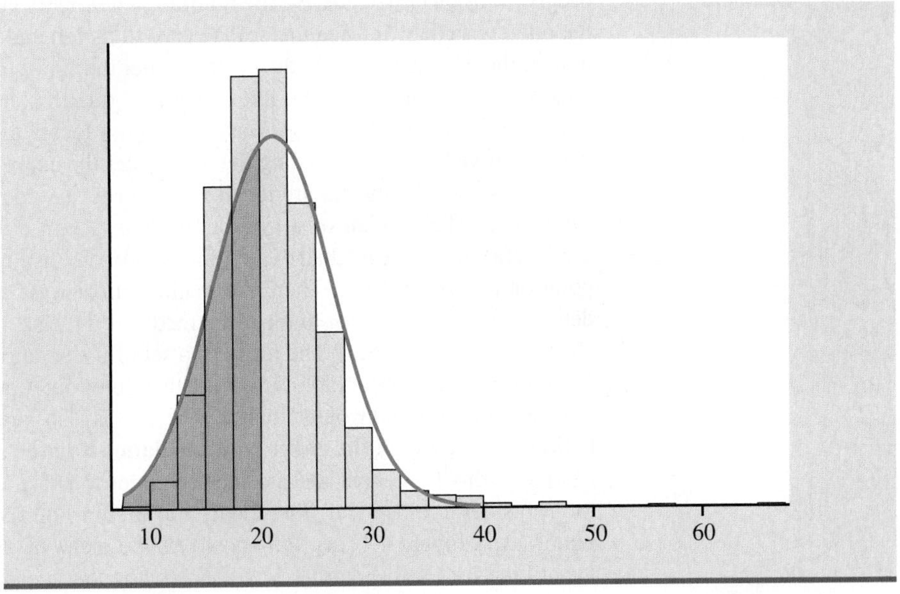

FIGURE 1.16(b) The proportion of gas mileages less than 20.0 from the density curve is 0.410, for Example 1.15.

vehicles with miles per gallon ratings of less than 20. This area is 0.410, only 0.039 away from the histogram result. You can see that areas under the density curve give quite good approximations of areas given by the histogram.

Density Curve

A **density curve** is a curve that

- is always on or above the horizontal axis, and
- has area exactly 1 underneath it.

A density curve describes the overall pattern of a distribution. The area under the curve and above any range of values is the proportion of all observations that fall in that range.

Normal curve

The density curve in Figures 1.15 and 1.16 is a **Normal curve.** Density curves, like distributions, come in many shapes. Figure 1.17 shows two density curves: a symmetric Normal density curve and a right-skewed curve. A density curve of the appropriate shape is often an adequate description of the overall pattern of a distribution. Outliers, which are deviations from the overall pattern, are not described by the curve. Of course, no set of real data is exactly described by a density curve. The curve is an approximation that is easy to use and accurate enough for practical purposes.

The median and mean of a density curve

Our measures of center and spread apply to density curves as well as to actual sets of observations. The median and quartiles are easy. Areas under a density curve represent proportions of the total number of observations. The median is the point with half the observations on either side. So **the median of a density curve is the equal-areas point,** the point with half the area under the curve to its left and the remaining half of the area to its right. The quartiles divide the area under the curve into quarters. One-fourth of the area under the curve is to the left of the first quartile, and three-fourths of the area is to the left of the third quartile. You can roughly locate the median and quartiles of any density curve by eye by dividing the area under the curve into four equal parts.

Because density curves are idealized patterns, a symmetric density curve is exactly symmetric. The median of a symmetric density curve is therefore at its center. Figure 1.17(a) shows the median of a symmetric curve. It isn't so easy to spot the equal-areas point on a skewed curve. There are mathematical ways of finding the median for any density curve. We did that to mark the median on the skewed curve in Figure 1.17(b).

What about the mean? The mean of a set of observations is their arithmetic average. If we think of the observations as weights strung out along a thin rod, the mean is the point at which the rod would balance. This fact is also true of density curves. **The mean is the point at which the curve would balance if made of solid material.** Figure 1.18 illustrates this fact about the mean. A symmetric curve balances at its center because the two sides are identical. **The mean and median of a symmetric density curve are equal**, as in Figure 1.17(a). We know that the mean of a skewed distribution is pulled toward the long tail. Figure 1.17(b) shows how the mean of a skewed density curve is

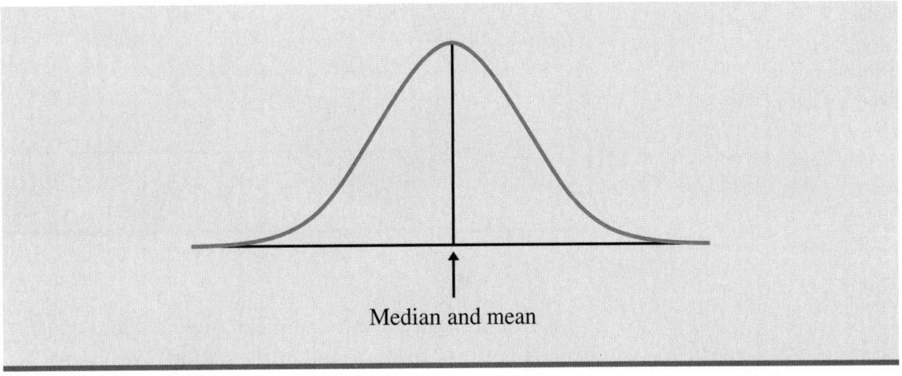

FIGURE 1.17(a) The median and mean of a symmetric density curve.

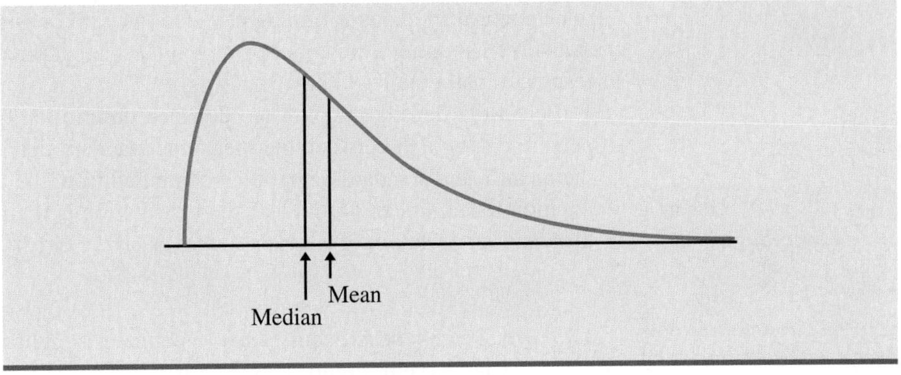

FIGURE 1.17(b) The median and mean of a right-skewed density curve.

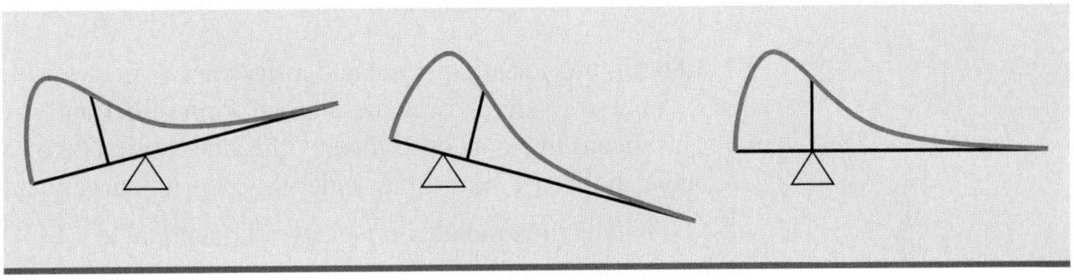

FIGURE 1.18 The mean is the balance point of a density curve.

pulled toward the long tail more than is the median. It's hard to locate the balance point by eye on a skewed curve. There are mathematical ways of calculating the mean for any density curve, so we are able to mark the mean as well as the median in Figure 1.17(b).

Median and Mean of a Density Curve

The **median** of a density curve is the equal-areas point, the point that divides the area under the curve in half.

The **mean** of a density curve is the balance point, at which the curve would balance if made of solid material.

The median and mean are the same for a symmetric density curve. They both lie at the center of the curve. The mean of a skewed curve is pulled away from the median in the direction of the long tail.

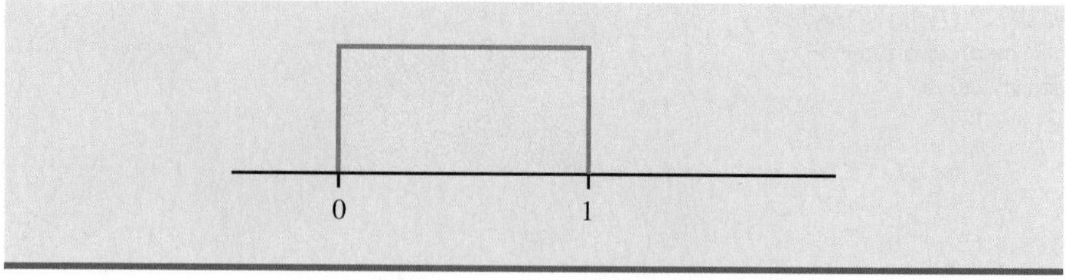

FIGURE 1.19 The density curve of a uniform distribution, for Exercise 1.80.

We can roughly locate the mean, median, and quartiles of any density curve by eye. This is not true of the standard deviation. When necessary, we can once again call on more advanced mathematics to learn the value of the standard deviation. The study of mathematical methods for doing calculations with density curves is part of theoretical statistics. Though we are concentrating on statistical practice, we often make use of the results of mathematical study.

mean μ
standard deviation σ

Because a density curve is an idealized description of the distribution of data, we need to distinguish between the mean and standard deviation of the density curve and the mean $\bar{x}$ and standard deviation s computed from the actual observations. The usual notation for the mean of an idealized distribution is μ (the Greek letter mu). We write the standard deviation of a density curve as σ (the Greek letter sigma).

APPLY YOUR KNOWLEDGE

1.79 (a) Sketch a density curve that is symmetric but has a shape different from that of the curve in Figure 1.17(a).

(b) Sketch a density curve that is strongly skewed to the left.

1.80 Figure 1.19 displays the density curve of a *uniform distribution.* The curve takes the constant value 1 over the interval from 0 to 1 and is 0 outside that range of values. This means that data described by this distribution take values that are uniformly spread between 0 and 1. Use areas under this density curve to answer the following questions.

(a) Why is the total area under this curve equal to 1?

(b) What percent of the observations lie above 0.8?

(c) What percent of the observations lie below 0.6?

(d) What percent of the observations lie between 0.25 and 0.75?

(e) What is the mean μ of this distribution?

1.81 Figure 1.20 displays three density curves, each with three points marked. At which of these points on each curve do the mean and the median fall?

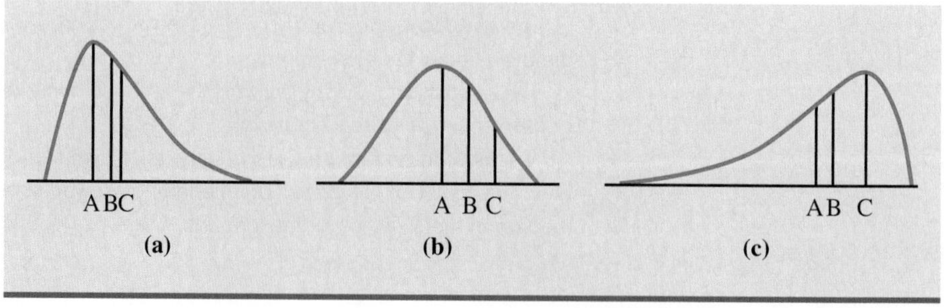

FIGURE 1.20 Three density curves, for Exercise 1.81.

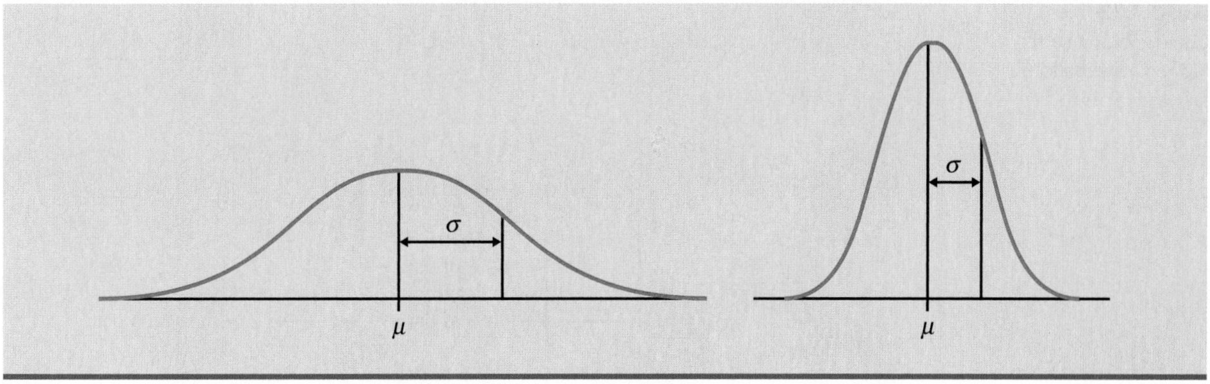

FIGURE 1.21 Two Normal curves, showing the mean μ and standard deviation σ.

Normal distributions

Normal distributions

One particularly important class of density curves has already appeared in Figures 1.15 and 1.17(a). These density curves are symmetric, single-peaked, and bell-shaped. They are called *Normal curves,* and they describe **Normal distributions.** All Normal distributions have the same overall shape. The exact density curve for a particular Normal distribution is described by giving its mean μ and its standard deviation σ. The mean is located at the center of the symmetric curve and is the same as the median. Changing μ without changing σ moves the Normal curve along the horizontal axis without changing its spread. The standard deviation σ controls the spread of a Normal curve. Figure 1.21 shows two Normal curves with different values of σ. The curve with the larger standard deviation is more spread out.

The standard deviation σ is the natural measure of spread for Normal distributions. Not only do μ and σ completely determine the shape of a Normal curve, but we can locate σ by eye on the curve. Here's how. Imagine that you are skiing down a mountain that has the shape of a Normal curve. At first, you descend at an ever-steeper angle as you go out from the peak:

Fortunately, before you find yourself going straight down, the slope begins to grow flatter rather than steeper as you go out and down:

The points at which this change of curvature takes place are located at distance σ on either side of the mean μ. You can feel the change as you run a pencil along a Normal curve, and so find the standard deviation. Remember that μ and σ alone do not specify the shape of most distributions, and that the shape of density curves in general does not reveal σ. These are special properties of Normal distributions.

Why are the Normal distributions important in statistics? Here are three reasons. First, Normal distributions are good descriptions for some distributions of *real data*. Distributions that are often close to Normal include scores on tests taken by many people (such as GMAT exams), repeated careful measurements of the same quantity (such as measurements taken from a production process), and characteristics of biological populations (such as yields of corn). Second, Normal distributions are good approximations

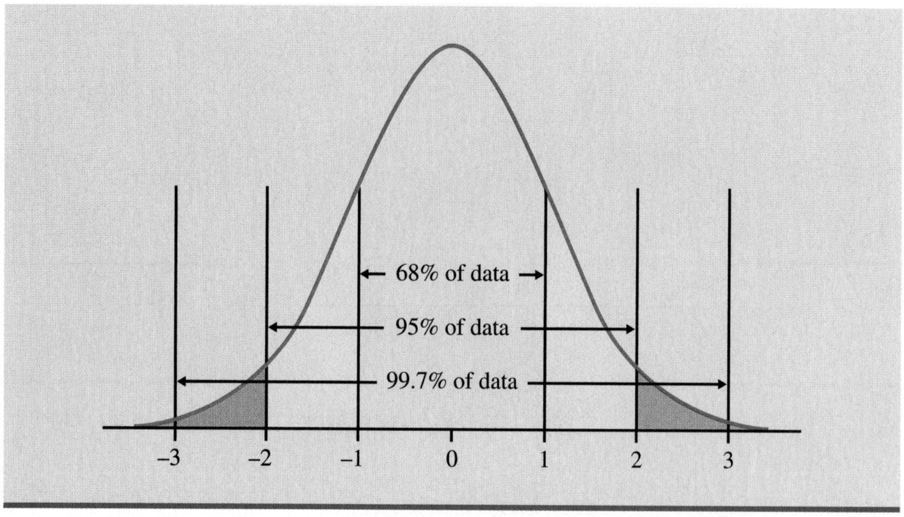

FIGURE 1.22 The 68–95–99.7 rule for Normal distributions.

to the results of many kinds of *chance outcomes,* such as tossing a coin many times. Third, and most important, we will see that many *statistical inference* procedures based on Normal distributions work well for other roughly symmetric distributions. However, even though many sets of data follow a Normal distribution, many do not. Most company salary distributions, for example, are skewed to the right and so are not Normal. Nonnormal data, like nonnormal people, not only are common but are sometimes more interesting than their normal counterparts.

The 68–95–99.7 rule

Although there are many Normal curves, they all have common properties. In particular, all Normal distributions obey the following rule.

The 68–95–99.7 Rule

In the Normal distribution with mean μ and standard deviation σ:

- **68%** of the observations fall within σ of the mean μ.
- **95%** of the observations fall within 2σ of μ.
- **99.7%** of the observations fall within 3σ of μ.

Figure 1.22 illustrates the 68–95–99.7 rule. By remembering these three numbers, you can think about Normal distributions without constantly making detailed calculations.

EXAMPLE 1.16 Using the 68–95–99.7 Rule

The distribution of weights of 9-ounce bags of a particular brand of potato chips is approximately Normal with mean $\mu = 9.12$ ounces and standard deviation $\sigma = 0.15$ ounce. Figure 1.23 shows what the 68–95–99.7 rule says about this distribution.

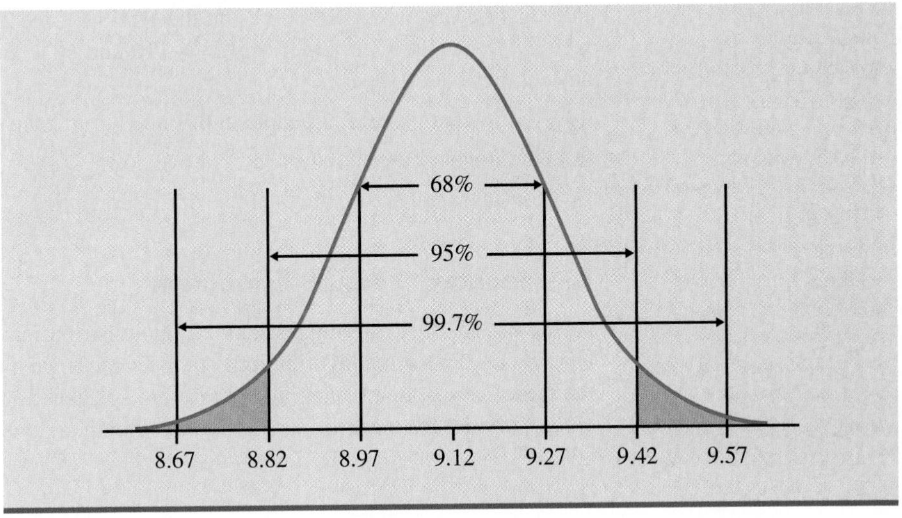

FIGURE 1.23 The 68–95–99.7 rule applied to the distribution of the weights of bags of potato chips, for Example 1.16. Here $\mu = 9.12$ ounces and $\sigma = 0.15$ ounce.

Two standard deviations is 0.3 ounces for this distribution. The 95 part of the 68–95–99.7 rule says that the middle 95% of 9-ounce bags weigh between $9.12 - 0.3$ and $9.12 + 0.3$ ounces, that is, between 8.82 ounces and 9.42 ounces. This fact is exactly true for an exactly Normal distribution. It is approximately true for the weights of 9-ounce bags of chips because the distribution of these weights is approximately Normal.

The other 5% of bags have weights outside the range from 8.82 to 9.42 ounces. Because the Normal distributions are symmetric, half of these bags are on the heavy side. So the heaviest 2.5% of 9-ounce bags are heavier than 9.42 ounces.

The 99.7 part of the 68–95–99.7 rule says that almost all bags (99.7% of them) have weights between $\mu - 3\sigma$ and $\mu + 3\sigma$. This range of weights is 8.67 to 9.57 ounces.

Because we will mention Normal distributions often, a short notation is helpful. We abbreviate the Normal distribution with mean μ and standard deviation σ as $N(\mu, \sigma)$. For example, the distribution of weights in the previous example is $N(9.12, 0.15)$.

APPLY YOUR KNOWLEDGE

1.82 Heights of young men. Product designers often must consider physical characteristics of their target population. For example, the distribution of heights of men aged 20 to 29 years is approximately Normal with mean 69 inches and standard deviation 2.5 inches. Draw a Normal curve on which this mean and standard deviation are correctly located. (*Hint:* Draw the curve first, locate the points where the curvature changes, then mark the horizontal axis.)

1.83 More on young men's heights. The distribution of heights of young men is approximately Normal with mean 69 inches and standard deviation 2.5 inches. Use the 68–95–99.7 rule to answer the following questions.

(a) What percent of these men are taller than 74 inches?

(b) Between what heights do the middle 95% of young men fall?

(c) What percent of young men are shorter than 66.5 inches?

1.84 IQ test scores. Employers may ask job applicants to take an IQ test if the test has been shown to predict performance on the job. One such test is the Wechsler Adult

Intelligence Scale (WAIS). Scores on the WAIS for the 20 to 34 age group are approximately Normally distributed with $\mu = 110$ and $\sigma = 25$. Use the 68–95–99.7 rule to answer these questions.

(a) About what percent of people in this age group have scores above 110?

(b) About what percent have scores above 160?

(c) In what range do the middle 95% of all scores lie?

The standard Normal distribution

As the 68–95–99.7 rule suggests, all Normal distributions share many common properties. In fact, all Normal distributions are the same if we measure in units of size σ about the mean μ as center. Changing to these units is called *standardizing*. To standardize a value, subtract the mean of the distribution and then divide by the standard deviation.

Standardizing and z-Scores

If x is an observation from a distribution that has mean μ and standard deviation σ, the **standardized value** of x is

$$z = \frac{x - \mu}{\sigma}$$

A standardized value is often called a **z-score.**

A z-score tells us how many standard deviations the original observation falls away from the mean, and in which direction. Observations larger than the mean are positive when standardized, and observations smaller than the mean are negative when standardized.

EXAMPLE 1.17 Standardizing Potato Chip Bag Weights

The weights of 9-ounce potato chip bags are approximately Normal with $\mu = 9.12$ ounces and $\sigma = 0.15$ ounce. The standardized weight is

$$z = \frac{\text{weight} - 9.12}{0.15}$$

A bag's standardized weight is the number of standard deviations by which its weight differs from the mean weight of all bags. A bag weighing 9.3 ounces, for example, has *standardized* weight

$$z = \frac{9.3 - 9.12}{0.15} = 1.2$$

or 1.2 standard deviations above the mean. Similarly, a bag weighing 8.7 ounces has standardized weight

$$z = \frac{8.7 - 9.12}{0.15} = -2.8$$

or 2.8 standard deviations below the mean bag weight.

If the variable we standardize has a Normal distribution, standardizing does more than give a common scale. It makes all Normal distributions into a single distribution, and this distribution is still Normal. Standardizing a variable that has any Normal distribution produces a new variable that has the *standard Normal distribution*.

Standard Normal Distribution

The **standard Normal distribution** is the Normal distribution $N(0, 1)$ with mean 0 and standard deviation 1.

If a variable x has any Normal distribution $N(\mu, \sigma)$ with mean μ and standard deviation σ, then the standardized variable

$$z = \frac{x - \mu}{\sigma}$$

has the standard Normal distribution.

APPLY YOUR KNOWLEDGE

1.85 SAT versus ACT. Eleanor scores 680 on the Mathematics part of the SAT. The distribution of SAT scores in a reference population is Normal, with mean 500 and standard deviation 100. Gerald takes the American College Testing (ACT) Mathematics test and scores 27. ACT scores are Normally distributed with mean 18 and standard deviation 6. Find the standardized scores for both students. Assuming that both tests measure the same kind of ability, who has the higher score?

Normal distribution calculations

An area under a density curve is a proportion of the observations in a distribution. Any question about what proportion of observations lies in some range of values can be answered by finding an area under the curve. Because all Normal distributions are the same when we standardize, we can find areas under any Normal curve from a single table, a table that gives areas under the curve for the standard Normal distribution.

EXAMPLE 1.18 Using the Standard Normal Distribution

What proportion of all 9-ounce bags of potato chips weigh less than 9.3 ounces? This proportion is the area under the $N(9.12, 0.15)$ curve to the left of the point 9.3. Because the standardized weight corresponding to 9.3 ounces is

$$z = \frac{x - \mu}{\sigma} = \frac{9.3 - 9.12}{0.15} = 1.2$$

this area is the same as the area under the standard Normal curve to the left of the point $z = 1.2$. Figure 1.24(a) shows this area.

Many calculators will give you areas under the standard Normal curve. In case your calculator or software does not, Table A in the back of the book gives some of these areas.

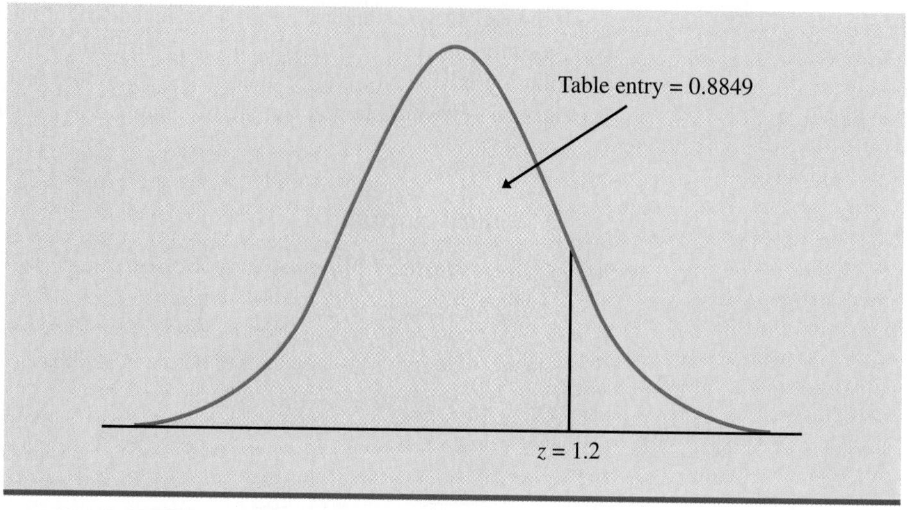

FIGURE 1.24(a) The area under a standard Normal curve to the left of the point $z = 1.2$ is 0.8849. Table A gives areas under the standard Normal curve.

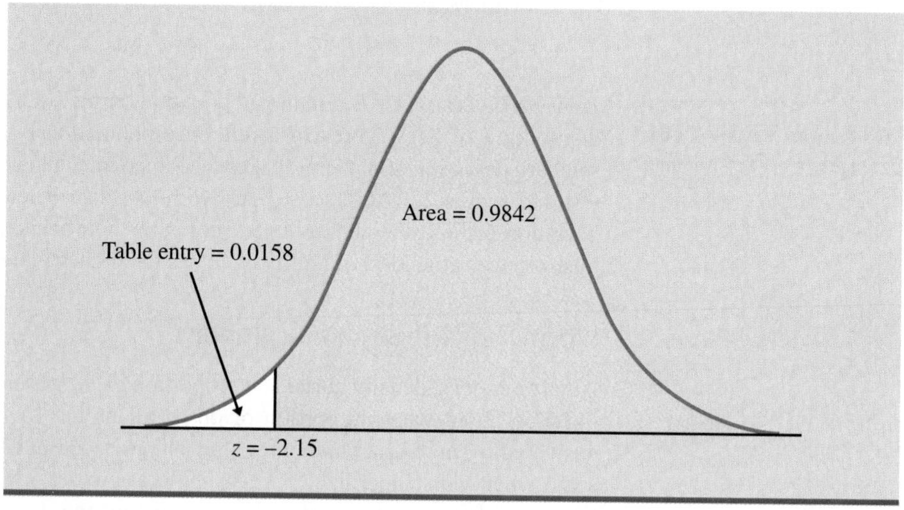

FIGURE 1.24(b) Areas under the standard Normal curve to the right and left of $z = -2.15$. Table A gives only areas to the left.

The Standard Normal Table

Table A is a table of areas under the standard Normal curve. The table entry for each value z is the area under the curve to the left of z.

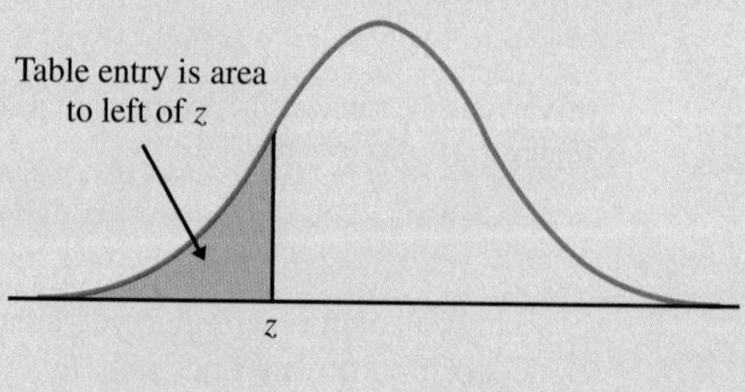

EXAMPLE 1.19 Using the Standard Normal Table

Problem: Find the proportion of observations from the standard Normal distribution that are less than 1.2.

Solution: To find the area to the left of 1.20, locate 1.2 in the left-hand column of Table A, then locate the remaining digit 0 as .00 in the top row. The entry opposite 1.2 and under .00 is 0.8849. This is the area we seek. Figure 1.23(a) illustrates the relationship between the value $z = 1.20$ and the area 0.8849. Because $z = 1.20$ is the standardized value of weight 9.3 ounces, the proportion of 9-ounce bags that weigh less than 9.3 ounces is 0.8849 (about 88.5%).

Problem: Find the proportion of observations from the standard Normal distribution that are greater than −2.15.

Solution: Enter Table A under $z = -2.15$. That is, find −2.1 in the left-hand column and .05 in the top row. The table entry is 0.0158. This is the area to the *left* of −2.15. Because the total area under the curve is 1, the area lying to the *right* of −2.15 is $1 - 0.0158 = 0.9842$. Figure 1.24(b) illustrates these areas.

We can answer any question about proportions of observations in a Normal distribution by standardizing and then using the standard Normal table. Here is an outline of the method for finding the proportion of the distribution in any region.

Finding Normal Proportions

1. State the problem in terms of the observed variable x.
2. Standardize x to restate the problem in terms of a standard Normal variable z. Draw a picture to show the area under the standard Normal curve.
3. Find the required area under the standard Normal curve using Table A and the fact that the total area under the curve is 1.

EXAMPLE 1.20 Normal Distribution Calculations

The annual rate of return on stock indexes (which combine many individual stocks) is approximately Normal. Since 1945, the Standard & Poor's 500 stock index has had a mean yearly return of about 12%, with a standard deviation of 16.5%. Take this Normal distribution to be the distribution of yearly returns over a long period. The market is down for the year if the return on the index is less than zero. In what proportion of years is the market down?

1. *State the problem.* Call the annual rate of return for Standard & Poor's 500 stock index x. The variable x has the $N(12, 16.5)$ distribution. We want the proportion of years with $x < 0$.
2. *Standardize.* Subtract the mean, then divide by the standard deviation, to turn x into a standard Normal z:

$$x < 0$$

$$\frac{x - 12}{16.5} < \frac{0 - 12}{16.5}$$

$$z < -0.73$$

Figure 1.25 shows the standard Normal curve with the area of interest shaded.

FIGURE 1.25 Areas under the standard Normal curve, for Example 1.20.

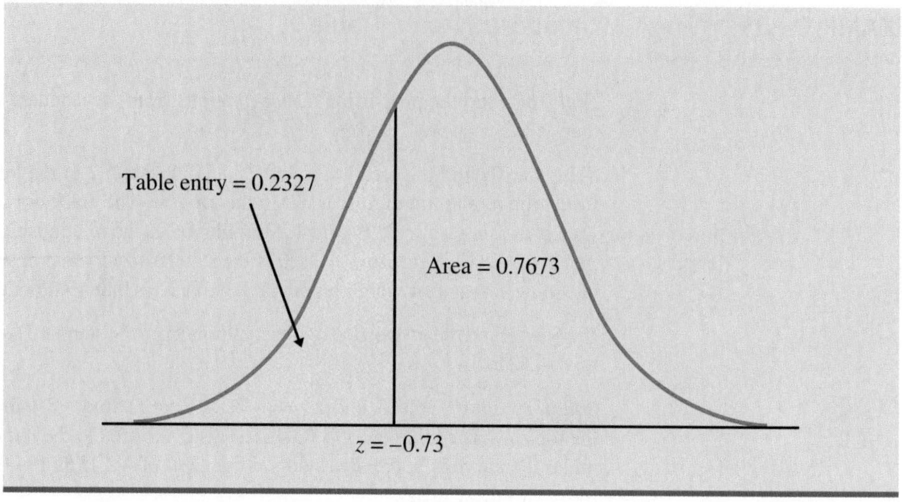

3. *Use the table*. From Table A, we see that the proportion of observations less than −0.73 is 0.2327. The market is down on an annual basis about 23.27% of the time. Notice that the area to the right of −0.73 is 1 − 0.2327 = 0.7673. This indicates that the market is up about 76.73% of the time.

In a Normal distribution, the proportion of observations with $x < 0$ is the same as the proportion with $x \leq 0$. There is no area under the curve and exactly over 0, so the areas under the curve with $x < 0$ and $x \leq 0$ are the same. This isn't true of the actual data. There may be a year with exactly a 0% return. The Normal distribution is an easy-to-use approximation, not a description of every detail in the actual data.

The key to using either software or Table A to do a Normal calculation is to sketch the area you want, then match that area with the areas that the table or software gives you. The interactive *Normal Curve* applet available at `www.whfreeman.com/pbs` allows you to work directly with any Normal curve, finding areas by changing a shaded area with your computer's mouse. You can use this applet to do any Normal distribution problem, though the accuracy of its output is limited. Here is another example of the use of Table A.

applet

EXAMPLE 1.21 More Normal Distribution Calculations

What percent of years have annual rates of return between 12% and 50%?

1. *State the problem.* We want the proportion of years with $12 \leq x \leq 50$.

2. *Standardize.*

$$12 \leq x \leq 50$$

$$\frac{12 - 12}{16.5} \leq \frac{x - 12}{16.5} \leq \frac{50 - 12}{16.5}$$

$$0 \leq z \leq 2.30$$

Figure 1.26 shows the area under the standard Normal curve.

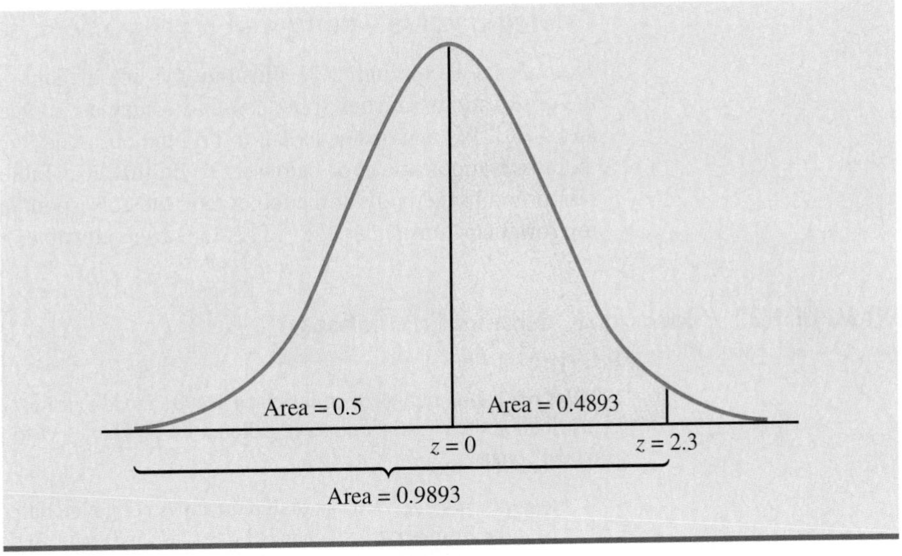

FIGURE 1.26 Areas under the standard Normal curve, for Example 1.21.

3. *Use the table*. The area between 0 and 2.30 is the area below 2.30 *minus* the area below 0. Look at Figure 1.26 to check this. From Table A,

$$\text{area between 0 and 2.30} = \text{area below 2.30} - \text{area below 0.00}$$
$$= 0.9893 - 0.5000 = 0.4893$$

About 49% of years have annual rates of return between 12% and 50%.

Sometimes we encounter a value of z more extreme than those appearing in Table A. For example, the area to the left of $z = -4$ is not given directly in the table. The z-values in Table A leave only area 0.0002 in each tail unaccounted for. For practical purposes, we can act as if there is zero area outside the range of Table A.

APPLY YOUR KNOWLEDGE

1.86 Use Table A to find the proportion of observations from a standard Normal distribution that satisfies each of the following statements. In each case, sketch a standard Normal curve and shade the area under the curve that is the answer to the question.

(a) $z < 2.85$

(b) $z > 2.85$

(c) $z > -1.66$

(d) $-1.66 < z < 2.85$

1.87 Gas mileage. The miles per gallon ratings for 2001 model vehicles vary according to an approximately Normal distribution with mean $\mu = 21.22$ miles per gallon and standard deviation $\sigma = 5.36$ miles per gallon.

(a) What percent of vehicles have miles per gallon ratings greater than 30?

(b) What percent of vehicles have miles per gallon ratings between 30 and 35?

(c) What percent of vehicles have miles per gallon ratings less than 12.45?

Finding a value when given a proportion

Examples 1.19 through 1.21 illustrate the use of Table A to find what proportion of the observations satisfies some condition, such as "annual rate of return between 12% and 50%." We may instead want to find the observed value with a given proportion of the observations above or below it. To do this, use Table A backward. Find the given proportion in the body of the table, read the corresponding z from the left column and top row, then "unstandardize" to get the observed value. Here is an example.

EXAMPLE 1.22 "Backward" Normal Calculations

Miles per gallon ratings of compact cars (2001 models) follow approximately the $N(25.7, 5.88)$ distribution. How many miles per gallon must a vehicle get to place in the top 10% of all 2001 model compact cars?

1. *State the problem.* We want to find the miles per gallon rating x with area 0.1 to its *right* under the Normal curve with mean $\mu = 25.7$ and standard deviation $\sigma = 5.88$. That's the same as finding the miles per gallon rating x with area 0.9 to its *left*. Figure 1.27 poses the question in graphical form. Because Table A gives the areas to the left of z-values, always state the problem in terms of the area to the left of x.

2. *Use the table.* Look in the body of Table A for the entry closest to 0.9. It is 0.8997. This is the entry corresponding to $z = 1.28$. So $z = 1.28$ is the standardized value with area 0.9 to its left.

3. *Unstandardize* to transform the solution from the z back to the original x scale. We know that the standardized value of the unknown x is $z = 1.28$. So x itself satisfies

$$\frac{x - 25.7}{5.88} = 1.28$$

Solving this equation for x gives

$$x = 25.7 + (1.28)(5.88) = 33.2$$

This equation should make sense: it says that x lies 1.28 standard deviations above the mean on this particular Normal curve. That is the "unstandardized" meaning of $z = 1.28$. We see

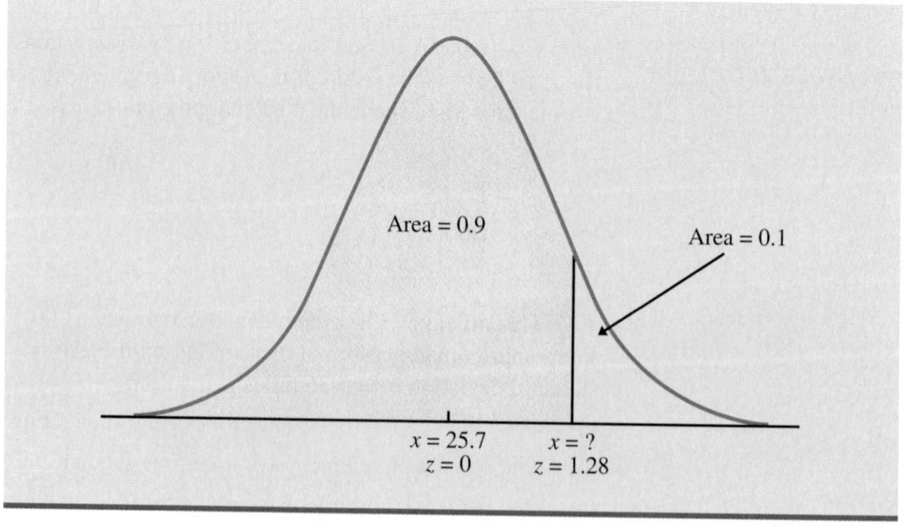

FIGURE 1.27 Locating the point on a Normal curve with area 0.10 to its right, for Example 1.22.

that a compact car must receive a rating of at least 33.2 miles per gallon to place in the highest 10%.

Here is the general formula for unstandardizing a z-score. To find the value x from the Normal distribution with mean μ and standard deviation σ corresponding to a given standard Normal value z, use

$$x = \mu + z\sigma$$

APPLY YOUR KNOWLEDGE

1.88 Use Table A to find the value z of a standard Normal variable that satisfies each of the following conditions. (Use the value of z from Table A that comes closest to satisfying the condition.) In each case, sketch a standard Normal curve with your value of z marked on the axis.

(a) The point z with 25% of the observations falling below it.

(b) The point z with 40% of the observations falling above it.

1.89 GMAT scores. Most graduate schools of business require applicants for admission to take the Graduate Management Admission Council's GMAT examination.[27] Total scores on the GMAT for the more than 500,000 people who took the exam between April 1997 and March 2000 are roughly Normally distributed with mean $\mu = 527$ and standard deviation $\sigma = 112$.

(a) What percent of test takers have scores above 500?

(b) What GMAT scores fall in the lowest 25% of the distribution?

(c) How high a GMAT score is needed to be in the highest 5%?

Assessing the Normality of data

The Normal distributions provide good models for some distributions of real data. Examples include the miles per gallon ratings of vehicles, average payrolls of Major League Baseball teams, and statewide unemployment rates. The distributions of some other common variables are usually skewed and therefore distinctly nonnormal. Examples include personal income, gross sales of business firms, and the service lifetime of mechanical or electronic components. While experience can suggest whether or not a Normal model is plausible in a particular case, it is risky to assume that a distribution is Normal without actually inspecting the data.

The decision to describe a distribution by a Normal model may determine the later steps in our analysis of the data. Both calculations of proportions and statistical inference based on such calculations follow from the choice of a model. How can we judge whether data are approximately Normal?

Normal quantile plot

A histogram or stemplot can reveal distinctly nonnormal features of a distribution, such as outliers, pronounced skewness, or gaps and clusters. If the stemplot or histogram appears roughly symmetric and single-peaked, however, we need a more sensitive way to judge the adequacy of a Normal model. The most useful tool for assessing Normality is another graph, the **Normal quantile plot.***

*Some software calls these graphs *Normal probability plots*. There is a technical distinction between the two types of graphs, but the terms are often used loosely.

Here is the idea of a simple version of a Normal quantile plot. It is not feasible to make Normal quantile plots by hand, but software makes them for us, using more sophisticated versions of this basic idea.

1. Arrange the observed data values from smallest to largest. Record what percentile of the data each value occupies. For example, the smallest observation in a set of 20 is at the 5% point, the second smallest is at the 10% point, and so on.

Normal scores

2. Find the same percentiles for the Normal distribution using Table A or statistical software. Percentiles of the standard Normal distribution are often called **Normal scores.** For example, $z = -1.645$ is the 5% point of the standard Normal distribution, and $z = -1.282$ is the 10% point.

3. Plot each data point x against the corresponding Normal score z. If the data distribution is close to standard Normal, the plotted points will lie close to the 45-degree line $x = z$. If the data distribution is close to any Normal distribution, the plotted points will lie close to some straight line.

Any Normal distribution produces a straight line on the plot because standardizing turns any Normal distribution into a standard Normal distribution. Standardizing is a linear transformation that can change the slope and intercept of the line in our plot but cannot turn a line into a curved pattern.

Use of Normal Quantile Plots

If the points on a Normal quantile plot lie close to a straight line, the plot indicates that the data are Normal. Systematic deviations from a straight line indicate a non-Normal distribution. Outliers appear as points that are far away from the overall pattern of the plot.

Figures 1.28 to 1.30 are Normal quantile plots for data we have met earlier. The data x are plotted vertically against the corresponding Normal scores z plotted horizontally. The z axis extends from -3 to 3 because almost all of a standard Normal curve lies between these values. These figures show how Normal quantile plots behave.

EXAMPLE 1.23 Interpreting Normal Quantile Plots

CASE 1.2

Figure 1.28 is a Normal quantile plot of the earnings of 15 black female hourly workers at National Bank. Most of the points lie close to a straight line, indicating that a Normal model fits well. The low outlier lies below the line formed by the other observations. That is, this observation is farther out in the low direction than we would expect in a Normal distribution. We can describe this distribution as "roughly Normal, with one low outlier." Compare the stemplot of these data in Figure 1.10 (page 31).

FIGURE 1.28 Normal quantile plot of the earnings of 15 black female hourly workers at National Bank, for Example 1.23. This distribution is roughly Normal except for one low outlier.

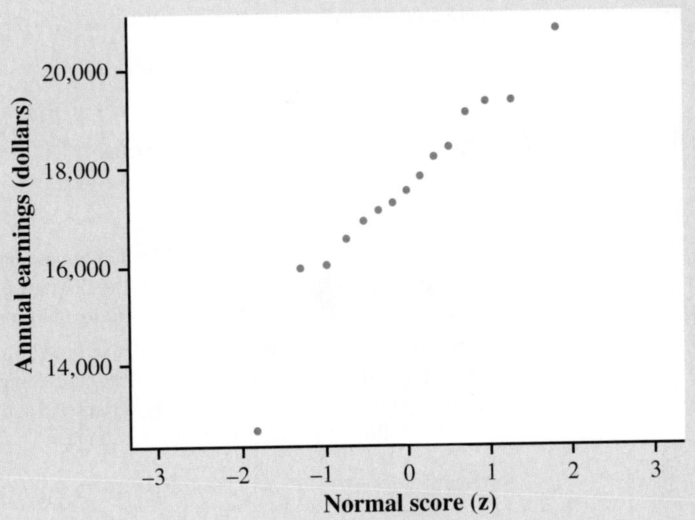

EXAMPLE 1.24  **Salary Data Aren't Normal**

Figure 1.29 is a Normal quantile plot of the Cincinnati Reds salary data. The histogram in Figure 1.4 (page 15) shows that the distribution is right-skewed. To see the right-skewness in the Normal quantile plot, draw a line through the points at the left of the plot, which correspond to the smaller observations. The larger observations fall systematically above this line. That is, the right-of-center observations have larger values than in a Normal distribution. *In a right-skewed distribution, the largest observations fall distinctly above a line drawn through the main body of points.* Similarly,

FIGURE 1.29 Normal quantile plot of the salaries of Cincinnati Reds players on opening day of the 2000 season, for Example 1.24. This distribution is skewed to the right.

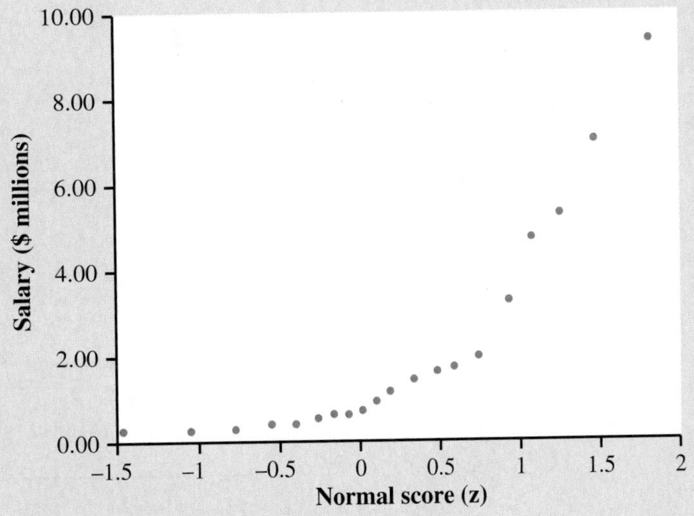

left-skewness is evident when the smallest observations fall below the line. Unlike Figure 1.28, there are no individual outliers.

EXAMPLE 1.25 Unemployment Rates are Roughly Normal

CASE 1.1

Figure 1.30 is a Normal quantile plot of the December 2004 unemployment rates in the 50 states, from Table 1.1. The plot is quite straight, showing good fit to a Normal model.

Normal quantile plots are designed specifically to assess Normality. The histograms in Figure 1.2 (ignoring Puerto Rico) (page 11) and the stemplots in Figure 1.6 (page 18) show us that the distribution of unemployment rates is symmetric and single-peaked, but they cannot tell us how closely it follows the distinctive Normal shape.

Figure 1.30 does, of course, show some deviation from a straight line. Real data almost always show some departure from the theoretical Normal model. It is important to confine your examination of a Normal quantile plot to searching for shapes that show *clear departures from Normality*. Don't overreact to minor wiggles in the plot. When we discuss statistical methods that are based on the Normal model, we will pay attention to the sensitivity of each method to departures from Normality. Many common methods work well as long as the data are reasonably symmetric and outliers are not present.

APPLY YOUR KNOWLEDGE

1.90 Process performance. Manufacturers measure dimensions of their products to monitor the performance of production processes. A maker of electric meters measures the distance between two mounting holes on 27 consecutive meters in a production run.[28] Figure 1.31 is a Normal quantile plot of these distances. The measurements are in hundredths of an inch. The large-scale pattern is quite Normal, but the measurements deviate from Normality in an interesting way. What explains the horizontal runs of points in the plot?

FIGURE 1.30 Normal quantile plot of the December 2004 unemployment rates in the 50 states, for Example 1.25. This distribution is quite Normal.

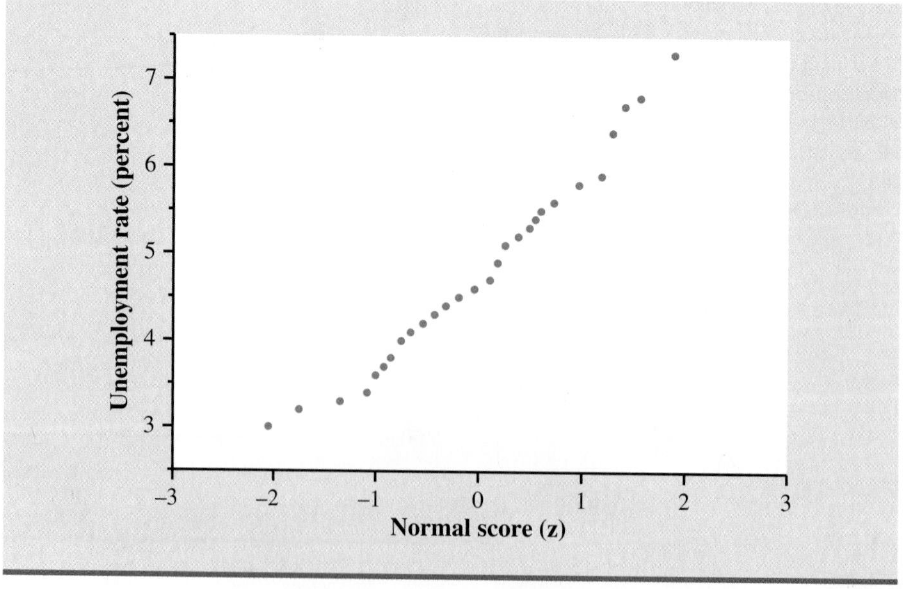

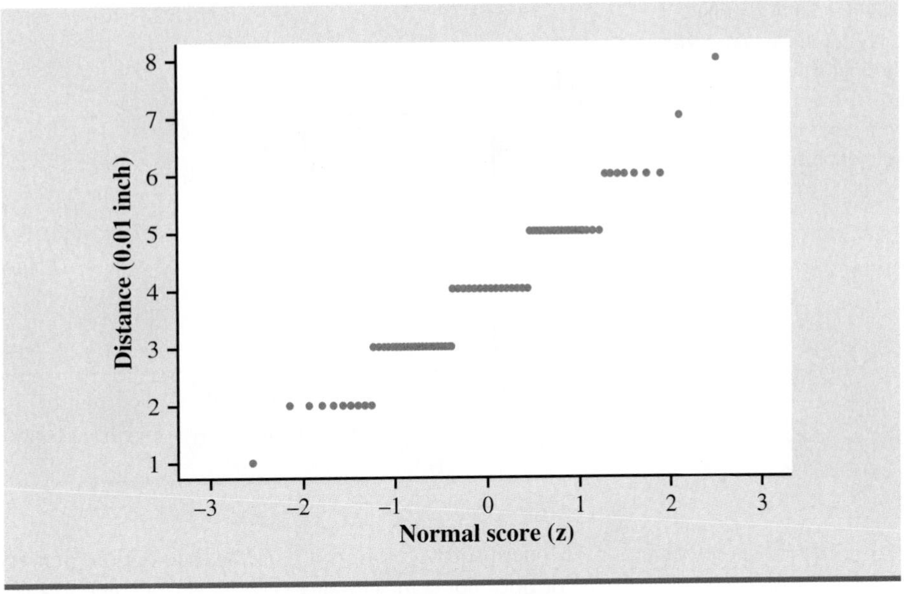

FIGURE 1.31 Normal quantile plot of the distances between two mounting holes on 27 electric meters, for Exercise 1.90.

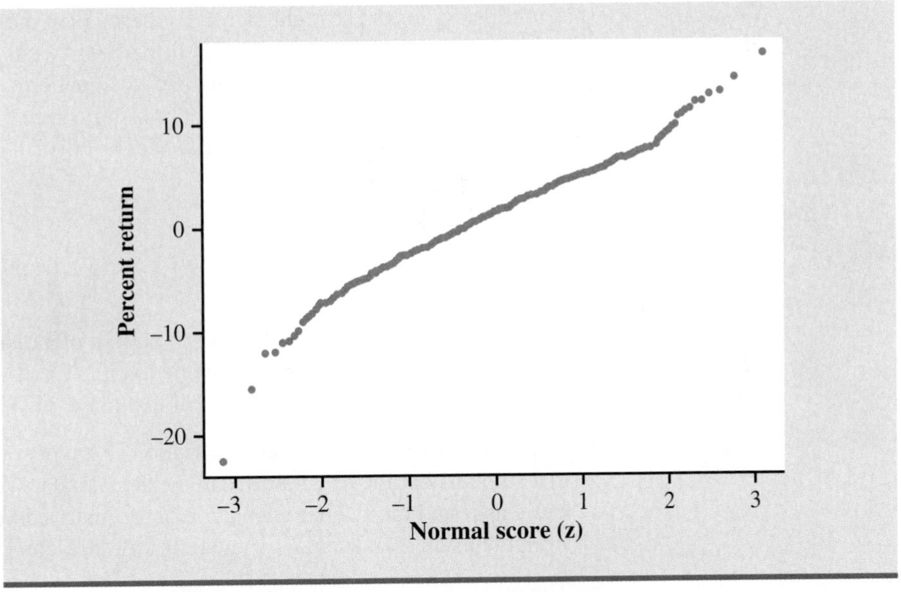

FIGURE 1.32 Normal quantile plot of the percent returns on U.S. common stocks in 601 consecutive months, for Exercise 1.91.

1.91 Stock returns. Figure 1.32 is a Normal quantile plot of the monthly percent returns on U.S. common stocks from June 1950 to June 2000. Because there are 601 observations, the individual points in the middle of the plot run together. In what way do monthly returns on stocks deviate from a Normal distribution?

BEYOND THE BASICS: DENSITY ESTIMATION

A density curve gives a compact summary of the overall shape of a distribution. Figure 1.15 (page 50) shows a Normal density curve that provides a good summary of the distribution of miles per gallon ratings for 2001 model vehicles. Many distributions do not have the Normal shape. There are other families of density curves that are used as mathematical models for various distribution shapes.

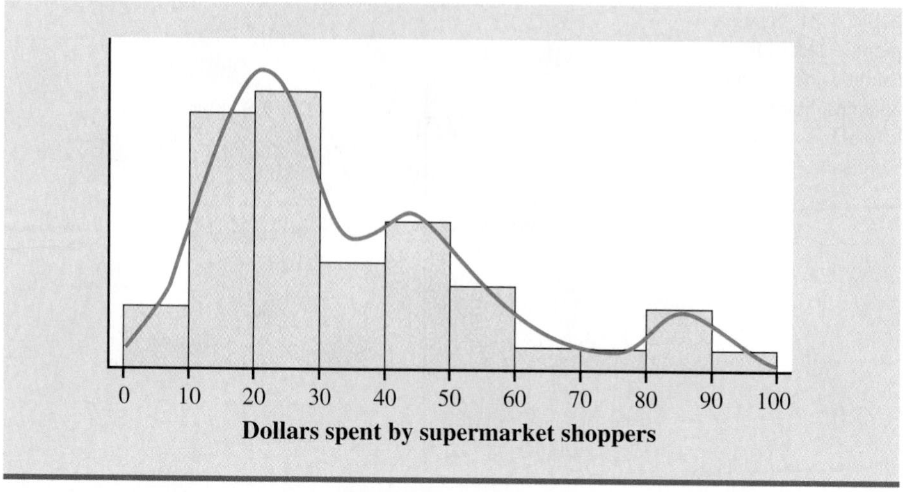

FIGURE 1.33 A density curve for the supermarket shopper data of Exercise 1.11, calculated from the data by density estimation software.

density estimation

Modern software offers a more flexible option, **density estimation.** A density estimator does not start with any specific shape, such as the Normal shape. It looks at the data and draws a density curve that describes the overall shape of the data. Figure 1.33 shows a histogram of the right-skewed supermarket shopper data from Exercise 1.11 (page 18). A density estimator produced the density curve drawn over the histogram. You can see that this curve does catch the overall pattern: the strong right-skewness, the major peak near \$20, and the two smaller clusters on the right side. Density estimation offers a quick way to picture the overall shapes of distributions. It is another useful tool for exploratory data analysis.

SECTION 1.3 SUMMARY

- We can sometimes describe the overall pattern of a distribution by a **density curve.** A density curve has total area 1 underneath it. An area under a density curve gives the proportion of observations that fall in a range of values.
- A density curve is an idealized description of the overall pattern of a distribution that smooths out the irregularities in the actual data. We write the mean of a density curve as μ and the standard deviation of a density curve as σ to distinguish them from the mean $\bar{x}$ and standard deviation s of the actual data.
- The mean, the median, and the quartiles of a density curve can be located by eye. The **mean** μ is the balance point of the curve. The **median** divides the area under the curve in half. The **quartiles** and the median divide the area under the curve into quarters. The **standard deviation** σ cannot be located by eye on most density curves.
- The mean and median are equal for symmetric density curves. The mean of a skewed curve is located farther toward the long tail than is the median.
- The **Normal distributions** are described by a special family of bell-shaped, symmetric density curves, called **Normal curves.** The mean μ and standard deviation σ completely specify a Normal distribution $N(\mu, \sigma)$. The mean is the center of the curve, and σ is the distance from μ to the change-of-curvature points on either side.

- To **standardize** any observation x, subtract the mean of the distribution and then divide by the standard deviation. The resulting **z-score**

$$z = \frac{x - \mu}{\sigma}$$

says how many standard deviations x lies from the distribution mean.

- All Normal distributions are the same when measurements are transformed to the standardized scale. In particular, all Normal distributions satisfy the **68–95–99.7 rule,** which describes what percent of observations lie within one, two, and three standard deviations of the mean.

- If x has the $N(\mu, \sigma)$ distribution, then the **standardized variable** $z = (x - \mu)/\sigma$ has the **standard Normal distribution** $N(0, 1)$ with mean 0 and standard deviation 1. Table A gives the proportions of standard Normal observations that are less than z for many values of z. By standardizing, we can use Table A for any Normal distribution.

- The adequacy of a Normal model for describing a distribution of data is best assessed by a **Normal quantile plot,** which is available in most statistical software packages. A pattern on such a plot that deviates substantially from a straight line indicates that the data are not Normal.

SECTION 1.3 Exercises

For Exercises 1.79 to 1.81, see page 54; for 1.82 to 1.84, see pages 57–58; for 1.85, see page 59; for 1.86 and 1.87, see page 63; for 1.88 and 1.89, see page 65; and for 1.90 and 1.91, see pages 68–69.

1.92 Stock performance. The 99.7 part of the 68–95–99.7 rule says that in practice Normal distributions are about six standard deviations wide. Exercise 1.57 (page 46) gives data on the real returns for the S&P 500 stock index over a 33-year period. The shape of the distribution is not close to Normal.

(a) Determine the mean and standard deviation of the real returns.

(b) What are the values three standard deviations above and below the mean, which would span the distribution if it were Normal?

(c) How do these values compare with the actual lowest and highest returns? (Remember that the 68–95–99.7 rule applies only to Normal distributions.)

1.93 Know your density. Sketch density curves that might describe distributions with the following shapes:

(a) Symmetric, but with two peaks (that is, two strong clusters of observations).

(b) Single peak and skewed to the left.

1.94 Selling apartment buildings. Owning an apartment building can be very profitable, as can selling an apartment building. The data file *ex01_094,* available on the CD that accompanies this book, contains selling prices (in dollars) and building square footages for 18 apartment buildings sold in a particular city during 2005.[29]

(a) Use statistical software to obtain histograms and Normal quantile plots of selling prices and building square footages.

(b) Do either of these variables appear to be Normally distributed? Explain in what way the plots match (or don't match) what you would expect to see for Normally distributed data.

(c) One apartment building appears to be an outlier with respect to both selling price and square footage. Report the selling price and square footage for this apartment building.

1.95 Selling apartment buildings. Continue with the data in the file *ex01_094.* Create a new variable (call it Sale Price Per Sqft) by dividing the selling price for each apartment building by the square footage for each apartment building.

(a) When plotting selling prices or building square footages, one apartment building stands out as an outlier. Does this same apartment building stand out in terms of the new variable you created for this exercise? Explain your response clearly.

(b) Use statistical software to obtain a histogram and a Normal quantile plot of the new variable Sale Price Per Sqft.

(c) Does the distribution of Sale Price Per Sqft appear to be Normal? Describe precisely what about the histogram and the Normal quantile plot leads you to your conclusion.

1.96 Selling apartment buildings. Continue with the variable Sale Price Per Sqft created in the previous exercise.

(a) Calculate the mean and standard deviation of the Sale Price Per Sqft values.

(b) Calculate the intervals $\bar{x} \pm s$, $\bar{x} \pm 2s$, and $\bar{x} \pm 3s$.

(c) Create a table that allows one to easily compare the distribution of Sale Price Per Sqft with the 68–95–99.7 rule for the three intervals calculated in part (b).

(d) Does your table from part (c) provide a clear indication of Normality (or non-Normality) for the data values?

1.97 Exploring Normal quantile plots.

(a) Create three data sets: one that is clearly skewed to the right, one that is clearly skewed to the left, and one that is clearly symmetric and mound-shaped. (As an alternative to creating data sets, you can look through this chapter and find an example of each type of data set requested.)

(b) Using statistical software, obtain Normal quantile plots for each of your three data sets.

(c) Clearly describe the pattern of each data set in the Normal quantile plots from part (b).

The table below contains data on a random sample of 22 telecom stocks—companies that specialize in telecommunication products. For each company, trading volume and revenue growth (over the last year) have been reported. Exercises 1.98 to 1.101 concern these data.[30]

Ticker symbol	Trading volume	Revenue growth
AATK	68,654	0.0482
ALLN	3,500	−0.03
ATGN	5,650	0.1514
AVCI	68,482	0.258
AXE	85,900	0.0739
CGN	100	−0.1098
COVD	2,410,204	−0.0166
CTV	254,600	−0.0437
CYBD	6,900	0
ETCIA	1,741	−0.2391
GCOM	27,392	0.4337
HLIT	690,026	−0.1765
PCTU	6,500	−0.2898
PTSC	314,680	−0.556
QCOM	6,696,185	0.2001
SRTI	2,000	−0.0006
TCCO	1,100	0.0856
TKLC	246,101	0.0009
VERA	25,000	0.0081
WJCI	59,408	−0.3544
XXIA	1,750,027	0.193
ZOOM	21,295	−0.1298

1.98 Telecom shares traded.

(a) Calculate the mean and standard deviation of the 22 trading-volume values.

(b) Calculate $\bar{x} \pm 3s$.

(c) Clearly explain why your calculations in part (b) show that the distribution of trading volume is not symmetric and mound-shaped.

1.99 Telecom revenue growth.

(a) Calculate the mean and standard deviation of the 22 revenue growth values.

(b) Calculate the ranges $\bar{x} \pm s$, $\bar{x} \pm 2s$, and $\bar{x} \pm 3s$.

(c) Determine the percent of revenue growth values that fall into each of the three ranges that you calculated in part (b). How do these percents compare with the 68–95–99.7 rule?

1.100 Telecom shares traded.

(a) Use statistical software to create a histogram of the trading volumes for these 22 telecom stocks.

(b) The histogram shows that these data are clearly right-skewed. Sketch what you think a Normal quantile plot of these data will look like.

(c) Use statistical software to create a Normal quantile plot of these data. How well does your sketch from part (b) match the plot generated by your software?

1.101 Telecom revenue growth.

(a) Construct a stemplot of the revenue growth for these 22 telecom stocks. You will need a 0 and a −0 on the stem. Use the tenths place of these values on the stem and the hundredths place as the leaves. For example, −0.556 rounds to −0.56 and would appear as −5|6 in the stemplot.

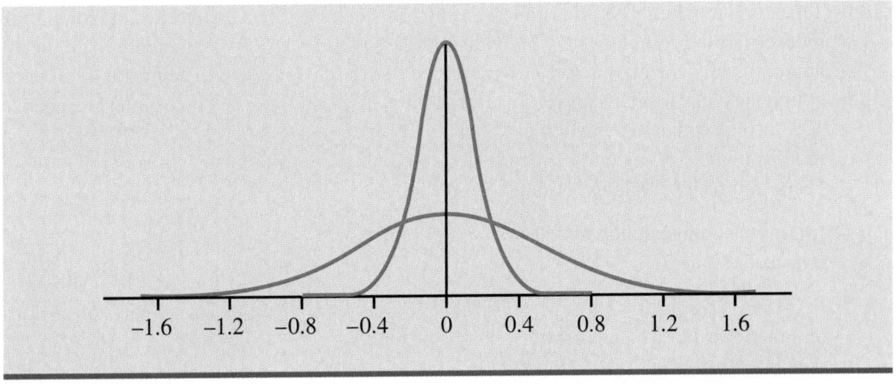

FIGURE 1.34 Two Normal curves with the same mean but different standard deviations, for Exercise 1.102.

(b) Describe the distribution of these revenue growth values. Sketch what you think a Normal quantile plot of these data will look like.

(c) Use statistical software to create a Normal quantile plot of these data. How well does your sketch from part (b) match the plot generated by your software?

1.102 **Visualizing the standard deviation.** Figure 1.34 shows two Normal curves, both with mean 0. Approximately what is the standard deviation of each of these curves?

1.103 **Variability of pollutants.** The Environmental Protection Agency requires that the exhaust of each model of motor vehicle be tested for the level of several pollutants. The level of oxides of nitrogen (NOX) in the exhaust of one light truck model was found to vary among individual trucks according to a Normal distribution with mean $\mu = 1.45$ grams per mile driven and standard deviation $\sigma = 0.40$ grams per mile. Sketch the density curve of this Normal distribution, with the scale of grams per mile marked on the horizontal axis. Also, using this Normal model, give an interval that contains the middle 95% of NOX levels in the exhaust of trucks.

1.104 **Length of pregnancies.** Some health insurance companies treat pregnancy as a "preexisting condition" when it comes to paying for maternity expenses for a new policyholder. Sometimes the exact date of conception is unknown, so the insurance company must count back from the expected due date to judge whether or not conception occurred before or after the new policy began. The length of human pregnancies from conception to birth varies according to a distribution that is approximately Normal with mean 266 days and standard deviation 16 days. Use the 68–95–99.7 rule to answer the following questions.

(a) Between what values do the lengths of the middle 95% of all pregnancies fall?

(b) How short are the shortest 2.5% of all pregnancies?

(c) How likely is it that a woman with an expected due date 218 days after her policy began conceived the child after her policy began?

1.105 Use Table A to find the proportion of observations from a standard Normal distribution that falls in each of the following regions. In each case, sketch a standard Normal curve and shade the area representing the region.

(a) $z \leq -2.25$

(b) $z \geq -2.25$

(c) $z > 1.77$

(d) $-2.25 < z < 1.77$

1.106 (a) Find the number z such that the proportion of observations that are less than z in a standard Normal distribution is 0.8.

(b) Find the number z such that 35% of all observations from a standard Normal distribution are greater than z.

1.107 **NCAA rules for athletes.** The National Collegiate Athletic Association (NCAA) requires Division I athletes to score at least 820 on the combined Mathematics and Verbal parts of the SAT to compete in their first college year. (Higher scores are required for students with poor high school grades.) In 2000, the scores of the 1,260,000 students taking the SATs were approximately Normal with mean 1019 and standard deviation 209. What percent of all students had scores less than 820?

1.108 **More NCAA rules.** The NCAA considers a student a "partial qualifier" eligible to practice and receive an athletic scholarship, but not to compete, if the combined SAT score is at least 720. Use the information in the previous exercise to find the percent of all SAT scores that are less than 720.

1.109 The stock market. The yearly rate of return on stock indexes (which combine many individual stocks) is approximately Normal. Between 1950 and 2000, U.S. common stocks had a mean yearly return of about 13%, with a standard deviation of about 17%. Take this Normal distribution to be the distribution of yearly returns over a long period.

(a) In what range do the middle 95% of all yearly returns lie?

(b) The market is down for the year if the return is less than zero. In what percent of years is the market down?

(c) In what percent of years does the index gain 25% or more?

1.110 Length of pregnancies. The length of human pregnancies from conception to birth varies according to a distribution that is approximately Normal with mean 266 days and standard deviation 16 days.

(a) What percent of pregnancies last less than 240 days (that's about 8 months)?

(b) What percent of pregnancies last between 240 and 270 days (roughly between 8 and 9 months)?

(c) How long do the longest 20% of pregnancies last?

1.111 Quartiles of Normal distributions. The median of any Normal distribution is the same as its mean. We can use Normal calculations to find the quartiles for Normal distributions.

(a) What is the area under the standard Normal curve to the left of the first quartile? Use this to find the value of the first quartile for a standard Normal distribution. Find the third quartile similarly.

(b) Your work in (a) gives the Normal scores z for the quartiles of any Normal distribution. What are the quartiles for the lengths of human pregnancies? (Use the distribution in the previous exercise.)

1.112 Deciles of Normal distributions. The ***deciles*** of any distribution are the 10th, 20th, . . . , 90th percentiles. The first and last deciles are the 10th and 90th percentiles, respectively.

(a) What are the first and last deciles of the standard Normal distribution?

(b) The weights of 9-ounce potato chip bags are approximately Normal with mean 9.12 ounces and standard deviation 0.15 ounce. What are the first and last deciles of this distribution?

The remaining exercises for this section require the use of software that will make Normal quantile plots.

1.113 Are monthly returns on a stock Normal? Is the distribution of monthly returns on Philip Morris stock approximately Normal with the exception of possible outliers? Make a Normal quantile plot of the data in Table 1.12 and report your conclusions.

1.114 Normal random numbers. Use software to generate 100 observations from the standard Normal distribution. Make a histogram of these observations. How does the shape of the histogram compare with a Normal density curve? Make a Normal quantile plot of the data. Does the plot suggest any important deviations from Normality? (Repeating this exercise several times is a good way to become familiar with how Normal quantile plots look when data actually are close to Normal.)

1.115 Uniform random numbers. Use software to generate 100 observations from the distribution described in Exercise 1.80 (page 54). (The software will probably call this a "uniform distribution.") Make a histogram of these observations. How does the histogram compare with the density curve in Figure 1.19? Make a Normal quantile plot of your data. According to this plot, how does the uniform distribution deviate from Normality?

STATISTICS IN SUMMARY

Data analysis is the art of describing data using graphs and numerical summaries. The purpose of data analysis is to describe the most important features of a set of data. This chapter introduces data analysis by presenting statistical ideas and tools for describing the distribution of a single variable. The Statistics in Summary figure on the next page will help you organize the big ideas. The question marks at the last two stages remind us that the usefulness of numerical summaries and models such as Normal distributions depends on what we find when we examine the data using graphs. Here is a review list of the most important skills you should have acquired from your study of this chapter.

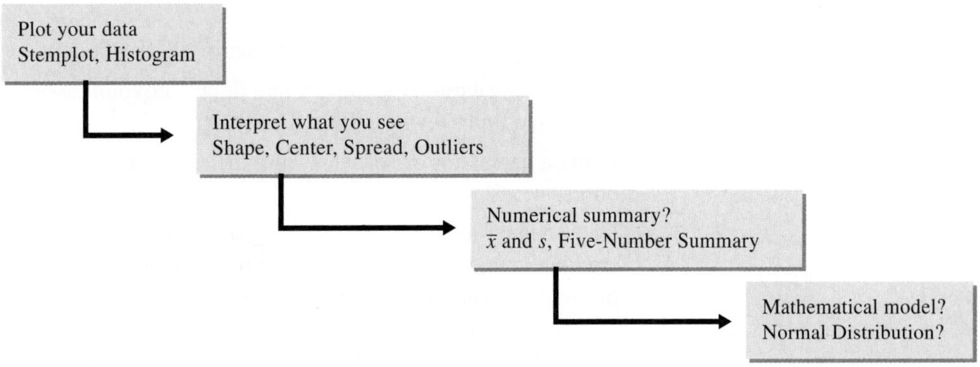

A. Data

1. Identify the individuals and variables in a set of data.
2. Identify each variable as categorical or quantitative. Identify the units in which each quantitative variable is measured.

B. Displaying Distributions

1. Make a bar graph, pie chart, and/or Pareto chart of the distribution of a categorical variable. Interpret bar graphs, pie charts, and Pareto charts.
2. Make a histogram of the distribution of a quantitative variable.
3. Make a stemplot of the distribution of a small set of observations. Round leaves or split stems as needed to make an effective stemplot.

C. Inspecting Distributions (Quantitative Variable)

1. Look for the overall pattern and for major deviations from the pattern.
2. Assess from a histogram or stemplot whether the shape of a distribution is roughly symmetric, distinctly skewed, or neither. Assess whether the distribution has one or more major peaks.
3. Describe the overall pattern by giving numerical measures of center and spread in addition to a verbal description of shape.
4. Decide which measures of center and spread are more appropriate: the mean and standard deviation (especially for symmetric distributions) or the five-number summary (especially for skewed distributions).
5. Recognize outliers.

D. Time Plots

1. Make a time plot of data, with the time of each observation on the horizontal axis and the value of the observed variable on the vertical axis.
2. Recognize strong trends or other patterns in a time plot.

E. Measuring Center

1. Find the mean $\bar{x}$ of a set of observations.
2. Find the median M of a set of observations.
3. Understand that the median is more resistant (less affected by extreme observations) than the mean. Recognize that skewness in a distribution moves the mean away from the median toward the long tail.

F. Measuring Spread

1. Find the quartiles Q_1 and Q_3 for a set of observations.
2. Give the five-number summary and draw a boxplot; assess center, spread, symmetry, and skewness from a boxplot.
3. Using a calculator or software, find the standard deviation s for a set of observations.
4. Know the basic properties of s: $s \geq 0$ always; $s = 0$ only when all observations are identical and increases as the spread increases; s has the same units as the original measurements; s is pulled strongly up by outliers or skewness.

G. Density Curves

1. Know that areas under a density curve represent proportions of all observations and that the total area under a density curve is 1.
2. Approximately locate the median (equal-areas point) and the mean (balance point) on a density curve.
3. Know that the mean and median both lie at the center of a symmetric density curve and that the mean moves farther toward the long tail of a skewed curve.

H. Normal Distributions

1. Recognize the shape of Normal curves and be able to estimate by eye both the mean and the standard deviation from such a curve.
2. Use the 68–95–99.7 rule and symmetry to state what percent of the observations from a Normal distribution fall between two points when both points lie at the mean or one, two, or three standard deviations on either side of the mean.
3. Find the standardized value (z-score) of an observation. Interpret z-scores and understand that any Normal distribution becomes standard Normal $N(0, 1)$ when standardized.
4. Given that a variable has the Normal distribution with a stated mean μ and standard deviation σ, calculate the proportion of values above a stated number, below a stated number, or between two stated numbers.
5. Given that a variable has the Normal distribution with a stated mean μ and standard deviation σ, calculate the point having a stated proportion of all values above it. Also calculate the point having a stated proportion of all values below it.
6. Assess the Normality of a set of data by inspecting a Normal quantile plot.

CHAPTER 1 Review Exercises

1.116 Customers' home state. A sample of 1095 customers entering a retail store were asked to fill out a brief survey. One question on the survey asked each person to identify his or her current state of residency. The data from this question are summarized in the table below.

(a) The state in which the retail store resides is easily deduced from the table. In which state is this store located?

(b) One way to make a pie chart of these data would be to use one slice in the pie chart for each state in the table. Give at least one reason why this would not result in a useful pie chart.

(c) Group all customers from states other than Iowa (IA) into a category called Other and make a pie chart with an Other slice. Be sure to include the percent or count for each slice of your pie chart.

State	Count	State	Count
AR	1	MI	2
AZ	1	MO	2
CA	2	MS	2
CO	1	NE	3
FL	1	NY	1
GA	2	OH	2
IA	1053	OK	1
ID	2	OR	5
IL	6	TN	1
KS	1	TX	1
LA	1	UT	1
MA	1	WI	2

1.117 Help-wanted advertising in newspapers. One source of revenue for newspapers is printing help-wanted ads for companies who are looking for new employees. The file *ex01_117* contains monthly data on help-wanted advertising in newspapers from January 1951 to April 2005. The time series uses an index value with 1987 as the base year. That is, the monthly average for 1987 is taken to be 100, so a month with an index value of 50 had only half as much help-wanted advertising in newspapers as the monthly average for 1987, while a month with an index value of 140 had 40% more help-wanted advertising in newspapers than the monthly average for 1987.[31]

(a) Using statistical software, obtain a time plot of the index values for help-wanted advertising in newspapers. Add a horizontal line to your time plot at the value of $\overline{x}$ for these data.

(b) What do you notice about the beginning years of the time series relative to the overall average of the time series? Which month in the time series is the first to be greater than the overall average?

(c) Describe the trend of the index values beginning from January 2000. Which month is the last month to be greater than the time series average?

(d) Propose at least one reasonable explanation for the observed trend in help-wanted advertising in newspapers since January 2000.

1.118 A closer look at customer refunds. A retail store specializing in children's clothing and toys has a relatively strict "no refunds" policy. Exceptions to this policy are sometimes granted in specific cases as determined by management. The store would like to look at refund activity for the year 2005. The file *ex01_118* contains the date, amount, and item count for all refund transactions in 2005. Of the 10,939 transactions conducted between the store and customers during 2005, only 103 of these transactions were refunds (less than 1%).

(a) Using statistical software, calculate the five-number summary for refund amounts. (*Note:* All refunds are recorded as negative numbers.)

(b) What percent of all refunds in 2005 were $10 or less?

(c) Construct a boxplot of the refund amounts based on your five-number summary.

(d) What does your boxplot indicate about the skewness of these data?

1.119 A closer look at customer refunds. Continue with the data on refunds described in the previous exercise. Upon inspection of the item counts for the refunds, we see that 83 of the 103 refunds were for one item. Using only this information and without using software or a calculator, answer the following questions.

(a) Provide the first four numbers of the five-number summary for the item counts. (You cannot determine the maximum item count using only the information given in this exercise.)

(b) Construct a boxplot for the item counts using 14 as the maximum item count. How long is the box in your boxplot? Explain why this makes sense, given the data on item counts.

(c) What does your boxplot indicate about the skewness of these data?

1.120 Telecom revenue growth. The data on revenue growth for a random sample of telecommunications companies displayed with Exercise 1.98 (page 72) closely follow a Normal distribution with a mean of -0.0224 and a standard deviation of 0.2180. Take as a model for telecom revenue growth the $N(-0.0224, 0.2180)$ distribution and answer the following questions.

(a) Calculate $\mu + 3\sigma$ for the model for telecom revenue growth.

(b) From the population of all telecom companies, what percent should we expect to have revenue growth greater than $\mu + 3\sigma$? Explain how you arrived at your response.

(c) What percent of the telecom companies in our sample have revenue growth greater than $\mu + 3\sigma$? Is this percent different from your response to part (b)? Clearly explain why these two percents being different is not inconsistent with our assumption of a Normal distribution for the model for telecom revenue growth.

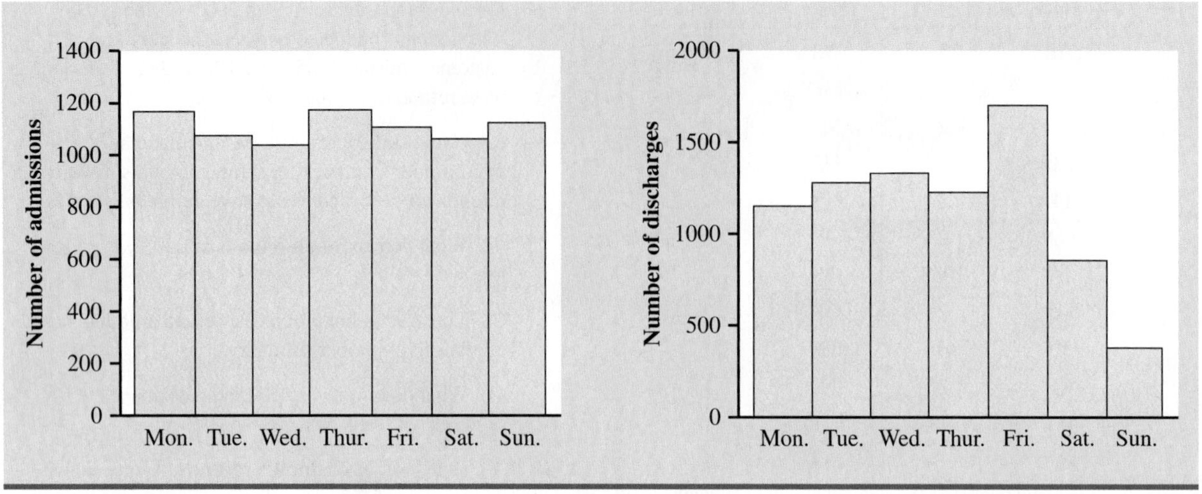

FIGURE 1.35 Bar graphs of the number of heart attack victims admitted and discharged on each day of the week by hospitals in Ontario, Canada, for Exercise 1.124.

1.121 Telecom revenue growth. Take the $N(-0.0224, 0.2180)$ distribution as the model for telecom revenue growth as described in the previous exercise and answer the following questions.

(a) What percent of telecom companies had negative revenue growth over the past year? Show your work.

(b) What does "negative revenue growth" mean for a company?

(c) What percent of telecom companies had revenue growth greater than 0.50 (50%)? Show your work.

(d) In terms of revenue growth, the top 25% of all telecom companies had revenue growth greater than what value? Show your work.

1.122 Household and family income. In government data, a household contains all people who live together in a residence. A family consists of two or more people living together and related by blood, marriage, or adoption. In 1999, the mean and median of household incomes were $40,816 and $54,842. The mean and median of family incomes were $48,950 and $62,636.

(a) Which of each pair is the mean and which is the median? How do you know?

(b) Why are the mean and median incomes higher for families than for households?

1.123 What influences buying? Product preference depends in part on the age, income, and gender of the consumer. A market researcher selects a large sample of potential car buyers. For each consumer, she records gender, age, household income, and automobile preference. Which of these variables are categorical and which are quantitative?

1.124 Never on Sunday? The Canadian province of Ontario carries out statistical studies of how Canada's national health care system is working in the province. The bar graphs in Figure 1.35 come from a study of admissions and discharges from community hospitals in Ontario.[32] They show the number of heart attack patients admitted and discharged on each day of the week during a 2-year period.

(a) Explain why you expect the number of patients admitted with heart attacks to be roughly the same for all days of the week. Do the data show that this is true?

(b) Describe how the distribution of the day on which patients are discharged from the hospital differs from that of the day on which they are admitted. What do you think explains the difference?

1.125 Yankee salaries. Few companies release their employees' salaries. The baseball players' union, however, makes player salaries public. Table 1.13 contains the salaries of the New York Yankees as of opening day of the 2001 season.[33] Describe the distribution of Yankee salaries, giving a graph and numerical measures to back up your description.

1.126 Stock returns. Table 1.12 (page 49) gives the monthly percent returns on Philip Morris stock for the period from June 1990 to July 2001. The data appear in time order reading from left to right across each row in turn, beginning with the 3.0% return in June 1990. Make a time plot of the data. This was a period of increasing action against smoking, so we might expect

Invoking Data Analysis ToolPak procedures

Once the **Data Analysis ToolPak** is installed, the statistical analysis routines are found by first selecting the **Data** tab found on the main toolbar. You will then see the **Data Analysis** command in the **Analysis** group. Figure App. 1.2 shows a blank Excel spreadsheet with the **Data Analysis** command invoked, resulting in the appearance of the **Data Analysis** menu box.

Within the **Data Analysis** menu box, there are 19 menu choices. When you select one of the menu choices, a box specific to the statistical routine will appear that calls for you to indicate where the data reside and where you want the output to be displayed. In particular, to indicate where the data for analysis reside, you specify the range of cells for the data in the **Input Range** box. This can be accomplished by first clicking the cursor in the **Input Range** box and then typing in the cell range, or more easily you can highlight the data by clicking and dragging the mouse over the cell range. The statistical output can be placed either in the current worksheet (placement indicated with **Output Range** box), in a new worksheet tabbed with the current workbook (**New Output Ply** option), or in an entirely new workbook (**New Workbook** option).

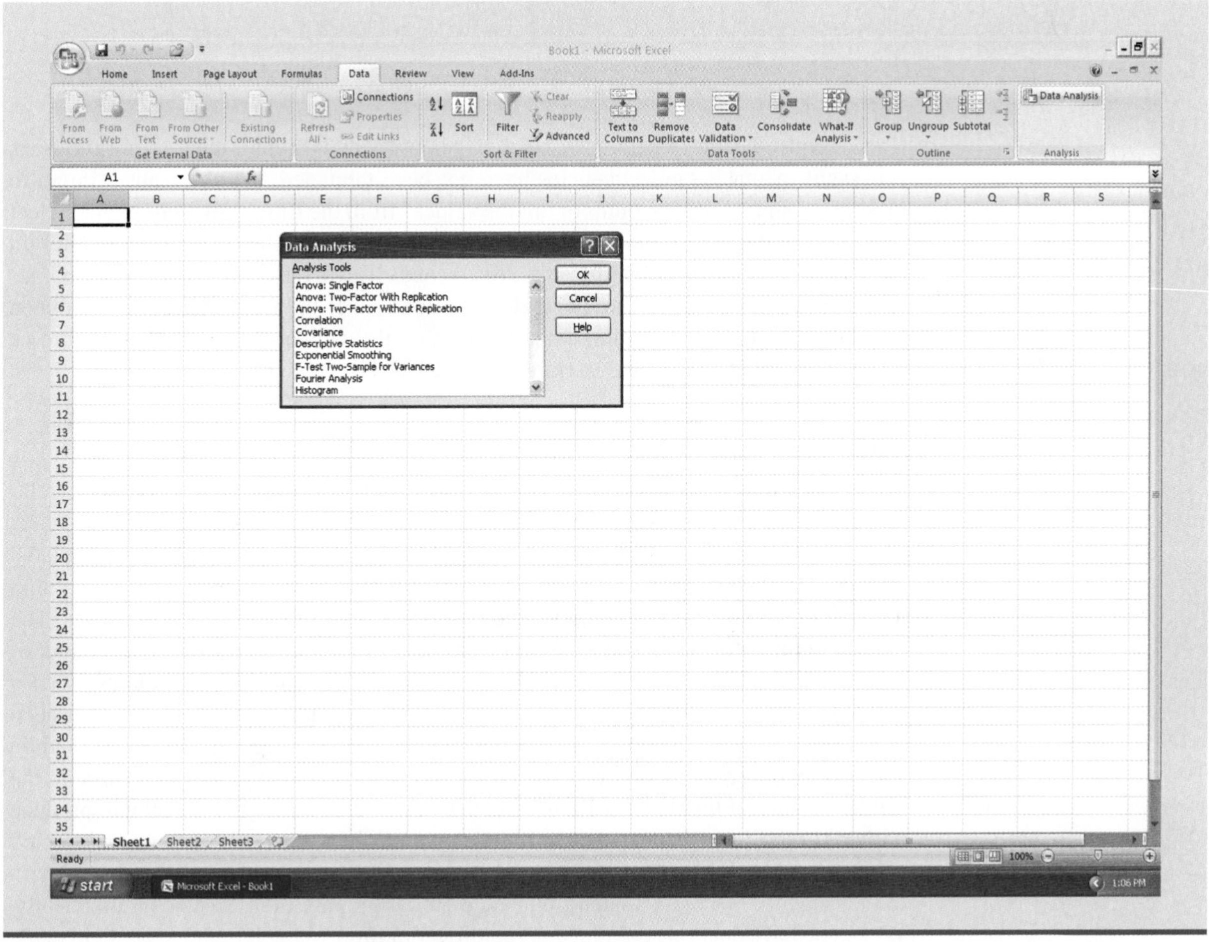

FIGURE App. 1.2 Excel blank spreadsheet with Data Analysis menu box.

Excel data files

As noted, we assume that you are familiar with the basics of Excel, including the saving and opening of files in Excel. It should be noted that files saved by Excel 2007 as an Excel Workbook cannot be opened by earlier versions of Excel. There is, however, an option to save workbooks as an Excel 97-2003 Workbook. Excel 2007 is backward compatible in terms of opening workbooks of older versions. Data files for selected examples and exercises provided on this book's CD are compatible with all versions of Excel. Data sets are named based on the chapter number and the figure, case, or exercise number. For example, data for Exercise 11.45 (in Chapter 11) will be in an Excel file named *ex11_045.XLS.* All data file naming conventions are described in the "To Students: What is Statistics?" section in the front of the book.

Using Minitab and Excel for Examining Distributions

Now that we have provided a general overview of Minitab and Excel, we discuss more specifically how these software programs can be used to create the graphs and numerical summaries presented in this chapter.

Bar Graphs

Minitab:

Graph ➤ Bar Chart

If the frequencies have been pretabulated, select "Values from a table" from the **Bars represent** menu. If the frequencies have not been tabulated and you want Minitab to make the counts, select "Counts of unique values" from the **Bars represent** menu. Select "Simple" for the type of bar graph, then click **OK.** For pretabulated frequencies, click-in the data column into the **Graph variables** box and click-in the column that has the names of the categories into the **Categorical variables** box. If the frequencies have not been pretabulated, click-in the column that has data on the categorical names that need to be counted into the **Categorical variables** box. Click **OK.**

Excel:

There are a few ways to create bar graphs in Excel. However, there is one particular approach that allows you to create bar graphs based on providing in the spreadsheet the total counts of each category or having Excel make the counts. For pretabulated frequencies, the spreadsheet should have two columns of information. With a column name in the top row, one column should have the names of the distinct categories. The other column, with its column name in the top row, should have the total counts of each category. If Excel needs to make the counts, there should be a column, with a column name in the top row, that has the data on the names of the categories that need to be counted. Once the one or two columns have been created, all the cells should be selected by dragging the mouse. Then click the **Insert** tab and click **PivotTable** in the **Tables** group and finally click **PivotChart.** You will then notice that Excel will produce a **PivotTable Field List** box. You will find that the column name(s) that you highlighted will be listed as fields. Select the field(s) presented to you by clicking a checkmark next to the name(s). For pretabulated frequencies, a bar graph will be created automatically. When you have only one column that requires counting, you will find that the field name appears in a section titled **Axis Fields (Categories).** You want to also have this field name in the section titled **Σ Values.** To do so, click and hold the field name and then drag the field from the field section into the **Σ Values** section. Excel will then automatically make the counts and create a corresponding bar graph.

Pie Charts

Minitab:

Graph ➤ Pie Chart

Making a pie chart is quite similar to making a bar graph. If the frequencies have been pretabulated, select the **Chart values from a table** option. If the frequencies have not been tabulated, select **Chart counts of unique values** option. For pretabulated frequencies, click-in the data column into the **Summary variables** box, and click-in the column that has the names of the categories into the **Categorical variables** box. If the frequencies have not been pretabulated, click-in the column that has data on the categorical names that need to be counted into the **Categorical variables** box. If you wish to have the pie slices labeled by categorical names and have percents reported (as in Figure 1.1(b)), click the **Label** button and then click the **Slice Labels** tab and finally place checkmarks next to the desired labels.

Excel:

To make a pie chart, you should follow the exact steps for making a bar graph. You want to now simply change the created bar graph into a pie chart. To do so, click the **Design** tab and then click the **Change Chart Type** in the **Type** group and finally select the **Pie** chart type. Alternatively, you can right-click on the bar graph and find the **Change Chart Type** option. To add labels to the pie slices, first right-click on one of the pie slices and then choose the **Add Data Labels** option. Once labels have been added, right-click again on one of the pie slices and then choose the **Format Data Labels** option and finally place checkmarks next to the desired labels.

Pareto Charts

Minitab:

Stat ➤ Quality Tools ➤ Pareto Chart

If the frequencies have been pretabulated, select the **Chart defects table** option. If the frequencies have not been tabulated, select the **Chart defects data in** option. For pretabulated frequencies, click-in the data column in the **Labels in** box and click-in the column that has the names of the categories in the **Frequencies in** box. If the frequencies have not been pretabulated, click-in the column that has data on the categorical names that need to be counted into the topmost box next to the **Chart defects data in** option. An alternative way to create a Pareto chart is to follow the steps for creating a bar graph but then click the **Chart Options** button and select the **Decreasing Y** option and place a checkmark next to the **Show Y as Percent** option.

Excel:

As a first step, create a bar graph as already described. You will find in the spreadsheet a PivotTable report made up of two columns: (1) a column labeled "Row Labels" and

(2) a column with the frequencies. Highlight the contents of the report (that is, the cells with the category names and the cells with the frequencies). Now click the **Data** tab and then click **Sort** in the **Sort & Filter** group. At this point, choose the **Descending (Z to A)** option and select the column associated with the frequency numbers in the menu box found immediately below the option. We now want to convert the counts into percent. To do so, click the field name found in the **Σ Values** section, select the **Value Field Setting** option, click the **Show values as** tab, finally select "% of total" from the **Show values as** menu and then click **OK.**

Histograms

Minitab:

Graph ➤ Histogram

Select "Simple" for the type of histogram, then click **OK.** Click-in the data column into the **Graph Variables** box and then click **OK.** If you wish to change the automatically selected classes, double-click on the horizontal axis to make the **Edit Scale** box appear. Now, click the **Binning** tab and then choose the **Midpoint/Cutpoint positions** option found in the **Interval Definition** section. Depending on whether you choose the **Interval type** as "Midpoint" or "Cutpoint," you then give the desired values of the midpoints (that is, the middle values of the classes) or the cutpoints (that is, lower and upper values of the classes).

Excel:

Select "Histogram" in the **Data Analysis** menu box and click **OK.** Enter the cell range of the data into the **Input Range** box. If you want Excel to automatically select the classes, leave the **Bin Range** box empty. Place a checkmark next to the **Chart Output** option. Click **OK.** Excel will then create a histogram with gaps between the data bars. To remove these gaps, right-click on any one of the bars and then select the **Format Data Series** option. You will then have the opportunity to set the gap width to 0%. With the bars now closed up to each other, it is a good idea to border the bars with line edges. Before closing the **Format Data Series** box, click the **Border Color** option and select the **Solid line** option and finally click **Close.** If you wish to change the automatically selected classes, enter upper values for each class into the spreadsheet and input their cell range in the **Bin Range** box.

Stemplots

Minitab:

Graph ➤ Stem-and-Leaf

Click-in the data column into the **Graph Variables** box and then click **OK.**

Excel:

Stemplots are available in neither standard Excel nor the enhanced add-on version of Excel.

Time Plots

Minitab:

Graph ➤ Time Series Plot

Select "Simple" for the type of time series plot, then click **OK.** Click-in the data column into the **Series** box. In default mode, Minitab will label the time periods as "1," "2," "3," and so on. If you wish to label the time periods by year, as in Figure 1.7, then click the **Time/Scale** button, select the **Calendar** option, select the desired time periods (for example, "Year") from the adjacent menu, and click **OK** to close the pop-up. Click **OK** to produce the plot.

Excel:

Click and drag the mouse to highlight the cell range of the data you wish to time plot (include the column name if you wish it to appear as a chart label). With the cell range highlighted, click the **Insert** tab and then click **Line** in the **Charts** group. Within the **2-D Line** choices, you can choose whether to have data symbols at the data values or not.

Numerical Summaries of Distribution

Minitab:

Stat ➤ Basic Statistics ➤ Display Descriptive Statistics

Click-in the data column(s) for which you want to get numerical summaries into the **Variables** box. To choose what numerical summaries you want reported, click the **Statistics** button, place checkmarks next to all desired measures, and then click **OK** to close the pop-up. Click **OK** to have the summaries reported in the Session window.

Excel:

Select "Descriptive Statistics" in the **Data Analysis** menu box and click **OK.** Enter the cell range of the data into the **Input Range** box. Place a checkmark next to the **Chart Output** option. Click **OK.** You will find that the first and third quartiles are not reported. If you wish to compute these quartiles, click an empty cell in the spreadsheet and then proceed to the **Statistical** function menu as described in the overview section of this Appendix. Scroll down the list of functions and double-click on the **QUARTILE** function choice. In the **Array** box, input the cell range of the data. In the **Quart** box, input the value "1" to get the first quartile or the value "3" to get the third quartile and then click **OK.**

Boxplots

Minitab:

Graph ➤ Boxplot

If you have only one variable, select "One Y Simple" for the type of boxplot, then click **OK.** If you have multiple boxplots that you want to display together, as in Figure 1.11, select "Multiple Y's Simple" for the type of boxplot, then click **OK.** In either case, click-in the data column(s) for which you want to construct boxplots into the **Graph variables** box. Click **OK.**

Excel:

Boxplots are not available in standard Excel but they are available in the enhanced add-on version of Excel.

Normal Distribution

Minitab:

Graph ➤ Probability Distribution Plot

This pull-down sequence will allow you to visualize areas under the Normal curve. Select "View Probability" and then click **OK.** The standard Normal distribution is the default distribution. You can change the values for the mean and/or standard deviation. Now click the **Shaded Area** tab. If you want to find the area under the curve associated with a specified value, select the **X Value** option. You can choose to find the area to the left or right of that specified value or even between two values by clicking the appropriate picture. You then enter the specified value(s) in the **X value** box. Click **OK.** As an exercise, you should be able to reproduce Figures 1.24, 1.25, and 1.26. To do backward Normal calculations, select the **Probability** option rather than the **X Value** option. Depending on whether you are considering the area to the left or to the right of a value, enter the desired area in the **Probability** box and click **OK.** If more accurate reporting of numbers is desired, then you can consider the following pull-down sequence:

Calc ➤ Probability Distributions ➤ Normal

Choose the **Cumulative probability** option if you wish to find the area to the left of a specified value. Choose the **Inverse cumulative probability** option if you wish to find the value associated with a specified area to the left of that value. You can then select the **Input constant** option. In the box next to this option enter the specified value of x or z or enter the specified area. Click **OK** to find the results reported in the Session window.

Excel:

Excel does not provide a means to visualize areas under the Normal curve but it can compute areas under the Normal curve or work backward. In either case, click an empty cell in the spreadsheet and then proceed to the **Statistical** function menu as described in the overview section of this Appendix. If you wish to find the area to the left of a specified value under the standard Normal curve, then scroll down the list of functions and double-click on the **NORMSDIST** function choice. Type the value of z in the **Z** box and click **OK.** To do backward standard Normal calculations, double-click on the **NORMSINV** function choice. Type the specified area in the **Probability** box and click **OK.**

Normal Quantile Plots

Minitab:

Stat ➤ Basic Statistics ➤ Normality Test

This pull-down sequence will produce a Normal probability plot. As noted in this chapter, there is a bit of a technical distinction between a Normal quantile plot and a Normal probability plot. However, the interpretation is the same in that the closer the data points plot to a straight line the closer is the conformity to the Normal distribution. Upon doing the noted pull-down sequence, click-in the data column of interest into the **Variable** box and then click **OK.**

Excel:

Neither Normal quantile plots nor Normal probability plots are available in standard Excel, but Normal probability plots are available in the enhanced add-on version of Excel.

CHAPTER 2

Examining Relationships

2.1 Scatterplots

2.2 Correlation

2.3 Least-Squares Regression

2.4 Cautions about Correlation and Regression

2.5 Relations in Categorical Data

PRELUDE: HOW MUCH FOR MY HOUSE?

As the mortgage officer for the local bank branch, Matthew helps individuals make decisions about buying and selling houses. A couple planning to buy a new house wonders how much their current house will sell for. The city assessor's office provides *assessed values* for all houses in town for tax purposes. An assessed value is an estimate of the value of a home used to determine property taxes. Matthew knows that most realtors in town tell someone trying to sell a house that they should expect to sell the house for approximately 10% above its assessed value, but he isn't sure about this "rule of thumb."

What is the relationship between selling price and assessed value for houses in town? Matthew took an introductory business statistics course in college, and he recalls studying relationships between two variables like selling price and assessed value. A trip to the city assessor's office provides a sample of the selling prices and assessed values for recently sold houses. A scatterplot shows that the relationship between selling prices and assessed values can be described by a line with a positive slope of approximately 1.07. The value of the slope indicates that selling prices are about 7% above assessed values in Matthew's sample of recently sold houses. While some houses did sell for 10% above their assessed value, others sold for smaller percents above assessed. Based on actual sales data, the slope of Matthew's line will provide his customers with a more reasonable assumption about selling prices than the "optimistic" 10% rule of thumb the realtors use.

Introduction

A marketing study finds that men spend more money online than women. An insurance group reports that heavier cars have fewer deaths per 10,000 vehicles registered than do lighter cars. These and many other statistical studies look at the relationship between two variables. To understand such a relationship, we must often examine other variables as well. To conclude that men spend more online, for example, the researchers had to eliminate the effect of other variables such as annual income. Our topic in this chapter is relationships between variables. One of our main themes is that the relationship between two variables can be strongly influenced by other variables that are lurking in the background.

Because variation is everywhere, statistical relationships are overall tendencies, not ironclad rules. They allow individual exceptions. Although smokers on the average die younger than nonsmokers, some people live to 90 while smoking three packs a day. To study a relationship between two variables, we measure both variables on the same individuals. Often, we think that one of the variables explains or influences the other.

Response Variable, Explanatory Variable

A **response variable** measures an outcome of a study. An **explanatory variable** explains or influences changes in a response variable.

independent variable
dependent variable

You will often find explanatory variables called **independent variables,** and response variables called **dependent variables.** The idea behind this language is that the response variable depends on the explanatory variable. Because the words "independent" and "dependent" have other meanings in statistics that are unrelated to the explanatory-response distinction, we prefer to avoid those words.

It is easiest to identify explanatory and response variables when we actually set values of one variable to see how it affects another variable.

EXAMPLE 2.1 The Best Price?

Price is important to consumers and therefore to retailers. Sales of an item typically increase as its price falls, except for some luxury items, where high price suggests exclusivity. The seller's profits for an item often increase as the price is reduced, due to increased sales, until the point at which lower profit per item cancels rising sales. A retail chain therefore introduces a new DVD player at several different price points and monitors sales. The chain wants to discover the price at which its profits are greatest. Price is the explanatory variable, and total profit from sales of the player is the response variable.

When we don't set the values of either variable but just observe both variables, there may or may not be explanatory and response variables. Whether there are depends on how we plan to use the data.

EXAMPLE 2.2 Inventory and Sales

Jim is a district manager for a retail chain. He wants to know how the average monthly inventory and monthly sales for the stores in his district are related to each other. Jim doesn't think that either inventory level or sales explains or causes the other. He has two related variables, and neither is an explanatory variable.

Sue manages another district for the same chain. She asks, "Can I predict a store's monthly sales if I know its inventory level?" Sue is treating the inventory level as the explanatory variable and the monthly sales as the response variable.

In Example 2.1, price differences actually *cause* differences in profits from sales of DVD players. There is no cause-and-effect relationship between inventory levels and sales in Example 2.2. Because inventory and sales are closely related, we can nonetheless use a store's inventory level to predict its monthly sales. We will learn how to do the prediction in Section 2.3. Prediction requires that we identify an explanatory variable and a response variable. Some other statistical techniques ignore this distinction. Do remember that calling one variable explanatory and the other response doesn't necessarily mean that changes in one *cause* changes in the other.

Most statistical studies examine data on more than one variable. Fortunately, statistical analysis of several-variable data builds on the tools we used to examine individual variables. The principles that guide our work also remain the same:

- First plot the data, then add numerical summaries.
- Look for overall patterns and deviations from those patterns.
- When the overall pattern is quite regular, use a compact mathematical model to describe it.

APPLY YOUR KNOWLEDGE

2.1 Independent and dependent variables. In each of the following situations, is it more reasonable to simply explore the relationship between the two variables or to view one of the variables as an explanatory variable and the other as a response variable? In the latter case, which is the explanatory variable and which is the response variable?

(a) The amount of time a student spends studying for a statistics exam and the grade on the exam

(b) The weight and height of a person

(c) The amount of yearly rainfall and the yield of a crop

(d) An employee's salary and number of sick days used

(e) The economic class of a father and of a son

2.2 Stock prices. How well does a stock's market price at the beginning of the year predict its price at the end of the year? To find out, record the prices of a large group of stocks at the beginning of the year, wait until the end of the year, then record their prices again. What are the explanatory and response variables here? Are these variables categorical or quantitative?

2.3 Hand wipes. Antibacterial hand wipes can irritate the skin. A company wants to compare two different formulas for new wipes. Investigators choose two groups of adults at random. Each group uses one type of wipes. After several weeks, a doctor assesses whether or not each person's skin appears abnormally irritated. What are the explanatory and response variables? Are they categorical or quantitative variables?

2.1 Scatterplots

CASE 2.1 SALES AT A RETAIL SHOP

Three entrepreneurial women open Duck Worth Wearing, a shop selling high-quality second-hand children's clothing, toys, and furniture. Items are consigned to the shop by individuals who then receive a percent of the selling price of their items. Table 2.1 displays daily data for April 2000 on sales at Duck Worth Wearing.[1] Larger retail establishments keep more elaborate records, particularly relating to sales of specific items or branded lines of goods. The consignment shop does not sell multiple copies of the same item, though records of sales by categories of item (clothing, toys, and so on) might be useful for planning and advertising.

The data in Table 2.1 concern each day's gross sales, broken down by method of payment (cash, check, credit card). "Gross sales" in retailing are overall dollar sales, not adjusted for returns or discounts. The data record the number of items sold and the dollar amount of gross sales for each payment method on each day. The three owners of Duck Worth Wearing would like to know what they should expect gross sales to be on a day when a particular number of items have been sold. Some discrepancies have arisen recently (coinciding with the hiring of two new employees) where daily gross sales have seemed unusually low given the number of items sold on a given day. In addition to this question, the owners would like to see how weekends compare to weekdays with respect to gross sales and items sold. We will examine relationships among some of these variables to help the owners answer their questions.

The most common way to display the relation between two quantitative variables is a *scatterplot*. Here is an example of a scatterplot.

EXAMPLE 2.3 Items Sold and Gross Sales

CASE 2.1

The owners of Duck Worth Wearing expect a clear relationship between the number of items sold per day and the gross sales per day. The data appear in columns B and C of Table 2.1.

TABLE 2.1 Gross sales and number of items sold

	A	B	C	D	E	F	G	H	I
1	Date	Gross Sales	Items	Gross Case	Cash Items	Gross Check	Check Items	Gross Credit Card	Credit Cards Items
2	4/1/2000	890.5	115	348.2	55	394.3	56	148	4
3	4/3/2000	197	17	42	8	44.5	3	110.5	6
4	4/4/2000	231	26	61	9	108.5	10	61.5	7
5	4/5/2000	170	21	94	16	76	5	0	0
6	4/6/2000	202.5	30	59.5	11	104	14	39	5
7	4/7/2000	225.5	35	164.5	26	54	8	7	1
8	4/8/2000	489.7	84	125.7	27	220.6	31	143.4	26
9	4/10/2000	234.8	42	110.8	19	97.5	18	26.5	5
10	4/11/2000	161.5	21	26	5	122	14	13.5	2
11	4/12/2000	284	44	109	18	104	14	71	12
12	4/13/2000	422	65	180	27	126	17	116	21
13	4/14/2000	300.7	59	211.8	36	39.4	14	49.5	9
14	4/15/2000	412.4	69	57.5	10	341.9	57	13	2
15	4/17/2000	346.8	59	115	20	126.8	23	105	16
16	4/18/2000	92.3	19	15.3	8	58	8	19	3
17	4/19/2000	255.8	42	97.3	15	114.5	13	44	14
18	4/20/2000	118.5	16	61	10	57.5	6	0	0
19	4/21/2000	286.5	39	84.5	15	178	21	24	3
20	4/22/2000	594	72	156.5	24	293.5	38	144	10
21	4/24/2000	263.29	43	87.56	15	113.18	17	62.55	11
22	4/25/2000	244.08	45	96.34	19	147.74	26	0	0
23	4/26/2000	394.28	64	201.53	33	178.95	28	13.8	3
24	4/27/2000	241.31	36	107.92	23	133.39	13	0	0
25	4/28/2000	299.97	40	158.19	21	118.03	15	23.75	4
26	4/29/2000	649.04	103	176.04	43	220.4	32	252.6	28
27									

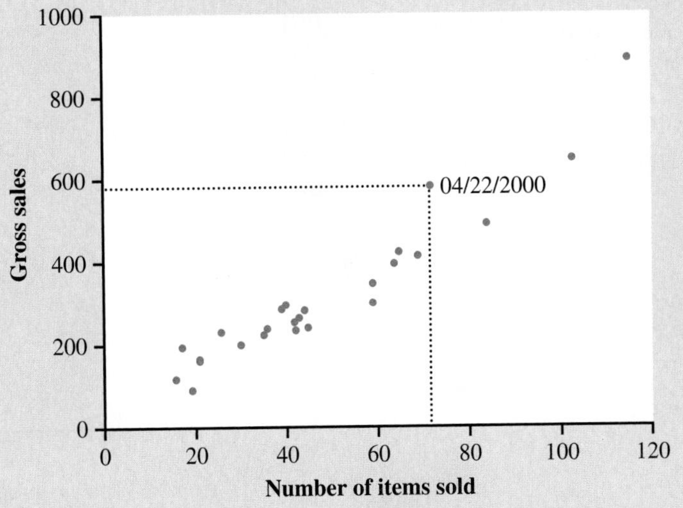

FIGURE 2.1 Scatterplot of the gross sales for each day in April 2000 against the number of items sold for the same day, from Table 2.1. The dotted lines intersect at the point (72, 594), the data for April 22, 2000.

The number of items sold should help explain gross sales. Therefore, "items sold" is the explanatory variable and "gross sales" is the response variable. We want to see how gross sales change when number of items sold changes, so we put number of items sold (the explanatory variable) on the horizontal axis. Figure 2.1 is the scatterplot. Each point represents a single day of transactions in April 2000. On April 22, 2000, for example, the shop sold 72 items, and the gross sales were $594. Find 72 on the x (horizontal) axis and 594 on the y (vertical) axis. April 22, 2000, appears as the point (72, 594) above 72 and to the right of 594. Figure 2.1 shows how to locate this point on the plot.

Scatterplot

A **scatterplot** shows the relationship between two quantitative variables measured on the same individuals. The values of one variable appear on the horizontal axis, and the values of the other variable appear on the vertical axis. Each individual in the data appears as the point in the plot fixed by the values of both variables for that individual.

Always plot the explanatory variable, if there is one, on the horizontal axis (the x axis) of a scatterplot. As a reminder, we usually call the explanatory variable x and the response variable y. If there is no explanatory-response distinction, either variable can go on the horizontal axis. The time plots in Section 1.1 (page 18) are special scatterplots where the explanatory variable x is a measure of time.

APPLY YOUR KNOWLEDGE

2.4 Architectural firms. Table 1.3 (page 13) contains data describing firms engaged in commercial architecture in the Indianapolis area.

(a) We want to examine the relationship between number of full-time staff members employed and total billings. Which is the explanatory variable?

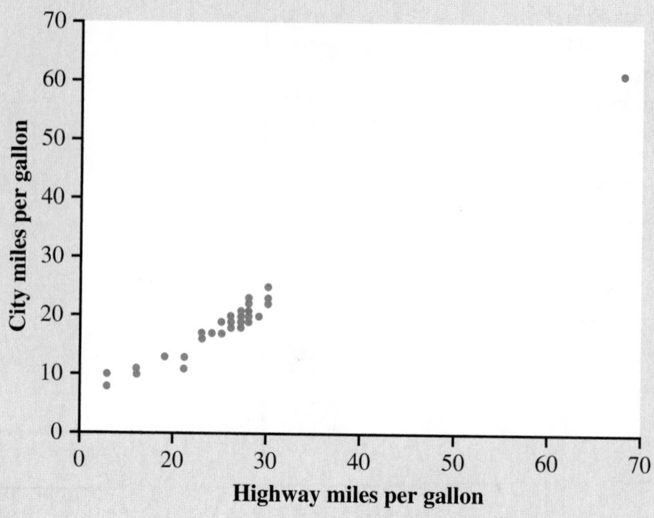

FIGURE 2.2 City and highway fuel consumption for 2001 model two-seater cars, for Exercise 2.5.

(b) Make a scatterplot of these data. (Be sure to label the axes with the variable names, not just x and y.) What does the scatterplot show about the relationship between these variables?

2.5 Your mileage may vary. Figure 2.2 plots the city and highway fuel consumption of 2001 model two-seater cars, from the Environmental Protection Agency's *Model Year 2001 Fuel Economy Guide*.

(a) There is one unusual observation, the Honda Insight. What are the approximate city and highway gas mileages for this car?

(b) Describe the pattern of the relationship between city and highway mileage. Explain why you might expect a relationship with this pattern.

(c) Does the Honda Insight observation fit the overall relationship portrayed by the other two-seater cars plotted?

Interpreting scatterplots

To interpret a scatterplot, apply the strategies of data analysis learned in Chapter 1.

Examining a Scatterplot

In any graph of data, look for the **overall pattern** and for striking **deviations** from that pattern.

You can describe the overall pattern of a scatterplot by the **form, direction,** and **strength** of the relationship.

An important kind of deviation is an **outlier,** an individual value that falls outside the overall pattern of the relationship.

linear relationship

cluster

Figure 2.1 shows a clear *form:* the data lie in a roughly straight-line, or **linear,** pattern. There are no clear outliers. That is, no points clearly fall outside the overall linear pattern. There appears to be a **cluster** of points at the left, representing low-sales days, with higher-sales days strung out to the right.

The relationship in Figure 2.1 also has a clear *direction:* days on which the shop sells more items tend to have higher gross sales, as we expect. This is a *positive association* between the two variables.

Positive Association, Negative Association

Two variables are **positively associated** when above-average values of one tend to accompany above-average values of the other and below-average values also tend to occur together.

Two variables are **negatively associated** when above-average values of one tend to accompany below-average values of the other, and vice versa.

The *strength* of a relationship in a scatterplot is determined by how closely the points follow a clear form. The overall relationship in Figure 2.1 is fairly moderate—days with similar numbers of items sold show some scatter in their gross sales. Here is an example of a stronger linear relationship.

EXAMPLE 2.4 Heating a House

The Sanchez household is about to install solar panels to reduce the cost of heating their house. To know how much the solar panels help, they record consumption of natural gas before the panels are installed. Gas consumption is higher in cold weather, so the relationship between outside temperature and gas consumption is important.

Table 2.2 gives data for 16 months.[2] The response variable y is the average amount of natural gas consumed each day during the month, in hundreds of cubic feet. The explanatory variable x is the average number of heating degree-days each day during the month. (Heating degree-days are the usual measure of demand for heating. One degree-day is accumulated for each degree a day's average temperature falls below 65°F. An average temperature of 20°F, for example, corresponds to 45 degree-days.)

TABLE 2.2 Average degree-days and natural-gas consumption for the Sanchez household

Month	Degree-days	Gas (100 cu. ft.)	Month	Degree-days	Gas (100 cu. ft.)
Nov.	24	6.3	July	0	1.2
Dec.	51	10.9	Aug.	1	1.2
Jan.	43	8.9	Sept.	6	2.1
Feb.	33	7.5	Oct.	12	3.1
Mar.	26	5.3	Nov.	30	6.4
Apr.	13	4.0	Dec.	32	7.2
May	4	1.7	Jan.	52	11.0
June	0	1.2	Feb.	30	6.9

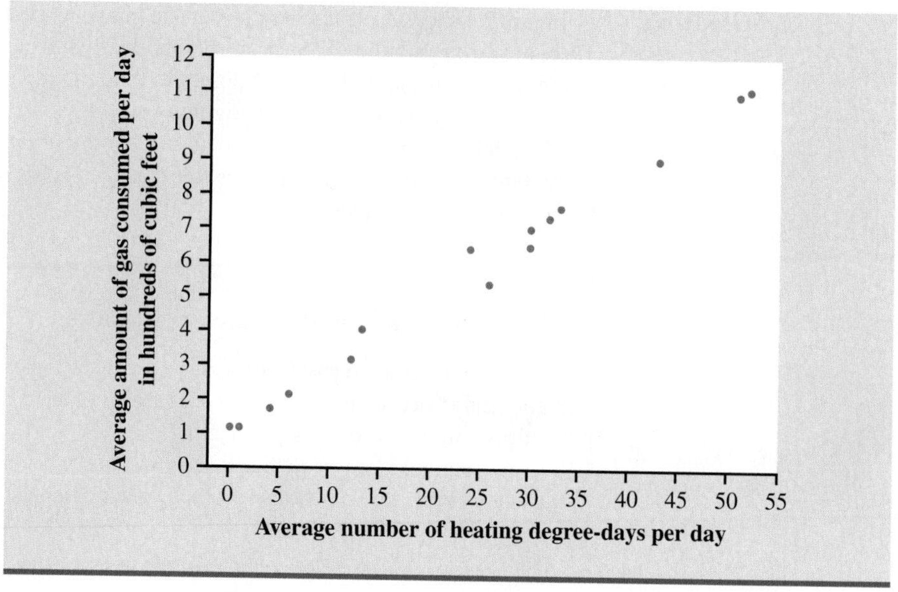

FIGURE 2.3 Scatterplot of the average amount of natural gas used per day by the Sanchez household in 16 months against the average number of heating degree-days per day in those months, from Table 2.2.

The scatterplot in Figure 2.3 shows a *strong positive linear association.* More degree-days means colder weather, so more gas is consumed. It is a strong linear relationship because the points lie close to a line, with little scatter. If we know how cold a month is, we can predict gas consumption quite accurately from the scatterplot.

Of course, not all relationships are linear. What is more, not all relationships have a clear direction that we can describe as positive association or negative association. Exercise 2.7 gives an example that is not linear and has no clear direction.

APPLY YOUR KNOWLEDGE

2.6 More on architectural firms. In Exercise 2.4 you made a scatterplot of number of full-time staff members employed and total billings.

(a) Describe the direction of the relationship. Are the variables positively or negatively associated?

(b) Describe the form of the relationship. Is it linear?

(c) Describe the strength of the relationship. Can the total billings of a firm be predicted accurately by the number of full-time staff members? If a firm maintains a full-time staff of 75 members, approximately what will its total billings be from year to year?

2.7 Does fast driving waste fuel? How does the fuel consumption of a car change as its speed increases? Here are data for a British Ford Escort. Speed is measured in kilometers per hour, and fuel consumption is measured in liters of gasoline used per 100 kilometers traveled.[3]

(a) Make a scatterplot. (Which is the explanatory variable?)

(b) Describe the form of the relationship. Why is it not linear? Explain why the form of the relationship makes sense.

(c) It does not make sense to describe the variables as either positively associated or negatively associated. Why?

(d) Is the relationship reasonably strong or quite weak? Explain your answer.

Speed (km/h)	Fuel used (liters/100 km)	Speed (km/h)	Fuel used (liters/100 km)
10	21.00	90	7.57
20	13.00	100	8.27
30	10.00	110	9.03
40	8.00	120	9.87
50	7.00	130	10.79
60	5.90	140	11.77
70	6.30	150	12.83
80	6.95		

Adding categorical variables to scatterplots

Every business has times of the day, days of the week, and periods in the year when sales are higher or the company is busier than other times. Duck Worth Wearing (Case 2.1) is open Monday through Saturday. The calendar provides an explanation of part of the pattern we observed in discussing Figure 2.1.

EXAMPLE 2.5 Are Saturdays Different?

CASE 2.1

Figure 2.4 enhances the scatterplot in Figure 2.1 by plotting the Saturdays with a different plot symbol (a colored **x**). The five days with the highest numbers of items sold are the five Saturdays in April 2000. While the Saturdays do stand out, Saturday sales still fit the same overall linear pattern as the weekdays.

Dividing the days into "Saturday" and "Weekday" introduces a third variable into the scatterplot. This is a categorical variable that has only two values. The two values

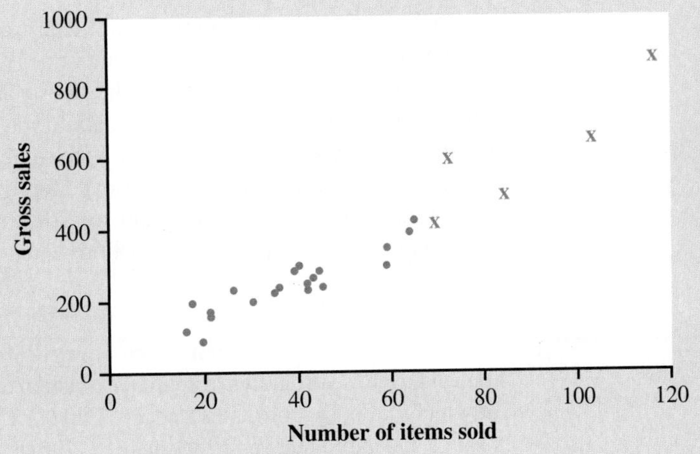

FIGURE 2.4 Gross sales at Duck Worth Wearing against number of items sold, with Saturdays highlighted, for Example 2.5.

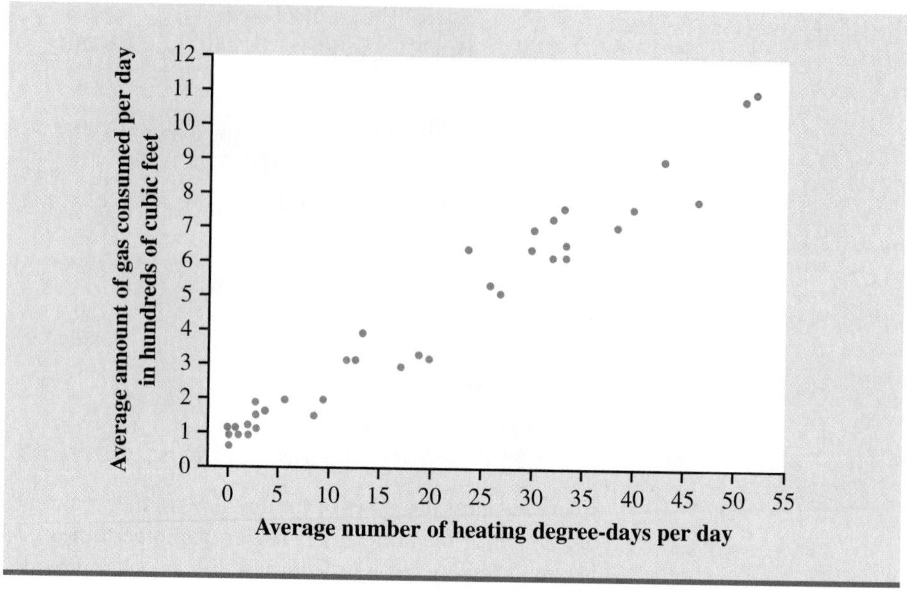

FIGURE 2.5 Natural-gas consumption against degree-days for the Sanchez household, for Example 2.6. The red observations are for 16 months before installing solar panels. The blue observations are for 23 months with the panels in use.

are displayed by the two different plotting symbols. **Use different colors or symbols to plot points when you want to add a categorical variable to a scatterplot.**[4]

EXAMPLE 2.6 Do Solar Panels Reduce Gas Use?

After the Sanchez household gathered the information recorded in Table 2.2 and Figure 2.3, they added solar panels to their house. They then measured their natural-gas consumption for 23 more months. To see how the solar panels affected gas consumption, add the degree-days and gas consumption for these months to the scatterplot. Figure 2.5 is the result. We use different colors to distinguish before from after. The "after" data form a linear pattern that is close to the "before" pattern in warm months (few degree-days). In colder months, with more degree-days, gas consumption after installing the solar panels is less than in similar months before the panels were added. The scatterplot shows the energy savings from the panels.

Our gas consumption example suffers from a common problem in drawing scatterplots that you may not notice when a computer does the work. When several individuals have exactly the same data, they occupy the same point on the scatterplot. Look at June and July in Table 2.2. Table 2.2 contains data for 16 months, but there are only 15 points in Figure 2.3. June and July both occupy the same point. You can use a different plotting symbol to call attention to points that stand for more than one individual. Some computer software does this automatically, but some does not. We recommend that you do use a different symbol for repeated observations when you plot a small number of observations by hand.

APPLY YOUR KNOWLEDGE

2.8 Do heavier people burn more energy? In judging the effectiveness of popular diet and exercise programs, researchers wish to take into account metabolic rate, the rate at which the body consumes energy. Table 2.3 gives data on the lean body mass and resting metabolic rate for 12 women and 7 men who are subjects in a study of dieting. Lean body mass, given in kilograms, is a person's weight leaving out all fat. Metabolic rate is measured in calories burned per 24 hours, the same calories used to describe the

TABLE 2.3 **Lean body mass and metabolic rate**

Subject	Sex	Mass (kg)	Rate (cal)	Subject	Sex	Mass (kg)	Rate (cal)
1	M	62.0	1792	11	F	40.3	1189
2	M	62.9	1666	12	F	33.1	913
3	F	36.1	995	13	M	51.9	1460
4	F	54.6	1425	14	F	42.4	1124
5	F	48.5	1396	15	F	34.5	1052
6	F	42.0	1418	16	F	51.1	1347
7	M	47.4	1362	17	F	41.2	1204
8	F	50.6	1502	18	M	51.9	1867
9	F	42.0	1256	19	M	46.9	1439
10	M	48.7	1614				

energy content of foods. The researchers believe that lean body mass is an important influence on metabolic rate.

(a) Make a scatterplot of the data for the female subjects. Which is the explanatory variable?

(b) Is the association between these variables positive or negative? What is the form of the relationship? How strong is the relationship?

(c) Now add the data for the male subjects to your graph, using a different color or a different plotting symbol. Does the pattern of the relationship that you observed in (b) hold for men also? How do the male subjects as a group differ from the female subjects as a group?

SECTION 2.1 SUMMARY

- To study relationships between variables, we must measure the variables on the same group of individuals.
- If we think that a variable x may explain or even cause changes in another variable y, we call x an **explanatory variable** and y a **response variable.**
- A **scatterplot** displays the relationship between two quantitative variables measured on the same individuals. Mark values of one variable on the horizontal axis (x axis) and values of the other variable on the vertical axis (y axis). Plot each individual's data as a point on the graph.
- Always plot the explanatory variable, if there is one, on the x axis of a scatterplot. Plot the response variable on the y axis.
- Plot points with different colors or symbols to see the effect of a categorical variable in a scatterplot.
- In examining a scatterplot, look for an overall pattern showing the **form, direction,** and **strength** of the relationship, and then for **outliers** or other deviations from this pattern.
- **Form: Linear relationships,** where the points show a straight-line pattern, are an important form of relationship between two variables. Curved relationships and **clusters** are other forms to watch for.

- **Direction:** If the relationship has a clear direction, we speak of either **positive association** (high values of the two variables tend to occur together) or **negative association** (high values of one variable tend to occur with low values of the other variable).
- **Strength:** The **strength** of a relationship is determined by how close the points in the scatterplot lie to a simple form such as a line.

SECTION 2.1 Exercises

For Exercises 2.1 to 2.3, see page 95; for 2.4 and 2.5, see pages 97–98; for 2.6 and 2.7, see pages 100–101; and for 2.8, see pages 102–103.

2.9 Paying for college. How well does the income of a college student's parents predict how much the student will borrow to pay for college? We have data on parents' income and college debt for a sample of 1200 recent college graduates. What are the explanatory and response variables? Are these variables categorical or quantitative? Do you expect a positive or negative association between these variables? Why?

2.10 T-bills and common stocks. What is the relationship between returns from buying Treasury bills and returns from buying common stocks? To buy a Treasury bill is to make a short-term loan to the U.S. government. This is much less risky than buying stock in a company, so (on the average) the returns on Treasury bills are lower than the returns on stocks. Figure 2.6 plots the annual returns on stocks for the years 1950 to 2003 against the returns on Treasury bills for the same years.

(a) The best year for stocks during this period was 1954. The worst year was 1974. About what were the returns on stocks in those two years?

(b) Treasury bills are a measure of the general level of interest rates. The years around 1980 saw very high interest rates. Treasury bill returns peaked in 1981. About what was the percent return that year?

(c) Some people say that high Treasury bill returns tend to go with low returns on stocks. Does such a pattern appear clearly in Figure 2.6? Does the plot have any clear pattern?

2.11 Sector fund returns. Fidelity Investments, like other large mutual funds companies, offers many "sector funds," which concentrate their investments in narrow segments of the stock market. These funds often rise or fall by much more than the market as a whole. We can group them by broader market sector to compare returns. Here are percent total returns for 23 Fidelity "Select Portfolios" funds for the year 2003, a year in which stocks rose sharply:[5]

Market sector	Fund returns (percent)						
Consumer	23.9	14.1	41.8	43.9	31.1		
Financial services	32.3	36.5	30.6	36.9	27.5		
Natural resources	22.9	7.6	32.1	28.7	29.5	19.1	
Technology	26.1	62.7	68.1	71.9	57.0	35.0	59.4

(a) Make a plot of total return against market sector (space the four market sectors equally on the horizontal axis). Compute the mean return for each sector, add the means to your plot, and connect the means with line segments.

(b) Based on the data, which of these market sectors were the best places in which to invest in 2003? Hindsight is wonderful.

(c) Does it make sense to speak of a positive or negative association between market sector and total return?

2.12 Sector fund returns. The data for 2003 in Exercise 2.11 make sector funds look attractive. Stocks rose sharply in 2003, after falling sharply in 2002 (and also in 2001 and 2000). Let's look at the percent returns for 2003 and 2002 for these same 23 funds.

2002 returns	2003 returns	2002 returns	2003 returns	2002 returns	2003 returns
−17.1	23.9	−0.7	36.9	−37.8	59.4
−6.7	14.1	−5.6	27.5	−11.5	22.9
−21.1	41.8	−26.9	26.1	−0.7	7.6
−12.8	43.9	−42.0	62.7	64.3	32.1
−18.9	31.1	−47.8	68.1	−9.6	28.7
−7.7	32.3	−50.5	71.9	−11.7	29.5
−17.2	36.5	−49.5	57.0	−2.3	19.1
−11.4	30.6	−23.4	35.0		

FIGURE 2.6 Scatterplot of percent return on common stocks versus percent return on Treasury bills, for Exercise 2.10.

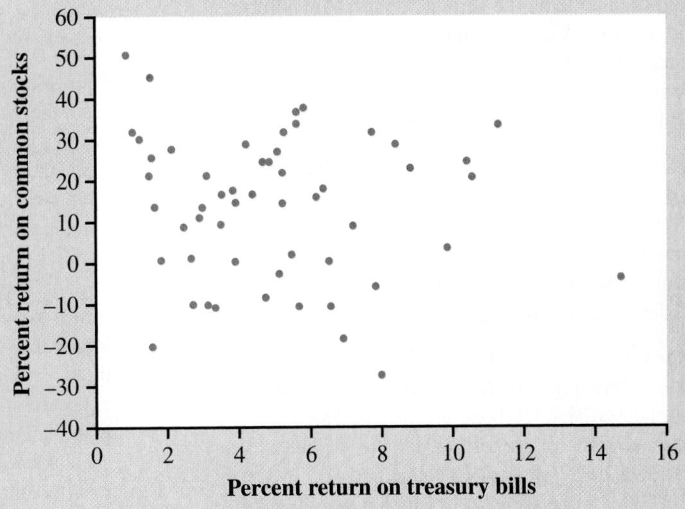

Do a careful graphical analysis of these data: side-by-side comparison of the distributions of returns in 2002 and 2003 and also a description of the relationship between the returns of the same funds in these two years. What are your most important findings? (The outlier is Fidelity Gold Fund.)

2.13 Online stock brokerages. How closely does the number of trading accounts relate to the total assets of the 10 largest online stock brokerages? The table below presents data on these brokerages. The number of accounts is in thousands, and assets are in billions of dollars.

Brokerage	Accounts (1000)	Assets ($ billions)
Ameritrade	428	19.5
Charles Schwab	2500	219.0
Datek	205	5.5
Discover	134	5.9
DLJ Direct	590	11.2
E* Trade	909	21.1
Fidelity	2300	160.0
National Discount Brokers	125	6.8
Suretrade	130	1.3
TD Waterhouse	615	38.8

(a) Does the wording of the initial question in this exercise indicate which variable should be treated as the response?

(b) Construct a scatterplot with Assets on the vertical axis and Accounts on the horizontal axis.

(c) Comment on the form, direction, and strength of the relationship between Assets and Accounts.

(d) Two brokerages stand out from the rest of the data. Identify these two brokerages by putting their names near their respective data points in your scatterplot.

2.14 Employment numbers. Where do most Americans work? Here are the numbers of paid employees in 1997 and in 2002 in the 10 kinds of business that employ the most people, according to a government census of business.[6]

Business type	2002 paid employees	1997 paid employees
Accommodation and food services	10,836,365	9,451,226
Administrative and support	8,002,725	7,066,658
Construction	6,943,582	5,664,853
Finance and insurance	6,663,714	5,835,214
Health care and social assistance	15,346,996	13,561,579
Information	3,845,583	3,066,167
Manufacturing	14,543,338	16,805,127
Professional, scientific, technical	7,508,866	5,361,210
Retail trade	15,029,339	13,991,103
Wholesale trade	6,034,579	5,796,557

(a) Construct a scatterplot with the number of paid employees in 2002 on the vertical axis and the number of paid employees in 1997 on the horizontal axis. Comment on the form, direction, and strength of the relationship between the two sets of values in the table. Also, identify any potential outliers in the data.

(b) Construct a scatterplot with the number of paid employees in 1997 on the vertical axis and the number of paid employees in 2002 on the horizontal axis. Comment on the form, direction, and strength of the relationship between the two sets of values in the table. Also, identify any potential outliers in the data.

(c) Are your comments on form, direction, and strength different in parts (a) and (b)? Clearly and carefully describe at least one scenario in which it would make sense to use a 1997 value to predict an unknown 2002 value in this context. Then, describe at least one scenario in which it would make sense to use a 2002 value to predict an unknown 1997 value.

2.15 Size and length of bear markets. Are longer bear markets associated with greater market declines? Figure 2.7 is a scatterplot of the data from Table 1.7 (page 27) on percent decline of the market versus duration of the bear market.

(a) Say in words what a positive association between decline and duration would mean. Does the plot show a positive association?

(b) What is the form of the relationship? Is it roughly linear? Is it very strong? Explain your answers.

(c) Without looking back at Table 1.7, what are the approximate decline and duration for the bear market that showed the greatest decline?

2.16 Health and wealth. Figure 2.8 is a scatterplot of data from the World Bank. The individuals are all the world's nations for which data are available. The explanatory variable is a measure of how rich a country is: the gross domestic product (GDP) per person. GDP is the total value of the goods and services produced in a country, here converted into dollars. The response variable is life expectancy at birth.[7] We expect people in richer countries to live longer. Describe the form, direction, and strength of the overall pattern. Does the graph confirm our expectation? The three African nations marked on the graph are outliers; a detailed study would ask what special factors explain the low life expectancy in these countries.

2.17 Rich states, poor states. One measure of a state's prosperity is the median income of its households. Another measure is the mean personal income per person in the state. Figure 2.9 is a scatterplot of these two variables, both measured in thousands of dollars. Because both variables have the same units, the plot uses equally spaced scales on both axes. The data appear in Table 1.9 (page 28).

(a) Explain why you expect a positive association between these variables. Also explain why you expect household income to be generally higher than income per person.

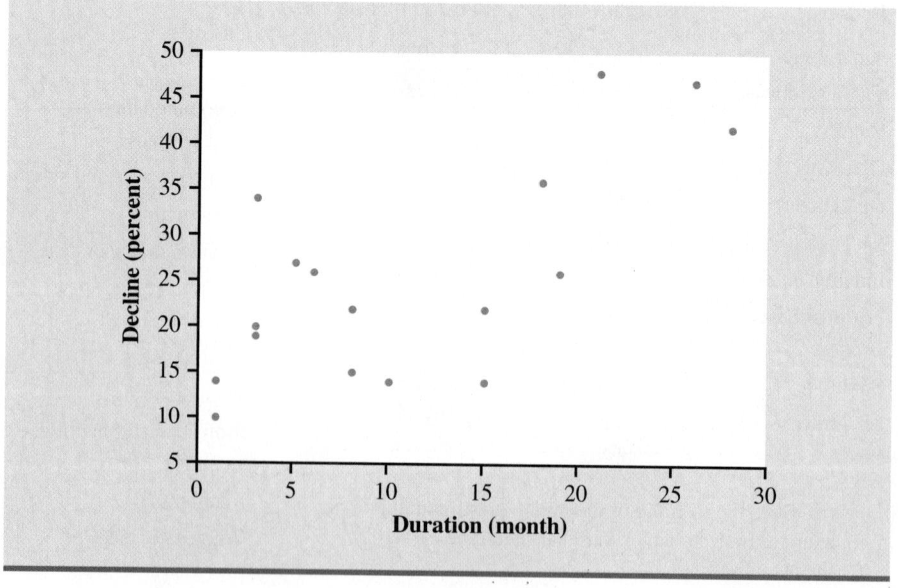

FIGURE 2.7 Scatterplot of percent decline versus duration in months of the bear markets in Table 1.7, for Exercise 2.15.

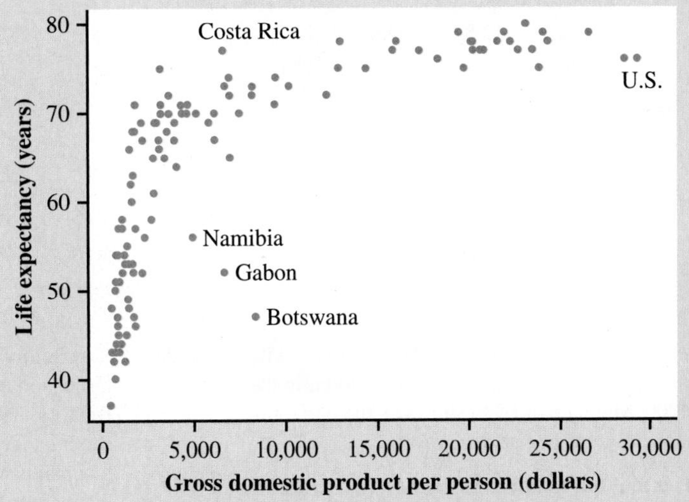

FIGURE 2.8 Scatterplot of life expectancy against gross domestic product per person for all the nations for which data are available, for Exercise 2.16.

(b) Nonetheless, the mean income per person in a state can be higher than the median household income. In fact, the District of Columbia has median income \$33,433 per household and mean income \$38,429 per person. Explain why this can happen.

(c) Describe the overall pattern of the plot, ignoring outliers.

(d) We have labeled New York on the graph because it is a large state in which mean individual income is high relative to median household income. There are two points that are outliers clearly more extreme than New York. Which observations do these points represent? What do you know that might help explain why these points are outliers?

2.18 Stocks and bonds. How is the flow of investors' money into stock mutual funds related to the flow of money into bond mutual funds? Here are data on the net new money flowing into stock and bond mutual funds in the years 1985 to 2000, in billions of dollars.[8] "Net" means that funds flowing out are subtracted from those flowing in. If more money leaves than arrives, the net flow will be negative. To eliminate the effect of

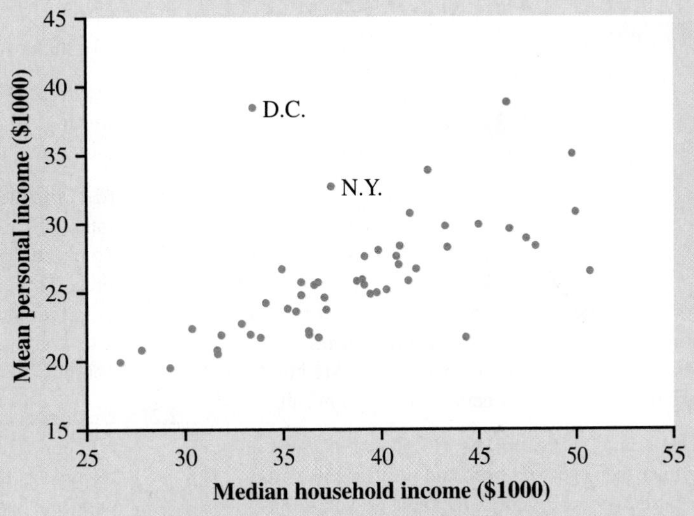

FIGURE 2.9 Scatterplot of mean income per person versus median income per household for the states, for Exercise 2.17.

Year	1985	1986	1987	1988	1989	1990	1991	1992
Stocks	12.8	34.6	28.8	−23.3	8.3	17.1	50.6	97.0
Bonds	100.8	161.8	10.6	−5.8	−1.4	9.2	74.6	87.1

Year	1993	1994	1995	1996	1997	1998	1999	2000
Stocks	151.3	133.6	140.1	238.2	243.5	165.9	194.3	309.0
Bonds	84.6	−72.0	−6.8	3.3	30.0	79.2	−6.2	−48.0

inflation, all dollar amounts are in "real dollars" with constant buying power equal to that of a dollar in the year 2000. Make a plot (with stocks on the horizontal axis) and describe the pattern it reveals.

2.19 Calories and salt in hot dogs. Are hot dogs that are high in calories also high in salt? Here are data for calories and salt content (milligrams of sodium) in 17 brands of meat hot dogs:[9]

Brand	Calories	Sodium (mg)
1	173	458
2	191	506
3	182	473
4	190	545
5	172	496
6	147	360
7	146	387
8	139	386
9	175	507
10	136	393
11	179	405
12	153	372
13	107	144
14	195	511
15	135	405
16	140	428
17	138	339

(a) Make a scatterplot of these data, with calories on the horizontal axis. Describe the overall form, direction, and strength of the relationship. Are hot dogs that are high in calories generally also high in salt?

(b) One brand, "Eat Slim Veal Hot Dogs," is made of veal rather than beef and pork and positions itself as a diet brand. Which brand in the table do you think this is?

2.20 How many corn plants are too many? Midwestern farmers make many business decisions before planting. Data can help. For example, how much corn per acre should a farmer plant to obtain the highest yield? Too few plants will give a low yield. On the other hand, if there are too many plants, they will compete with each other for moisture and nutrients, and yields will fall. To find the best planting rate, plant at different rates on several plots of ground and measure the harvest. (Be sure to treat all the plots the same except for the planting rate.) Here are data from such an experiment:[10]

Plants per acre	Yield (bushels per acre)			
12,000	150.1	113.0	118.4	142.6
16,000	166.9	120.7	135.2	149.8
20,000	165.3	130.1	139.6	149.9
24,000	134.7	138.4	156.1	
28,000	119.0	150.5		

(a) Is yield or planting rate the explanatory variable?

(b) Make a scatterplot of yield and planting rate.

(c) Describe the overall pattern of the relationship. Is it linear? Is there a positive or negative association, or neither?

(d) Find the mean yield for each of the five planting rates. Plot each mean yield against its planting rate on your scatterplot and connect these five points with lines. This combination of numerical description and graphing makes the relationship clearer. What planting rate would you recommend to a farmer whose conditions were similar to those in the experiment?

2.21 Business starts and failures. Table 2.4 lists the number of businesses started and the number of businesses that failed by state for one year. We might expect an association to exist between these economic measures.[11]

TABLE 2.4 Business starts and failures

State	Starts	Failures	State	Starts	Failures
AL	2,645	546	MT	397	201
AK	271	177	NE	565	383
AZ	2,868	1,225	NV	1,465	677
AR	1,091	748	NH	708	322
CA	21,582	17,679	NJ	6,412	2,024
CO	3,041	2,483	NM	887	585
CT	2,069	580	NY	13,403	4,233
DE	508	28	NC	4,371	846
DC	537	75	ND	229	144
FL	13,029	2,047	OH	4,829	2,524
GA	5,471	800	OK	1,367	990
HI	593	781	OR	1,823	1,109
ID	639	441	PA	5,525	2,641
IL	5,542	3,291	RI	544	150
IN	2,611	473	SC	2,023	410
IA	1,020	244	SD	281	275
KS	967	1,140	TN	2,835	1,369
KY	1,824	270	TX	10,936	6,785
LA	1,849	377	UT	1,417	388
ME	577	259	VT	261	80
MD	3,139	1,283	VA	3,502	860
MA	3,425	1,200	WA	2,956	2,528
MI	4,293	1,551	WV	623	305
MN	2,111	1,711	WI	2,357	1,005
MS	1,347	177	WY	213	166
MO	2,163	1,321			

(a) Make a scatterplot of business failures against business starts. Take business starts as the explanatory variable.

(b) The plot shows a positive association between the two variables. Why do we say that the association is positive?

(c) Find the point for Florida in the scatterplot and circle it.

(d) There is an outlier at the upper right of the plot. Which state is this?

(e) We wonder about clusters and gaps in the data display. There is a relatively clear cluster of states at the lower left of the plot. Four states are outside this cluster. Which states are these? Are they mainly from one part of the country?

2.22 Transforming data. Data analysts often look for a *transformation* of data that simplifies the overall pattern. Here is an example of how transforming the response variable can simplify the pattern of a scatterplot. The data show the growth of world crude-oil production between 1880 and 1990.[12]

Year	1880	1890	1900	1910	1920	1930	1940
Millions of barrels	30	77	149	328	689	1412	2150

Year	1950	1960	1970	1980	1990
Millions of barrels	3803	7674	16,690	21,722	22,100

(a) Make a scatterplot of production (millions of barrels) against year. Briefly describe the pattern of world crude-oil production growth.

(b) Now take the logarithm of the production in each year (use the `log` button on your calculator). Plot the logarithms against year. What is the overall pattern on this plot?

2.23 Categorical explanatory variable. A scatterplot shows the relationship between two quantitative variables. Here is a similar plot to study the relationship between a categorical explanatory variable and a quantitative response variable.

Fidelity Investments, like other large mutual funds companies, offers many "sector funds," which concentrate their investments in narrow segments of the stock market. These funds often rise or fall by much more than the market as a whole. We can group them by broader market sector to compare returns. Below are percent total returns for 23 Fidelity "Select Portfolios" funds for the year 2000, a year in which stocks declined and technology shares were especially hard-hit.[13]

(a) Make a plot of total return against market sector (space the four market sectors equally on the horizontal axis). Compute the mean return for each sector, add the means to your plot, and connect the means with line segments.

(b) Based on the data, which market sectors were good places to invest in 2000? Hindsight is wonderful.

(c) Does it make sense to speak of a positive or negative association between market sector and total return?

2.24 Where the stores are. Target and Wal-Mart are two of the largest retail chains in the United States. In 2000, Target had 977 stores and Wal-Mart had 2624 stores. The file *ex02_024* on the CD that accompanies this book has the number of Target stores and Wal-Mart stores listed by state.

(a) Use software to create a scatterplot of the number of Target stores versus the number of Wal-Mart stores for each of the 50 states.

(b) Identify any unusual observations in your scatterplot by labeling the point with the state abbreviation. Describe specifically what about the observation makes it stand out in the scatterplot.

(c) Comment on the form, direction, and strength of the relationship between the number of Target stores and the number of Wal-Mart stores per state.

Market sector	Fund returns (percent)						
Consumer	−9.3	29.8	−24.4	−23.1	−11.3		
Financial services	18.3	28.1	28.5	50.2	53.3		
Technology	−1.6	−30.4	−28.8	−17.5	−20.2	−32.3	−37.4
Utilities and natural resources	31.8	50.3	−18.1	71.3	30.4	−13.5	

2.2 Correlation

A scatterplot displays the form, direction, and strength of the relationship between two quantitative variables. Linear relations are particularly important because a straight line is a simple pattern that is quite common. We say a linear relation is strong if the points lie close to a straight line, and weak if they are widely scattered about a line. Our eyes are not good judges of how strong a linear relationship is. The two scatterplots in Figure 2.10 depict exactly the same data, but the lower plot is drawn smaller in a large field. The lower plot seems to show a stronger linear relationship. Our eyes can be fooled by changing the plotting scales or the amount of white space around the cloud of points in a scatterplot.[14] We need to follow our strategy for data analysis by using a numerical measure to supplement the graph. *Correlation* is the measure we use.

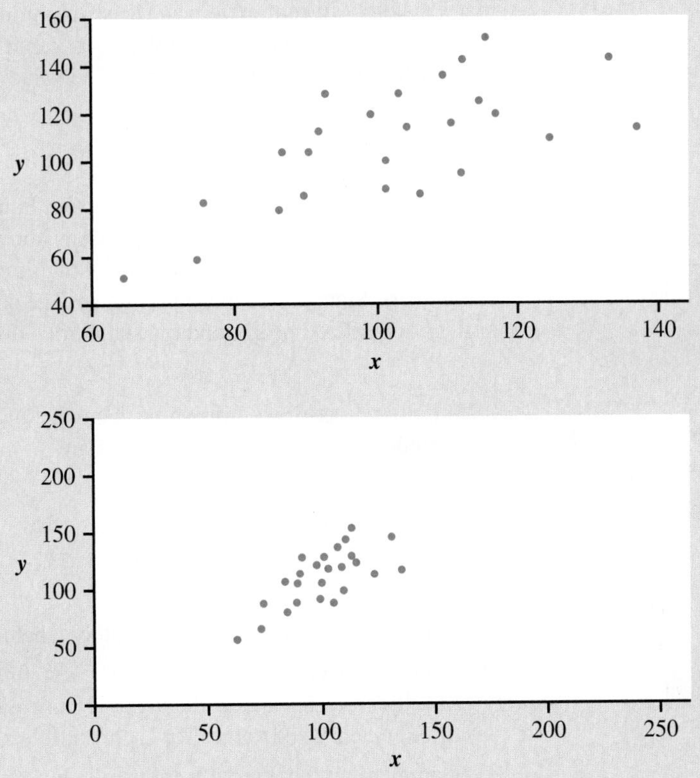

FIGURE 2.10 Two scatterplots of the same data. The straight-line pattern in the lower plot appears stronger because of the surrounding open space.

The correlation r

Correlation

The **correlation** measures the direction and strength of the linear relationship between two quantitative variables. Correlation is usually written as r.

Suppose that we have data on variables x and y for n individuals. The values for the first individual are x_1 and y_1, the values for the second individual are x_2 and y_2, and so on. The means and standard deviations of the two variables are $\bar{x}$ and s_x for the x-values, and $\bar{y}$ and s_y for the y-values. The correlation r between x and y is

$$r = \frac{1}{n-1} \sum \left(\frac{x_i - \bar{x}}{s_x} \right) \left(\frac{y_i - \bar{y}}{s_y} \right)$$

As always, the summation sign $\sum$ means "add these terms for all the individuals." The formula for the correlation r is a bit complex. It helps us to see what correlation is, but in practice you should use software or a calculator that finds r from keyed-in values of two variables x and y. Exercises 2.25 and 2.26 ask you to calculate correlations step-by-step from the definition to solidify the meaning.

The formula for r begins by standardizing the observations. Suppose, for example, that x is height in centimeters and y is weight in kilograms and that we have height and weight measurements for n people. Then $\overline{x}$ and s_x are the mean and standard deviation of the n heights, both in centimeters. The value

$$\frac{x_i - \overline{x}}{s_x}$$

is the standardized height of the ith person, familiar from Chapter 1. The standardized height says how many standard deviations above or below the mean a person's height lies. Standardized values have no units—in this example, they are no longer measured in centimeters. Standardize the weights also. The correlation r is an average of the products of the standardized height and the standardized weight for the n people.

APPLY YOUR KNOWLEDGE

2.25 Four-wheel-drive minivans. The city and highway miles per gallon for all three 2001 model four-wheel-drive minivans are

City MPG	18.6	19.2	18.8
Highway MPG	28.7	29.3	29.2

(a) Make a scatterplot with appropriately labeled axes.

(b) Find the correlation r step-by-step. First, find the mean and standard deviation of the city mileages and of the highway mileages. (Use a calculator.) Then find the three standardized values for each variable and use the formula for r.

(c) Comment on the direction and strength of the relationship.

2.26 The price of a gigabyte. Here are data on the size in gigabytes (GB) and the wholesale price in dollars of several internal hard-drive models from one manufacturer:

Size (GB)	80	60	180	300	200	100	30
Price ($)	31	29	50	80	47	33	15

(a) Make a scatterplot. Be sure to label the axes appropriately. Comment on the form, direction, and strength of the relationship.

(b) Find the correlation r step-by-step. First, find the mean and standard deviation of the sizes and of the prices (use your calculator). Then find the seven standardized values for these variables and use the formula for r.

(c) Enter these data into your calculator and use the calculator's correlation function to find r. Check that you get the same result as in (b).

Facts about correlation

The formula for correlation helps us see that r is positive when there is a positive association between the variables. Height and weight, for example, have a positive association. People who are above average in height tend also to be above average in weight. Both the standardized height and the standardized weight are positive. People who are below average in height tend also to have below-average weight. Then both standardized height and standardized weight are negative. In both cases, the products in the formula for r are mostly positive and so r is positive. In the same way, we can see that r is negative when the association between x and y is negative. More detailed study of the formula gives more detailed properties of r. Here is what you need to know to interpret correlation.

1. Correlation makes no distinction between explanatory and response variables. It makes no difference which variable you call x and which you call y in calculating the correlation.

2. Correlation requires that both variables be quantitative, so that it makes sense to do the arithmetic indicated by the formula for r. We cannot calculate a correlation between the incomes of a group of people and what city they live in, because city is a categorical variable.

3. Because r uses the standardized values of the observations, r does not change when we change the units of measurement of x, y, or both. Measuring height in inches rather than centimeters and weight in pounds rather than kilograms does not change the correlation between height and weight. The correlation r itself has no unit of measurement; it is just a number.

4. Positive r indicates positive association between the variables, and negative r indicates negative association.

5. The correlation r is always a number between -1 and 1. Values of r near 0 indicate a very weak linear relationship. The strength of the linear relationship increases as r moves away from 0 toward either -1 or 1. Values of r close to -1 or 1 indicate that the points in a scatterplot lie close to a straight line. The extreme values $r = -1$ and $r = 1$ occur only in the case of a perfect linear relationship, when the points lie exactly along a straight line.

6. Correlation measures the strength of only a linear relationship between two variables. Correlation does not describe curved relationships between variables, no matter how strong they are.

7. Like the mean and standard deviation, the correlation is not resistant: r is strongly affected by a few outlying observations. The correlation for Figure 2.9 (page 107) is $r = 0.6287$ when all 51 observations are included but rises to $r = 0.7789$ when we omit Alaska and the District of Columbia. Use r with caution when outliers appear in the scatterplot.

The scatterplots in Figure 2.11 illustrate how values of r closer to 1 or -1 correspond to stronger linear relationships. To make the meaning of r clearer, the standard deviations of both variables in these plots are equal and the horizontal and vertical scales are the same. In general, it is not so easy to guess the value of r from the appearance of a scatterplot. Remember that changing the plotting scales in a scatterplot may mislead our eyes, but it does not change the correlation.

The real data we have examined also illustrate how correlation measures the strength and direction of linear relationships. Figure 2.3 (page 100) shows a very strong positive linear relationship between degree-days and natural-gas consumption. The correlation is $r = 0.9953$. Check this on your calculator or software from the data in Table 2.2. Figure 2.8 (page 107) shows a positive but curved relationship. The correlation, which measures only the strength of the *linear* relationship for this plot, is $r = 0.7177$.

Do remember that **correlation is not a complete description of two-variable data,** even when the relationship between the variables is linear. You should give the means and standard deviations of both x and y along with the correlation. (Because the formula for correlation uses the means and standard deviations, these measures are the proper

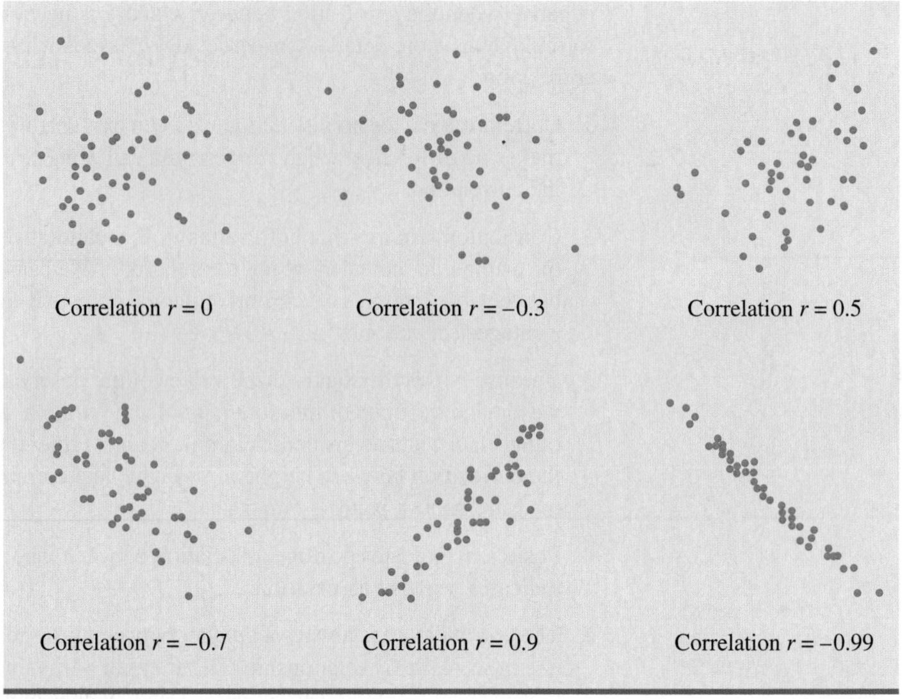

FIGURE 2.11 How correlation measures the strength of a linear relationship. Patterns closer to a straight line have correlations closer to 1 or −1.

choice to accompany a correlation.) Conclusions based on correlations alone may require rethinking in the light of a more complete description of the data.

EXAMPLE 2.7 Forecasting Earnings

Stock analysts regularly forecast the earnings per share (EPS) of companies they follow. EPS is calculated by dividing a company's net income for a given time period by the number of common stock shares outstanding. We have two analysts' EPS forecasts for a computer manufacturer for the next 6 quarters. How well do the two forecasts agree? The correlation between them is $r = 0.9$, but the mean of the first analyst's forecasts is 3 dollars per share lower than the second analyst's mean.

These facts do not contradict each other. They are simply different kinds of information. The means show that the first analyst predicts lower EPS than the second. But because the first analyst's EPS predictions are about 3 dollars per share lower than the second analyst's *for every quarter,* the correlation remains high. Adding or subtracting the same number to all values of either x or y does not change the correlation. The two analysts agree on which quarters will see higher EPS values. The high r shows this agreement, despite the fact that the actual predicted values differ by 3 dollars per share.

APPLY YOUR KNOWLEDGE

2.27 Thinking about correlation. Figure 2.7 (page 106) is a scatterplot of percent decline versus duration in months for 15 bear markets.

(a) Is the correlation r for these data near −1, clearly negative but not near −1, near 0, clearly positive but not near 1, or near 1? Explain your answer.

(b) Figure 2.2 (page 98) shows the highway and city gas mileage for 2001 model two-seater cars. Is the correlation here closer to 1 than that for Figure 2.7 or closer to 0? Explain your answer.

2.28 Brand names and generic products.

(a) If a store always prices its generic "store brand" products at 90% of the brand name products' prices, what would be the correlation between the prices of the brand name products and the store brand products? (*Hint:* Draw a scatterplot for several prices.)

(b) If the store always prices its generic products \$1 less than the corresponding brand name products, then what would be the correlation between the prices of the brand name products and the store brand products?

2.29 Strong association but no correlation. The gas mileage of an automobile first increases and then decreases as the speed increases. Suppose that this relationship is very regular, as shown by the following data on speed (miles per hour) and mileage (miles per gallon):

Speed	20	30	40	50	60
MPG	24	28	30	28	24

Make a scatterplot of mileage versus speed. Show that the correlation between speed and mileage is $r = 0$. Explain why the correlation is 0 even though there is a strong relationship between speed and mileage.

SECTION 2.2 SUMMARY

- The **correlation** r measures the strength and direction of the linear association between two quantitative variables x and y. Although you can calculate a correlation for any scatterplot, r measures only straight-line relationships.
- Correlation indicates the direction of a linear relationship by its sign: $r > 0$ for a positive association and $r < 0$ for a negative association.
- Correlation always satisfies $-1 \leq r \leq 1$ and indicates the strength of a relationship by how close it is to -1 or 1. Perfect correlation, $r = \pm 1$, occurs only when the points on a scatterplot lie exactly on a straight line.
- Correlation ignores the distinction between explanatory and response variables. The value of r is not affected by changes in the unit of measurement of either variable. Correlation is not resistant, so outliers can greatly change the value of r.

SECTION 2.2 Exercises

For Exercises 2.25 and 2.26, see page 112; and for 2.27 to 2.29, see pages 114–115.

2.30 Sector fund returns. Exercise 2.12 gives data on the returns from 23 Fidelity "sector funds" in 2002 (a down-year for stocks) and 2003 (an up-year).

(a) Make a scatterplot. Fidelity Gold Fund, the only fund with a positive return in both years, is an extreme outlier.

(b) To demonstrate that correlation is not resistant, find r for all 23 funds and then find r for the 22 funds other than Gold. Explain from Gold's position in your plot why omitting this point makes r more negative.

2.31 Coffee and deforestation. Coffee is a leading export from several developing countries. When coffee prices are high, farmers often clear forest to plant more coffee trees. Here are data for five years on prices paid to coffee growers in Indonesia and the rate of deforestation in a national park that lies in a coffee-producing region:[15]

Price (cents per pound)	Deforestation (percent)
29	0.49
40	1.59
54	1.69
55	1.82
72	3.10

(a) Make a scatterplot. Which is the explanatory variable? What kind of pattern does your plot show?

(b) Find the correlation r step-by-step. That is, find the mean and standard deviation of the two variables. Then find the five standardized values for each variable and use the formula for r. Explain how your value for r matches your graph in (a).

(c) Next, enter these data into your calculator or software and use the correlation function to find r. Check that you get the same result as in (b), up to roundoff error.

2.32 Coffee and deforestation. Coffee is currently priced in dollars. If it were priced in euros, and the dollar prices in Exercise 2.31 were translated into the equivalent prices in euros, would the correlation between coffee price and percent deforestation change? Explain your answer.

2.33 Coffee and deforestation. Exercise 2.31 gives data showing that deforestation in a national park in Indonesia goes up when high prices for coffee encourage farmers to clear forest in order to plant more coffee. There are only 5 observations, so we worry that the apparent relationship may be just chance.

(a) Make a scatterplot and find the correlation r.

(b) Assume that we know that coffee prices and deforestation rates are unrelated. Add at least 20 points (by hand) to the scatterplot you made in part (a) to create a scatterplot that corresponds to this assumption. Use a different marking symbol for these new points than that used for the 5 data points in part (a).

(c) What would be the approximate correlation of your points in part (b)?

2.34 Online stock brokerages. The table in Exercise 2.13 (page 105) presents data on the number of accounts and the total assets of 10 online stock brokerages.

(a) Calculate the correlation between Accounts and Assets.

(b) Rather than reporting assets of these brokerages in billions of dollars, divide each asset value by 10 and record the new values. The new asset values are now reported in units of 10 billion dollars (that's 10,000,000,000). Recalculate the correlation between Accounts and Assets.

(c) Did changing the units from billions of dollars to tens of billions of dollars affect the correlation? Is this what you expected? Explain your response.

2.35 Online stock brokerages. The table in Exercise 2.13 (page 105) presents data on the number of accounts and the total assets of 10 online stock brokerages.

(a) Calculate the correlation between Accounts and Assets.

(b) Recalculate the correlation between Accounts and Assets excluding Charles Schwab and Fidelity.

(c) When outliers are excluded from a data set, the correlation will tend to rise upon recalculation. Based on your calculations in parts (a) and (b), would you conclude that Charles Schwab and Fidelity are outliers with respect to this data set? Explain your response.

2.36 Match the correlation. The *Correlation and Regression* applet at `www.whfreeman.com/pbs` allows you to create a scatterplot by clicking and dragging with the mouse. The applet calculates and displays the correlation as you change the plot. You will use this applet to make scatterplots with 10 points that have correlation close to 0.7. The lesson is that many patterns can have the same correlation. Always plot your data before you trust a correlation.

(a) Stop after adding the first 2 points. What is the value of the correlation? Why does it have this value?

(b) Make a lower-left to upper-right pattern of 10 points with correlation about $r = 0.7$. (You can drag points up or down to adjust r after you have 10 points.) Make a rough sketch of your scatterplot.

(c) Make another scatterplot with 9 points in a vertical stack at the left of the plot. Add one point far to the right and move it until the correlation is close to 0.7. Make a rough sketch of your scatterplot.

(d) Make yet another scatterplot with 10 points in a curved pattern that starts at the lower left, rises to the right, then falls again at the far right. Adjust the points up or down until you have a quite smooth curve with correlation close to 0.7. Make a rough sketch of this scatterplot also.

2.37 Mutual fund performance. Many mutual funds compare their performance with that of a benchmark, an index of the returns on all securities of the kind that the fund buys. The Vanguard International Growth Fund, for example, takes as its benchmark the Morgan Stanley Europe, Australasia, Far East (EAFE) index of overseas stock market performance. Here are the percent returns for the fund and for the EAFE from 1982 (the first full year of the fund's existence) to 2000:[16]

Year	Fund	EAFE	Year	Fund	EAFE
1982	5.27	−0.86	1992	−5.79	−11.85
1983	43.08	24.61	1993	44.74	32.94
1984	−1.02	7.86	1994	0.76	8.06
1985	56.94	56.72	1995	14.89	11.55
1986	56.71	69.94	1996	14.65	6.36
1987	12.48	24.93	1997	4.12	2.06
1988	11.61	28.59	1998	16.93	20.33
1989	24.76	10.80	1999	26.34	27.30
1990	−12.05	−23.20	2000	−8.60	−13.96
1991	4.74	12.50			

Make a scatterplot suitable for predicting fund returns from EAFE returns. Is there a clear straight-line pattern? How strong is this pattern? (Give a numerical measure.) Are there any extreme outliers from the straight-line pattern?

2.38 How many calories? A food industry group asked 3368 people to guess the number of calories in each of several common foods. Table 2.5 displays the averages of their guesses and the correct number of calories.[17]

(a) We think that how many calories a food actually has helps explain people's guesses of how many calories it has. With this in mind, make a scatterplot of these data.

(b) Find the correlation r. Explain why your r is reasonable based on the scatterplot.

(c) The guesses are all higher than the true calorie counts. Does this fact influence the correlation in any way? How would r change if every guess were 100 calories higher?

(d) The guesses are much too high for spaghetti and the snack cake. Circle these points on your scatterplot. Calculate r for the other eight foods, leaving out these two points. Explain why r changed in the direction that it did.

2.39 Stretching a scatterplot. Changing the units of measurement can greatly alter the appearance of a scatterplot. Consider the following data:

x	−4	−4	−3	3	4	4
y	0.5	−0.6	−0.5	0.5	0.5	−0.6

(a) Draw x and y axes each extending from −6 to 6. Plot the data on these axes.

(b) Calculate the values of new variables $x^* = x/10$ and $y^* = 10y$, starting from the values of x and y. Plot y^* against x^* on the same axes using a different plotting symbol. The two plots are very different in appearance.

(c) Find the correlation between x and y. Then find the correlation between x^* and y^*. How are the two correlations related? Explain why this isn't surprising.

2.40 Where the stores are. Exercise 2.24 (page 110) looked at data on the number of Target and Wal-Mart stores in each state.

(a) Use software to calculate the correlation of these data.

(b) Predict whether the correlation will increase or decrease if California's data are excluded, then recalculate the correlation without the data for California. Why did the correlation change in this way?

TABLE 2.5 Guessed and true calories in 10 foods

Food	Guessed calories	Correct calories	Food	Guessed calories	Correct calories
8 oz. whole milk	196	159	2-oz. candy bar	364	260
5 oz. spaghetti with tomato sauce	394	163	Saltine cracker	74	12
5 oz. macaroni with cheese	350	269	Medium-size apple	107	80
One slice wheat bread	117	61	Medium-size potato	160	88
One slice white bread	136	76	Cream-filled snack cake	419	160

(c) Start again with all 50 observations and predict whether the correlation will increase or decrease if the data for Texas are excluded. Recalculate the correlation without the Texas data. Why did the correlation change in this way?

2.41 CEO compensation and stock market performance. An academic study concludes, "The evidence indicates that the correlation between the compensation of corporate CEOs and the performance of their company's stock is close to zero." A business magazine reports this as "A new study shows that companies that pay their CEOs highly tend to perform poorly in the stock market, and vice versa." Explain why the magazine's report is wrong. Write a statement in plain language (don't use the word "correlation") to explain the study's conclusion.

2.42 Investment diversification. A mutual funds company's newsletter says, "A well-diversified portfolio includes assets with low correlations." The newsletter includes a table of correlations between the returns on various classes of investments. For example, the correlation between municipal bonds and large-cap stocks is 0.50, and the correlation between municipal bonds and small-cap stocks is 0.21.[18]

(a) Rachel invests heavily in municipal bonds. She wants to diversify by adding an investment whose returns do not closely follow the returns on her bonds. Should she choose large-cap stocks or small-cap stocks for this purpose? Explain your answer.

(b) If Rachel wants an investment that tends to increase when the return on her bonds drops, what kind of correlation should she look for?

2.43 Outliers and correlation. Both Figures 2.2 and 2.9 contain outliers. In Figure 2.9 removing the outlier *increases* the correlation r, but in Figure 2.2 removing the outlier *decreases* r. Explain why this is true.

2.44 Driving speed and fuel consumption. The data in Exercise 2.29 were made up to create an example of a strong curved relationship for which, nonetheless, $r = 0$. Exercise 2.7 (pages 100–101) gives actual data on gas used versus speed for a small car. Make a scatterplot if you did not do so in Exercise 2.7. Calculate the correlation, and explain why r is close to 0 despite a strong relationship between speed and gas used.

2.45 Sloppy writing about correlation. Each of the following statements contains a blunder. Explain in each case what is wrong.

(a) "There is a high correlation between the gender of American workers and their income."

(b) "We found a high correlation ($r = 1.09$) between students' ratings of faculty teaching and ratings made by other faculty members."

(c) "The correlation between planting rate and yield of corn was found to be $r = 0.23$ bushel."

2.46 Mutual funds and correlation. Financial experts use statistical measures to describe the performance of investments such as mutual funds. In the past, fund companies feared that investors would not understand statistical descriptions, but investor demand for better information is moving standard deviations and correlations into published reports.

(a) The T. Rowe Price mutual funds group reports the standard deviation of yearly percent returns for its funds. Recently, Equity Income Fund had standard deviation 9.94%, and Science & Technology Fund had standard deviation 23.77%. Explain to someone who knows no statistics how these standard deviations help investors compare the two funds.

(b) Some mutual funds act much like the stock market as a whole, as measured by a market index such as the Standard & Poor's 500 stock index (S&P 500). Others are very different from the overall market. We can use correlation to describe the association. Monthly returns from Fidelity Magellan Fund have correlation $r = 0.85$ with the S&P 500. Fidelity Small Cap Stock Fund has correlation $r = 0.55$ with the S&P 500. Explain to someone who knows no statistics how these correlations help investors compare the two funds.

2.3 Least-Squares Regression

Correlation measures the direction and strength of the straight-line (linear) relationship between two quantitative variables. If a scatterplot shows a linear relationship, we would like to summarize this overall pattern by drawing a line on the scatterplot. A *regression line* summarizes the relationship between two variables, but only in a specific setting: when one of the variables helps explain or predict the other. That is, regression describes a relationship between an explanatory variable and a response variable.

Regression Line

A **regression line** is a straight line that describes how a response variable y changes as an explanatory variable x changes. We often use a regression line to predict the value of y for a given value of x.

EXAMPLE 2.8 Predicting Natural-Gas Consumption

Figure 2.12 is another scatterplot of the natural-gas consumption data from Table 2.2. There is a strong linear relationship between the average outside temperature (measured by heating degree-days) in a month and the average amount of natural gas that the Sanchez household uses per day during the month. The correlation is $r = 0.9953$, close to the $r = 1$ of points that lie exactly on a line. The regression line drawn through the points in Figure 2.12 describes these data very well.

prediction

The Sanchez household wants to use this line to predict their natural-gas consumption. "If a month averages 20 degree-days per day (that's 45°F), how much gas will we use?" To **predict** gas consumption at 20 degree-days, first locate 20 on the x axis. Then go "up and over" as in the figure to find the gas consumption y that corresponds to $x = 20$. We predict that the Sanchez household will use about 4.9 hundreds of cubic feet of gas each day in such a month.

The least-squares regression line

Different people might draw different lines by eye on a scatterplot. This is especially true when the points are more widely scattered than those in Figure 2.12. We need a way to draw a regression line that doesn't depend on our guess as to where the line should

FIGURE 2.12 The Sanchez household gas consumption data, with a regression line for predicting gas consumption from degree-days, for Example 2.8. The dashed lines illustrate how to use the regression line to predict gas consumption for a month averaging 20 degree-days per day.

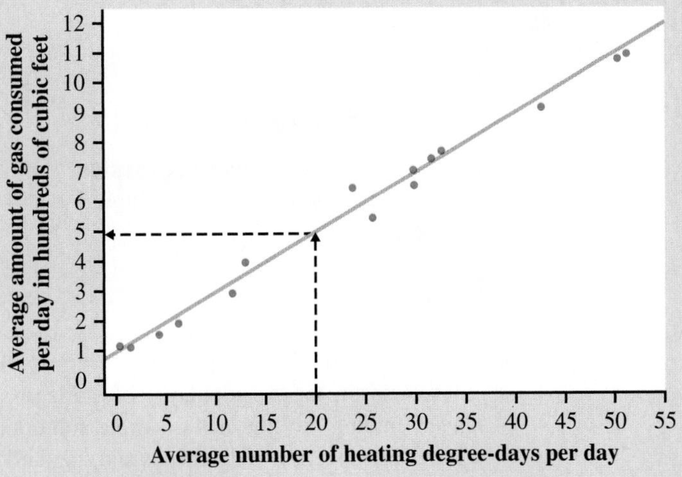

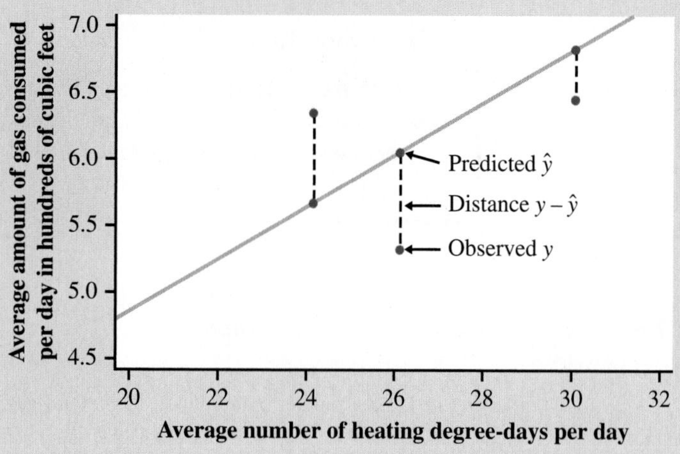

FIGURE 2.13 The least-squares idea. For each observation, find the vertical distance of each point on the scatterplot from a regression line. The least-squares regression line makes the sum of the squares of these distances as small as possible.

go. We will use the line to predict y from x, so the prediction errors we make are errors in y, the vertical direction in the scatterplot. If we predict 4.9 hundreds of cubic feet for a month with 20 degree-days and the actual use turns out to be 5.1 hundreds of cubic feet, our prediction error is

$$\begin{aligned}\text{error} &= \text{observed } y - \text{predicted } y \\ &= 5.1 - 4.9 = 0.2\end{aligned}$$

No line will pass exactly through all the points in the scatterplot. We want the *vertical* distances of the points from the line to be as small as possible. Figure 2.13 illustrates the idea. This plot shows three of the points from Figure 2.12, along with the line, on an expanded scale. The line passes above two of the points and below one of them. The vertical distances of the data points from the line appear as vertical line segments. There are many ways to make the collection of vertical distances "as small as possible." The most common is the *least-squares* method.

Least-Squares Regression Line

The **least-squares regression line** of y on x is the line that makes the sum of the squares of the vertical distances of the data points from the line as small as possible.

One reason for the popularity of the least-squares regression line is that the problem of finding the line has a simple solution. We can give the recipe for the least-squares line in terms of the means and standard deviations of the two variables and their correlation.

Equation of the Least-Squares Regression Line

We have data on an explanatory variable x and a response variable y for n individuals. From the data, calculate the means $\bar{x}$ and $\bar{y}$ and the standard deviations s_x and s_y of the two variables, and their correlation r. The least-squares regression line is the line

$$\hat{y} = b_0 + b_1 x$$

with **slope**

$$b_1 = r\frac{s_y}{s_x}$$

and **intercept**

$$b_0 = \bar{y} - b_1\bar{x}$$

We write $\hat{y}$ (read "y hat") in the equation of the regression line to emphasize that the line gives a *predicted* response $\hat{y}$ for any x. Because of the scatter of points about the line, the predicted response will usually not be exactly the same as the actually *observed* response y. In practice, you don't need to calculate the means, standard deviations, and correlation first. Statistical software or your calculator will give the slope b_1 and intercept b_0 of the least-squares line from keyed-in values of the variables x and y. You can then concentrate on understanding and using the regression line. Be warned—different software packages and calculators label the slope and intercept differently in their output, so remember that the slope is the value that multiplies x in the equation.

EXAMPLE 2.9 Using a Regression Line

The line in Figure 2.12 is in fact the least-squares regression line of gas consumption on degree-days. Enter the data from Table 2.2 into your calculator or software and check that the equation of this line is

$$\hat{y} = 1.0892 + 0.1890x$$

slope

The **slope** of a regression line is almost always important for interpreting the data. The slope is the rate of change, the amount of change in $\hat{y}$ when x increases by 1. The slope $b_1 = 0.1890$ in this example says that each additional degree-day predicts consumption of about 0.19 more hundreds of cubic feet of natural gas per day.

intercept

The **intercept** of the regression line is the value of $\hat{y}$ when $x = 0$. Although we need the value of the intercept to draw the line, it is statistically meaningful only when x can actually take values close to zero. In our example, $x = 0$ occurs when the average outdoor temperature is at least 65°F. We predict that the Sanchez household will use an average of $b_0 = 1.0892$ hundreds of cubic feet of gas per day when there are no degree-days. They use this gas for cooking and heating water, activities that continue in warm weather.

prediction

The equation of the regression line makes **prediction** easy. Just substitute an x-value into the equation. To predict gas consumption at 20 degree-days, substitute $x = 20$:

$$\hat{y} = 1.0892 + (0.1890)(20)$$
$$= 1.0892 + 3.78 = 4.869$$

plotting a line

To **plot the line** on the scatterplot, use the equation to find $\hat{y}$ for two values of x, one near each end of the range of x in the data. Plot each $\hat{y}$ above its x and draw the line through the two points. ■

(a)

```
LinReg
  y=ax+b
  a=.1889989538
  b=1.089210843
  r2=.9905504416
  r=.995264006
```

(b)

```
The regression equation is
Gas Used = 1.09 + 0.189 Degree-Days

Predictor          Coef    SE Coef       T      P
Constant         1.0892     0.1389    7.84  0.000
Degree-Days    0.188999   0.004934   38.31  0.000

S = 0.338928   R-Sq = 99.1%   R-Sq(adj) = 99.0%

Analysis of Variance

Source           DF      SS      MS        F      P
Regression        1  168.58  168.58  1467.55  0.000
Residual Error   14    1.61    0.11
Total            15  170.19
```

(c)

Regression Statistics	
Multiple R	0.995264006
R Square	0.990550442
Adjusted R Square	0.989875473
Standard Error	0.338928399
Observations	16

ANOVA

	df	*SS*	*MS*	*F*	*Significance F*
Regression	1	168.5811606	168.5811606	1467.55072	1.41518E-15
Residual	14	1.608214432	0.114872459		
Total	15	170.189375			

	Coefficients	*Standard Error*	*t Stat*	*P-value*	*Lower 95%*	*Upper 95%*
Intercept	1.089210843	0.138914661	7.840863106	1.72896E-06	0.791268528	1.387153159
Degree-Days	0.188998954	0.004933588	38.30862462	1.41518E-15	0.178417461	0.199580447

FIGURE 2.14 Least-squares regression output for the gas consumption data from a graphing calculator, a statistical software package, and a spreadsheet. (a) The TI-83 calculator. (b) Minitab. (c) Microsoft Excel.

Figure 2.14 displays the regression output for the gas consumption data from a graphing calculator, a statistical software package, and a spreadsheet. Each output records the slope and intercept of the least-squares line, calculated to more decimal places than we need. The software also provides information that we do not yet need—part of the art of using such tools is to ignore the extra information that is almost always present. You must also inspect the output with care. For example, the graphing calculator presents the least-squares line in the form $y = ax + b$, so a is the calculator's symbol for the slope rather than our symbol b_1.

APPLY YOUR KNOWLEDGE

2.47 Example 2.9 gives the equation of the regression line of gas consumption y on degree-days x for the data in Table 2.2 as

$$\hat{y} = 1.0892 + 0.1890x$$

Enter the data from Table 2.2 into your calculator or software.

(a) Use the regression function to find the equation of the least-squares regression line.

(b) Find the mean and standard deviation of both x and y and their correlation r. Find the slope b_1 and intercept b_0 of the regression line from these, using the facts in the box Equation of the Least-Squares Regression Line. Verify that in both part (a) and part (b) you get the equation in Example 2.9. (Results may differ slightly because of rounding.)

2.48 Architectural firms. Table 1.3 (page 13) contains data describing firms engaged in commercial architecture in the Indianapolis area. The regression line for predicting total billings from number of full-time staff members employed is

$$\text{billings} = 0.2821 + (0.0917 \times \text{employed})$$

(a) Make a scatterplot and draw this regression line on the plot. Using the regression equation, predict the total billings of an architectural firm in Indianapolis with 111 full-time staff members.

(b) Compare the observed total billings for the firm with 111 full-time staff members with your prediction from part (a) by calculating the prediction error. How accurate was your prediction?

Facts about least-squares regression

Regression is one of the most common statistical settings, and least squares is the most common method for fitting a regression line to data. Here are some facts about least-squares regression lines.

Fact 1. The distinction between explanatory and response variables is essential in regression. Least-squares regression looks at the distances of the data points from the line only in the y direction. If we reverse the roles of the two variables, we get a different least-squares regression line.

EXAMPLE 2.10 Gross Sales and Item Count

CASE 2.1

Figure 2.15 is a scatterplot of the data in columns B and C of Table 2.1 (page 96). They are daily gross sales and number of items sold per day for Duck Worth Wearing, the children's consignment shop described in Case 2.1. There is a positive linear relationship, with $r = 0.9540$ indicating a strong linear relationship.

The two lines on the plot are the two least-squares regression lines. The regression line of gross sales on item count is solid. The regression line of item count on gross sales is dashed. *Regression of gross sales on item count and regression of item count on gross sales give different lines.* In the regression setting, you must decide which variable is explanatory.

Fact 2. There is a close connection between correlation and the slope of the least-squares line. The slope is

$$b_1 = r\frac{s_y}{s_x}$$

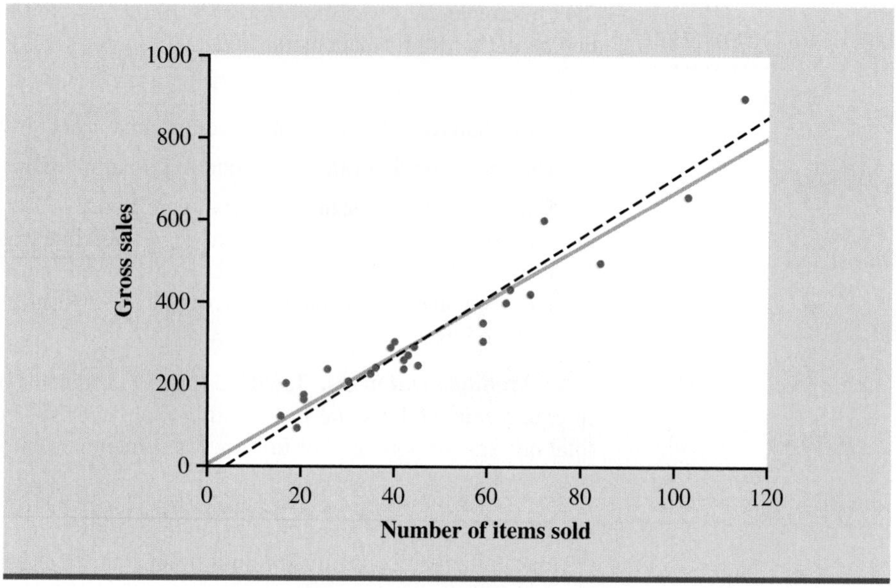

FIGURE 2.15 Scatterplot of the gross sales at Duck Worth Wearing for each day in April 2000 against the number of items sold for the same day, from Table 2.1. The two lines are the two least-squares regression lines: of gross sales on item count (solid) and of item count on gross sales (dashed).

This equation says that along the regression line, **a change of one standard deviation in x corresponds to a change of r standard deviations in y.** When the variables are perfectly correlated ($r = 1$ or $r = -1$), the change in the predicted response $\hat{y}$ is the same (in standard deviation units) as the change in x. Otherwise, because $-1 \leq r \leq 1$, the change in $\hat{y}$ is less than the change in x. As the correlation grows less strong, the prediction $\hat{y}$ moves less in response to changes in x.

Fact 3. The least-squares regression line always passes through the point $(\bar{x}, \bar{y})$ on the graph of y against x. So the least-squares regression line of y on x is the line with slope rs_y/s_x that passes through the point $(\bar{x}, \bar{y})$. We can describe regression entirely in terms of the basic descriptive measures $\bar{x}$, s_x, $\bar{y}$, s_y, and r.

Fact 4. The correlation r describes the strength of a straight-line relationship. In the regression setting, this description takes a specific form: **the square of the correlation r^2 is the fraction of the variation in the values of y that is explained by the least-squares regression of y on x.**

The idea is that when there is a linear relationship, some of the variation in y is accounted for by the fact that as x changes it pulls y along with it. Look again at Figure 2.12 (page 119). There is a lot of variation in the observed y's, the gas consumption data. They range from a low of about 1 to a high of 11. The scatterplot shows that most of this variation in y is accounted for by the fact that outdoor temperature (measured by degree-days x) was changing and pulled gas consumption along with it. There is only a little remaining variation in y, which appears in the scatter of points about the line. The points in Figure 2.15, on the other hand, are more scattered. Linear dependence on item count does explain much of the observed variation in gross sales. You would guess a higher value for the gross sales y knowing that $x = 100$ than you would if you were told that $x = 20$. But there is still considerable variation in y even when x is held relatively constant—look at the variability in the gross sales for points in Figure 2.15 near $x = 40$.

This idea can be expressed in algebra, though we won't do it. It is possible to separate the total variation in the observed values of y into two parts. One part is the variation we expect as x moves and $\hat{y}$ moves with it along the regression line. The other measures the variation of the data points about the line. The squared correlation r^2 is the first of these as a fraction of the whole:

$$r^2 = \frac{\text{variation in } \hat{y} \text{ as } x \text{ pulls it along the line}}{\text{total variation in observed values of } y}$$

EXAMPLE 2.11 Using r^2

The correlation between degree-days and gas use (Figure 2.12) is $r = 0.9953$. So $r^2 = 0.99$, and the straight-line relationship explains 99% of the month-to-month variation in gas use. In Figure 2.15, $r = 0.9540$ and $r^2 = 0.91$. The linear relationship between gross sales and item count explains 91% of the variation in either variable. There are two regression lines, but just one correlation, and r^2 helps interpret both regressions.

The relationship between life expectancy and gross domestic product (Figure 2.8, page 107) is positive but curved and has correlation $r = 0.7177$. Here, $r^2 = 0.515$, so that regressing life expectancy on GDP explains only about half of the variation in life expectancy among nations.

When you report a regression, give r^2 as a measure of how successful the regression was in explaining the response. All the software outputs in Figure 2.14 include r^2, either in decimal form or as a percent. When you see a correlation, square it to get a better feel for the strength of the association. Perfect correlation ($r = -1$ or $r = 1$) means the points lie exactly on a line. Then $r^2 = 1$ and all of the variation in one variable is accounted for by the linear relationship with the other variable. If $r = -0.7$ or $r = 0.7$, $r^2 = 0.49$ and about half the variation is accounted for by the linear relationship. In the r^2 scale, correlation ± 0.7 is about halfway between 0 and ± 1.

These facts are special properties of least-squares regression. They are not true for other methods of fitting a line to data. Another reason that least squares is the most common method for fitting a regression line to data is that it has many convenient special properties.

APPLY YOUR KNOWLEDGE

2.49 The "January effect." Some people think that the behavior of the stock market in January predicts its behavior for the rest of the year. Take the explanatory variable x to be the percent change in a stock market index in January and the response variable y to be the change in the index for the entire year. We expect a positive correlation between x and y because the change during January contributes to the full year's change. Calculation based on 38 years of data gives

$$\bar{x} = 1.75\% \qquad s_x = 5.36\% \qquad r = 0.596$$
$$\bar{y} = 9.07\% \qquad s_y = 15.35\%$$

(a) What percent of the observed variation in yearly changes in the index is explained by a straight-line relationship with the change during January?

(b) What is the equation of the least-squares line for predicting full-year change from January change?

(c) The mean change in January is $\bar{x} = 1.75\%$. Use your regression line to predict the change in the index in a year in which the index rises 1.75% in January. Why could you have given this result (up to roundoff error) without doing the calculation?

2.50 Is regression useful? In Exercise 2.36 (page 116) you used the *Correlation and Regression* applet to create three scatterplots having correlation about $r = 0.7$ between the horizontal variable x and the vertical variable y. Create three similar scatterplots again, after clicking the "Show least-squares line" box to display the regression line. Correlation $r = 0.7$ is considered reasonably strong in many areas of work. Because there is a reasonably strong correlation, we might use a regression line to predict y from x. In which of your three scatterplots does it make sense to use a straight line for prediction?

Residuals

A regression line is a mathematical model for the overall pattern of a linear relationship between an explanatory variable and a response variable. Deviations from the overall pattern are also important. In the regression setting, we see deviations by looking at the scatter of the data points about the regression line. The vertical distances from the points to the least-squares regression line are as small as possible in the sense that they have the smallest possible sum of squares. Because they represent "leftover" variation in the response after fitting the regression line, these distances are called *residuals*.

Residuals

A **residual** is the difference between an observed value of the response variable and the value predicted by the regression line. That is,

$$\text{residual} = \text{observed}\,y - \text{predicted}\,y$$
$$= y - \hat{y}$$

EXAMPLE 2.12 Predicting Credit Card Sales

CASE 2.1

Table 2.1 (page 96) contains data on daily sales by Duck Worth Wearing for April 2000. We are now interested in credit card sales. The final two columns in the spreadsheet display gross credit card sales and the number of items purchased with a credit card for each day. We will ignore the four days on which no customer used a credit card.

Figure 2.16 is a scatterplot of these data, with items purchased as the explanatory variable x and gross sales as the response variable y. The plot shows a positive association—days with more items purchased with a credit card tend to be the days with higher credit card sales. The overall pattern is moderately linear. The correlation describes both the direction and strength of the linear relationship. It is $r = 0.7718$.

The line on the plot is the least-squares regression line of credit card sales on item count. Its equation is

$$\hat{y} = 14.3908 + 6.1739x$$

For Observation 11, the day with 9 items purchased with credit cards, we predict the credit card sales to be

$$\hat{y} = 14.3908 + (6.1739)(9) = 69.96$$

This day's actual credit card sales were \$49.50. The residual is

$$\text{residual} = \text{observed } y - \text{predicted } y$$
$$= 49.50 - 69.96 = -20.46$$

The residual is negative because the data point lies below the regression line.

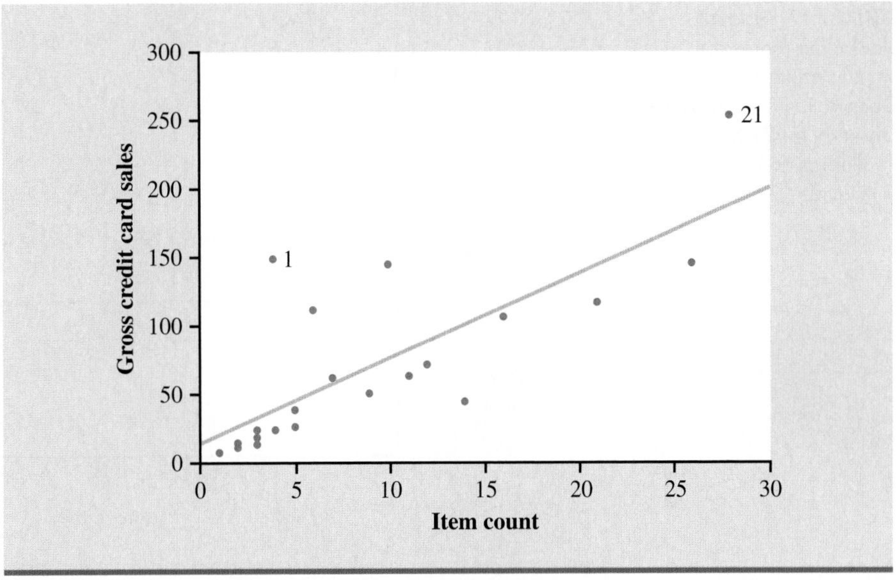

FIGURE 2.16 Scatterplot of gross credit card sales at Duck Worth Wearing versus number of items purchased with a credit card for 21 days, from Table 2.1. The line is the least-squares regression line for predicting sales from item count.

There is a residual for each data point. Finding the residuals with a calculator is a bit unpleasant, because you must first find the predicted response for every x. Statistical software gives you the residuals all at once. Here are the 21 residuals for the credit card data, from regression software:

```
residuals:
  108.9135  59.0657   3.8917  -6.2604 -13.5647 -31.5128 -18.7604
  -13.2386 -17.4779 -28.0432 -20.4561 -13.7386  -8.1736 -13.9126
  -56.8257  -8.9126  67.8700 -19.7540 -19.1126 -15.3365  65.3394
```

Because the residuals show how far the data fall from our regression line, examining the residuals helps assess how well the line describes the data. Although residuals can be calculated from any model fitted to data, the residuals from the least-squares line have a special property: **the mean of the least-squares residuals is always zero.**

Compare the scatterplot in Figure 2.16 with the *residual plot* for the same data in Figure 2.17. The horizontal line at zero in Figure 2.17 helps orient us. It corresponds to the regression line in Figure 2.16.

Residual Plots

A **residual plot** is a scatterplot of the regression residuals against the explanatory variable. Residual plots help us assess the fit of a regression line.

If the regression line captures the overall relationship between x and y, the residuals should have no systematic pattern. The residual plot will look something like the pattern

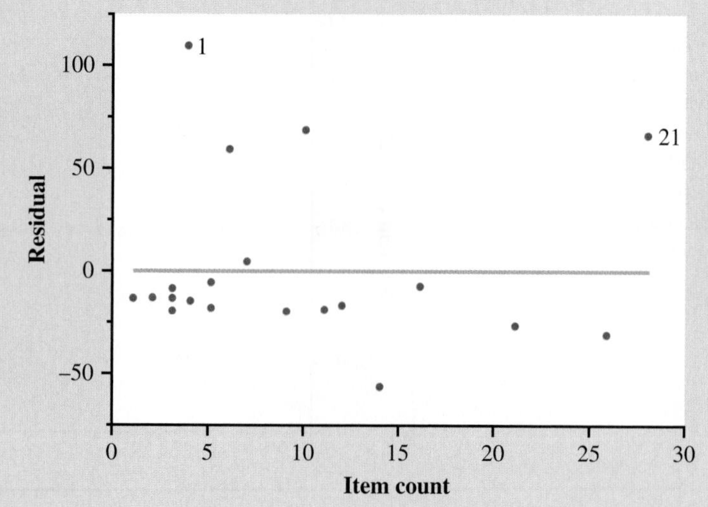

FIGURE 2.17 Residual plot for the regression of sales on item count. Observation 1 is an outlier. Observation 21 has a smaller residual but is more influential.

in Figure 2.18(a). That plot shows a scatter of the points about the fitted line, with no unusual individual observations or systematic change as x increases. Here are some things to look for when you examine a residual plot:

- **A curved pattern** shows that the relationship is not linear. Figure 2.18(b) is a simplified example. A straight line is not a good summary for such data. The residuals for Figure 2.8 (page 107) would have this form.
- **Increasing or decreasing spread about the line** as x increases. Figure 2.18(c) is a simplified example. Prediction of y will be less accurate for larger x in that example.
- **Individual points with large residuals,** like Observation 1 in Figures 2.16 and 2.17. Such points are outliers in the vertical (y) direction because they lie far from the line that describes the overall pattern.
- **Individual points that are extreme in the** x **direction,** like Observation 21 in Figures 2.16 and 2.17. Such points may not have large residuals, but they can be very important. We address such points next.

Influential observations

Observations 1 and 21 are both unusual in the credit card sales example. They are unusual in different ways. Observation 1 lies far from the regression line. This day's credit card sales figure is so high that we should check for a mistake in recording it. In fact, the amount is correct. Observation 21 is closer to the line but far out in the x direction. This day had more items purchased with credit cards than the other days in the sample. *Because of its extreme position on the item count scale, this point has a strong influence on the position of the regression line.* Figure 2.19 adds a second regression line, calculated after leaving out Observation 21. You can see that this one point moves the line quite a bit. We call such points *influential.*

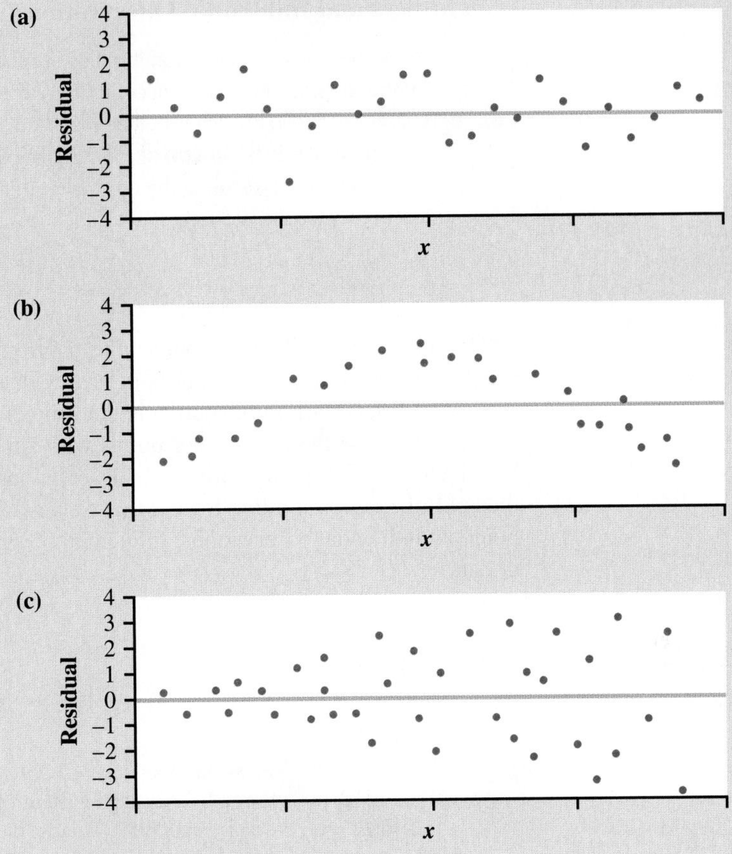

FIGURE 2.18 Idealized patterns in plots of least-squares residuals. Plot (a) indicates that the regression line fits the data well. The data in plot (b) have a curved pattern, so a straight line fits poorly. The response variable y in plot (c) has more spread for larger values of the explanatory variable x, so prediction will be less accurate when x is large.

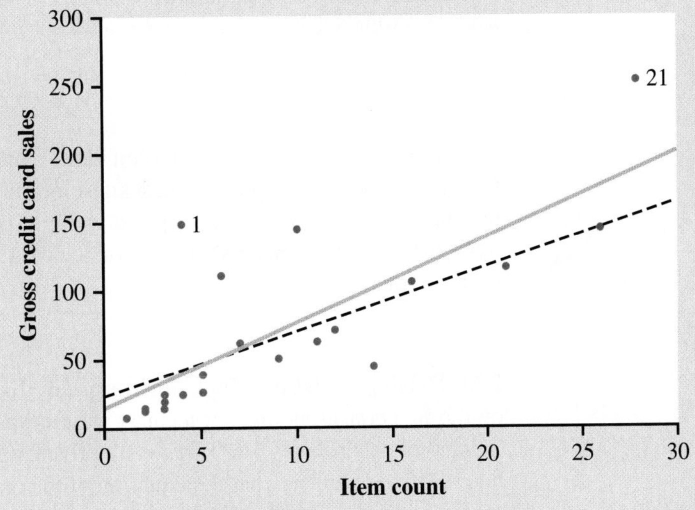

FIGURE 2.19 Two least-squares regression lines of sales on item count. The solid line is calculated from all the data. The dashed line was calculated leaving out observation 21. Observation 21 is an influential observation because leaving out this point moves the regression line quite a bit.

Outliers and Influential Observations in Regression

An **outlier** is an observation that lies outside the overall pattern of the other observations. Points that are outliers in the y direction of a scatterplot have large regression residuals, but other outliers need not have large residuals.

An observation is **influential** for a statistical calculation if removing it would markedly change the result of the calculation. Points that are extreme in the x direction of a scatterplot are often influential for the least-squares regression line.

Observations 1 and 21 are both quite far from the original regression line in Figure 2.19. Observation 21 influences the least-squares line because it is far out in the x direction. Observation 1 is an outlier in the y direction. It has less influence on the regression line because the many other points with similar values of x anchor the line well below the outlying point. Influential observations may have small residuals, because they pull the regression line toward themselves. That is, you can't rely on residuals to point out influential observations. Influential observations can change the interpretation of data.

EXAMPLE 2.13 An Influential Observation

CASE 2.1

The strong influence of Observation 21 makes the original regression of credit card sales on item count a bit misleading. The original data have $r^2 = 0.5957$. That is, the number of items purchased with credit cards explains about 60% of the variation in daily credit card sales. This relationship is strong enough to be interesting to the store's owners. If we leave out Observation 21, r^2 drops to only 43%. The unexamined regression suggests that items sold predict sales quite well, but much of this is due to a single day's results.

What should we do with Observation 21? If this unusual day resulted from a special promotion, we might remove it when predicting results for ordinary business days. Otherwise, the influential observation reminds us of the hazard of prediction using small sets of data. More data may include other days with high item counts and so reduce the influence of this one observation.

The best way to grasp the important idea of influence is to use an interactive animation that allows you to move points on a scatterplot and observe how correlation and regression respond. The *Correlation and Regression* applet on the companion Web site for this book, `www.whfreeman.com/pbs`, allows you to do this. Exercises 2.77 and 2.78 guide the use of this applet.

applet

APPLY YOUR KNOWLEDGE

2.51 Driving speed and fuel consumption. Exercise 2.7 (pages 100–101) gives data on the fuel consumption y of a car at various speeds x. Fuel consumption is measured in liters of gasoline per 100 kilometers driven, and speed is measured in kilometers per hour. Software tells us that the equation of the least-squares regression line is

$$\hat{y} = 11.058 - 0.01466x$$

The residuals, in the same order as the observations, are

10.09	2.24	−0.62	−2.47	−3.33	−4.28	−3.73	−2.94
−2.17	−1.32	−0.42	0.57	1.64	2.76	3.97	

(a) Make a scatterplot of the observations and draw the regression line on your plot.

(b) Would you use the regression line to predict y from x? Explain your answer.

(c) Check that the residuals have sum zero (up to roundoff error).

(d) Make a plot of the residuals against the values of x. Draw a horizontal line at height zero on your plot. Notice that the residuals show the same pattern about this line as the data points show about the regression line in the scatterplot in (a).

2.52 Doctors and poverty. We might expect states with more poverty to have fewer doctors. Table 1.9 (page 28) gives data on the percent of each state's residents living below the poverty line and on the number of doctors per 100,000 residents in each state.

(a) Make a scatterplot and calculate a regression line suitable for predicting doctors per 100,000 residents from poverty rate. Draw the line on your plot. Surprise: the slope is positive, so poverty and doctors go up together.

(b) The District of Columbia is an outlier, with both very many doctors and a high poverty rate. (D.C. is a city rather than a state.) Circle the point for D.C. on your plot and explain why this point may strongly influence the least-squares line.

(c) Calculate the regression line for the 50 states, omitting D.C. Add the new line to your scatterplot. Was this point highly influential? Does the number of doctors now go down with increasing poverty, as we initially expected?

2.53 Influential or not? We have seen that Observation 21 in the credit card data in Table 2.1 is an influential observation. Now we will examine the effect of Observation 1, which is also an outlier in Figure 2.16.

(a) Find the least-squares regression line of credit card sales on item count, leaving out Observation 1. Example 2.12 gives the regression line from all the data. Plot both lines on the same graph. (You do not have to make a scatterplot of all the points; just plot the two lines.) Would you call Observation 1 very influential? Why?

(b) How does removing Observation 1 change the r^2 for this regression? Explain why r^2 changes in this direction when you drop Observation 1.

BEYOND THE BASICS: SCATTERPLOT SMOOTHERS

A scatterplot provides a complete picture of the relationship between two quantitative variables. A complete picture is often too detailed for easy interpretation, so we try to describe the plot in terms of an overall pattern and deviations from that pattern. If the pattern is roughly linear, we can fit a regression line to describe it. Modern software offers a method more flexible than fitting a specific model such as a straight line. **Scatterplot smoothing** uses algorithms that extract an overall pattern by looking at the y-values for points in the neighborhood of each x-value.

smoothing

FIGURE 2.20 Two scatterplot smoothing algorithms applied to the data on national gross domestic product per person and life expectancy, for Example 2.14. Both portray the overall pattern of the plot.

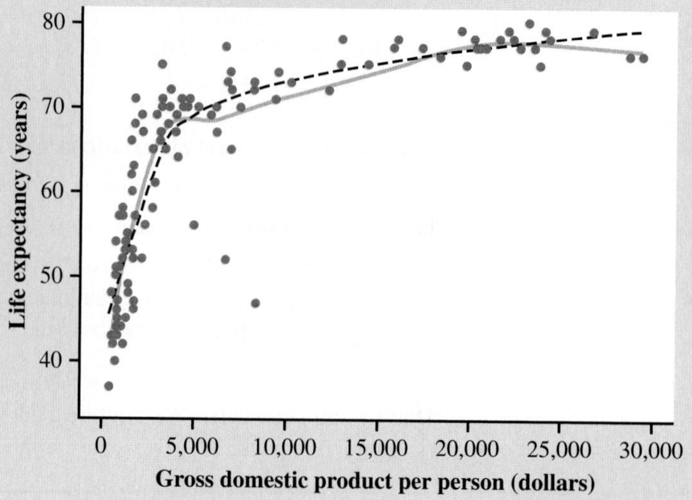

EXAMPLE 2.14 Smoothing a Nonlinear Pattern

Figure 2.8 displays the relationship between gross domestic product (GDP) per person and life expectancy for all the world's nations for which data are available. There is a strong pattern with positive association, but the pattern is not linear. Figure 2.20 shows the result of applying a scatterplot smoother to these data. The smoother accurately catches the rapid rise in life expectancy as GDP increases up to roughly $5000 per person, followed by a much more gradual rise in wealthier nations.

Scatterplot smoothing is not quite automatic—you can decide how smooth you want your result to be. Figure 2.20 shows the results of two choices. The dashed line is very smooth, while the solid line pays more attention to local detail. For example, the solid line is pulled down a bit around $5000 GDP by the three low outliers.

Scatterplot smoothers help us see overall patterns, especially when these patterns are not simple. They do not, however, provide a handy equation for prediction and other purposes. Least-squares regression, whether fitting a straight line or more complex models, remains more widely used.

SECTION 2.3 SUMMARY

- A **regression line** is a straight line that describes how a response variable y changes as an explanatory variable x changes.
- The most common method of fitting a line to a scatterplot is least squares. The **least-squares regression line** is the straight line $\hat{y} = b_0 + b_1 x$ that minimizes the sum of the squares of the vertical distances of the observed points from the line.
- You can use a regression line to **predict** the value of y for any value of x by substituting this x into the equation of the line.
- The **slope** b_1 of a regression line $\hat{y} = b_0 + b_1 x$ is the rate at which the predicted response $\hat{y}$ changes along the line as the explanatory variable x changes. Specifically, b_1 is the change in $\hat{y}$ when x increases by 1.

- The **intercept** b_0 of a regression line $\hat{y} = b_0 + b_1 x$ is the predicted response $\hat{y}$ when the explanatory variable $x = 0$. This prediction is of no statistical use unless x can actually take values near 0.
- The least-squares regression line of y on x is the line with slope $b_1 = rs_y/s_x$ and intercept $b_0 = \overline{y} - b_1\overline{x}$. This line always passes through the point $(\overline{x}, \overline{y})$.
- **Correlation and regression** are closely connected. The correlation r is the slope of the least-squares regression line when we measure both x and y in standardized units. The square of the correlation r^2 is the fraction of the variance of one variable that is explained by least-squares regression on the other variable.
- You can examine the fit of a regression line by studying the **residuals,** which are the differences between the observed and predicted values of y. Be on the lookout for outlying points with unusually large residuals and also for nonlinear patterns and uneven variation about the line.
- Also look for **influential observations,** individual points that substantially change the regression line. Influential observations are often outliers in the x direction, but they need not have large residuals.

SECTION 2.3 Exercises

For Exercises 2.47 and 2.48, see pages 122–123; for 2.49 and 2.50, see pages 125–126; and for 2.51 to 2.53, see pages 130–131.

2.54 Review of straight lines. A company manufactures batteries for cell phones. The overhead expenses of keeping the factory operational for a month—even if no batteries are made—total \$500,000. Batteries are manufactured in lots (1000 batteries per lot) costing \$10,000 to make. In this scenario, \$500,000 is the *fixed* cost associated with producing cell phone batteries, and \$10,000 is the *marginal* (or *variable*) cost of producing each lot of batteries. The total monthly cost y of producing x lots of cell phone batteries is given by the equation

$$y = 500{,}000 + 10{,}000x$$

(a) Draw a graph of this equation. (Choose two values of x, such as 0 and 10. Compute the corresponding values of y from the equation. Plot these two points on graph paper and draw the straight line joining them.)

(b) What will it cost to produce 20 lots of batteries (20,000 batteries)?

(c) If each lot cost \$20,000 instead of \$10,000 to produce, what is the equation that describes total monthly cost for x lots produced?

2.55 Review of straight lines. A local consumer electronics store sells exactly 4 DVD players of a particular model each week. The store expects no more shipments of this particular model, and they have 96 such units in their current inventory.

(a) Give an equation for the number of DVD players of this particular model in inventory after x weeks. What is the slope of this line?

(b) Draw a graph of this line between now (Week 0) and Week 10.

(c) Would you be willing to use this line to predict the inventory after 25 weeks? Do the prediction and think about the reasonableness of the result.

2.56 Review of straight lines. A cellular telephone company offers two plans. Plan A charges \$20 a month for up to 75 minutes of airtime and \$0.45 per minute above 75 minutes. Plan B charges \$30 a month for up to 250 minutes and \$0.40 per minute above 250 minutes.

(a) Draw a graph of the Plan A charge against minutes used from 0 to 250 minutes.

(b) How many minutes a month must the user talk in order for Plan B to be less expensive than Plan A?

2.57 T-bills and common stocks. The scatterplot for Exercise 2.10 (page 104) suggests that returns on common stocks may be somewhat lower in years with high interest rates. Here is part of the output from software for the regression of stock returns on the Treasury bill returns for the same years:

```
Stock = 16.639318 - 0.67974913 Tbill
Sample size: 54
R (correlation coefficient) = -0.113
R-sq = 0.01275773
Estimate of error standard deviation:
17.680649
```

If you knew the return on Treasury bills for next year, do you think you could predict the return on stocks quite accurately? Use the scatterplot in Figure 2.6 as well as a number from the regression output to justify your answer.

2.58 Sector fund returns. Exercise 2.12 gives the returns of 23 Fidelity "sector funds" for the years 2002 and 2003. These mutual funds invest in narrow segments of the stock market. They often rise faster than the overall market in up-years such as 2003 and fall faster than the market in down-years such as 2002. A scatterplot shows that Fidelity Gold Fund—the only fund that went up in 2002—is an outlier. In Exercise 2.30, you showed that this outlier has a strong effect on the correlation. The least-squares line, like the correlation, is not resistant.

(a) Find the equations of two least-squares lines for predicting 2003 return from 2002 return, one for all 23 funds and one omitting Fidelity Gold Fund. Make a scatterplot with both lines drawn on it. The two lines are very different.

(b) Starting with the least-squares idea, explain why adding Fidelity Gold Fund to the other 22 funds moves the line in the direction that your graph shows.

2.59 Stock index returns. How well have stocks done over the past generation? The Standard & Poor's 500 stock index describes the average performance of the stocks of 500 leading companies. Because the average is weighted by the total market value of each company's stock, the index emphasizes larger companies. Here are the real (that is, adjusted for the changing buying power of the dollar) returns on the S&P 500 for the years from 1971 to 2003:

Year	Return	Year	Return	Year	Return
1971	10.691	1982	17.033	1993	7.127
1972	15.070	1983	18.075	1994	−1.316
1973	−21.522	1984	2.253	1995	34.167
1974	−34.540	1985	26.896	1996	19.008
1975	28.353	1986	17.390	1997	31.138
1976	18.177	1987	0.783	1998	26.534
1977	−12.992	1988	11.677	1999	17.881
1978	−2.264	1989	25.821	2000	−12.082
1979	4.682	1990	−8.679	2001	−13.230
1980	17.797	1991	26.594	2002	−23.909
1981	−12.710	1992	4.584	2003	26.311

(a) Plot real returns against time. To bring out the pattern in these highly variable returns, use a vertical scale from −60% to 60%. Describe this pattern.

(b) Because of the curved pattern and the large amount of scatter about the pattern, a straight line doesn't describe the data well. Regress real return on year, and add the regression line to your plot. What is the value of r^2, and what does this value tell you about the usefulness of the regression line?

2.60 Coffee and deforestation. Continue your analysis of the effect of coffee prices on deforestation, begun in Exercise 2.31 (page 115). The slope of the regression line for predicting percent of deforestation from coffee price is an important measure of how serious the problem is.

(a) What does the slope tell us? Specifically, the slope for these data is $b = 0.0543$. What does this number say about the relationship between coffee price and deforestation?

(b) What does the estimated intercept's value of −0.976 seem to imply about deforestation rates and coffee prices?

2.61 Florida condo sales. Florida reappraises real estate every year, and the county appraiser's Web site lists the current "fair market value" of each piece of property. Property usually sells for somewhat more than the appraised market value. Here are the appraised market values and actual selling prices of condominium units sold in a beachfront building over a 19-month period (in thousands of dollars):[19]

Selling price	Appraised value	Month	Selling price	Appraised value	Month
850	758	0	790	605.9	13
900	812.7	1	700	483.8	14
625	504	2	715	585.8	14
1075	956.7	2	825	707.6	14
890	747.9	8	675	493.9	17
810	717.7	8	1050	802.6	17
650	576.6	9	1325	1031.8	18
845	648.3	12	845	586.7	19

(a) Make a scatterplot. It appears that appraised market value can be used to predict selling price.

(b) Find the least-squares line for predicting selling price from appraised value. Add this line to your scatterplot. Another unit in this building has appraised value $802,600. What do you predict that it will sell for?

2.62 Florida condo sales. Prices for beachfront property were rising rapidly during the period for which the previous exercise gives data. Because property is reassessed just once a year, selling prices might pull away from appraised values over time. The data in the previous exercise are in order by date of the sale, and we have given the number of months from the start of the data period. The residuals from the regression of selling price on appraised value are (rounded):

−70.60	−77.85	−29.76	−53.56
−20.03	−68.42	−80.75	39.21
28.59	66.38	−25.38	−42.85
30.81	82.72	117.83	103.68

(a) Plot the residuals against the explanatory variable (appraised value). To make the pattern clearer, use vertical limits −200 to 200. Explain why the pattern you see implies that a straight line is a good summary of these data.

(b) Next, plot the residuals against month. Explain why the pattern fits the fact that selling prices were rising rapidly.

2.63 Online stock brokerages. The table in Exercise 2.13 presents data on the number of accounts and the total assets of 10 online stock brokerages. Our goal is to predict total assets based on number of accounts. Part of this exercise requires that you calculate the slope and intercept of the least-squares regression line "by hand" using several summary statistics. Least-squares calculations like these are best done by statistical software. However, the connections among means, standard deviations, correlation, slope, and intercept are often lost when the computer *always* does the calculations for us.

(a) Use the following summary statistics and the formulas of this section to calculate the least-squares slope and intercept for these data. Be sure to show at least one intermediate step in your calculations.

$$\bar{x} = 793.6 \qquad \bar{y} = 48.9$$

$$s_x = 886.3337 \qquad s_y = 76.1639$$

$$r = 0.9683$$

(b) Demonstrate that Fact 3 (page 124) is true for the least-squares line you calculated in part (a).

(c) In light of Fact 4 (page 124), calculate and interpret the value of r^2 in the context of these data.

2.64 Online stock brokerages. Continuing with the brokerage data in the previous exercise, use statistical software to complete this exercise.

(a) Report the least-squares regression line from your statistical software and compare the estimated intercept and slope to the estimates from the previous exercise.

(b) Report the 10 residuals from the model fitted in part (a) and provide a residual plot of these values.

(c) Does the residual plot display a systematic pattern of any kind? If so, describe the pattern in a sentence or two. If not, then what does the lack of systematic pattern indicate?

(d) Identify the two unusual points on the far right of the residual plot by brokerage name. Are these points mostly unusual because of their residual value or their x-value (number of accounts)?

2.65 Online stock brokerages. Refer to the data and model in Exercise 2.64 for this exercise. Show at least one intermediate step in all calculations.

(a) Use the equation of the least-squares regression line to calculate a prediction of total assets for DLJ Direct.

(b) Is the prediction for DLJ Direct an overestimate or an underestimate of the actual total assets of this brokerage? How far off is the prediction from the actual total assets of DLJ Direct?

(c) Calculate the residual for DLJ Direct using the equation on page 126. Would knowing the value of the residual for DLJ Direct allow you to answer *both* questions in part (b)?

2.66 Online stock brokerages. Refer to the data and model in Exercise 2.64 for this exercise. Use statistical software to answer these questions.

(a) Provide a scatterplot of total assets (vertical axis) versus number of accounts (horizontal axis).

(b) Fit the least-squares regression line to these data, and plot the fitted line on the scatterplot from part (a).

(c) Repeat part (b) after excluding the data for Charles Schwab and Fidelity. How do the two regression lines compare?

(d) Calculate the absolute change and the percent change in both the intercept and the slope when Charles Schwab and Fidelity were excluded from the analysis.

(e) Do these two points appear to be influential observations? Explain your response based on your work in this exercise.

2.67 Employment numbers. Refer to the data on number of paid employees presented in Exercise 2.14 (page 105).

(a) Use statistical software to calculate the least-squares regression line for predicting the number of paid employees in 2002 from the number of paid employees in 1997. Report the estimated intercept, the estimated slope, and the value of r^2.

(b) Now report the number of paid employees with the units "millions of employees" rather than just a count of employees (for example, 10,836,365 employees is 10.836365 million employees). Using these values, repeat part (a).

(c) Are all three values (intercept, slope, r^2) affected by the change in units from "employees" to "millions of employees"? Compare and comment on the differences in the three values in parts (a) and (b).

2.68 Employment numbers. Refer to the data on number of paid employees presented in Exercise 2.14 (page 105).

(a) Use statistical software to calculate the residuals from the least-squares regression line for predicting the number of paid employees in 2002 from the number of paid employees in 1997.

(b) Construct a residual plot and be sure to draw a horizontal line at zero on the residual plot.

(c) If the least-squares regression line captures the overall pattern in the data, then the residual plot should have no systematic pattern. Using this criterion, do you conclude that the regression line captures the overall pattern in the data? Explain your response.

2.69 Florida condo sales. Consider the Florida condo sales data in Exercise 2.61.

(a) Make a scatterplot with selling prices on the vertical axis and appraised values on the horizontal axis if you have not already done so. Does the plot suggest a linear relationship?

(b) Report the correlation for these data. From the correlation, calculate r^2 and interpret its value in the context of these data.

(c) Find the least-squares line for predicting selling price from appraised value. Add this line to your scatterplot.

(d) If another unit in this building is appraised at $688,750, what do you predict that it will sell for?

(e) Calculate the average of the selling prices and compare this with your answer in part (d). What do you now know about the value $688,750?

2.70 Florida condo sales. Consider the Florida condo sales data in Exercise 2.61.

(a) Use statistical software to calculate the residuals from the least-squares regression line for predicting selling prices from appraised values.

(b) Construct a residual plot. Does the residual plot indicate that the line fits the data well? Explain your response.

2.71 Moving in step? One reason to invest abroad is that markets in different countries don't move in step. When American stocks go down, foreign stocks may go up. So an investor who holds both bears less risk. That's the theory. Now we read, "The correlation between changes in American and European share prices has risen from 0.4 in the mid-1990s to 0.8 in 2000."[20] Explain to an investor who knows no statistics why this fact reduces the protection provided by buying European stocks.

2.72 Interpreting correlation. The same article that claims that the correlation between changes in stock prices in Europe and the United States was 0.8 in 2000 goes on to say, "Crudely, that means that movements on Wall Street can explain 80% of price movements in Europe." Is this true? What is the correct percent explained if $r = 0.8$?

2.73 Size and length of bear markets. Figure 2.7 (page 106) is a scatterplot of the data from Table 1.7 (page 27) on percent decline of the market versus duration of the bear market. Calculation shows that the mean and standard deviation of the durations are

$$\bar{x} = 10.73 \qquad s_x = 8.20$$

For the declines,

$$\bar{y} = 24.67 \qquad s_y = 11.20$$

The correlation between duration and decline is $r = 0.6285$.

(a) Find the equation of the least-squares line for predicting decline from duration.

(b) What percent of the observed variation in these declines can be attributed to the linear relationship between decline and duration?

(c) One bear market has a duration of 15 months but a very low decline of 14%. What is the predicted decline for a bear market with duration = 15? What is the residual for this particular bear market?

2.74 CASE 2.1 **Cash or credit?** We might expect credit card purchases to differ from cash purchases at the same store. Let's compare regressions for credit card and cash purchases using the consignment shop data in Table 2.1 (page 96).

(a) Make a scatterplot of daily gross sales y versus items sold x for credit card purchases. Using a separate plot symbol or color, add daily gross sales and items sold for cash. It is somewhat difficult to compare the two patterns by eye.

TABLE 2.6 **Annual total return on overseas and U.S. stocks**

Year	Overseas % return	U.S. % return	Year	Overseas % return	U.S. % return
1971	29.6	14.6	1986	69.4	18.6
1972	36.3	18.9	1987	24.6	5.1
1973	−14.9	−14.8	1988	28.5	16.8
1974	−23.2	−26.4	1989	10.6	31.5
1975	35.4	37.2	1990	−23.0	−3.1
1976	2.5	23.6	1991	12.8	30.4
1977	18.1	−7.4	1992	−12.1	7.6
1978	32.6	6.4	1993	32.9	10.1
1979	4.8	18.2	1994	6.2	1.3
1980	22.6	32.3	1995	11.2	37.6
1981	−2.3	−5.0	1996	6.4	23.0
1982	−1.9	21.5	1997	2.1	33.4
1983	23.7	22.4	1998	20.3	28.6
1984	7.4	6.1	1999	27.2	21.0
1985	56.2	31.6	2000	−14.0	−9.1

(b) Regression can help. Find the equations of the two least-squares regression lines of gross sales on items sold, for credit card sales and for cash sales. Draw these lines on your plot. What are the slopes of the two regression lines? Explain carefully what comparing the slopes says about credit card purchases versus cash purchases.

2.75 **Keeping water clean.** Manufacturing companies (and the Environmental Protection Agency) monitor the quality of the water near their facilities. Measurements of pollutants in water are indirect—a typical analysis involves forming a dye by a chemical reaction with the dissolved pollutant, then passing light through the solution and measuring its "absorbance." To calibrate such measurements, the laboratory measures known standard solutions and uses regression to relate absorbance to pollutant concentration. This is usually done every day. Here is one series of data on the absorbance for different levels of nitrates. Nitrates are measured in milligrams per liter of water.[21]

(a) Chemical theory says that these data should lie on a straight line. If the correlation is not at least 0.997, something went wrong and the calibration procedure is repeated. Plot the data and find the correlation. Must the calibration be done again?

(b) What is the equation of the least-squares line for predicting absorbance from concentration? If the lab analyzed a specimen with 500 milligrams of nitrates per liter, what do you expect the absorbance to be? Based on your plot and the correlation, do you expect your predicted absorbance to be very accurate?

Nitrates	50	50	100	200	400	800	1200	1600	2000	2000
Absorbance	7.0	7.5	12.8	24.0	47.0	93.0	138.0	183.0	230.0	226.0

2.76 **Investing at home and overseas.** Investors ask about the relationship between returns on investments in the United States and on investments overseas. Table 2.6 gives the total returns on U.S. and overseas common stocks over a 30-year period. (The total return is change in price plus any dividends paid, converted into U.S. dollars. Both returns are averages over many individual stocks.)[22]

(a) Make a scatterplot suitable for predicting overseas returns from U.S. returns.

(b) Find the correlation and r^2. Describe the relationship between U.S. and overseas returns in words, using r and r^2 to make your description more precise.

(c) Find the least-squares regression line of overseas returns on U.S. returns. Draw the line on the scatterplot.

Are you confident that predictions using the regression line will be quite accurate? Why?

(d) Circle the point that has the largest residual (either positive or negative). What year is this? Are there any points that seem likely to be very influential?

2.77 Influence on correlation. The *Correlation and Regression* applet at www.whfreeman.com/pbs allows you to create a scatterplot and to move points by dragging with the mouse. Click to create a group of 10 points in the lower-left corner of the scatterplot with a strong straight-line pattern (correlation about 0.9).

(a) Add 1 point at the upper right that is in line with the first 10. How does the correlation change?

(b) Drag this last point down until it is opposite the group of 10 points. How small can you make the correlation? Can you make the correlation negative? You see that a single outlier can greatly strengthen or weaken a correlation. Always plot your data to check for outlying points.

2.78 Influence in regression. As in the previous exercise, create a group of 10 points in the lower-left corner of the scatterplot with a strong straight-line pattern (correlation at least 0.9). Click the "Show least-squares line" box to display the regression line.

(a) Add 1 point at the upper right that is far from the other 10 points but exactly on the regression line. Why does this outlier have no effect on the line even though it changes the correlation?

(b) Now drag this last point down until it is opposite the group of 10 points. You see that one end of the least-squares line chases this single point, while the other end remains near the middle of the original group of 10. What about the last point makes it so influential?

2.79 How many calories? Table 2.5 (page 117) gives data on the true calories in 10 foods and the average guesses made by a large group of people. Exercise 2.38 explored the influence of two outlying observations on the correlation.

(a) Make a scatterplot suitable for predicting guessed calories from true calories. Circle the points for spaghetti and snack cake on your plot. These points lie outside the linear pattern of the other 8 points.

(b) Find the least-squares regression line of guessed calories on true calories. Do this twice, first for all 10 data points and then leaving out spaghetti and snack cake.

(c) Plot both lines on your graph. (Make one dashed so you can tell them apart.) Are spaghetti and snack cake, taken together, influential observations? Explain your answer.

2.80 Always plot your data! Table 2.7 presents four sets of data prepared by the statistician Frank Anscombe to illustrate the dangers of calculating without first plotting the data.[23]

(a) Without making scatterplots, find the correlation and the least-squares regression line for all four data sets. What do you notice? Use the regression line to predict y for $x = 10$.

(b) Make a scatterplot for each of the data sets and add the regression line to each plot.

TABLE 2.7 Four data sets for exploring correlation and regression

Data Set A											
x	10	8	13	9	11	14	6	4	12	7	5
y	8.04	6.95	7.58	8.81	8.33	9.96	7.24	4.26	10.84	4.82	5.68
Data Set B											
x	10	8	13	9	11	14	6	4	12	7	5
y	9.14	8.14	8.74	8.77	9.26	8.10	6.13	3.10	9.13	7.26	4.74
Data Set C											
x	10	8	13	9	11	14	6	4	12	7	5
y	7.46	6.77	12.74	7.11	7.81	8.84	6.08	5.39	8.15	6.42	5.73
Data Set D											
x	8	8	8	8	8	8	8	8	8	8	19
y	6.58	5.76	7.71	8.84	8.47	7.04	5.25	5.56	7.91	6.89	12.50

(c) In which of the four cases would you be willing to use the regression line to describe the dependence of y on x? Explain your answer in each case.

2.81 What's my grade? In Professor Friedman's economics course, the correlation between the students' total scores before the final examination and their final examination scores is $r = 0.6$. The pre-exam totals for all students in the course have mean 280 and standard deviation 30. The final-exam scores have mean 75 and standard deviation 8. Professor Friedman has lost Julie's final exam but knows that her total before the exam was 300. He decides to predict her final-exam score from her pre-exam total.

(a) What is the slope of the least-squares regression line of final-exam scores on pre-exam total scores in this course? What is the intercept?

(b) Use the regression line to predict Julie's final-exam score.

(c) Julie doesn't think this method accurately predicts how well she did on the final exam. Calculate r^2 and use the value you get to argue that her actual score could have been much higher (or much lower) than the predicted value.

2.82 Investing at home and overseas. Exercise 2.76 examined the relationship between returns on U.S. and overseas stocks. Investors also want to know what typical returns are and how much year-to-year variability (called *volatility* in finance) there is. Regression and correlation do not answer these questions.

(a) Find the five-number summaries for both U.S. and overseas returns, and make side-by-side boxplots to compare the two distributions.

(b) Were returns generally higher in the United States or overseas during this period? Explain your answer.

(c) Were returns more volatile (more variable) in the United States or overseas during this period? Explain your answer.

2.83 Missing work. Data on number of days of work missed and annual salary increase for a company's employees show that in general employees who missed more days of work during the year received smaller raises than those who missed fewer days. Number of days missed explained 64% of the variation in salary increases. What is the numerical value of the correlation between number of days missed and salary increase?

2.84 Your mileage may vary. Figure 2.2 (page 98) displays a scatterplot of city versus highway mileages for 2001 model two-seater cars. Calculation shows that the mean and standard deviation of the highway mileages are

$$\bar{x} = 25.83 \qquad s_x = 8.53$$

For the city mileages,

$$\bar{y} = 18.86 \qquad s_y = 8.38$$

The correlation between city and highway mileages is $r = 0.9840$.

(a) Find the equation of the least-squares line for predicting city mileage from highway mileage for 2001 model two-seater cars.

(b) What percent of the observed variation in these city mileages can be attributed to the linear relationship between city mileage and highway mileage?

(c) One car, the Mercedes-Benz SL600, has a highway rating of 19 miles per gallon. What is the predicted city mileage for a 2001 model two-seater with a highway mileage of 19? What is the residual for this particular car if its city mileage is actually 13?

2.85 Will I bomb the final? We expect that students who do well on the midterm exam in a course will usually also do well on the final exam. Gary Smith of Pomona College looked at the exam scores of all 346 students who took his statistics class over a 10-year period.[24] The least-squares line for predicting final-exam score from midterm exam score was $\hat{y} = 46.6 + 0.41x$.

Octavio scores 10 points above the class mean on the midterm. How many points above the class mean do you predict that he will score on the final? (*Hint:* Use the fact that the least-squares line passes through the point $(\bar{x}, \bar{y})$ and the fact that Octavio's midterm score is $\bar{x} + 10$. This is an example of the phenomenon that gave "regression" its name: students who do well on the midterm will on the average do less well, but still above average, on the final.)

2.86 Four-wheel-drive minivans. Exercise 2.25 (page 112) displays data on all three 2001 model four-wheel-drive minivans. The least-squares regression line for these data is

$$\hat{y} = -4.5742 + 0.8065x$$

(a) If the minivan with a highway mileage of 28.7 had a city mileage of 19.3 rather than 18.6, how would the least-squares regression line change? Find the least-squares line for the altered data. In words, describe the change in the line resulting from the change in this one observation. What name is given to an observation like this one?

(b) If a fourth observation were added with a highway mileage equal to the average of the highway mileages of the three minivans ($\bar{x} = 29.0667$) and a city mileage of 20, the least-squares regression line for the data set with four observations would be

$\hat{y} = -4.2909 + 0.8065x$. In words, describe the change in the line resulting from adding this particular "new" observation. (This illustrates the effect an outlier has on the least-squares regression line.)

2.87 Where the stores are. Exercise 2.24 (page 110) looks at data on the number of Target and Wal-Mart stores in each of the 50 states.

(a) Use software to calculate the least-squares regression line for predicting the number of Target stores from the number of Wal-Mart stores.

(b) Using the line from (a), predict the number of Target stores in Texas based on the number of Wal-Mart stores in Texas (254 Wal-Mart stores). What is the residual for the Texas point?

(c) Use software to calculate the least-squares regression line for predicting the number of Wal-Mart stores from the number of Target stores.

(d) Using the line from (c), predict the number of Wal-Mart stores in Texas based on the number of Target stores in Texas (90 Target stores). What is the residual for the Texas point here? (This illustrates how essential the distinction between explanatory and response variables is in regression.)

2.4 Cautions about Correlation and Regression

Correlation and regression are powerful tools for describing the relationship between two variables. When you use these tools, you must be aware of their limitations, beginning with the fact that **correlation and regression describe only linear relationships.** Also remember that **the correlation r and the least-squares regression line are not resistant.** One influential observation or incorrectly entered data point can greatly change these measures. Always plot your data before interpreting regression or correlation. Here are some other cautions to keep in mind when you apply correlation and regression or read accounts of their use.

Beware extrapolation

Associations for variables can be trusted only for the range of values for which data have been collected. Even a very strong relationship may not hold outside the data's range.

EXAMPLE 2.15 Predicting the Future

Here are data on the number of Target stores in operation at the end of each year in the early 1990s:[25]

Year (x)	1990	1991	1992	1993
Stores (y)	420	463	506	554

These points lie almost exactly on a straight line, with $r = 0.9996$. The least-squares regression line for these data predicts 864 Target stores in operation by the end of 2000. However, the Target 2000 Annual Report shows 977 stores in operation at the end of 2000. The very strong linear trend evident in the 1990–1993 data did not continue to the year 2000.

Predictions made far beyond the range for which data have been collected can't be trusted. Few relationships are linear for *all* values of x. It is risky to stray far from the range of x-values that actually appear in your data.

Extrapolation

Extrapolation is the use of a regression line for prediction far outside the range of values of the explanatory variable x that you used to obtain the line. Such predictions are often not accurate.

APPLY YOUR KNOWLEDGE

2.88 The declining farm population. The number of people living on American farms has declined steadily during the 20th century. Here are data on farm population (millions of persons) from 1935 to 1980:

Year	1935	1940	1945	1950	1955	1960	1965	1970	1975	1980
Population	32.1	30.5	24.4	23.0	19.1	15.6	12.4	9.7	8.9	7.2

(a) Make a scatterplot of these data and find the least-squares regression line of farm population on year.

(b) According to the regression line, how much did the farm population decline each year on the average during this period? What percent of the observed variation in farm population is accounted for by linear change over time?

(c) Use the regression equation to predict the number of people living on farms in 1990. Is this result reasonable? Why?

Beware correlations based on averaged data

Many regression and correlation studies work with averages or other measures that combine information from many individuals. You should note this carefully and resist the temptation to apply the results of such studies to individuals. Figure 2.3 (page 100) shows a strong relationship between outside temperature and the Sanchez household's natural-gas consumption. Each point on the scatterplot represents a month. Both degree-days and gas consumed are averages over all the days in the month. The data for individual days would form a cloud around each month's averages—they would have more scatter and lower correlation. Averaging over an entire month smooths out the day-to-day variation due to doors left open, house guests using more gas to heat water, and so on. **Correlations based on averages are usually too high when applied to individuals.** This is another reminder that it is important to note exactly what variables were measured in a statistical study.

APPLY YOUR KNOWLEDGE

2.89 Stock market indexes. The Standard & Poor's 500 stock index is an average of the price of 500 stocks. There is a moderately strong correlation (roughly $r = 0.6$) between how much this index changes in January and how much it changes during the entire year. If we looked instead at data on all 500 individual stocks, we would find a quite different correlation. Would the correlation be higher or lower? Why?

Beware the lurking variable

Correlation and regression describe the relationship between two variables. Often the relationship between two variables is strongly influenced by other variables. We try to measure potentially influential variables. We can then use more advanced statistical methods to examine all of the relationships revealed by our data. Sometimes, however, the relationship between two variables is influenced by other variables that we did not measure or even think about. Variables lurking in the background, measured or not, often help explain statistical associations.

Lurking Variable

A **lurking variable** is a variable that is not among the explanatory or response variables in a study and yet may influence the interpretation of relationships among those variables.

A lurking variable can falsely suggest a strong relationship between x and y, or it can hide a relationship that is really there. Here are examples of each of these effects.

EXAMPLE 2.16 Discrimination in Medical Treatment?

Studies show that men who complain of chest pain are more likely to get detailed tests and aggressive treatment such as bypass surgery than are women with similar complaints. Is this association between gender and treatment due to discrimination?

Perhaps not. Men and women develop heart problems at different ages—women are on the average between 10 and 15 years older than men when they develop heart problems. Aggressive treatments are more risky for older patients, so doctors may hesitate to recommend them. Lurking variables—the patient's age and condition—may explain the relationship between gender and doctors' decisions. As the author of one study of the issue said, "When men and women are otherwise the same and the only difference is gender, you find that treatments are very similar."[26]

EXAMPLE 2.17 Measuring Inadequate Housing

A study of housing conditions in the city of Hull, England, measured several variables for each of the city's wards. Figure 2.21 is a simplified version of one of the study's findings. The variable x measures how crowded the ward is. The variable y measures the fraction of housing units that have no indoor toilet. We expect inadequate housing to be crowded (high x) and lack toilets (high y). That is, we expect a strong correlation between x and y. In fact, the correlation was only $r = 0.08$. How can this be?

Figure 2.21 shows that there are two clusters of wards. The wards in the lower cluster have a lot of public housing. These wards are crowded (high values of x), but they have low values of y because public housing always includes indoor toilets. The wards in the upper cluster lack public housing and have high values of both x and y. Within wards of each type, there is a strong positive association between x and y. In Figure 2.21, $r = 0.85$ and $r = 0.91$ in the two clusters. However, because similar values of x correspond to quite different values of y in the two clusters, x alone is of little value for predicting y. Analyzing all wards together ignores the lurking variable—amount of public housing—and hides the nature of the relationship between x and y.[27]

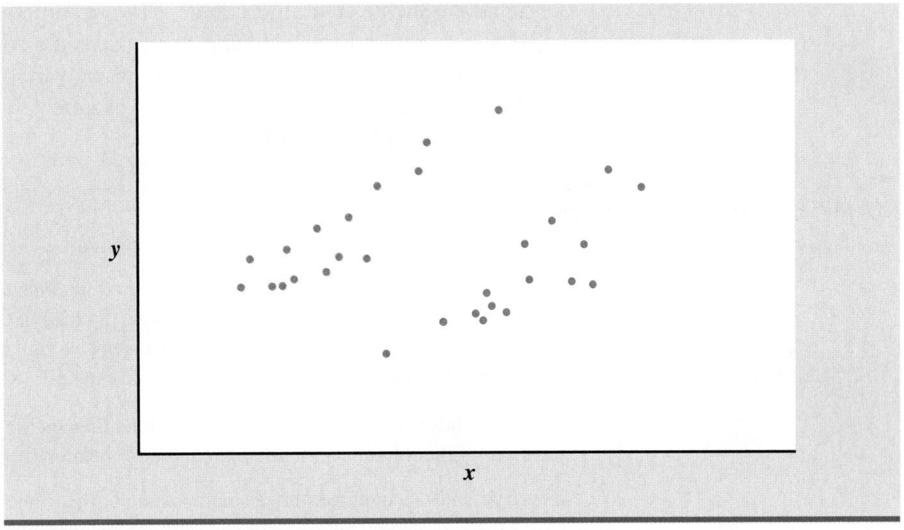

FIGURE 2.21 The variables in this scatterplot, for Example 2.17, have a small correlation even though there is a strong correlation within each of the two clusters.

APPLY YOUR KNOWLEDGE

2.90 Education and income. There is a strong positive correlation between years of education and income for economists employed by business firms. In particular, economists with doctorates earn more than economists with only a bachelor's degree. There is also a strong positive correlation between years of education and income for economists employed by colleges and universities. But when all economists are considered, there is a *negative* correlation between education and income. The explanation for this is that business pays high salaries and employs mostly economists with bachelor's degrees, while colleges pay lower salaries and employ mostly economists with doctorates. Sketch a scatterplot with two groups of cases (business and academic) illustrating how a strong positive correlation within each group and a negative overall correlation can occur together. (*Hint:* Begin by studying Figure 2.21.)

Association is not causation

When we study the relationship between two variables, we often hope to show that changes in the explanatory variable *cause* changes in the response variable. But a strong association between two variables is not enough to draw conclusions about cause and effect. Sometimes an observed association really does reflect cause and effect. The Sanchez household uses more natural gas in colder months because cold weather requires burning more gas to stay warm. In other cases, an association is explained by lurking variables, and the conclusion that x causes y is either wrong or not proved. Here are several examples.

EXAMPLE 2.18 Does Television Extend Life?

Measure the number of television sets per person x and the average life expectancy y for the world's nations. There is a high positive correlation: nations with many TV sets have higher life expectancies.

The basic meaning of causation is that by changing x we can bring about a change in y. Could we lengthen the lives of people in Rwanda by shipping them TV sets? No. Rich nations have more TV sets than poor nations. Rich nations also have longer life expectancies because they offer better nutrition, clean water, and better health care. There is no cause-and-effect tie between TV sets and length of life.

Correlations such as that in Example 2.18 are sometimes called "nonsense correlations." The correlation is real. What is nonsense is the conclusion that changing one of the variables causes changes in the other. A lurking variable—such as national wealth in Example 2.18—that influences both x and y can create a high correlation even though there is no direct connection between x and y.

EXAMPLE 2.19 Firestone Tires

Example 1.2 (page 6) presented data on the different Firestone tire models involved in 2969 accidents believed to be caused by defective tires. Most (84.6%) of the accidents involved the Wilderness, Wilderness AT, or ATX tire models, but this is not enough information to conclude that these 3 models are the worst of the 9 models listed in the example. At least two scenarios are possible:

- If these brands account for most of the Firestone tires on the road, then we would expect to see more of them fail because there are more of them on the road.
- If these brands account for only a small portion of the Firestone tires on the road, then it seems that a large percent of these particular models are failing, indicating a potential problem with these 3 models.

The lurking variable here is number of each tire model in use. The failure rate (number failed/number in use) of each tire model is the real variable of interest in identifying defective models.

These and other examples lead us to the most important caution about correlation, regression, and statistical association between variables in general.

Association Does Not Imply Causation

An association between an explanatory variable x and a response variable y, even if it is very strong, is not by itself good evidence that changes in x actually cause changes in y.

experiment

The best way to get good evidence that x causes y is to do an **experiment** in which we change x and keep lurking variables under control. We will discuss experiments in Chapter 3. When experiments cannot be done, finding the explanation for an observed association is often difficult and controversial. Many of the sharpest disputes in which statistics plays a role involve questions of causation that cannot be settled by experiment. Does gun control reduce violent crime? Does using cell phones cause brain tumors? Has increased free trade widened the gap between the incomes of more-educated and less-educated American workers? All of these questions have become public issues. All concern associations among variables. And all have this in common: they try to pinpoint cause and effect in a setting involving complex relations among many interacting variables.

EXAMPLE 2.20 Does Smoking Cause Lung Cancer?

Despite the difficulties, it is sometimes possible to build a strong case for causation in the absence of experiments. The evidence that smoking causes lung cancer is about as strong as nonexperimental evidence can be.

Doctors had long observed that most lung cancer patients were smokers. Comparison of smokers and "similar" nonsmokers showed a very strong association between smoking and death from lung cancer. Could the association be explained by lurking variables? Might there be, for example, a genetic factor that predisposes people both to nicotine addiction and to lung cancer? Smoking and lung cancer would then be positively associated even if smoking had no direct effect on the lungs. How were these objections overcome?

Let's answer this question in general terms: what are the criteria for establishing causation when we cannot do an experiment?

- *The association is strong.* The association between smoking and lung cancer is very strong.
- *The association is consistent.* Many studies of different kinds of people in many countries link smoking to lung cancer. That reduces the chance that a lurking variable specific to one group or one study explains the association.
- *Higher doses are associated with stronger responses.* People who smoke more cigarettes per day or who smoke over a longer period get lung cancer more often. People who stop smoking reduce their risk.
- *The alleged cause precedes the effect in time.* Lung cancer develops after years of smoking. The number of men dying of lung cancer rose as smoking became more common, with a lag of about 30 years. Lung cancer kills more men than any other form of cancer. Lung cancer was rare among women until women began to smoke. Lung cancer in women rose along with smoking, again with a lag of about 30 years, and has now passed breast cancer as the leading cause of cancer death among women.
- *The alleged cause is plausible.* Experiments with animals show that tars from cigarette smoke do cause cancer.

Medical authorities do not hesitate to say that smoking causes lung cancer. A U.S. surgeon general has stated that cigarette smoking is "the largest avoidable cause of death and disability in the United States."[28] The evidence for causation is overwhelming—but it is not as strong as evidence provided by well-designed experiments.

APPLY YOUR KNOWLEDGE

2.91 Do firefighters make fires worse? Someone says, "There is a strong positive correlation between the number of firefighters at a fire and the amount of damage the fire does. So sending lots of firefighters just causes more damage." Explain why this reasoning is wrong.

2.92 How's your self-esteem? People who do well tend to feel good about themselves. Perhaps helping people feel good about themselves will help them do better in their jobs and in life. For a time, raising self-esteem became a goal in many schools and companies. Can you think of explanations for the association between high self-esteem and good performance other than "Self-esteem causes better work"?

2.93 Are big hospitals bad for you? A study shows that there is a positive correlation between the size of a hospital (measured by its number of beds x) and the median number of days y that patients remain in the hospital. Does this mean that you can shorten a hospital stay by choosing a small hospital? Why?

BEYOND THE BASICS: DATA MINING

Chapters 1 and 2 of this book are devoted to the important aspect of statistics called *exploratory data analysis* (EDA). We use graphs and numerical summaries to examine data, searching for patterns and paying attention to striking deviations from the patterns we find. In discussing regression, we advanced to using the pattern we find (in this case, a linear pattern) for prediction.

Suppose now that we have a truly enormous data base, such as all purchases recorded by the cash register scanners of our retail chain during the past week. Surely this trove of data contains patterns that might guide business decisions. If we could see clearly the types of activewear preferred in large California cities and compare the preferences of small Midwest cities—right now, not at the end of the season—we might improve profits in both parts of the country by matching stock with demand. This sounds much like EDA, and indeed it is. There is, however, a saying in computer science that a big enough difference of scale amounts to a difference of kind. Exploring really large data bases in the hope of finding useful patterns is called **data mining.** Here are some distinctive features of data mining:

data mining

- When you have 100 gigabytes of data, even straightforward calculations and graphics become impossibly time-consuming. So efficient algorithms are very important.
- The structure of the data base and the process of storing the data, perhaps by unifying data scattered across many departments of a large corporation, require careful thought. The fashionable term is *data warehousing.*
- Data mining requires automated tools that work based on only vague queries by the user. The process is too complex to do step-by-step as we have done in EDA.

All of these features point to the need for sophisticated computer science as a basis for data mining. Indeed, data mining is often thought of as a part of computer science. Yet many statistical ideas and tools—mostly tools for dealing with multidimensional data, not the sort of thing that appears in a first statistics course—are very helpful. Like many modern developments, data mining crosses the boundaries of traditional fields of study.

Do remember that the perils we find with blind use of correlation and regression are yet more perilous in data mining, where the fog of an immense data base prevents clear vision. Extrapolation, ignoring lurking variables, and confusing association with causation are traps for the unwary data miner.

SECTION 2.4 SUMMARY

- Correlation and regression must be **interpreted with caution. Plot the data** to be sure the relationship is roughly linear and to detect outliers and influential observations.
- Avoid **extrapolation,** the use of a regression line for prediction for values of the explanatory variable far outside the range of the data from which the line was calculated.
- Remember that **correlations based on averages** are usually too high when applied to individuals.

TABLE 2.10 Marital status and job level

	Marital Status				
Job grade	**Single**	**Married**	**Divorced**	**Widowed**	**Total**
1	58	874	15	8	955
2	222	3927	70	20	4239
3	50	2396	34	10	2490
4	7	533	7	4	551
Total	337	7730	126	42	8235

nature. Other categorical variables are created by grouping values of a quantitative variable into classes. Published data often appear in grouped form to save space. To analyze categorical data, we use the *counts* or *percents* of individuals that fall into various categories.

CASE 2.2

MARITAL STATUS AND JOB LEVEL

We sometimes read in popular magazines that getting married is good for your career. Table 2.10 presents data from one of the studies behind this generalization. To avoid gender effects, the investigators looked only at men. The data describe the marital status and the job level of all 8235 male managers and professionals employed by a large manufacturing firm.[31] The firm assigns each position a grade that reflects the value of that particular job to the company. The authors of the study grouped the many job grades into quarters. Grade 1 contains jobs in the lowest quarter of the job grades, and Grade 4 contains those in the highest quarter.

two-way table

row and column variables

Table 2.10 is a **two-way table** because it describes two categorical variables. Job grade is the **row variable** because each row in the table describes one job grade group. Marital status is the **column variable** because each column describes one marital status group. The entries in the table are the counts of men in each marital-status-by-job-grade class. Both marital status and job grade in this table are categorical variables. Job grade has a natural order from lowest to highest. The order of the rows in Table 2.10 reflects the order of the job grades.

Marginal distributions

How can we best grasp the information contained in Table 2.10? First, *look at the distribution of each variable separately*. The distribution of a categorical variable says how often each outcome occurred. The "Total" column at the right of the table contains the totals for each of the rows. These row totals give the distribution of job grade (the row variable) among all men in the study: 955 are at Grade 1, 4239 are at Grade 2, and so on. In the same way, the "Total" row at the bottom of the table gives the marital status distribution. If the row and column totals are missing, the first thing to do in studying a two-way table is to calculate them. The distributions of job grade alone and marital status alone are called **marginal distributions** because they appear at the right and bottom margins of the two-way table.

marginal distribution

Percents are often more informative than counts. We can display the marginal distribution of job grade in terms of percents by dividing each row total by the table total and converting to a percent.

EXAMPLE 2.21 Calculating a Marginal Distribution

CASE 2.2

The percent of men in the study who have a Grade 1 job is

$$\frac{\text{total with Grade 1}}{\text{table total}} = \frac{955}{8235} = 0.1160 = 11.60\%$$

Do three more such calculations to obtain the marginal distribution of job grade in percents. Here it is:

Job grade	1	2	3	4
Percent	11.60	51.48	30.24	6.69

The total should be 100% because everyone in the study is in one of the job grade categories. The total is in fact 100.01%, due to roundoff error.

Each marginal distribution from a two-way table is a distribution for a single categorical variable. As we saw in Example 1.2 (page 6), we can use a bar graph or a pie chart to display such a distribution. Figure 2.23 is a bar graph of the distribution of job grade. We see that men with jobs of Grade 2 make up about half of the total.

In working with two-way tables, you must calculate lots of percents. Here's a tip to help decide what fraction gives the percent you want. Ask, "What group represents the total that I want a percent of?" The count for that group is the denominator of the fraction that leads to the percent. In Example 2.21, we wanted a percent "of men in the study," so the table total is the denominator.

APPLY YOUR KNOWLEDGE

2.108 Marital status. CASE 2.2 Give the marginal distribution of marital status (in percents) for the men in the study of Case 2.2, starting from the counts in Table 2.10.

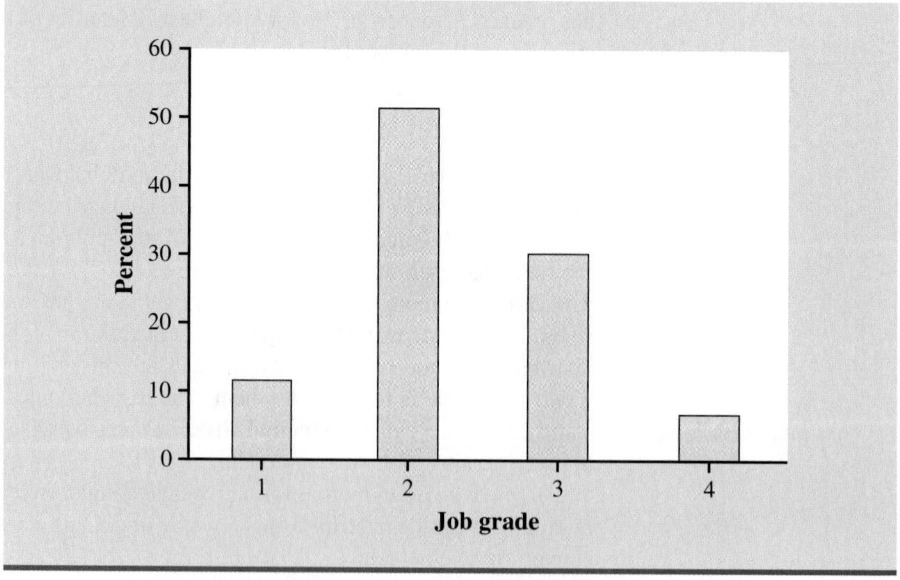

FIGURE 2.23 A bar graph of the distribution of job grade for the men described in Case 2.2. This is one of the marginal distributions for Table 2.10.

2.109 Smoking by students and their parents. Advertising by tobacco companies is believed to encourage students to smoke and use other tobacco products. Another source of "encouragement" may be the example set by parents with respect to tobacco use. Here are data from eight high schools on smoking among students and among their parents:[32]

	Neither parent smokes	One parent smokes	Both parents smoke
Student does not smoke	1168	1823	1380
Student smokes	188	416	400

(a) How many students do these data describe?

(b) What percent of these students smoke?

(c) Give the marginal distribution of parents' smoking behavior, both in counts and in percents.

Describing relationships

Table 2.10 contains much more information than the two marginal distributions of marital status alone and job grade alone. The nature of the relationship between marital status and job grade cannot be deduced from the separate distributions but requires the full table. **Relationships among categorical variables are described by calculating appropriate percents from the counts given.** We use percents because counts are often hard to compare. For example, 874 married men have Grade 1 jobs, and only 58 single men have Grade 1 jobs. These counts do not accurately describe the association, however, because there are many more married men in the study.

EXAMPLE 2.22 How Common Are Grade 1 Jobs?

CASE 2.2

What percent of single men have Grade 1 jobs? This is the count of those who are single and have Grade 1 jobs as a percent of the single group total:

$$\frac{58}{337} = 0.1721 = 17.21\%$$

In the same way, find the percent of men in each marital status group who have Grade 1 jobs. The comparison of all four groups is

Marital status	Single	Married	Divorced	Widowed
Percent with Grade 1 jobs	17.21	11.31	11.90	19.05

These percents make it clear that Grade 1 jobs are less common among married and divorced men than among single and widowed men. Don't leap to any causal conclusions: single men as a group, for example, are probably younger and so have not yet advanced to higher-grade jobs.

APPLY YOUR KNOWLEDGE

2.110 The top jobs. Using the counts in Table 2.10, find the percent of men in each marital status group who have Grade 4 jobs. Draw a bar graph that compares these percents. Explain briefly what the data show.

CASE 2.2

2.111 Smoking by students. Using the table in Exercise 2.109 on smoking by students and parents, calculate the percent of students in each group (neither parent smokes, one parent smokes, both parents smoke) who smoke. One might believe that parents' smoking increases smoking in their children. Do the data support that belief? Briefly explain your response.

Conditional distributions

Example 2.22 does not compare the complete distributions of job grade in the four marital status groups. It compares only the percents who have Grade 1 jobs. Let's look at the complete picture.

EXAMPLE 2.23 Calculating a Conditional Distribution

CASE 2.2 

Information about single men occupies the first column in Table 2.10. To find the complete distribution of job grade in this marital status group, look only at that column. Compute each count as a percent of the column total, which is 337. Here is the distribution:

Job grade	1	2	3	4
Percent	17.21	65.88	14.84	2.08

conditional distribution

These percents should add to 100% because all single men fall in one of the job grade categories. (In fact, they add to 100.01% because of roundoff error.) The four percents together are the **conditional distribution** of job grade, given that a man is single. We use the term "conditional" because the distribution refers only to men who satisfy the condition that they are single.

Now focus in turn on the second column (married men) and then the third column (divorced men) and finally the fourth column (widowed men) of Table 2.10 to find three more conditional distributions. Statistical software can speed the task of finding each entry in a two-way table as a percent of its column total. Figure 2.24 displays the output.

Each cell in this table contains a count from Table 2.10 along with that count as a percent of the column total. The percents in each column form the conditional distribution of job grade for one marital status group. The percents in each column add to 100% (up to

FIGURE 2.24 JMP output of the two-way table of job grade by marital status with the four conditional distributions of job grade, one for each marital status group. The percents in each column add to 100% (up to roundoff error).

Marital Status

Job Grade: Count / Col%	Single	Married	Divorced	Widowed	
1	58 17.21	874 11.31	15 11.90	8 19.05	955
2	222 65.88	3927 50.80	70 55.56	20 47.62	4239
3	50 14.84	2396 31.00	34 26.98	10 23.81	2490
4	7 2.08	533 6.90	7 5.56	4 9.52	551
	337	7730	126	42	8235

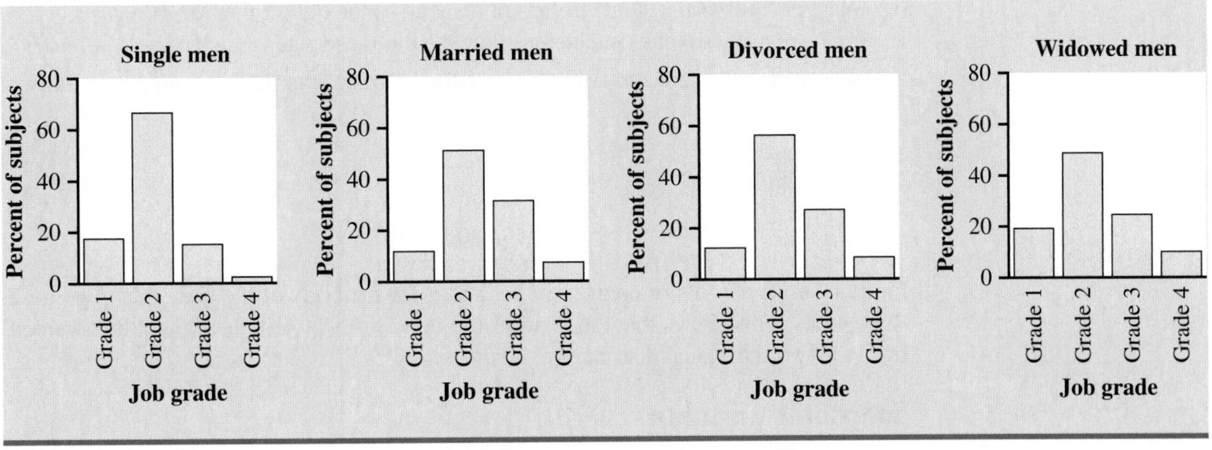

FIGURE 2.25 Bar graphs comparing the distribution of job grade level within each of four marital status groups. These are conditional distributions of job grade, given a specific marital status.

roundoff error) because everyone in the marital status group is accounted for. Figure 2.25 presents all four conditional distributions for comparison with each other and with the overall distribution in Figure 2.23. Comparing these conditional distributions reveals the nature of the association between marital status and job grade. The distributions of job grade in the married, divorced, and widowed groups are quite similar, but Grade 4 jobs are less common in the single group.

No single graph (such as a scatterplot) portrays the form of the relationship between categorical variables. No single numerical measure (such as the correlation) summarizes the strength of the association. Bar graphs are flexible enough to be helpful, but you must think about what comparisons you want to display. For numerical measures, we rely on well-chosen percents. You must decide which percents you need. Here is a hint: compare the conditional distributions of the response variable (job grade) for the separate values of the explanatory variable (marital status). That's what we did in Figure 2.25.

APPLY YOUR KNOWLEDGE

2.112 Who holds the top jobs? Find the conditional distribution of marital status among men with Grade 4 jobs, starting from the counts in Table 2.10. (To do this, look only at the "Job grade 4" row in the table.)

CASE 2.2

2.113 Majors for men and women in business. To study the career plans of young women and men, questionnaires were sent to all 722 members of the senior class in the College of Business Administration at the University of Illinois. One question asked which major within the business program the student had chosen. Here are the data from the students who responded:[33]

	Female	Male
Accounting	68	56
Administration	91	40
Economics	5	6
Finance	61	59

(a) Find the two conditional distributions of major, one for women and one for men. Based on your calculations, describe the differences between women and men with a graph and in words.

(b) What percent of the students did not respond to the questionnaire? The nonresponse weakens conclusions drawn from these data.

2.114 Here are the row and column totals for a two-way table with two rows and two columns:

a	b	50
c	d	50
60	40	100

Find *two different* sets of counts a, b, c, and d for the body of the table that give these same totals. This shows that the relationship between two variables cannot be obtained from the two individual distributions of the variables.

Simpson's paradox

As is the case with quantitative variables, the effects of lurking variables can change or even reverse relationships between two categorical variables. Here is an example that demonstrates the surprises that can await the unsuspecting user of data.

EXAMPLE 2.24 Which Airline Is on Time?

Air travelers would like their flights to arrive on time. Airlines collect data on on-time arrivals and report them to the government. Following are one month's data for flights from several western cities for two airlines:

	Alaska Airlines	America West
On time	3274	6438
Delayed	501	787
Total	3775	7225

Alaska Airlines is delayed 13.3% (501/3775) of the time, and America West is delayed only 10.9% (787/7225) of the time. It seems that you should choose America West to minimize delays.

Some cities are more likely to have delays than others, however. If we consider which city the flights left from in our analysis, we obtain a more complete picture of the two airlines' on-time flights. Here are the data broken down by which city each flight left from.[34] Check that the entries in the original two-way table are just the sums of the city entries in this table.

	Alaska Airlines		America West	
	On time	Delayed	On time	Delayed
Los Angeles	497	62	694	117
Phoenix	221	12	4840	415
San Diego	212	20	383	65
San Francisco	503	102	320	129
Seattle	1841	305	201	61

Alaska Airlines beats America West for flights from Los Angeles: only 11.1% (62/559) delayed compared with 14.4% (117/811) for America West. Alaska Airlines wins again for flights from Phoenix, with 5.2% (12/233) delayed versus 7.9% (415/5255). In fact, if you calculate the percent of delayed flights for each city individually, Alaska Airlines has a lower percent of late flights at *all* of these cities. So Alaska Airlines is the better choice no matter which of the five cities you are flying from.

The city of origin for each flight is a lurking variable when we compare the late-flight percents of the two airlines. When we ignore the lurking variable, America West seems better, even though Alaska Airlines does better for each city. How can Alaska Airlines do better for all cities, yet do worse overall? Look at the data: America West flies most often from sunny Phoenix, where there are few delays. Alaska Airlines flies most often from Seattle, where fog and rain cause frequent delays. The original two-way table, which did not take account of the city of origin for each flight, was misleading. Example 2.24 illustrates *Simpson's paradox.*

Simpson's Paradox

An association or comparison that holds for all of several groups can reverse direction when the data are combined to form a single group. This reversal is called **Simpson's paradox.**

The lurking variables in Simpson's paradox are categorical. That is, they break the individuals into groups, as when flights are classified by city of origin. Simpson's paradox is just an extreme form of the fact that observed associations can be misleading when there are lurking variables.

APPLY YOUR KNOWLEDGE

2.115 Which hospital is safer? Insurance companies and consumers are interested in the performance of hospitals. The government releases data about patient outcomes in hospitals that can be useful in making informed health care decisions. Here is a two-way table of data on the survival of patients after surgery in two hospitals. All patients undergoing surgery in a recent time period are included. "Survived" means that the patient lived at least 6 weeks following surgery.

	Hospital A	Hospital B
Died	63	16
Survived	2037	784
Total	2100	800

(a) What percent of Hospital A patients died? What percent of Hospital B patients died? These are the numbers one might see reported in the media.

Not all surgery cases are equally serious, however. Patients are classified as being in either "poor" or "good" condition before surgery. Here are the data broken down by patient condition. Check that the entries in the original two-way table are just the sums of the "poor" and "good" entries in this pair of tables.

	Good Condition	
	Hospital A	Hospital B
Died	6	8
Survived	594	592
Total	600	600

	Poor Condition	
	Hospital A	Hospital B
Died	57	8
Survived	1443	192
Total	1500	200

(b) Find the percent of Hospital A patients who died who were classified as "poor" before surgery. Do the same for Hospital B. In which hospital do "poor" patients fare better?

(c) Repeat (b) for patients classified as "good" before surgery.

(d) What is your recommendation to someone facing surgery and choosing between these two hospitals?

(e) How can Hospital A do better in both groups, yet do worse overall? Look at the data and carefully explain how this can happen.

SECTION 2.5 SUMMARY

- A **two-way table** of counts organizes data about two categorical variables. Values of the **row variable** label the rows that run across the table, and values of the **column variable** label the columns that run down the table. Two-way tables are often used to summarize large amounts of information by grouping outcomes into categories.
- The **row totals** and **column totals** in a two-way table give the **marginal distributions** of the two individual variables. It is clearer to present these distributions as percents of the table total. Marginal distributions tell us nothing about the relationship between the variables.
- To find the **conditional distribution** of the row variable for one specific value of the column variable, look only at that one column in the table. Find each entry in the column as a percent of the column total.
- There is a conditional distribution of the row variable for each column in the table. Comparing these conditional distributions is one way to describe the association between the row and the column variables. It is particularly useful when the column variable is the explanatory variable.
- **Bar graphs** are a flexible means of presenting categorical data. There is no single best way to describe an association between two categorical variables.
- A comparison between two variables that holds for each individual value of a third variable can be changed or even reversed when the data for all values of the third variable are combined. This is **Simpson's paradox.** Simpson's paradox is an example of the effect of lurking variables on an observed association.

SECTION 2.5 Exercises

For Exercises 2.108 and 2.109, see pages 152–153; for 2.110 and 2.111, see pages 153–154; for 2.112 to 2.114, see pages 155–156; and for 2.115, see page 157.

2.116 Advertising to divers. How far in advance do scuba divers plan diving trips to the Florida Keys? The answer will help in planning advertising to divers. Here are counts from a survey of people on the mailing list of a diving agency:[35]

	Months in Advance			
	Less than 1	1 to 3	4 to 6	7 or more
Men	11	18	10	4
Women	4	9	11	3

(a) Give the marginal distribution (in percents) of how long before a trip divers do their planning. If you want to mail a brochure advertising a diving expedition that will take place in April, when would you mail it?

(b) Find the conditional distributions of advance planning for men and for women. What are the most important differences between the sexes?

2.117 Impulse purchasing. We might expect that shoppers are more likely to use credit cards for "impulse purchases," which they decide to make on the spot, as opposed to purchases they had in mind when they went to the store. Stop every third person leaving a department store with a purchase. A few questions allow us to classify the purchase as impulse or not. Here are the data on how the customer paid:[36]

	Payment Method		
	Cash	Check	Credit card
Impulse purchases	14	4	13
Planned purchases	20	11	35

Describe the relationship between type of purchase and payment method by finding and commenting on several percents. What do you think might explain the choice of payment method for impulse purchases?

College undergraduates. *Exercises 2.118 to 2.122 are based on Table 2.11. This two-way table reports data on all undergraduate students enrolled in U.S. colleges and universities in the fall of 1997 whose age was known.*[37]

2.118 College undergraduates.

(a) How many undergraduate students were enrolled in colleges and universities?

(b) What percent of all undergraduate students were 18 to 24 years old in the fall of the academic year?

(c) Find the percent of the undergraduates enrolled in each of the four types of programs who were 18 to 24 years old. Make a bar graph to compare these percents.

(d) The 18 to 24 group is the traditional age group for college students. Briefly summarize what you have learned from the data about the extent to which this group predominates in different kinds of college programs.

2.119 Two-year college students.

(a) An association of two-year colleges asks: "What percent of students enrolled part-time at 2-year colleges are 25 to 39 years old?" Find the percent.

(b) A bank that makes education loans to adults asks: "What percent of all 25- to 39-year-old students are enrolled part-time at 2-year colleges?" Find the percent.

2.120 Students' ages.

(a) Find the marginal distribution of age among all undergraduate students, first in counts and then in percents. Make a bar graph of the distribution in percents.

(b) Find the conditional distribution of age (in percents) among students enrolled part-time in 2-year colleges and make a bar graph of this distribution.

(c) Briefly describe the most important differences between the two age distributions.

(d) The sum of the entries in the "2-year full-time" column is not the same as the total given for that column. Why is this?

2.121 Older students. Call students aged 40 and up "older students." Compare the presence of older students in the four types of program with numbers, a graph, and a brief summary of your findings.

2.122 Nontraditional students. With a little thought, you can extract from Table 2.11 information other than marginal and conditional distributions. The traditional college age group is ages 18 to 24 years.

(a) What percent of all undergraduates fall in this age group?

(b) What percent of students at 2-year colleges fall in this age group?

TABLE 2.11 Undergraduate college enrollment, fall 1997 (thousands of students)

Age	2-year full-time	2-year part-time	4-year full-time	4-year part-time
Under 18	45	170	83	55
18 to 24	1478	1202	4759	562
25 to 39	421	1344	1234	1273
40 and up	121	748	236	611
Total	2065	3464	6312	2501

(c) What percent of part-time students fall in this group?

2.123 Hiring practices. A company has been accused of age discrimination in hiring for operator positions. Lawyers for both sides look at data on applicants for the past 3 years. They compare hiring rates for applicants less than 40 years old and those aged 40 years or greater.

Age	Hired	Not hired
< 40	79	1148
≥ 40	1	163

(a) Find the two conditional distributions of hired/not hired, one for applicants who are less than 40 years old and one for applicants who are not less than 40 years old.

(b) Based on your calculations, make a graph to show the differences in distribution for the two age categories.

(c) Describe the company's hiring record in words. Does the company appear to discriminate on the basis of age?

(d) What lurking variables might be involved here?

2.124 Nonresponse in a survey. A business school conducted a survey of companies in its state. They mailed a questionnaire to 200 small companies, 200 medium-sized companies, and 200 large companies. The rate of nonresponse is important in deciding how reliable survey results are. Here are the data on response to this survey:

	Small	Medium	Large
Response	125	81	40
No response	75	119	160
Total	200	200	200

(a) What was the overall percent of nonresponse?

(b) Describe how nonresponse is related to the size of the business. (Use percents to make your statements precise.)

(c) Draw a bar graph to compare the nonresponse percents for the three size categories.

2.125 Helping cocaine addicts. Cocaine addiction is hard to break. Addicts need cocaine to feel any pleasure, so perhaps giving them an antidepressant drug will help. A 3-year study with 72 chronic cocaine users compared an antidepressant drug called desipramine (manufactured by Hoechst-Marion-Roussel) with lithium and a placebo. (Lithium is a standard drug to treat cocaine addiction. A placebo is a dummy drug, used so that the effect of being in the study but not taking any drug can be seen.) One-third of the subjects, chosen at random, received each drug. Here are the results:[38]

	Desipramine	Lithium	Placebo
Relapse	10	18	20
No relapse	14	6	4
Total	24	24	24

(a) Compare the effectiveness of the three treatments in preventing relapse. Use percents and draw a bar graph.

(b) Do you think that this study gives good evidence that desipramine actually *causes* a reduction in relapses?

2.126 Employee performance. Four employees are responsible for handling the cash register at your store. One item that needs to be recorded for each sale is the type of payment: cash, check, or credit card. For a number of transactions this information is missing, though. Are certain employees responsible, or is everyone equally guilty in forgetting to record this information? Below is a table summarizing the last 3501 transactions.[39]

	Not recorded	Recorded
Employee 1	68	897
Employee 2	62	679
Employee 3	90	1169
Employee 4	39	497

(a) What percent of all transactions do not have the payment terms recorded?

(b) Compare the reliability of the four employees in recording the payment terms for each transaction they handle. Use percents and draw a bar graph.

(c) Do you think these data provide good evidence that a certain employee (or subset of employees) is causing the high percent of transactions without payment terms recorded?

2.127 Demographics and new products. Companies planning to introduce a new product to the market must define the "target" for the product. Who do we hope to attract with our new product? Age and gender are two of the most important demographic variables. The following two-way table describes the age and marital status of American women in 1999.[40] The table entries are in thousands of women.

Age (years)	Marital Status: Never married	Married	Widowed	Divorced	Total
18 to 24	10,240	2,598	9	184	13,031
25 to 39	7,640	20,129	193	2,930	30,891
40 to 64	3,234	28,923	2,357	6,764	41,278
≥ 65	751	8,270	8,385	1,263	18,667
Total	21,865	59,918	10,944	11,141	103,867

(a) Find the sum of the entries in the "Married" column. Why does this sum differ from the "Total" entry for that column?

(b) Give the marginal distribution of marital status for all adult women (use percents). Draw a bar graph to display this distribution.

2.128 Demographics, continued.

(a) Using the data in the previous exercise, compare the conditional distributions of marital status for women aged 18 to 24 and women aged 40 to 64. Briefly describe the most important differences between the two groups of women, and back up your description with percents.

(b) Your company is planning a magazine aimed at women who have never been married. Find the conditional distribution of age among never-married women and display it in a bar graph. What age group or groups should your magazine aim to attract?

2.129 Discrimination? Wabash Tech has two professional schools, business and law. Here are two-way tables of applicants to both schools, categorized by gender and admission decision. (Although these data are made up, similar situations occur in reality.)[41]

Business	Admit	Deny
Male	480	120
Female	180	20

Law	Admit	Deny
Male	10	90
Female	100	200

(a) Make a two-way table of gender by admission decision for the two professional schools together by summing entries in these tables.

(b) From the two-way table, calculate the percent of male applicants who are admitted and the percent of female applicants who are admitted. Wabash admits a higher percent of male applicants.

(c) Now compute separately the percents of male and female applicants admitted by the business school and by the law school. Each school admits a higher percent of female applicants.

(d) This is Simpson's paradox: both schools admit a higher percent of the women who apply, but overall Wabash admits a lower percent of female applicants than of male applicants. Explain carefully, as if speaking to a skeptical reporter, how it can happen that Wabash appears to favor males when each school individually favors females.

2.130 Obesity and health. Recent studies have shown that earlier reports underestimated the health risks associated with being overweight. The error was due to overlooking lurking variables. In particular, smoking tends both to reduce weight and to lead to earlier death. Illustrate Simpson's paradox by a simplified version of this situation. That is, make up tables of overweight (yes or no) by early death (yes or no) by smoker (yes or no) such that

- Overweight smokers and overweight nonsmokers both tend to die earlier than those not overweight.
- But when smokers and nonsmokers are combined into a two-way table of overweight by early death, persons who are not overweight tend to die earlier.

STATISTICS IN SUMMARY

Chapter 1 dealt with data analysis for a single variable. In this chapter, we have studied analysis of data for two or more variables. The proper analysis depends on whether the variables are categorical or quantitative and on whether one is an explanatory variable and the other a response variable.

When you have a categorical explanatory variable and a quantitative response variable, use the tools of Chapter 1 to compare the distributions of the response variable for the

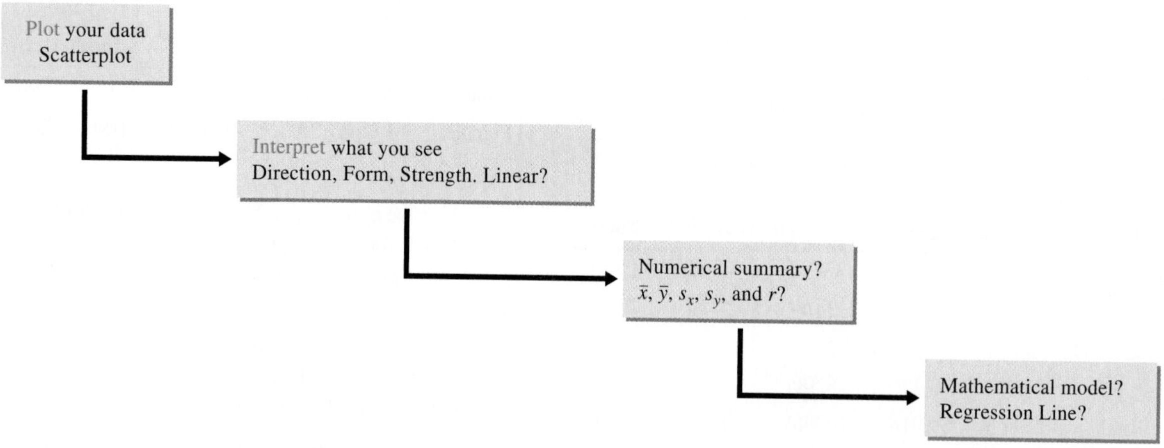

different categories of the explanatory variable. Make side-by-side boxplots, stemplots, or histograms and compare medians or means. If both variables are categorical, there is no satisfactory graph (though bar graphs can help). We describe the relationship numerically by comparing percents. The optional Section 2.5 explains how to do this.

Most of this chapter concentrates on relations between two quantitative variables. The Statistics in Summary figure on this page organizes the main ideas in a way that stresses that our tactics are the same as when we faced single-variable data in Chapter 1. Here is a review list of the most important skills you should have gained from studying this chapter.

A. Data

1. Recognize whether each variable is quantitative or categorical.
2. Identify the explanatory and response variables in situations where one variable explains or influences another.

B. Scatterplots

1. Make a scatterplot to display the relationship between two quantitative variables. Place the explanatory variable (if any) on the horizontal scale of the plot.
2. Add a categorical variable to a scatterplot by using a different plotting symbol or color.
3. Describe the form, direction, and strength of the overall pattern of a scatterplot. In particular, recognize positive or negative association and linear (straight-line) patterns. Recognize outliers in a scatterplot.

C. Correlation

1. Using a calculator or software, find the correlation r between two quantitative variables.
2. Know the basic properties of correlation: r measures the strength and direction of only linear relationships; $-1 \le r \le 1$ always; $r = \pm 1$ only for perfect straight-line relations; r moves away from 0 toward ± 1 as the linear relation gets stronger.

D. Straight lines

1. Explain what the slope b_1 and the intercept b_0 mean in the equation $y = b_0 + b_1 x$ of a straight line.
2. Draw a graph of the straight line when you are given its equation.

E. Regression

1. Using a calculator or software, find the least-squares regression line of a response variable y on an explanatory variable x from data.
2. Find the slope and intercept of the least-squares regression line from the means and standard deviations of x and y and their correlation.
3. Use the regression line to predict y for a given x. Recognize extrapolation and be aware of its dangers.
4. Use r^2 to describe how much of the variation in one variable can be accounted for by a straight-line relationship with another variable.
5. Recognize outliers and potentially influential observations from a scatterplot with the regression line drawn on it.
6. Calculate the residuals and plot them against the explanatory variable x or against other variables. Recognize unusual patterns.

F. Limitations of Correlation and Regression

1. Understand that both r and the least-squares regression line can be strongly influenced by a few extreme observations.
2. Recognize that a correlation based on averages of several observations is usually stronger than the correlation for individual observations.
3. Recognize possible lurking variables that may explain the observed association between two variables x and y.
4. Understand that even a strong correlation does not mean that there is a cause-and-effect relationship between x and y.

G. Categorical Data (Optional)

1. From a two-way table of counts, find the marginal distributions of both variables by obtaining the row sums and column sums.
2. Express any distribution in percents by dividing the category counts by their total.
3. Describe the relationship between two categorical variables by computing and comparing percents. Often this involves comparing the conditional distributions of one variable for the different categories of the other variable.
4. Recognize Simpson's paradox and be able to explain it.

CHAPTER 2 Review Exercises

2.131 Faculty salaries. Data on the salaries of full professors in an engineering department at a large midwestern university are given at right. The salaries are for the academic years 2002–2003 and 2005–2006.

2002 salary ($)	2005 salary ($)	2002 salary ($)	2005 salary ($)
95,600	113,400	102,300	144,200
93,800	114,500	112,500	133,100
104,200	113,300	113,100	131,100
119,000	134,000	122,500	134,400
100,600	115,000	121,100	130,000
108,200	128,000	124,000	133,700
92,100	100,800	153,300	172,800
106,700	115,700	138,500	144,500

(a) Construct a scatterplot with the 2005 salaries on the vertical axis and the 2002 salaries on the horizontal axis.

(b) Comment on the form, direction, and strength of the data.

(c) Identify the point in the scatterplot corresponding to the ninth row in the data set, and mark it with a different plotting symbol than what you used to mark the points in part (a). Do any other professors in the data set have a 2002 salary like this one? Do any other professors in the data set have a 2005 salary like this one? Does this point follow the same overall pattern as the other points? Describe precisely what is unusual about this point. Is this what we describe as an outlier?

(d) Repeat part (c) for the fifteenth row of the data set.

2.132 Faculty salaries. Data on the salaries of full professors in an engineering department at a large midwestern university were presented in the previous exercise. Use statistical software to perform the calculations required in this exercise.

(a) Make a scatterplot of the salary data with the 2005 salaries on the vertical axis and the 2002 salaries on the horizontal axis.

(b) Call the original data set DATA-A, and consider two variations of DATA-A. First, call DATA-B the data set that results from deleting row 9 from DATA-A. Second, call DATA-C the data set that results from deleting row 15 from DATA-A. Now, let r_A be the correlation for DATA-A, r_B the correlation for DATA-B, and r_C the correlation for DATA-C. Before doing any calculations, attempt to put the three correlations in order from smallest to largest.

(c) Calculate the three correlations described in part (b) and report them in order from smallest to largest. Compare your answer to part (b) with the calculated correlations in part (c). How well did you guess?

2.133 Florida condo sales. Florida reappraises real estate every year, and the county appraiser's Web site lists the current "fair market value" of each piece of property. Property usually sells for somewhat more than the appraised market value. Here are the appraised market values and actual selling prices of condominium units sold in a beachfront building over a 19-month period (in thousands of dollars):

These data were also presented in Exercise 2.61.

(a) Make a scatterplot using the default ranges that your software chooses for the axes.

(b) Make a scatterplot with both axes ranging from 0 to 1500.

(c) Make a scatterplot with both axes ranging from 0 to 3000.

(d) Comment on the effects of changing the range of values represented by the axes.

2.134 Florida condo sales. Refer to the Florida condo sales data in the previous exercise.

(a) Make a scatterplot using the default ranges that your software chooses for the axes.

(b) Make a scatterplot with the horizontal axis ranging from 0 to 1500 and the vertical axis ranging from 0 to 5000.

(c) Make a scatterplot with the horizontal axis ranging from 0 to 5000 and the vertical axis ranging from 0 to 1500.

(d) Comment on the effects of changing the range of values represented by the axes.

2.135 Employment numbers. Refer to the data on number of paid employees presented in Exercise 2.14 (page 105) to answer the following questions. Use statistical software for the calculations.

(a) Calculate the correlation between the number of paid employees in 1997 and 2002.

(b) Report the values in the units "millions of employees" rather than as a count of employees (for example, 10,836,365 employees is reported as 10.836365 million employees) and calculate the correlation for the new values.

(c) Now, round the values from part (b) to one decimal place (for example, 10.836365 rounds to 10.8) and calculate the correlation for the rounded data.

Selling price	Appraised value	Month	Selling price	Appraised value	Month
850	758	0	790	605.9	13
900	812.7	1	700	483.8	14
625	504	2	715	585.8	14
1075	956.7	2	825	707.6	14
890	747.9	8	675	493.9	17
810	717.7	8	1050	802.6	17
650	576.6	9	1325	1031.8	18
845	648.3	12	845	586.7	19

(d) How do the calculated correlations in parts (a) and (b) compare? Is this a special case or an example of a general fact? Explain your response.

(e) How do the calculated correlations in parts (b) and (c) compare? Rounding data can sometimes have a considerable effect on subsequent calculations. Comment on the effect of rounding in calculating the correlation for this particular data set.

2.136 Faculty salaries. Data on the salaries of full professors in an engineering department at a large midwestern university were presented in Exercise 2.131.

(a) Report the least-squares line for predicting 2005 salaries from 2002 salaries. In addition to the equation of the line, report s and r^2.

(b) Interpret the value of the estimated slope within the context of these data.

(c) Interpret the value of r^2 within the context of these data.

2.137 Faculty salaries. Continue with the least-squares model from the previous exercise.

(a) With the mathematical definition of the y intercept in mind, interpret the value of the estimated intercept. Is your interpretation a "practical" one given the context of the data? Explain your response.

(b) One might believe that the intercept in this context should be zero. Make a scatterplot of these data with the least-squares regression line superimposed. Adjust the horizontal and vertical axes so that both include the value zero; that is, the point (0, 0) should be visible on your scatterplot. Now, sketch the line one obtains if you replace the least-squares intercept with zero (and leave the slope as it is).

(c) Comment on the fit of the "zero intercept" line compared to the least-squares line. What does the value of the estimated intercept accomplish in addition to its interpretation (or in spite of the interpretation, whichever the case may be)?

2.138 Faculty salaries. Data on the salaries of full professors in an engineering department at a large midwestern university were presented in Exercise 2.131. Consider fitting a line to the data with the 2005 salaries as the response variable and the 2002 salaries as the explanatory variable.

(a) Calculate the residuals from the least-squares regression and use them to create a residual plot. Also, report the values of s and r^2 for the model.

(b) Row 9 appears to be an outlier. Delete this point from the data set and redo part (a).

(c) Contrast the residual plots in parts (a) and (b).

(d) Describe the change in the values of s and r^2 when row 9 is deleted.

2.139 Faculty salaries. Continue your analysis of the faculty salary data presented in Exercise 2.131.

(a) Row 15 has the potential to be an influential observation because of its unusual x-value. Report the least-squares line for these data with and without row 15. Also, report s and r^2 for both regressions.

(b) Would you classify row 15 as an influential observation? Explain your response.

2.140 Circular saws. The following table gives the weight (in pounds) and amps for 19 circular saws. Saws with higher amp ratings tend to also be heavier than saws with lower amp ratings. We can quantify this fact using regression.

Weight	Amps	Weight	Amps	Weight	Amps
11	15	9	10	11	13
12	15	11	15	13	14
11	15	12	15	10	12
11	15	12	14	11	12
12	15	10	10	11	12
11	15	12	13	10	12
13	15				

(a) Make a scatterplot of the data. What do you notice about the weight and amp values?

(b) Report the equation of the least-squares regression line along with the values of s and r^2.

(c) Interpret the value of the estimated slope.

(d) How much of an increase in weight would you expect to correspond to a one amp increase in the power consumption of a saw, on average, when comparing two saws?

(e) Create a residual plot for the model in part (b). Does the model indicate curvature in the data?

2.141 Circular saws. The table in the previous exercise gives the weight (in pounds) and amps for 19 circular saws. The data contain only five different amp ratings among the 19 saws.

(a) Calculate the correlation between the weights and the amps of the 19 saws.

(b) Calculate the average weight of the saws for each of the five amp ratings.

(c) Calculate the correlation between the average weights and the amps. Is the correlation between

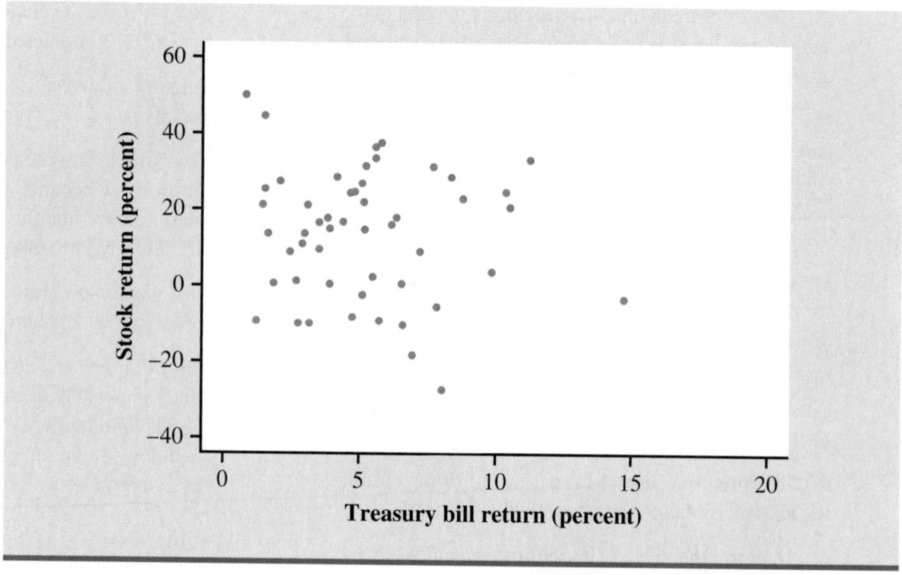

FIGURE 2.26 Annual returns on U.S. common stocks versus returns on Treasury bills for the years 1950 to 2000, for Exercise 2.143.

average weights and amps greater than, less than, or equal to the correlation between individual weights and amps?

2.142 Florida condo sales. Consider the Florida condo sales data in Exercise 2.61.

(a) Calculate the correlation, r^2, and the least-squares regression line for these data. Also, create a residual plot.

(b) Add one more condo's data and redo part (a). The additional condo has an appraised value of $688,750 and a selling price of $1,248,125.

(c) What do you conclude about the additional condo by inspecting the residual plot from part (b)?

(d) Describe how the additional data point affected the correlation, r^2, the estimated intercept, and the estimated slope.

(e) If the additional data point was for a condo with an appraised value of $688,750 and a selling price of $448,125, then how would you expect the correlation, r^2, the estimated intercept, and the estimated slope to change?

2.143 Are high interest rates bad for stocks? When interest rates are high, investors may shun stocks because they can get high returns with less risk. Figure 2.26 plots the annual returns on U.S. common stocks for the years 1950 to 2000 against the returns on Treasury bills for the same years.[42] (The interest rate paid by Treasury bills is a measure of how high interest rates were that year.) Describe the pattern you see. Are high interest rates bad for stocks? Is there a strong relationship between interest rates and stock returns?

2.144 Are high interest rates bad for stocks? The scatterplot in Figure 2.26 suggests that returns on common stocks may be somewhat lower in years with high interest rates. Here is part of the Excel output for the regression of stock returns on the bill returns for the same years:

Regression Statistics	
Multiple R	0.097538007
R Square	0.009513663
Adjusted R Square	−0.010700344
Standard Error	17.16003473
Observations	51

ANOVA

	df	*SS*	*MS*	*F*	*Significance F*
Regression	1	138.5899296	138.5899296	0.470647059	0.495923077
Residual	49	14428.87281	294.4667921		
Total	50	14567.46274			

	Coefficients	*Standard Error*	*t Stat*	*P-value*	*Lower 95%*	*Upper 95%*
Intercept	16.23521332	4.960252104	3.27306213	0.001954308	6.267213705	26.20321293
T-Bill return	−0.572668524	0.834748484	−0.686037214	0.495923077	−2.250158374	1.104821326

(a) What is the equation of the least-squares line? Use this line to predict the percent return on stocks in a year when Treasury bills return 5%.

(b) Explain what the slope of the regression line tells us. Does the slope confirm that high interest rates are in general bad for stocks?

(c) If you knew the return on Treasury bills for next year, do you think you could predict the return on stocks quite accurately? Use both the scatterplot in Figure 2.26 and the regression output to justify your answer.

2.145 Influence? The scatterplot in Figure 2.26 contains an outlier: in 1981, inflation reached a peak and the return on Treasury bills was 14.72%. Would removing this point increase or decrease the correlation between returns on T-bills and stocks? Why? Is the location of this point such that it could strongly influence the regression line? Why?

2.146 A hot stock? It is usual in finance to describe the returns from investing in a single stock by regressing the stock's returns on the returns from the stock market as a whole. This helps us see how closely the stock follows the market. We analyzed the monthly percent total return y on Philip Morris common stock and the monthly return x on the Standard & Poor's 500 stock index, which represents the market, for the period between July 1990 and May 1997. Here are the results:

$$\bar{x} = 1.304 \qquad s_x = 3.392 \qquad r = 0.5251$$
$$\bar{y} = 1.878 \qquad s_y = 7.554$$

A scatterplot shows no very influential observations.

(a) Find the equation of the least-squares line from this information. What percent of the variation in Philip Morris stock is explained by the linear relationship with the market as a whole?

(b) Explain carefully what the slope of the line tells us about how Philip Morris stock responds to changes in the market. This slope is called "beta" in investment theory.

(c) Returns on most individual stocks have a positive correlation with returns on the entire market. That is, when the market goes up, an individual stock tends also to go up. Explain why an investor should prefer stocks with beta > 1 when the market is rising and stocks with beta < 1 when the market is falling.

2.147 What correlation doesn't say. Investment reports now often include correlations. Following a table of correlations among mutual funds, a report adds: "Two funds can have perfect correlation, yet different levels of risk. For example, Fund A and Fund B may be perfectly correlated, yet Fund A moves 20% whenever Fund B moves 10%." Write a brief explanation, for someone who knows no statistics, of how this can happen. Include a sketch to illustrate your explanation.

2.148 A computer game. A multimedia statistics learning system includes a test of skill in using the computer's mouse. The software displays a circle at a random location on the computer screen. The subject tries to click in the circle with the mouse as quickly as possible. A new circle appears as soon as the subject clicks the old one. Table 2.12 gives data for one subject's trials, 20 with each hand. Distance is the distance from the cursor location to the center of the new circle, in units whose actual size depends on the size of the screen. Time is the time required to click in the new circle, in milliseconds.[43]

(a) We suspect that time depends on distance. Make a scatterplot of time against distance, using separate symbols for each hand.

(b) Describe the pattern. How can you tell that the subject is right-handed?

(c) Find the regression line of time on distance separately for each hand. Draw these lines on your plot. Which regression does a better job of predicting time from distance? Give numerical measures that describe the success of the two regressions.

(d) It is possible that the subject got better in later trials due to learning. It is also possible that he got worse due to fatigue. Plot the residuals from each regression against the time order of the trials (down the columns in Table 2.12). Is either of these systematic effects of time visible in the data?

2.149 Wood products. A wood product manufacturer is interested in replacing solid-wood building material by less-expensive products made from wood flakes. The company collected the following data to examine the relationship between the length (in inches) and the strength (in pounds per square inch) of beams made from wood flakes:

Length	5	6	7	8	9	10	11	12	13	14
Strength	446	371	334	296	249	254	244	246	239	234

(a) Make a scatterplot that shows how the length of a beam affects its strength.

(b) Describe the overall pattern of the plot. Are there any outliers?

(c) Fit a least-squares line to the entire set of data. Graph the line on your scatterplot. Does a straight line adequately describe these data?

TABLE 2.12 Reaction times in a computer game

Time	Distance	Hand	Time	Distance	Hand
115	190.70	right	240	190.70	left
96	138.52	right	190	138.52	left
110	165.08	right	170	165.08	left
100	126.19	right	125	126.19	left
111	163.19	right	315	163.19	left
101	305.66	right	240	305.66	left
111	176.15	right	141	176.15	left
106	162.78	right	210	162.78	left
96	147.87	right	200	147.87	left
96	271.46	right	401	271.46	left
95	40.25	right	320	40.25	left
96	24.76	right	113	24.76	left
96	104.80	right	176	104.80	left
106	136.80	right	211	136.80	left
100	308.60	right	238	308.60	left
113	279.80	right	316	279.80	left
123	125.51	right	176	125.51	left
111	329.80	right	173	329.80	left
95	51.66	right	210	51.66	left
108	201.95	right	170	201.95	left

(d) The scatterplot suggests that the relation between length and strength can be described by *two* straight lines, one for lengths of 5 to 9 inches and another for lengths of 9 to 14 inches. Fit least-squares lines to these two subsets of the data, and draw the lines on your plot. Do they describe the data adequately? What question would you now ask the wood experts?

2.150 Heating a business. Joan is concerned about the amount of energy she uses to heat her small business. She keeps a record of the natural gas she consumes each month over one year's heating season. The variables are the same as in Example 2.4 (page 99) for the Sanchez home. Here are Joan's data:[44]

(a) Make a scatterplot of these data. There is a strong linear pattern with no outliers.

(b) Find the equation of the least-squares regression line for predicting gas use from degree-days. Draw this line on your graph. Explain in simple language what the slope of the regression line tells us about how gas use responds to outdoor temperature.

(c) Joan adds some insulation during the summer, hoping to reduce her gas consumption. Next February averages 40 degree-days per day, and her gas consumption is 870 cubic feet per day. Predict from the regression equation how much gas the business would have used at 40 degree-days per day last winter before the extra insulation. Did the insulation reduce gas consumption?

2.151 Heating a business. Find the mean and standard deviation of the degree-day and gas consumption data in the previous exercise. Find the correlation between the two variables. Use these five numbers to find the equation of the regression line for predicting gas use from degree-days. Verify that your work agrees with your previous results. Use the same five numbers to find the equation of the regression line for predicting

	Oct.	Nov.	Dec.	Jan.	Feb.	Mar.	Apr.	May	June
Degree-days per day	15.6	26.8	37.8	36.4	35.5	18.6	15.3	7.9	0.0
Gas consumed per day	520	610	870	850	880	490	450	250	110

degree-days from gas use. What units does each of these slopes have?

2.152 Size and selling price of houses. Table 2.13 provides information on a random sample of 50 houses sold in Ames, Iowa, in the year 2000.[45]

(a) Describe the distribution of selling price with a graph and a numerical summary. What are the main features of this distribution?

(b) Make a scatterplot of selling price versus square feet and describe the relationship between these two variables.

(c) Calculate the least-squares regression line for these data. On average, how much does each square foot add to the selling price of a house?

(d) What would you expect the selling price of a 1600-square-foot house in Ames to be?

(e) What percent of the variability in these 50 selling prices can be attributed to differences in square footage?

2.153 Age and selling price of houses.

(a) Using the data in Table 2.13, calculate the least-squares regression line for predicting selling price from age at time of sale, that is, in 2000.

(b) What would you expect for the selling price of a house built in 2000? 1999? 1998? 1997? Describe specifically how age relates to selling price.

(c) Would you trust this regression line for predicting the selling price of a house that was built in 1900?

TABLE 2.13 Houses sold in Ames, Iowa

Selling price ($)	Square footage	Age (years)	Selling price ($)	Square footage	Age (years)
268,380	1897	1	169,900	1686	35
131,000	1157	15	180,000	2054	34
112,000	1024	35	127,000	1386	50
112,000	935	35	242,500	2603	10
122,000	1236	39	152,900	1582	3
127,900	1248	32	171,600	1790	1
157,600	1620	33	195,000	1908	6
135,000	1124	33	83,100	1378	72
145,900	1248	35	125,000	1668	55
126,000	1139	39	60,500	1248	100
142,000	1329	40	85,000	1229	59
107,500	1040	45	117,000	1308	60
110,000	951	42	57,000	892	90
187,000	1628	1	110,000	1981	72
94,000	816	43	127,250	1098	70
99,500	1060	24	119,000	1858	80
78,000	800	68	172,500	2010	60
55,790	492	79	123,000	1680	86
70,000	792	80	161,715	1670	1
53,600	980	62	179,797	1938	1
157,000	1629	3	117,250	1120	36
166,730	1889	0	116,500	914	4
340,000	2759	6	117,000	1008	23
195,000	1811	3	177,500	1920	32
215,850	2400	27	132,000	1146	37

1899? 1850? Explain your responses. (What would this line predict for a house built in 1850?)

(d) Calculate and interpret the correlation between selling price and age.

2.154 Beta. Exercise 2.146 introduced the financial concept of a stock's "beta." Beta measures the volatility of a stock relative to the overall market. A beta of less than 1 indicates lower risk than the market; a beta of more than 1 indicates higher risk than the market. In February 2001, the information on Apple Computer, Inc., at `finance.yahoo.com` listed a beta of 1.24; the information on Apple Computer, Inc., at `www.nasdaq.com` listed a beta of 1.69. Both Web sites use the S&P 500 to measure changes in the overall market. Using the 60 monthly returns from March 1996 to February 2001, we find the least-squares regression line $\hat{y} = 0.30 + 1.35x$ (y is Apple return, x is S&P 500 return).[46]

(a) The correlation for our 60 months of data is 0.3481. Interpret this correlation in terms of using the movement of the overall market to predict movement in Apple stock.

(b) We have three different beta values for Apple stock: 1.24, 1.35, and 1.69. What is a likely explanation for this discrepancy?

The following exercises concern material in the optional Section 2.5.

2.155 Aspirin and heart attacks. Does taking aspirin regularly help prevent heart attacks? "Nearly five decades of research now link aspirin to the prevention of stroke and heart attacks." So says the Bayer Aspirin Web site, `www.bayeraspirin.com`. The most important evidence for this claim comes from the Physicians' Health Study. The subjects were 22,071 healthy male doctors at least 40 years old. Half the subjects, chosen at random, took aspirin every other day. The other half took a placebo, a dummy pill that looked and tasted like aspirin. Here are the results.[47] (The row for "None of these" is left out of the two-way table.)

	Aspirin group	Placebo group
Fatal heart attacks	10	26
Other heart attacks	129	213
Strokes	119	98
Total	11,037	11,034

What do the data show about the association between taking aspirin and heart attacks and stroke? Use percents to make your statements precise. Do you think the study provides evidence that aspirin actually reduces heart attacks (cause and effect)?

2.156 More smokers live at least 20 more years! You can see the headlines "More smokers than nonsmokers live at least 20 more years after being contacted for study!" A medical study contacted randomly chosen people in a district in England. Here are data on the 1314 women contacted who were either current smokers or who had never smoked. The tables classify these women by their smoking status and age at the time of the survey and whether they were still alive 20 years later.[48]

Age 18 to 44	Smoker	Not
Dead	19	13
Alive	269	327

Age 45 to 64	Smoker	Not
Dead	78	52
Alive	167	147

Age 65+	Smoker	Not
Dead	42	165
Alive	7	28

(a) From these data make a two-way table of smoking (yes or no) by dead or alive. What percent of the smokers stayed alive for 20 years? What percent of the nonsmokers survived? It seems surprising that a higher percent of smokers stayed alive.

(b) The age of the women at the time of the study is a lurking variable. Show that within each of the three age groups in the data, a higher percent of nonsmokers remained alive 20 years later. This is another example of Simpson's paradox.

(c) The study authors give this explanation: "Few of the older women (over 65 at the original survey) were smokers, but many of them had died by the time of follow-up." Compare the percent of smokers in the three age groups to verify the explanation.

2.157 Recycled product quality. Recycling is supposed to save resources. Some people think recycled products are lower in quality than other products, a fact that makes recycling less practical. People who actually use a recycled product may have different opinions from those who don't use it. Here are data on attitudes toward coffee filters made of recycled paper among people who do and don't buy these filters:[49]

	Think the quality of the recycled product is:		
	Higher	The same	Lower
Buyers	20	7	9
Nonbuyers	29	25	43

(a) Find the marginal distribution of opinion about quality. Assuming that these people represent all users of coffee filters, what does this distribution tell us?

(b) How do the opinions of buyers and nonbuyers differ? Use conditional distributions as a basis for your answer. Can you conclude that using recycled filters causes more favorable opinions? If so, giving away samples might increase sales.

CHAPTER 2 Case Study Exercises

CASE STUDY EXERCISE 1: Wal-Mart stores. The file *ex02_24* on the CD that accompanies this book contains data on the number of the nation's 2624 Wal-Mart stores in each state. Table 1.9 gives the populations of the states.

A. Stores and population. How well does least-squares regression on state population predict the number of Wal-Mart stores in a state? Do an analysis that includes graphs, calculations, and a discussion of your findings. If a state's population increases by a million people, about how many more Wal-Marts would you expect? What other state-to-state differences might account for differences in number of Wal-Mart stores per state?

B. California. Is California unusual with respect to number of Wal-Mart stores per million people? Does looking at graphs suggest that California may be influential for either correlation or the least-squares line? Redo parts of your analysis without California and draw conclusions about the influence of the largest state on this statistical study.

CASE STUDY EXERCISE 2: Predicting college grades. The data set CSDATA, described in the Data Appendix, contains information about all 224 students who entered a large university in a single year and who planned to major in computer science. We are interested in predicting GPA (grade point average) after three semesters of college from information available before the student enters college. To do this effectively, we must use several explanatory variables together. This is *multiple regression,* the topic of Chapter 11. In this Case Study, you will look at individual explanatory variables.

A. Correlations. What are the correlations of all the explanatory variables with GPA? Explain why knowing the correlations tells us which variables will best predict GPA in a regression with just one explanatory variable. What are the two best predictor variables? Does your finding seem reasonable for computer science majors?

B. Prediction. Make scatterplots, with the least-squares line added, for GPA versus each of the two best explanatory variables. How well do each of these variables predict GPA? Do the scatterplots contain unusual observations? In what way is each of these observations unusual?

CASE STUDY EXERCISE 3: Predicting coffee exports. The data set COFFEEXPORTS, described in the Data Appendix, contains information on the number of 60-kilogram bags of coffee exported from 48 countries in 2000 and 2001. In this Case Study, you will consider three prediction scenarios.

A. Using December 2000 exports to predict 2001 exports. What is the correlation between December 2000 exports and total exports for 2001? Make a scatterplot with the least-squares line added for predicting 2001 exports using December 2000 exports. What does the value of r^2 tell you? Identify any unusual values by country name.

B. Using 2000 exports to predict 2001 exports. What is the correlation between 2000 exports and 2001 exports? Make a scatterplot with the least-squares line added for predicting 2001 exports using 2000 exports. What does the value of r^2 tell you in this setting? For the countries listed as having unusual values in part A, find their data points on the scatterplot in part B. Are these countries' values unusual in this data set? Do you recommend using 2000 total exports or December 2000 exports for predicting 2001 exports? Briefly explain your choice.

C. Using December 2000 exports to predict December 2001 exports. What is the correlation between December 2000 exports and December 2001 exports? Make a scatterplot with the least-squares line added for predicting December 2001 exports using December 2000 exports. What does the value of r^2 tell you here? This r^2-value should be higher than the r^2-values in parts A and B. Explain intuitively why one might expect the highest r^2 to be in part C.

CHAPTER 2 Appendix

Using Minitab and Excel for Examining Relationships

Scatterplots

Minitab:

Graph ➤ Scatterplot

Select "Simple" for the type of scatterplot, then click **OK.** Click-in the data column associated with the *y* (response) variable into row 1 of the **Y variables** box, and click-in the data column associated with the *x* (explanatory) variable into row 1 of the **X variables** box. Click **OK.**

Excel:

To create a scatterplot in Excel, the data for the two variables should be placed in two adjacent columns, with the column associated with the *y* variable being in the column to the right of the column associated with the *x* variable. Click and drag the mouse to highlight the cells of the two columns of data. With the cell range highlighted, click the **Insert** tab and then click **Scatter** in the **Charts** group. You want to now choose the scatterplot option with no line connections. If the gridlines are not desired, you can click on them and delete them by hitting the delete key or by right-clicking and selecting **Delete.** The layout of the scatterplot can also be manipulated by choosing among a variety of options offered within the **Charts Layouts** group found under the **Design** tab.

Correlation

Minitab:

Stat ➤ Basic Statistics ➤ Correlation

Click-in the *y* variable data column and the *x* variable data column into the **Variables** box and then click **OK.**

Excel:

Select "Correlation" in the **Data Analysis** menu box and click **OK.** Enter the cell range of the data on the two variables (placed in adjacent columns) into the **Input Range** box. Click **OK.**

Least-squares regression

Minitab:

Stat ➤ Regression ➤ Regression

Click-in the response variable data column into the **Response** box, and click-in the explanatory variable data column into the **Predictors** box. If you want the residual values, then click the **Storage** button and place a checkmark next to the **Residuals** option and then click **OK** to close the pop-up box. Select the **Fits** option if you want the predicted

Observation versus Experiment

An **observational study** observes individuals and measures variables of interest but does not attempt to influence the responses.

An **experiment** deliberately imposes some treatment on individuals to observe their responses.

Observational studies are essential sources of data about topics from public attitudes toward business to the behavior of online shoppers. But an observational study, even one based on a statistical sample, is a poor way to gauge the effect of an intervention. To see the response to a change, we must actually impose the change. When our goal is to understand cause and effect, experiments are the only source of fully convincing data.

EXAMPLE 3.1 Do Cell Phones Cause Brain Cancer?

As cell phone use grows, concerns about exposure to radiation from long-term use of the phones have also grown. Reports of cell phone users suffering from brain cancer make headlines and plant seeds of fear in some wireless phone users. Are the observed cases of cell phone users with brain cancer evidence that cell phones *cause* brain cancer? Careful observational studies look at large groups, not at isolated cases. To date, they find no consistent relationship between cell phone use and cancer. But observation cannot answer the cause-and-effect question directly. Even if observational data did show a relationship, cell phone users might have some other common characteristics that contribute to the development of brain cancer. For example, they are more likely than nonusers to live in metropolitan areas. That means higher exposure to many types of pollution, some of which might cause cancer.

To see if cell phone radiation actually causes brain cancer, we might carry out an experiment. Choose two similar groups of people. Expose one group to cell phone radiation regularly and forbid the other group any close contact with cell phones. Wait a few years, then compare the rates of brain cancer in the two groups. This experiment would answer our question, but it is neither practical nor ethical to force people to accept or avoid cell phones. Experimenters can and do use mice or rats, exposing some to cell phone radiation while keeping others free from it. The experiments have not (yet) been conclusive—those that show more tumors in mice exposed to radiation used mice bred to be prone to cancer and radiation more intense than that produced by phones.[2]

When we simply observe cell phone use and brain cancer, any effect of radiation on the occurrence of brain cancer is *confounded* (mixed up) with such lurking variables as age, occupation, and place of residence.

Confounding

Two variables (explanatory variables or lurking variables) are **confounded** when their effects on a response variable cannot be distinguished from each other.

Observational studies of the effect of one variable on another often fail because the explanatory variable is confounded with lurking variables. We will see that well-designed experiments take steps to defeat confounding.

APPLY YOUR KNOWLEDGE

3.1 Gender and consumer choices. Men and women differ in their choices for many product categories. Are there gender differences in preferences for health insurance plans as well? A market researcher interviews a large sample of consumers, both men and women. She asks each consumer which of two health plans he or she prefers. Is this study an experiment? Why or why not? What are the explanatory and response variables?

3.2 Teaching economics. An educational software company wants to compare the effectiveness of its computer animation for teaching about supply, demand, and market clearing with that of a textbook presentation. The company tests the economic knowledge of each of a group of first-year college students, then divides them into two groups. One group uses the animation, and the other studies the text. The company retests all the students and compares the increase in economic understanding in the two groups. Is this an experiment? Why or why not? What are the explanatory and response variables?

3.3 Does job training work? A state institutes a job-training program for manufacturing workers who lose their jobs. After five years, the state reviews how well the program works. Critics claim that because the state's unemployment rate for manufacturing workers was 6% when the program began and 10% five years later, the program is ineffective. Explain why higher unemployment does not necessarily mean that the training program failed. In particular, identify some lurking variables whose effect on unemployment may be confounded with the effect of the training program.

3.1 Designing Samples

A major food producer wants to know what fraction of the public worries about use of genetically modified corn in taco shells. A quality engineer must estimate what fraction of the bearings rolling off an assembly line are defective. Government economists inquire about household income. In all these situations, we want to gather information about a large group of people or things. Time, cost, and inconvenience prevent inspecting every bearing or contacting every household. In such cases, we gather information about only part of the group to draw conclusions about the whole.

Population, Sample

The **population** in a statistical study is the entire group of individuals about which we want information.

A **sample** is the part of the population from which we actually collect information used to draw conclusions about the whole.

Notice that the population is defined in terms of our desire for knowledge. If we wish to draw conclusions about all U.S. college students, that group is our population even if only local students are available for questioning. The sample is the part from which we draw conclusions about the whole. The **design** of a sample refers to the method used to choose the sample from the population. Poor sample designs can produce misleading conclusions.

sample design

EXAMPLE 3.2 A "Good" Sample Isn't a Good Idea

A mill produces large coils of thin steel for use in manufacturing home appliances. A quality engineer wants to submit a sample of 5-centimeter squares to detailed laboratory examination. She asks a technician to cut a sample of 10 such squares. Wanting to provide "good" pieces of steel, the technician carefully avoids the visible defects in the steel when cutting the sample. The laboratory results are wonderful, but the customers complain about the material they are receiving.

EXAMPLE 3.3 Call-in Opinion Polls

Television news programs like to conduct call-in polls of public opinion. The program announces a question and asks viewers to call one telephone number to respond "Yes" and another for "No." Telephone companies charge for these calls. The ABC network program *Nightline* once asked whether the United Nations should continue to have its headquarters in the United States. More than 186,000 callers responded, and 67% said "No."

People who spend the time and money to respond to call-in polls are not representative of the entire adult population. In fact, they tend to be the same people who call radio talk shows. People who feel strongly, especially those with strong negative opinions, are more likely to call. It is not surprising that a properly designed sample showed that 72% of adults want the UN to stay.[3]

Call-in opinion polls are an example of *voluntary response sampling.* A voluntary response sample can easily produce 67% "No" when the truth about the population is close to 72% "Yes."

Voluntary Response Sample

A **voluntary response sample** consists of people who choose themselves by responding to a general appeal. Voluntary response samples are biased because people with strong opinions, especially negative opinions, are most likely to respond.

convenience sampling

Voluntary response is one common type of bad sample design. Another is **convenience sampling,** which chooses the individuals easiest to reach. Here is an example of convenience sampling.

EXAMPLE 3.4 Interviewing at the Mall

Manufacturers and advertising agencies often use interviews at shopping malls to gather information about the habits of consumers and the effectiveness of ads. A sample of mall shoppers is fast and cheap. "Mall interviewing is being propelled primarily as a budget issue," one expert told the *New York Times.* But people contacted at shopping malls are not representative of the entire U.S. population. They are richer, for example, and more likely to be teenagers or retired. Moreover, mall interviewers tend to select neat, safe-looking individuals from the stream of customers. Decisions based on mall interviews may not reflect the preferences of all consumers.[4]

Both voluntary response samples and convenience samples produce samples that are almost guaranteed not to represent the entire population. These sampling methods display *bias,* or systematic error, in favoring some parts of the population over others.

Bias

The design of a study is **biased** if it systematically favors certain outcomes.

APPLY YOUR KNOWLEDGE

3.4 Sampling employed women. A sociologist wants to know the opinions of employed adult women about government funding for day care. She obtains a list of the 520 members of a local business and professional women's club and mails a questionnaire to 100 of these women selected at random. Only 48 questionnaires are returned. What is the population in this study? What is the sample from whom information is actually obtained? What is the rate (percent) of nonresponse?

3.5 What is the population? For each of the following sampling situations, identify the population as exactly as possible. That is, say what kind of individuals the population consists of and say exactly which individuals fall in the population. If the information given is not sufficient, complete the description of the population in a reasonable way.

(a) Each week, the Gallup Poll questions a sample of about 1500 adult U.S. residents to determine national opinion on a wide variety of issues.

(b) The 2000 census tried to gather basic information from every household in the United States. Also, a "long form" requesting much additional information was sent to a sample of about 17% of households.

(c) A machinery manufacturer purchases voltage regulators from a supplier. There are reports that variation in the output voltage of the regulators is affecting the performance of the finished products. To assess the quality of the supplier's production, the manufacturer sends a sample of 5 regulators from the last shipment to a laboratory for study.

3.6 Is that movie any good? You wonder if that new "blockbuster" movie is really any good. Some of your friends like the movie, but you decide to check the Internet Movie Database (`www.imdb.com`) to see others' ratings. You find that 2497 people chose to rate this movie, with an average rating of only 3.7 out of 10. You are surprised that most of your friends liked the movie, while many people gave low ratings to the movie online. Are you convinced that a majority of those who saw the movie would give it a low rating? What type of sample are your friends? What type of sample are the raters on the Internet Movie Database?

Simple random samples

In a voluntary response sample, people choose whether to respond. In a convenience sample, the interviewer makes the choice. In both cases, personal choice produces bias. The statistician's remedy is to allow impersonal chance to choose the sample. A sample chosen by chance allows neither favoritism by the sampler nor self-selection by respondents. Choosing a sample by chance attacks bias by giving all individuals an equal chance to be chosen. Rich and poor, young and old, black and white, all have the same chance to be in the sample.

The simplest way to use chance to select a sample is to place names in a hat (the population) and draw out a handful (the sample). This is the idea of *simple random sampling.*

Simple Random Sample

A **simple random sample (SRS)** of size n consists of n individuals from the population chosen in such a way that every set of n individuals has an equal chance to be the sample actually selected.

An SRS not only gives each individual an equal chance to be chosen (thus avoiding bias in the choice) but also gives every possible sample an equal chance to be chosen. There are other random sampling designs that give each individual, but not each sample, an equal chance. Exercise 3.29 describes one such design, called systematic random sampling.

The idea of an SRS is to choose our sample by drawing names from a hat. In practice, computer software can choose an SRS almost instantly from a list of the individuals in the population. For example, the *Simple Random Sample* applet available on the Web site for this book can choose an SRS of any size up to $n = 40$ from a population of any size up to 500. If you don't use software, you can randomize by using a *table of random digits.*

applet

Random Digits

A **table of random digits** is a long string of the digits 0, 1, 2, 3, 4, 5, 6, 7, 8, 9 with these two properties:

1. Each entry in the table is equally likely to be any of the 10 digits 0 through 9.
2. The entries are independent of each other. That is, knowledge of one part of the table gives no information about any other part.

Table B at the back of the book is a table of random digits. You can think of Table B as the result of asking an assistant (or a computer) to mix the digits 0 to 9 in a hat, draw one, then replace the digit drawn, mix again, draw a second digit, and so on. The assistant's mixing and drawing save us the work of mixing and drawing when we need to randomize. Table B begins with the digits 19223950340575628713. To make the table easier to read, the digits appear in groups of five and in numbered rows. The groups and rows have no meaning—the table is just a long list of randomly chosen digits. Because the digits in Table B are random:

- Each entry is equally likely to be any of the 10 possibilities 0, 1, . . . , 9.
- Each pair of entries is equally likely to be any of the 100 possible pairs 00, 01, . . . , 99.
- Each triple of entries is equally likely to be any of the 1000 possibilities 000, 001, . . . , 999; and so on.

These "equally likely" facts make it easy to use Table B to choose an SRS. Here is an example that shows how.

EXAMPLE 3.5 How to Choose an SRS

Joan's accounting firm serves 30 small business clients. Joan wants to interview a sample of 5 clients in detail to find ways to improve client satisfaction. To avoid bias, she chooses an SRS of size 5.

Step 1. **Label.** Give each client a numerical label, using as few digits as possible. Two digits are needed to label 30 clients, so we use labels

01, 02, 03, . . . , 29, 30

It is also correct to use labels 00 to 29 or even another choice of 30 two-digit labels. Here is the list of clients, with labels attached.

01	A-1 Plumbing	16	JL Records
02	Accent Printing	17	Johnson Commodities
03	Action Sport Shop	18	Keiser Construction
04	Anderson Construction	19	Liu's Chinese Restaurant
05	Bailey Trucking	20	MagicTan
06	Balloons Inc.	21	Peerless Machine
07	Bennett Hardware	22	Photo Arts
08	Best's Camera Shop	23	River City Books
09	Blue Print Specialties	24	Riverside Tavern
10	Central Tree Service	25	Rustic Boutique
11	Classic Flowers	26	Satellite Services
12	Computer Answers	27	Scotch Wash
13	Darlene's Dolls	28	Sewing Center
14	Fleisch Realty	29	Tire Specialties
15	Hernandez Electronics	30	Von's Video Store

Step 2. **Table.** Enter Table B anywhere and read two-digit groups. Suppose we enter at line 130, which is

69051 64817 87174 09517 84534 06489 87201 97245

The first 10 two-digit groups in this line are

69 05 16 48 17 87 17 40 95 17

Each successive two-digit group is a label. The labels 00 and 31 to 99 are not used in this example, so we ignore them. The first 5 labels between 01 and 30 that we encounter in the table choose our sample. Of the first 10 labels in line 130, we ignore 5 because they are too high (over 30). The others are 05, 16, 17, 17, and 17. The clients labeled 05, 16, and 17 go into the sample. Ignore the second and third 17s because that client is already in the sample. Now run your finger across line 130 (and continue to line 131 if needed) until 5 clients are chosen.

The sample is the clients labeled 05, 16, 17, 20, 19. These are Bailey Trucking, JL Records, Johnson Commodities, MagicTan, and Liu's Chinese Restaurant.

Choosing an SRS

Choose an SRS in two steps:

Step 1. **Label.** Assign a numerical label to every individual in the population.

Step 2. **Table.** Use Table B to select labels at random.

You can assign labels in any convenient manner, such as alphabetical order for names of people. Be certain that all labels have the same number of digits. Only then will all individuals have the same chance to be chosen. Use the shortest possible labels: one digit for a population of up to 10 members, two digits for 11 to 100 members, three digits for 101 to 1000 members, and so on. As standard practice, we recommend that you begin with label 1 (or 01 or 001, as needed). You can read digits from Table B in any order—across a row, down a column, and so on—because the table has no order. As standard practice, we recommend reading across rows.

APPLY YOUR KNOWLEDGE

3.7 Sampling employees. A firm wants to understand the attitudes of its minority managers toward its system for assessing management performance. Below is a list of all the firm's managers who are members of minority groups. Use Table B at line 139 to choose 6 to be interviewed in detail about the performance appraisal system.

Agarwal	Dewald	Huang	Puri
Anderson	Fernandez	Kim	Richards
Baxter	Fleming	Liao	Rodriguez
Bowman	Garcia	Mourning	Santiago
Brown	Gates	Naber	Shen
Castillo	Goel	Peters	Vega
Cross	Gomez	Pliego	Wang

3.8 Focus group sampling. Thirty individuals in your target audience have been using a new product. Each person has filled out short evaluations of the product periodically during the test period. At the end of the period, you decide to select 4 of the individuals at random for a lengthy interview. The list of participants appears below. Choose an SRS of 4, using the table of random digits, beginning at line 145.

Armstrong	Gonzalez	Kempthorne	Robertson
Aspin	Green	Laskowsky	Sanchez
Bennett	Gupta	Liu	Sosa
Bock	Gutierrez	Montoya	Tran
Breiman	Harter	Patnaik	Trevino
Collins	Henderson	Pirelli	Wu
Dixon	Hughes	Rao	
Edwards	Johnson	Rider	

3.9 Sampling retail locations. You must choose an SRS of 10 of the 440 retail outlets in New York that sell your company's products. How would you label this population? Use Table B, starting at line 105, to choose your sample.

Stratified samples

The general framework for statistical sampling is a *probability sample.*

Probability Sample

A **probability sample** is a sample chosen by chance. We must know what samples are possible and what chance, or probability, each possible sample has.

Some probability sampling designs (such as an SRS) give each member of the population an equal chance to be selected. This may not be true in more elaborate sampling designs. In every case, however, the use of chance to select the sample is the essential principle of statistical sampling.

Designs for sampling from large populations spread out over a wide area are usually more complex than an SRS. For example, it is common to sample important groups within the population separately, then combine these samples. This is the idea of a *stratified random sample.*

Stratified Random Sample

To select a **stratified random sample,** first divide the population into groups of similar individuals, called **strata.** Then choose a separate SRS in each stratum and combine these SRSs to form the full sample.

Choose the strata based on facts known before the sample is taken. For example, a population of consumers might be divided into strata according to age, gender, and other demographic information. A stratified design can produce more exact information than an SRS of the same size by taking advantage of the fact that individuals in the same stratum are similar to one another. If all individuals in each stratum are identical, for example, just one individual from each stratum is enough to completely describe the population.

EXAMPLE 3.6 Who Wrote That Song?

A radio station that broadcasts a piece of music owes a royalty to the composer. The organization of composers (called ASCAP) collects these royalties for all its members by charging stations a license fee for the right to play members' songs. ASCAP has 4 million songs in its catalog and collects $435 million in fees each year. How should ASCAP distribute this income among its members? By sampling: ASCAP tapes about 60,000 hours from the 53 million hours of local radio programs across the country each year.

Radio stations are stratified by type of community (metropolitan, rural), geographic location (New England, Pacific, etc.), and the size of the license fee paid to ASCAP, which reflects the size of the audience. In all, there are 432 strata. Tapes are made at random hours for randomly selected members of each stratum. The tapes are reviewed by experts who can recognize almost every piece of music ever written, and the composers are then paid according to their popularity.[5]

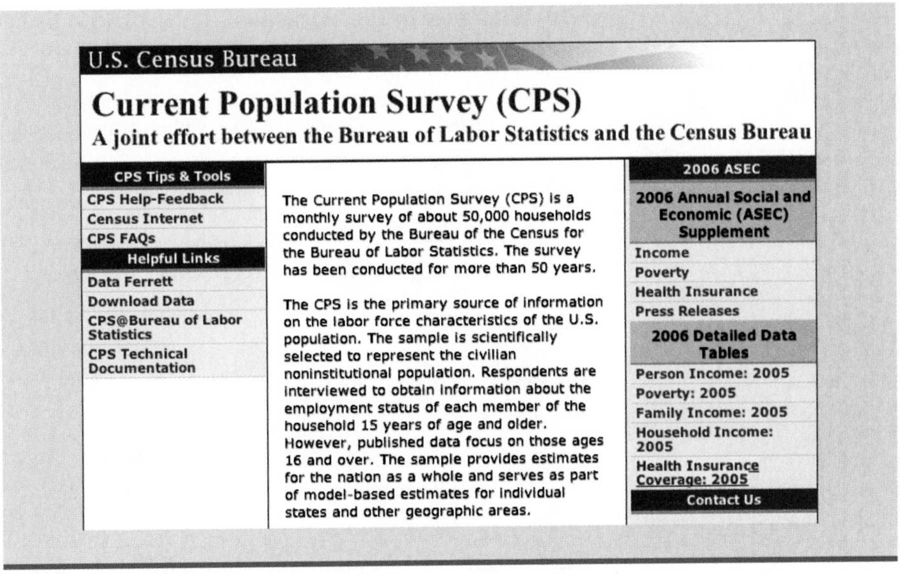

FIGURE 3.1 The monthly Current Population Survey is one of the most important sample surveys in the United States. You can find information and data from the survey on its Web page, `www.bls.census.gov/cps`.

Multistage samples

Current Population Survey

multistage sample

Another common type of probability sample chooses the sample in stages. This is usual practice for national samples of households or people. For example, government data on employment and unemployment are gathered by the **Current Population Survey** (Figure 3.1), which conducts interviews in about 55,000 households each month. It is not practical to maintain a list of all U.S. households from which to select an SRS. Moreover, the cost of sending interviewers to the widely scattered households in an SRS would be too high. The Current Population Survey therefore uses a **multistage sample design.** The final sample consists of clusters of nearby households. Most opinion polls and other national samples are also multistage, though interviewing in most national samples today is done by telephone rather than in person, eliminating the economic need for clustering. The Current Population Survey sampling design is roughly as follows:[6]

Stage 1. Divide the United States into 2007 geographical areas called Primary Sampling Units, or PSUs. Select a sample of 754 PSUs. This sample includes the 428 PSUs with the largest populations and a stratified sample of 326 of the others.

Stage 2. Divide each PSU selected at Stage 1 into small areas called "census blocks." Stratify the blocks using ethnic and other information and take a stratified sample of the blocks in each PSU.

Stage 3. Group the housing units in each block into clusters of four nearby units. Interview the households in a random sample of these clusters.

Analysis of data from sampling designs more complex than an SRS takes us beyond basic statistics. But the SRS is the building block of more elaborate designs, and analysis of other designs differs more in complexity of detail than in fundamental concepts.

APPLY YOUR KNOWLEDGE

3.10 Who goes to the workshop? A small advertising firm has 30 junior associates and 10 senior associates. The junior associates are

Abel	Fisher	Huber	Miranda	Reinmann
Chen	Ghosh	Jimenez	Moskowitz	Santos
Cordoba	Griswold	Jones	Neyman	Shaw
David	Hein	Kim	O'Brien	Thompson
Deming	Hernandez	Klotz	Pearl	Utts
Elashoff	Holland	Lorenz	Potter	Varga

The senior associates are

Andrews	Fernandez	Kim	Moore	West
Besicovitch	Gupta	Lightman	Vicario	Yang

The firm will send 4 junior associates and 2 senior associates to a workshop on current trends in market research. It decides to choose those who will go by random selection. Use Table B to choose a stratified random sample of 4 junior associates and 2 senior associates. Start at line 121 to choose your sample.

3.11 Sampling by accountants. Accountants use stratified samples during audits to verify a company's records of such things as accounts receivable. The stratification is based on the dollar amount of the item and often includes 100% sampling of the largest items. One company reports 5000 accounts receivable. Of these, 100 are in amounts over $50,000; 500 are in amounts between $1000 and $50,000; and the remaining 4400 are in amounts under $1000. Using these groups as strata, you decide to verify all of the largest accounts and to sample 5% of the midsize accounts and 1% of the small accounts. How would you label the two strata from which you will sample? Use Table B, starting at line 115, to select *only the first 5* accounts from each of these strata.

Cautions about sample surveys

Random selection eliminates bias in the choice of a sample from a list of the population. When the population consists of human beings, however, accurate information from a sample requires much more than a good sampling design.[7] To begin, we need an accurate and complete list of the population. Because such a list is rarely available, most samples suffer from some degree of *undercoverage.* A sample survey of households, for example, will miss not only homeless people but prison inmates and students in dormitories, too. An opinion poll conducted by telephone will miss the 6% of American households without residential phones. The results of national sample surveys therefore have some bias if the people not covered—who most often are poor people—differ from the rest of the population.

A more serious source of bias in most sample surveys is *nonresponse,* which occurs when a selected individual cannot be contacted or refuses to cooperate. Nonresponse to sample surveys often reaches 50% or more, even with careful planning and several callbacks. Because nonresponse is higher in urban areas, most sample surveys substitute other people in the same area to avoid favoring rural areas in the final sample. If the people contacted differ from those who are rarely at home or who refuse to answer questions, some bias remains.

Undercoverage and Nonresponse

Undercoverage occurs when some groups in the population are left out of the process of choosing the sample.

Nonresponse occurs when an individual chosen for the sample can't be contacted or refuses to cooperate.

EXAMPLE 3.7 How Bad Is Nonresponse?

The Current Population Survey has the lowest nonresponse rate of any poll we know: only about 6% or 7% of the households in the CPS sample don't respond. People are more likely to respond to a government survey such as the CPS, and the CPS contacts its sample in person before doing later interviews by phone.

The General Social Survey, conducted by the University of Chicago's National Opinion Research Center, is the nation's most important social science survey. The GSS also contacts its sample in person, and it is run by a university. Despite these advantages, its most recent survey had a 30% rate of nonresponse.

What about polls done by the media and by market research and opinion-polling firms? We don't know their rates of nonresponse, because they don't say. That itself is a bad sign. The Pew Research Center imitated a careful telephone survey and published the results: out of 2879 households called, 1658 were never at home, refused, or would not finish the interview. That's a nonresponse rate of 58%.[8]

response bias

In addition, the behavior of the respondent or of the interviewer can cause **response bias** in sample results. Respondents may lie, especially if asked about illegal or unpopular behavior. The sample then underestimates the presence of such behavior in the population. An interviewer whose attitude suggests that some answers are more desirable than others will get these answers more often. The race or sex of the interviewer can influence responses to questions about race relations or attitudes toward feminism. Answers to questions that ask respondents to recall past events are often inaccurate because of faulty memory. For example, many people "telescope" events in the past, bringing them forward in memory to more recent time periods. "Have you visited a dentist in the last 6 months?" will often draw a "Yes" from someone who last visited a dentist 8 months ago.[9] Careful training of interviewers and careful supervision to avoid variation among the interviewers can greatly reduce response bias. Good interviewing technique is another aspect of a well-done sample survey.

wording effects

The **wording of questions** is the most important influence on the answers given to a sample survey. Confusing or leading questions can introduce strong bias, and even minor changes in wording can change a survey's outcome. Here are two examples.

EXAMPLE 3.8 Should We Ban Disposable Diapers?

A survey paid for by makers of disposable diapers found that 84% of the sample opposed banning disposable diapers. Here is the actual question:

> It is estimated that disposable diapers account for less than 2% of the trash in today's landfills. In contrast, beverage containers, third-class mail and yard wastes are estimated

> to account for about 21% of the trash in landfills. Given this, in your opinion, would it be fair to ban disposable diapers?[10]

This question gives information on only one side of an issue, then asks an opinion. That's a sure way to bias the responses. A different question that described how long disposable diapers take to decay and how many tons they contribute to landfills each year would draw a quite different response.

EXAMPLE 3.9 A Few Words Make a Big Difference

How do Americans feel about government help for the poor? Only 13% think we are spending too much on "assistance to the poor," but 44% think we are spending too much on "welfare." How do the Scots feel about the movement to become independent from England? Well, 51% would vote for "independence for Scotland," but only 34% support "an independent Scotland separate from the United Kingdom."[11]

It seems that "assistance to the poor" and "independence" are nice, hopeful words. "Welfare" and "separate" are negative words. Small changes in how a question is worded can make a big difference in the response.

Never trust the results of a sample survey until you have read the exact questions posed. The amount of nonresponse and the date of the survey are also important. Good statistical design is a part, but only a part, of a trustworthy survey.

APPLY YOUR KNOWLEDGE

sampling frame

3.12 Random digit dialing. The list of individuals from which a sample is actually selected is called the **sampling frame.** Ideally, the frame should list every individual in the population, but in practice this is often difficult. A frame that leaves out part of the population is a common source of undercoverage.

(a) Suppose that a sample of households in a community is selected at random from the telephone directory. What households are omitted from this frame? What types of people do you think are likely to live in these households? These people will probably be underrepresented in the sample.

(b) It is usual in telephone surveys to use random digit dialing equipment that selects the last four digits of a telephone number at random after being given the exchange (the first three digits). Which of the households that you mentioned in your answer to (a) will be included in the sampling frame by random digit dialing?

3.13 Ring-no-answer. A common form of nonresponse in telephone surveys is "ring-no-answer." That is, a call is made to an active number, but no one answers. The Italian National Statistical Institute looked at nonresponse to a government survey of households in Italy during two periods, January 1 to Easter and July 1 to August 31. All calls were made between 7 and 10 P.M., but 21.4% gave "ring-no-answer" in one period versus 41.5% "ring-no-answer" in the other period.[12] Which period do you think had the higher rate of no answers? Why? Explain why a high rate of nonresponse makes sample results less reliable.

3.14 Campaign contributions. Here are two wordings for the same question. The first question was asked by presidential candidate Ross Perot, and the second by a *Time*/CNN Poll, both in March 1993.[13]

1. Should laws be passed to eliminate all possibilities of special interests giving huge sums of money to candidates?
2. Should laws be passed to prohibit interest groups from contributing to campaigns, or do groups have a right to contribute to the candidates they support?

One of these questions drew 40% favoring banning contributions; the other drew 80% with this opinion. Which question produced the 40% and which got 80%? Explain why the results were so different.

BEYOND THE BASICS: CAPTURE-RECAPTURE SAMPLING

Pacific salmon return to reproduce in the river where they were hatched three or four years earlier. How many salmon made it back this year? The answer will help determine quotas for commercial fishing on the west coast of Canada and the United States. Biologists estimate the size of animal populations with a special kind of repeated sampling, called *capture-recapture sampling*. More recently, capture-recapture methods have been used on human populations as well.

EXAMPLE 3.10 Counting Salmon

The old method of counting returning salmon involved placing a "counting fence" in a stream and counting all the fish caught by the fence. This is expensive and difficult. For example, fences are often damaged by high water. Sampling using small nets is more practical.[14]

During this year's spawning run in the Chase River in British Columbia, Canada, you net 200 coho salmon, tag the fish, and release them. Later in the week, your nets capture 120 coho salmon in the river, of which 12 have tags.

The proportion of your second sample that have tags should estimate the proportion in the entire population of returning salmon that are tagged. So if N is the unknown number of coho salmon in the Chase River this year, we should have approximately

$$\text{proportion tagged in sample} = \text{proportion tagged in population}$$

$$\frac{12}{120} = \frac{200}{N}$$

Solve for N to estimate that the total number of salmon in this year's spawning run in the Chase River is approximately

$$N = 200 \times \frac{120}{12} = 2000$$

The capture-recapture idea extends the use of a sample proportion to estimate a population proportion. The idea works well if both samples are SRSs from the population and the population remains unchanged between samples. In practice, complications arise. For example, some tagged fish might be caught by bears or otherwise die between the first and second samples. Variations on capture-recapture samples are widely used in wildlife studies and are now finding other applications. One way to estimate the census undercount in a district is to consider the census as "capturing and marking" the households that respond. Census workers then visit the district, take an SRS of households, and see how many of those counted by the census show up in the sample. Capture-recapture estimates the total count of households in the district. As with estimating wildlife populations, there are many practical pitfalls. Our final word is as before: the real world is less orderly than statistics textbooks imply.

SECTION 3.1 SUMMARY

- We can produce data intended to answer specific questions by **observational studies** or **experiments. Sample surveys** that select a part of a population of interest to represent the whole are one type of observational study. **Experiments,** unlike observational studies, actively impose some treatment on the subjects of the experiment.
- A sample survey selects a **sample** from the **population** of all individuals about which we desire information. We base conclusions about the population on data about the sample.
- The **design** of a sample refers to the method used to select the sample from the population. **Probability sampling** designs use random selection to select the sample, thus avoiding bias due to personal choice.
- The basic probability sample is a **simple random sample (SRS).** An SRS gives every possible sample of a given size the same chance to be chosen.
- Choose an SRS by labeling the members of the population and using a **table of random digits** to select the sample. Software can automate this process.
- To choose a **stratified random sample,** divide the population into **strata,** groups of individuals that are similar in some way that is important to the response. Then choose a separate SRS from each stratum.
- Failure to use probability sampling often results in **bias,** or systematic errors in the way the sample represents the population. **Voluntary response samples,** in which the respondents choose themselves, are particularly prone to large bias.
- In human populations, even probability samples can suffer from bias due to **undercoverage** or **nonresponse,** from **response bias,** or from misleading results due to **poorly worded questions.** Sample surveys must deal expertly with these potential problems in addition to using a probability sampling design.

SECTION 3.1 Exercises

For Exercises 3.1 to 3.3, see page 178; for 3.4 to 3.6, see page 180; for 3.7 to 3.9, see page 183; for 3.10 and 3.11, see page 186; and for 3.12 to 3.14, see pages 188–189.

3.15 Make it an experiment! In the following observational studies, describe changes that could be made to the data collection process that would result in an experiment rather than an observation study. Also, offer suggestions about unseen biases or lurking variables that may be present in the studies as they are described here.

(a) In a sample of 50 members of a local health club, you find that 12 of these members meet weekly with a physical fitness trainer and that the average body mass index (BMI) of these 12 members is less than the average BMI of the other 38 club members in your sample.

(b) In a sample of 12 bank tellers at a local branch office, the 7 tellers who have completed the advanced training program offered by the bank have a lower average error rate in the processing of transactions than the remaining 5 tellers.

3.16 Aren't voluntary response samples convenient? You are asked to develop an ad campaign for a headache relief product. You decide to collect information from potential customers on what their most common causes of headaches are, so that you might gear the ads toward these causes and thus connect with the potential customers.

(a) Describe how you could obtain a voluntary response sample from the population of potential customers. What bias might your sample have as a result of your data collection method?

(b) Describe how you could obtain a convenience sample from the population of potential customers. What bias might your sample have as a result of your data collection method?

3.17 Table B or not Table B. Numbering the members of a population in sequence (001, 002, 003, . . .) and using Table B to select a random sample of integers corresponding to members of the numbered population is only one way of choosing an SRS. Most statistical software programs have random number generators, and some will select a random sample from any list of numbers or text that you provide. Note that not all random number generators and sampling programs are equally good at their task. Be sure to investigate your software's reputation for random number generation. Another option is to use the random number generation features available on some Web sites. The same caution applies here though: be sure to investigate a site's reputation for random number generation before depending on the site for random samples.

(a) Inspect the Web site `www.random.org`. Write a short description, in your own words, of how Random.org generates random numbers.

(b) Does Random.org offer any evidence of how well it generates random numbers? Describe what evidence you find at the site.

(c) Use the site to generate a random sample for Example 3.5 (page 182). Report the 5 companies in your random sample.

(d) Repeat part (c) and report this second random sample of 5 companies. Is there any overlap between your two random samples?

3.18 Table B or not Table B. Another Web site for random numbers is `www.randomizer.org`. Randomizer.org uses a different method of generating random numbers than the one used by Random.org.

(a) Inspect the Web site `www.randomizer.org`. Write a short description, in your own words, of how Randomizer.org generates random numbers.

(b) Does Randomizer.org offer any evidence of how well it generates random numbers? Describe what evidence you find at the site.

(c) Use the site to complete Exercise 3.7 (page 183).

(d) Repeat part (c) and report your second random sample of managers. Is there any overlap between your two random samples?

3.19 Students as customers. A committee on community relations in a college town plans to survey local businesses about the importance of students as customers. From telephone book listings, the committee chooses 150 businesses at random. Of these, 73 return the questionnaire mailed by the committee.

(a) What is the population for this sample survey?

(b) What is the sample?

(c) What is the rate (percent) of nonresponse?

(d) Will the use of telephone book listings miss any members of the population of interest? Explain your response.

3.20 Survey follow-up. In the previous exercise, 73 businesses returned the survey to the committee. The committee decides to sample 5 of these companies for an in-depth follow-up survey.

(a) Use Table B, starting at line 171, to select a random sample of 5 of the 73 companies.

(b) Use Random.org to select a random sample of 5 of the 73 companies.

3.21 What is the population? For each of the following sampling situations, identify the population as exactly as possible. That is, say what kind of individuals the population consists of and say exactly which individuals fall in the population. If the information given is not sufficient, complete the description of the population in a reasonable way.

(a) A business school researcher wants to know what factors affect the survival and success of small businesses. She selects a sample of 150 eating-and-drinking establishments from those listed in the telephone directory Yellow Pages for a large city.

(b) A member of Congress wants to know whether his constituents support proposed legislation on health care. His staff reports that 228 letters have been received on the subject, of which 193 oppose the legislation.

(c) An insurance company wants to monitor the quality of its procedures for handling loss claims from its auto insurance policyholders. Each month the company examines in detail an SRS from all auto insurance claims filed that month.

3.22 Instant opinion. The Excite Poll was found online at `poll.excite.com`. The question appeared on the screen, and you simply clicked buttons to vote "Yes," "No," or "Not sure." On January 25, 2000, the question was "Should female athletes be paid the same as men for the work they do?" In all, 13,147 respondents (44%) said "Yes," another 15,182 (50%) said "No," and the remaining 1448 said "Don't know."

(a) What is the sample size for this poll?

(b) That's a much larger sample than standard sample surveys. In spite of this, we can't trust the result to give good information about any clearly defined population. Why?

(c) It is still true that more men than women use the Web. How might this fact affect the poll results?

3.23 Mail to Congress. You are on the staff of a member of Congress who is considering a bill that would require all employers to provide health insurance for their employees. You report that 1128 letters dealing with the issue have been received, of which 871 oppose the legislation. "I'm surprised that most of my constituents oppose the bill. I thought it would be quite popular," says the congresswoman. Are you convinced that a majority of the voters opposes the bill? State briefly how you would explain the statistical issue to the congresswoman.

3.24 Design your own bad sample. Your college wants to gather student opinion about parking for students on campus. It isn't practical to contact all students.

(a) Give an example of a way to choose a sample of students that is poor practice because it depends on voluntary response.

(b) Give an example of a bad way to choose a sample that doesn't use voluntary response.

3.25 Quality control sampling. A manufacturer of chemicals chooses 3 containers from each lot of 25 containers of a reagent to test for purity and potency. Below are the control numbers stamped on the bottles in the current lot. Use Table B at line 111 to choose an SRS of 3 of these bottles.

A1096	A1097	A1098	A1101	A1108
A1112	A1113	A1117	A2109	A2211
A2220	B0986	B1011	B1096	B1101
B1102	B1103	B1110	B1119	B1137
B1189	B1223	B1277	B1286	B1299

3.26 Apartment living. You are planning a report on apartment living in a college town. You decide to select three apartment complexes at random for in-depth interviews with residents. Use Table B, starting at line 117, to select a simple random sample of three of the following apartment complexes.

Ashley Oaks	Country View	Mayfair Village
Bay Pointe	Country Villa	Nobb Hill
Beau Jardin	Crestview	Pemberly Courts
Bluffs	Del-Lynn	Peppermill
Brandon Place	Fairington	Pheasant Run
Briarwood	Fairway Knolls	Richfield
Brownstone	Fowler	Sagamore Ridge
Burberry	Franklin Park	Salem Courthouse
Cambridge	Georgetown	Village Manor
Chauncey Village	Greenacres	Waterford Court
Country Squire	Lahr House	Williamsburg

3.27 Sampling from a census tract. The Census Bureau divides the entire country into "census tracts" that contain about 4000 people. Each tract is in turn divided into small "blocks," which in urban areas are bounded by local streets. An SRS of blocks from a census tract is often the next-to-last stage in a multistage sample. Figure 3.2 shows part of census tract 8051.12, in Cook County, Illinois, west of Chicago. The 41 blocks in this tract are divided into three "block groups." Group 1 contains 5 blocks numbered 1000 to 1005. Group 2 (outlined in Figure 3.2) contains 11 blocks numbered 2000 to 2011. Group 3 contains 25 blocks numbered 3000 to 3025. Use Table B, beginning at line 125, to choose an SRS of 5 of the 41 blocks in this census tract. Explain carefully how you labeled the blocks.

3.28 Random digits. Which of the following statements are true of a table of random digits, and which are false? Briefly explain your answers.

(a) There are exactly four 0s in each row of 40 digits.

(b) Each pair of digits has chance $1/100$ of being 00.

(c) The digits 0000 can never appear as a group, because this pattern is not random.

3.29 Systematic random samples. The last stage of the Current Population Survey chooses clusters of households within small areas called blocks. The method used is ***systematic random sampling.*** An example will illustrate the idea of a systematic sample. Suppose that we must choose 4 clusters out of 100. Because $100/4 = 25$, we can think of the list as four lists of 25 clusters. Choose 1 of the first 25 at random, using Table B. The sample will contain this cluster and the clusters 25, 50, and 75 places down the list from it. If 13 is chosen, for example, then the systematic

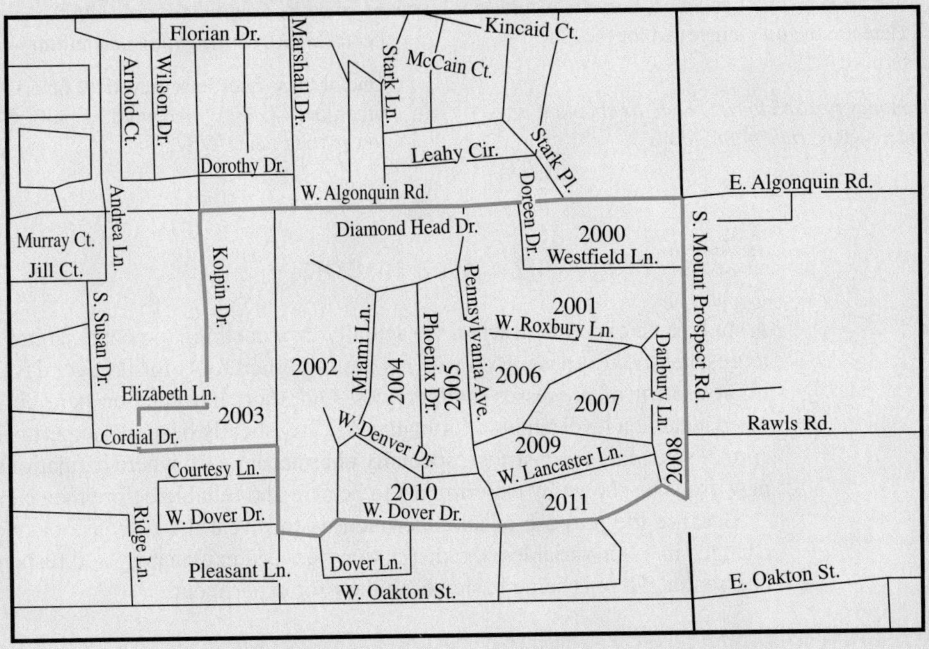

FIGURE 3.2 Census blocks in Cook County, Illinois. The outlined area is a block group. (From factfinder.census.gov.)

random sample consists of the clusters numbered 13, 38, 63, and 88.

(a) Use Table B to choose a systematic random sample of 5 clusters from a list of 200. Enter the table at line 120.

(b) Like an SRS, a systematic sample gives all individuals the same chance to be chosen. Explain why this is true, then explain carefully why a systematic sample is nonetheless *not* an SRS.

3.30 Is this an SRS? A company employs 2000 male and 500 female engineers. A stratified random sample of 50 female and 200 male engineers gives each engineer one chance in 10 to be chosen. This sample design gives every individual in the population the same chance to be chosen for the sample. Is it an SRS? Explain your answer.

3.31 A stratified sample. A company employs 2000 male and 500 female engineers. The human resources department wants to poll the opinions of a random sample of engineers about the company's performance review system. To give adequate attention to female opinion, you will choose a stratified random sample of 200 males and 200 females. You have alphabetized lists of female and male engineers. Explain how you would assign labels and use random digits to choose the desired sample. Enter Table B at line 122 and give the labels of the first 5 females and the first 5 males in the sample.

3.32 Wording survey questions. Comment on each of the following as a potential sample survey question. Is the question clear? Is it slanted toward a desired response?

(a) Some cell phone users have developed brain cancer. Should all cell phones come with a warning label explaining the danger of using cell phones?

(b) In view of escalating environmental degradation and incipient resource depletion, would you favor economic incentives for recycling of resource-intensive consumer goods?

3.33 Bad survey questions. Write your own examples of bad sample survey questions.

(a) Write a biased question designed to get one answer rather than another.

(b) Write a question that is confusing, so that it is hard to answer.

3.34 Do the people want a tax cut? During the 2000 presidential campaign, the candidates debated what to do with the large government surplus. The Pew

Research Center asked two questions of random samples of adults. Both said that Social Security would be "fixed." Here are the uses suggested for the remaining surplus:

Should the money be used for a tax cut, or should it be used to fund new government programs?

Should the money be used for a tax cut, or should it be spent on programs for education, the environment, health care, crime-fighting and military defense?

One of these questions drew 60% favoring a tax cut; the other, only 22%. Which wording pulls respondents toward a tax cut? Why?

3.2 Designing Experiments

A study is an experiment when we actually do something to people, animals, or objects to observe the response. Experiments are important tools for product development and improvement of processes and services. Our short introduction here concentrates on basic ideas at a level suitable for managers. Statistically designed experiments are at the core of some large industries, especially pharmaceuticals, where regulations require that new drugs be shown by experiments to be safe and reliable before they can be sold.

Because the purpose of an experiment is to reveal the response of one variable to changes in other variables, the distinction between explanatory and response variables is essential. Here is some basic vocabulary for experiments.

Subjects, Factors, Treatments

The individuals studied in an experiment are often called **subjects,** especially if they are people.

The explanatory variables in an experiment are often called **factors.**

A **treatment** is any specific experimental condition applied to the subjects. If an experiment has several factors, a treatment is a combination of a specific value (often called a **level**) of each of the factors.

EXAMPLE 3.11 Absorption of a Drug

Researchers at a pharmaceutical company studying the absorption of a drug into the bloodstream inject the drug (the treatment) into 25 people (the subjects). The response variable is the concentration of the drug in a subject's blood, measured 30 minutes after the injection. This experiment has a single factor with only one level. If three different doses of the drug are injected, there is still a single factor (the dosage of the drug), now with three levels. The three levels of the single factor are the treatments that the experiment compares.

EXAMPLE 3.12 Effects of TV Advertising

What are the effects of repeated exposure to an advertising message? The answer may depend both on the length of the ad and on how often it is repeated. An experiment investigates this question using undergraduate students as subjects. All subjects view a 40-minute television program that

Factor A Length	Factor B Repetitions: 1 time	3 times	5 times
30 seconds	1	2	3
90 seconds	4	5	6

FIGURE 3.3 The treatments in the experimental design of Example 3.12. Combinations of levels of the two factors form six treatments.

includes ads for a digital camera. Some subjects see a 30-second commercial; others, a 90-second version. The same commercial is repeated either 1, 3, or 5 times during the program. After viewing, all of the subjects answer questions about their recall of the ad, their attitude toward the camera, and their intention to purchase it. These are the response variables.[15]

This experiment has two factors: length of the commercial, with 2 levels; and repetitions, with 3 levels. The 6 combinations of one level of each factor form 6 treatments. Figure 3.3 shows the layout of the treatments.

Examples 3.11 and 3.12 illustrate the advantages of experiments over observational studies. Experimentation allows us to study the effects of the specific treatments we are interested in. Moreover, we can control the environment of the subjects to hold constant the factors that are of no interest to us, such as the specific product advertised in Example 3.12. The ideal case is a laboratory experiment in which we control all lurking variables and so see only the effect of the treatments on the response. Like most ideals, such control is not always realized in practice.

Another advantage of experiments is that we can study the combined effects of several factors simultaneously. The interaction of several factors can produce effects that could not be predicted from looking at the effect of each factor alone. Perhaps longer commercials increase interest in a product, and more commercials also increase interest, but if we both make a commercial longer and show it more often, viewers get annoyed and their interest in the product drops. The two-factor experiment in Example 3.12 will help us find out.

APPLY YOUR KNOWLEDGE

3.35 Sickle-cell disease. Sickle-cell disease is an inherited disorder of the red blood cells that in the United States affects mostly blacks. It can cause severe pain and many complications. Bristol-Myers Squibb markets Hydrea—a brand name for the drug hydroxyurea—to treat sickle-cell disease. Federal regulations allow the sale of a new drug only after statistically designed experiments (called clinical trials in medical language) show that the drug is safe and effective. A clinical trial at the National Institutes of Health gave hydroxyurea to 150 sickle-cell sufferers and a placebo (a dummy medication) to another 150. The researchers then counted the episodes of pain reported by each subject. What are the subjects, the factors, the treatments, and the response variables?

3.36 Sealing food packages. A manufacturer of food products uses package liners that are sealed at the top by applying heated jaws after the package is filled. The customer peels the sealed pieces apart to open the package. What effect does the temperature of the jaws have on the force needed to peel the liner? To answer this question, engineers prepare 20 pairs of pieces of package liner. They seal 5 pairs at each of 250°F, 275°F, 300°F, and 325°F. Then they measure the force needed to peel each seal.

(a) What are the individuals studied?

(b) There is one factor (explanatory variable). What is it, and what are its levels?

(c) What is the response variable?

3.37 An industrial experiment. A chemical engineer is designing the production process for a new product. The chemical reaction that produces the product may have higher or lower yield, depending on the temperature and the stirring rate in the vessel in which the reaction takes place. The engineer decides to investigate the effects of combinations of two temperatures (50°C and 60°C) and three stirring rates (60 rpm, 90 rpm, and 120 rpm) on the yield of the process. She will process two batches of the product at each combination of temperature and stirring rate.

(a) What are the individuals and the response variable in this experiment?

(b) How many factors are there? How many treatments? Use a diagram like that in Figure 3.3 to lay out the treatments.

(c) How many individuals are required for the experiment?

Comparative experiments

Experiments in the laboratory often have a simple design: impose the treatment and see what happens. We can outline that design like this:

Subjects ⟶ Treatment ⟶ Response

In the laboratory, we try to avoid confounding by rigorously controlling the environment of the experiment so that nothing except the experimental treatment influences the response. Once we get out of the laboratory, however, there are almost always lurking variables waiting to confound us. When our subjects are people or animals rather than electrons or chemical compounds, confounding can happen even in the controlled environment of a laboratory or medical clinic. Here is an example that helps explain why careful experimental design is a key issue for pharmaceutical companies and other makers of medical products.

EXAMPLE 3.13 Gastric Freezing to Treat Ulcers

"Gastric freezing" is a clever treatment for ulcers. The patient swallows a deflated balloon with tubes attached, then a refrigerated liquid is pumped through the balloon for an hour. The idea is that cooling the stomach will reduce its production of acid and so relieve ulcers. An experiment reported in the *Journal of the American Medical Association* showed that gastric freezing did reduce acid production and relieve ulcer pain. The treatment was widely used for several years. The design of the experiment was

Subjects ⟶ Gastric freezing ⟶ Observe pain relief

placebo effect

This experiment is poorly designed. The patients' response may be due to the **placebo effect.** A placebo is a dummy treatment. Many patients respond favorably to *any* treatment, even a placebo, presumably because of trust in the doctor and expectations of a cure. This response to a dummy treatment is the placebo effect.

A later experiment divided ulcer patients into two groups. One group was treated by gastric freezing as before. The other group received a placebo treatment in which the liquid in the balloon was at body temperature rather than freezing. The results: 34% of the 82 patients in the treatment group improved, but so did 38% of the 78 patients in the placebo group. This and other properly designed experiments showed that gastric freezing was no better than a placebo, and its use was abandoned.[16]

The first gastric-freezing experiment was *biased.* It systematically favored gastric freezing because the placebo effect was confounded with the effect of the treatment. Fortunately, the remedy is simple. Experiments should *compare* treatments rather than attempt to assess a single treatment in isolation. When we compare the two groups of patients in the second gastric-freezing experiment, the placebo effect and other lurking variables operate on both groups. The only difference between the groups is the actual effect of gastric freezing. The group of patients who receive a sham treatment is called a **control group,** because it enables us to control the effects of lurking variables on the outcome.

control group

Randomized comparative experiments

The design of an experiment first describes the response variables, the factors (explanatory variables), and the layout of the treatments, with *comparison* as the leading principle. The second aspect of design is the rule used to assign the subjects to the treatments. Comparison of the effects of several treatments is valid only when all treatments are applied to similar groups of subjects. If one corn variety is planted on more fertile ground, or if one cancer drug is given to less seriously ill patients, comparisons among treatments are biased. How can we assign individuals to treatments in a way that is fair to all the treatments?

Our answer is the same as in sampling: let impersonal chance make the assignment. The use of chance to divide subjects into groups is called **randomization.** Groups formed by randomization don't depend on any characteristic of the subjects or on the judgment of the experimenter. An experiment that uses both comparison and randomization is a **randomized comparative experiment.** Here is an example.

randomization

randomized comparative experiment

EXAMPLE 3.14 Testing a Breakfast Food

A food company assesses the nutritional quality of a new "instant breakfast" product by feeding it to newly weaned male white rats. The response variable is a rat's weight gain over a 28-day period. A control group of rats eats a standard diet but otherwise receives exactly the same treatment as the experimental group.

This experiment has one factor (the diet) with two levels. The researchers use 30 rats for the experiment and so must divide them into two groups of 15. To do this in an unbiased fashion, put the cage numbers of the 30 rats in a hat, mix them up, and draw 15. These rats form the experimental group and the remaining 15 make up the control group. *Each group is an SRS of the available rats.* Figure 3.4 outlines the design of this experiment.

We can use software or the table of random digits to randomize. Label the rats 01 to 30. Enter Table B at (say) line 130. Run your finger along this line (and continue to lines 131 and 132 as needed) until 15 rats are chosen. They are the rats labeled

05 16 17 20 19 04 25 29 18 07 13 02 23 27 21

These rats form the experimental group; the remaining 15 are the control group.

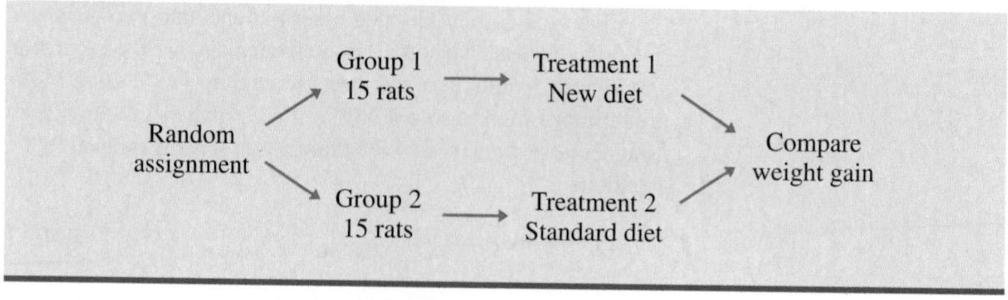

FIGURE 3.4 Outline of a randomized comparative experiment, for Example 3.14.

Completely randomized designs

The design in Figure 3.4 combines comparison and randomization to arrive at the simplest statistical design for an experiment. This "flowchart" outline presents all the essentials: randomization, the sizes of the groups and which treatment they receive, and the response variable. There are, as we will see later, statistical reasons for generally using treatment groups that are about equal in size. We call designs like that in Figure 3.4 *completely randomized.*

Completely Randomized Design

In a **completely randomized** experimental design, all the subjects are allocated at random among all the treatments.

Completely randomized designs can compare any number of treatments. Here is an example that compares three treatments.

EXAMPLE 3.15 Conserving Energy

Many utility companies have introduced programs to encourage energy conservation among their customers. An electric company considers placing electronic meters in households to show what the cost would be if the electricity use at that moment continued for a month. Will meters reduce electricity use? Would cheaper methods work almost as well? The company decides to design an experiment.

One cheaper approach is to give customers a chart and information about monitoring their electricity use. The experiment compares these two approaches (meter, chart) and also a control. The control group of customers receives information about energy conservation but no help in monitoring electricity use. The response variable is total electricity used in a year. The company finds 60 single-family residences in the same city willing to participate, so it assigns 20 residences at random to each of the 3 treatments. Figure 3.5 outlines the design.

To carry out the random assignment, label the 60 households 01 to 60. Enter Table B (or use software) to select an SRS of 20 to receive the meters. Continue in Table B, selecting 20 more to receive charts. The remaining 20 form the control group.

Examples 3.14 and 3.15 describe completely randomized designs that compare levels of a single factor. In Example 3.14, the factor is the diet fed to the rats. In Example 3.15,

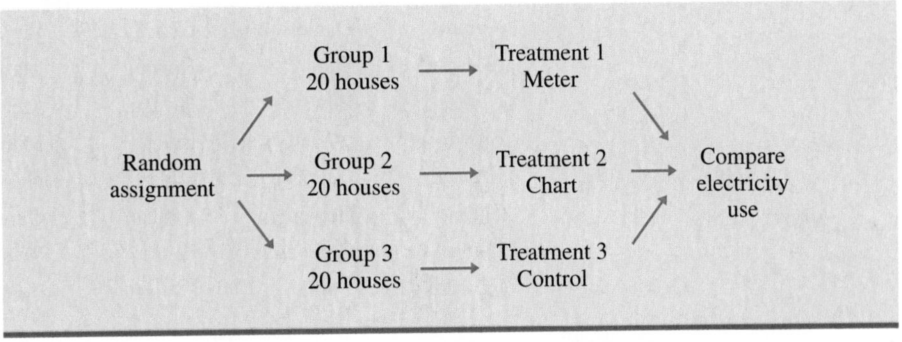

FIGURE 3.5 Outline of a completely randomized design comparing three treatments, for Example 3.15.

it is the method used to encourage energy conservation. Completely randomized designs can have more than one factor. The advertising experiment of Example 3.12 has two factors: the length and the number of repetitions of a television commercial. Their combinations form the six treatments outlined in Figure 3.3 (page 195). A completely randomized design assigns subjects at random to these six treatments. Once the layout of treatments is set, the randomization needed for a completely randomized design is tedious but straightforward.

APPLY YOUR KNOWLEDGE

3.38 Gastric freezing. Example 3.13 describes an experiment that helped end the use of gastric freezing to treat ulcers. The subjects were 160 ulcer patients.

(a) Make a diagram to outline the design of this experiment, using the information in Example 3.13. (Show the size of the groups, the treatment each group receives, and the response variable. Figures 3.4 and 3.5 are models to follow.)

(b) The 82 patients in the gastric-freezing group are an SRS of the 160 subjects. Label the subjects and use Table B, starting at line 131, to choose the first 5 members of the gastric-freezing group.

3.39 Sealing food packages. Use a diagram to describe a completely randomized experimental design for the package liner experiment of Exercise 3.36. (Show the size of the groups, the treatment each group receives, and the response variable. Figures 3.4 and 3.5 are models to follow.) Use software or Table B, starting at line 120, to do the randomization required by your design.

3.40 Does child care help recruit employees? Will providing child care for employees make a company more attractive to women, even those who are unmarried? You are designing an experiment to answer this question. You prepare recruiting material for two fictitious companies, both in similar businesses in the same location. Company A's brochure does not mention child care. There are two versions of Company B's material, identical except that one describes the company's on-site child care facility. Your subjects are 40 unmarried women who are college seniors seeking employment. Each subject will read recruiting material for both companies and choose the one she would prefer to work for. You will give each version of Company B's brochure to half the women. You expect that a higher percent of those who read the description that includes child care will choose Company B.

(a) Outline an appropriate design for the experiment.

(b) The names of the subjects appear below. Use Table B, beginning at line 131, to do the randomization required by your design. List the subjects who will read the version that mentions child care.

Abrams	Danielson	Gutierrez	Lippman	Rosen
Adamson	Durr	Howard	Martinez	Sugiwara
Afifi	Edwards	Hwang	McNeill	Thompson
Brown	Fluharty	Iselin	Morse	Travers
Cansico	Garcia	Janle	Ng	Turing
Chen	Gerson	Kaplan	Quinones	Ullmann
Cortez	Green	Kim	Rivera	Williams
Curzakis	Gupta	Lattimore	Roberts	Wong

The logic of randomized comparative experiments

Randomized comparative experiments are designed to give good evidence that differences in the treatments actually *cause* the differences we see in the response. The logic is as follows:

- Random assignment of subjects forms groups that should be similar in all respects before the treatments are applied.
- Comparative design ensures that influences other than the experimental treatments operate equally on all groups.
- Therefore, differences in average response must be due either to the treatments or to the play of chance in the random assignment of subjects to the treatments.

That "either-or" deserves more thought. In Example 3.14, we cannot say that *any* difference in the average weight gains of rats fed the two diets must be caused by a difference between the diets. There would be some difference even if both groups received the same diet because the natural variability among rats means that some grow faster than others. Chance assigns the faster-growing rats to one group or the other, and this creates a chance difference between the groups. We would not trust an experiment with just one rat in each group, for example. The results would depend on which group got lucky and received the faster-growing rat. If we assign many rats to each diet, however, the effects of chance will average out and there will be little difference in the average weight gains in the two groups unless the diets themselves cause a difference. "Use enough subjects to reduce chance variation" is the third big idea of statistical design of experiments.

Principles of Experimental Design

1. **Control** the effects of lurking variables on the response, most simply by comparing two or more treatments.
2. **Randomize**—use impersonal chance to assign subjects to treatments.
3. **Replicate** each treatment on enough subjects to reduce chance variation in the results.

We hope to see a difference in the responses so large that it is unlikely to happen just because of chance variation. We can use the laws of probability, which give a mathematical description of chance behavior, to learn if the treatment effects are larger than we would expect to see if only chance were operating. If they are, we call them *statistically significant.*

Statistical Significance

An observed effect so large that it would rarely occur by chance is called **statistically significant.**

If we observe statistically significant differences among the groups in a comparative randomized experiment, we have good evidence that the treatments actually caused these differences. You will often see the phrase "statistically significant" in reports of investigations in many fields of study. The great advantage of randomized comparative experiments is that they can produce data that give good evidence for a cause-and-effect relationship between the explanatory and response variables. We know that in general a strong association does not imply causation. A statistically significant association in data from a well-designed experiment does imply causation.

APPLY YOUR KNOWLEDGE

3.41 Conserving energy. Example 3.15 describes an experiment to learn whether providing households with electronic meters or charts will reduce their electricity consumption. An executive of the electric company objects to including a control group. He says, "It would be simpler to just compare electricity use last year (before the meter or chart was provided) with consumption in the same period this year. If households use less electricity this year, the meter or chart must be working." Explain clearly why this design is inferior to that in Example 3.15.

3.42 Exercise and heart attacks. Does regular exercise reduce the risk of a heart attack? Here are two ways to study this question. Explain clearly why the second design will produce more trustworthy data.

1. A researcher finds 2000 men over 40 who exercise regularly and have not had heart attacks. She matches each with a similar man who does not exercise regularly, and she follows both groups for 5 years.
2. Another researcher finds 4000 men over 40 who have not had heart attacks and are willing to participate in a study. She assigns 2000 of the men to a regular program of supervised exercise. The other 2000 continue their usual habits. The researcher follows both groups for 5 years.

3.43 Statistical significance. The financial aid office of a university asks a sample of students about their employment and earnings. The report says that "for academic year earnings, a significant difference was found between the sexes, with men earning more on the average. No significant difference was found between the earnings of black and white students." Explain the meaning of "a significant difference" and "no significant difference" in plain language.

Cautions about experimentation

The logic of a randomized comparative experiment depends on our ability to treat all the subjects identically in every way except for the actual treatments being compared.

Good experiments therefore require careful attention to details. For example, the subjects in both groups of the second gastric-freezing experiment (Example 3.13, page 196) all got the same medical attention over the several years of the study. The researchers paid attention to such details as ensuring that the tube in the mouth of each subject was cold, whether or not the fluid in the balloon was refrigerated. Moreover, the study was **double-blind**—neither the subjects themselves nor the medical personnel who worked with them knew which treatment any subject had received. The double-blind method avoids unconscious bias by, for example, a doctor who doesn't think that "just a placebo" can benefit a patient.

double-blind

lack of realism

The most serious potential weakness of experiments is **lack of realism.** The subjects or treatments or setting of an experiment may not realistically duplicate the conditions we really want to study. Here are two examples.

EXAMPLE 3.16 Response to Advertising

The study of television advertising in Example 3.12 showed a 40-minute videotape to students who knew an experiment was going on. We can't be sure that the results apply to everyday television viewers. The student subjects described their reactions but did not actually decide whether to buy the camera. Many experiments in marketing and decision making use as subjects students who know they are taking part in an experiment. That's not a realistic setting.

EXAMPLE 3.17 Center Brake Lights

Do those high center brake lights, required on all cars sold in the United States since 1986, really reduce rear-end collisions? Randomized comparative experiments with fleets of rental and business cars, done before the lights were required, showed that the third brake light reduced rear-end collisions by as much as 50%. Alas, requiring the third light in all cars led to only a 5% drop.

What happened? Most cars did not have the extra brake light when the experiments were carried out, so it caught the eye of following drivers. Now that almost all cars have the third light, they no longer capture attention.

Lack of realism can limit our ability to apply the conclusions of an experiment to the settings of greatest interest. Most experimenters want to generalize their conclusions to some setting wider than that of the actual experiment. Statistical analysis of the original experiment cannot tell us how far the results will generalize. Nonetheless, the randomized comparative experiment, because of its ability to give convincing evidence for causation, is one of the most important ideas in statistics.

APPLY YOUR KNOWLEDGE

3.44 Does meditation reduce anxiety? Some companies employ consultants to train their managers in meditation in the hope that this practice will relieve stress and make the managers more effective on the job. An experiment that claimed to show that meditation reduces anxiety proceeded as follows. The experimenter interviewed the subjects and rated their level of anxiety. Then the subjects were randomly assigned to two groups. The experimenter taught one group how to meditate and they meditated daily for a month. The other group was simply told to relax more. At the end of the month, the experimenter interviewed all the subjects again and rated their anxiety level. The meditation group now had less anxiety. Psychologists said that the results were suspect because the ratings were not blind. Explain what this means and how lack of blindness could bias the reported results.

3.45 Frustration and teamwork. A psychologist wants to study the effects of failure and frustration on the relationships among members of a work team. She forms a team of students, brings them to the psychology laboratory, and has them play a game that requires teamwork. The game is rigged so that they lose regularly. The psychologist observes the students through a one-way window and notes the changes in their behavior during an evening of game playing. Why is it doubtful that the findings of this study tell us much about the effect of working for months developing a new product that never works right and is finally abandoned by your company?

Matched pairs designs

Completely randomized designs are the simplest statistical designs for experiments. They illustrate clearly the principles of control, randomization, and replication of treatments on a number of subjects. However, completely randomized designs are often inferior to more elaborate statistical designs. In particular, matching the subjects in various ways can produce more precise results than simple randomization.

matched pairs design

One common design that combines matching with randomization is the **matched pairs design.** A matched pairs design compares just two treatments. Choose pairs of subjects that are as closely matched as possible. Assign one of the treatments to each subject in a pair by tossing a coin or reading odd and even digits from Table B. Sometimes each "pair" in a matched pairs design consists of just one subject, who gets both treatments one after the other. Each subject serves as his or her own control. The *order* of the treatments can influence the subject's response, so we randomize the order for each subject, again by a coin toss.

EXAMPLE 3.18 Coke versus Pepsi

Pepsi wanted to demonstrate that Coke drinkers prefer Pepsi when they taste both colas blind. The subjects, all people who said they were Coke drinkers, tasted both colas from glasses without brand markings and said which they liked better. This is a matched pairs design in which each subject compares the two colas. Because responses may depend on which cola is tasted first, the order of tasting should be chosen at random for each subject.

When more than half the Coke drinkers chose Pepsi, Coke claimed that the experiment was biased. The Pepsi glasses were marked *M* and the Coke glasses were marked *Q*. Aha, said Coke, this just shows that people like the letter *M* better than the letter *Q*. A careful experiment would in fact take care to avoid any distinction other than the actual treatments.[17]

Block designs

Matched pairs designs apply the principles of comparison of treatments, randomization, and replication. However, the randomization is not complete—we do not randomly assign all the subjects at once to the two treatments. Instead, we only randomize within each matched pair. This allows matching to reduce the effect of variation among the subjects. Matched pairs are an example of *block designs.*

Block Design

A **block** is a group of subjects that are known before the experiment to be similar in some way expected to affect the response to the treatments. In a **block design,** the random assignment of individuals to treatments is carried out separately within each block.

A block design combines the idea of creating equivalent treatment groups by matching with the principle of forming treatment groups at random. Blocks are another form of *control.* They control the effects of some outside variables by bringing those variables into the experiment to form the blocks. Here is a typical example of a block design.

EXAMPLE 3.19 Men, Women, and Advertising

Women and men respond differently to advertising. An experiment to compare the effectiveness of three television commercials for the same product will want to look separately at the reactions of men and women, as well as assess the overall response to the ads.

A completely randomized design considers all subjects, both men and women, as a single pool. The randomization assigns subjects to three treatment groups without regard to their sex. This ignores the differences between men and women. A better design considers women and men separately. Randomly assign the women to three groups, one to view each commercial. Then separately assign the men at random to three groups. Figure 3.6 outlines this improved design.

A block is a group of subjects formed before an experiment starts. We reserve the word "treatment" for a condition that we impose on the subjects. We don't speak of 6 treatments in Example 3.19 even though we can compare the responses of 6 groups of

FIGURE 3.6 Outline of a block design, for Example 3.19. The blocks consist of male and female subjects. The treatments are three television commercials.

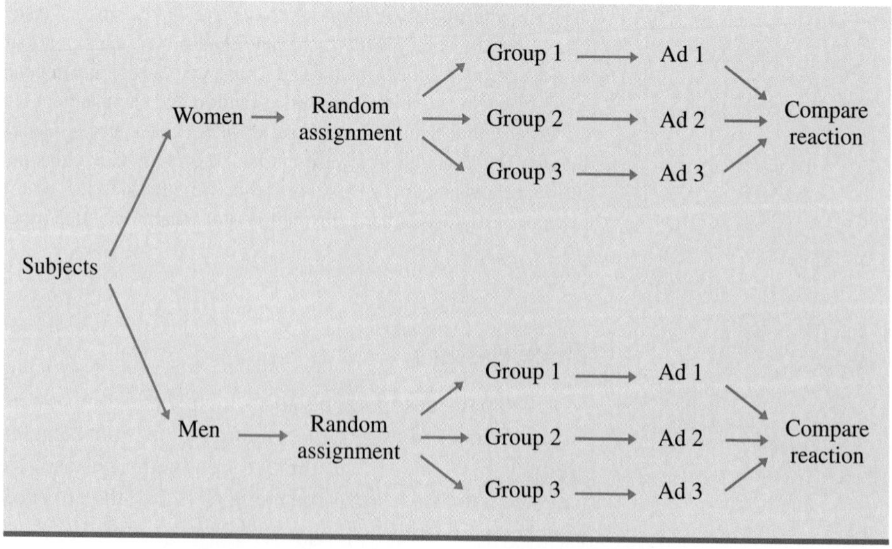

subjects formed by the 2 blocks (men, women) and the 3 commercials. Block designs are similar to stratified samples. Blocks and strata both group similar individuals together. We use two different names only because the idea developed separately for sampling and experiments. The advantages of block designs are the same as the advantages of stratified samples. Blocks allow us to draw separate conclusions about each block—for example, about men and women in the advertising study in Example 3.19. Blocking also allows more precise overall conclusions because the systematic differences between men and women can be removed when we study the overall effects of the three commercials. The idea of blocking is an important additional principle of statistical design of experiments. A wise experimenter will form blocks based on the most important unavoidable sources of variability among the experimental subjects. Randomization will then average out the effects of the remaining variation and allow an unbiased comparison of the treatments.

Like the design of samples, the design of complex experiments is a job for experts. Now that we have seen a bit of what is involved, we will usually just act as if most experiments were completely randomized.

APPLY YOUR KNOWLEDGE

3.46 Does charting help investors? Some investment advisers believe that charts of past trends in the prices of securities can help predict future prices. Most economists disagree. In an experiment to examine the effects of using charts, business students trade (hypothetically) a foreign currency at computer screens. There are 20 student subjects available, named for convenience A, B, C, . . . , T. Their goal is to make as much money as possible, and the best performances are rewarded with small prizes. The student traders have the price history of the foreign currency in dollars in their computers. They may or may not also have software that highlights trends. Describe two designs for this experiment, a completely randomized design and a matched pairs design in which each student serves as his or her own control. In both cases, carry out the randomization required by the design.

3.47 Comparing weight-loss treatments. Twenty overweight females have agreed to participate in a study of the effectiveness of 4 weight-loss treatments: A, B, C, and D. The company researcher first calculates how overweight each subject is by comparing the subject's actual weight with her "ideal" weight. The subjects and their excess weights in pounds are

Birnbaum	35	Hernandez	25	Moses	25	Smith	29
Brown	34	Jackson	33	Nevesky	39	Stall	33
Brunk	30	Kendall	28	Obrach	30	Tran	35
Cruz	34	Loren	32	Rodriguez	30	Wilansky	42
Deng	24	Mann	28	Santiago	27	Williams	22

The response variable is the weight lost after 8 weeks of treatment. Because a subject's excess weight will influence the response, a block design is appropriate.

(a) Arrange the subjects in order of increasing excess weight. Form 5 blocks of 4 subjects each by grouping the 4 least overweight, then the next 4, and so on.

(b) Use Table B to randomly assign the 4 subjects in each block to the 4 weight-loss treatments. Be sure to explain exactly how you used the table.

SECTION 3.2 SUMMARY

- In an experiment, we impose one or more **treatments** on the **subjects.** Each treatment is a combination of levels of the explanatory variables, which we call **factors.**
- The **design** of an experiment describes the choice of treatments and the manner in which the subjects are assigned to the treatments.
- The basic principles of statistical design of experiments are **control, randomization,** and **replication.**
- The simplest form of control is **comparison.** Experiments should compare two or more treatments in order to avoid **confounding** of the effect of a treatment with other influences, such as lurking variables.
- **Randomization** uses chance to assign subjects to the treatments. Randomization creates treatment groups that are similar (except for chance variation) before the treatments are applied. Randomization and comparison together prevent **bias,** or systematic favoritism, in experiments.
- You can carry out randomization by giving numerical labels to the subjects and using a **table of random digits** to choose treatment groups.
- **Replication** of each treatment on many subjects reduces the role of chance variation and makes the experiment more sensitive to differences among the treatments.
- Good experiments require attention to detail as well as good statistical design. Many behavioral and medical experiments are **double-blind. Lack of realism** in an experiment can prevent us from generalizing its results.
- In addition to comparison, a second form of control is to restrict randomization by forming **blocks** of subjects that are similar in some way that is important to the response. Randomization is then carried out separately within each block.
- **Matched pairs** are a common form of blocking for comparing just two treatments. In some matched pairs designs, each subject receives both treatments in a random order. In others, the subjects are matched in pairs as closely as possible, and one subject in each pair receives each treatment.

SECTION 3.2 Exercises

For Exercises 3.35 to 3.37, see pages 195–196; for 3.38 to 3.40, see pages 199–200; for 3.41 to 3.43, see page 201; for 3.44 and 3.45, see pages 202–203; and for 3.46 and 3.47, see page 205.

3.48 Survivor guilt in layoffs. Workers who survive a layoff of other employees at their location may suffer from "survivor guilt." A study of survivor guilt and its effects used as subjects 120 students who were offered an opportunity to earn extra course credit by doing proofreading. Each subject worked in the same cubicle as another student, who was an accomplice of the experimenters. At a break midway through the work, one of three things happened:

Treatment 1: The accomplice was told to leave; it was explained that this was because she performed poorly.

Treatment 2: It was explained that unforeseen circumstances meant there was only enough work for one person. By "chance," the accomplice was chosen to be laid off.

Treatment 3: Both students continued to work after the break.

The subjects' work performance after the break was compared with performance before the break.[18]

(a) Outline the design of this completely randomized experiment. Follow the model of Figure 3.5 (page 199).

(b) If you are using software, choose the subjects for Treatment 1. If not, use Table B at line 123 to choose the first four subjects for Treatment 1.

3.49 Drug use and willingness to work. How does smoking marijuana affect willingness to work? Canadian researchers persuaded young adult men who used marijuana to live for 98 days in a "planned environment." The men earned money by weaving belts. They used their earnings to pay for meals and other consumption and could keep any money left over. One group smoked two potent marijuana cigarettes every evening. The other group smoked two weak marijuana cigarettes. All subjects could buy more cigarettes but were given strong or weak cigarettes, depending on their group. Did the weak and strong groups differ in work output and earnings?[19]

(a) Outline the design of this experiment.

(b) Here are the names of the 20 subjects. Use software or Table B at line 131 to carry out the randomization your design requires.

Abate	Dubois	Gutierrez	Lucero	Rosen
Afifi	Engel	Hwang	McNeill	Thompson
Brown	Fluharty	Iselin	Morse	Travers
Chen	Gerson	Kaplan	Quinones	Ullmann

3.50 Attractive price cuts. Stores advertise price reductions to attract customers. What type of price cut is most attractive? Market researchers prepared ads for athletic shoes announcing different levels of discounts (20%, 40%, or 60%). The student subjects who read the ads were also given "inside information" about the fraction of shoes on sale (50% or 100%). Each subject then rated the attractiveness of the sale on a scale of 1 to 7.[20]

(a) There are two factors. Make a sketch like Figure 3.3 (page 195) that displays the treatments formed by all combinations of levels of the factors.

(b) Outline a completely randomized design using 60 student subjects. Use software or Table B at line 111 to choose the subjects for the first treatment.

3.51 I'll have a Mocha Light. Here's the opening of a press release from June 2004: "Starbucks Corp. on Monday said it would roll out a line of blended coffee drinks intended to tap into the growing popularity of reduced-calorie and reduced-fat menu choices for Americans." You wonder if Starbucks customers like the new "Mocha Frappuccino Light" as well as the regular version of this drink.

(a) Describe a matched pairs design to answer this question. Be sure to include proper blinding of your subjects.

(b) You have 20 regular Starbucks customers on hand. Use Table B at line 141 to do the randomization that your design requires.

3.52 Cash bonuses for the unemployed. Will cash bonuses speed the return to work of unemployed people? The Illinois Department of Employment Security designed an experiment to find out. The subjects were 10,065 people aged 20 to 54 who were filing claims for unemployment insurance. Some were offered \$500 if they found a job within 11 weeks and held it for at least 4 months. Others could tell potential employers that the state would pay the employer \$500 for hiring them. A control group got neither kind of bonus.[21]

(a) Suggest a few response variables of interest to the state and outline the design of the experiment.

(b) How will you label the subjects for random assignment? Use Table B at line 127 to choose the first 3 subjects for the first treatment.

3.53 Poultry-processing plants. The air in poultry-processing plants often contains fungus spores. Inadequate ventilation can affect the health of the workers. The problem is most serious during the summer. To measure the presence of spores, air samples are pumped to an agar plate, and "colony-forming units (CFUs)" are counted after an incubation period. Here are data from two locations in a plant that processes 37,000 turkeys per day, taken on four days in the summer. The units are CFUs per cubic meter of air.[22]

	Day 1	Day 2	Day 3	Day 4
Kill room	3175	2526	1763	1090
Processing	529	141	362	224

(a) Explain carefully why these are matched pairs data.

(b) The spore count is clearly higher in the kill room. Give sample means to demonstrate the difference for these data.

3.54 Public housing. A study of the effect of living in public housing on the income and other variables in poverty-level households was carried out as follows. The researchers obtained a list of all applicants for public housing during the previous year. Some applicants had been accepted, while others had been turned down by the housing authority. Both groups were interviewed and compared. Is this study an experiment or an observational study? Why? What are the explanatory and response variables? Why will confounding make it difficult to see the effect of the explanatory variable on the response variables?

3.55 Effects of price promotions. A researcher studying the effect of price promotions on consumers' expectations makes up a history of the store price of a hypothetical brand of laundry detergent for the past year. Students in a marketing course view the price history on a computer. Some students see a steady price, while others see regular promotions that temporarily cut the price. Then the students are asked what price they would expect to pay for the detergent. Is this study an experiment? Why? What are the explanatory and response variables?

3.56 Computer telephone calls. You can use your computer to make telephone calls over the Internet. How will the cost affect the behavior of users of this service? You will offer the service to all 200 rooms in a college dormitory. Some rooms will pay a low flat rate. Others will pay higher rates at peak periods and very low rates off-peak. You are interested in the amount and time of use and in the effect on the congestion of the network. Outline the design of an experiment to study the effect of rate structure.

3.57 Marketing to children. If children are given more choices within a class of products, will they tend to prefer that product to a competing product that offers fewer choices? Marketers want to know. An experiment prepared three sets of beverages. Set 1 contained two milk drinks and two fruit drinks. Set 2 had two fruit drinks and four milk drinks. Set 3 contained four fruit drinks but only two milk drinks. The researchers divided 210 children aged 4 to 12 years into three groups at random. They offered each group one of the sets. As each child chose a beverage to drink from the set presented, the researchers noted whether the choice was a milk drink or a fruit drink.

(a) What are the experimental subjects?

(b) What is the factor and what are its levels? What is the response variable?

(c) Use a diagram to outline a completely randomized design for the study.

(d) Explain how you would assign labels to the subjects. Use Table B at line 125 to choose the first 5 subjects assigned to the first treatment.

3.58 Clinical trial basics. Fizz Laboratories, a pharmaceutical company, has developed a new pain-relief medication. Three hundred patients suffering from arthritis and needing pain relief are available. Each patient will be treated and asked an hour later, "About what percent of pain relief did you experience?"

(a) Why should Fizz not simply administer the new drug and record the patients' responses?

(b) Outline the design of an experiment to compare the drug's effectiveness with that of aspirin and of a placebo.

(c) Should patients be told which drug they are receiving? How would this knowledge probably affect their reactions?

(d) If patients are not told which treatment they are receiving, the experiment is single-blind. Should this experiment be double-blind also? Explain.

3.59 Treating prostate disease. A large study used records from Canada's national health care system to compare the effectiveness of two ways to treat prostate disease. The two treatments are traditional surgery and a new method that does not require surgery. The records described many patients whose doctors had chosen each method. The study found that patients treated by the new method were significantly more likely to die within 8 years.[23]

(a) Further study of the data showed that this conclusion was wrong. The extra deaths among patients who got the new method could be explained by lurking variables. What lurking variables might be confounded with a doctor's choice of surgical or nonsurgical treatment?

(b) You have 300 prostate patients who are willing to serve as subjects in an experiment to compare the two methods. Use a diagram to outline the design of a randomized comparative experiment.

3.60 Aspirin and heart attacks. "Nearly five decades of research now link aspirin to the prevention of stroke and heart attacks." So says the Bayer Aspirin Web site, `www.bayeraspirin.com`. The most important evidence for this claim comes from the Physicians' Health Study, a large medical experiment involving 22,000 male physicians. One group of about 11,000 physicians took an aspirin every second day, while the rest took a placebo. After several years the study found that subjects in the aspirin group had significantly fewer heart attacks than subjects in the placebo group.

(a) Identify the experimental subjects, the factor and its levels, and the response variable in the Physicians' Health Study.

(b) Use a diagram to outline a completely randomized design for the Physicians' Health Study.

(c) What does it mean to say that the aspirin group had "significantly fewer heart attacks"?

3.61 Prayer and meditation. Not all effective medical treatments come from pharmaceutical companies. You read in a magazine that "nonphysical treatments such as meditation and prayer have been shown to be effective in controlled scientific studies for such ailments as high blood pressure, insomnia, ulcers, and asthma." Explain in simple language what the article means by "controlled scientific studies" and why such studies can show that meditation and prayer are effective treatments for some medical problems.

3.62 Sickle-cell disease. Exercise 3.35 (page 195) describes a medical study of a new treatment for sickle-cell disease.

(a) Use a diagram to outline the design of this experiment.

(b) Use of a placebo is considered ethical if there is no effective standard treatment to give the control group. It might seem humane to give all the subjects hydroxyurea in the hope that it will help them. Explain clearly why this would not provide information about the effectiveness of the drug. (In fact, the experiment was stopped ahead of schedule because the hydroxyurea group had only half as many pain episodes as the control group. Ethical standards required stopping the experiment as soon as significant evidence became available.)

3.63 Reducing health care spending. Will people spend less on health care if their health insurance requires them to pay some part of the cost themselves? An experiment on this issue asked if the percent of medical costs that are paid by health insurance has an effect either on the amount of medical care that people use or on their health. The treatments were four insurance plans. Each plan paid all medical costs above a ceiling. Below the ceiling, the plans paid 100%, 75%, 50%, or 0% of costs incurred.

(a) Outline the design of a randomized comparative experiment suitable for this study.

(b) Describe briefly the practical and ethical difficulties that might arise in such an experiment.

3.64 Effects of TV advertising. You decide to use a completely randomized design in the two-factor experiment on response to advertising described in Example 3.12 (page 194). The 36 students named below will serve as subjects. Outline the design. Then use Table B at line 130 to randomly assign the subjects to the 6 treatments.

Alomar	Edwards	Imrani	O'Brian	Tullock
Asihiro	Farouk	James	Ogle	Valasco
Bennett	Fleming	Kaplan	Padilla	Vaughn
Bikalis	George	Liang	Plochman	Wei
Chao	Han	Maldonado	Rosen	Wilder
Clemente	Howard	Marsden	Solomon	Willis
Denman	Hruska	Montoya	Trujillo	Zhang
Durr				

3.65 Temperature and work performance. An expert on worker performance is interested in the effect of room temperature on the performance of tasks requiring manual dexterity. She chooses temperatures of 20°C (68°F) and 30°C (86°F) as treatments. The response variable is the number of correct insertions, during a 30-minute period, in a peg-and-hole apparatus that requires the use of both hands simultaneously. Each subject is trained on the apparatus and then asked to make as many insertions as possible in 30 minutes of continuous effort.

(a) Outline a completely randomized design to compare dexterity at 20° and 30°. Twenty subjects are available.

(b) Because individuals differ greatly in dexterity, the wide variation in individual scores may hide the systematic effect of temperature unless there are many subjects in each group. Describe in detail the design of a matched pairs experiment in which each subject serves as his or her own control.

3.66 Reaching Mexican Americans. Advertising that hopes to attract Mexican Americans must keep in mind the cultural orientation of these consumers. There are several psychological tests available to measure the extent to which Mexican Americans are oriented toward Mexican/Spanish or Anglo/English culture. Two such tests are the Bicultural Inventory (BI) and the Acculturation Rating Scale for Mexican Americans (ARSMA). To study the relationship between the scores on these two tests, researchers will give both tests to a group of 22 Mexican Americans.

(a) Briefly describe a matched pairs design for this study. In particular, how will you use randomization in your design?

(b) You have an alphabetized list of the subjects (numbered 1 to 22). Carry out the randomization required by your design and report the result.

3.67 Absorption of a drug. Example 3.11 (page 194) describes a study in which a maker of pharmaceuticals compares the concentration of a drug in the blood of patients 30 minutes after injecting one of three doses.

Use a diagram to outline a completely randomized design for this experiment.

3.68 Absorption of a drug: another step. The drug studied in Exercise 3.67 can be administered by injection, by a skin patch, or by intravenous drip. Concentration in the blood may depend both on the dose and on the method of administration. Make a sketch that describes the treatments formed by combining dosage and method. Then use a diagram to outline a completely randomized design for this two-factor experiment.

3.69 Potatoes. A horticulturist is comparing two methods (call them A and B) of growing potatoes. Standard potato cuttings will be planted in small plots of ground. The response variables are number of tubers per plant and fresh weight (weight when just harvested) of vegetable growth per plant. There are 20 plots available for the experiment. Sketch a rectangular field divided into 5 rows of 4 plots each. Then diagram the experimental design and do the required randomization. (If you use Table B, start at line 145.) Mark on your sketch which growing method you will use in each plot.

3.3 Toward Statistical Inference

A market research firm interviews a random sample of 2500 adults. Result: 66% find shopping for clothes frustrating and time-consuming. That's the truth about the 2500 people in the sample. What is the truth about the almost 210 million American adults who make up the population? Because the sample was chosen at random, it's reasonable to think that these 2500 people represent the entire population pretty well. So the market researchers turn the *fact* that 66% of the *sample* find shopping frustrating into an *estimate* that about 66% of *all adults* feel this way. That's a basic move in statistics: use a fact about a sample to estimate the truth about the whole population. We call this **statistical inference** because we infer conclusions about the wider population from data on selected individuals. To think about inference, we must keep straight whether a number describes a sample or a population. Here is the vocabulary we use.

statistical inference

Parameters and Statistics

A **parameter** is a number that describes the **population.** A parameter is a fixed number, but in practice we do not know its value.

A **statistic** is a number that describes a **sample.** The value of a statistic is known when we have taken a sample, but it can change from sample to sample. We often use a statistic to estimate an unknown parameter.

CASE 3.1 IS CLOTHES SHOPPING FRUSTRATING?

Changing consumer attitudes toward shopping are of great interest to retailers and makers of consumer goods. The Yankelovich market research firm specializes in the study of "consumer trends" that go beyond preferences for one or another product. The firm promises its clients that its work "reveals the reasons why consumers are changing their behavior to create the lifestyle they want. We also show you how smart businesses are using that knowledge to make smarter marketing decisions."[24]

One trend of concern to marketers is that fewer people enjoy shopping than in the past. Yankelovich conducts an annual survey of consumer attitudes. The population is all U.S. residents aged 18 and over. A recent survey asked a nationwide random sample of 2500 adults if they agreed or disagreed that "I like buying new clothes, but shopping is often frustrating and time-consuming." Of the respondents, 1650 said they agreed. That's 66%, a percent high enough to encourage development of alternatives such as online sales.

The proportion of the Yankelovich sample who agreed that clothes shopping is often frustrating is

$$\hat{p} = \frac{1650}{2500} = 0.66 = 66\%$$

The number $\hat{p} = 0.66$ is a *statistic*. The corresponding *parameter* is the proportion (call it p) of all adult U.S. residents who would have said "Agree" if asked the same question. We don't know the value of the parameter p, so we use the statistic $\hat{p}$ as an estimate.

APPLY YOUR KNOWLEDGE

3.70 Unlisted telephone numbers. A telemarketing firm in Los Angeles uses a device that dials residential telephone numbers in that city at random. Of the first 100 numbers dialed, **43** are unlisted. This is not surprising, because **52%** of all Los Angeles residential phones are unlisted. Which of the bold numbers is a parameter and which is a statistic?

3.71 Indianapolis voters. Voter registration records show that **68%** of all voters in Indianapolis are registered as Republicans. To test a random digit dialing device, you use the device to call 150 randomly chosen residential telephones in Indianapolis. Of the registered voters contacted, **73%** are registered Republicans. Which of the bold numbers is a parameter and which is a statistic?

Sampling variability, sampling distributions

If the Yankelovich firm took a second random sample of 2500 adults, the new sample would have different people in it. It is almost certain that there would not be exactly 1650 positive responses. That is, the value of the statistic $\hat{p}$ will *vary* from sample to sample. Could it happen that one random sample finds that 66% of adults find clothes shopping frustrating and a second random sample finds that only 42% feel this way? Random samples eliminate *bias* from the act of choosing a sample, but they can still be wrong because of the *variability* that results when we choose at random. If the variation when we take repeat samples from the same population is too great, we can't trust the results of any one sample.

We are saved by the second great advantage of random samples. The first advantage is that choosing at random eliminates favoritism. That is, random sampling attacks bias. The second advantage is that if we take lots of random samples of the same size from the same population, the variation from sample to sample will follow a predictable pattern. **All of statistical inference is based on one idea: to see how trustworthy a procedure is, ask what would happen if we repeated it many times.**

To understand why sampling variability is not fatal, we therefore ask, "What would happen if we took many samples?" Here's how to answer that question:

- Take a large number of samples from the same population.
- Calculate the sample proportion $\hat{p}$ for each sample.
- Make a histogram of the values of $\hat{p}$.
- Examine the distribution displayed in the histogram for shape, center, and spread, as well as outliers or other deviations.

We can't afford to actually take many samples from a large population such as all adult U.S. residents. But we can imitate many samples by using random digits. Using random digits from a table or computer software to imitate chance behavior is called **simulation.**

simulation

EXAMPLE 3.20 Lots of Samples

CASE 3.1

Suppose that in fact (unknown to Yankelovich), exactly 60% of all adults find shopping for clothes frustrating and time-consuming. That is, the truth about the population is that $p = 0.6$. What if we select an SRS of size 100 from this population and use the sample proportion $\hat{p}$ to estimate the unknown value of the population proportion p? Using software, we simulated doing this 1000 times.

Figure 3.7 illustrates the process of choosing many samples and finding $\hat{p}$ for each one. In the first sample, 56 of the 100 people say they find shopping frustrating, so $\hat{p} = 56/100 = 0.56$. Only 46 in the next sample feel this way, so for that sample $\hat{p} = 0.46$. Choose 1000 samples and make a histogram of the 1000 values of $\hat{p}$. That's the graph at the right of Figure 3.7.

Of course, Yankelovich interviewed 2500 people, not just 100. Figure 3.8 shows the process of choosing 1000 SRSs, each of size 2500, from a population in which the true sample proportion is $p = 0.6$. The 1000 values of $\hat{p}$ from these samples form the histogram at the right of the figure.

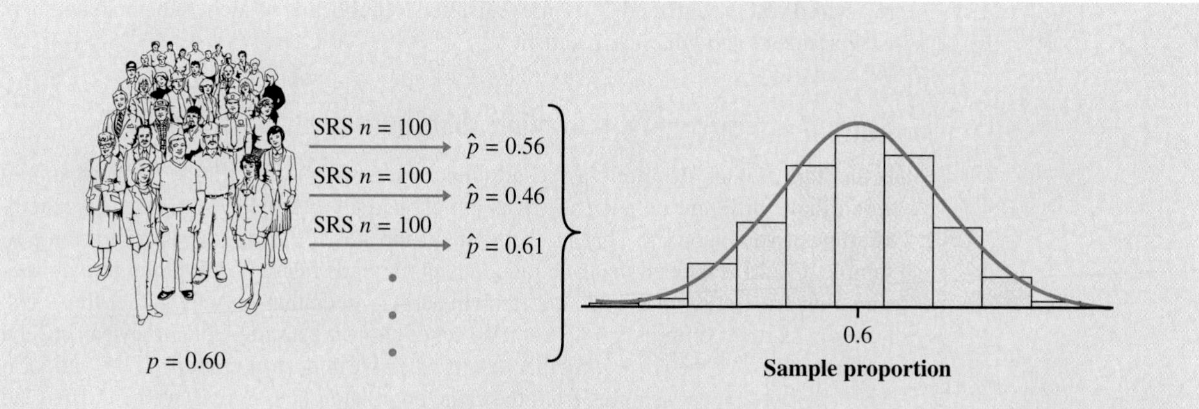

FIGURE 3.7 The results of many SRSs have a regular pattern. Here, we draw 1000 SRSs of size 100 from the same population. The population proportion is $p = 0.60$. The histogram shows the distribution of the 1000 sample proportions $\hat{p}$.

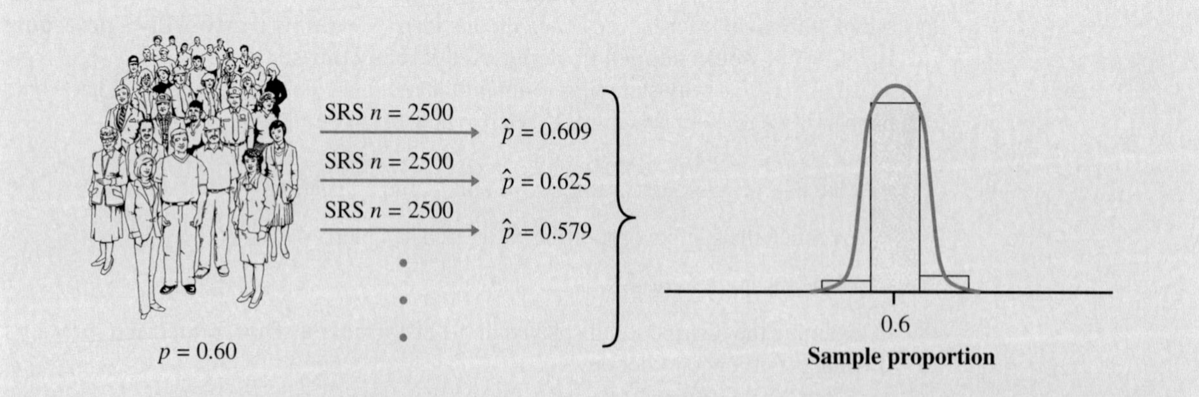

FIGURE 3.8 The distribution of sample proportions $\hat{p}$ for 1000 SRSs of size 2500 drawn from the same population as in Figure 3.7. The two histograms have the same scale. The statistic from the larger sample is less variable.

Figures 3.7 and 3.8 are drawn on the same scale. Comparing them shows what happens when we increase the size of our samples from 100 to 2500. These histograms display the *sampling distribution* of the statistic $\hat{p}$ for two sample sizes.

Sampling Distribution

The **sampling distribution** of a statistic is the distribution of values taken by the statistic in all possible samples of the same size from the same population.

Strictly speaking, the sampling distribution is the ideal pattern that would emerge if we looked at all possible samples of the same size from our population. A distribution obtained from a fixed number of samples, like the 1000 samples in Figures 3.7 and 3.8, is only an approximation to the sampling distribution. One of the uses of probability theory in statistics is to obtain sampling distributions without simulation. The interpretation of a sampling distribution is the same, however, whether we obtain it by simulation or by the mathematics of probability.

We can use the tools of data analysis to describe any distribution. Let's apply those tools to Figures 3.7 and 3.8.

- **Shape:** The histograms look Normal. Figure 3.9 is a Normal quantile plot of the values of $\hat{p}$ for our samples of size 100. It confirms that the distribution in Figure 3.7 is close to Normal. The 1000 values for samples of size 2500 in Figure 3.8 are even closer to Normal. The Normal curves drawn through the histograms describe the overall shape quite well.
- **Center:** In both cases, the values of the sample proportion $\hat{p}$ vary from sample to sample, but the values are centered at 0.6. Recall that $p = 0.6$ is the true population parameter. Some samples have a $\hat{p}$ less than 0.6 and some greater, but there is no tendency to be always low or always high. That is, $\hat{p}$ has no *bias* as an estimator

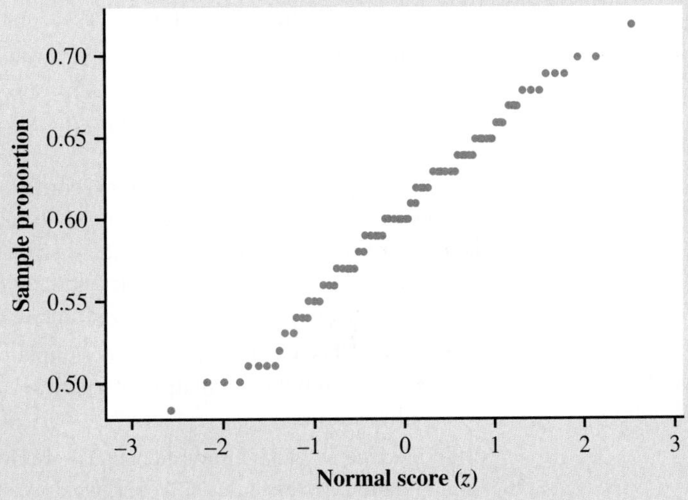

FIGURE 3.9 Normal quantile plot of the sample proportions in Figure 3.7. The distribution is close to Normal except for some granularity due to the fact that sample proportions from a sample of size 100 can take only values that are multiples of 0.01. Because a plot of 1000 points is hard to read, this plot presents only every 10th value.

of p. This is true for both large and small samples. (Want the details? The mean of the 1000 values of $\hat{p}$ is 0.598 for samples of size 100 and 0.6002 for samples of size 2500. The median value of $\hat{p}$ is exactly 0.6 for samples of both sizes.)

- **Spread:** The values of $\hat{p}$ from samples of size 2500 are much less spread out than the values from samples of size 100. In fact, the standard deviations are 0.051 for Figure 3.7 and 0.0097, or about 0.01, for Figure 3.8.

Although these results describe just two sets of simulations, they reflect facts that are true whenever we use random sampling.

APPLY YOUR KNOWLEDGE

3.72 Simulation by hand. You can use a table of random digits to simulate sampling from a population. Suppose that 60% of the population find shopping frustrating. That is, the population proportion is $p = 0.6$.

CASE 3.1

(a) Let each digit in the table stand for one person in this population. Digits 0 to 5 stand for people who find shopping frustrating, and 6 to 9 stand for people who do not. Why does looking at one digit from Table B simulate drawing one person at random from a population with $p = 0.6$?

(b) The first 100 entries in Table B contain 63 digits between 0 and 5, so $\hat{p} = 63/100 = 0.63$ for this sample. Why do the first 100 digits simulate drawing 100 people at random?

(c) Simulate a second SRS from this population, using 100 entries in Table B, starting at line 104. What is $\hat{p}$ for this sample? You see that the two sample results are different, and neither is equal to the true population value $p = 0.6$. That's the issue we face in this section.

3.73 Making movies, making money. During the 1990s, a total of 1986 movies were released in the United States. We used statistical software to choose several SRSs of size 25 from this population. Our first sample of 25 movies had mean domestic gross sales 33.916 million dollars, standard deviation 50.2697 million dollars, and median 16.1 million dollars. A second random sample of 25 movies had mean 38.712 million dollars, standard deviation 58 million dollars, and median 14.1 million dollars. Table 3.1 lists the members of a third SRS.[25]

(a) Calculate the mean domestic gross $\bar{x}$ for the sample in Table 3.1. How does it compare with the means of the first two samples?

(b) Calculate the standard deviation s. How does it compare with those of the first two samples?

(c) Calculate the median M. How does it compare with the previous two medians?

3.74 Making movies, making money, continued. There are over 1.5×10^{57} different samples of size 25 possible from the 1986 movies released in the 1990s. Table 3.1 displays just one of these samples. The distribution of the 1.5×10^{57} values of $\bar{x}$ from all these samples is the sampling distribution of the sample mean. Let's look at just 1000 samples to get a rough picture of this sampling distribution.

(a) Figure 3.10 is a histogram of 1000 sample means based on 1000 different samples of size 25 from the population of movies. Describe the shape, center, and spread of this distribution.

(b) In practice, we take a sample because we don't have access to the entire population. In this case, however, we know the mean domestic gross for the population of movies released in the 1990s. It is 27.77 million dollars. Given this

TABLE 3.1 Sample of 25 movies released in the 1990s

Movie name (year)	Domestic gross ($ millions)
Aces: Iron Eagle III (1992)	2.5
BASEketball (1998)	7.0
Body of Evidence (1993)	13.3
Car 54, Where Are You? (1994)	1.2
City of Angels (1998)	78.9
Coneheads (1993)	21.3
Days of Thunder (1990)	82.7
Death Warrant (1990)	16.9
Desperate Hours (1990)	2.7
Ernest Scared Stupid (1991)	14.1
Executive Decision (1996)	68.8
For Love of the Game (1999)	35.2
I Come in Peace (1990)	4.3
Jumanji (1995)	100.2
Kika (1993)	2.1
Miami Rhapsody (1995)	5.2
Mighty, The (1998)	2.6
Perez Family, The (1995)	2.8
Revenge (1990)	15.7
Shine (1996)	35.8
So I Married an Axe Murderer (1993)	11.6
Thinner (1996)	15.2
Wedding Singer, The (1998)	80.2
Wing Commander (1999)	11.6
Xizao (1999)	1.2

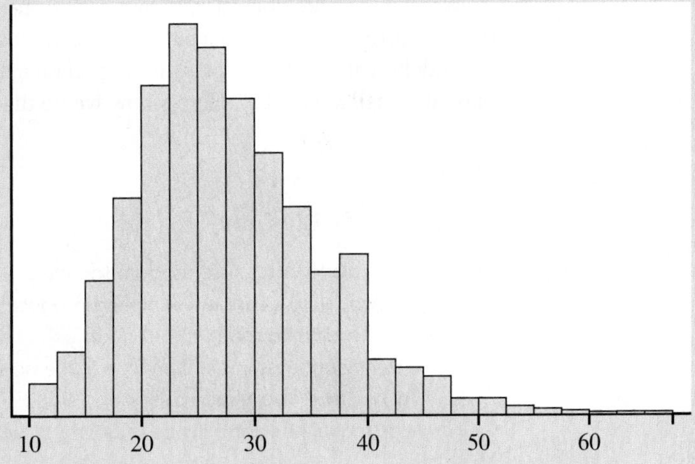

FIGURE 3.10 The distribution of sample means $\bar{x}$ for 1000 SRSs of size 25 from the domestic gross sales (millions of dollars) of all movies released in the United States in the 1990s (for Exercise 3.74).

information and the histogram in Figure 3.10, what can you say about how far a particular sample mean might be from the target of 27.77 million dollars?

Bias and variability

Our simulations show that a sample of size 2500 will almost always give an estimate $\hat{p}$ that is close to the truth about the population. Figure 3.8 illustrates this fact for just one population, but it is true for any population. Samples of size 100, on the other hand, might give an estimate of 50% or 70% when the truth is 60%.

Thinking about Figures 3.7 and 3.8 helps us restate the idea of bias when we use a statistic like $\hat{p}$ to estimate a parameter like p. It also reminds us that variability matters as much as bias.

Bias and Variability

Bias concerns the center of the sampling distribution. A statistic used to estimate a parameter is **unbiased** if the mean of its sampling distribution is equal to the true value of the parameter being estimated.

The **variability of a statistic** is described by the spread of its sampling distribution. This spread is determined by the sampling design and the sample size n. Statistics from larger samples have smaller spreads.

We can think of the true value of the population parameter as the bull's-eye on a target, and of the sample statistic as an arrow fired at the bull's-eye. Bias and variability describe what happens when an archer fires many arrows at the target. *Bias* means that the aim is off, and the arrows land consistently off the bull's-eye in the same direction. The sample values do not center about the population value. Large *variability* means that repeated shots are widely scattered on the target. Repeated samples do not give similar results but differ widely among themselves. Figure 3.11 shows this target illustration of the two types of error.

Notice that small variability (repeated shots are close together) can accompany large bias (the arrows are consistently away from the bull's-eye in one direction). And small bias (the arrows center on the bull's-eye) can accompany large variability (repeated shots are widely scattered). A good sampling scheme, like a good archer, must have both small bias and small variability. Here's how we do this.

Managing Bias and Variability

To reduce bias, use random sampling. When we start with a list of the entire population, simple random sampling produces **unbiased estimates**—the values of a statistic computed from an SRS neither consistently overestimate nor consistently underestimate the value of the population parameter.

To reduce the variability of a statistic from an SRS, use a larger sample. You can make the variability as small as you want by taking a large enough sample.

In practice, Yankelovich takes only one sample. We don't know how close to the truth an estimate from this one sample is, because we don't know what the truth about the population is. But *large random samples almost always give an estimate that is close to the truth.* Looking at the pattern of many samples shows that we can trust the result of one sample. The Current Population Survey's sample of 55,000 households estimates the national unemployment rate very accurately. Of course, only probability samples carry this guarantee. *Nightline*'s voluntary response sample (Example 3.3) is worthless even though 186,000 people called in. Using a probability sampling design and taking care to deal with practical difficulties reduce bias in a sample. The size of the sample then determines how close to the population truth the sample result is likely to fall. Results from a sample survey usually come with a *margin of error* that sets bounds on the size of the likely error. How to do this is part of the detail of statistical inference. We will describe the reasoning in Chapter 6.

APPLY YOUR KNOWLEDGE

3.75 Making movies, making money, continued. During the 1990s, a total of 1986 movies were released in the United States. We want to estimate the mean domestic gross sales of this population. We will take an SRS and use the sample mean $\overline{x}$ as our estimate.

(a) Figure 3.10 is a histogram of 1000 sample means from 1000 different samples of size 25. What is the approximate range (smallest to largest) of these sample means?

(b) Figure 3.12 is a histogram of 1000 sample means from 1000 different samples of size 10. What is the approximate range of these sample means? How does this compare with the spread in part (a)?

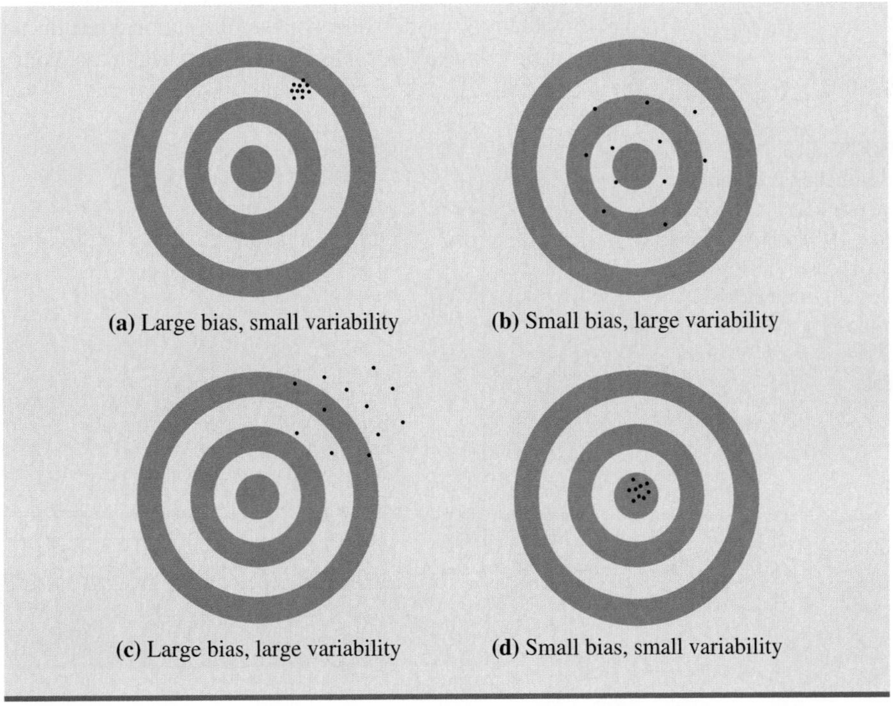

FIGURE 3.11 Bias and variability in shooting arrows at a target. Bias means the archer systematically misses in the same direction. Variability means that the arrows are scattered.

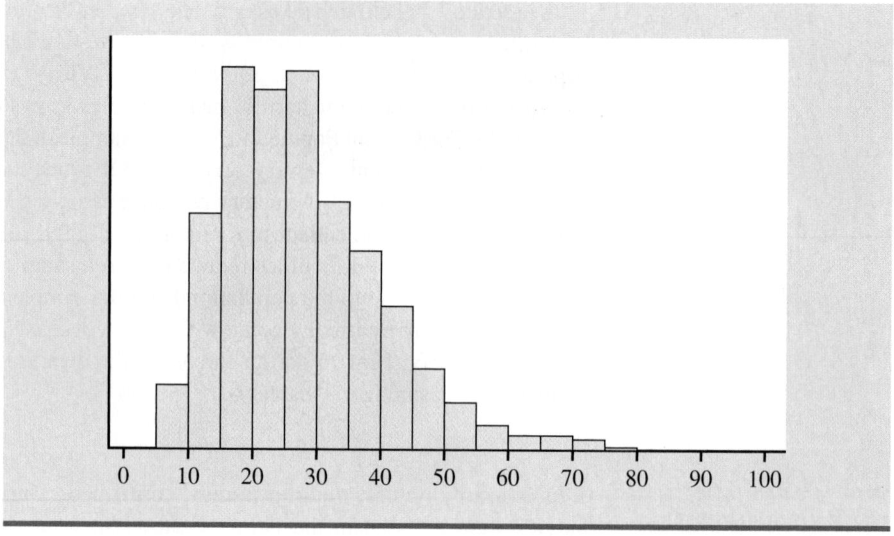

FIGURE 3.12 The distribution of sample means $\bar{x}$ for 1000 SRSs of size 10 from the domestic gross sales (millions of dollars) of all movies released in the United States in the 1990s (for Exercise 3.75).

(c) Figure 3.13 is a histogram of 1000 sample means from 1000 different samples of size 100. What is the approximate range? How does this compare with the spread in part (a)? In part (b)?

(d) What important fact do these three sampling distributions illustrate?

3.76 Ask more people. Just before a presidential election, a national opinion-polling firm increases the size of its weekly sample from the usual 1500 people to 4000 people. Why do you think the firm does this?

3.77 Canada's national health care. The Ministry of Health in the Canadian province of Ontario wants to know whether the national health care system is achieving its goals in the province. Much information about health care comes from patient records, but that

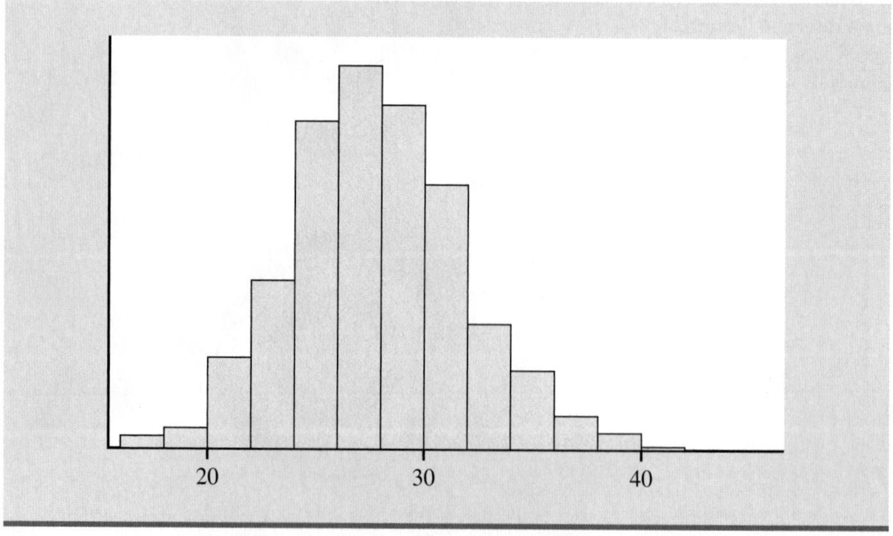

FIGURE 3.13 The distribution of sample means $\bar{x}$ for 1000 SRSs of size 100 from the domestic gross sales (millions of dollars) of all movies released in the United States in the 1990s (for Exercise 3.75.)

source doesn't allow us to compare people who use health services with those who don't. So the Ministry of Health conducted the Ontario Health Survey, which interviewed a probability sample of 61,239 people who live in Ontario.[26]

(a) What is the population for this sample survey? What is the sample?

(b) The survey found that 76% of males and 86% of females in the sample had visited a general practitioner at least once in the past year. Do you think these estimates are close to the truth about the entire population? Why?

Sampling from large populations

Yankelovich's sample of 2500 adults is only about 1 out of every 85,000 adults in the United States. Does it matter whether we sample 1 in 100 individuals in the population or 1 in 85,000?

Population Size Doesn't Matter

The variability of a statistic from a random sample does not depend on the size of the population, as long as the population is at least 100 times larger than the sample.

Why does the size of the population have little influence on the behavior of statistics from random samples? To see why this is plausible, imagine sampling harvested corn by thrusting a scoop into a lot of corn kernels. The scoop doesn't know whether it is surrounded by a bag of corn or by an entire truckload. As long as the corn is well mixed (so that the scoop selects a random sample), the variability of the result depends only on the size of the scoop.

The fact that the variability of sample results is controlled by the size of the sample has important consequences for sampling design. An SRS of size 2500 from the 280 million residents of the United States gives results as precise as an SRS of size 2500 from the 740,000 inhabitants of San Francisco. This is good news for designers of national samples but bad news for those who want accurate information about the citizens of San Francisco. If both use an SRS, both must use the same size sample to obtain equally trustworthy results.

Why randomize?

Why randomize? The act of randomizing guarantees that our data are subject to the laws of probability. The behavior of statistics is described by a sampling distribution. The form of the distribution is known, and in many cases is approximately Normal. Often, the center of the distribution lies at the true parameter value, so the notion that randomization eliminates bias is made more precise. The spread of the distribution describes the variability of the statistic and can be made as small as we wish by choosing a large enough sample. Randomized experiments behave similarly: we can reduce variability by choosing larger groups of subjects for each treatment.

These facts are at the heart of formal statistical inference. Later chapters will have much to say in more technical language about sampling distributions and the way statistical conclusions are based on them. What any user of statistics must understand is that all the technical talk has its basis in a simple question: What would happen if the sample or the experiment were repeated many times? The reasoning applies not only to an SRS but also to the complex sampling designs actually used by opinion polls and other national sample surveys. The same conclusions hold as well for randomized experimental designs. The details vary with the design but the basic facts are true whenever randomization is used to produce data.

Remember that proper statistical design is not the only aspect of a good sample or experiment. The sampling distribution shows only how a statistic varies due to the operation of chance in randomization. It reveals nothing about possible bias due to undercoverage or nonresponse in a sample or to lack of realism in an experiment. The true distance of a statistic from the parameter it is estimating can be much larger than the sampling distribution suggests. What is worse, there is no way to say how large the added error is. The real world is less orderly than statistics textbooks imply.

SECTION 3.3 SUMMARY

- A number that describes a population is a **parameter.** A number that can be computed from the data is a **statistic.** The purpose of sampling or experimentation is usually to use statistics to make statements about unknown parameters.
- A statistic from a probability sample or randomized experiment has a **sampling distribution** that describes how the statistic varies in repeated data production. The sampling distribution answers the question "What would happen if we repeated the sample or experiment many times?" Formal statistical inference is based on the sampling distributions of statistics.
- A statistic as an estimator of a parameter may suffer from **bias** or from high **variability.** Bias means that the center of the sampling distribution is not equal to the true value of the parameter. The variability of the statistic is described by the spread of its sampling distribution.
- Properly chosen statistics from randomized data production designs have no bias resulting from the way the sample is selected or the way the subjects are assigned to treatments. We can reduce the variability of the statistic by increasing the size of the sample or the size of the experimental groups.

SECTION 3.3 Exercises

For Exercises 3.70 and 3.71, see page 211; for 3.72 to 3.74, see pages 214–216; and for 3.75 to 3.77, see pages 217–219.

How successful are customer support chats? *Exercises 3.78 to 3.83 deal with the following scenario.*

Some companies now offer customer support via online live chats with customer support staff. The records of the last 96,621 online chats at one company's online customer support Web site are to be sampled and studied to estimate the success rate of these chats in satisfying the customers who use them. The method that will eventually be used to estimate p, the proportion of chats that are successful, is as follows:

1. *Obtain an SRS of 150 chats from the 96,621 available chat records, and*

2. *count the number of successful chats out of the 150 (call this x), then*

3. *calculate the proportion of successful chats in the sample as $\hat{p} = x/150$.*

We should not think that our $\hat{p}$ will equal p. The probability of this is zero. The real question to be addressed is how far off could our $\hat{p}$ be from p? This question gets at the heart of how well the method of estimating p described above works.

3.78 Step 1: Worst possible cases. The value of p (whatever it happens to be) is a number between 0 and 1, including both of those values as possibilities. The same statement is true about *any* $\hat{p}$-value that we might obtain from an application of the method described above.

(a) For the moment, take only the fact that both p and $\hat{p}$ are numbers between 0 and 1 and explain how far off $\hat{p}$ could be from p. Provide a sketch to support your conclusion.

(b) Now, imagine that, instead of the method described above, we simply take $\hat{p}$ to *always* be 0.5. Using this method, how far off could $\hat{p}$ be from p? Provide a sketch to support your conclusion.

3.79 Step 2: What-if cases.

(a) What if the proportion of successful chats is (unknown to us) actually 0.2? Taking the fact that any $\hat{p}$-value we end up with is a number between 0 and 1, explain how far off $\hat{p}$ could be from p. Provide a sketch to support your conclusion.

(b) If we were to use the "always use 0.5 as your estimate" approach described in part (b) of Step 1, how far off could $\hat{p}$ be from p? Provide a sketch to support your conclusion.

3.80 Step 3: More what-if cases.

(a) Repeat parts (a) and (b) of Step 2, assuming that p is actually 0.7.

(b) Repeat parts (a) and (b) of Step 2, assuming that p is actually 0.5.

3.81 Step 4: Finally, some data. You decide that you have a handle on how estimating p works based on the previous exercises, so you decide to apply the method to the 96,621 chat records. You obtain an SRS of 150 chats and find that 122 of them were successful.

(a) Calculate the value of $\hat{p}$ for this sample.

(b) How far off *could* this $\hat{p}$ be from p? Explain your calculation and/or your reasoning.

(c) How far off *is* this $\hat{p}$ from p? Explain your calculation and/or your reasoning.

3.82 Step 5: How well did it work? Your work so far should convince you that evaluating *how well a method works* is best done by applying the method in a case where the answer is known. In this series of exercises, this means applying the method in a case where p is known. This is an important point. If we already know the value of p, then we are (obviously) *not* applying the method to *estimate* p. Rather, we are applying the method to see how well the method works, and to see how well the method works we must apply it in a case where we already know the answer. The task of inspecting all 96,621 chat records is undertaken. The end result is that 83,384 of the chats are found to be successful; that is, $p = 83{,}384/96{,}621 = 0.863$ (rounded to three decimal places). Notice that if our *only* goal is to estimate p, then we are done now. In fact, we've done better than estimate p; we have actually *calculated* p. However, our goal is to see how well the prescribed method works in general, not just to estimate p for this one scenario.

(a) For the SRS obtained in Step 4, how well did the method of estimating p work?

(b) Another SRS of size 150 is obtained from the 96,621 chat records. For this SRS, the number of successful chats is 133. Calculate $\hat{p}$ for this sample. How well did the method work for this sample?

(c) You now have accomplished two realizations of the method of estimating p. Can you say how well the method of estimating p works *in general?* Why or why not? If not, what would you need in order to evaluate how well the method works in general?

3.83 Step 6: How well does it work? The method of estimating p is applied to the 96,621 chat records a total of 1200 times. The resulting 1200 $\hat{p}$-values have the following characteristics:

- The average of the 1200 $\hat{p}$-values is 0.8634.
- The standard deviation of the 1200 $\hat{p}$-values is 0.0281.
- The histogram of the 1200 $\hat{p}$-values is distinctly symmetric and mound-shaped.

(a) Sketch the histogram of the 1200 $\hat{p}$-values.

(b) Given the shape of the distribution of the 1200 $\hat{p}$-values, we can apply the 68–95–99.7 rule of Section 1.3 to these $\hat{p}$-values. Approximately 95% of the $\hat{p}$-values are inside what interval?

FIGURE 3.14 Which of these sampling distributions displays high or low bias and high or low variability? (For Exercise 3.86.)

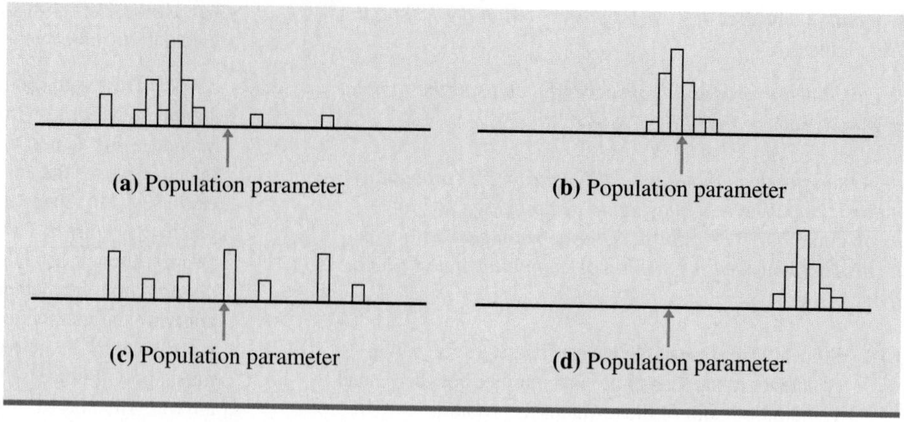

(c) Explain how the interval in part (b) provides a reasonable response to the question "How far off could $\hat{p}$ be from p?"

3.84 Unemployment. The Bureau of Labor Statistics announces that last month it interviewed all members of the labor force in a sample of 55,000 households; **6.2%** of the people interviewed were unemployed. Is the bold number a parameter or a statistic? Why?

3.85 Acceptance sampling. A carload lot of ball bearings has a mean diameter of **2.503** centimeters (cm). This is within the specifications for acceptance of the lot by the purchaser. The inspector happens to inspect 100 bearings from the lot with a mean diameter of **2.515** cm. This is outside the specified limits, so the lot is mistakenly rejected. Is each of the bold numbers a parameter or a statistic? Explain your answers.

3.86 Bias and variability. Figure 3.14 shows histograms of four sampling distributions of statistics intended to estimate the same parameter. Label each distribution relative to the others as high or low bias and as high or low variability.

3.87 Sampling students. A management student is planning to take a survey of student attitudes toward part-time work while attending college. He develops a questionnaire and plans to ask 25 randomly selected students to fill it out. His faculty adviser approves the questionnaire but urges that the sample size be increased to at least 100 students. Why is the larger sample helpful?

3.88 Sampling in the states. The Internal Revenue Service plans to examine an SRS of individual federal income tax returns from each state. One variable of interest is the proportion of returns claiming itemized deductions. The total number of individual tax returns in a state varies from 14 million in California to 227,000 in Wyoming.

(a) Will the variability of the sample proportion vary from state to state if an SRS of size 2000 is taken in each state? Explain your answer.

(b) Will the variability of the sample proportion change from state to state if an SRS of 1/10 of 1% (0.001) of the state's population is taken in each state? Explain your answer.

3.89 Margin of error. A *New York Times* opinion poll on women's issues contacted a sample of 1025 women and 472 men by randomly selecting telephone numbers. The *Times* publishes descriptions of its polling methods. Here is part of the description for this poll:

In theory, in 19 cases out of 20 the results based on the entire sample will differ by no more than three percentage points in either direction from what would have been obtained by seeking out all adult Americans.

The potential sampling error for smaller subgroups is larger. For example, for men it is plus or minus five percentage points.[27]

Explain why the margin of error is larger for conclusions about men alone than for conclusions about all adults.

3.90 Coin tossing. Coin tossing can illustrate the idea of a sampling distribution. The population is all outcomes (heads or tails) we would get if we tossed a coin forever. The parameter p is the proportion of heads in this population. We suspect that p is close to 0.5. That is, we think the coin will show about one-half heads in the long run. The sample is the outcomes of 20 tosses, and the statistic $\hat{p}$ is the proportion of heads in these 20 tosses.

(a) Toss a coin 20 times and record the value of $\hat{p}$.

(b) Repeat this sampling process 10 times. Make a stemplot of the 10 values of $\hat{p}$. Is the center of this distribution close to 0.5? (Ten repetitions give only a crude approximation to the sampling distribution. If possible, pool your work with that of other students to obtain at least 100 repetitions and make a histogram of the values of $\hat{p}$.)

3.91 Sampling invoices. We will illustrate the idea of a sampling distribution in the case of a very small sample from a very small population. The population contains 10 past due invoices. Here are the number of days each invoice is past due:

Invoice	0	1	2	3	4	5	6	7	8	9
Days past due	8	12	10	5	7	3	15	9	7	6

The parameter of interest is the mean of this population, which is 8.2. The sample is an SRS of $n = 4$ invoices drawn from the population. Because the invoices are labeled 0 to 9, a single random digit from Table B chooses one invoice for the sample.

(a) Use Table B to draw an SRS of size 4 from this population. Write the past due values for the days in your sample and calculate their mean $\overline{x}$. This statistic is an estimate of the population parameter

(b) Repeat this process 10 times. Make a histogram of the 10 values of $\overline{x}$. You are constructing the sampling distribution of $\overline{x}$. Is the center of your histogram close to 8.2? (Ten repetitions give only a crude approximation to the sampling distribution. If possible, pool your work with that of other students—using different parts of Table B—to obtain at least 100 repetitions. A histogram of these values of $\overline{x}$ is a better approximation to the sampling distribution.)

3.92 A sampling applet experiment. The *Simple Random Sample* applet available at `www.whfreeman.com/pbs` can animate the idea of a sampling distribution. Form a population labeled 1 to 100. We will choose an SRS of 10 of these numbers. That is, in this exercise the numbers themselves are the population, not just labels for 100 individuals. The proportion of the whole numbers 1 to 100 that are equal to or less than 60 is $p = 0.6$. This is the population proportion.

(a) Use the applet to choose an SRS of size 25. Which 25 numbers were chosen? Count the numbers ≤ 60 in your sample and divide this count by 25. This is the sample proportion $\hat{p}$.

(b) Although the population and the parameter $p = 0.6$ remain fixed, the sample proportion changes as we take more samples. Take another SRS of size 25. (Use the "Reset" button to return to the original population before taking the second sample.) What are the 25 numbers in your sample? What proportion of these is ≤ 60? This is another value of $\hat{p}$.

(c) Take 8 more SRSs from this same population and record their sample proportions. You now have 10 values of the statistic $\hat{p}$ from 10 SRSs of the same size from the same population. Make a histogram of the 10 values and mark the population parameter $p = 0.6$ on the horizontal axis. Are your 10 sample values roughly centered at the population value p? (If you kept going forever, your $\hat{p}$-values would form the sampling distribution of the sample proportion; the population proportion p would indeed be the center of this distribution.)

3.93 CASE 3.1 **A sampling experiment.** Figures 3.7 and 3.8 show how the sample proportion $\hat{p}$ behaves when we take many samples from a population in which the population proportion is $p = 0.6$. You can follow the steps in this process on a small scale.

Figure 3.15 is a small population. Each circle represents an adult. The white circles are people who find clothes shopping frustrating, and the colored circles are people who do not. You can check that 60 of the 100 circles are white, so in this population the proportion who find shopping frustrating is $p = 60/100 = 0.6$.

(a) The circles are labeled 00, 01, ..., 99. Use line 101 of Table B to draw an SRS of size 5. What is the proportion $\hat{p}$ of the people in your sample who find shopping frustrating?

(b) Take 9 more SRSs of size 5 (10 in all), using lines 102 to 110 of Table B, a different line for each sample. You now have 10 values of the sample proportion $\hat{p}$.

(c) Because your samples have only 5 people, the only values $\hat{p}$ can take are $0/5$, $1/5$, $2/5$, $3/5$, $4/5$, and $5/5$. That is, $\hat{p}$ is always 0, 0.2, 0.4, 0.6, 0.8, or 1. Mark these numbers on a line and make a histogram of your 10 results by putting a bar above each number to show how many samples had that outcome.

(d) Taking samples of size 5 from a population of size 100 is not a practical setting, but let's look at your results anyway. How many of your 10 samples estimated the population proportion $p = 0.6$ exactly correctly? Is the true value 0.6 roughly in the center of your sample values? Explain why 0.6 would be in the center of the sample values if you took a large number of samples.

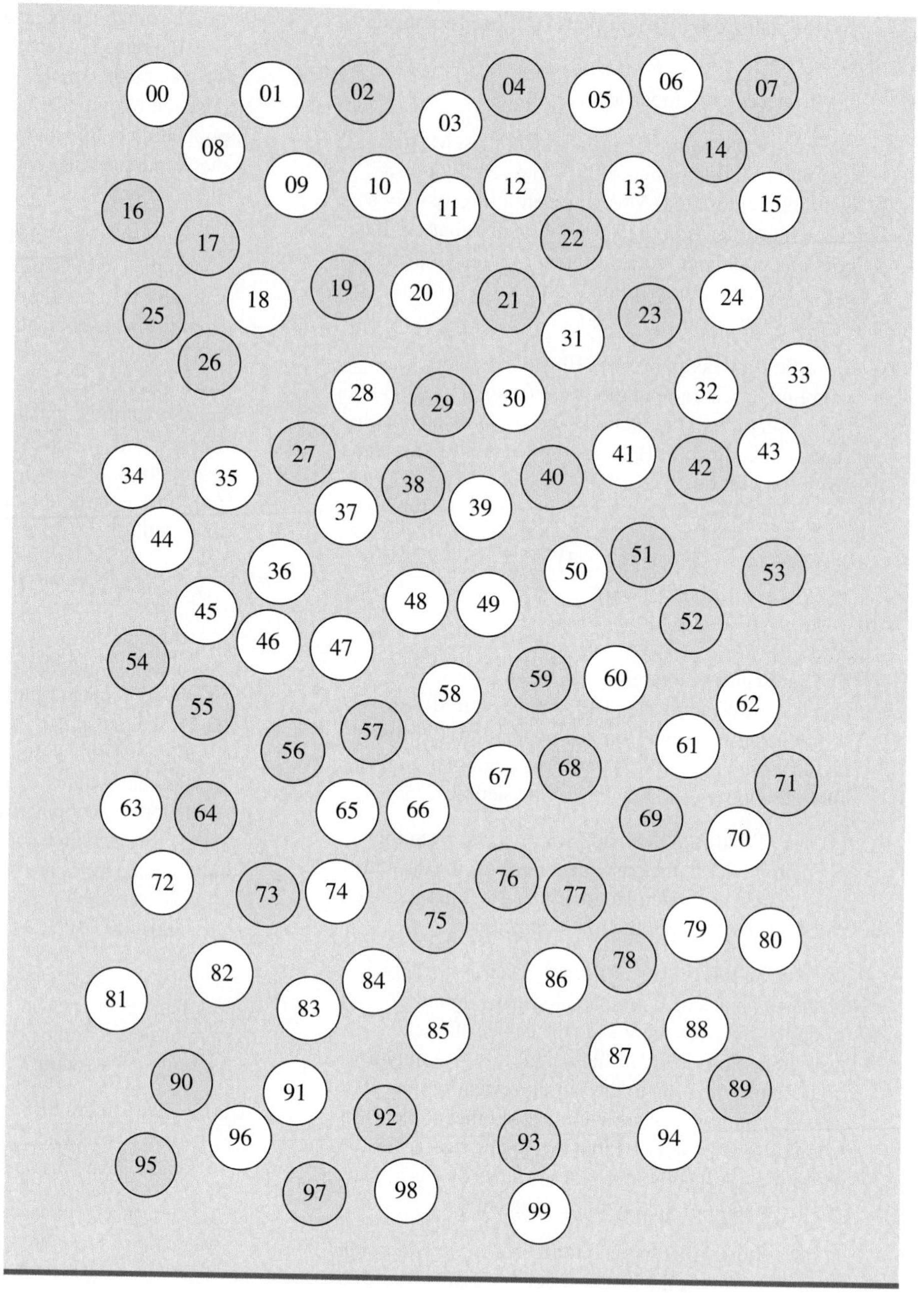

FIGURE 3.15 A population of 100 individuals for Exercise 3.93. Some individuals (white circles) find clothes shopping frustrating, and the others do not.

3.4 Commentary: Data Ethics*

The production and use of data, like all human endeavors, raise ethical questions. We won't discuss the telemarketer who begins a telephone sales pitch with "I'm conducting a survey." Such deception is clearly unethical. It enrages legitimate survey organizations,

*This short essay concerns a very important topic, but the material is not needed to read the rest of the book.

which find the public less willing to talk with them. Neither will we discuss those few researchers who, in the pursuit of professional advancement, publish fake data. There is no ethical question here—faking data to advance your career is just wrong. It will end your career when uncovered. But just how honest must researchers be about real, unfaked data? Here is an example that suggests the answer is "More honest than they often are."

EXAMPLE 3.21 The Whole Truth?

Papers reporting scientific research are supposed to be short, with no extra baggage. Brevity, however, can allow researchers to avoid complete honesty about their data. Did they choose their subjects in a biased way? Did they report data on only some of their subjects? Did they try several statistical analyses and report only the ones that looked best? The statistician John Bailar screened more than 4000 medical papers in more than a decade as consultant to the *New England Journal of Medicine*. He says, "When it came to the statistical review, it was often clear that critical information was lacking, and the gaps nearly always had the practical effect of making the authors' conclusions look stronger than they should have."[28] The situation is no doubt worse in fields that screen published work less carefully.

The most complex issues of data ethics arise when we collect data from people. The ethical difficulties are more severe for experiments that impose some treatment on people than for sample surveys that simply gather information. Trials of new medical treatments, for example, can do harm as well as good to their subjects. Here are some basic standards of data ethics that must be obeyed by any study that gathers data from human subjects, whether sample survey or experiment.

Basic Data Ethics

The organization that carries out the study must have an **institutional review board** that reviews all planned studies in advance in order to protect the subjects from possible harm.

All individuals who are subjects in a study must give their **informed consent** before data are collected.

All individual data must be kept **confidential.** Only statistical summaries for groups of subjects may be made public.

The law requires that studies carried out or funded by the federal government obey these principles.[29] But neither the law nor the consensus of experts is completely clear about the details of their application.

Institutional review boards

The purpose of an institutional review board is not to decide whether a proposed study will produce valuable information or whether it is statistically sound. The board's purpose is, in the words of one university's board, "to protect the rights and welfare of human subjects (including patients) recruited to participate in research activities." The board reviews the plan of the study and can require changes. It reviews the consent form to ensure that subjects are informed about the nature of the study and about any potential risks. Once research begins, the board monitors the study's progress at least once a year.

The most pressing issue concerning institutional review boards is whether their workload has become so large that their effectiveness in protecting subjects drops. When the government temporarily stopped human-subject research at Duke University Medical Center in 1999 due to inadequate protection of subjects, more than 2000 studies were going on. That's a lot of review work. There are shorter review procedures for projects that involve only minimal risks to subjects, such as most sample surveys. When a board is overloaded, there is a temptation to put more proposals in the minimal-risk category to speed the work.

Informed consent

Both words in the phrase "informed consent" are important, and both can be controversial. Subjects must be *informed* in advance about the nature of a study and any risk of harm it may bring. In the case of a sample survey, physical harm is not possible. The subjects should be told what kinds of questions the survey will ask and about how much of their time it will take. Experimenters must tell subjects the nature and purpose of the study and outline possible risks. Subjects must then *consent* in writing.

EXAMPLE 3.22 Who Can Consent?

Are there some subjects who can't give informed consent? It was once common, for example, to test new vaccines on prison inmates who gave their consent in return for good-behavior credit. Now we worry that prisoners are not really free to refuse, and the law forbids almost all medical research in prisons.

Children can't give fully informed consent, so the usual procedure is to ask their parents. A study of new ways to teach reading is about to start at a local elementary school, so the study team sends consent forms home to parents. Many parents don't return the forms. Can their children take part in the study because the parents did not say "No," or should we allow only children whose parents returned the form and said "Yes"?

What about research into new medical treatments for people with mental disorders? What about studies of new ways to help emergency room patients who may be unconscious? In most cases, there is not time to get the consent of the family. Does the principle of informed consent bar realistic trials of new treatments for unconscious patients?

These are questions without clear answers. Reasonable people differ strongly on all of them. There is nothing simple about informed consent.[30]

The difficulties of informed consent do not vanish even for capable subjects. Some researchers, especially in medical trials, regard consent as a barrier to getting patients to participate in research. They may not explain all possible risks; they may not point out that there are other therapies that might be better than those being studied; they may be too optimistic in talking with patients even when the consent form has all the right details. On the other hand, mentioning every possible risk leads to very long consent forms that really are barriers. "They are like rental car contracts," one lawyer said. Some subjects don't read forms that run five or six printed pages. Others are frightened by the large number of possible (but unlikely) disasters that might happen and so refuse to participate. Of course, unlikely disasters sometimes happen. When they do, lawsuits follow and the consent forms become yet longer and more detailed.

Confidentiality

Ethical problems do not disappear once a study has been cleared by the review board, has obtained consent from its subjects, and has actually collected data about the subjects. It is important to protect the subjects' privacy by keeping all data about individuals confidential. The report of an opinion poll may say what percent of the 1200 respondents felt that legal immigration should be reduced. It may not report what *you* said about this or any other issue.

anonymity

Confidentiality is not the same as **anonymity.** Anonymity means that subjects are anonymous—their names are not known even to the director of the study. Anonymity is rare in statistical studies. Even where it is possible (mainly in surveys conducted by mail), anonymity prevents any follow-up to improve nonresponse or inform subjects of results.

Any breach of confidentiality is a serious violation of data ethics. The best practice is to separate the identity of the subjects from the rest of the data at once. Sample surveys, for example, use the identification only to check on who did or did not respond. In an era of advanced technology, however, it is no longer enough to be sure that each individual set of data protects people's privacy. The government, for example, maintains a vast amount of information about citizens in many separate data bases—census responses, tax returns, Social Security information, data from surveys such as the Current Population Survey, and so on. Many of these data bases can be searched by computers for statistical studies. A clever computer search of several data bases might be able, by combining information, to identify you and learn a great deal about you even if your name and other identification have been removed from the data available for search. A colleague from Germany once remarked that "female full professor of statistics with PhD from the United States" was enough to identify her among all the 83 million residents of Germany. Privacy and confidentiality of data are hot issues among statisticians in the computer age.

EXAMPLE 3.23 Uncle Sam Knows

Citizens are required to give information to the government. Think of tax returns and Social Security contributions. The government needs these data for administrative purposes—to see if we paid the right amount of tax and how large a Social Security benefit we are owed when we retire. Some people feel that individuals should be able to forbid any other use of their data, even with all identification removed. This would prevent using government records to study, say, the ages, incomes, and household sizes of Social Security recipients. Such a study could well be vital to debates on reforming Social Security.

Clinical trials

Clinical trials are experiments that study the effectiveness of medical treatments on actual patients. Medical treatments can harm as well as heal, so clinical trials spotlight the ethical problems of experiments with human subjects. Here are the starting points for a discussion:

- Randomized comparative experiments are the only way to see the true effects of new treatments. Without them, risky treatments that are no more effective than placebos will become common.
- Clinical trials produce great benefits, but most of these benefits go to future patients. The trials also pose risks, and these risks are borne by the subjects of the trial. So we must balance future benefits against present risks.
- Both medical ethics and international human rights standards say that "the interests of the subject must always prevail over the interests of science and society."

The quoted words are from the 1964 Helsinki Declaration of the World Medical Association, the most respected international standard. The most outrageous examples of unethical experiments are those that ignore the interests of the subjects.

EXAMPLE 3.24 The Tuskegee Study

In the 1930s, syphilis was common among black men in the rural South, a group that had almost no access to medical care. The Public Health Service Tuskegee study recruited 399 poor black sharecroppers with syphilis and 201 others without the disease in order to observe how syphilis progressed when no treatment was given. Beginning in 1943, penicillin became available to treat syphilis. The study subjects were not treated. In fact, the Public Health Service prevented any treatment until word leaked out and forced an end to the study in the 1970s.

The Tuskegee study is an extreme example of investigators following their own interests and ignoring the well-being of their subjects. A 1996 review said, "It has come to symbolize racism in medicine, ethical misconduct in human research, paternalism by physicians, and government abuse of vulnerable people." In 1997, President Clinton formally apologized to the surviving participants in a White House ceremony.[31]

Because "the interests of the subject must always prevail," medical treatments can be tested in clinical trials only when there is reason to hope that they will help the patients who are subjects in the trials. Future benefits aren't enough to justify experiments with human subjects. Of course, if there is already strong evidence that a treatment works and is safe, it is unethical *not* to give it. Here are the words of Dr. Charles Hennekens of the Harvard Medical School, who directed the large clinical trial that showed that aspirin reduces the risk of heart attacks:

> *There's a delicate balance between when to do or not do a randomized trial. On the one hand, there must be sufficient belief in the agent's potential to justify exposing half the subjects to it. On the other hand, there must be sufficient doubt about its efficacy to justify withholding it from the other half of subjects who might be assigned to placebos.*[32]

Why is it ethical to give a control group of patients a placebo? Well, we know that placebos often work. Moreover, placebos have no harmful side effects. So in the state of balanced doubt described by Dr. Hennekens, the placebo group may be getting a better treatment than the drug group. If we *knew* which treatment was better, we would give it to everyone. When we don't know, it is ethical to try both and compare them.

Behavioral and social science experiments

When we move from medicine to the behavioral and social sciences, the direct risks to experimental subjects are less acute, but so are the possible benefits to the subjects. Consider, for example, the experiments conducted by psychologists in their study of human behavior.

EXAMPLE 3.25 Psychologists in the Men's Room

Psychologists observe that people have a "personal space" and are uneasy if others come too close to them. We don't like strangers to sit at our table in a coffee shop if other tables are available, and we see people move apart in elevators if there is room to do so. Americans tend to require more personal space than people in most other cultures. Can violations of personal space have physical, as well as emotional, effects?

Investigators set up shop in a men's public restroom. They blocked off urinals to force men walking in to use either a urinal next to an experimenter (treatment group) or a urinal separated from the experimenter (control group). Another experimenter, using a periscope from a toilet stall, measured how long the subject took to start urinating and how long he continued.[33]

This personal space experiment illustrates the difficulties facing those who plan and review behavioral studies.

- There is no risk of harm to the subjects, although they would certainly object to being watched through a periscope. What should we protect subjects from when physical harm is unlikely? Possible emotional harm? Undignified situations? Invasion of privacy?
- What about informed consent? The subjects did not even know they were participating in an experiment. Many behavioral experiments rely on hiding the true purpose of the study. The subjects would change their behavior if told in advance what the investigators were looking for. Subjects are asked to consent on the basis of vague information. They receive full information only after the experiment.

The "Ethical Principles" of the American Psychological Association require consent unless a study merely observes behavior in a public place. They allow deception only when it is necessary to the study, does not hide information that might influence a subject's willingness to participate, and is explained to subjects as soon as possible. The personal space study (from the 1970s) does not meet current ethical standards.

We see that the basic requirement for informed consent is understood differently in medicine and psychology. Here is an example of another setting with yet another interpretation of what is ethical. The subjects get no information and give no consent. They don't even know that an experiment may be sending them to jail for the night.

EXAMPLE 3.26 Reducing Domestic Violence

How should police respond to domestic-violence calls? In the past, the usual practice was to remove the offender and order him to stay out of the household overnight. Police were reluctant to make arrests because the victims rarely pressed charges. Women's groups argued that arresting offenders would help prevent future violence even if no charges were filed. Is there evidence that arrest will reduce future offenses? That's a question that experiments have tried to answer.

A typical domestic-violence experiment compares two treatments: arrest the suspect and hold him overnight, or warn the suspect and release him. When police officers reach the scene of a domestic-violence call, they calm the participants and investigate. Weapons or death threats require an arrest. If the facts permit an arrest but do not require it, an officer radios headquarters for instructions. The person on duty opens the next envelope in a file prepared in advance by a statistician. The envelopes contain the treatments in random order. The police either arrest the suspect or warn and release him, depending on the contents of the envelope. The researchers then watch police records and visit the victim to see if the domestic violence reoccurs.

Such experiments show that arresting domestic-violence suspects does reduce their future violent behavior.[34] As a result of this evidence, arrest has become the common police response to domestic violence.

The domestic-violence experiments shed light on an important issue of public policy. Because there is no informed consent, the ethical rules that govern clinical trials and most social science studies would forbid these experiments. They were cleared by review boards because, in the words of one domestic-violence researcher, "These people became subjects by committing acts that allow the police to arrest them. You don't need consent to arrest someone."

SECTION 3.4 SUMMARY

- The purpose of an **institutional review board** is to protect the rights and welfare of the human subjects in a study. Institutional review boards review **informed consent** forms that subjects will agree to in writing before participating in a study.
- Information about individuals in a study must be kept **confidential** while statistical summaries of groups of individuals may be made public.
- **Clinical trials** are experiments that study the effectiveness of medical treatments on actual patients.
- Some studies in the **behavioral** and **social sciences** are observational while others are designed experiments.

SECTION 3.4 Exercises

Most of these exercises pose issues for discussion. There are no right or wrong answers, but there are more and less thoughtful answers.

3.94 **Minimal risk?** You are a member of your college's institutional review board. You must decide whether several research proposals qualify for lighter review because they involve only minimal risk to subjects. Federal regulations say that "minimal risk" means the risks are no greater than "those ordinarily encountered in daily life or during the performance of routine physical or psychological examinations or tests." That's vague. Which of these do you think qualifies as "minimal risk"?

(a) Draw a drop of blood by pricking a finger in order to measure blood sugar.

(b) Draw blood from the arm for a full set of blood tests.

(c) Insert a tube that remains in the arm, so that blood can be drawn regularly.

3.95 **Who reviews?** Government regulations require that institutional review boards consist of at least five people, including at least one scientist, one nonscientist, and one person from outside the institution. Most boards are larger, but many contain just one outsider.

(a) Why should review boards contain people who are not scientists?

(b) Do you think that one outside member is enough? How would you choose that member? (For example, would you prefer a medical doctor? A member of the clergy? An activist for patients' rights?)

3.96 Getting consent. A researcher suspects that traditional religious beliefs tend to be associated with an authoritarian personality. She prepares a questionnaire that measures authoritarian tendencies and also asks many religious questions. Write a description of the purpose of this research to be read by subjects in order to obtain their informed consent. You must balance the conflicting goals of not deceiving the subjects as to what the questionnaire will tell about them and of not biasing the sample by scaring off religious people.

3.97 No consent needed? In which of the circumstances below would you allow collecting personal information without the subjects' consent?

(a) A government agency takes a random sample of income tax returns to obtain information on the average income of people in different occupations. Only the incomes and occupations are recorded from the returns, not the names.

(b) A social psychologist attends public meetings of a religious group to study the behavior patterns of members.

(c) A social psychologist pretends to be converted to membership in a religious group and attends private meetings to study the behavior patterns of members.

3.98 Studying your blood. Long ago, doctors drew a blood specimen from you as part of treating minor anemia. Unknown to you, the sample was stored. Now researchers plan to use stored samples from you and many other people to look for genetic factors that may influence anemia. It is no longer possible to ask your consent. Modern technology can read your entire genetic makeup from the blood sample.

(a) Do you think it violates the principle of informed consent to use your blood sample if your name is on it but you were not told that it might be saved and studied later?

(b) Suppose that your identity is not attached. The blood sample is known only to come from (say) "a 20-year-old white female being treated for anemia." Is it now OK to use the sample for research?

(c) Perhaps we should use biological materials such as blood samples only from patients who have agreed to allow the material to be stored for later use in research. It isn't possible to say in advance what kind of research, so this falls short of the usual standard for informed consent. Is it nonetheless acceptable, given complete confidentiality and the fact that using the sample can't physically harm the patient?

3.99 Anonymous? Confidential? One of the most important nongovernment surveys in the United States is the National Opinion Research Center's General Social Survey. The GSS regularly monitors public opinion on a wide variety of political and social issues. Interviews are conducted in person in the subject's home. Are a subject's responses to GSS questions anonymous, confidential, or both? Explain your answer.

3.100 Anonymous? Confidential? Texas A&M, like many universities, offers free screening for HIV, the virus that causes AIDS. The announcement says, "Persons who sign up for the HIV Screening will be assigned a number so that they do not have to give their name." They can learn the results of the test by telephone, still without giving their name. Does this practice offer *anonymity* or just *confidentiality?*

3.101 Political polls. The presidential election campaign is in full swing, and the candidates have hired polling organizations to take sample surveys to find out what the voters think about the issues. What information should the pollsters be required to give out?

(a) What does the standard of informed consent require the pollsters to tell potential respondents?

(b) The standards accepted by polling organizations also require giving respondents the name and address of the organization that carries out the poll. Why do you think this is required?

(c) The polling organization usually has a professional name such as "Samples Incorporated," so respondents don't know that the poll is being paid for by a political party or candidate. Would revealing the sponsor to respondents bias the poll? Should the sponsor always be announced whenever poll results are made public?

3.102 Making poll results public. Some people think that the law should require that all political poll results be made public. Otherwise, the possessors of poll results can use the information to their own advantage. They can act on the information, release only selected parts of it, or time the release for best effect. A candidate's organization replies that they are paying for the poll in order to gain information for their own use, not to amuse the public. Do you favor requiring complete disclosure of political poll results? What about other private surveys, such as market research surveys of consumer tastes?

3.103 Student subjects. Students taking Psychology 001 are required to serve as experimental subjects. Students in Psychology 002 are not required to serve, but they are given extra credit if they do so. Students in Psychology 003 are required either to sign up as subjects or to write a term paper. Serving as an experimental subject may be educational, but current ethical standards frown on using "dependent subjects" such as prisoners or charity medical patients. Students are certainly somewhat dependent on their teachers. Do you object to any of these course policies? If so, which ones, and why?

3.104 Unequal benefits. Researchers on aging proposed to investigate the effect of supplemental health services on the quality of life of older people. Eligible patients on the rolls of a large medical clinic were to be randomly assigned to treatment and control groups. The treatment group would be offered hearing aids, dentures, transportation, and other services not available without charge to the control group. The review board felt that providing these services to some but not other persons in the same institution raised ethical questions. Do you agree?

3.105 How many have HIV? Researchers from Yale, working with medical teams in Tanzania, wanted to know how common infection with HIV, the virus that causes AIDS, is among pregnant women in that African country. To do this, they planned to test blood samples drawn from pregnant women.

Yale's institutional review board insisted that the researchers get the informed consent of each woman and tell her the results of the test. This is the usual procedure in developed nations. The Tanzanian government did not want to tell the women why blood was drawn or tell them the test results. The government feared panic if many people turned out to have an incurable disease for which the country's medical system could not provide care. The study was canceled. Do you think that Yale was right to apply its usual standards for protecting subjects?

3.106 AIDS trials in Africa. Effective drugs for treating AIDS are very expensive, so some African nations cannot afford to give them to large numbers of people. Yet AIDS is more common in parts of Africa than anywhere else. Several clinical trials are looking at ways to prevent pregnant mothers infected with HIV from passing the infection to their unborn children, a major source of HIV infections in Africa. Some people say these trials are unethical because they do not give effective AIDS drugs to their subjects, as would be required in rich nations. Others reply that the trials are looking for treatments that can work in the real world in Africa and that they promise benefits at least to the children of their subjects. What do you think?

3.107 AIDS trials in Africa. One of the most important goals of AIDS research is to find a vaccine that will protect against HIV infection. Because AIDS is so common in parts of Africa, that is the easiest place to test a vaccine. It is likely, however, that a vaccine would be so expensive that it could not (at least at first) be widely used in Africa. Is it ethical to test in Africa if the benefits go mainly to rich countries? The treatment group of subjects would get the vaccine, and the placebo group would later be given the vaccine if it proved effective. So the actual subjects would benefit—it is the future benefits that would go elsewhere. What do you think?

3.108 Asking teens about sex. The Centers for Disease Control and Prevention, in a survey of teenagers, asked the subjects if they were sexually active. Those who said "Yes" were then asked, "How old were you when you had sexual intercourse for the first time?" Should consent of parents be required to ask minors about sex, drugs, and other such issues, or is consent of the minors themselves enough? Give reasons for your opinion.

3.109 Deceiving subjects. Students sign up to be subjects in a psychology experiment. When they arrive, they are told that interviews are running late and are taken to a waiting room. The experimenters then stage a theft of a valuable object left in the waiting room. Some subjects are alone with the thief, and others are in pairs—these are the treatments being compared. Will the subject report the theft?

The students had agreed to take part in an unspecified study, and the true nature of the experiment is explained to them afterward. Do you think this study is ethically OK?

3.110 Deceiving subjects. A psychologist conducts the following experiment: she measures the attitude of subjects toward cheating, then has them play a game rigged so that winning without cheating is impossible. The computer that organizes the game also records—unknown to the subjects—whether or not they cheat. Then attitude toward cheating is retested.

Subjects who cheat tend to change their attitudes to find cheating more acceptable. Those who resist the temptation to cheat tend to condemn cheating more strongly on the second test of attitude. These results confirm the psychologist's theory.

This experiment tempts subjects to cheat. The subjects are led to believe that they can cheat secretly when in fact they are observed. Is this experiment ethically objectionable? Explain your position.

STATISTICS IN SUMMARY

Designs for producing data are essential parts of statistics in practice. The Statistics in Summary figure on this page displays the big ideas visually. Random sampling and randomized comparative experiments are perhaps the most important statistical inventions of the twentieth century. Both were slow to gain acceptance, and you will still see many voluntary response samples and uncontrolled experiments. This chapter has explained good techniques for producing data and has also explained why bad techniques often produce worthless data.

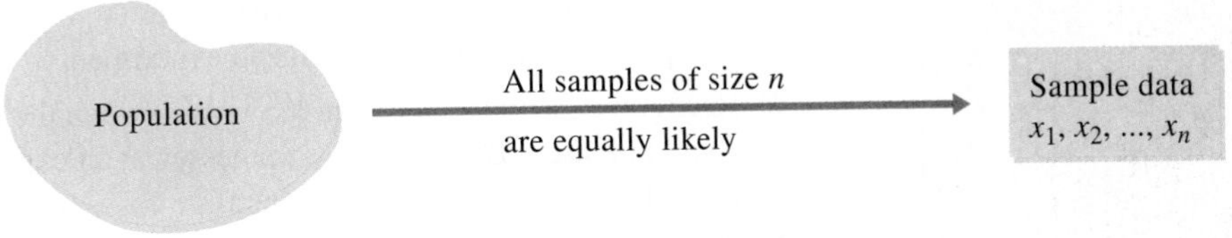

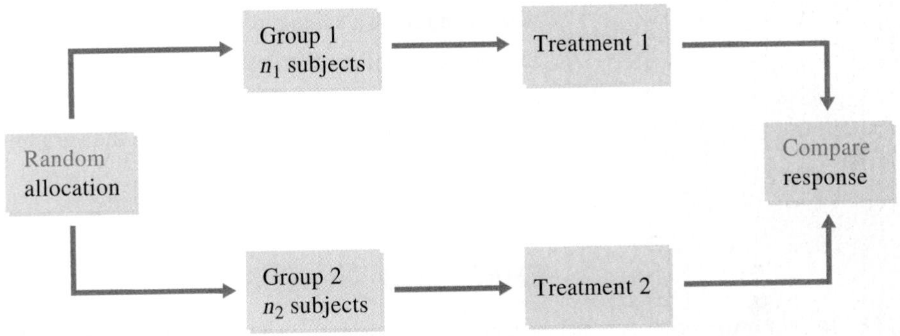

The deliberate use of chance in producing data is a central idea in statistics. It allows use of the laws of probability to analyze data, as we will see in the following chapters. Here are the major skills you should have now that you have studied this chapter.

A. Sampling

1. Identify the population in a sampling situation.
2. Recognize bias due to voluntary response samples and other inferior sampling methods.
3. Use software or Table B of random digits to select a simple random sample (SRS) from a population.
4. Recognize the presence of undercoverage and nonresponse as sources of error in a sample survey. Recognize the effect of the wording of questions on the responses.
5. Use random digits to select a stratified random sample from a population when the strata are identified.

B. Experiments

1. Recognize whether a study is an observational study or an experiment.
2. Recognize bias due to confounding of explanatory variables with lurking variables in either an observational study or an experiment.
3. Identify the factors (explanatory variables), treatments, response variables, and individuals or subjects in an experiment.
4. Outline the design of a completely randomized experiment using a diagram like those in Figures 3.4 and 3.5. The diagram in a specific case should show the sizes of the groups, the specific treatments, and the response variable.
5. Use Table B of random digits to carry out the random assignment of subjects to groups in a completely randomized experiment.
6. Recognize the placebo effect. Recognize when the double-blind technique should be used. Be aware of weaknesses in an experiment, especially lack of realism that makes it hard to generalize conclusions.
7. Explain why a randomized comparative experiment can give good evidence for cause-and-effect relationships.

C. Toward Inference

1. Identify parameters and statistics in a sample or experiment.
2. Recognize the fact of sampling variability: a statistic will take different values when you repeat a sample or experiment.
3. Interpret a sampling distribution as describing the values taken by a statistic in all possible repetitions of a sample or experiment under the same conditions.
4. Understand the effect of sample size on the variability of sample statistics.

CHAPTER 3 Review Exercises

3.111 In your own words. A friend mentions a report about high rates of the disease lupus appearing to coincide with high rates of discarded petroleum products in several nearby counties. Using this scenario, write a paragraph or two explaining to your friend the concepts of *observational study, experiment,* and *confounding.*

3.112 Coupon effect? A researcher studying the effect of coupons on consumers' expectations makes up two different series of ads for a hypothetical brand of cola for the past year. Students in a family science course view one or the other sequence of ads on a computer. Some students see a sequence of ads with no coupon offered on the cola, while others see regular coupon offerings that effectively lower the price of the cola temporarily. Next, the students are asked what price they would expect to pay for the cola.

(a) Is this study an experiment? Why?

(b) What are the explanatory and response variables?

3.113 California area codes. A poll of opinion in California uses random digit dialing to choose telephone numbers at random. Numbers are selected separately within each California area code. The size of the sample in each area code is proportional to the population living there.

(a) What is the name for this kind of sampling design?

(b) California area codes, in rough order from north to south, are

530	707	916	209	415	925	510
650	408	831	805	559	760	661
818	213	626	323	562	709	310
949	909	858	619			

Another California survey does not call numbers in all area codes but starts with an SRS of 10 area codes. Choose such an SRS. If you use Table B, start at line 111.

3.114 Can you remember how many? An opinion poll calls 1800 randomly chosen residential telephone numbers, then asks to speak with an adult member of the household. The interviewer asks, "How many movies have you watched in a movie theater in the past 12 months?"

(a) What population do you think the poll has in mind?

(b) In all, 1131 people respond. What is the rate (percent) of nonresponse?

(c) What source of response error is likely for the question asked?

(d) Write a variation on this question that would be likely to lessen the associated response error.

3.115 Calcium and blood pressure. Your company produces a dietary supplement that contains a significant amount of calcium as one of its ingredients. The company would like to be able to market this fact successfully to one of the target groups for the supplement: men with high blood pressure. To this end, you must design an experiment to demonstrate that added calcium in the diet reduces blood pressure. You have available 40 men with high blood pressure who are willing to serve as subjects.

(a) Outline an appropriate design for the experiment, taking the placebo effect into account.

(b) The names of the subjects appear below. Do the randomization required by your design, and list the subjects to whom you will give the drug. (If you use Table B, enter the table at line 141.)

Alomar	Denman	Han	Liang	Rosen
Asihiro	Durr	Howard	Maldonado	Solomon
Bennett	Edwards	Hruska	Marsden	Tompkins
Bikalis	Farouk	Imrani	Moore	Townsend
Chen	Fratianna	James	O'Brian	Tullock
Clemente	George	Kaplan	Ogle	Underwood
Cranston	Green	Krushchev	Plochman	Willis
Curtis	Guillen	Lawless	Rodriguez	Zhang

3.116 Child care benefits. Will providing child care for employees make a company more attractive to women, even those who are unmarried? You are designing an experiment to answer this question. You prepare recruiting material for two fictitious companies, both in similar businesses in the same location. Company A's brochure does not mention child care. There are two versions of Company B's material, identical except that one describes the company's on-site child care facility. Your subjects are 40 unmarried women who are college seniors seeking employment. Each subject will read recruiting material for both companies and choose the one she would prefer to work for. You will give each version of Company B's brochure to half the women. You suspect that a higher percent of those who read the description that includes child care will choose Company B.

(a) Outline the design of the experiment. Be sure to identify the response variable.

(b) The names of the subjects appear below. Do the randomization required by your design and list the subjects who will read the version that mentions child care. (If you use Table B, begin at line 161.)

Abrams	Danielson	Gutierrez	Lippman	Rosen
Adamson	Durr	Howard	Martinez	Sugiwara
Afifi	Edwards	Hwang	McNeill	Thompson
Brown	Fluharty	Iselin	Morse	Travers
Cansico	Garcia	Janle	Ng	Turing
Chen	Gerson	Kaplan	Quinones	Ullmann
Cortez	Green	Kim	Rivera	Williams
Curzakis	Gupta	Lattimore	Roberts	Wong

3.117 Employee meditation. You see a news report of an experiment that claims to show that a meditation technique increased job satisfaction of employees. The experimenter interviewed the employees and assessed their levels of job satisfaction. The subjects then learned how to meditate and did so regularly for a month. The experimenter reinterviewed them at the end of the month and assessed their job satisfaction levels again.

(a) There was no control group in this experiment. Why is this a blunder? What lurking variables might be confounded with the effect of meditation?

(b) The experimenter who diagnosed the effect of the treatment knew that the subjects had been meditating. Explain how this knowledge could bias the experimental conclusions.

(c) Briefly discuss a proper experimental design, with controls and blind diagnosis, to assess the effect of meditation on job satisfaction.

3.118 Physical fitness and leadership. A study of the relationship between physical fitness and leadership uses as subjects middle-aged executives who have volunteered for an exercise program. The executives are divided into a low-fitness group and a high-fitness group on the basis of a physical examination. All subjects then take a psychological test designed to measure leadership, and the results for the two groups are compared. Is this an observational study or an experiment? Explain your answer.

3.119 Taste testing. Before a new variety of frozen muffins is put on the market, it is subjected to extensive taste testing. People are asked to taste the new muffin and a competing brand and to say which they prefer. (Both muffins are unidentified in the test.) Is this an observational study or an experiment? Why?

3.120 **A hot fund.** A large mutual funds group assigns a young securities analyst to manage its small biotechnology stock fund. The fund's share value increases an impressive 43% during the first year under the new manager. Explain why this performance does not necessarily establish the manager's ability.

3.121 **Are you sure?** Spain's Centro de Investigaciónes Sociológicos carried out a sample survey on the attitudes of Spaniards toward private business and state intervention in the economy.[35] Of the 2496 adults interviewed, 72% agreed that "employees with higher performance must get higher pay." On the other hand, 71% agreed that "everything a society produces should be distributed among its members as equally as possible and there should be no major differences." Use these conflicting results as an example in a short explanation of why opinion polls often fail to reveal public attitudes clearly.

3.122 **Daytime running lights.** Canada requires that cars be equipped with "daytime running lights," headlights that automatically come on at a low level when the car is started. Some manufacturers are now equipping cars sold in the United States with running lights. Will running lights reduce accidents by making cars more visible?

(a) Briefly discuss the design of an experiment to help answer this question. In particular, what response variables will you examine?

(b) Example 3.17 (page 202) discusses center brake lights. What cautions do you draw from that example that apply to an experiment on the effects of running lights?

3.123 **Learning about markets.** Your economics professor wonders if playing market games online will help students understand how markets set prices. You suggest an experiment: have some students use the online games, while others discuss markets in recitation sections. The course has two lectures, at 8:30 A.M. and 2:30 P.M. There are 10 recitation sections attached to each lecture. The students are already assigned to recitations. For practical reasons, all students in each recitation must follow the same program.

(a) The professor says, "Let's just have the 8:30 group do online work in recitation and the 2:30 group do discussion." Why is this a bad idea?

(b) Outline the design of an experiment with the 20 recitation sections as individuals. Carry out your randomization and include in your outline the recitation numbers assigned to each treatment.

3.124 **How much do students earn?** A university's financial aid office wants to know how much it can expect students to earn from summer employment. This information will be used to set the level of financial aid. The population contains 3478 students who have completed at least one year of study but have not yet graduated. The university will send a questionnaire to an SRS of 100 of these students, drawn from an alphabetized list.

(a) Describe how you will label the students in order to select the sample.

(b) Use Table B, beginning at line 105, to select the first 5 students in the sample.

3.125 **Sampling entrepreneurs.** A group of business school researchers wanted information on "why some firms survive while other firms with equal economic performance do not." Here are some bare facts about the study's data. Write a brief discussion of the difficulty of gathering data from this population, using this study as an example. Include nonresponse rates in percents.

The researchers sent approximately 13,000 questionnaires to members of the National Federation of Independent Businesses who reported that they had recently become business owners. Responses were obtained from 4814 entrepreneurs, of whom 2294 had become owners during the preceding 17 months. Followup questionnaires were sent to these 2294 people after one year and after two years. After two years, 963 replied that their firms had survived and 171 firms had been sold. From other sources, the authors could identify 611 firms that no longer existed. The remaining businesses did not respond and could not be identified as discontinued or sold. The study then compared the 963 surviving firms with the 611 known to have failed.[36]

3.126 **The price of digital cable TV.** A cable television provider plans to introduce "digital cable" to its current market. Digital cable offers more channels and features than standard cable television, but at a higher price. The provider wants to gauge how many consumers would sign up for digital service. You must plan a sample survey of households in the company's service area. You feel that these groups may respond differently:

- Households that currently subscribe to standard cable television service.
- Households that currently subscribe to some other form of television service such as satellite television.

- Households that do not subscribe to any pay television service.

Briefly discuss the design of your sample.

3.127 Sampling college faculty. A labor organization wants to study the attitudes of college faculty members toward collective bargaining. These attitudes appear to be different depending on the type of college. The American Association of University Professors classifies colleges as follows:

Class I. Offer doctorate degrees and award at least 15 per year.

Class IIA. Award degrees above the bachelor's but are not in Class I.

Class IIB. Award no degrees beyond the bachelor's.

Class III. Two-year colleges.

Discuss the design of a sample of faculty from colleges in your state, with total sample size about 200.

3.128 Sampling students. You want to investigate the attitudes of students at your school about the labor practices of factories that make college-brand apparel. You have a grant that will pay the costs of contacting about 500 students.

(a) Specify the exact population for your study. For example, will you include part-time students?

(b) Describe your sample design. Will you use a stratified sample?

(c) Briefly discuss the practical difficulties that you anticipate. For example, how will you contact the students in your sample?

3.129 Did you vote? When the Current Population Survey asked the adults in its sample of 55,000 households if they had voted in the 1996 presidential election, 54% said they had. In fact, only 49% of the adult population voted in that election. Why do you think the CPS result missed by much more than its margin of error?

3.130 Treating drunk drivers. Once a person has been convicted of drunk driving, one purpose of court-mandated treatment or punishment is to prevent future offenses of the same kind. Suggest three different treatments that a court might require. Then outline the design of an experiment to compare their effectiveness. Be sure to specify the response variables you will measure.

3.131 Do antioxidants prevent cancer? People who eat lots of fruits and vegetables have lower rates of colon cancer than those who eat little of these foods. Fruits and vegetables are rich in "antioxidants" such as vitamins A, C, and E. Will taking antioxidants help prevent colon cancer? A clinical trial studied this question with 864 people who were at risk of colon cancer. The subjects were divided into four groups: daily beta-carotene, daily vitamins C and E, all three vitamins every day, and daily placebo. After four years, the researchers were surprised to find no significant difference in colon cancer among the groups.[37]

(a) What are the explanatory and response variables in this experiment?

(b) Outline the design of the experiment. Use your judgment in choosing the group sizes.

(c) Assign labels to the 864 subjects and use Table B, starting at line 118, to choose the first 5 subjects for the beta-carotene group.

(d) The study was double-blind. What does this mean?

(e) What does "no significant difference" mean in describing the outcome of the study?

(f) Suggest some lurking variables that could explain why people who eat lots of fruits and vegetables have lower rates of colon cancer. The experiment suggests that these variables, rather than the antioxidants, may be responsible for the observed benefits of fruits and vegetables.

3.132 Stocks go down on Monday. Puzzling but true: stocks tend to go down on Mondays, both in the United States and in overseas markets. There is no convincing explanation for this fact. A recent study looked at this "Monday effect" in more detail, using data on the daily returns of stocks on several U.S. exchanges over a 30-year period. Here are some of the findings:

To summarize, our results indicate that the well-known Monday effect is caused largely by the Mondays of the last two weeks of the month. The mean Monday return of the first three weeks of the month is, in general, not significantly different from zero and is generally significantly higher than the mean Monday return of the last two weeks. Our finding seems to make it more difficult to explain the Monday effect.[38]

A friend thinks that "significantly" in this article has its plain English meaning, roughly "I think this is important." Explain in simple language what "significantly higher" and "not significantly different from zero" actually tell us here.

3.133 Potatoes for french fries. Few people want to eat discolored french fries. Potatoes are kept refrigerated before being cut for french fries to prevent spoiling and preserve flavor. But immediate processing of cold potatoes causes discoloring due to complex chemical reactions. The potatoes must therefore be brought to room temperature before processing. Fast-food chains and other sellers of french fries must understand potato behavior. Design an experiment in which tasters will rate the color and flavor of french fries prepared from several groups of potatoes. The potatoes will be freshly harvested or stored for a month at room temperature or stored for a month refrigerated. They will then be sliced and cooked either immediately or after an hour at room temperature.

(a) What are the factors and their levels, the treatments, and the response variables?

(b) Describe and outline the design of this experiment.

(c) It is efficient to have each taster rate fries from all treatments. How will you use randomization in presenting fries to the tasters?

3.134 **Speeding the mail?** Statistical studies can often help service providers assess the quality of their service. The United States Postal Service is one such provider of services. We wonder if the number of days a letter takes to reach another city is affected by the time of day it is mailed and whether or not the zip code is used. Describe briefly the design of a two-factor experiment to investigate this question. Be sure to specify the treatments exactly and to tell how you will handle lurking variables such as the day of the week on which the letter is mailed.

3.135 **McDonald's versus Wendy's.** The food industry uses taste tests to improve products and for comparison with competitors. Do consumers prefer the taste of a cheeseburger from McDonald's or from Wendy's in a blind test in which neither burger is identified? Describe briefly the design of a matched pairs experiment to investigate this question. How will you be sure the comparison is "blind"?

3.136 **Design your own experiment.** The previous two exercises illustrate the use of statistically designed experiments to answer questions of interest to consumers as well as to businesses. Select a question of interest to you that an experiment might answer and briefly discuss the design of an appropriate experiment.

3.137 **Randomization at work.** To demonstrate how randomization reduces confounding, return to the nutrition experiment described in Example 3.14 (page 197). Label the 30 rats 01 to 30. Suppose that, unknown to the experimenter, the 10 rats labeled 01 to 10 have a genetic defect that will cause them to grow more slowly than normal rats. If the experimenter simply puts rats 01 to 15 in the experimental group and rats 16 to 30 in the control group, this lurking variable will bias the experiment against the new food product.

Use Table B to assign 15 rats at random to the experimental group as in Example 3.14. Record how many of the 10 rats with genetic defects are placed in the experimental group and how many are in the control group. Repeat the randomization using different lines in Table B until you have done five random assignments. What is the mean number of genetically defective rats in experimental and control groups in your five repetitions?

Simulating samples. *Statistical software offers a shortcut to simulate the results of, say, 100 SRSs of size n drawn from a population in which proportion p would say "Yes" to a certain question. We will see in Chapter 5 that "binomial" is the key word to look for in the software menus. Set the sample size n and the sample proportion p. The software will generate the number of "Yes" answers in an SRS. You can divide by n to get the sample proportion $\hat{p}$. Use simulation to complete Exercises 3.138 and 3.139.*

3.138 **Changing the population.** Draw 100 samples of size $n = 50$ from populations with $p = 0.1$, $p = 0.3$, and $p = 0.5$. Make a stemplot of the 100 values of $\hat{p}$ obtained in each simulation. Compare your three stemplots. Do they show about the same variability? How does changing the parameter p affect the sampling distribution? If your software permits, make a Normal quantile plot of the $\hat{p}$-values from the population with $p = 0.5$. Is the sampling distribution approximately Normal?

3.139 **Changing the sample size.** Draw 100 samples of each of the sizes $n = 50$, $n = 200$, and $n = 800$ from a population with $p = 0.6$. Make a histogram of the $\hat{p}$-values for each simulation, using the same horizontal and vertical scales so that the three graphs can be compared easily. How does increasing the size of an SRS affect the sampling distribution of $\hat{p}$?

CHAPTER 3 Case Study Exercises

CASE STUDY EXERCISE 1: Consumer preferences in car colors. The most popular colors for cars and light trucks sold in recent years are white and silver. A survey shows that 17.6% of cars and trucks made in North America in 2000 were silver and 17.2% were white.[39] ("White" includes various shades of "pearl" and "cream.") The preferences of some groups of consumers may of course differ from national patterns. Undertake a study to determine the most popular colors among the vehicles driven by students at your school. You might collect data by questioning a sample of students or by looking at cars in student parking areas. Explain carefully how you attempted to get data that are close to an SRS of student cars, including how you used random selection. Then report your findings on student preferences in motor vehicle colors.

CASE STUDY EXERCISE 2: Individual incomes. The Data Appendix describes the file *individuals,* which contains the total incomes of 55,899 people between the ages of 25 and 65. We will illustrate sampling variability and sampling distributions in a case study that considers these people as a population. This is similar to sampling the employees of a major corporation. For example, Microsoft employs roughly as many people as are represented in this data file.

A. **The population.** Describe the distribution of the 55,899 incomes in the population. Include a histogram and the five-number summary.

B. **Samples and sampling distributions.** Choose an SRS of 500 members from this population. Make a histogram of the 500 incomes in the sample and find the five-number summary. Briefly compare the shape, center, and spread of the income distributions in the sample and in the population. Then repeat the process of choosing an SRS of size 500 four more times (five in all). Does it seem reasonable to you from this small trial that an SRS of 500 people will usually produce a sample whose shape is generally representative of the population?

C. **Statistical estimation.** Do the medians and quartiles of the samples provide reasonable estimates of the population median and quartiles? Explain why we expect that the minimum and maximum of a sample will *not* satisfactorily estimate the population minimum and maximum. Now examine estimation of mean income in more detail. Use your software to choose 50 SRSs of size 500 from this population. Find the mean income for each sample and save these 50 sample means in a separate file. Make a histogram of the distribution of the 50 sample means. How do the shape, center, and spread of this distribution compare with the distribution of individual incomes from part A? Does it appear that the sample mean from an SRS of size 500 is usually a reasonable estimator of the population mean? (The sampling distribution of the sample mean for samples of size 500 from this population is the distribution of the means of all possible samples. Your 50 samples give a rough idea of the nature of the sampling distribution.)

CASE STUDY EXERCISE 3: Random or *truly* random? If you have not completed parts (a) and (b) of Exercises 3.17 and 3.18 (page 191), do so now.

Part One. Summarize your research related to these two Web sites in a short report. Be sure to indicate the strengths and weaknesses of each site. Be sure to consider user-friendliness as well as technical differences in the methods used by each site. How easy is it to generate random samples? How easy is it to extract the random sample from the site for your own use?

Part Two. If you are using software (or a calculator) in your course to generate random numbers, see if you can find research related to your software's ability to generate "good" random numbers. Summarize your findings in a short report (or add this information to the report from Part One).

CHAPTER 3 Appendix

Using Minitab and Excel for Simple Random Sample

Simple Random Sample

Minitab:

Calc ➤ Random Data ➤ Sample from Columns

With this option, Minitab is basically picking from a hat. You can have a list of population elements in a worksheet column. For example, the 30 names of "A-1 Plumbing, . . . , Von's Video Store" from Example 3.5 can be placed in a column of Minitab. Alternatively, as explained in Section 3.1, you can assign a numerical label to each population element and place these numerical labels in a worksheet column. Input the value of n (sample size) in the **Number of rows to sample** box. Click-in the column that has the list of population elements of the numerical labels into the **From columns** box and then type in the column name in the **Store Samples in** box to indicate where you want to place the simple random sample. Click **OK** to find the random sample in the worksheet.

If the randomly generated sample is a column of numerical values and you wish to sort them in ascending order, then you can do the following pull-down sequence:

Data ➤ Sort

Click-in the column which has the random numbers into the **Sort column(s)** box and then click-in the same column into the **By column** box. To put the sorted numbers into the current worksheet, select the **Column(s) of current worksheet** option and then type in the column name in the box below to indicate where you want to place the sorted numbers. Click **OK.**

Excel:

To conduct random sampling in Excel, you need to assign a numerical label in the form of an integer to each population element. For example, as suggested with Example 3.5, we would design the numbers 1, . . . , 30 to the 30 population elements. These numerical labels should be put in a column in the spreadsheet. Now select "Sampling" in the **Data Analysis** menu box and click **OK.** Enter the cell range of the numerical labels into the **Input Range** box. Choose the **Random** option and input the number of random selections you wish Excel to make. Repeated selections are possible, so it is advisable that you generate several more random numbers than the sample size. Click **OK** and find the random numbers outputted to a new worksheet ply. If you wish to sort the random numbers, you should first highlight the cells to be sorted and then click the **Sort & Filter** option, found under the **Home** tab. You can now pick the option to have the numbers sorted from smallest to largest.

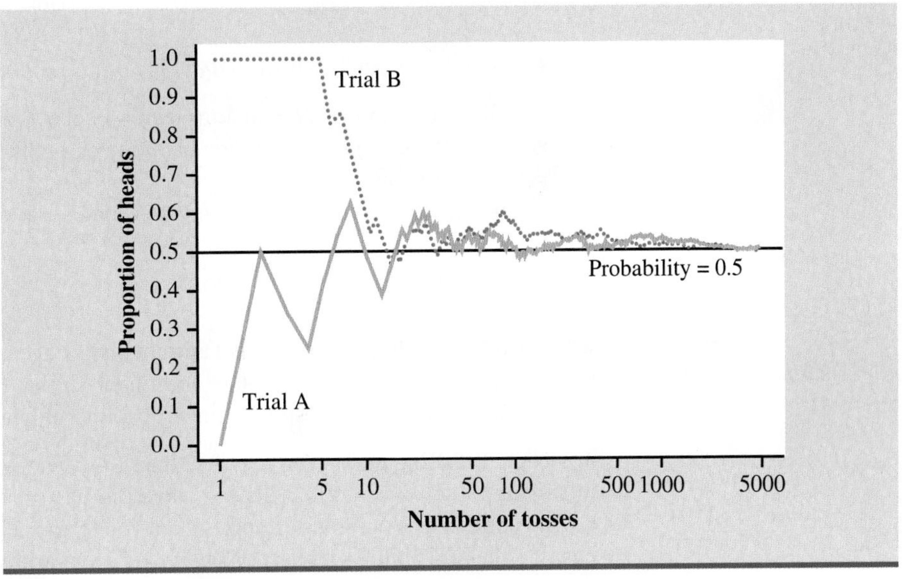

FIGURE 4.1 The proportion of tosses of a coin that give a head changes as we make more tosses. Eventually, however, the proportion approaches 0.5, the probability of a head. This figure shows the results of two trials of 5000 tosses each.

of a head and simulate any number of tosses of a coin with that probability. Experience shows that the proportion of heads gradually settles down close to the probability. Equally important, it also shows that the proportion in a small or moderate number of tosses can be far from the probability. Probability describes *only* what happens in the long run.

"Random" in statistics is not a synonym for "haphazard" but a description of a kind of order that emerges only in the long run. We often encounter the unpredictable side of randomness in our everyday experience, but we rarely see enough repetitions of the same random phenomenon to observe the long-term regularity that probability describes. You can see that regularity emerging in Figure 4.1. In the very long run, the proportion of tosses that give a head is 0.5. This is the intuitive idea of probability. Probability 0.5 means "occurs half the time in a very large number of trials."

We might suspect that a coin has probability 0.5 of coming up heads just because the coin has two sides. As Exercises 4.1 and 4.2 illustrate, such suspicions are not always correct. The idea of probability is *empirical.* That is, it is based on observation rather than theorizing. Probability describes what happens in very many trials, and we must actually observe many trials to pin down a probability. In the case of tossing a coin, some diligent people have in fact made thousands of tosses.

EXAMPLE 4.2 Some Coin Tossers

The French naturalist Count Buffon (1707–1788) tossed a coin 4040 times. Result: 2048 heads, or proportion 2048/4040 = 0.5069 for heads.

Around 1900, the English statistician Karl Pearson heroically tossed a coin 24,000 times. Result: 12,012 heads, a proportion of 0.5005.

While imprisoned by the Germans during World War II, the South African mathematician John Kerrich tossed a coin 10,000 times. Result: 5067 heads, a proportion of 0.5067.

Randomness and Probability

We call a phenomenon **random** if individual outcomes are uncertain but there is nonetheless a regular distribution of outcomes in a large number of repetitions.

The **probability** of any outcome of a random phenomenon is the proportion of times the outcome would occur in a very long series of repetitions.

APPLY YOUR KNOWLEDGE

4.1 Nickels spinning. Hold a nickel upright on its edge under your forefinger on a hard surface, then snap it with your other forefinger so that it spins for some time before falling. Based on 50 spins, estimate the probability of heads.

4.2 Nickels falling over. You may feel that it is obvious that the probability of a head in tossing a coin is about 1/2 because the coin has two faces. Such opinions are not always correct. The previous exercise asked you to spin a nickel rather than toss it—that changes the probability of a head. Now try another variation. Stand a nickel on edge on a hard, flat surface. Pound the surface with your hand so that the nickel falls over. What is the probability that it falls with heads upward? Make at least 50 trials to estimate the probability of a head.

Thinking about randomness

That some things are random is an observed fact about the world. The outcome of a coin toss, the time between customers arriving at an ATM machine, and the price of a share of a company's stock at the close of the market are all random. So is the outcome of a random sample or a randomized experiment. Probability theory is the branch of mathematics that describes random behavior. Of course, we can never observe a probability exactly. We could always continue tossing the coin, for example. Mathematical probability is an idealization based on imagining what would happen in an indefinitely long series of trials.

The best way to understand randomness is to observe random behavior—not only the long-run regularity but the unpredictable results of short runs. You can do this with physical devices, as in Exercises 4.1 and 4.2, but computer simulations (imitations) of random behavior allow faster exploration. Exercises 4.11 to 4.15 suggest some simulations of random behavior. As you explore randomness, remember:

independence

- You must have a long series of **independent** trials. That is, the outcome of one trial must not influence the outcome of any other. Imagine a crooked gambling house where the operator of a roulette wheel can stop it where she chooses—she can prevent the proportion of "red" from settling down to a fixed number. These trials are not independent.
- The idea of probability is empirical. Computer simulations start with given probabilities and imitate random behavior, but we can estimate a real-world probability only by actually observing many trials.
- Nonetheless, computer simulations are very useful because we need long runs of trials. In situations such as coin tossing, the proportion of an outcome often requires several hundred trials to settle down to the probability of that outcome. The kinds of physical techniques suggested in the exercises are too slow for this. Short runs give only rough estimates of a probability.

SECTION 4.1 SUMMARY

- A **random phenomenon** has outcomes that we cannot predict but that nonetheless have a regular distribution in very many repetitions.
- The **probability** of an event is the proportion of times the event occurs in many repeated trials of a random phenomenon.

SECTION 4.1 Exercises

For Exercises 4.1 and 4.2, see page 246.

4.3 Financial fraud. In December 2006, the Experian-Gallup Personal Credit Index survey found that 17% of fraud victims knew the perpetrator as a friend or acquaintance. Financial fraud includes crimes like unauthorized credit card charges, withdrawal of money from a savings or checking account, and opening an account in someone else's name. Because 17% is approximately 1-in-6, a single fair die can be used to study the probability that a fraud victim knew the perpetrator. Each roll of the die will represent the random selection of a single fraud victim. If the die lands with the number 6 facing up, record this as a fraud victim who knew the perpetrator. If the die lands with a 1, 2, 3, 4, or 5 facing up, record this as a fraud victim who did not know the perpetrator.

(a) Roll the die 6 times. How many of these 6 simulated fraud victims knew their perpetrators? If your 6 rolls did not result in exactly 1 fraud victim who knew the perpetrator, do you have reason to doubt the fairness of the die?

(b) Roll the die a total of 30 times. How many of these 30 simulated fraud victims knew their perpetrators?

(c) If possible, combine your 30 rolls with the rolls of fellow students. How many fraud victims are represented by the combined rolls? How many knew their perpetrators? Compare the percent who knew their perpetrators in your combined rolls with 1-in-6 (16.67%).

4.4 Credit monitoring. In a recent study of consumers, 25% reported purchasing a credit-monitoring product that alerts them to any activity on their credit report. To study this situation with a physical device providing the randomness as opposed to a computer simulation, we will need to be a bit more clever than flipping a single coin or rolling a single die. When flipping 2 fair coins, there are 4 possible results: HH, HT, TH, TT. Each of these possibilities has a 25% chance of happening. Each flip of a pair of fair coins will represent the random selection of a single consumer. If our coin flip results in HH (both coins land "heads up"), record this as a consumer who purchased a credit-monitoring product.

(a) Flip two fair coins 8 times. How many of the 8 flips resulted in a consumer who purchased a credit-monitoring product?

(b) Steve comments: "You should always get two HH flips out of 8 coin flips like those described in part (a)." Respond to Steve's statement.

(c) Suggest another physical mechanism for studying this situation.

4.5 Random digits. The table of random digits (Table B) was produced by a random mechanism that gives each digit probability 0.1 of being a 0. What proportion of the first 200 digits in the table are 0s? This proportion is an estimate, based on 200 repetitions, of the true probability, which in this case is known to be 0.1.

4.6 How many tosses to get a head? When we toss a penny, experience shows that the probability (long-term proportion) of a head is close to 1/2. Suppose now that we toss the penny repeatedly until we get a head. What is the probability that the first head comes up in an odd number of tosses (1, 3, 5, and so on)? To find out, repeat this experiment 50 times, and keep a record of the number of tosses needed to get a head on each of your 50 trials.

(a) From your experiment, estimate the probability of a head on the first toss. What value should we expect this probability to have?

(b) Use your results to estimate the probability that the first head appears on an odd-numbered toss.

4.7 Tossing a thumbtack. Toss a thumbtack on a hard surface 100 times. How many times did it land with the point up? What is the approximate probability of landing point up?

4.8 Three of a kind. You read in a book on poker that the probability of being dealt three of a kind in a five-card poker hand is 1/50. Explain in simple language what this means.

4.9 Thinking about probability statements. Probability is a measure of how likely an event is to occur. Match one of the probabilities that follow with each statement of likelihood given. (The probability is usually a more exact measure of likelihood than is the verbal statement.)

0 0.01 0.3 0.6 0.99 1

(a) This event is impossible. It can never occur.

(b) This event is certain. It will occur on every trial.

(c) This event is very unlikely, but it will occur once in a while in a long sequence of trials.

(d) This event will occur more often than not.

4.10 What probability doesn't say. The idea of probability is that the *proportion* of heads in many tosses of a balanced coin eventually gets close to 0.5. But does the actual *count* of heads get close to one-half the number of tosses? Let's find out. Set the "Probability of heads" in the *What Is Probability?* applet to 0.5 and the number of tosses to 40. You can extend the number of tosses by clicking "Toss" again to get 40 more. Don't click "Reset" during this exercise.

(a) After 40 tosses, what is the proportion of heads? What is the count of heads? What is the difference between the count of heads and 20 (one-half the number of tosses)?

(b) Keep going to 120 tosses. Again record the proportion and count of heads and the difference between the count and 60 (half the number of tosses).

(c) Keep going. Stop at 240 tosses and again at 480 tosses to record the same facts. Although it may take a long time, the laws of probability say that the proportion of heads will always get close to 0.5 and also that the difference between the count of heads and half the number of tosses will always grow without limit.

4.11 Simulating consumer behavior. About half of the customers entering a local computer store will purchase a new computer before leaving the store. Use the *What Is Probability?* applet or your statistical software to simulate 100 customers independently entering the store with each having a probability of 0.5 of purchasing a new computer on this visit to the store. (In most software, the key phrase to look for is "Bernoulli trials." This is the technical term for independent trials with Yes/No outcomes. Our outcomes here are "buy" and "not buy.")

(a) What percent of the 100 simulated customers bought a new computer?

(b) Examine the sequence of "buys" and "not buys." How long was the longest run of "buys"? Of "not buys"? (Sequences of random outcomes often show runs longer than our intuition thinks likely.)

4.12 Simulating an opinion poll. A recent opinion poll showed that about 65% of the American public have a favorable opinion of the software company Microsoft.[2] Suppose that this is exactly true. Choosing a person at random then has probability 0.65 of getting one who has a favorable opinion of Microsoft. Use the *What Is Probability?* applet or your statistical software to simulate choosing many people independently. (In most software, the key phrase to look for is "Bernoulli trials." This is the technical term for independent trials with Yes/No outcomes. Our outcomes here are "favorable" or not.)

(a) Simulate drawing 20 people, then 80 people, then 320 people. What proportion have a favorable opinion of Microsoft in each case? We expect (but because of chance variation we can't be sure) that the proportion will be closer to 0.65 in larger runs of trials.

(b) Simulate drawing 20 people 10 times and record the percents in each trial who have a favorable opinion of Microsoft. Then simulate drawing 320 people 10 times and again record the 10 percents. Which set of 10 results is less variable? We expect the results of larger trials to be more predictable (less variable) than the results of smaller trials. That is "long-run regularity" showing itself.

4.13 More efficient simulation. Continue the exploration begun in Exercise 4.12. Software allows you to simulate many independent Yes/No trials more quickly if all you want to save is the count of Yes outcomes. The key word "Binomial" simulates n independent Bernoulli trials, each with probability p of a Yes, and records just the count of Yes outcomes.

(a) Simulate 100 draws of 20 people from the population in Exercise 4.12. Record the number who have a favorable opinion of Microsoft on each draw. What is the approximate probability that out of 20 people drawn at random at least 14 have a favorable opinion of Microsoft?

(b) Convert the "favorable" counts into percents of the 20 people in each trial. Make a histogram of these 100 percents. Describe the shape, center, and spread of this distribution.

(c) Now simulate drawing 320 people. Do this 100 times and record the percent who respond "favorable" on each of the 100 draws. Make a histogram of the percents and describe the shape, center, and spread of the distribution.

(d) In what ways are the distributions in parts (b) and (c) alike? In what ways do they differ? (Because regularity emerges in the long run, we expect the results of drawing 320 individuals many times to be less variable than the results of drawing 20 individuals many times.)

4.14 **Financial fraud.** Continue with the Experian-Gallup Personal Credit Index survey described in Exercise 4.3. In Exercise 4.3, a fair die was used to simulate the selection of a fraud victim. The die provided a 1-in-6 (or 16.66667%) chance of a fraud victim's knowing the perpetrator of the fraud. The survey result was actually reported as 17% though. Use your statistical software to complete this exercise. (In most software, the key phrase to look for is "Bernoulli trials.")

(a) Set the probability for Bernoulli trials to 1/6 (or 0.166667 if your software doesn't allow you to enter a fraction). Generate 300 Bernoulli trials. How many of the 300 trials resulted in a "success" (likely represented by a number 1 in your software)? What percent of the trials does this represent? (*Note:* The word "success" is simply a label to describe the event of interest, which in this case is the event that a randomly selected fraud victim knew the perpetrator.)

(b) Now generate 30,000 Bernoulli trials. How many of the 30,000 trials resulted in a "success"? What percent of the trials does this represent?

(c) Redo parts (a) and (b) with the Bernoulli probability set to 0.17.

(d) In which simulation (300 trials or 30,000 trials) did the difference between 1/6 and 17% make the most difference in the results? How is this consistent with the definition of probability given in this section?

4.15 **Customer returns.** Shoppers return about 6% of everything they buy. Use your statistical software to complete this exercise.

(a) Set the probability for Bernoulli trials to 0.06. Generate 100 Bernoulli trials. How many of the 100 trials resulted in a "success"? What percent of the trials does this represent?

(b) Write a clear explanation of what the simulation in part (a) actually represents in terms of "Shoppers return about 6% of everything they buy." Your explanation provides the context for the statistical simulation of part (a).

4.2 Probability Models

CASE 4.1 UNCOVERING FRAUD BY DIGITAL ANALYSIS

"Digital analysis" is one of the big new tools among auditors and investigators looking for fraud. Faked numbers in tax returns, payment records, invoices, expense account claims, and many other settings often display patterns that aren't present in legitimate records. Some patterns, like too many round numbers, are obvious and easily avoided by a clever crook. Others are more subtle. It is a striking fact that the first digits of numbers in legitimate records often follow a distribution known as *Benford's law.* Here it is:

First digit	1	2	3	4	5	6	7	8	9
Proportion	0.301	0.176	0.125	0.097	0.079	0.067	0.058	0.051	0.046

These proportions are in fact *probabilities.* That is, they are the proportions specified by Benford's law if we examine a very large number of similar records. Set a computer to work comparing invoices from your company's vendors with this distribution. Aha—here is a vendor whose invoices show a very different pattern. All the invoices were approved by the same manager. Confronted, he admits that he was raising the amounts of the invoices and buying from his wife's company at the inflated amounts. Digital analysis has uncovered another case of fraud.

Of course, not all sets of data follow Benford's law. Numbers that are assigned, such as Social Security numbers, do not. Nor do data with a fixed maximum, such as deductible contributions to individual retirement accounts (IRAs). Nor of course do random numbers. But a surprising variety of data from natural science, social affairs, and business obeys this distribution.[3]

Gamblers have known for centuries that the fall of coins, cards, and dice displays clear patterns in the long run. Benford's law says that first digits also follow a clear pattern. The idea of probability rests on the observed fact that the average result of many thousands of chance outcomes can be known with near certainty. How can we give a mathematical description of long-run regularity?

To see how to proceed, think first about a very simple random phenomenon, tossing a coin once. When we toss a coin, we cannot know the outcome in advance. What do we know? We are willing to say that the outcome will be either heads or tails. We believe that each of these outcomes has probability 1/2. This description of coin tossing has two parts:

- a list of possible outcomes
- a probability for each outcome

This description is the basis for all probability models. Here is the vocabulary we use.

Probability Models

The **sample space** of a random phenomenon is the set of all possible outcomes. S is used to denote sample space.

An **event** is an outcome or a set of outcomes of a random phenomenon. That is, an event is a subset of the sample space.

A **probability model** is a mathematical description of a random phenomenon. The model has two parts: a sample space S and a way of assigning probabilities to events.

The sample space S can be very simple or very complex. When we toss a coin once, there are only two outcomes, heads and tails. The sample space is $S = \{H, T\}$. If we draw a random sample of 55,000 U.S. households, as the Current Population Survey does, the sample space contains all possible choices of 55,000 of the 106 million households in the country. This S is extremely large. Each member of S is a possible sample, which explains the term *sample space.*

EXAMPLE 4.3 Rolling Dice

Rolling two dice is a common way to lose money in casinos. There are 36 possible outcomes when we roll two dice and record the up-faces in order (first die, second die). Figure 4.2 displays these outcomes. They make up the sample space S. "Roll a 5" is an event, call it A, that contains four of these 36 outcomes:

$A = \{$  $\}$

In craps and other games, all that matters is the *sum* of the spots on the up-faces. Let's change the random outcomes we are interested in: roll two dice and count the spots on the up-faces. Now there are only 11 possible outcomes, from a sum of 2 for rolling a double one through 3, 4, 5, and on up to 12 for rolling a double six. The sample space is now

$$S = \{2, 3, 4, 5, 6, 7, 8, 9, 10, 11, 12\}$$

Comparing this S with Figure 4.2 reminds us that we can change S by changing the detailed description of the random phenomenon we are describing.

FIGURE 4.2 The 36 possible outcomes in rolling two dice.

APPLY YOUR KNOWLEDGE

4.16 Describing sample spaces. In each of the following situations, describe a sample space S for the random phenomenon. In some cases, you have some freedom in your choice of S.

(a) A new business is started. After two years, it is either still in business or it has closed.

(b) A rust prevention treatment is applied to a new car. The response variable is the length of time before rust begins to develop on the vehicle.

(c) A student enrolls in a statistics course and at the end of the semester receives a letter grade.

(d) A quality inspector examines four portable CD players and rates each as either "acceptable" or "unacceptable." You record the sequence of ratings.

(e) A quality inspector examines four portable CD players and rates each as either "acceptable" or "unacceptable." You record the number of units rated "acceptable."

4.17 Describing sample spaces. In each of the following situations, describe a sample space S for the random phenomenon. In some cases you have some freedom in specifying S, especially in setting the largest and the smallest value in S.

(a) Choose a student in your class at random. Ask how much time that student spent studying during the past 24 hours.

(b) The Physicians' Health Study asked 11,000 physicians to take an aspirin every other day and observed how many of them had a heart attack in a 5-year period.

(c) In a test of a new package design, you drop a carton of a dozen eggs from a height of 1 foot and count the number of broken eggs.

(d) Choose a Fortune 500 company at random. Look up how much the CEO of the company makes annually.

(e) A nutrition researcher feeds a new diet to a young male white rat. The response variable is the weight (in grams) that the rat gains in 8 weeks.

Probability rules

The true probability of any outcome—say, "roll a 5 when we toss two dice"—can be found only by actually tossing two dice many times, and then only approximately. How then can we describe probability mathematically? Rather than try to give "correct" probabilities, we start by laying down facts that must be true for any assignment of probabilities. These facts follow from the idea of probability as "the long-run proportion of repetitions in which an event occurs."

1. **Any probability is a number between 0 and 1.** Any proportion is a number between 0 and 1, so any probability is also a number between 0 and 1. An event with probability 0 never occurs, and an event with probability 1 occurs on every trial. An event with probability 0.5 occurs in half the trials in the long run.
2. **All possible outcomes together must have probability 1.** Because some outcome must occur on every trial, the sum of the probabilities for all possible outcomes must be exactly 1.
3. **The probability that an event does not occur is 1 minus the probability that the event does occur.** If an event occurs in (say) 70% of all trials, it fails to occur in the other 30%. The probability that an event occurs and the probability that it does not occur always add to 100%, or 1.
4. **If two events have no outcomes in common, the probability that one or the other occurs is the sum of their individual probabilities.** If one event occurs in 40% of all trials, a different event occurs in 25% of all trials, and the two can never occur together, then one or the other occurs on 65% of all trials because $40\% + 25\% = 65\%$.

We can use mathematical notation to state Facts 1 to 4 more concisely. Capital letters near the beginning of the alphabet denote events. If A is any event, we write its probability as $P(A)$. Here are our probability facts in formal language. As you apply these rules, remember that they are just another form of intuitively true facts about long-run proportions.

Probability Rules

Rule 1. The probability $P(A)$ of any event A satisfies $0 \leq P(A) \leq 1$.

Rule 2. If S is the sample space in a probability model, then $P(S) = 1$.

Rule 3. The **complement** of any event A is the event that A does not occur, written as A^c. The **complement rule** states that

$$P(A^c) = 1 - P(A)$$

Rule 4. Two events A and B are **disjoint** if they have no outcomes in common and so can never occur simultaneously. If A and B are disjoint,

$$P(A \text{ or } B) = P(A) + P(B)$$

This is the **addition rule for disjoint events.**

EXAMPLE 4.4 Benford's Law

CASE 4.1

The probabilities assigned to first digits by Benford's law are all between 0 and 1. They add to 1 because the first digits listed make up the sample space S. (Note that a first digit can't be 0.)

The probability that a first digit is anything other than 1 is, by Rule 3,

$$\begin{aligned} P(\text{not a } 1) &= 1 - P(\text{first digit is } 1) \\ &= 1 - 0.301 = 0.699 \end{aligned}$$

That is, if 30.1% of first digits are 1s, the other 69.9% are not 1s.

"First digit is a 1" and "first digit is a 2" are disjoint events. So the addition rule (Rule 4) says

$$\begin{aligned} P(1 \text{ or } 2) &= P(1) + P(2) \\ &= 0.301 + 0.176 = 0.477 \end{aligned}$$

About 48% of first digits in data governed by Benford's law are 1s or 2s. Fraudulent records generally have many fewer 1s and 2s.

EXAMPLE 4.5 Probabilities for Rolling Dice

Figure 4.2 displays the 36 possible outcomes of rolling two dice. What probabilities shall we assign to these outcomes?

Casino dice are carefully made. Their spots are not hollowed out, which would give the faces different weights, but are filled with white plastic of the same density as the colored plastic of the body. For casino dice it is reasonable to assign the same probability to each of the 36 outcomes in Figure 4.2. Because all 36 outcomes together must have probability 1 (Rule 2), each outcome must have probability 1/36.

What is the probability of rolling a 5? Because the event "roll a 5" contains the four outcomes displayed in Example 4.3, the addition rule (Rule 4) says that its probability is

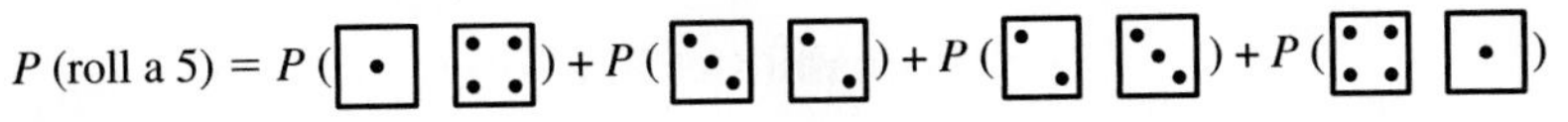

$$\begin{aligned} &= \frac{1}{36} + \frac{1}{36} + \frac{1}{36} + \frac{1}{36} \\ &= \frac{4}{36} = 0.111 \end{aligned}$$

What about the probability of rolling a 7? In Figure 4.2 you will find six outcomes for which the sum of the spots is 7. The probability is 6/36, or about 0.167.

APPLY YOUR KNOWLEDGE

4.18 Moving up. An economist studying economic class mobility finds that the probability that the son of a lower-class father remains in the lower class is 0.46. What is the probability that the son moves to one of the higher classes?

4.19 Causes of death. Government data on job-related deaths assign a single occupation for each such death that occurs in the United States. The data on occupational deaths in 1999 show that the probability is 0.134 that a randomly chosen death was agriculture related, and 0.119 that it was manufacturing related. What is the probability that a death was either agriculture related or manufacturing related? What is the probability that the death was related to some other occupation?

4.20 Rating the economy. A Gallup Poll (June 11–17, 2001) interviewed a random sample of 1004 adults (18 years or older). The people in the sample were asked how they would rate economic conditions in the United States today. Here are the results:

Outcome	Probability
Excellent	0.03
Good	0.39
Fair	?
Poor	0.12
No opinion	0.01

These proportions are probabilities for the random phenomenon of choosing an adult at random and asking the person's opinion on current economic conditions.

(a) What must be the probability that the person chosen says "fair"? Why?

(b) The official press release focused on the percent of adults giving the economy a "positive" rating where positive is defined as "good" or "excellent." What is this probability?

Assigning probabilities: finite number of outcomes

Examples 4.4 and 4.5 illustrate one way to assign probabilities to events: assign a probability to every individual outcome, then add these probabilities to find the probability of any event. If such an assignment is to satisfy the rules of probability, the probabilities of all the individual outcomes must sum to exactly 1.

Probabilities in a Finite Sample Space

Assign a probability to each individual outcome. These probabilities must be numbers between 0 and 1 and must have sum 1.

The probability of any event is the sum of the probabilities of the outcomes making up the event.

EXAMPLE 4.6 Random Digits versus Benford's Law

CASE 4.1 You might think that first digits in financial records are distributed "at random" among the digits 1 to 9. The 9 possible outcomes would then be equally likely. The sample space for a single digit is

$$S = \{1, 2, 3, 4, 5, 6, 7, 8, 9\}$$

Call a randomly chosen first digit X for short. The probability model for X is completely described by this table:

First digit X	1	2	3	4	5	6	7	8	9
Probability	1/9	1/9	1/9	1/9	1/9	1/9	1/9	1/9	1/9

The probability that a first digit is equal to or greater than 6 is

$$P(X \geq 6) = P(X = 6) + P(X = 7) + P(X = 8) + P(X = 9)$$
$$= \frac{1}{9} + \frac{1}{9} + \frac{1}{9} + \frac{1}{9} = \frac{4}{9} = 0.444$$

Note that this is not the same as the probability that a random digit is strictly greater than 6, $P(X > 6)$. The outcome $X = 6$ is included in the event $\{X \geq 6\}$ and is omitted from $\{X > 6\}$.

Compare this with the probability of the same event among first digits from financial records that obey Benford's law. A first digit V chosen from such records has the distribution

First digit V	1	2	3	4	5	6	7	8	9
Probability	0.301	0.176	0.125	0.097	0.079	0.067	0.058	0.051	0.046

The probability that this digit is equal to or greater than 6 is

$$P(V \geq 6) = 0.067 + 0.058 + 0.051 + 0.046 = 0.222$$

Benford's law allows easy detection of phony financial records based on randomly generated numbers. These records tend to have too few 1s and 2s as first digits and too many first digits of 6 or greater.

probability histogram

We can use histograms to display probability distributions as well as distributions of data. Figure 4.3 displays **probability histograms** that compare the probability model for random digits with the model given by Benford's law. The height of each bar shows the

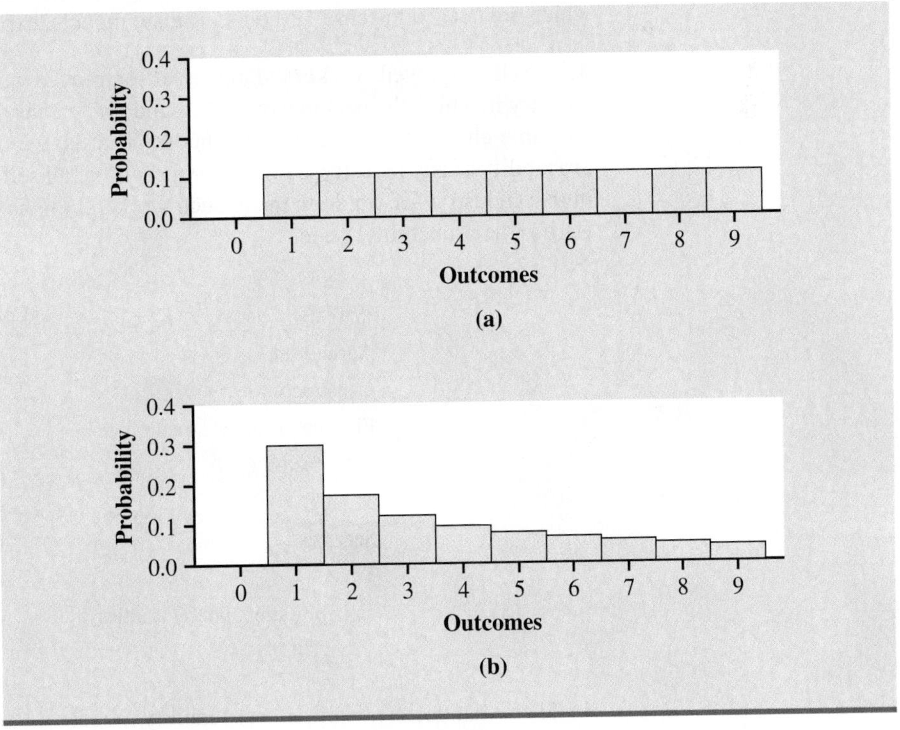

FIGURE 4.3 Probability histograms for (a) random digits 1 to 9 and (b) Benford's law. The height of each bar shows the probability assigned to a single outcome.

FIGURE 4.4 Four assignments of probabilities to the six faces of a die, for Exercise 4.21.

	Probability			
Outcome	Model 1	Model 2	Model 3	Model 4
⚀	1/7	1/3	1/3	1
⚁	1/7	1/6	1/6	1
⚂	1/7	1/6	1/6	2
⚃	1/7	0	1/6	1
⚄	1/7	1/6	1/6	1
⚅	1/7	1/6	1/6	2

probability of the outcome at its base. Because the heights are probabilities, they add to 1. As usual, all the bars in a histogram have the same width. So the areas also display the assignment of probability to outcomes. Think of these histograms as idealized pictures of the results of very many trials.

APPLY YOUR KNOWLEDGE

4.21 Rolling a die. Figure 4.4 displays several assignments of probabilities to the six faces of a die. We can learn which assignment is actually *accurate* for a particular die only by rolling the die many times. However, some of the assignments are not *legitimate* assignments of probability. That is, they do not obey the rules. Which are legitimate and which are not? In the case of the illegitimate models, explain what is wrong.

4.22 Self-employed workers. Draw a self-employed worker at random and record the industry in which the person works. "At random" means that we give every such person the same chance to be the one we choose. That is, we choose an SRS of size 1. The probability of any industry is just the proportion of all self-employed workers who work in that industry—if we drew many such workers, this is the proportion we would get. Here is the probability model:[4]

Industry	Probability
Agriculture	0.130
Construction	0.147
Finance, insurance, real estate	0.059
Manufacturing	0.042
Mining	0.002
Services	0.419
Trade	0.159
Transportation, public utilities	0.042

(a) Show that this is a legitimate probability model.

(b) What is the probability that a randomly chosen worker does not work in agriculture?

(c) What is the probability that a randomly chosen worker works in construction, manufacturing, or mining?

4.23 Job satisfaction. We can use the results of a poll on job satisfaction to give a probability model for the job satisfaction rating of a randomly chosen employed (full-time or part-time) American.[5] Here is the model:

Rating	Completely satisfied	Somewhat satisfied	Somewhat dissatisfied	Completely dissatisfied
Probability	?	0.47	0.12	0.02

(a) What is the probability of a randomly selected employed American being completely satisfied with his or her job? Why?

(b) What is the probability that a randomly selected employed American will be dissatisfied with his or her job?

Assigning probabilities: intervals of outcomes

A software random number generator is designed to produce a number between 0 and 1 chosen at random. It is only a slight idealization to consider *any* number in this range as a possible outcome. The sample space is then

$$S = \{\text{all numbers between 0 and 1}\}$$

Call the outcome of the random number generator Y for short. How can we assign probabilities to such events as $\{0.3 \le Y \le 0.7\}$? As in the case of selecting a random digit, we would like all possible outcomes to be equally likely. But we cannot assign probabilities to each individual value of Y and then add them, because there are infinitely many possible values.

We use a new way of assigning probabilities directly to events—as *areas under a density curve.* Any density curve has area exactly 1 underneath it, corresponding to total probability 1. We first met density curves as models for data in Chapter 1 (page 50).

EXAMPLE 4.7 Random Numbers

uniform density curve

The random number generator will spread its output uniformly across the entire interval from 0 to 1 as we allow it to generate a long sequence of numbers. The results of many trials are represented by the **uniform density curve,** as shown in Figure 4.5. This density curve has height 1 over the interval from 0 to 1. The area under the curve is 1, and the probability of any event is the area under the curve and above the event in question.

As Figure 4.5(a) illustrates, the probability that the random number generator produces a number between 0.3 and 0.7 is

$$P(0.3 \le X \le 0.7) = 0.4$$

because the area under the density curve and above the interval from 0.3 to 0.7 is 0.4. The height of the curve is 1 and the area of a rectangle is the product of height and length, so the probability of any interval of outcomes is just the length of the interval.

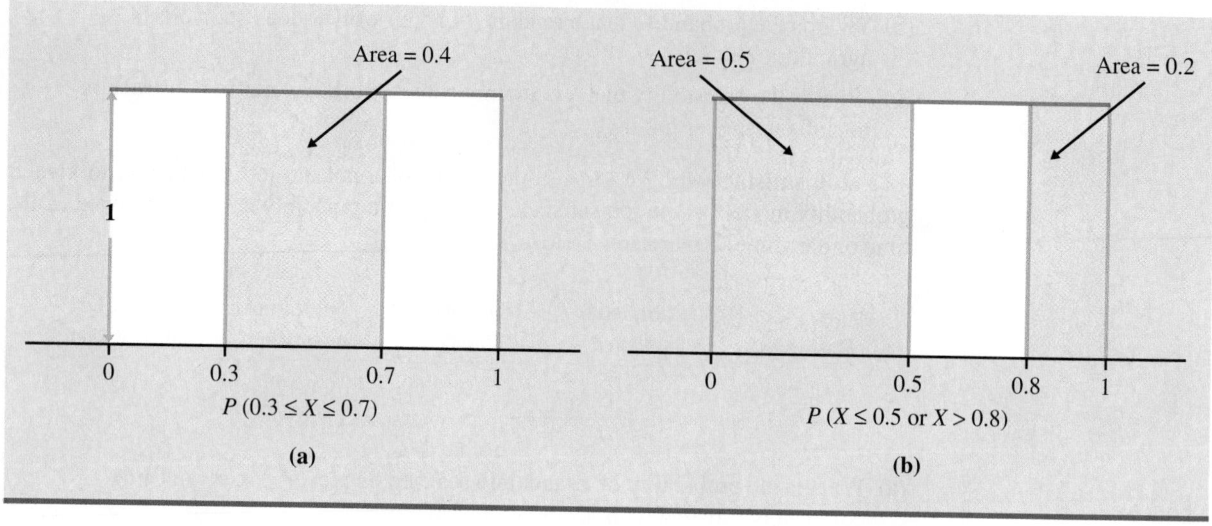

FIGURE 4.5 Probability as area under a density curve, for Example 4.7. These uniform density curves spread probability evenly between 0 and 1.

Similarly,

$$P(X \leq 0.5) = 0.5$$
$$P(X > 0.8) = 0.2$$
$$P(Y \leq 0.5 \text{ or } Y > 0.8) = 0.7$$

Notice that the last event consists of two nonoverlapping intervals, so the total area above the event is found by adding two areas, as illustrated by Figure 4.5(b). This assignment of probabilities obeys all of our rules for probability.

Compare the density curves in Figure 4.5 with the probability histogram in Figure 4.3(a). Both describe uniform distributions. In 4.3(a), there are only 9 possible outcomes, the whole numbers 1, 2, ..., 9. In Figure 4.5, the outcome can be any number between 0 and 1. In both figures, probability is given by area. Although the mathematics required to deal with density curves is more advanced, the most important ideas of probability apply to both kinds of probability models.

APPLY YOUR KNOWLEDGE

4.24 Random numbers. Let Y be a random number between 0 and 1 produced by the idealized uniform random number generator described in Example 4.7 and Figure 4.5. Find the following probabilities:

(a) $P(0 \leq Y \leq 0.4)$

(b) $P(0.4 \leq Y \leq 1)$

(c) $P(0.3 \leq Y \leq 0.5)$

(d) $P(0.3 < Y < 0.5)$

4.25 Adding random numbers. Generate two random numbers between 0 and 1 and take T to be their sum. The sum T can take any value between 0 and 2. The density curve of T is the triangle shown in Figure 4.6.

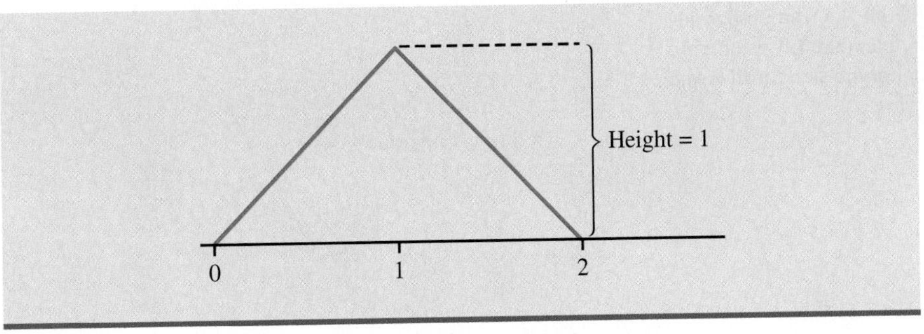

FIGURE 4.6 The density curve for the sum of two random numbers, for Exercise 4.25. This density curve spreads probability between 0 and 2.

(a) Verify by geometry that the area under this curve is 1.

(b) What is the probability that T is less than 1? (Sketch the density curve, shade the area that represents the probability, then find that area. Do this for (c) also.)

(c) What is $P(T < 0.5)$?

Normal probability models

Any density curve can be used to assign probabilities. The density curves that are most familiar to us are the Normal curves introduced in Section 1.3. So **Normal distributions are probability models.** There is a close connection between a Normal distribution as an idealized description for data and a Normal probability model. If we look at the weights of all 9-ounce bags of a particular brand of potato chip, we find that they closely follow the Normal distribution with mean $\mu = 9.12$ ounces and standard deviation $\sigma = 0.15$ ounces, $N(9.12, 0.15)$. That is a distribution for a large set of data. Now choose one 9-ounce bag at random. Call its weight W. If we repeat the random choice very many times, the distribution of values of W is the same Normal distribution.

EXAMPLE 4.8 The Weight of Bags of Potato Chips

What is the probability that a randomly chosen 9-ounce bag has weight between 9.33 and 9.45 ounces?

The weight W of the bag we choose has the $N(9.12, 0.15)$ distribution. Find the probability by standardizing and using Table A, the table of standard Normal probabilities. We will reserve capital Z for a standard Normal variable, $N(0, 1)$.

$$\begin{aligned} P(9.33 \le W \le 9.45) &= P\left(\frac{9.33 - 9.12}{0.15} \le \frac{W - 9.12}{0.15} \le \frac{9.45 - 9.12}{0.15}\right) \\ &= P(1.4 \le Z \le 2.2) \\ &= 0.9861 - 0.9192 = 0.0669 \end{aligned}$$

Figure 4.7 shows the areas under the standard Normal curve. The calculation is the same as those we did in Chapter 1. Only the language of probability is new.

APPLY YOUR KNOWLEDGE

4.26 Miles per gallon for 2001 vehicles. The Normal distribution with mean $\mu = 21.2$ miles per gallon and standard deviation $\sigma = 5.4$ mpg is an approximate model for the city gas mileage of 2001 model vehicles. Figure 1.15 (page 50) pictures this distribution. Let X be the city mpg of one 2001 vehicle chosen at random.

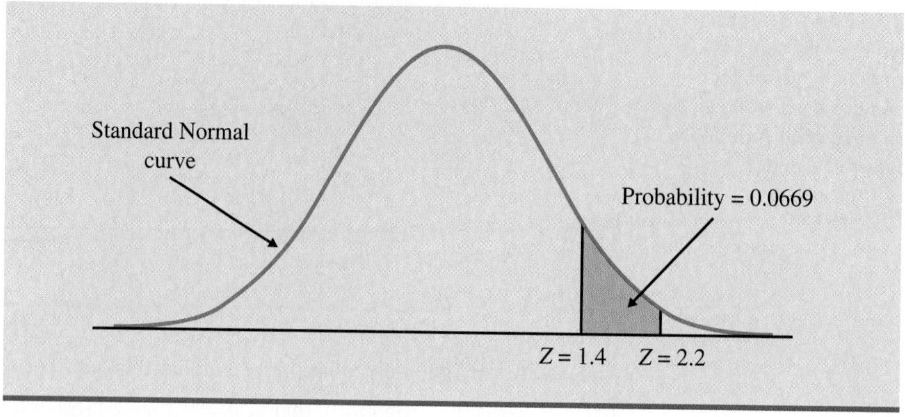

FIGURE 4.7 The probability in Example 4.8 as an area under the standard Normal curve.

(a) Write the event "the vehicle chosen has a city MPG of 32 or higher" in terms of X.

(b) Find the probability of this event.

4.27 NAEP math scores. Scores on the National Assessment of Educational Progress 12th-grade mathematics test for the year 2000 were approximately Normal with mean 300 points (out of 500 possible) and standard deviation 35 points. Let Y stand for the score of a randomly chosen student. Express each of the following events in terms of Y and use the 68–95–99.7 rule to give the approximate probability.

(a) The student has a score above 300.

(b) The student's score is above 370.

SECTION 4.2 SUMMARY

- A **probability model** for a random phenomenon consists of a sample space S and an assignment of probabilities P.
- The **sample space** S is the set of all possible outcomes of the random phenomenon. Sets of outcomes are called **events.** P assigns a number $P(A)$ to an event A as its probability.
- Any assignment of probability must obey the rules that state the basic properties of probability:
  1. $0 \leq P(A) \leq 1$ for any event A.
  2. $P(S) = 1$.
  3. For any event A, $P(A \text{ does not occur}) = 1 - P(A)$.
  4. **Addition rule:** Events A and B are **disjoint** if they have no outcomes in common. If A and B are disjoint, then $P(A \text{ or } B) = P(A) + P(B)$.
- When a sample space S contains finitely many possible outcomes, a probability model assigns each of these outcomes a probability between 0 and 1 such that the sum of all the probabilities is exactly 1. The probability of any event is the sum of the probabilities of all the outcomes that make up the event.
- A sample space can contain all values in some interval of numbers. A probability model assigns probabilities as **areas under a density curve.** The probability of any event is the area under the curve above the outcomes that make up the event.

SECTION 4.2 Exercises

For Exercises 4.16 and 4.17, see page 251; for 4.18 to 4.20, see pages 253–254; for 4.21 to 4.23, see pages 256–257; for 4.24 and 4.25, see pages 258–259; and for 4.26 and 4.27, see pages 259–260.

4.28 Demographics—language. Canada has two official languages, English and French. Choose a Canadian at random and ask, "What is your mother tongue?" Here is the distribution of responses, combining many separate languages from the broad Asian/Pacific region:[6]

Language	English	French	Asian/Pacific	Other
Probability	0.59	0.23	0.07	?

(a) What probability should replace "?" in the distribution?

(b) What is the probability that a Canadian's mother tongue is not English?

4.29 Filtering junk mail. A majority of email messages are now "spam," or junk mail. Email providers, including colleges, businesses, Internet service providers (ISPs), and free-email providers (like Yahoo and Google), are engaged in fighting the onslaught of junk mail. Some kinds of spam messages are more bothersome to email users than others. Consider choosing a spam email message at random. Here is the distribution of topics:[7]

Topic	Probability
Adult	0.145
Financial	0.162
Health	0.073
Leisure	0.078
Products	0.210
Scams	0.142

(a) What is the probability that a spam email does not concern one of these topics?

(b) Corinne is particularly annoyed by spam offering "adult" content (that is, pornography) and scams. What is the probability that a randomly chosen spam email falls into one or the other of these categories?

(c) What are the chances that a randomly chosen spam message is not selling a product?

4.30 Spill or spell? Spell-checking software catches "nonword errors" that result in a string of letters that is not a word, as when "the" is typed as "teh." When undergraduates are asked to write a 250-word essay (without spell-checking), the number X of nonword errors has the following distribution:

Value of X	0	1	2	3	4
Probability	0.1	0.2	0.3	0.3	0.1

(a) Write the event "at least one nonword error" in terms of X. What is the probability of this event?

(b) Describe the event $X \leq 2$ in words. What is its probability? What is the probability that $X < 2$?

4.31 Great Britain household size. In government data, a household consists of all occupants of a dwelling unit. Here is the distribution of household size in Great Britain according to the 2005 General Household Survey:

Occupants	1	2	3	4	5	6+
Probability	0.31	0.35	0.15	0.13	0.04	0.02

Choose a Great Britain household at random and let the random variable Y be the number of persons living in the household.

(a) Express "more than one person lives in this household" in terms of Y. What is the probability of this event?

(b) What is $P(2 < Y \leq 4)$?

(c) What is $P(Y \neq 2)$?

4.32 World Internet usage. According to information summarized by `InternetWorldStats.com`, approximately 16.6% of the world's population uses the Internet (as of January 2007). Furthermore, a randomly chosen Internet user has the following probabilities of being from the given region of the world:

Region	Probability
Asia	0.356
Europe	0.286
North America	0.212
Latin America/Caribbean	0.081
Other	?

Color	Silver	White	Black	Dark green	Dark blue	Medium red
Probability	0.176	0.172	0.113	0.089	0.088	0.067

(a) What is the probability of a randomly chosen Internet user not being from one of the four regions explicitly listed in this table?

(b) What is the probability of a randomly chosen Internet user living in either Asia or Europe?

(c) What is the probability of a randomly chosen Internet user not living in North America?

4.33 Broadband preferences. According to information presented by the National Telecommunications and Information Administration (NTIA), approximately 19.9% of all U.S. households have high-speed (broadband) Internet (as of October 2003). Of these broadband Internet households, the following broadband technologies are in use, with the specified percents:

Technology	Cable	DSL	MMDS	Satellite
Percent of broadband users	56.4	41.6	01.1	00.9

(a) Do all broadband households appear to be accounted for by this table? Explain your response.

(b) What is the probability of a randomly chosen broadband household having neither cable nor DSL Internet access?

(c) What is the probability of a randomly chosen U.S. household having broadband Internet access?

4.34 Stock price movements. You watch the price of Cisco Systems stock for four days. Give a sample space for each of the following random phenomena.

(a) You record the sequence of up-days and down-days.

(b) You record the number of up-days.

4.35 Land in Iowa. Choose an acre of land in Iowa at random. The probability is 0.92 that it is farmland and 0.01 that it is forest.

(a) What is the probability that the acre chosen is not farmland?

(b) What is the probability that it is either farmland or forest?

(c) What is the probability that a randomly chosen acre in Iowa is something other than farmland or forest?

4.36 Car colors. Choose a new car or light truck at random and note its color. At the top of this page are the probabilities of the most popular colors for cars made in North America in 2000.[8]

What is the probability that the car you choose has any color other than the six listed? What is the probability that a randomly chosen car is either silver or white?

4.37 Colors of M&M's. The colors of candies such as M&M's are carefully chosen to match consumer preferences. The color of an M&M drawn at random from a bag has a probability distribution determined by the proportions of colors among all M&M's of that type.

(a) Here is the distribution for plain M&M's:

Color	Brown	Red	Yellow	Green	Orange	Blue
Probability	0.3	0.2	0.2	0.1	0.1	?

What must be the probability of drawing a blue candy?

(b) The probabilities for peanut M&M's are a bit different. Here they are:

Color	Brown	Red	Yellow	Green	Orange	Blue
Probability	0.2	0.2	0.2	0.1	0.1	?

What is the probability that a peanut M&M chosen at random is blue?

(c) What is the probability that a plain M&M is any of red, yellow, or orange? What is the probability that a peanut M&M has one of these colors?

4.38 Crispy M&M's. Exercise 4.37 gives the probabilities that an M&M candy is each of brown, red, yellow, green, orange, and blue. "Crispy Chocolate" M&M's are equally likely to be any of these colors. What is the probability of any one color?

4.39 Legitimate probabilities? In each of the following situations, state whether or not the given assignment of probabilities to individual outcomes is legitimate, that is, satisfies the rules of probability. If not, give specific reasons for your answer.

(a) When a coin is spun, $P(\text{H}) = 0.55$ and $P(\text{T}) = 0.45$.

(b) When two coins are tossed, $P(\text{HH}) = 0.4$, $P(\text{HT}) = 0.4$, $P(\text{TH}) = 0.4$, and $P(\text{TT}) = 0.4$.

Acres	< 10	10–49	50–99	100–179	180–499	500–999	1000–1999	≥ 2000
Probability	0.09	0.20	0.15	0.16	0.22	0.09	0.05	0.04

(c) Plain M&M's have not always had the mixture of colors given in Exercise 4.37. In the past there were no red candies and no blue candies. Tan had probability 0.10, and the other four colors had the same probabilities that are given in Exercise 4.37.

4.40 Who goes to Paris? Abby, Deborah, Sam, Tonya, and Roberto work in a firm's public relations office. Their employer must choose two of them to attend a conference in Paris. To avoid unfairness, the choice will be made by drawing two names from a hat. (This is an SRS of size 2.)

(a) Write down all possible choices of two of the five names. This is the sample space.

(b) The random drawing makes all choices equally likely. What is the probability of each choice?

(c) What is the probability that Tonya is chosen?

(d) What is the probability that neither of the two men (Sam and Roberto) is chosen?

4.41 How big are farms? Choose an American farm at random and measure its size in acres. At the top of the page are the probabilities that the farm chosen falls in several acreage categories.

Let A be the event that the farm is less than 50 acres in size, and let B be the event that it is 500 acres or more.

(a) Find $P(A)$ and $P(B)$.

(b) Describe the event "A does not occur" in words and find its probability by Rule 3.

(c) Describe the event "A or B" in words and find its probability by the addition rule.

4.42 Roulette. A roulette wheel has 38 slots, numbered 0, 00, and 1 to 36. The slots 0 and 00 are colored green, 18 of the others are red, and 18 are black. The dealer spins the wheel and at the same time rolls a small ball along the wheel in the opposite direction. The wheel is carefully balanced so that the ball is equally likely to land in any slot when the wheel slows. Gamblers can bet on various combinations of numbers and colors.

(a) What is the probability of any one of the 38 possible outcomes? Explain your answer.

(b) If you bet on "red," you win if the ball lands in a red slot. What is the probability of winning?

(c) The slot numbers are laid out on a board on which gamblers place their bets. One column of numbers on the board contains all multiples of 3, that is, 3, 6, 9, . . . , 36. You place a "column bet" that wins if any of these numbers comes up. What is your probability of winning?

4.43 Consumer preference. Suppose that half of all computer users prefer the new version of your company's best-selling software, and half prefer the old version. If you randomly choose three consumers and record their preferences, there are 8 possible outcomes. For example, NNO means the first two consumers prefer the new (N) version and the third consumer prefers the old version (O). All 8 arrangements are equally likely.

(a) Write down all 8 arrangements of preferences of three consumers. What is the probability of any one of these arrangements?

(b) Let X be the number of consumers who prefer the new version of the product. What is the probability that $X = 2$?

(c) Starting from your work in (a), list the values X can take and the probability for each value.

4.44 Moving up. A study of class mobility in England looked at the economic class reached by the sons of lower-class fathers. Economic classes are numbered from 1 (low) to 5 (high). Take X to be the class of a randomly chosen son of a father in Class 1. The study found that the probability model for X is

Son's class X	1	2	3	4	5
Probability	0.48	0.38	0.08	0.05	0.01

(a) Check that this distribution satisfies the two requirements for a legitimate assignment of probabilities to individual outcomes.

(b) What is $P(X \leq 3)$? (Be careful: the event "$X \leq 3$" includes the value 3.)

(c) What is $P(X < 3)$?

(d) Write the event "a son of a lower-class father reaches one of the two highest classes" in terms of values of X. What is the probability of this event?

4.45 How large are households? Choose an American household at random and let X be the number of persons living in the household. If we ignore the few

Household size X	1	2	3	4	5	6	7
Probability	0.25	0.32	0.17	0.15	0.07	0.03	0.01

households with more than seven inhabitants, the probability model for X is shown above.

(a) Verify that this is a legitimate probability distribution.

(b) What is $P(X \geq 5)$?

(c) What is $P(X > 5)$?

(d) What is $P(2 < X \leq 4)$?

(e) What is $P(X \neq 1)$?

(f) Write the event that a randomly chosen household contains more than two persons in terms of X. What is the probability of this event?

4.46 Random numbers. Many random number generators allow users to specify the range of the random numbers to be produced. Suppose that you specify that the random number Y can take any value between 0 and 2. Then the density curve of the outcomes has constant height between 0 and 2, and height 0 elsewhere.

(a) What is the height of the density curve between 0 and 2? Draw a graph of the density curve.

(b) Use your graph from (a) and the fact that probability is area under the curve to find $P(Y \leq 1)$.

(c) Find $P(0.5 < Y < 1.3)$.

(d) Find $P(Y \geq 0.8)$.

4.3 Random Variables

Not all sample spaces are made up of numbers. When we toss a coin four times, we can record the outcome as a string of heads and tails, such as HTTH. In statistics, however, we are most often interested in numerical outcomes such as the count of heads in the four tosses. It is convenient to use a shorthand notation: Let X be the number of heads. If our outcome is HTTH, then $X = 2$. If the next outcome is TTTH, the value of X changes to $X = 1$. The possible values of X are 0, 1, 2, 3, and 4. Tossing a coin four times will give X one of these possible values. Tossing four more times will give X another and probably different value. We call X a *random variable* because its values vary when the coin tossing is repeated. Examples 4.6 and 4.7 used this shorthand notation. In Example 4.8, we let W stand for the weight of a randomly chosen 9-ounce bag of potato chips. We know that W would take a different value if we took another random sample. Because its value changes from one sample to another, W is also a random variable.

Random Variable

A **random variable** is a variable whose value is a numerical outcome of a random phenomenon.

We usually denote random variables by capital letters near the end of the alphabet, such as X or Y. Of course, the random variables of greatest interest to us are outcomes such as the mean $\overline{x}$ of a random sample, for which we will keep the familiar notation.[9] As we progress from general rules of probability toward statistical inference, we will concentrate on random variables. When a random variable X describes a random phenomenon, the sample space S just lists the possible values of the random variable. We usually do not mention S separately.

We will meet two types of random variables, corresponding to two ways of assigning probability: *discrete* and *continuous*. Compare the random variable X in Example 4.6 (page 254) and the random variable Y in Example 4.7 (page 257). Both have uniform distributions that distribute probability evenly across the possible outcomes, but one is discrete and the other is continuous.

The possible values of X in Example 4.6 are the whole numbers $\{1, 2, 3, 4, 5, 6, 7, 8, 9\}$. These nine values are separated on the number line by other numbers that are not possible values of X:

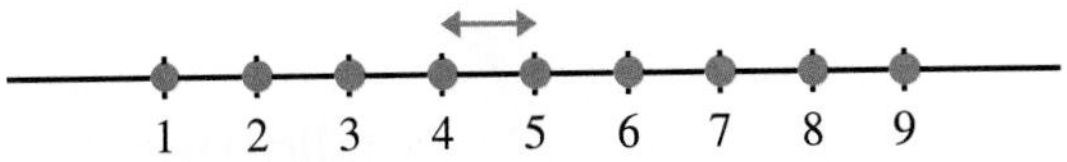

discrete random variable

X is a **discrete random variable.** "Discrete" describes the nature of the sample space for X. In contrast, the sample space for Y in Example 4.7 is {all numbers between 0 and 1}. These possible values are not separated on the number line. As you move continuously from the value 0 to the value 1, you do not leave the sample space for Y:

continuous random variable

Y is a **continuous random variable.** Once again, "continuous" describes the nature of the sample space.

APPLY YOUR KNOWLEDGE

4.47 Discrete or continuous? For each exercise listed below, decide whether the random variable described is discrete or continuous and give a brief explanation for your response.

(a) Exercise 4.16(b), page 251

(b) Exercise 4.16(e), page 251

(c) Exercise 4.26, page 259

(d) Exercise 4.45, page 263

4.48 Discrete or continuous? For each exercise listed below, decide whether the random variable described is discrete or continuous and sketch the sample space on a number line.

(a) Exercise 4.17(a), page 251

(b) Exercise 4.17(c), page 251

(c) Exercise 4.17(e), page 251

Probability distributions

The starting point for studying any random variable is its probability distribution, which is just the probability model for the outcomes.

Probability Distribution

The **probability distribution** of a random variable X tells us what values X can take and how to assign probabilities to those values.

Because of the difference in the nature of sample spaces for discrete and continuous random variables, we describe probability distributions for the two types of random variables separately.

Discrete random variables

A discrete random variable like the uniform random digit X in Example 4.6 (page 254) has a finite number of possible values.[10] The probability distribution of X therefore simply lists the values and their probabilities.

Discrete Probability Distributions

The **probability distribution** of a discrete random variable X lists the possible values of X and their probabilities:

Value of X	x_1	x_2	x_3	$\cdots$	x_k
Probability	p_1	p_2	p_3	$\cdots$	p_k

The probabilities p_i must satisfy two requirements:

1. Every probability p_i is a number between 0 and 1, $0 \leq p_i \leq 1$.
2. The sum of the probabilities is exactly 1, $p_1 + p_2 + \cdots + p_k = 1$.

To find the probability of any event, add the probabilities p_i of the individual values x_i that make up the event.

We can use a probability histogram to display a discrete distribution. Figure 4.3 (page 255) compares the distributions of random digits and first digits that obey Benford's law.

EXAMPLE 4.9 Hard-Drive Sizes

Buyers of a laptop computer model may choose to purchase either a 40 GB (gigabyte), 60 GB, 80 GB, or 100 GB internal hard drive. Choose customers from the last 60 days at random to ask what influenced their choice of computer. To "choose at random" means to give every customer of the last 60 days the same chance to be chosen. The size (in gigabytes) of the internal hard drive chosen by a randomly selected customer is a random variable X.

The value of X changes when we repeatedly choose customers at random, but it is always one of 40, 60, 80, or 100 GB. Here is the distribution of X:

Hard-drive size X	40	60	80	100
Probability	0.50	0.25	0.15	0.10

The probability histogram in Figure 4.8 pictures this distribution.

The probability that a randomly selected customer chose at least an 80 GB hard drive is

$$P(\text{size is 80 or 100}) = P(X = 80) + P(X = 100)$$
$$= 0.15 + 0.10 = 0.25$$

CASE 4.2 PORTFOLIO ANALYSIS *(Continued)*

Investors want high returns, but they also want safety. Apple's stock price has often halved or doubled within a few months. The variability of returns, called *volatility* in finance, is a measure of the risk of an investment. A highly volatile stock, which may go either up or down a lot, is more risky than a Treasury bill, whose return is very predictable.

A *portfolio* is a collection of investments held by an individual or an institution. *Portfolio analysis* begins by studying how the risk and return of a portfolio are determined by the risk and return of the individual investments it contains. That's where statistics comes in: the return on an investment over some period of time is a random variable. We are interested in the *mean* return and we measure volatility by the *standard deviation* of returns. Let's say that Sadie's portfolio places 20% of her funds in Treasury bills and 80% in an "index fund" that represents all U.S. common stocks. If X is the annual return on T-bills and Y the annual return on stocks, the portfolio rate of return is

$$R = 0.2X + 0.8Y$$

How can we find the mean and standard deviation of the portfolio return R starting from information about X and Y? We must now develop the machinery to do this.

Think first not about investments but about making refrigerators. Dimples and paint sags are two kinds of flaws in the painted finish of refrigerators. Not all refrigerators have the same number of dimples: many have none, some have one, some two, and so on. The inspectors report finding an average of 0.7 dimples and 1.4 sags per refrigerator. How many total imperfections of both kinds (on the average) are on a refrigerator? That's easy: if the average number of dimples is 0.7 and the average number of sags is 1.4, then counting both gives an average of $0.7 + 1.4 = 2.1$ flaws.

In more formal language, the number of dimples on a refrigerator is a random variable X that varies as we inspect one refrigerator after another. We know only that the mean number of dimples is $\mu_X = 0.7$. The number of paint sags is a second random variable Y having mean $\mu_Y = 1.4$. (As usual, the subscripts keep straight which variable we are talking about.) The total number of both dimples and sags is another random variable, the sum $X + Y$. Its mean μ_{X+Y} is the average number of dimples and sags together. It is just the sum of the individual means μ_X and μ_Y. That's an important rule for how means of random variables behave.

Here's another rule. A large lot of plastic coffee-can lids has mean diameter 4.2 inches. What is the mean in centimeters? There are 2.54 centimeters in an inch, so the diameter in centimeters of any lid is 2.54 times its diameter in inches. If we multiply every observation by 2.54, we also multiply their average by 2.54. The mean in centimeters must be 2.54×4.2, or about 10.7 centimeters. More formally, the diameter in inches of a lid chosen at random from the lot is a random variable X with mean μ_X. The diameter in centimeters is $2.54X$, and this new random variable has mean $2.54\mu_X$.

The point of these examples is that means behave like averages. Here are the rules we need.

Rules for Means

Rule 1. If X is a random variable and a and b are fixed numbers, then

$$\mu_{a+bX} = a + b\mu_X$$

Rule 2. If X and Y are random variables, then

$$\mu_{X+Y} = \mu_X + \mu_Y$$

This is the **addition rule for means.**

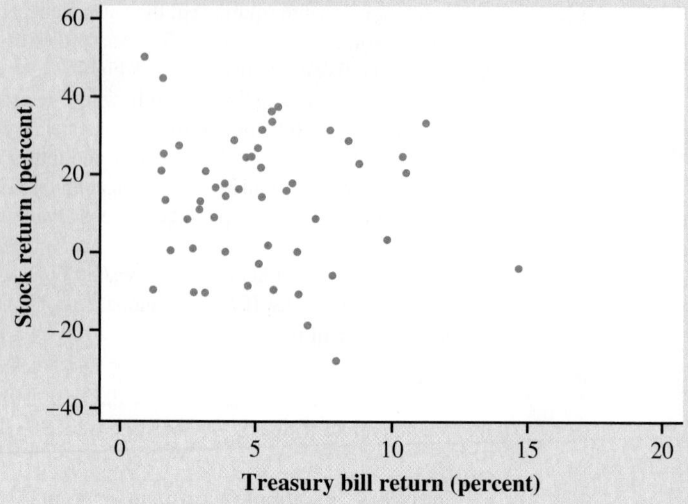

FIGURE 4.14 Annual returns on U.S. common stocks versus returns on Treasury bills for the years 1950 to 2000, for Example 4.15.

EXAMPLE 4.15 Portfolio Analysis

CASE 4.2 

The past behavior of the two securities in Sadie's portfolio is pictured in Figure 4.14, which plots the annual returns on Treasury bills and common stocks for the years 1950 to 2000. We can calculate mean returns from the data behind the plot:[12]

$$X = \text{annual return on T-bills} \qquad \mu_X = 5.2\%$$
$$Y = \text{annual return on stocks} \qquad \mu_Y = 13.3\%$$

Sadie invests 20% in T-bills and 80% in stocks. We can find the mean return on her portfolio by combining Rules 1 and 2:

$$\begin{aligned} R &= 0.2X + 0.8Y \\ \mu_R &= 0.2\mu_X + 0.8\mu_Y \\ &= (0.2)(5.2) + (0.8)(13.3) = 11.68\% \end{aligned}$$

This calculation uses historical data on returns. Next year may of course be very different. It is usual in finance to use the term *expected return* in place of mean return. Remember our warning that we can't generally expect a future value to be close to the mean. ■

EXAMPLE 4.16 Gain Communications

Gain Communications sells aircraft communications units to both the military and the civilian markets. Next year's sales depend on market conditions that cannot be predicted exactly. Gain follows the modern practice of using probability estimates of sales. The military division estimates its sales as follows:

Units sold	1000	3000	5000	10,000
Probability	0.1	0.3	0.4	0.2

These are *personal probabilities* that express the informed opinion of Gain's executives. The corresponding sales estimates for the civilian division are

Units sold	300	500	750
Probability	0.4	0.5	0.1

Take X to be the number of military units sold and Y the number of civilian units sold. From the probability distributions we compute that

$$\begin{aligned}\mu_X &= (1000)(0.1) + (3000)(0.3) + (5000)(0.4) + (10{,}000)(0.2) \\ &= 100 + 900 + 2000 + 2000 = 5000 \text{ units} \\ \mu_Y &= (300)(0.4) + (500)(0.5) + (750)(0.1) \\ &= 120 + 250 + 75 = 445 \text{ units}\end{aligned}$$

Gain makes a profit of \$2000 on each military unit sold and \$3500 on each civilian unit. Next year's profit from military sales will be $2000X$, \$2000 times the number X of units sold. By Rule 1 for means, the mean military profit is

$$\mu_{2000X} = 2000\mu_X = (2000)(5000) = \$10{,}000{,}000$$

Similarly, the civilian profit is $3500Y$, and the mean profit from civilian sales is

$$\mu_{3500Y} = 3500\mu_Y = (3500)(445) = \$1{,}557{,}500$$

The total profit is the sum of the military and civilian profit:

$$Z = 2000X + 3500Y$$

Rule 2 for means says that the mean of this sum of two variables is the sum of the two individual means:

$$\begin{aligned}\mu_Z &= \mu_{2000X} + \mu_{3500Y} \\ &= \$10{,}000{,}000 + \$1{,}557{,}500 \\ &= \$11{,}557{,}500\end{aligned}$$

This mean is the company's best estimate of next year's profit, combining the probability estimates of the two divisions. We can do this calculation more quickly by combining Rules 1 and 2:

$$\begin{aligned}\mu_Z &= \mu_{2000X+3500Y} \\ &= 2000\mu_X + 3500\mu_Y \\ &= (2000)(5000) + (3500)(445) = \$11{,}557{,}500\end{aligned}$$

APPLY YOUR KNOWLEDGE

4.55 Selling mobile phones. You own a mobile-phone store with two locations, one in the local mall and one downtown on Main Street. Let X be the number of phones sold during the next month at the mall location, and let Y be the number of phones sold during the next month at the downtown location. For the mall location, you estimate the following probability distribution:

Phones sold	200	300	400
Probability	0.4	0.4	0.2

For the downtown location, your estimated distribution is

Phones sold	100	200	300	400
Probability	0.3	0.5	0.15	0.05

(a) Calculate μ_X and μ_Y.

(b) Your rental cost is higher at the mall location. You make $25 profit on each phone sold at the mall location and $35 profit on each phone sold at the downtown location. Calculate the mean profit for each location.

(c) Calculate the mean profit for both locations combined.

4.56 Mutual funds. The addition rule for means extends to sums of any number of random variables. Let's look at a portfolio containing three mutual funds. CASE 4.2 The monthly returns on Fidelity Magellan Fund, Fidelity Real Estate Fund, and Fidelity Japan Fund for the 36 months ending in December 2000 had approximately these means:[13]

W = Magellan monthly return	$\mu_W = 1.14\%$
X = Real Estate monthly return	$\mu_X = 0.16\%$
Y = Japan monthly return	$\mu_Y = 1.59\%$

What is the mean monthly return for a portfolio consisting of 50% Magellan, 30% Real Estate, and 20% Japan?

The variance of a random variable

The mean portfolio return in Example 4.15 is less than the mean return for stocks because Sadie added 20% Treasury bills. What does she gain by giving up some average return? T-bills are much less volatile than stocks, so she hopes that her portfolio returns will vary less from year to year than would be the case if she invested all her funds in stocks. The mean is a measure of the center of a distribution. Even the most basic numerical description requires in addition a measure of the spread or variability of the distribution.

The variance and the standard deviation are the measures of spread that accompany the choice of the mean to measure center. Just as for the mean, we need a distinct symbol to distinguish the variance of a random variable from the variance s^2 of a data set. We write the variance of a random variable X as σ_X^2. The definition of the variance σ_X^2 of a random variable is similar to the definition of the sample variance s^2 given in Chapter 1. That is, the variance is an average of the squared deviations $(X - \mu_X)^2$ of the variable X from its mean μ_X. As for the mean, the average we use is a weighted average in which each outcome is weighted by its probability to take account of outcomes that are not equally likely. Calculating this weighted average is straightforward for discrete random variables but requires advanced mathematics in the continuous case. Here is the definition.

Variance of a Discrete Random Variable

Suppose that X is a discrete random variable whose distribution is

Value of X	x_1	x_2	x_3	$\cdots$	x_k
Probability	p_1	p_2	p_3	$\cdots$	p_k

and that μ is the mean of X. The **variance** of X

$$\sigma_X^2 = (x_1 - \mu_X)^2 p_1 + (x_2 - \mu_X)^2 p_2 + \cdots + (x_k - \mu_X)^2 p_k$$
$$= \sum (x_i - \mu_X)^2 p_i$$

The **standard deviation** σ_X of X is the square root of the variance.

EXAMPLE 4.17 Gain Communications

In Example 4.16 we saw that the number X of communications units that the Gain Communications military division hopes to sell has distribution

Units sold	1000	3000	5000	10,000
Probability	0.1	0.3	0.4	0.2

We can find the mean and variance of X by arranging the calculation in the form of a table. Both μ_X and σ_X^2 are sums of columns in this table.

x_i	p_i	$x_i p_i$	$(x_i - \mu_X)^2 p_i$
1,000	0.1	100	$(1{,}000 - 5{,}000)^2(0.1) = 1{,}600{,}000$
3,000	0.3	900	$(3{,}000 - 5{,}000)^2(0.3) = 1{,}200{,}000$
5,000	0.4	2,000	$(5{,}000 - 5{,}000)^2(0.4) = 0$
10,000	0.2	2,000	$(10{,}000 - 5{,}000)^2(0.2) = 5{,}000{,}000$
		$\mu_X = 5{,}000$	$\sigma_X^2 = 7{,}800{,}000$

We see that $\sigma_X^2 = 7{,}800{,}000$. The standard deviation of X is $\sigma_X = \sqrt{7{,}800{,}000} = 2792.8$. The standard deviation is a measure of how variable the number of units sold is. As in the case of distributions for data, the standard deviation of a probability distribution is easiest to understand for Normal distributions.

APPLY YOUR KNOWLEDGE

4.57 Civilian sales. Example 4.16 also gives the distribution of Gain's civilian sales Y. Find the variance σ_Y^2 and the standard deviation σ_Y.

4.58 Hard-drive sizes. Example 4.9 (page 266) gives the distribution of hard-drive sizes for sales of a particular model computer. You found the mean hard-drive size in Exercise 4.53 (page 274). Find the standard deviation of the distribution of hard-drive sizes.

4.59 Selling mobile phones. Exercise 4.55 gives the distribution of weekly mobile-phone sales in two locations.

(a) Calculate the variance and the standard deviation of the number of phones sold at the mall location.

(b) Calculate σ_Y^2 and σ_Y for the downtown location.

Rules for variances

What are the facts for variances that parallel Rules 1 and 2 for means? The mean of a sum of random variables is always the sum of their means, but this addition rule is not always true for variances. To understand why, take X to be the percent of a family's after-tax income that is spent and Y the percent that is saved. When X increases, Y decreases by the same amount. Though X and Y may vary widely from year to year, their sum $X + Y$ is always 100% and does not vary at all. It is the association between the variables X and Y that prevents their variances from adding. If random variables are *independent,* this kind of association between their values is ruled out and their variances do add. *independence* Two random variables X and Y are **independent** if knowing that any event involving X alone did or did not occur tells us nothing about the occurrence of any event involving Y alone. Probability models often assume independence when the random variables describe outcomes that appear unrelated to each other. You should ask in each instance whether the assumption of independence seems reasonable.

When random variables are not independent, the variance of their sum depends on the *correlation* **correlation** between them as well as on their individual variances. In Chapter 2, we met the correlation r between two observed variables measured on the same individuals. We defined (page 111) the correlation r as an average of the products of the standardized x and y observations. The correlation between two random variables is defined in the same way, once again using a weighted average with probabilities as weights. We won't give the details—it is enough to know that the correlation between two random variables has the same basic properties as the correlation r calculated from data. We use ρ, the Greek letter rho, for the correlation between two random variables. The correlation ρ is a number between -1 and 1 that measures the direction and strength of the linear relationship between two variables. **The correlation between two independent random variables is zero.**

Returning to family finances, if X is the percent of a family's after-tax income that is spent and Y the percent that is saved, then $Y = 100 - X$. This is a perfect linear relationship with a negative slope, so the correlation between X and Y is $\rho = -1$. With the correlation at hand, we can state the rules for manipulating variances.

Rules for Variances

Rule 1. If X is a random variable and a and b are fixed numbers, then

$$\sigma^2_{a+bX} = b^2\sigma^2_X$$

Rule 2. If X and Y are independent random variables, then

$$\sigma^2_{X+Y} = \sigma^2_X + \sigma^2_Y$$
$$\sigma^2_{X-Y} = \sigma^2_X + \sigma^2_Y$$

This is the **addition rule for variances of independent random variables.**

Rule 3. If X and Y have correlation ρ, then

$$\sigma^2_{X+Y} = \sigma^2_X + \sigma^2_Y + 2\rho\sigma_X\sigma_Y$$
$$\sigma^2_{X-Y} = \sigma^2_X + \sigma^2_Y - 2\rho\sigma_X\sigma_Y$$

This is the **general addition rule for variances of random variables.**

Notice that because a variance is the average of *squared* deviations from the mean, multiplying X by a constant b multiplies σ^2_X by the *square* of the constant. Adding a constant a to a random variable changes its mean but does not change its variability. The variance of $X + a$ is therefore the same as the variance of X. Because the square of -1 is 1, the addition rule says that the variance of a difference of independent random variables is the *sum* of the variances. For independent random variables, the difference $X - Y$ is more variable than either X or Y alone because variations in both X and Y contribute to variation in their difference.

As with data, we prefer the standard deviation to the variance as a measure of the variability of a random variable. Rule 2 for variances implies that standard deviations of independent random variables do *not* add. To combine standard deviations, use the rules for variances rather than trying to remember separate rules for standard deviations. For example, the standard deviations of $2X$ and $-2X$ are both equal to $2\sigma_X$ because this is the square root of the variance $4\sigma^2_X$.

EXAMPLE 4.18 Pick 3

The payoff X of a \$1 ticket in the Tri-State Pick 3 game is \$500 with probability 1/1000 and 0 the rest of the time. Here is the combined calculation of mean and variance:

x_i	p_i	$x_i p_i$	$(x_i - \mu_X)^2 p_i$	
0	0.999	0	$(0 - 0.5)^2(0.999) =$	0.24975
500	0.001	0.5	$(500 - 0.5)^2(0.001) =$	249.50025
		$\mu_X = 0.5$	$\sigma^2_X =$	249.75

The standard deviation is $\sigma_X = \sqrt{249.75} = \$15.80$. Games of chance usually have large standard deviations because large variability makes gambling exciting.

If you buy a Pick 3 ticket, your net winnings are $W = X - 1$ because the dollar you pay for the ticket must be subtracted from the payoff. By the rules for means, the mean amount you win is

$$\mu_W = \mu_X - 1 = -\$0.50$$

That is, you lose an average of 50 cents on a ticket. The rules for variances remind us that the variance and standard deviation of the winnings $W = X - 1$ are the same as those of the payoff X. Subtracting a fixed number changes the mean but not the variance.

Suppose now that you buy a \$1 ticket on each of two different days. The payoffs X and Y on the two tickets are independent because separate drawings are held each day. Your total payoff $X + Y$ has mean

$$\mu_{X+Y} = \mu_X + \mu_Y = \$0.50 + \$0.50 = \$1.00$$

Because X and Y are independent, the variance of $X + Y$ is

$$\sigma^2_{X+Y} = \sigma^2_X + \sigma^2_Y = 249.75 + 249.75 = 499.5$$

The standard deviation of the total payoff is

$$\sigma_{X+Y} = \sqrt{499.5} = \$22.35$$

This is not the same as the sum of the individual standard deviations, which is \$15.80 + \$15.80 = \$31.60. Variances of independent random variables add; standard deviations do not.

EXAMPLE 4.19 SAT Scores

A college uses SAT scores as one criterion for admission. Experience has shown that the distribution of SAT scores among the college's entire population of applicants is such that

$$\begin{aligned} X &= \text{SAT Math score} & \mu_X &= 625 & \sigma_X &= 90 \\ Y &= \text{SAT Verbal score} & \mu_Y &= 590 & \sigma_Y &= 100 \end{aligned}$$

What are the mean and standard deviation of the total score $X + Y$ among students applying to this college?

The mean overall SAT score is

$$\mu_{X+Y} = \mu_X + \mu_Y = 625 + 590 = 1215$$

The variance and standard deviation of the total *cannot be computed* from the information given. SAT Verbal and Math scores are not independent, because students who score high on one exam tend to score high on the other also. Therefore, Rule 2 does not apply and we need to know ρ, the correlation between X and Y, to apply Rule 3.

Nationally, the correlation between SAT Math and Verbal scores is about $\rho = 0.7$. If this is true for these students,

$$\begin{aligned} \sigma^2_{X+Y} &= \sigma^2_X + \sigma^2_Y + 2\rho\sigma_X\sigma_Y \\ &= (90)^2 + (100)^2 + (2)(0.7)(90)(100) \\ &= 30{,}700 \end{aligned}$$

The variance of the sum $X + Y$ is greater than the sum of the variances $\sigma_X^2 + \sigma_Y^2$ because of the positive correlation between SAT Math scores and SAT Verbal scores. We find the standard deviation from the variance,

$$\sigma_{X+Y} = \sqrt{30{,}700} = 175$$

EXAMPLE 4.20 Portfolio Analysis

CASE 4.2

Now we can complete our initial analysis of Sadie's portfolio. Based on annual returns between 1950 and 2000, we have

X = annual return on T-bills	$\mu_X = 5.2\%$	$\sigma_X = 2.9\%$
Y = annual return on stocks	$\mu_Y = 13.3\%$	$\sigma_Y = 17.0\%$
Correlation between X and Y:	$\rho = -0.1$	

We see that stocks had higher returns than Treasury bills on the average but were also much more volatile. This is a basic relationship in finance: a more volatile investment must offer a higher return to compensate investors for its greater risk. For the return R on Sadie's portfolio of 20% T-bills and 80% stocks,

$$\begin{aligned} R &= 0.2X + 0.8Y \\ \mu_R &= 0.2\mu_X + 0.8\mu_Y \\ &= (0.2 \times 5.2) + (0.8 \times 13.3) = 11.68\% \end{aligned}$$

To find the variance of the portfolio return, combine Rules 1 and 3:

$$\begin{aligned} \sigma_R^2 &= \sigma_{0.2X}^2 + \sigma_{0.8Y}^2 + 2\rho\sigma_{0.2X}\sigma_{0.8Y} \\ &= (0.2)^2\sigma_X^2 + (0.8)^2\sigma_Y^2 + 2\rho(0.2 \times \sigma_X)(0.8 \times \sigma_Y) \\ &= (0.2)^2(2.9)^2 + (0.8)^2(17.0)^2 + (2)(-0.1)(0.2 \times 2.9)(0.8 \times 17.0) \\ &= 183.719 \\ \sigma_R &= \sqrt{183.719} = 13.55\% \end{aligned}$$

The portfolio has a smaller mean return than an all-stock portfolio, but it is also less volatile. As a proportion of the all-stock values, the reduction in standard deviation is greater than the reduction in mean return. That's why Sadie put some funds into Treasury bills.

Example 4.20 illustrates the first step in modern finance, using mean and standard deviation to describe the behavior of a portfolio. The next step is to seek best-possible portfolios based on a given set of securities by finding the combination with the highest return for a specified level of risk. The investor says how much risk (measured as standard deviation of returns) she is willing to bear; the best portfolio has the highest mean return for this standard deviation. Our examples also suggest the characteristic weakness of portfolio analysis: risk and return in the future may be very different from the σ and μ we get from past returns. You can find out more about statistical aspects of portfolio analysis in Chapter 14.

APPLY YOUR KNOWLEDGE

4.60 Comparing sales. Tamara and Derek are sales associates in a large electronics and appliance store. Their store tracks each associate's daily sales in dollars. Tamara's sales total X varies from day to day with mean and standard deviation

$$\mu_X = \$1100 \quad \text{and} \quad \sigma_X = \$100$$

Derek's sales total Y also varies, with

$$\mu_Y = \$1000 \quad \text{and} \quad \sigma_Y = \$80$$

Because the store is large and Tamara and Derek work in different departments, we might assume that their daily sales totals vary independently of each other. What are the mean and standard deviation of the difference $X - Y$ between Tamara's daily sales and Derek's daily sales? Tamara sells more on the average. Do you think she sells more every day? Why?

4.61 Comparing sales. It is unlikely that the daily sales of Tamara and Derek in the previous problem are independent. They will both sell more during the Christmas season, for example. Suppose that the correlation between their sales is $\rho = 0.4$. What are now the mean and standard deviation of the difference $X - Y$? Can you explain conceptually why positive correlation between two variables reduces the variability of the difference between them?

4.62 Exercise 4.55 (page 277) gives the distributions of X, the number of wireless phones sold at the mall location of a store during the next month, and Y, the number of wireless phones sold at the downtown location during the next month. You did some useful variance calculations in Exercise 4.59 (page 280). Each phone sold at the mall location results in \$25 profit, and each phone sold at the downtown location results in \$35 profit.

(a) Calculate the standard deviation of the profit for each location using Rule 1 for variances.

(b) Assuming phone sales at the two locations are independent, calculate the standard deviation for total profit of both locations combined.

(c) Assuming $\rho = 0.8$, calculate the standard deviation for total profit of both locations combined.

(d) Assuming $\rho = 0$, calculate the standard deviation for total profit of both locations combined. How does this compare with your result in part (b)? In part (c)?

(e) Assuming $\rho = -0.8$, calculate the standard deviation for total profit of both locations combined. How does this compare with your result in part (b)? In part (c)? In part (d)?

SECTION 4.3 SUMMARY

- A **random variable** is a variable taking numerical values determined by the outcome of a random phenomenon. The **probability distribution** of a random variable X tells us what the possible values of X are and how probabilities are assigned to those values.

even though the roulette wheel does not. Can you beat the odds with a system based on the outcomes of past plays? No. Mathematicians have established a stronger version of the law of large numbers that says that if you do not have an infinite fortune to gamble with, your long-run average winnings μ remain the same as long as successive trials of the game (such as spins of the roulette wheel) are independent.

What if observations are not independent?
You are in charge of a process that manufactures video screens for computer monitors. Your equipment measures the tension on the metal mesh that lies behind each screen and is critical to its image quality. You want to estimate the mean tension μ for the process by the average $\bar{x}$ of the measurements. Alas, the tension measurements are not independent. If the tension on one screen is a bit too high, the tension on the next is more likely to also be high. Many real-world processes are like this—the process stays stable in the long run, but observations made close together are likely to be both above or both below the long-run mean. Again the mathematicians come to the rescue: as long as the dependence dies out fast enough as we take measurements farther and farther apart in time, the law of large numbers still holds.

APPLY YOUR KNOWLEDGE

4.96 Help this man.

(a) A gambler knows that red and black are equally likely to occur on each spin of a roulette wheel. He observes five consecutive reds and bets heavily on red at the next spin. Asked why, he says that "red is hot" and that the run of reds is likely to continue. Explain to the gambler what is wrong with this reasoning.

(b) After hearing you explain why red and black remain equally probable after five reds on the roulette wheel, the gambler moves to a poker game. He is dealt five straight red cards. He remembers what you said and assumes that the next card dealt in the same hand is equally likely to be red or black. Is the gambler right or wrong? Why?

4.97 The "law of averages." The baseball player Tony Gwynn got a hit about 34% of the time over his 20-year career. After he failed to hit safely in six straight at-bats, the TV commentator said, "Tony is due for a hit by the law of averages." Is that right? Why?

4.98 The law of large numbers. Figure 4.2 (page 251) shows the 36 possible outcomes of rolling two dice and counting the spots on the up-faces. These 36 outcomes are equally likely. You can calculate that the mean for the sum of the two up-faces is $\mu = 7$. This is the population mean μ for the idealized population that contains the results of rolling two dice forever. The law of large numbers says that the average $\bar{x}$ from a finite number of rolls gets closer and closer to 7 as we do more and more rolls.

(a) Go to the *Mean of a Random Variable* applet. Click "More dice" once to get two dice. Click "Show mean" to see the mean 7 on the graph. Leaving the number of rolls at 1, click "Roll dice" three times. Note the count of spots for each roll (what were they?) and the average for the three rolls. You see that the graph displays at each point the average number of spots for all rolls up to the last one. Now you understand the display.

(b) Set the number of rolls to 100 and click "Roll dice." The applet rolls the two dice 100 times. The graph shows how the average count of spots changes as we make more rolls. That is, the graph shows $\bar{x}$ as we continue to roll the dice. Make a rough sketch of the final graph.

(c) Repeat your work from (b). Click "Reset" to start over, then roll two dice 100 times. Make a sketch of the final graph of the mean $\bar{x}$ against the number of rolls. Your two graphs will often look very different. What they have in common is that the average eventually gets close to the population mean $\mu = 7$. The law of large numbers says that this will *always* happen if you keep on rolling the dice.

Sampling distributions

The law of large numbers assures us that if we measure enough subjects, the statistic $\bar{x}$ will eventually get very close to the unknown parameter μ. But our study in Example 4.21 had just 10 subjects. What can we say about $\bar{x}$ from 10 subjects as an estimate of μ? We ask: "What would happen if we took many samples of 10 subjects from this population?" We learned in Section 3.3 how to answer this question:

- Take a large number of samples of size 10 from the same population.
- Calculate the sample mean $\bar{x}$ for each sample.
- Make a histogram of the values of $\bar{x}$. This histogram shows how $\bar{x}$ varies in many samples.

In Section 3.3 (page 210) we used computer simulation to take many samples in a different setting. The histogram of values of the statistic approximates the *sampling distribution* that we would see if we kept on sampling forever. The idea of a sampling distribution is the foundation of statistical inference. One reason for studying probability is that the laws of probability can tell us about sampling distributions without the need to actually choose or simulate a large number of samples.

The mean and the standard deviation of $\bar{x}$

The first important fact about the sampling distribution of $\bar{x}$ follows from using the rules for means and variances, though we won't do the algebra. Here is the result.[20]

Mean and Standard Deviation of a Sample Mean

Suppose that $\bar{x}$ is the mean of an SRS of size n drawn from a large population with mean μ and standard deviation σ. Then the **mean** of the sampling distribution of $\bar{x}$ is μ and its **standard deviation** is $\sigma/\sqrt{n}$.

Both the mean and the standard deviation of the sampling distribution of $\bar{x}$ have important implications for statistical inference.

- The mean of the statistic $\bar{x}$ is always the same as the mean μ of the population. The sampling distribution of $\bar{x}$ is centered at μ. In repeated sampling, $\bar{x}$ will sometimes fall above the true value of the parameter μ and sometimes below, but there is no systematic tendency to overestimate or underestimate the parameter. This makes the

unbiased estimator

idea of lack of bias in the sense of "no favoritism" more precise. Because the mean of $\overline{x}$ is equal to μ, we say that the statistic $\overline{x}$ is an **unbiased estimator** of the parameter μ.

- An unbiased estimator is "correct on the average" in many samples. How close the estimator falls to the parameter in most samples is determined by the spread of the sampling distribution. If individual observations have standard deviation σ, then sample means $\overline{x}$ from samples of size n have standard deviation $\sigma/\sqrt{n}$. **Averages are less variable than individual observations.**

Not only is the standard deviation of the distribution of $\overline{x}$ smaller than the standard deviation of individual observations, but it gets smaller as we take larger samples. **The results of large samples are less variable than the results of small samples.** If n is large, the standard deviation of $\overline{x}$ is small and almost all samples will give values of $\overline{x}$ that lie very close to the true parameter μ. That is, the sample mean from a large sample can be trusted to estimate the population mean accurately. Notice, however, that the standard deviation of the sampling distribution gets smaller only at the rate $\sqrt{n}$. To cut the standard deviation of $\overline{x}$ in half, we must take four times as many observations, not just twice as many.

APPLY YOUR KNOWLEDGE

4.99 Generating a sampling distribution. Let's illustrate the idea of a sampling distribution in the case of a very small sample from a very small population. The population is the sizes of 10 medium-sized businesses where size is measured in terms of the number of employees. For convenience, the 10 companies have been labeled with the integers 0 to 9.

Company	0	1	2	3	4	5	6	7	8	9
Size	82	62	80	58	72	73	65	66	74	62

The parameter of interest is the mean size μ in this population. The sample is an SRS of size $n = 4$ drawn from the population. Because the companies are labeled 0 to 9, a single random digit from Table B chooses one company for the sample.

(a) Find the mean of the 10 sizes in the population. This is the population mean μ.

(b) Use Table B to draw an SRS of size 4 from this population. Write the four sizes in your sample and calculate the mean $\overline{x}$ of the sample sizes. This statistic is an estimate of μ.

(c) Repeat this process 10 times using different parts of Table B. Make a histogram of the 10 values of $\overline{x}$. You are constructing the sampling distribution of $\overline{x}$. Is the center of your histogram close to μ?

4.100 Measurements on the production line. Sodium content (in milligrams) is measured for bags of potato chips sampled from a production line. The standard deviation of the sodium content measurements is $\sigma = 10$ mg. The sodium content is measured 3 times and the mean $\overline{x}$ of the 3 measurements is recorded.

(a) What is the standard deviation of the mean result? (That is, if you kept on making 3 measurements and averaging them, what would be the standard deviation of all the $\overline{x}$'s?)

(b) How many times must we repeat the measurement to reduce the standard deviation of $\overline{x}$ to 5? Explain to someone who knows no statistics the advantage of reporting the average of several measurements rather than the result of a single measurement.

4.101 Measuring blood cholesterol. A study of the health of teenagers plans to measure the blood cholesterol level of an SRS of youth of ages 13 to 16 years. The researchers will report the mean $\overline{x}$ from their sample as an estimate of the mean cholesterol level μ in this population.

(a) Explain to someone who knows no statistics what it means to say that $\overline{x}$ is an "unbiased" estimator of μ.

(b) The sample result $\overline{x}$ is an unbiased estimator of the population truth μ no matter what size SRS the study chooses. Explain to someone who knows no statistics why a large sample gives more trustworthy results than a small sample.

The central limit theorem

We have described the center and spread of the sampling distribution of a sample mean $\overline{x}$, but not its shape. The shape of the distribution of $\overline{x}$ depends on the shape of the population distribution. Here is one important case: if the population distribution is Normal, then so is the distribution of the sample mean.

Sampling Distribution of a Sample Mean

If a population has the $N(\mu, \sigma)$ distribution, then the sample mean $\overline{x}$ of n independent observations has the $N(\mu, \sigma/\sqrt{n})$ distribution.

EXAMPLE 4.23 Estimating Odor Thresholds

Adults differ in the smallest amount of DMS they can detect in wine. Extensive studies have found that the DMS odor threshold of adults follows roughly a Normal distribution with mean $\mu = 25$ micrograms per liter (μg/l) and standard deviation $\sigma = 7$ μg/l. Because the population distribution is Normal, the sampling distribution of $\overline{x}$ is also Normal. Figure 4.16 displays the Normal curve

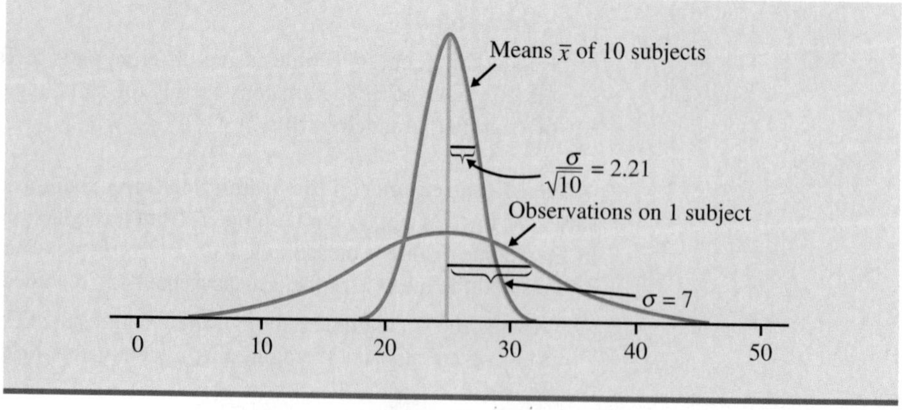

FIGURE 4.16 The distribution of single observations compared with the distribution of the means $\overline{x}$ of 10 observations, for Example 4.23. Averages are less variable than individual observations.

for odor thresholds in the adult population and also the Normal curve for the average threshold in random samples of size 10.

Both distributions have the same mean. But means $\bar{x}$ from samples of 10 adults vary less than do measurements on individual adults. The standard deviation of $\bar{x}$ is

$$\frac{\sigma}{\sqrt{n}} = \frac{7}{\sqrt{10}} = 2.21\mu\text{g/l}$$

What happens when the population distribution is not Normal? As the sample size increases, the distribution of $\bar{x}$ changes shape: it looks less like that of the population and more like a Normal distribution. When the sample is large enough, the distribution of $\bar{x}$ is very close to Normal. This is true no matter what shape the population distribution has, as long as the population has a finite standard deviation σ. This famous fact of probability theory is called the *central limit theorem.* It is much more useful than the fact that the distribution of $\bar{x}$ is exactly Normal if the population is exactly Normal.

Central Limit Theorem

Draw an SRS of size n from any population with mean μ and finite standard deviation σ. When n is large, the sampling distribution of the sample mean $\bar{x}$ is approximately Normal:

$$\bar{x} \text{ is approximately } N\left(\mu, \frac{\sigma}{\sqrt{n}}\right)$$

More general versions of the central limit theorem say that the distribution of a sum or average of many small random quantities is close to Normal. This is true even if the quantities are not independent (as long as they are not too highly correlated) and even if they have different distributions (as long as no one random quantity is so large that it dominates the others). The central limit theorem suggests why the Normal distributions are common models for observed data. Any variable that is a sum of many small influences will have approximately a Normal distribution.

How large a sample size n is needed for $\bar{x}$ to be close to Normal depends on the population distribution. More observations are required if the shape of the population distribution is far from Normal.

EXAMPLE 4.24 The Central Limit Theorem in Action

Figure 4.17 shows how the central limit theorem works for a very non-Normal population. Figure 4.17(a) displays the density curve of a single observation, that is, of the population. The distribution is strongly right-skewed, and the most probable outcomes are near 0. The mean μ of this distribution is 1, and its standard deviation σ is also 1. This particular distribution is called an *exponential distribution.* Exponential distributions are used as models for the lifetime in service of electronic components and for the time required to serve a customer or repair a machine.

Figures 4.17(b), (c), and (d) are the density curves of the sample means of 2, 10, and 25 observations from this population. As n increases, the shape becomes more Normal. The mean remains

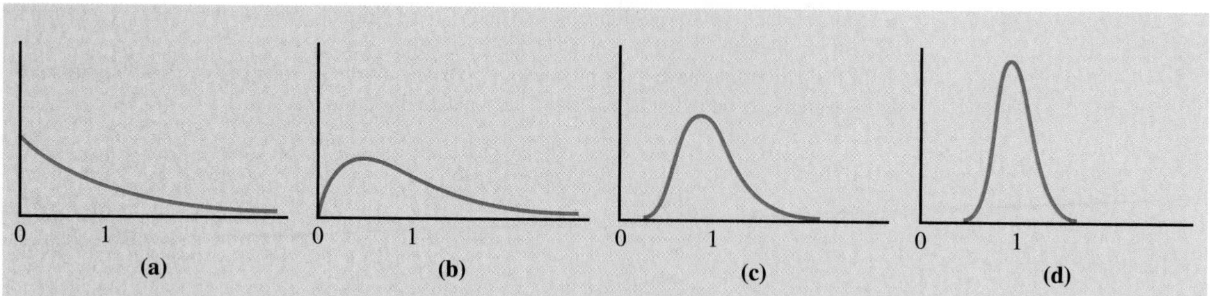

FIGURE 4.17 The central limit theorem in action: the distribution of sample means $\bar{x}$ from a strongly non-Normal population becomes more Normal as the sample size increases. (a) The distribution of 1 observation. (b) The distribution of $\bar{x}$ for 2 observations. (c) The distribution of $\bar{x}$ for 10 observations. (d) The distribution of $\bar{x}$ for 25 observations.

at $\mu = 1$, and the standard deviation decreases, taking the value $1/\sqrt{n}$. The density curve for the sample mean of 10 observations is still somewhat skewed to the right but already resembles a Normal curve having $\mu = 1$ and $\sigma = 1/\sqrt{10} = 0.32$. The density curve for $n = 25$ is yet more Normal. The contrast between the shapes of the population distribution and of the distribution of the mean of 10 or 25 observations is striking.

The central limit theorem allows us to use Normal probability calculations to answer questions about sample means from many observations even when the population distribution is not Normal.

EXAMPLE 4.25 Maintaining Air Conditioners

The time X that a technician requires to perform preventive maintenance on an air-conditioning unit is governed by the exponential distribution whose density curve appears in Figure 4.17(a). The mean time is $\mu = 1$ hour and the standard deviation is $\sigma = 1$ hour. Your company operates 70 of these units. What is the probability that their average maintenance time exceeds 50 minutes?

The central limit theorem says that the sample mean time $\bar{x}$ (in hours) spent working on 70 units has approximately the Normal distribution with mean equal to the population mean $\mu = 1$ hour and standard deviation

$$\frac{\sigma}{\sqrt{70}} = \frac{1}{\sqrt{70}} = 0.12 \text{ hour}$$

The distribution of $\bar{x}$ is therefore approximately $N(1, 0.12)$. This Normal curve is the solid curve in Figure 4.18.

Because 50 minutes is 50/60 of an hour, or 0.83 hour, the probability we want is $P(\bar{x} > 0.83)$. A Normal distribution calculation gives this probability as 0.9222. This is the area to the right of 0.83 under the solid Normal curve in Figure 4.18.

Using more mathematics, we could start with the exponential distribution and find the actual density curve of $\bar{x}$ for 70 observations. This is the dashed curve in Figure 4.18. You can see that the solid Normal curve is a good approximation. The exactly correct probability is the area under the dashed density curve. It is 0.9294. The central limit theorem Normal approximation is off by only about 0.007.

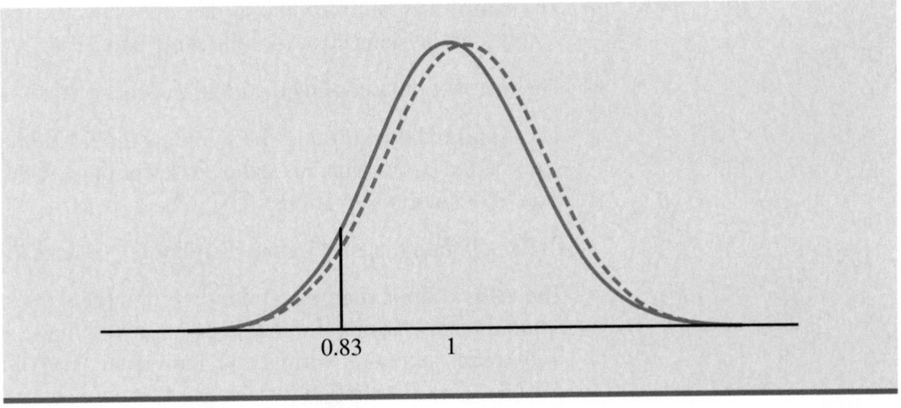

FIGURE 4.18 The exact distribution (dashed) and the Normal approximation from the central limit theorem (solid) for the average time needed to maintain an air conditioner, for Example 4.25.

APPLY YOUR KNOWLEDGE

4.102 ACT scores. The scores of students on the ACT college entrance examination in a recent year had the Normal distribution with mean $\mu = 18.6$ and standard deviation $\sigma = 5.9$.

(a) What is the probability that a single student randomly chosen from all those taking the test scores 21 or higher?

(b) Now take an SRS of 50 students who took the test. What are the mean and standard deviation of the sample mean score $\overline{x}$ of these 50 students?

(c) What is the probability that the mean score $\overline{x}$ of these students is 21 or higher?

4.103 Flaws in carpets. The number of flaws per square yard in a type of carpet material varies with mean 1.6 flaws per square yard and standard deviation 1.2 flaws per square yard. The population distribution cannot be Normal, because a count takes only whole-number values. An inspector samples 200 square yards of the material, records the number of flaws found in each square yard, and calculates $\overline{x}$, the mean number of flaws per square yard inspected. Use the central limit theorem to find the approximate probability that the mean number of flaws exceeds 2 per square yard.

4.104 Returns on stocks. The distribution of annual returns on common stocks is roughly symmetric, but extreme observations are somewhat more frequent than in Normal distributions. Because the distribution is not strongly non-Normal, the mean return over a number of years is close to Normal. We have seen that annual returns on common stocks (not adjusted for inflation) have varied with mean about 13% and standard deviation about 17%. Andrew plans to retire in 45 years. He assumes (this is dubious) that the past pattern of variation will continue. What is the probability that the mean annual return on common stocks over the next 45 years will exceed 15%? What is the probability that the mean return will be less than 7%?

SECTION 4.4 SUMMARY

- When we want information about the **population mean** μ for some variable, we often take an SRS and use the **sample mean** $\overline{x}$ to estimate the unknown parameter μ.
- The **law of large numbers** states that the actually observed mean outcome $\overline{x}$ must approach the mean μ of the population as the number of observations increases.

- The **sampling distribution** of $\overline{x}$ describes how the statistic $\overline{x}$ varies in all possible samples of the same size from the same population.
- The **mean** of the sampling distribution is μ, so that $\overline{x}$ is an **unbiased estimator** of μ.
- The **standard deviation** of the sampling distribution of $\overline{x}$ is $\sigma/\sqrt{n}$ for an SRS of size n if the population has standard deviation σ. That is, averages are less variable than individual observations.
- If the population has a Normal distribution, so does $\overline{x}$.
- The **central limit theorem** states that for large n the sampling distribution of $\overline{x}$ is approximately Normal for any population with finite standard deviation σ. That is, averages are more Normal than individual observations. We can use the $N(\mu, \sigma/\sqrt{n})$ distribution to calculate approximate probabilities for events involving $\overline{x}$.

SECTION 4.4 Exercises

For Exercises 4.93 to 4.95, see page 293; for 4.96 to 4.98, see pages 295–296; for 4.99 to 4.101, see pages 297–298; and for 4.102 to 4.104, see page 301.

4.105 Legal music downloads. According to Apple, Inc. press reports, the iTunes Music Store sold **500,000,000** songs between July 17, 2005, and February 24, 2006. In an analysis of over 2 million credit and debit card transactions, Forrester Research (`Forrester.com`) calculated that "iTunes households" make an average of **5.6** iTunes transactions per year. Is each of the bold numbers a parameter or a statistic?

4.106 What Americans buy. In a story on consumer spending, *Time* magazine reports that Americans buy **34** Porsche 911s and **88,163** Apple iPods each day. Is each of the bold numbers a parameter or a statistic?

4.107 Business employees. There are more than 5 million businesses in the United States. The mean number of employees in these businesses is about **19.** A university selects a random sample of 100 businesses in North Dakota and finds that they average about **14** employees. Is each of the bold numbers a parameter or a statistic?

4.108 Personal income. The Annual Demographic Supplement to the Current Population Survey interviewed more than 128,000 people in March 2001. The Census Bureau reports that the mean income of the Hispanic males interviewed was **\$22,771.** The mean income for the non-Hispanic white males interviewed was **\$41,798.** Is each of the bold numbers a parameter or a statistic?

4.109 Roulette. A roulette wheel has 38 slots, of which 18 are black, 18 are red, and 2 are green. When the wheel is spun, the ball is equally likely to come to rest in any of the slots. One of the simplest wagers chooses red or black. A bet of \$1 on red returns \$2 if the ball lands in a red slot. Otherwise, the player loses his dollar. When gamblers bet on red or black, the two green slots belong to the house. Because the probability of winning \$2 is 18/38, the mean payoff from a \$1 bet is twice 18/38, or 94.7 cents. Explain what the law of large numbers tells us about what will happen if a gambler makes a large number of bets on red.

4.110 Generating a sampling distribution. Table 1.15 (page 81) gives the population counts of the 58 counties in California. Consider these counties to be the population of interest.

(a) Make a histogram of the 58 counts. This is the population distribution. It is strongly skewed to the right.

(b) Find the mean of the 58 counts. This is the population mean μ. Mark μ on the x axis of your histogram.

(c) Label the members of the population 01 to 58 and use Table B to choose an SRS of size $n = 10$. What is $\overline{x}$ for your sample? Mark the value of $\overline{x}$ with a point on the axis of your histogram from (a).

(d) Choose four more SRSs of size 10, using different parts of Table B. Find $\overline{x}$ for each sample and mark the values on the axis of your histogram from (a). Would you be surprised if all five $\overline{x}$'s fell on the same side of μ? Why?

(e) If you chose a large number of SRSs of size 10 from this population and made a histogram of the $\overline{x}$-values, where would you expect the center of this sampling distribution to lie?

4.111 Dust in coal mines. A laboratory weighs filters from a coal mine to measure the amount of dust in the mine atmosphere. Repeated measurements of the weight of dust on the same filter vary Normally with standard deviation $\sigma = 0.08$ milligram (mg) because the weighing is not perfectly precise. The dust on a particular filter actually weighs 123 mg. Repeated weighings will then have the Normal distribution with mean 123 mg and standard deviation 0.08 mg.

(a) The laboratory reports the mean of 3 weighings. What is the distribution of this mean?

(b) What is the probability that the laboratory reports a weight of 124 mg or higher for this filter?

4.112 Making auto parts. An automatic grinding machine in an auto parts plant prepares axles with a target diameter $\mu = 40.125$ millimeters (mm). The machine has some variability, so the standard deviation of the diameters is $\sigma = 0.002$ mm. A sample of 4 axles is inspected each hour for process control purposes, and records are kept of the sample mean diameter. What will be the mean and standard deviation of the numbers recorded?

4.113 Safe flying weight. In response to the increasing weight of airline passengers, in 2003 the Federal Aviation Administration told airlines to assume that passengers average 190 pounds in the summer, including clothing and carry-on baggage. But passengers vary: the FAA gave a mean but not a standard deviation. A reasonable standard deviation is 35 pounds. Weights are not Normally distributed, especially when the population includes both men and women, but they are not very non-Normal. A commuter plane carries 19 passengers. What is the approximate probability that the total weight of the passengers exceeds 4000 pounds? (*Hint:* To apply the central limit theorem, restate the problem in terms of the mean weight.)

4.114 Cotton clothing treatment. "Durable press" cotton fabrics are treated to improve their recovery from wrinkles after washing. Unfortunately, the treatment also reduces the strength of the fabric. The breaking strength of untreated fabric is Normally distributed with mean 58 pounds and standard deviation 2.3 pounds. The same type of fabric after treatment has Normally distributed breaking strength with mean 30 pounds and standard deviation 1.6 pounds.[21] A clothing manufacturer tests 5 specimens of each fabric. All 10 strength measurements are independent.

(a) What is the probability that the mean breaking strength of the 5 untreated specimens exceeds 50 pounds?

(b) What is the probability that the mean breaking strength of the 5 untreated specimens is at least 25 pounds greater than the mean strength of the 5 treated specimens?

4.115 The cost of Internet access. The amount that households pay service providers for access to the Internet varies quite a bit, but the mean monthly fee is \$28 and the standard deviation is \$10. The distribution is not Normal: many households pay about \$10 for limited dial-up access or about \$25 for unlimited dial-up access, but many pay more for broadband connections. A sample survey asks an SRS of 500 households with Internet access how much they pay. What is the probability that the average fee paid by the sample households exceeds \$29?

4.116 The business of insurance. The idea of insurance is that we all face risks that are unlikely but carry high cost. Think of a fire destroying your home. So we form a group to share the risk: we all pay a small amount, and the insurance policy pays a large amount to those few of us whose homes burn down. An insurance company looks at the records for millions of homeowners and sees that the mean loss from fire in a year is $\mu = \$250$ per house and that the standard deviation of the loss is $\sigma = \$1000$. (The distribution of losses is extremely right-skewed: most people have \$0 loss, but a few have large losses.) The company plans to sell fire insurance for \$250 plus enough to cover its costs and profit.

(a) Explain clearly why it would be unwise to sell only 12 policies. Then explain why selling many thousands of such policies is a safe business.

(b) If the company sells 10,000 policies, what is the approximate probability that the average loss in a year will be greater than \$275?

4.117 Bottling cola. A bottling company uses a filling machine to fill plastic bottles with cola. The bottles are supposed to contain 300 milliliters (ml). In fact, the contents vary according to a Normal distribution with mean $\mu = 298$ ml and standard deviation $\sigma = 3$ ml.

(a) What is the probability that an individual bottle contains less than 295 ml?

(b) What is the probability that the mean contents of the bottles in a six-pack is less than 295 ml?

4.118 Glucose testing and medical costs. Shelia's doctor is concerned that she may suffer from gestational diabetes (high blood glucose levels during pregnancy). There is variation both in the actual glucose level and in the blood test that measures the level. A patient is classified as having gestational diabetes if the glucose level is above 140 milligrams per deciliter one hour after a sugary drink is ingested. Shelia's measured glucose level one hour after ingesting the sugary drink varies according to the Normal distribution with $\mu = 125$ mg/dl and $\sigma = 10$ mg/dl.

(a) If a single glucose measurement is made, what is the probability that Shelia is diagnosed as having gestational diabetes?

(b) If measurements are made instead on 4 separate days and the mean result is compared with the criterion 140 mg/dl, what is the probability that Shelia is diagnosed as having gestational diabetes?

(c) If Shelia is incorrectly diagnosed with gestational diabetes, then she (and her insurance company) will incur unnecessary additional expenses (insulin, needles, doctor visits) for treating the condition during the remainder of her pregnancy. These additional expenses are greater than the cost of repeating the test on three additional days as suggested in (b). Considering the probabilities you calculated in (a) and (b), comment on which testing method seems more appropriate given that Shelia has an acceptable mean glucose level of 125 mg/dl.

4.119 Manufacturing defects. Newly manufactured automobile radiators may have small leaks. Most have no leaks, but some have 1, 2, or more. The number of leaks in radiators made by one supplier has mean 0.15 and standard deviation 0.4. The distribution of number of leaks cannot be Normal because only whole-number counts are possible. The supplier ships 400 radiators per day to an auto assembly plant. Take $\bar{x}$ to be the mean number of leaks in these 400 radiators. Over several years of daily shipments, what range of values will contain the middle 95% of the many $\bar{x}$'s?

4.120 Auto accidents. The number of accidents per week at a hazardous intersection varies with mean 2.2 and standard deviation 1.4. This distribution takes only whole-number values, so it is certainly not Normal.

(a) Let $\bar{x}$ be the mean number of accidents per week at the intersection during a year (52 weeks). What is the approximate distribution of $\bar{x}$ according to the central limit theorem?

(b) What is the approximate probability that $\bar{x}$ is less than 2?

(c) What is the approximate probability that there are fewer than 100 accidents at the intersection in a year? (*Hint:* Restate this event in terms of $\bar{x}$.)

4.121 Budgeting for expenses. Weekly postage expenses for your company have a mean of \$312 and a standard deviation of \$58. Your company has allowed \$400 for postage per week in its budget.

(a) What is the approximate probability that the average weekly postage expense for the past 52 weeks will exceed the budgeted amount of \$400?

(b) What information would you need to determine the probability that postage for one particular week will exceed \$400? Why wasn't this information required for (a)?

4.122 Pollutants in auto exhausts. The level of nitrogen oxides (NOX) in the exhaust of a particular car model varies with mean 0.9 grams per mile (g/mi) and standard deviation 0.15 g/mi. A company has 125 cars of this model in its fleet.

(a) What is the approximate distribution of the mean NOX emission level $\bar{x}$ for these cars?

(b) What is the level L such that the probability that $\bar{x}$ is greater than L is only 0.01? (*Hint:* This requires a backward Normal calculation. See page 64 of Chapter 1 if you need to review.)

4.123 Glucose testing and medical costs. In Exercise 4.118, Shelia's measured glucose level one hour after ingesting the sugary drink varies according to the Normal distribution with $\mu = 125$ mg/dl and $\sigma = 10$ mg/dl. Find the level L such that there is probability only 0.05 that the mean glucose level of 4 test results falls above L for Shelia's glucose level distribution. What is the value of L? (*Hint:* This requires a backward Normal calculation. See page 64 of Chapter 1 if you need to review.)

STATISTICS IN SUMMARY

This chapter lays the foundations for the study of statistical inference. Statistical inference uses data to draw conclusions about the population or process from which the data come. What is special about inference is that the conclusions include a statement, in the language of probability, about how reliable they are. The statement gives a probability that answers the question "What would happen if I used this method very many times?" The probabilities we need come from the sampling distributions of sample statistics.

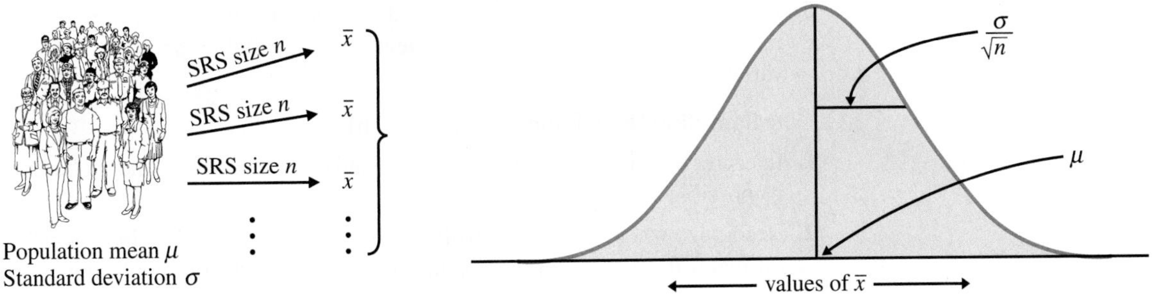

Sampling distributions are the key to understanding statistical inference. The Statistics in Summary figure above summarizes the facts about the sampling distribution of $\bar{x}$ in a way that reminds us of the big idea of a sampling distribution. Keep taking random samples of size n from a population with mean μ. Find the sample mean $\bar{x}$ for each sample. Collect all the $\bar{x}$'s and display their distribution. That's the sampling distribution of $\bar{x}$. Keep this figure in mind as you go forward.

To think more effectively about sampling distributions, we use the language of probability. Probability, the mathematics that describes randomness, is important in many areas of study. Here, we concentrate on informal probability as the conceptual foundation for statistical inference. Because random samples and randomized comparative experiments use chance, their results vary according to the laws of probability. Here is a review list of the most important things you should be able to do after studying this chapter.

A. Probability

1. Recognize that some phenomena are random. Probability describes the long-run regularity of random phenomena.
2. Understand that the probability of an event is the proportion of times the event occurs in very many repetitions of a random phenomenon. Use the idea of probability as long-run proportion to think about probability.
3. Know the rules that are obeyed by any legitimate assignment of probabilities to events. Use these rules to find the probabilities of events that are formed from other events.
4. Know what properties an assignment of probabilities to a finite number of outcomes must satisfy. Find probabilities of events in a finite sample space by adding the probabilities of their outcomes.
5. Know what a density curve is. Find probabilities of events as areas under a density curve.

B. Random Variables

1. Use the language of random variables to give compact descriptions of events and their probabilities, such as $P(X \geq 2.5)$.
2. Verify that the probability distribution of a discrete random variable is legitimate. Use the distribution to find probabilities of events involving the random variable.
3. Use the density curve of a continuous random variable to find probabilities of events involving the random variable.
4. Calculate the mean and standard deviation of a discrete random variable from its probability distribution.

5. Know and use the rules for means and variances of sums and differences of random variables, both for independent random variables and correlated random variables.

C. The Sampling Distribution of a Sample Mean

1. Interpret the sampling distribution of a statistic as describing the probabilities of its possible values.
2. Recognize when a problem involves the mean $\overline{x}$ of a sample. Understand that $\overline{x}$ estimates the mean μ of the population from which the sample is drawn.
3. Use the law of large numbers to describe the behavior of $\overline{x}$ as the size of the sample increases.
4. Find the mean and standard deviation of a sample mean $\overline{x}$ from an SRS of size n when the mean μ and standard deviation σ of the population are known.
5. Understand that $\overline{x}$ is an unbiased estimator of μ and that the variability of $\overline{x}$ about its mean μ gets smaller as the sample size increases.
6. Understand that $\overline{x}$ has approximately a Normal distribution when the sample is large (central limit theorem). Use this Normal distribution to calculate probabilities that concern $\overline{x}$.

CHAPTER 4 Review Exercises

4.124 Insuring an asset. Consider an insurance policy that will pay the holder of the policy the market price of her house if the house is completely destroyed by fire. The market price of a particular house is set at \$220,000. The probability of this house being completely destroyed by fire during the next year is determined by the insurance company to be 0.3%, and the cost of the policy is set at \$1280 for the next year. Let X represent the value of the insurance policy to the holder of the policy at the end of the next year, and let Y represent the value of the house at the end of the next year. Assume the house will be worth \$220,000 unless it is completely destroyed by fire.

(a) If the house is completely destroyed by fire in the next year, the value of the policy will be $220{,}000 - 1280 = 218{,}720$ dollars. If the house is not completely destroyed by fire in the next year, what will be the value of the policy?

(b) Write down the probability distribution of X in the form of a table.

(c) Write down the probability distribution of Y in the form of a table.

4.125 Insuring an asset. Continue analyzing the insurance scenario described in the previous exercise.

(a) Calculate the mean and standard deviation of X, the value of the insurance policy at the end of the next year.

(b) Calculate the mean and standard deviation of Y, the value of the house at the end of the next year.

(c) What do you notice about the risk (as measured by the standard deviation) of owning the house compared to the risk of holding the insurance policy?

4.126 Insuring an asset. Continue analyzing the insurance scenario described in the previous two exercises. Consider the value of holding the insurance policy *and* owning the house, $X + Y$. Let $W = X + Y$ in this exercise.

(a) Write down the probability distribution of W in the form of a table. What do you notice about the possible values of W? What does this mean for the owner of the house who also is the holder of the insurance policy?

(b) Calculate the mean value of W.

(c) Calculate the standard deviation of W. What does this imply about the risk associated with owning the house *and* holding the insurance policy on the house?

(d) X and Y are perfectly correlated. What is the value of ρ in this case?

4.127 Weights of bags of potato chips. In Example 4.8 (page 259), the weight of a single 9-ounce bag of potato chips has an $N(9.12, 0.15)$ distribution. Samuel works on the production line that manufactures these bags of chips. He weighs 3 randomly chosen bags and records their mean.

(a) What is the standard deviation of Samuel's mean result?

(b) How many bags must Samuel weigh to reduce the standard deviation of his mean to 0.05 ounces?

(c) Explain to someone who knows no statistics the advantage of reporting the average of several weights rather than just a single weight.

4.128 Weights of bags of potato chips. In Example 4.8 (page 259), the probability of a single randomly chosen 9-ounce bag weighing between 9.33 and 9.45 ounces was calculated to be 0.0669. In the setting of the previous exercise, Samuel regularly samples 3 bags of chips and calculates their average weight.

(a) What is the probability of Samuel's 3-bag average falling between 9.33 and 9.45 ounces?

(b) What is the probability of a 6-bag average falling between 9.33 and 9.45 ounces?

4.129 Weights of bags of potato chips. In Example 4.8 (page 259), the weight of a single 9-ounce bag of potato chips has an $N(9.12, 0.15)$ distribution. Consider taking a sample of bags of chips and calculating the average weight of the sample.

(a) What is the probability of a 3-bag average falling between 9.08 and 9.16 ounces?

(b) What is the probability of a 30-bag average falling between 9.08 and 9.16 ounces?

(c) What is the probability of a 150-bag average falling between 9.08 and 9.16 ounces?

(d) If the weights were known to have a mean of 9.12 ounces and a standard deviation of 0.15 ounces but the distribution of the weights was unknown, what would you be able to say about the probabilities you calculated in parts (a), (b), and (c)? Would any of them still be reasonably accurate?

4.130 Customer backgrounds. A company that offers courses to prepare would-be MBA students for the GMAT examination has the following information about its customers: 20% are currently undergraduate students in business; 15% are undergraduate students in other fields of study; 60% are college graduates who are currently employed; and 5% are college graduates who are not employed.

(a) This is a legitimate assignment of probabilities to customer backgrounds. Why?

(b) What percent of customers are currently undergraduates?

4.131 Who gets promoted? Exactly one of Brown, Chavez, and Williams will be promoted to partner in the law firm that employs them all. Brown thinks that she has probability 0.25 of winning the promotion and that Williams has probability 0.2. What probability does Brown assign to the outcome that Chavez is the one promoted?

4.132 Predicting the ACC champion. Las Vegas Zeke, when asked to predict the Atlantic Coast Conference basketball champion, follows the modern practice of giving probabilistic predictions. He says, "North Carolina's probability of winning is twice Duke's. North Carolina State and Virginia each have probability 0.1 of winning, but Duke's probability is three times that. Nobody else has a chance." Has Zeke given a legitimate assignment of probabilities to the eight teams in the conference? Explain your answer.

4.133 Classifying occupations. Choose an American worker at random and assign his or her occupation to one of the following classes. These classes are used in government employment data.

A Managerial and professional
B Technical, sales, administrative support
C Service occupations
D Precision production, craft, and repair
E Operators, fabricators, and laborers
F Farming, forestry, and fishing

The table below gives the probabilities that a randomly chosen worker falls into each of 12 sex-by-occupation classes:

Class	A	B	C	D	E	F
Male	0.14	0.11	0.06	0.11	0.12	0.03
Female	0.09	0.20	0.08	0.01	0.04	0.01

(a) Verify that this is a legitimate assignment of probabilities to these outcomes.

(b) What is the probability that the worker is female?

(c) What is the probability that the worker is not engaged in farming, forestry, or fishing?

(d) Classes D and E include most mechanical and factory jobs. What is the probability that the worker holds a job in one of these classes?

(e) What is the probability that the worker does not hold a job in Classes D or E?

4.134 Rolling dice. Figure 4.2 (page 251) shows the possible outcomes for rolling two dice. If the dice are carefully made, each of these 36 outcomes has probability 1/36. The outcome of interest to a gambler is the sum of the spots on the two up-faces. Call this random variable X. Example 4.5 shows that $P(X = 5) = 4/36$.

(a) Give the complete probability distribution of X in the form of a table of the possible values and their probabilities. Draw a probability histogram to display the distribution.

(b) One bet available in craps wins if a 7 or an 11 comes up on the next roll of two dice. What is the probability of rolling a 7 or an 11 on the next roll?

(c) Several bets in craps lose if a 7 is rolled. If any outcome other than 7 occurs, these bets either win or continue to the next roll. What is the probability that anything other than a 7 is rolled?

4.135 Nonstandard dice. You have two balanced, six-sided dice. One is a standard die, with faces having 1, 2, 3, 4, 5, and 6 spots. The other die has three faces with 0 spots and three faces with 6 spots. Find the probability distribution for the total number of spots Y on the up-faces when you roll these two dice.

4.136 An IQ test. The Wechsler Adult Intelligence Scale (WAIS) is a common "IQ test" for adults. The distribution of WAIS scores for persons over 16 years of age is approximately Normal with mean 100 and standard deviation 15.

(a) What is the probability that a randomly chosen individual has a WAIS score of 105 or higher?

(b) What are the mean and standard deviation of the average WAIS score $\bar{x}$ for an SRS of 60 people?

(c) What is the probability that the average WAIS score of an SRS of 60 people is 105 or higher?

(d) Would your answers to any of (a), (b), or (c) be affected if the distribution of WAIS scores in the adult population were distinctly non-Normal?

4.137 Weights of eggs. The weight of the eggs produced by a certain breed of hen is Normally distributed with mean 65 grams (g) and standard deviation 5 g. Think of cartons of such eggs as SRSs of size 12 from the population of all eggs. What is the probability that the weight of a carton falls between 750 and 825 g?

4.138 How many people in a car? A study of rush-hour traffic in San Francisco counts the number of people in each car entering a freeway at a suburban interchange. Suppose that this count has mean 1.5 and standard deviation 0.75 in the population of all cars that enter at this interchange during rush hours.

(a) Could the exact distribution of the count be Normal? Why or why not?

(b) Traffic engineers estimate that the capacity of the interchange is 700 cars per hour. According to the central limit theorem, what is the approximate distribution of the mean number of persons $\bar{x}$ in 700 randomly selected cars at this interchange?

(c) What is the probability that 700 cars will carry more than 1075 people? (*Hint:* Restate this event in terms of the mean number of people $\bar{x}$ per car.)

4.139 A grade distribution. North Carolina State University posts the grade distributions for its courses online.[22] You can find that the distribution of grades in Accounting 210 in the spring 2001 semester was

Grade	A	B	C	D	F
Probability	0.18	0.32	0.34	0.09	0.07

(a) Verify that this is a legitimate assignment of probabilities to grades.

(b) Using the common scale A = 4, B = 3, C = 2, D = 1, F = 0, what is the mean grade in Accounting 210?

4.140 Simulating a mean. One consequence of the law of large numbers is that once we have a probability distribution for a random variable, we can find its mean by simulating many outcomes and averaging them. The law of large numbers says that if we take enough outcomes, their average value is sure to approach the mean of the distribution.

I have a little bet to offer you. Toss a coin 10 times. If there is no run of three or more straight heads or tails in the 10 outcomes, I'll pay you \$2. If there is a run of three or more, you pay me just \$1. Surely you will want to take advantage of me and play this game?

Simulate enough plays of this game (the outcomes are +\$2 if you win and −\$1 if you lose) to estimate the mean outcome. Is it to your advantage to play?

Insurance. *The business of selling insurance is based on probability and the law of large numbers. Consumers (including businesses) buy insurance because we all face risks that are unlikely but carry high cost—think of a fire destroying your home. So we form a group to share the risk: we all pay a small amount, and the insurance policy pays a large amount to those few of us whose homes burn down. The insurance company sells many policies, so it can rely* *on the law of large numbers. Exercises 4.141 to 4.146 explore aspects of insurance.*

4.141 Fire insurance. An insurance company looks at the records for millions of homeowners and sees that the mean loss from fire in a year is $\mu = \$400$ per person. (Most of us have no loss, but a few lose their homes. The \$400 is the average loss.) The company plans to sell fire insurance for \$400 plus enough to cover its costs and profit. Explain clearly why it would be stupid to sell only 10 policies. Then explain why selling thousands of such policies is a safe business.

4.142 More about fire insurance. In fact, the insurance company sees that in the entire population of homeowners, the mean loss from fire is $\mu = \$400$ and the standard deviation of the loss is $\sigma = \$300$. The distribution of losses is strongly right-skewed: many policies have \$0 loss, but a few have large losses. If the company sells 10,000 policies, what is the approximate probability that the average loss will be greater than \$410?

4.143 Life insurance. A life insurance company sells a term insurance policy to a 21-year-old male that pays \$100,000 if the insured dies within the next 5 years. The probability that a randomly chosen male will die each year can be found in mortality tables. The company collects a premium of \$250 each year as payment for the insurance. The amount X that the company earns on this policy is \$250 per year, less the \$100,000 that it must pay if the insured dies. At the bottom of this page is the distribution of X. Fill in the missing probability in the table and calculate the mean earnings μ_X.

4.144 More about life insurance. It would be quite risky for you to insure the life of a 21-year-old friend under the terms of Exercise 4.143. There is a high probability that your friend would live and you would gain \$1250 in premiums. But if he were to die, you would lose almost \$100,000. Explain carefully why selling insurance is not risky for an insurance company that insures many thousands of 21-year-old men.

4.145 The risk of selling insurance. We have seen that the risk of an investment is often measured by the standard deviation of the return on the investment. The more variable the return is (the larger σ is), the riskier the investment. We can measure the great risk of insuring one person's life in Exercise 4.143 by computing the standard deviation of the income X that the insurer will receive. Find σ_X, using the distribution and mean you found in Exercise 4.143.

4.146 The risk of selling insurance, continued. The risk of insuring one person's life is reduced if we insure many people. Use the result of the previous exercise and the rules for means and variances to answer the following questions.

(a) Suppose that we insure two 21-year-old males, and that their ages at death are independent. If X and Y are the insurer's income from the two insurance policies, the insurer's average income on the two policies is

$$Z = \frac{X + Y}{2} = 0.5X + 0.5Y$$

Find the mean and standard deviation of Z. You see that the mean income is the same as for a single policy but the standard deviation is less.

(b) If four 21-year-old men are insured, the insurer's average income is

$$Z = \frac{1}{4}(X_1 + X_2 + X_3 + X_4)$$

where X_i is the income from insuring one man. The X_i are independent and each has the same distribution as before. Find the mean and standard deviation of Z. Compare your results with the results of (a). We see that averaging over many insured individuals reduces risk.

4.147 Finite sample spaces. Choose one employee of your company at random and let X be the number of years that person has been employed by the company (rounded to the nearest year).

(a) Give a reasonable sample space S for the possible values of X.

(b) Is X a discrete random variable or a continuous random variable? Why?

(c) How many possible values of X did you include in your definition of S?

4.148 Infinite sample spaces, Part I (optional). Buy one share of Apple Computer (AAPL) stock, and let Y be the number of days until the closing market value of

Age at death	21	22	23	24	25	≥ 26
Earnings X	−\$99,750	−\$99,500	−\$99,250	−\$99,000	−\$98,750	\$1250
Probability	0.00183	0.00186	0.00189	0.00191	0.00193	?

your share is double what you initially paid for the share.

(a) Give the sample space S for the possible values of Y.

(b) Is Y a discrete random variable or a continuous random variable? Why?

(c) How many possible values of Y did you include in your definition of S? (This exercise illustrates that "discrete" and "finite" are not the same thing, though we have made use of only finite discrete sample spaces.)[23]

4.149 Infinite sample spaces, Part II (optional). Randomly choose one 30-milliliter (ml) ink cartridge from the lot of cartridges produced at your plant in the last hour. Let W be the actual amount of ink in the cartridge. The cartridges are supposed to contain 30 ml of ink but are designed to hold up to a maximum of 35 ml of ink.

(a) Give a reasonable sample space S for the possible values of W.

(b) Is W a discrete random variable or a continuous random variable? Why?

(c) How many possible values of W did you include in your definition of S?

CHAPTER 4 Case Study Exercises

CASE STUDY 1: Benford's law. Case 4.1 (page 249) concerns Benford's law, which gives the distribution of first digits in many sets of data from business and science. Locate at least two long tables whose entries could plausibly begin with any digit 1 through 9. You may choose data tables, such as populations of many cities or the number of shares traded on the New York Stock Exchange on many days, or mathematical tables such as logarithms or square roots. We hope it's clear that you can't use the table of random digits. Let's require that your examples each contain at least 300 numbers. Tally the first digits of all entries in each table. Report the distributions (in percents) and compare them with each other, with Benford's law, and with the "equally likely" distribution.

CASE STUDY 2: State lotteries. Most American states and Canadian provinces operate lotteries. State lotteries combine probability with economics and politics. States sometimes add opportunities for gambling in hard times to increase their take from operating the games or from taxing games run by others. Investigate the presence of legal gambling in your state. Include probability aspects, such as the probability of winning and the expected payoff on different games. Also look at economic aspects of gambling: how much does the state earn? What percent of the state budget is this? Has the state's take from gambling changed in recent years? Probability and economics are related, because a state lottery keeps only what it doesn't pay out in winnings to gamblers. What percent of the money bet in the lottery does the state pay out in prizes? How does this compare with casino games?

CHAPTER 5

Probability Theory*

PRELUDE: THE CASE OF THE PENTIUM BUG

Intel's Pentium processors power a majority of the world's computers. In 1994, a bug was discovered in the Pentium chip. The bug, which came to be known as the Pentium FDIV bug, caused some floating-point division operations to give incorrect values. Intel claimed that the probability of an error was only 1 in 9 billion. At that rate, said the chip firm, a spreadsheet user who performs 1000 floating-point divisions per day will encounter an incorrect division only about once in 25,000 years. The probability of one or more errors due to the FDIV bug in 365 working days is only about 0.00004.

An IBM research group disagreed. Based on the results of probability simulations, IBM concluded that a more reasonable estimate of the probability of a floating-point division error was 1 in 100 million, 90 times the estimate given by Intel. What is more, simulations of typical financial calculations done by spreadsheet users found that an average user would perform nearly 4.2 million divisions per day. The probability of one or more errors due to the FDIV bug in 365 days, said IBM, is not 0.00004 but 0.9999998.

At first, Intel claimed that the bug would cause errors so rarely that it would not replace the faulty chips that had already been sold—as many as 2 million chips. However, faced with results like IBM's and growing consumer concern, Intel agreed to replace the chips for anyone who wanted a replacement. The Pentium FDIV bug incident is reported to have cost Intel approximately 475 million dollars.[1]

*This more advanced chapter gives more detail about probability. It is not needed to read the rest of the book.

Introduction

The mathematics of probability can provide models to describe the flow of traffic through a highway system, a telephone interchange, or a computer processor; the product preferences of consumers; the spread of epidemics or computer viruses; and the rate of return on risky investments. Although we are interested in probability because of its usefulness in statistics, the mathematics of chance is important in many fields of study. This chapter presents a bit more of the theory of probability.

5.1 General Probability Rules

Our study of probability in Chapter 4 concentrated on sampling distributions. Now we return to the general laws of probability. With more probability at our command, we can model more complex random phenomena. We have already met and used four rules.

Rules of Probability

Rule 1. $0 \leq P(A) \leq 1$ for any event A

Rule 2. $P(S) = 1$

Rule 3. Complement rule: For any event A,

$$P(A^c) = 1 - P(A)$$

Rule 4. Addition rule: If A and B are **disjoint** events, then

$$P(A \text{ or } B) = P(A) + P(B)$$

complement

The complement rule takes its name from the fact that the set of all outcomes that are *not* in an event A is often called the **complement** of A. As a convenient short notation, we will write the complement of A as A^c. For example, if A is the event that a randomly chosen corporate CEO is female, then A^c is the event that the CEO is male.

Independence and the multiplication rule

Rule 4, the addition rule for disjoint events, describes the probability that *one or the other* of two events A and B occurs when A and B cannot occur together. Now we will describe the probability that *both* events A and B occur, again only in a special situation.

Venn diagram

You may find it helpful to draw a picture to display relations among several events. A picture like Figure 5.1 that shows the sample space S as a rectangular area and events as areas within S is called a **Venn diagram.** The events A and B in Figure 5.1 are disjoint because they do not overlap. The Venn diagram in Figure 5.2 illustrates two events that are not disjoint. The event $\{A \text{ and } B\}$ appears as the overlapping area that is common to both A and B.

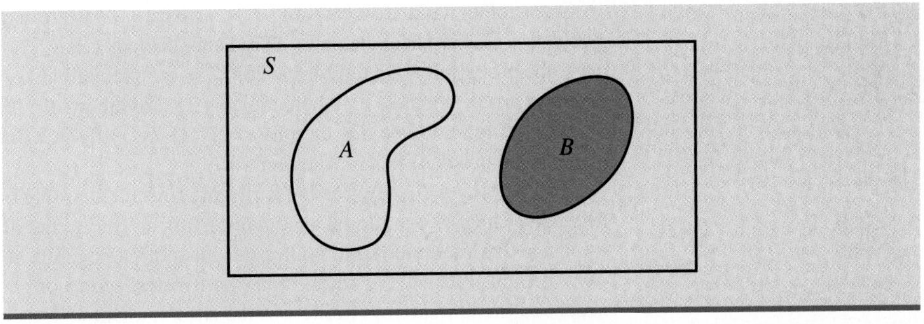

FIGURE 5.1 Venn diagram showing disjoint events A and B.

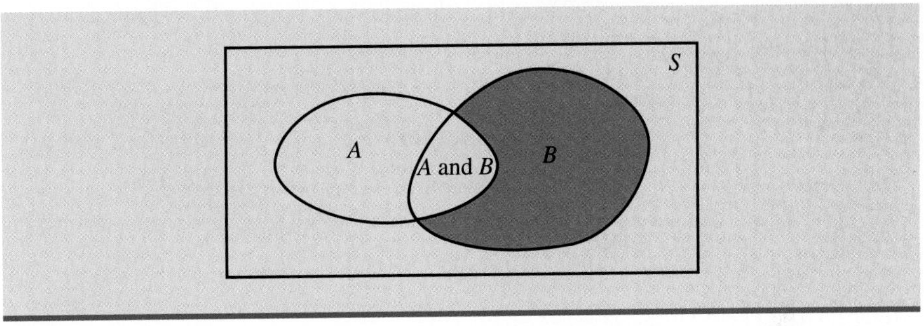

FIGURE 5.2 Venn diagram showing events A and B that are not disjoint. The event $\{A \text{ and } B\}$ consists of outcomes common to A and B.

Suppose that you toss a balanced coin twice. You are counting heads, so two events of interest are

$$A = \text{first toss is a head}$$
$$B = \text{second toss is a head}$$

The events A and B are not disjoint. They occur together whenever both tosses give heads. We want to find the probability of the event $\{A \text{ and } B\}$ that *both* tosses are heads.

The coin tossing of Buffon, Pearson, and Kerrich described at the beginning of Chapter 4 makes us willing to assign probability $1/2$ to a head when we toss a coin. So

$$P(A) = 0.5$$
$$P(B) = 0.5$$

What is $P(A \text{ and } B)$? Our common sense says that it is $1/4$. The first coin will give a head half the time and then the second will give a head on half of those trials, so both coins will give heads on $1/2 \times 1/2 = 1/4$ of all trials in the long run. This reasoning assumes that the second coin still has probability $1/2$ of a head after the first has given a head. This is true—we can verify it by tossing two coins many times and observing the proportion of heads on the second toss after the first toss has produced a head. We say that the events "head on the first toss" and "head on the second toss" are **independent.** Independence means that the outcome of the first toss cannot influence the outcome of the second toss.

independence

EXAMPLE 5.1 Independent or Not?

Because a coin has no memory and most coin tossers cannot influence the fall of the coin, it is safe to assume that successive coin tosses are independent. For a balanced coin this means that, after we see the outcome of the first toss, we still assign probability $1/2$ to heads on the second toss.

On the other hand, the colors of successive cards dealt from the same deck are not independent. A standard 52-card deck contains 26 red and 26 black cards. For the first card dealt from a shuffled deck, the probability of a red card is $26/52 = 0.50$ (equally likely outcomes). Once we see that the first card is red, we know that there are only 25 reds among the remaining 51 cards. The probability that the second card is red is therefore only $25/51 = 0.49$. Knowing the outcome of the first deal changes the probabilities for the second.

If an employer does two tests for illegal drugs on the same blood sample from a job applicant, it is reasonable to assume that the two results are independent because the first result does not influence the instrument that makes the second reading. But if the applicant takes an IQ test or other mental test twice in succession, the two test scores are not independent. The learning that occurs on the first attempt influences the second attempt.

Multiplication Rule for Independent Events

Two events A and B are **independent** if knowing that one occurs does not change the probability that the other occurs. If A and B are independent,

$$P(A \text{ and } B) = P(A)P(B)$$

EXAMPLE 5.2 Mendel's Peas

Gregor Mendel used garden peas in some of the experiments that revealed that inheritance operates randomly. The seed color of Mendel's peas can be either green or yellow. Two parent plants are "crossed" (one pollinates the other) to produce seeds. Each parent plant carries two genes for seed color, and each of these genes has probability 1/2 of being passed to a seed. The two genes that the seed receives, one from each parent, determine its color. The parents contribute their genes independently of each other.

Suppose that both parents carry the G (green) and the Y (yellow) genes. The seed will be green if both parents contribute a G gene; otherwise it will be yellow. If M is the event that the male contributes a G gene and F is the event that the female contributes a G gene, then the probability of a green seed is

$$\begin{aligned} P(M \text{ and } F) &= P(M)P(F) \\ &= (0.5)(0.5) = 0.25 \end{aligned}$$

In the long run, 1/4 of all seeds produced by crossing these plants will be green.

The multiplication rule $P(A \text{ and } B) = P(A)P(B)$ holds if A and B are *independent* but not otherwise. The addition rule $P(A \text{ or } B) = P(A) + P(B)$ holds if A and B are *disjoint* but not otherwise. Resist the temptation to use these simple rules when the circumstances that justify them are not present. You must also be certain not to confuse disjointness and independence. If A and B are disjoint, then the fact that A occurs tells us that B cannot occur—look again at Figure 5.1. So disjoint events are not independent. Unlike disjointness, we cannot picture independence in a Venn diagram, because it involves the probabilities of the events rather than just the outcomes that make up the events.

APPLY YOUR KNOWLEDGE

5.1 High school rank. Select a first-year college student at random and ask what his or her academic rank was in high school. Here are the probabilities, based on proportions from a large sample survey of first-year students:

Rank	Top 20%	Second 20%	Third 20%	Fourth 20%	Lowest 20%
Probability	0.41	0.23	0.29	0.06	0.01

(a) Choose two first-year college students at random. Why is it reasonable to assume that their high school ranks are independent?

(b) What is the probability that both were in the top 20% of their high school classes?

(c) What is the probability that the first was in the top 20% and the second was in the lowest 20%?

5.2 College-educated laborers? Government data show that 27% of employed people have at least 4 years of college and that 14% of employed people work as laborers or operators of machines or vehicles. Can you conclude that because $(0.27)(0.14) = 0.038$ about 3.8% of employed people are college-educated laborers or operators? Explain your answer.

Applying the multiplication rule

If two events A and B are independent, the event that A does not occur is also independent of B, and so on. Suppose, for example, that 75% of all registered voters in a suburban district are Republicans. If an opinion poll interviews two voters chosen independently, the probability that the first is a Republican and the second is not a Republican is $(0.75)(0.25) = 0.1875$. The multiplication rule also extends to collections of more than two events, provided that all are independent. Independence of events A, B, and C means that no information about any one or any two can change the probability of the remaining events. Independence is often assumed in setting up a probability model when the events we are describing seem to have no connection. We can then use the multiplication rule freely, as in this example.

EXAMPLE 5.3 Undersea Cables

The first successful transatlantic telegraph cable was laid in 1866. The first telephone cable across the Atlantic did not appear until 1956—the barrier was designing "repeaters," amplifiers needed to boost the signal, that could operate for years on the sea bottom. This first cable had 52 repeaters. The last copper cable, laid in 1983 and retired in 1994, had 662 repeaters. The first fiber-optic cable was laid in 1988 and has 109 repeaters. There are now more than 400,000 miles of undersea cable, with more being laid every year to handle the flood of Internet traffic.

Repeaters in undersea cables must be very reliable. To see why, suppose that each repeater has probability 0.999 of functioning without failure for 25 years. Repeaters fail independently of each other. (This assumption means that there are no "common causes" such as earthquakes that would affect several repeaters at once.) Denote by A_i the event that the ith repeater operates successfully for 25 years.

The probability that 2 repeaters both last 25 years is

$$\begin{aligned} P(A_1 \text{ and } A_2) &= P(A_1)P(A_2) \\ &= 0.999 \times 0.999 = 0.998 \end{aligned}$$

For a cable with 10 repeaters the probability of no failures in 25 years is

$$P(A_1 \text{ and } A_2 \text{ and } \dots \text{ and } A_{10}) = P(A_1)P(A_2)\cdots P(A_{10})$$
$$= 0.999 \times 0.999 \times \cdots \times 0.999$$
$$= 0.999^{10} = 0.990$$

Cables with 2 or 10 repeaters would be quite reliable. Unfortunately, the last copper transatlantic cable had 662 repeaters. The probability that all 662 work for 25 years is

$$P(A_1 \text{ and } A_2 \text{ and } \dots \text{ and } A_{662}) = 0.999^{662} = 0.516$$

This cable will fail to reach its 25-year design life about half the time if each repeater is 99.9% reliable over that period. The multiplication rule for probabilities shows that repeaters must be much more than 99.9% reliable.

By combining the rules we have learned, we can compute probabilities for rather complex events. Here is an example.

EXAMPLE 5.4 False-Positives in HIV Testing

Screening large numbers of blood samples for HIV, the virus that causes AIDS, uses an enzyme immunoassay (EIA) test that detects antibodies to the virus. Samples that test positive are retested using a more accurate "Western blot" test. Applied to people who have no HIV antibodies, EIA has probability about 0.006 of producing a false-positive. If the 140 employees of a medical clinic are tested and all 140 are free of HIV antibodies, what is the probability that at least 1 false-positive will occur?

It is reasonable to assume as part of the probability model that the test results for different individuals are independent. The probability that the test is positive for a single person is 0.006, so the probability of a negative result is $1 - 0.006 = 0.994$ by the complement rule. The probability of at least 1 false-positive among the 140 people tested is therefore

$$P(\text{at least one positive}) = 1 - P(\text{no positives})$$
$$= 1 - P(140 \text{ negatives})$$
$$= 1 - 0.994^{140}$$
$$= 1 - 0.431 = 0.569$$

The probability is greater than $1/2$ that at least 1 of the 140 people will test positive for HIV even though no one has the virus.

APPLY YOUR KNOWLEDGE

5.3 Telemarketing. Telephone marketers and opinion polls use random digit dialing equipment to call residential telephone numbers at random. The telephone polling firm Zogby International reports that the probability that a call reaches a live person is 0.2.[2] Calls are independent.

(a) A telemarketer places 5 calls. What is the probability that none of them reaches a person?

(b) When calls are made to New York City, the probability of reaching a person is only 0.08. What is the probability that none of 5 calls made to New York City reaches a person?

5.4 Detecting drug use. An employee suspected of having used an illegal drug is given two tests that operate independently of each other. Test A has probability 0.9 of being

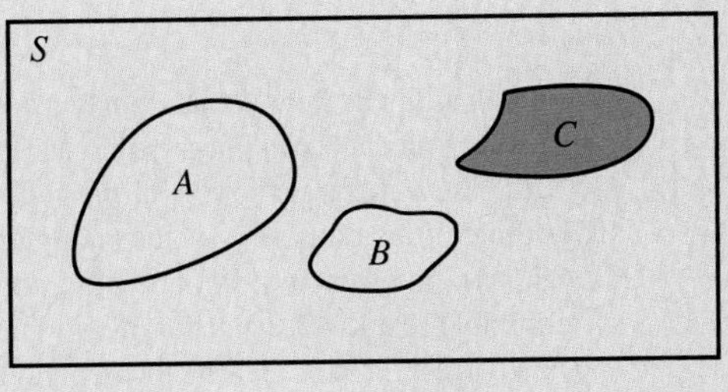

FIGURE 5.3 The addition rule for disjoint events: $P(A \text{ or } B \text{ or } C) = P(A) + P(B) + P(C)$ when events A, B, and C are disjoint.

positive if the illegal drug has been used. Test B has probability 0.8 of being positive if the illegal drug has been used. What is the probability that *neither* test is positive if the illegal drug has been used?

5.5 Bright lights? A string of holiday lights contains 20 lights. The lights are wired in series, so that if any light fails the whole string will go dark. Each light has probability 0.02 of failing during a 3-year period. The lights fail independently of each other. What is the probability that the string of lights will remain bright for 3 years?

The general addition rule

We know that if A and B are disjoint events, then $P(A \text{ or } B) = P(A) + P(B)$. This addition rule extends to more than two events that are disjoint in the sense that no two have any outcomes in common. The Venn diagram in Figure 5.3 shows three disjoint events A, B, and C. The probability that one of these events occurs is $P(A) + P(B) + P(C)$.

If events A and B are *not* disjoint, they can occur simultaneously. The probability that one or the other occurs is then *less* than the sum of their probabilities. As Figure 5.4 suggests, the outcomes common to both are counted twice when we add probabilities, so we must subtract this probability once. Here is the addition rule for any two events, disjoint or not.

General Addition Rule for Any Two Events

For any two events A and B,

$$P(A \text{ or } B) = P(A) + P(B) - P(A \text{ and } B)$$

If A and B are disjoint, the event $\{A \text{ and } B\}$ that both occur contains no outcomes and therefore has probability 0. So the general addition rule includes Rule 4, the addition rule for disjoint events.

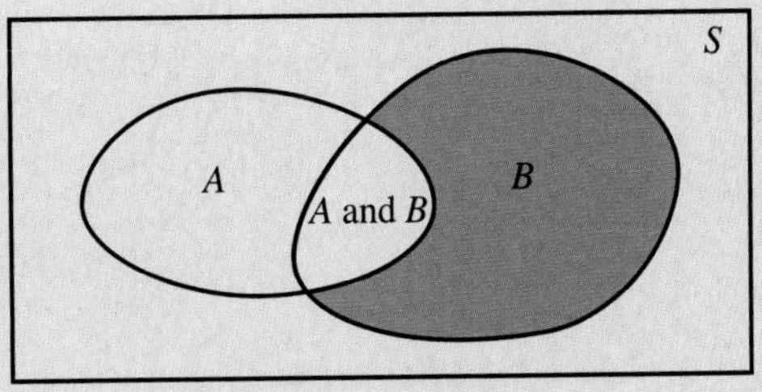

FIGURE 5.4 The general addition rule: $P(A \text{ or } B) = P(A) + P(B) - P(A \text{ and } B)$ for any events A and B.

EXAMPLE 5.5 Making Partner

Deborah and Matthew are anxiously awaiting word on whether they have been made partners of their law firm. Deborah guesses that her probability of making partner is 0.7 and that Matthew's is 0.5. (These are personal probabilities reflecting Deborah's assessment of chance.) This assignment of probabilities does not give us enough information to compute the probability that at least one of the two is promoted. In particular, adding the individual probabilities of promotion gives the impossible result 1.2. If Deborah also guesses that the probability that *both* she and Matthew are made partners is 0.3, then by the general addition rule

$$P(\text{at least one is promoted}) = 0.7 + 0.5 - 0.3 = 0.9$$

The probability that *neither* is promoted is then 0.1 by the complement rule.

Venn diagrams are a great help in finding probabilities because you can just think of adding and subtracting areas. Figure 5.5 shows some events and their probabilities for Example 5.5. What is the probability that Deborah is promoted and Matthew is not? The Venn diagram shows that this is the probability that Deborah is promoted minus the probability that both are promoted, $0.7 - 0.3 = 0.4$. Similarly, the probability that Matthew is promoted and Deborah is not is $0.5 - 0.3 = 0.2$. The four probabilities that appear in the figure add to 1 because they refer to four disjoint events that make up the entire sample space.

APPLY YOUR KNOWLEDGE

5.6 Prosperity and education. Call a household prosperous if its income exceeds \$100,000. Call the household educated if the householder completed college. Select an American household at random, and let A be the event that the selected household is prosperous and B the event that it is educated. According to the Current Population Survey, $P(A) = 0.134$, $P(B) = 0.254$, and the probability that a household is both prosperous and educated is $P(A \text{ and } B) = 0.080$.

(a) Draw a Venn diagram that shows the relation between the events A and B. What is the probability $P(A \text{ or } B)$ that the household selected is either prosperous or educated?

(b) In your diagram, shade the event that the household is educated but not prosperous. What is the probability of this event?

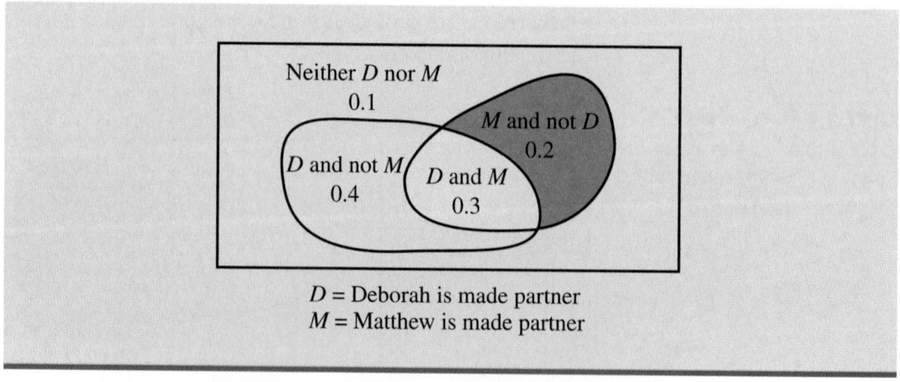

FIGURE 5.5 Venn diagram and probabilities for Example 5.5.

5.7 Caffeine in the diet. Common sources of caffeine are coffee, tea, and cola drinks. Suppose that

55% of adults drink coffee
25% of adults drink tea
45% of adults drink cola

and also that

15% drink both coffee and tea
5% drink all three beverages
25% drink both coffee and cola
5% drink only tea

Draw a Venn diagram marked with this information. Use it along with the addition rules to answer the following questions.

(a) What percent of adults drink only cola?

(b) What percent drink none of these beverages?

SECTION 5.1 SUMMARY

- Events A and B are **disjoint** if they have no outcomes in common. Events A and B are **independent** if knowing that one event occurs does not change the probability we would assign to the other event.
- Any assignment of probability obeys these more general rules in addition to those stated in Chapter 4:

  Addition rule: If events $A, B, C, \ldots$ are all **disjoint** in pairs, then

  $$P(\text{at least one of these events occurs}) = P(A) + P(B) + P(C) + \cdots$$

  Multiplication rule: If events A and B are **independent,** then

  $$P(A \text{ and } B) = P(A)P(B)$$

  General addition rule: For any two events A and B,

  $$P(A \text{ or } B) = P(A) + P(B) - P(A \text{ and } B)$$

SECTION 5.1 Exercises

For Exercises 5.1 and 5.2, see page 315; for 5.3 to 5.5, see pages 316–317; and for 5.6 and 5.7, see pages 318–319.

5.8 Using Internet sources. Internet sites often vanish or move, so that references to them can't be followed. In fact, 13% of Internet sites referenced in major scientific journals are lost within two years after publication.

(a) If a paper contains seven Internet references, what is the probability that all seven are still good two years later?

(b) What specific assumptions did you make in order to calculate this probability?

5.9 Demographics in an SRS. The Census Bureau reports that 27% of California residents are foreign-born. Suppose that you choose three Californians at random, so that each has probability 0.27 of being foreign-born and the three are independent of each other. Let W be the number of foreign-born people you chose.

(a) What are the possible values of W?

(b) Look at your three people in order. There are eight possible arrangements of foreign (F) and domestic (D) birth. For example, FFD means the first two are foreign-born and the third is not. What is the probability of each arrangement? (Use the multiplication rule.)

(c) What is the value of W for each arrangement in (b)? What is the probability of each possible value of W? (This is the distribution of a Yes/No response for an SRS of size 3. In principle, the same idea works for an SRS of any size.)

5.10 I'll switch! In a February 2007 buying-intention survey, the investment bank Goldman Sachs found that 71% of the respondents indicated interest in buying an Apple mobile phone. Of the respondents interested in buying an Apple mobile phone, 15% indicated that they would switch cellular carriers to get an Apple mobile phone. Consider randomly selecting one survey respondent. Let A be the event that the respondent is interested in buying an Apple mobile phone, and let B be the event that the respondent would switch carriers to get an Apple mobile phone.

(a) Draw a Venn diagram that shows the relation between the events A and B.

(b) Apply the general addition rule to calculate $P(A \text{ or } B)$.

(c) Calculate $P(A \text{ and } B)$ and calculate $P(A)P(B)$. Are the two calculations equal? Are A and B independent?

5.11 Everyone gets audited. Wallen Accounting Services specializes in tax preparation for individual tax returns. Data collected from past records reveals that 9% of the returns prepared by Wallen have been selected for audit by the Internal Revenue Service. Today, Wallen has six new customers. Assume the chances of these six customers being audited are independent.

(a) What is the probability that all six new customers will be selected for audit?

(b) What is the probability that none of the six new customers will be selected for audit?

(c) What is the probability that exactly one of the six new customers will be selected for audit?

5.12 Hiring strategy. A chief executive officer (CEO) has resources to hire one vice-president or three managers. He believes that he has probability 0.6 of successfully recruiting the vice-president candidate and probability 0.8 of successfully recruiting each of the manager candidates. The three candidates for manager will make their decisions independently of each other. The CEO must successfully recruit either the vice-president or all three managers to consider his hiring strategy a success. Which strategy should he choose?

5.13 Playing the lottery. An instant lottery game gives you probability 0.02 of winning on any one play. Plays are independent of each other. If you play 5 times, what is the probability that you win at least once?

5.14 Nonconforming chips. Automobiles use semiconductor chips for engine and emission control, repair diagnosis, and other purposes. An auto manufacturer buys chips from a supplier. The supplier sends a shipment of which 5% fail to conform to performance specifications. Each chip chosen from this shipment has probability 0.05 of being nonconforming, and each automobile uses 12 chips selected independently. What is the probability that all 12 chips in a car will work properly?

5.15 A random walk on Wall Street? The "random walk" theory of securities prices holds that price movements in disjoint time periods are independent of each other. Suppose that we record only whether the price is up or down each year, and that the probability that our portfolio rises in price in any one year is 0.65. (This probability is approximately correct for a portfolio containing equal dollar amounts of all common stocks listed on the New York Stock Exchange.)

(a) What is the probability that our portfolio goes up for three consecutive years?

(b) If you know that the portfolio has risen in price 2 years in a row, what probability do you assign to the event that it will go down next year?

(c) What is the probability that the portfolio's value moves in the same direction in both of the next 2 years?

5.16 Getting into an MBA program. Ramon has applied to MBA programs at both Harvard and Stanford. He thinks the probability that Harvard will admit him is 0.4, the probability that Stanford will admit him is 0.5, and the probability that both will admit him is 0.2.

(a) Make a Venn diagram with the probabilities given marked.

(b) What is the probability that neither university admits Ramon?

(c) What is the probability that he gets into Stanford but not Harvard?

5.17 Will we get the jobs? Consolidated Builders has bid on two large construction projects. The company president believes that the probability of winning the first contract (event A) is 0.6, that the probability of winning the second (event B) is 0.5, and that the probability of winning both jobs (event $\{A \text{ and } B\}$) is 0.3. What is the probability of the event $\{A \text{ or } B\}$ that Consolidated will win at least one of the jobs?

5.18 Tastes in music. Musical styles other than rock and pop are becoming more popular. A survey of college students finds that 40% like country music, 30% like gospel music, and 10% like both.

(a) Make a Venn diagram with these results.

(b) What percent of college students like country but not gospel?

(c) What percent like neither country nor gospel?

5.19 Independent? In the setting of Exercise 5.17, are events A and B independent? Do a calculation that proves your answer.

Blood types. *All human blood can be "ABO-typed" as one of O, A, B, or AB, but the distribution of the types varies a bit among groups of people. Here is the distribution of blood types for a randomly chosen person in the United States:*

Blood type	O	A	B	AB
U.S. probability	0.45	0.40	0.11	0.04

Choose a married couple at random. It is reasonable to assume that the blood types of husband and wife are independent and follow this distribution. Exercises 5.20 to 5.23 concern this setting.

5.20 Is transfusion safe? Someone with type B blood can safely receive transfusions only from persons with type B or type O blood. What is the probability that the husband of a woman with type B blood is an acceptable blood donor for her?

5.21 Same type? What is the probability that a wife and husband share the same blood type?

5.22 Blood types, continued. What is the probability that the wife has type A blood and the husband has type B? What is the probability that one of the couple has type A blood and the other has type B?

5.23 Don't forget Rh. Human blood is typed as O, A, B, or AB and also as Rh-positive or Rh-negative. ABO type and Rh-factor type are independent because they are governed by different genes. In the American population, 84% of people are Rh-positive. Give the probability distribution of blood type (ABO and Rh together) for a randomly chosen person.

5.24 Age effects in medical care. The type of medical care a patient receives may vary with the age of the patient. A large study of women who had a breast lump investigated whether or not each woman received a mammogram and a biopsy when the lump was discovered. Here are some probabilities estimated by the study. The entries in the table are the probabilities that *both* of two events occur; for example, 0.321 is the probability that a patient is under 65 years of age *and* the tests were done. The four probabilities in the table have sum 1 because the table lists all possible outcomes.

	Tests Done?	
Age	Yes	No
Under 65	0.321	0.124
65 or over	0.365	0.190

(a) What is the probability that a patient in this study is under 65? That a patient is 65 or over?

(b) What is the probability that the tests were done for a patient? That they were not done?

(c) Are the events $A = \{\text{the patient was 65 or older}\}$ and $B = \{\text{the tests were done}\}$ independent? Were the tests omitted on older patients more or less frequently than would be the case if testing were independent of age?

5.25 Playing the odds? A writer on casino games says that the odds against throwing an 11 in the dice game craps are 17 to 1. He then says that the odds against three 11s in a row are $17 \times 17 \times 17$ to 1, or 4913 to 1.[3]

(a) What is the probability that the sum of the up-faces is 11 when you throw two balanced dice? (See Figure 4.2 on page 251.) What is the probability of three 11s in three independent throws?

(b) If an event A has probability P, the odds against A are

$$\text{odds against } A = \frac{1-P}{P}$$

Gamblers often speak of odds rather than probabilities. The odds against an event that has probability 1/3 are 2 to 1, for example. Find the odds against throwing an 11 and the odds against throwing three straight 11s. Which of the writer's statements are correct?

5.2 The Binomial Distributions

A company's human resources manager asks 100 employees if job stress is affecting their personal lives. How many will say "Yes"? A new treatment for pancreatic cancer is tried on 25 patients. How many will survive for 5 years? A store sells 10 computers with 1-year warranties. How many will not need repair within 1 year? In all these situations, we want a probability model for a *count* of successful outcomes.

The binomial setting

The distribution of a count depends on how the data are produced. Here is a common situation.

The Binomial Setting

1. There are a fixed number n of observations.
2. The n observations are all **independent.** That is, knowing the result of one observation tells you nothing about the other observations.
3. Each observation falls into one of just two categories, which for convenience we call "success" and "failure."
4. The probability of a success, call it p, is the same for each observation.

Think of tossing a coin n times as an example of the binomial setting. Each toss gives either heads or tails. Knowing the outcome of one toss doesn't tell us anything about other tosses, so the n tosses are independent. If we call heads a success, then p is the probability of a head and remains the same as long as we toss the same coin. The number of heads we count is a random variable X. The distribution of X is called a *binomial distribution.*

Binomial Distribution

The distribution of the count X of successes in the binomial setting is the **binomial distribution** with parameters n and p. The parameter n is the number of observations, and p is the probability of a success on any one observation. The possible values of X are the whole numbers from 0 to n.

The binomial distributions are an important class of probability distributions. Pay attention to the binomial setting, because not all counts have binomial distributions.

EXAMPLE 5.6 Determining Consumer Preferences

Market research to determine the product preferences of consumers is an increasingly important area in the intersection of business and statistics. With some companies competing in markets with little product discrimination, determining what features consumers most prefer is critical to the success of a product. Market research is interested in finding the probability of a "typical" consumer purchasing a product with a particular combination of features.

Suppose that your product is actually preferred over competitors' products by 25% of all consumers. If X is the count of the number of consumers who prefer your product in a group of 5 consumers, then X has a binomial distribution with $n = 5$ and $p = 0.25$, provided the 5 consumers make choices independently. Some business schools and companies are doing research on innovative ways to collect independent consumer data for use in statistical analyses.[4]

EXAMPLE 5.7 Dealing Cards

Deal 10 cards from a shuffled deck and count the number X of red cards. There are 10 observations, and each gives either a red or a black card. A "success" is a red card. But the observations are *not* independent. If the first card is black, the second is more likely to be red because there are more red cards than black cards left in the deck. The count X does *not* have a binomial distribution.

CASE 5.1 INSPECTING A SUPPLIER'S PRODUCTS

A manufacturing firm purchases components for its products from suppliers. Good practice calls for suppliers to manage their production processes to ensure good quality. You can find some discussion of statistical methods for managing and improving quality in Chapter 12. There have, however, been quality lapses in the switches supplied by a regular vendor. While working with the supplier to improve its processes, the manufacturing firm temporarily institutes an *acceptance sampling* plan to assess the quality of shipments of switches. If a random sample from a shipment contains too many switches that don't conform to specifications, the firm will not accept the shipment.

An engineer at the firm chooses an SRS of 10 switches from a shipment of 10,000 switches. Suppose that (unknown to the engineer) 10% of the switches in the shipment are nonconforming. The engineer counts the number X of nonconforming switches in the sample.

This is not quite a binomial setting. Just as removing 1 card in Example 5.7 changed the makeup of the deck, removing 1 switch changes the proportion of nonconforming switches remaining in the shipment. If there are initially 1000 nonconforming switches, the proportion remaining is $1000/9999 = 0.10001$ if the first switch drawn is OK and $999/9999 = 0.09991$ if the first switch fails inspection. That is, the state of the second switch chosen is not independent of the first. But removing 1 switch from a shipment of 10,000 changes the makeup of the remaining 9999 switches very little. In practice, the distribution of X is very close to the binomial distribution with $n = 10$ and $p = 0.1$.

Case 5.1 shows how we can use the binomial distributions in the statistical setting of selecting an SRS. When the population is much larger than the sample, a count of successes in an SRS of size n has approximately the binomial distribution with n equal to the sample size and p equal to the proportion of successes in the population.

APPLY YOUR KNOWLEDGE

In each of Exercises 5.26 to 5.28, X is a count. Does X have a binomial distribution? Give your reasons in each case.

5.26 Births. You observe the sex of the next 20 children born at a local hospital; X is the number of girls among them.

5.27 First girl. A couple decides to continue to have children until their first girl is born; X is the total number of children the couple has.

5.28 Teaching office software. A company uses a computer-based system to teach clerical employees new office software. After a lesson, the computer presents 10 exercises. The student solves each exercise and enters the answer. The computer gives additional instruction between exercises if the answer is wrong. The count X is the number of exercises that the student gets right.

Binomial probabilities*

We can find a formula for the probability that a binomial random variable takes any value by adding probabilities for the different ways of getting exactly that many successes in n observations. An example will guide us toward the formula we want.

EXAMPLE 5.8 Determining Consumer Preferences

Each consumer has probability 0.25 of preferring your product over competitors' products. If we question 5 consumers, what is the probability that exactly 2 of them prefer your product?

The count of consumers preferring your product is a binomial random variable X with $n = 5$ tries and probability $p = 0.25$ of a success on each try. We want $P(X = 2)$.

Because the method doesn't depend on the specific example, let's use "S" for success and "F" for failure for short. Do the work in two steps.

Step 1. Find the probability that a specific 2 of the 5 tries, say the first and the third, give successes. This is the outcome SFSFF. Because tries are independent, the multiplication rule for independent events applies. The probability we want is

$$\begin{aligned} P(\text{SFSFF}) &= P(S)P(F)P(S)P(F)P(F) \\ &= (0.25)(0.75)(0.25)(0.75)(0.75) \\ &= (0.25)^2(0.75)^3 \end{aligned}$$

Step 2. Observe that the probability of *any one* arrangement of 2 S's and 3 F's has this same probability. This is true because we multiply together 0.25 twice and 0.75 three times whenever we have 2 S's and 3 F's. The probability that $X = 2$ is the probability of getting 2 S's and 3 F's in any arrangement whatsoever. Here are all the possible arrangements:

SSFFF	SFSFF	SFFSF	SFFFS	FSSFF
FSFSF	FSFFS	FFSSF	FFSFS	FFFSS

There are 10 of them, all with the same probability. The overall probability of 2 successes is therefore

$$P(X = 2) = 10(0.25)^2(0.75)^3 = 0.2637$$

Approximately 26% of the time, samples of 5 independent consumers will produce exactly 2 who prefer your product over competitors' products.

*The derivation and use of the exact formula for binomial probabilities are optional.

The pattern of this calculation works for any binomial probability. To use it, we must count the number of arrangements of k successes in n observations. We use the following fact to do the counting without actually listing all the arrangements.

Binomial Coefficient

The number of ways of arranging k successes among n observations is given by the **binomial coefficient**

$$\binom{n}{k} = \frac{n!}{k!\,(n-k)!}$$

for $k = 0, 1, 2, \ldots, n$.

factorial

The formula for binomial coefficients uses the **factorial** notation. For any positive whole number n, its factorial $n!$ is

$$n! = n \times (n-1) \times (n-2) \times \cdots \times 3 \times 2 \times 1$$

Also, $0! = 1$ by definition.

The larger of the two factorials in the denominator of a binomial coefficient will cancel much of the $n!$ in the numerator. For example, the binomial coefficient we need for Example 5.8 is

$$\begin{aligned}\binom{5}{2} &= \frac{5!}{2!\,3!}\\ &= \frac{(5)(4)(3)(2)(1)}{(2)(1) \times (3)(2)(1)}\\ &= \frac{(5)(4)}{(2)(1)} = \frac{20}{2} = 10\end{aligned}$$

The notation $\binom{n}{k}$ is *not* related to the fraction $\frac{n}{k}$. A helpful way to remember its meaning is to read it as "binomial coefficient n choose k." Binomial coefficients have many uses in mathematics, but we are interested in them only as an aid to finding binomial probabilities. The binomial coefficient $\binom{n}{k}$ counts the number of different ways in which k successes can be arranged among n observations. The binomial probability $P(X = k)$ is this count multiplied by the probability of any specific arrangement of the k successes. Here is the result we seek.

Binomial Probability

If X has the binomial distribution with n observations and probability p of success on each observation, the possible values of X are $0, 1, 2, \ldots, n$. If k is any one of these values,

$$P(X = k) = \binom{n}{k} p^k (1-p)^{n-k}$$

EXAMPLE 5.9 Inspecting Switches

CASE 5.1 

The number X of switches that fail inspection in Case 5.1 closely follows the binomial distribution with $n = 10$ and $p = 0.1$.

The probability that no more than 1 switch fails is

$$
\begin{aligned}
P(X \le 1) &= P(X = 1) + P(X = 0) \\
&= \binom{10}{1}(0.1)^1(0.9)^9 + \binom{10}{0}(0.1)^0(0.9)^{10} \\
&= \frac{10!}{1!\,9!}(0.1)(0.3874) + \frac{10!}{0!\,10!}(1)(0.3487) \\
&= (10)(0.1)(0.3874) + (1)(1)(0.3487) \\
&= 0.3874 + 0.3487 = 0.7361
\end{aligned}
$$

This calculation uses the facts that $0! = 1$ and that $a^0 = 1$ for any number a other than 0. We see that about 74% of all samples will contain no more than 1 bad switch. In fact, 35% of the samples will contain no bad switches. A sample of size 10 cannot be trusted to alert the engineer to the presence of unacceptable items in the shipment. Calculations such as this are used to design acceptance sampling schemes.

APPLY YOUR KNOWLEDGE

5.29 Inheriting blood type. Genetics says that children receive genes from their parents independently. Each child of a particular pair of parents has probability 0.25 of having type O blood. If these parents have 5 children, the number who have type O blood is the count X of successes in 5 independent trials with probability 0.25 of a success on each trial. So X has the binomial distribution with $n = 5$ and $p = 0.25$.

(a) What are the possible values of X?

(b) Find the probability of each value of X. Draw a probability histogram to display this distribution. (Because probabilities are long-run proportions, a histogram with the probabilities as the heights of the bars shows what the distribution of X would be in very many repetitions.)

5.30 Hispanic representation. A factory employs several thousand workers, of whom 30% are Hispanic. If the 15 members of the union executive committee were chosen from the workers at random, the number of Hispanics on the committee would have the binomial distribution with $n = 15$ and $p = 0.3$.

(a) What is the probability that exactly 3 members of the committee are Hispanic?

(b) What is the probability that 3 or fewer members of the committee are Hispanic?

5.31 Do our athletes graduate? A university claims that 80% of its basketball players get degrees. An investigation examines the fate of all 20 players who entered the program over a period of several years that ended six years ago. Of these players, 11 graduated and the remaining 9 are no longer in school. If the university's claim is true, the number of players who graduate among the 20 should have the binomial distribution with $n = 20$ and $p = 0.8$. What is the probability that exactly 11 out of 20 players graduate?

Finding binomial probabilities: tables

The formula given on page 325 for binomial probabilities is practical for hand calculations when n is small. However, in practice, you will rarely have to use this formula for

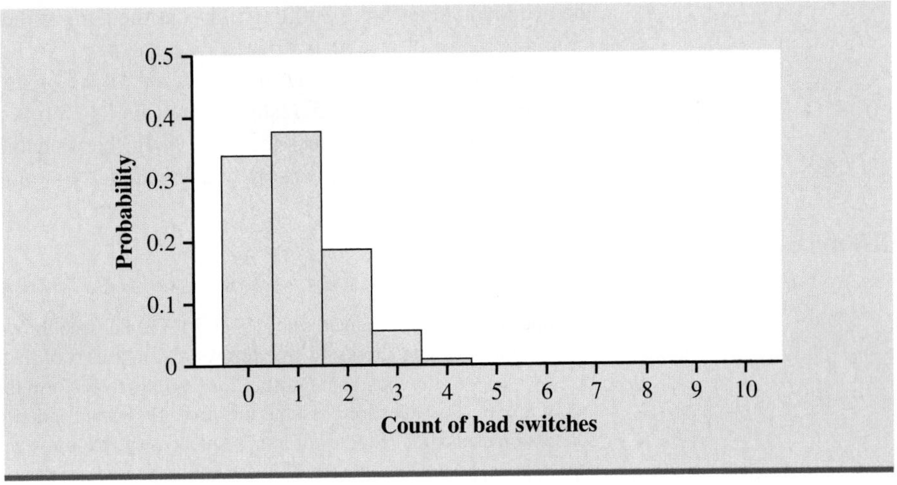

FIGURE 5.6 Probability histogram for the binomial distribution with $n = 10$ and $p = 0.1$, for Example 5.10.

calculations. Some calculators and most statistical software packages calculate binomial probabilities. If you do not have suitable computing facilities, you can look up the probabilities for some values of n and p in Table C in the back of this book. The entries in the table are the probabilities $P(X = k)$ of individual outcomes for a binomial random variable X.

EXAMPLE 5.10 Inspecting Switches

CASE 5.1

The quality engineer in Case 5.1 inspects an SRS of 10 switches from a large shipment of which 10% fail to conform to specifications. What is the probability that no more than 1 of the 10 switches in the sample fails inspection?

The count X of nonconforming switches in the sample has approximately the binomial distribution with $n = 10$ and $p = 0.1$. Figure 5.6 is a probability histogram for this distribution. The distribution is strongly skewed. Although X can take any whole-number value from 0 to 10, the probabilities of values larger than 5 are so small that they do not appear in the histogram.

We want to calculate

$$P(X \leq 1) = P(X = 1) + P(X = 0)$$

when X is binomial with $n = 10$ and $p = 0.1$. Your software may do this—look for the key word "Binomial." To use Table C for this calculation, look opposite $n = 10$ and under $p = 0.10$. This part of the table appears at the left. The entry opposite each k is $P(X = k)$. We find

$$P(X \leq 1) = P(X = 1) + P(X = 0)$$
$$= 0.3874 + 0.3487 = 0.7361$$

About 74% of all samples will contain no more than 1 bad switch. This matches our calculation in Example 5.9.

		p
n	k	0.10
10	0	0.3487
	1	0.3874
	2	0.1937
	3	0.0574
	4	0.0112
	5	0.0015
	6	0.0001
	7	0.0000
	8	0.0000
	9	0.0000
	10	0.0000

The excerpt from Table C in the margin contains the full binomial distribution for $n = 10$ and $p = 0.1$. The probabilities are rounded to four decimal places. Outcomes larger than 6 do not have probability exactly 0, but their probabilities are so small that the rounded values are 0.0000. Check that the sum of the probabilities given is 1, as it should be.

The values of p that appear in Table C are all 0.5 or smaller. When the probability of a success is greater than 0.5, restate the problem in terms of the number of failures. The probability of a failure is less than 0.5 when the probability of a success exceeds 0.5. When using the table, always stop to ask whether you must count successes or failures.

EXAMPLE 5.11 Free Throws

Corinne is a basketball player who makes 75% of her free throws over the course of a season. In a key game, Corinne shoots 12 free throws and misses 5 of them. The fans think that she failed because she was nervous. Is it unusual for Corinne to perform this poorly?

To answer this question, assume that free throws are independent with probability 0.75 of a success on each shot. (Studies of long sequences of free throws have found no evidence that they are dependent, so this is a reasonable assumption.) Because the probability of making a free throw is greater than 0.5, we count misses in order to use Table C. The probability of a miss is $1 - 0.75$, or 0.25. The number X of misses in 12 attempts has the binomial distribution with $n = 12$ and $p = 0.25$.

We want the probability of missing 5 or more. This is

$$\begin{aligned} P(X \geq 5) &= P(X = 5) + P(X = 6) + \cdots + P(X = 12) \\ &= 0.1032 + 0.0401 + \cdots + 0.0000 = 0.1576 \end{aligned}$$

Corinne will miss 5 or more out of 12 free throws about 16% of the time, or roughly one of every six games. While below her average level, her performance in this game was well within the range of the usual chance variation in her shooting.

APPLY YOUR KNOWLEDGE

5.32 Restaurant survey. You operate a restaurant. You read that a sample survey by the National Restaurant Association shows that 40% of adults are committed to eating nutritious food when eating away from home. To help plan your menu, you decide to conduct a sample survey in your own area. You will use random digit dialing to contact an SRS of 20 households by telephone.

(a) If the national result holds in your area, it is reasonable to use the binomial distribution with $n = 20$ and $p = 0.4$ to describe the count X of respondents who seek nutritious food when eating out. Explain why.

(b) Ten of the 20 respondents say they are concerned about nutrition. Is this reason to believe that the percent in your area is higher than the national 40%? To answer this question, use software or Table C to find the probability that X is 10 or larger if $p = 0.4$ is true. If this probability is very small, that is reason to think that p is actually greater than 0.4 in your area.

Binomial mean and standard deviation

If a count X has the binomial distribution based on n observations with probability p of success, what is its mean μ? That is, in very many repetitions of the binomial setting, what will be the average count of successes? We can guess the answer. If a basketball player makes 75% of her free throws, the mean number made in 12 tries should be 75% of 12, or 9. In general, the mean of a binomial distribution should be $\mu = np$. Here are the facts.

Binomial Mean and Standard Deviation

If a count X has the binomial distribution with number of observations n and probability of success p, the **mean** and **standard deviation** of X are

$$\mu = np$$
$$\sigma = \sqrt{np(1-p)}$$

Remember that these short formulas are good only for binomial distributions. They can't be used for other distributions.

EXAMPLE 5.12 Inspecting Switches

CASE 5.1

Continuing Case 5.1, the count X of bad switches is binomial with $n = 10$ and $p = 0.1$. The mean and standard deviation of this binomial distribution are

$$\begin{aligned}\mu &= np \\ &= (10)(0.1) = 1 \\ \sigma &= \sqrt{np(1-p)} \\ &= \sqrt{(10)(0.1)(0.9)} = \sqrt{0.9} = 0.9487\end{aligned}$$

In Figure 5.7, we have added the mean to the probability histogram of the distribution.

APPLY YOUR KNOWLEDGE

5.33 Restaurant survey. As in Exercise 5.32, you ask an SRS of 20 adults from your restaurant's target area if they are concerned about nutrition when eating away from home. If the national proportion $p = 0.4$ holds in your area, what will be the mean number of "Yes" responses? What is the standard deviation of the count of "Yes" answers?

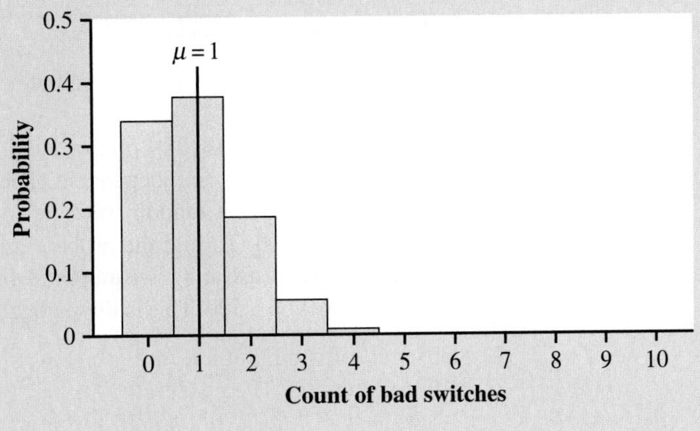

FIGURE 5.7 Probability histogram for the binomial distribution with $n = 10$ and $p = 0.1$ and with the mean $\mu = 1$ marked, for Example 5.12.

5.34 Hispanic representation.

(a) What is the mean number of Hispanics on randomly chosen committees of 15 workers in Exercise 5.30?

(b) What is the standard deviation σ of the count X of Hispanic members?

(c) Suppose that 10% of the factory workers were Hispanic. Then $p = 0.1$. What is σ in this case? What is σ if $p = 0.01$? What does your work show about the behavior of the standard deviation of a binomial distribution as the probability of a success gets closer to 0?

5.35 Do our athletes graduate?

(a) Find the mean number of graduates out of 20 players in the setting of Exercise 5.31 if the university's claim is true.

(b) Find the standard deviation σ of the count X.

(c) Suppose that the 20 players came from a population of which $p = 0.9$ graduated. What is the standard deviation σ of the count of graduates? If $p = 0.99$, what is σ? What does your work show about the behavior of the standard deviation of a binomial distribution as the probability p of success gets closer to 1?

The Normal approximation to binomial distributions

The binomial probability formula and tables are practical only when the number of trials n is small. Even software and statistical calculators are unable to handle calculations for very large n. Here is another alternative: *as the number of trials n gets larger, the binomial distribution gets close to a Normal distribution.* When n is large, we can use Normal probability calculations to approximate hard-to-calculate binomial probabilities. For an example, we return to the survey discussed in Case 3.1 (page 210).

EXAMPLE 5.13 Is Clothes Shopping Frustrating?

CASE 3.1

Sample surveys show that fewer people enjoy shopping than in the past. A recent survey asked a nationwide random sample of 2500 adults if they agreed or disagreed that "I like buying new clothes, but shopping is often frustrating and time-consuming."[5] The population that the poll wants to draw conclusions about is *all* U.S. residents aged 18 and over. Suppose that in fact 60% of *all* adult U.S. residents would say "agree" if asked the same question. What is the probability that 1520 or more of the sample agree?

Because there are almost 220 million adults, we can take the responses of 2500 randomly chosen adults to be independent. The number in our sample who agree that shopping is frustrating is a random variable X having the binomial distribution with $n = 2500$ and $p = 0.6$. To find the probability that at least 1520 of the people in the sample find shopping frustrating, we must add the binomial probabilities of all outcomes from $X = 1520$ to $X = 2500$. This isn't practical. Here are three ways to do this problem:

1. Statistical software (but not some versions of the Excel spreadsheet program) can do the calculation. The result is

$$P(X \geq 1520) = 0.2131$$

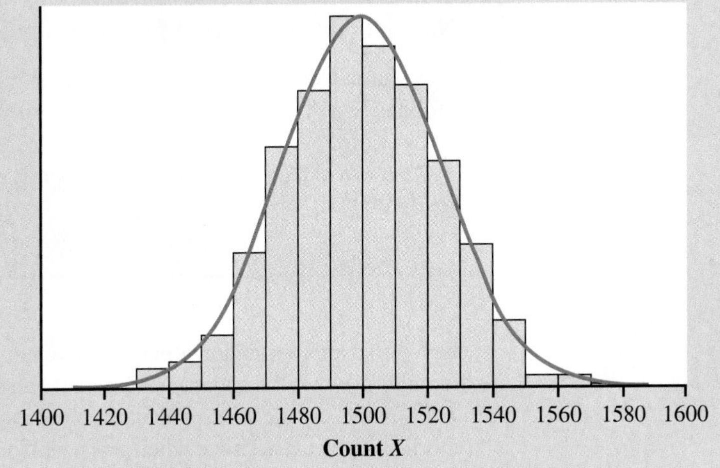

FIGURE 5.8 Histogram of 1000 binomial counts ($n = 2500$, $p = 0.6$) and the Normal density curve that approximates this binomial distribution.

2. We can simulate a large number of repetitions of the sample. Figure 5.8 displays a histogram of the counts X from 1000 samples of size 2500 when the truth about the population is $p = 0.6$. Because 221 of these 1000 samples have X at least 1520, the probability estimated from the simulation is

$$P(X \geq 1520) = \frac{221}{1000} = 0.221$$

3. Both of the previous methods require software. Instead, look at the Normal curve in Figure 5.8. This is the density curve of the Normal distribution with the same mean and standard deviation as the binomial variable X:

$$\mu = np = (2500)(0.6) = 1500$$
$$\sigma = \sqrt{np(1-p)} = \sqrt{(2500)(0.6)(0.4)} = 24.49$$

As the figure shows, this Normal distribution approximates the binomial distribution quite well. So we can do a Normal calculation.

EXAMPLE 5.14 Normal Calculation of a Binomial Probability

CASE 3.1 

Act as though the count X had the $N(1500, 24.49)$ distribution. Here is the probability we want, using Table A:

$$P(X \geq 1520) = P\left(\frac{X - 1500}{24.49} \geq \frac{1520 - 1500}{24.49}\right)$$
$$= P(Z \geq 0.82)$$
$$= 1 - 0.7939 = 0.2061$$

The Normal approximation 0.2061 differs from the software result 0.2131 by only 0.007.

Normal Approximation for Binomial Distributions

Suppose that a count X has the binomial distribution with n trials and success probability p. When n is large, the distribution of X is approximately Normal, $N(np, \sqrt{np(1-p)})$.

As a rule of thumb, we will use the Normal approximation when n and p satisfy $np \geq 10$ and $n(1-p) \geq 10$.

The Normal approximation is easy to remember because it says that X is Normal with its binomial mean and standard deviation. The accuracy of the Normal approximation improves as the sample size n increases. It is most accurate for any fixed n when p is close to $1/2$, and least accurate when p is near 0 or 1. Whether or not you use the Normal approximation should depend on how accurate your calculations need to be. For most statistical purposes great accuracy is not required. Our "rule of thumb" for use of the Normal approximation reflects this judgment.

APPLY YOUR KNOWLEDGE

5.36 Restaurant survey. Return to the survey described in Exercise 5.32. You plan to use random digit dialing to contact an SRS of 200 households by telephone rather than just 20.

(a) What are the mean and standard deviation of the number of nutrition-conscious people in your sample if $p = 0.4$ is true?

(b) What is the probability that X lies between 75 and 85? (Use the Normal approximation.)

5.37 The effect of sample size. The SRS of size 200 described in the previous exercise finds that 100 of the 200 respondents are concerned about nutrition. We wonder if this is reason to conclude that the percent in your area is higher than the national 40%.

(a) Find the probability that X is 100 or larger if $p = 0.4$ is true. If this probability is very small, that is reason to think that p is actually greater than 0.4 in your area.

(b) In Exercise 5.32, you found $P(X \geq 10)$ for a sample of size 20. In (a), you have found $P(X \geq 100)$ for a sample of size 200 from the same population. Both of these probabilities answer the question "How likely is a sample with at least 50% successes when the population has 40% successes?" What does comparing these probabilities suggest about the importance of sample size?

SECTION 5.2 SUMMARY

- A count X of successes has a **binomial distribution** in the **binomial setting:** the number of observations n is fixed in advance; the observations are independent of each other; each observation results in a success or a failure; and each observation has the same probability p of a success.
- The binomial distribution with n observations and probability p of success gives a good approximation to the sampling distribution of the count of successes in an SRS of size n from a large population containing proportion p of successes.

- If X has the binomial distribution with parameters n and p, the possible values of X are the whole numbers $0, 1, 2, \ldots, n$. The **binomial probability** that X takes any value is

$$P(X = k) = \binom{n}{k} p^k (1 - p)^{n-k}$$

Binomial probabilities are most easily found by software. This formula is practical for calculations when n is small. Table C contains binomial probabilities for some values of n and p. For large n, you can use the Normal approximation.

- The **binomial coefficient**

$$\binom{n}{k} = \frac{n!}{k!\,(n - k)!}$$

counts the number of ways k successes can be arranged among n observations. Here the **factorial** $n!$ is

$$n! = n \times (n - 1) \times (n - 2) \times \cdots \times 3 \times 2 \times 1$$

for positive whole numbers n, and $0! = 1$.

- The **mean** and **standard deviation** of a binomial count X are

$$\mu = np$$
$$\sigma = \sqrt{np(1 - p)}$$

- The **Normal approximation** to the binomial distribution says that if X is a count having the binomial distribution with parameters n and p, then when n is large, X is approximately $N(np, \sqrt{np(1 - p)})$. We will use this approximation when $np \geq 10$ and $n(1 - p) \geq 10$.

SECTION 5.2 Exercises

For Exercises 5.26 to 5.28, see pages 323–324; for 5.29 to 5.31, see page 326; for 5.32, see page 328; for 5.33 to 5.35, see pages 329–330; and for 5.36 and 5.37, see page 332.

All of the binomial probability calculations required in these exercises can be done by using Table C or the Normal approximation. Your instructor may request that you use the binomial probability formula or software.

5.38 Web site traffic. What kinds of Web sites do males aged 18 to 34 visit most often? Pornographic sites take first place, but about 50% of male Internet users in this age group visit an auction site such as eBay at least once a month. Interview a random sample of 12 male Internet users aged 18 to 34.

(a) What is the distribution of the number who have visited an online auction site in the past month?

(b) What is the probability that exactly 8 of the 12 have visited an auction site in the past month? If you have software, also find the probability that at least 8 of the 12 have visited an auction site in the past month.

5.39 Web site traffic. Suppose that 50% of male Internet users aged 18 to 34 have visited an auction site at least once in the past month.

(a) If you interview 12 at random, what is the mean of the count X who have visited an auction site? What is the mean of the proportion $\hat{p}$ in your sample who have visited an auction site?

(b) Repeat the calculations in (a) for samples of size 120 and 1200. What happens to the mean count of successes as the sample size increases? What happens to the mean proportion of successes?

5.40 Carpooling stats. Although cities encourage carpooling to reduce traffic congestion, most vehicles carry only one person. For example, 70% of vehicles on the roads in the Minneapolis–St. Paul metropolitan area are occupied by just the driver.

(a) If you choose 10 vehicles at random, what is the probability that more than half (that is, 6 or more) carry just one person?

(b) If you choose 100 vehicles at random, what is the probability that more than half (that is, 51 or more) carry just one person?

5.41 Internet postings. Suppose (as is roughly true) that 20% of all Internet users have posted photos online. A sample survey interviews an SRS of 1555 Internet users.

(a) What is the actual distribution of the number X in the sample who have posted photos online?

(b) What is the probability that 300 or fewer of the people in the sample have posted photos online? (Use software or a suitable approximation.)

5.42 Binomial setting? In each situation below, is it reasonable to use a binomial distribution for the random variable X? Give reasons for your answer in each case.

(a) An auto manufacturer chooses one car from each hour's production for a detailed quality inspection. One variable recorded is the count X of finish defects (dimples, ripples, etc.) in the car's paint.

(b) Joe buys a ticket in his state's "Pick 3" lottery game every week; X is the number of times in a year that he wins a prize.

5.43 Binomial setting? In each of the following cases, decide whether or not a binomial distribution is an appropriate model, and give your reasons.

(a) A firm uses a computer-based training module to prepare 20 machinists to use new numerically controlled lathes. The module contains a test at the end of the course; X is the number who perform satisfactorily on the test.

(b) The list of potential product testers for a new product contains 100 persons chosen at random from the adult residents of a large city. Each person on the list is asked whether he or she would participate in the study if given the chance; X is the number who say "Yes."

5.44 Random digits. Each entry in a table of random digits like Table B has probability 0.1 of being a 0, and digits are independent of each other.

(a) What is the probability that a group of five digits from the table will contain at least one 0?

(b) What is the mean number of 0s in lines 40 digits long?

5.45 Unmarried women. Among employed women, 25% have never been married. Select 10 employed women at random.

(a) The number in your sample who have never been married has a binomial distribution. What are n and p?

(b) What is the probability that exactly 2 of the 10 women in your sample have never been married?

(c) What is the probability that 2 or fewer have never been married?

(d) What is the mean number of women in such samples who have never been married? What is the standard deviation?

5.46 Generic brand soda. In a taste test of a generic soda versus a brand name soda, 25% of tasters can distinguish between the colas. Twenty tasters are asked to take the taste test and guess which cup contains the brand name soda. The tests are done independently in separate locations, so that the tasters do not interact with each other during the test.

(a) The count of correct guesses in 20 taste tests has a binomial distribution. What are n and p?

(b) What is the mean number of correct guesses in many repetitions?

(c) What is the probability of exactly 5 correct guesses?

5.47 Random stock prices. A believer in the "random walk" theory of stock markets thinks that an index of stock prices has probability 0.65 of increasing in any year. Moreover, the change in the index in any given year is not influenced by whether it rose or fell in earlier years. Let X be the number of years among the next 5 years in which the index rises.

(a) X has a binomial distribution. What are n and p?

(b) What are the possible values that X can take?

(c) Find the probability of each value of X. Draw a probability histogram for the distribution of X.

(d) What are the mean and standard deviation of this distribution? Mark the location of the mean on your histogram.

5.48 Lie detectors. A federal report finds that lie detector tests given to truthful persons have probability about 0.2 of suggesting that the person is deceptive.[6]

(a) A company asks 12 job applicants about thefts from previous employers, using a lie detector to assess their truthfulness. Suppose that all 12 answer truthfully. What is the probability that the lie detector says all 12 are truthful? What is the probability that the lie detector says at least 1 is deceptive?

(b) What is the mean number among 12 truthful persons who will be classified as deceptive? What is the standard deviation of this number?

(c) What is the probability that the number classified as deceptive is less than the mean?

5.49 Multiple-choice tests. Here is a simple probability model for multiple-choice tests. Suppose that each student has probability p of correctly answering a question chosen at random from a universe of possible questions. (A strong student has a higher p than a weak student.) Answers to different questions are independent. Jodi is a good student for whom $p = 0.75$.

(a) Use the Normal approximation to find the probability that Jodi scores 70% or lower on a 100-question test.

(b) If the test contains 250 questions, what is the probability that Jodi will score 70% or lower?

5.50 Mark McGwire's home runs. In 1998, Mark McGwire of the St. Louis Cardinals hit 70 home runs, a new major league record. Was this feat as surprising as most of us thought? In the three seasons before 1998, McGwire hit a home run in 11.6% of his times at bat. He went to bat 509 times in 1998. McGwire's home run count in 509 times at bat has approximately the binomial distribution with $n = 509$ and $p = 0.116$.

(a) What is the mean number of home runs he will hit in 509 times at bat?

(b) What is the probability of 70 or more home runs? Use the Normal approximation.

(c) Compare your answer in (b) to the actual probability of 0.0764 found using software.

	A	B	C
1	1-BINOMDIST(69,509,0.116,1)=	0.076374	
2			

5.51 Planning a survey. You are planning a sample survey of small businesses in your area. You will choose an SRS of businesses listed in the telephone book's Yellow Pages. Experience shows that only about half the businesses you contact will respond.

(a) If you contact 150 businesses, it is reasonable to use the binomial distribution with $n = 150$ and $p = 0.5$ for the number X who respond. Explain why.

(b) What is the expected number (the mean) who will respond?

(c) What is the probability that 70 or fewer will respond? (Use the Normal approximation.)

(d) How large a sample must you take to increase the mean number of respondents to 100?

5.52 Are we shipping on time? Your mail-order company advertises that it ships 90% of its orders within three working days. You select an SRS of 100 of the 5000 orders received in the past week for an audit. The audit reveals that 86 of these orders were shipped on time.

(a) If the company really ships 90% of its orders on time, what is the probability that 86 or fewer in an SRS of 100 orders are shipped on time?

(b) A critic says, "Aha! You claim 90%, but in your sample the on-time percent is only 86%. So the 90% claim is wrong." Explain in simple language why your probability calculation in (a) shows that the result of the sample does not refute the 90% claim.

5.53 Checking for survey errors. One way of checking the effect of undercoverage, nonresponse, and other sources of error in a sample survey is to compare the sample with known facts about the population. About 12% of American adults are black. The number X of blacks in a random sample of 1500 adults should therefore vary with the binomial ($n = 1500$, $p = 0.12$) distribution.

(a) What are the mean and standard deviation of X?

(b) Use the Normal approximation to find the probability that the sample will contain 170 or fewer blacks. Be sure to check that you can safely use the approximation.

5.3 The Poisson Distributions

Not all counts have binomial distributions. It is common to meet counts that are open-ended, that is, that do not have the fixed number of observations required by the binomial model. Count the number of finish defects in the sheet metal of a car or a refrigerator: the count could be 0, 1, 2, 3, and so on indefinitely. A bank counts the number of automatic teller machine (ATM) customers arriving at a particular ATM between 2:00 P.M. and 4:00 P.M. A railyard counts the number of work injuries that happen in a month. All of these count examples share common characteristics.

The Poisson setting

The Poisson distribution is another distribution for count random variables. Count the number of events (call them "successes") that occur in some fixed unit of measure such as an area of sheet metal, a period of time, or a length of cable. The Poisson distribution is appropriate in the following situation.

The Poisson Setting

1. The number of successes that occur in any unit of measure is **independent** of the number of successes that occur in any nonoverlapping unit of measure.
2. The probability that a success will occur in a unit of measure is the same for all units of equal size and is proportional to the size of the unit.
3. The probability that 2 or more successes will occur in a unit approaches 0 as the size of the unit becomes smaller.

For binomial distributions, the important quantities were n, the fixed number of observations, and p, the probability of success on any given observation. The quantity important in specifying Poisson distributions is the mean number of successes occurring per unit of measure.

Poisson Distribution

The distribution of the count X of successes in the Poisson setting is the **Poisson distribution** with **mean** μ. The parameter μ is the mean number of successes per unit of measure. The possible values of X are the whole numbers $0, 1, 2, 3, \ldots$. If k is any whole number 0 or greater, then*

$$P(X = k) = \frac{e^{-\mu}\mu^k}{k!}$$

The **standard deviation** of the distribution is $\sqrt{\mu}$.

*The quantity e in the Poisson probability formula is a mathematical constant, $e = 2.71828$ to six significant digits. Many calculators have an e^x function.

EXAMPLE 5.15 Flaws in Carpets

A carpet manufacturer knows that the number of flaws per square yard in a type of carpet material varies with an average of 1.6 flaws per square yard. The count X of flaws per square yard can be modeled by the Poisson distribution with $\mu = 1.6$. The unit of measure is a square yard of carpet material. What is the probability of no more than 2 defects in a randomly chosen square yard of this material?

We will calculate $P(X \leq 2)$ in two ways:

1. Software can do the calculation:

	A	B	C
1	Poisson(0,1.6,0)=	0.2019	
2	Poisson(1,1.6,0)=	0.3230	
3	Poisson(2,1.6,0)=	0.2584	
4	SUM(B1:B3)=	0.7834	
5			

2. We can use the Poisson probability formula:

$$\begin{aligned} P(X \leq 2) &= P(X = 0) + P(X = 1) + P(X = 2) \\ &= \frac{e^{-1.6}(1.6)^0}{0!} + \frac{e^{-1.6}(1.6)^1}{1!} + \frac{e^{-1.6}(1.6)^2}{2!} \\ &= 0.2019 + 0.3230 + 0.2584 = 0.7833 \end{aligned}$$

The software answer and the hand calculation differ by 0.0001 due to roundoff error in the hand calculation. The software calculates the individual probabilities to many significant digits even though it displays only four significant digits.

cumulative probability

Recall that Table A gives **cumulative probabilities** of the form $P(X \leq k)$ for the standard Normal distribution. Most software will calculate cumulative probabilities for other distributions, including the Poisson family. Cumulative probability calculations make solving many problems less tedious.

EXAMPLE 5.16 Counting ATM Customers

Suppose the number of persons using an ATM in any given hour can be modeled by a Poisson distribution with $\mu = 5.5$. What is the probability of more than 8 persons using the machine during the next hour? Calculating this probability requires two steps:

1. Write $P(X > 8)$ as an expression involving a cumulative probability:

$$P(X > 8) = 1 - P(X \leq 8)$$

2. Calculate $P(X \leq 8)$ and subtract the value from 1.

	A	B	C
1	1-Poisson(8,5.5,1)=	0.1056	
2			

This is quicker and less prone to error than the method of Example 5.15, which would require specifying nine individual probabilities and summing their values.

The Poisson model

If we add counts of successes in nonoverlapping areas of space or time, we are just counting the successes in a larger area. That count still meets the conditions of the Poisson setting. Put more formally, if X is a Poisson random variable with mean μ_X and Y is a Poisson random variable with mean μ_Y and Y is independent of X, then $X + Y$ is a Poisson random variable with mean $\mu_X + \mu_Y$. This fact is important in using Poisson models. We can combine areas or look at just a portion of an area and still use Poisson distributions for counts of successes.

EXAMPLE 5.17 Paint Finish Flaws

Auto bodies are painted during manufacture by robots programmed to move in such a way that the paint is uniform in thickness and quality. You are testing a newly programmed robot by counting paint sags caused by small areas receiving too much paint. Sags are more common on vertical surfaces. Suppose that counts of sags on the roof follow the Poisson model with mean 0.7 sags per square yard and that counts on the side panels of the auto body follow the Poisson model with mean 1.4 sags per square yard. Counts in nonoverlapping areas are independent. Then

- The number of sags in 2 square yards of roof is a Poisson random variable with mean $0.7 + 0.7 = 1.4$.
- The total roof area of the auto body is 4.8 square yards. The number of paint sags on a roof is a Poisson random variable with mean $4.8 \times 0.7 = 3.36$.
- A square foot is 1/9 square yard. The number of paint sags in a square foot of roof is a Poisson random variable with mean $1/9 \times 0.7 = 0.078$.
- If we examine 1 square yard of roof and 1 square yard of side panel, the number of sags is a Poisson random variable with mean $0.7 + 1.4 = 2.1$.

APPLY YOUR KNOWLEDGE

5.54 Industrial accidents. A large manufacturing plant has averaged 7 "reportable accidents" per month. Suppose that accident counts over time follow a Poisson distribution with mean 7 per month.

(a) What is the probability of exactly 7 accidents in a month?

(b) What is the probability of 7 or fewer accidents in a month?

5.55 A safety initiative. This year, a "safety culture change" initiative attempts to reduce the number of accidents at the plant described in the previous exercise. There are 66 reportable accidents during the year. Suppose that the Poisson distribution of the previous exercise continues to apply.

(a) What is the distribution of the number of reportable accidents in a year?

(b) What is the probability of 66 or fewer accidents in a year? (Use software.) The probability is small, which is evidence that the initiative did reduce the accident rate.

BEYOND THE BASICS: MORE DISTRIBUTION APPROXIMATIONS

In Section 5.2, we observed that the Normal distribution could be used to calculate binomial probabilities when n, the number of trials, is large (page 330). When n is large, the binomial probability histogram has the familiar mound shape of the Normal density curve. This fact allows us to use Normal probabilities and to avoid tedious hand calculations or the need to use software to calculate binomial probabilities.

Using the Normal distribution to approximate the binomial distribution is just one example of using one distribution to approximate another to make probability calculations more convenient. With the distributions we have studied, two more approximations are common:

- **Normal approximation to the Poisson.** Some versions of the Excel spreadsheet program return an error when asked to calculate $P(X \le 142)$ for a Poisson random variable X with mean $\mu = 150$. What can we do if our software cannot handle Poisson distributions with large means? Fortunately, when μ is large, Poisson probabilities can be approximated using the Normal distribution with mean μ and standard deviation $\sqrt{\mu}$. The following table compares $P(X \le k)$ for a Poisson random variable X with $\mu = 150$ with approximations using the $N(150, 12.247)$ distribution.

k	Poisson	Normal
142	0.2730	0.2568
150	0.5217	0.5000
160	0.8054	0.7929

  The Normal approximation is adequate for many practical purposes, but we recommend statistical software that can give exact Poisson probabilities.

- **Poisson approximation to the binomial.** We recommend using the Normal approximation to a binomial distribution only when n and p satisfy $np \ge 10$ and $n(1-p) \ge 10$. In cases where p is so small that $np < 10$, using the Poisson distribution with $\mu = np$ to calculate binomial probabilities yields more accurate results. The following table compares $P(X \le k)$ for a binomial distribution with $n = 1000$ and $p = 0.001$ with Poisson probabilities calculated using $\mu = np = (1000)(0.001) = 1$.

k	Binomial	Poisson
0	0.3677	0.3679
1	0.7358	0.7358
2	0.9198	0.9197
3	0.9811	0.9810
4	0.9964	0.9963
5	0.9994	0.9994
6	0.9999	0.9999
7	1.0000	1.0000

  The Poisson approximation gives very accurate probability calculations for the binomial distribution with $n = 1000$ and $p = 0.001$.

Even statistical software has its limits, and some binomial and Poisson probability calculations can exceed those limits. In many cases, however, one of the approximations we have discussed will make calculations possible.

SECTION 5.3 SUMMARY

- A count X of successes has a **Poisson distribution** in the **Poisson setting:** the number of successes in any unit of measure is independent of the number of successes in any other nonoverlapping unit; the probability of a success in a unit of measure is the same for all units of equal size and is proportional to the size of the unit; the probability of 2 or more successes in a unit approaches 0 as the size of the unit becomes smaller.
- If X has the Poisson distribution with mean μ, then the standard deviation of X is $\sqrt{\mu}$, and the possible values of X are all the whole numbers 0, 1, 2, 3, and so on. The **Poisson probability** that X takes any one of these values is

$$P(X = k) = \frac{e^{-\mu}\mu^k}{k!} \qquad k = 0, 1, 2, 3, \ldots$$

- Poisson probabilities are most easily found by software. The formula above is practical when only a small number of probabilities is needed and k is not large.
- Sums of independent Poisson random variables also have the Poisson distribution. In a Poisson model with mean μ per unit of space or time, the count of successes in a units is a Poisson random variable with mean $a\mu$.

SECTION 5.3 Exercises

For Exercises 5.54 and 5.55, see page 318.

Use software to calculate the Poisson probabilities in the following exercises.

5.56 How many calls? Calls to the customer service department of a cable TV provider are made randomly and independently at a rate of 11 per minute. The company has a staff of 20 customer service specialists who handle all the calls. Assume that none of the specialists are on a call at this moment and that a Poisson model is appropriate for the number of incoming calls per minute.

(a) What is the probability of the customer service department receiving more than 20 calls in the next minute?

(b) What is the probability of the customer service department receiving exactly 20 calls in the next minute?

(c) What is the probability of the customer service department receiving fewer than 11 calls in the next minute?

5.57 Hospitalization claims. A national home improvement and hardware chain provides health insurance to its full-time employees. On the basis of past experience with companies similar to this one, the insurance carrier for this chain of stores expects 6 hospitalizations per month, on average. Employee turnover within the chain of stores is approximately 32%; however, the overall size and general demographic characteristics of the workforce remain fairly consistent over time. This stability within the workforce makes the Poisson model reasonable.

(a) What assumption must be made about hospitalizations for different employees?

(b) What is the probability of 2 or fewer hospitalizations in the next month?

(c) What is the probability of more than 2 hospitalizations in the next month?

(d) What is the probability of at least 8 hospitalizations in the next month?

5.58 Bad checks. Duck Worth Wearing, the children's consignment shop featured in Case 2.1 (page 96), accepts cash, check, and credit card for payment. About 30% of all transactions are paid by check. Duck Worth Wearing anticipates only 3 bad checks per month, on average. Assume that the number of bad checks per month can be modeled as a Poisson random variable.

(a) What is the probability of no bad checks in the next month?

(b) What is the probability of one or more bad checks in the next month?

(c) What is the probability of more than 7 bad checks in the next month?

5.59 Switchboard errors. At a large software company, calls coming to the general contact phone number are answered by a switchboard operator. The operator's job is to manually forward calls to the desired party within the company. The switchboard operator's past performance indicates that he forwards calls incorrectly at a rate of 2.5 per week. Assuming a Poisson model is appropriate, answer the following questions.

(a) What is the probability of no call-forwarding errors in the next week?

(b) What is the probability of 4 or more call-forwarding errors in the next week?

5.60 Too much email? According to email logs, one employee at your company receives an average of 110 emails per week. Suppose the count of emails received can be adequately modeled as a Poisson random variable.

(a) What is the probability of this employee receiving exactly 110 emails in a given week?

(b) What is the probability of receiving 100 or fewer emails in a given week?

(c) What is the probability of receiving more than 125 emails in a given week?

(d) What is the probability of receiving 125 or more emails in a given week? (Be careful: this is not the same event as in part (c).)

5.61 Traffic model. The number of vehicles passing a particular mile marker during 15-minute units of time can be modeled as a Poisson random variable. Counting devices show that the average number of vehicles passing the mile marker per 15 minutes is 48.7.

(a) What is the probability of 50 or more vehicles passing the marker during a 15-minute time period?

(b) What is the standard deviation of the number of vehicles passing the marker in a 15-minute time period? A 30-minute time period?

(c) What is the probability of 100 or more vehicles passing the marker during a 30-minute time period?

5.62 Too much email? According to email logs, one employee at your company receives an average of 110 emails per week. Suppose the count of emails received can be adequately modeled as a Poisson random variable.

(a) What is the distribution of the number of emails in a two-week period?

(b) What is the probability of receiving 200 or fewer emails in a two-week period?

5.63 Work-related deaths. Work-related deaths in the United States have a mean of 17 per day. Suppose the count of work-related deaths per day follows an approximate Poisson distribution.

(a) What is the standard deviation for daily work-related deaths?

(b) What is the probability of 10 or fewer work-related deaths in one day?

(c) What is the probability of more than 30 work-related deaths in one day?

5.64 Flaws in carpets. Flaws in carpet material follow the Poisson model with mean 1.6 flaws per square yard. An inspector examines 100 randomly selected square yard specimens of the material, records the number of flaws found in each specimen, and calculates $\overline{x}$, the average number of flaws per square yard inspected.

(a) The total number of flaws $100\overline{x}$ is a Poisson random variable. What is its mean?

(b) What is the probability that the total number of flaws $100\overline{x}$ exceeds 110?

(c) We can use the central limit theorem (page 299) to calculate the same probability as in part (b) by realizing that $P(100\overline{x} > 110) = P(\overline{x} > 110/100)$. What is the probability found using the central limit theorem?

(d) Compare your answers to (b) and (c). How close are the two answers? Which one is more accurate and why?

5.65 Calling tech support. The number of calls received between 8 A.M. and 9 A.M. by a software developer's technical support line has a Poisson distribution with a mean of 14.

(a) What is the probability of at least 5 calls between 8 A.M. and 9 A.M.?

(b) What is the probability of at least 5 calls between 8:15 A.M. and 8:45 A.M.?

(c) What is the probability of at least 5 calls between 8:15 A.M. and 8:30 A.M.?

5.66 Web site hits. A "hit" for a Web site is a request for a file from the Web site's server computer. Some popular Web sites have thousands of hits per minute. One popular Web site boasts an average of 6500 hits per minute between the hours of 9 A.M. and 6 P.M. Some weaker software packages will have trouble calculating Poisson probabilities with such a large value of μ.

(a) Try calculating the probability of 6400 or more hits during the minute beginning at 10:05 A.M. using the software that you have available. Did you get an answer? If not, how did the software respond?

(b) Now, use the central limit theorem to calculate the probability of 6400 or more hits during the minute beginning at 10:05 A.M. To do this, think of the number of hits in this minute as the sum of the number of hits for each of the 60 seconds in this minute. We can express P(sum of hits for each of the 60 seconds $\geq$ 6400) as $P(\bar{x} \geq 6400/60)$ where $\bar{x}$ is the average number of hits per second for the 60 seconds in the minute of interest.

5.67 Credit card manufacturing. Large sheets of plastic are cut into smaller pieces to be pressed into credit cards. One manufacturer uses sheets of plastic known to have approximately 2.3 defects per square yard. The number of defects can be modeled as a Poisson random variable X.

(a) What is the standard deviation of the number of defects per square yard?

(b) What is the probability of an inspector finding more than 5 defects in a randomly chosen square yard?

(c) Using trial and error with your software, find the largest value k such that $P(X > k) \geq 0.15$.

5.68 Initial public offerings. The number of companies making their initial public offering of stock (IPO) can be modeled by a Poisson distribution with a mean of 15 per month.

(a) What is the probability of fewer than 3 IPOs in a month?

(b) What is the probability of fewer than 15 IPOs in a month?

(c) What is the probability of fewer than 30 IPOs in a two-month period?

(d) What is the probability of fewer than 180 IPOs in a year?

5.4 Conditional Probability

In Section 2.5 we met the idea of a *conditional distribution,* the distribution of a variable, given that a condition is satisfied. Now we will introduce the probability language for this idea.

EXAMPLE 5.18 Employment Revisited

CASE 1.1

The discussion of unemployment rates in Case 1.1 (page 9) pointed out that the government has very specific definitions of terms like "in the labor force" and "unemployed." Using those definitions, the following table contains counts (in thousands) of persons aged 16 to 24 who are enrolled in school, classified by gender and employment status:

	Employed	Unemployed	Not in labor force	Total
Male	3,927	520	4,611	9,058
Female	4,313	446	4,357	9,116
Total	8,240	966	8,968	18,174

Randomly choose a person aged 16 to 24 who is enrolled in school. What is the probability that the person is employed? Because "choose at random" gives all 18,174,000 such persons the same chance, the probability is just the proportion that are employed. In thousands,

$$P(\text{employed}) = \frac{8{,}240}{18{,}174} = 0.4534$$

Now we are told that the person chosen is female. The probability that the person is employed, *given the information that the person is female,* is

$$P(\text{employed} \mid \text{female}) = \frac{4{,}313}{9{,}116} = 0.4731$$

conditional probability

This is a **conditional probability.**

The conditional probability 0.4731 in Example 5.18 gives the probability of one event (the person chosen is employed) under the condition that we know another event (the person is female). You can read the bar | as "given the information that." We found the conditional probability by applying common sense to the two-way table.

We want to turn this common sense into something more general. To do this, we reason as follows. To find the proportion of 16- to 24-year-olds enrolled in school who are *both* female *and* employed, first find the proportion of females in the group of interest (16- to 24-year-olds enrolled in school). Then multiply by the proportion of these females who are employed. If 20% are female and half of these are employed, then half of 20%, or 10%, are females who are employed. The actual proportions from Example 5.18 are

$$\begin{aligned} P(\text{female } \textit{and } \text{employed}) &= P(\text{female}) \times P(\text{employed} \mid \text{female}) \\ &= (0.5016)(0.4731) = 0.2373 \end{aligned}$$

You can check that this is right: the probability that a randomly chosen person from this group is a female who is employed is

$$P(\text{female and employed}) = \frac{4{,}313}{18{,}174} = 0.2373$$

Try to think your way through this in words before looking at the formal notation. We have just discovered the general multiplication rule of probability.

General Multiplication Rule for Any Two Events

The probability that both of two events A and B happen together can be found by

$$P(A \text{ and } B) = P(A)P(B \mid A)$$

Here $P(B \mid A)$ is the conditional probability that B occurs, given the information that A occurs.

In words, this rule says that for both of two events to occur, first one must occur and then, given that the first event has occurred, the second must occur.

EXAMPLE 5.19 Focus Group Probabilities

A focus group of 10 consumers has been selected to view a new TV commercial. After the viewing, 2 members of the focus group will be randomly selected and asked to answer detailed questions about the commercial. The group contains 4 men and 6 women. What is the probability that the 2 chosen to answer questions will both be women?

To find the probability of randomly selecting 2 women, first calculate

$$P(\text{first person is female}) = \frac{6}{10}$$
$$P(\text{second person is female} \mid \text{first person is female}) = \frac{5}{9}$$

Both probabilities are found by counting group members. The probability that the first person selected is a female is $6/10$ because 6 of the 10 group members are female. If the first person is a female, that leaves 5 females among the 9 remaining people. So the *conditional* probability of another female is $5/9$. The multiplication rule now says that

$$P(\text{both people are female}) = \frac{6}{10} \times \frac{5}{9} = \frac{1}{3} = 0.3333$$

One-third of the time, randomly picking 2 people from a group of 4 males and 6 females will result in a pair of females.

Remember that events A and B play different roles in the conditional probability $P(B \mid A)$. Event A represents the information we are given, and B is the event whose probability we are computing.

EXAMPLE 5.20 Internet Users

About 20% of all Web surfers use Macintosh computers. About 90% of all Macintosh users surf the Web. If you know someone who uses a Macintosh computer, then the probability that that person surfs the Web is

$$P(\text{surfs the Web} \mid \text{Macintosh user}) = 0.90$$

The 20% is a different conditional probability that does not apply when you are considering someone who you know uses a Macintosh computer.

The general multiplication rule also extends to the probability that all of several events occur. The key is to condition each event on the occurrence of *all* of the preceding events. For example, for three events A, B, and C,

$$P(A \text{ and } B \text{ and } C) = P(A)P(B \mid A)P(C \mid A \text{ and } B)$$

EXAMPLE 5.21 The Future of High School Athletes

Only 5% of male high school basketball, baseball, and football players go on to play at the college level. Of these, only 1.7% enter major league professional sports. About 40% of the athletes who compete in college and then reach the pros have a career of more than 3 years.[7] Define these events:

$$A = \{\text{competes in college}\}$$
$$B = \{\text{competes professionally}\}$$
$$C = \{\text{pro career longer than 3 years}\}$$

4. Use binomial tables to find binomial probabilities.
5. Find the mean and standard deviation of a binomial count X.
6. Recognize when you can use the Normal approximation to a binomial distribution. Use the Normal approximation to calculate probabilities that concern a binomial count X.

C. Poisson Distributions

1. Recognize the Poisson setting: we are counting the number of successes in a fixed unit of measure (time, area, volume, or length).
2. Given a Poisson model with stated mean count per unit, find the Poisson distribution for the count in a multiple or a fractional number of units.
3. Use software to calculate Poisson probabilities.
4. Find the mean and standard deviation of a Poisson count X.
5. Use the central limit theorem to approximate Poisson probabilities when μ is too large for your software by dividing the basic unit of measure into many smaller units of measure and viewing the Poisson random variable as the sum of many independent Poisson random variables.

D. Conditional Probability

1. Understand the idea of conditional probability. Identify the two events required from a verbal description of conditional probability. Find conditional probabilities for individuals chosen at random from a two-way table of counts of outcomes.
2. Use the general multiplication rule to find $P(A \text{ and } B)$ from $P(A)$ and the conditional probability $P(B \mid A)$.
3. Use a tree diagram to organize several-stage probability models.
4. Use Bayes's rule to calculate conditional probabilities when given other "reverse" conditional probabilities.

CHAPTER 5 Review Exercises

5.94 Motor vehicle sales. Motor vehicles sold to individuals are classified as either cars or light trucks (including SUVs) and as either domestic or imported. In early 2004, 69% of vehicles sold were light trucks, 78% were domestic, and 55% were domestic light trucks.

(a) Draw a Venn diagram that represents the given percents.

(b) Calculate the probability that a randomly selected vehicle is a car.

(c) Calculate the probability that a randomly selected vehicle is an imported car.

5.95 Using a mailing list. The mailing list of an agency that markets scuba-diving trips to the Florida Keys contains 70% males and 30% females. The agency calls 30 people chosen at random from its list.

(a) What is the probability that 20 of the 30 are men? (Use the binomial probability formula.)

(b) What is the probability that the first woman is reached on the fourth call? (That is, the first 4 calls give MMMF.)

(c) List any assumptions necessary for using the binomial distribution in this context.

5.96 Motor vehicle sales. Using the information in Exercise 5.94, answer these questions.

(a) Given that a vehicle is imported, what is the conditional probability that it is a car?

(b) Are the events "vehicle is a car" and "vehicle is imported" independent? Justify your answer.

5.97 Human spell-checker. Spelling errors in a text can be either nonword errors or word errors. Nonword errors make up 25% of all errors. A human proofreader will catch 90% of nonword errors and 70% of word errors. What percent of all errors will the proofreader catch? (Draw a tree diagram to organize the information given.)

5.98 Playing the slots. Slot machines are now video games, with winning determined by electronic random number generators. In the old days, slot machines worked like this: you pull the lever to spin three wheels; each wheel has 20 symbols, all equally likely to show when the wheel stops spinning; the three wheels are independent of each other. Suppose that the middle wheel has 9 bells among its 20 symbols, and the left and right wheels have 1 bell each.

(a) You win the jackpot if all three wheels show bells. What is the probability of winning the jackpot?

(b) What is the probability that the wheels stop with exactly 2 bells showing?

5.99 Leaking gas tanks. Leakage from underground gasoline tanks at service stations can damage the environment. It is estimated that 25% of these tanks leak. You examine 15 tanks chosen at random, independently of each other.

(a) What is the mean number of leaking tanks in such samples of 15?

(b) What is the probability that 10 or more of the 15 tanks leak?

(c) Now you do a larger study, examining a random sample of 1000 tanks nationally. What is the probability that at least 275 of these tanks are leaking?

5.100 Environmental credits. An opinion poll asks an SRS of 500 adults whether they favor tax credits for companies that demonstrate a commitment to preserving the environment. Suppose that in fact 45% of the population favor this idea. What is the probability that more than half of the sample are in favor?

5.101 Computer training. Macintosh users make up about 5% of all computer users. A computer training school that wants to attract Macintosh users mails an advertising flyer to 25,000 computer users.

(a) If the mailing list can be considered a random sample of the population, what is the mean number of Macintosh users who will receive the flyer?

(b) What is the probability that at least 1245 Macintosh users will receive the flyer?

5.102 Is this coin balanced? While he was a prisoner of the Germans during World War II, John Kerrich tossed a coin 10,000 times. He got 5067 heads. Take Kerrich's tosses to be an SRS from the population of all possible tosses of his coin. If the coin is perfectly balanced, $p = 0.5$. Is there reason to think that Kerrich's coin gave too many heads to be balanced? To answer this question, find the probability that a balanced coin would give 5067 or more heads in 10,000 tosses. What do you conclude?

5.103 Who is driving? A sociology professor asks her class to observe cars having a man and a woman in the front seat and record which of the two is the driver.

(a) Explain why it is reasonable to use the binomial distribution for the number of male drivers in n cars if all observations are made in the same location at the same time of day.

(b) Explain why the binomial model may not apply if half the observations are made outside a church on Sunday morning and half are made on campus after a dance.

(c) The professor requires students to observe 10 cars during business hours in a retail district close to campus. Past observations have shown that the man is driving about 85% of cars in this location. What is the probability that the man is driving 8 or fewer of the 10 cars?

(d) The class has 10 students, who will observe 100 cars in all. What is the probability that the man is driving 80 or fewer of these?

5.104 Income and savings. A sample survey chooses a sample of households and measures their annual income and their savings. Some events of interest are

$A =$ the household chosen has income at least \$100,000

$C =$ the household chosen has at least \$50,000 in savings

Based on this sample survey, we estimate that $P(A) = 0.13$ and $P(C) = 0.25$.

(a) We want to find the probability that a household has either income at least \$100,000 *or* savings at least \$50,000. Explain why we do not have enough information to find this probability. What additional information is needed?

(b) We want to find the probability that a household has income at least \$100,000 *and* savings at least \$50,000. Explain why we do not have enough information to find this probability. What additional information is needed?

5.105 Medical risks. You have torn a tendon and are facing surgery to repair it. The surgeon explains the risks to you: infection occurs in 3% of such operations, the repair fails in 14%, and both infection and failure occur together in 1%. What percent of these operations succeed and are free from infection?

Working. *In the language of government statistics, you are "in the labor force" if you are available for work and either working or actively seeking work. The unemployment rate is the proportion of the labor force (not of the entire population) who are unemployed. Here are data from the Current Population Survey for the civilian population aged 25 years and over. The table entries are counts in thousands of people. Exercises 5.106 to 5.108 concern these data.*

Highest education	Total population	In labor force	Employed
Did not finish high school	27,325	12,073	11,139
High school but no college	57,221	36,855	35,137
Less than bachelor's degree	45,471	33,331	31,975
College graduate	47,371	37,281	36,259

5.106 Unemployment rates. Find the unemployment rate for people with each level of education. How does the unemployment rate change with education? Explain carefully why your results show that level of education and being employed are not independent.

5.107 Education and work.

(a) What is the probability that a randomly chosen person 25 years of age or older is in the labor force?

(b) If you know that the person chosen is a college graduate, what is the conditional probability that he or she is in the labor force?

(c) Are the events "in the labor force" and "college graduate" independent? How do you know?

5.108 Education and work, continued. You know that a person is employed. What is the conditional probability that he or she is a college graduate? You know that a second person is a college graduate. What is the conditional probability that he or she is employed?

5.109 Testing for HIV. Enzyme immunoassay (EIA) tests are used to screen blood specimens for the presence of antibodies to HIV, the virus that causes AIDS. Antibodies indicate the presence of the virus. The test is quite accurate but is not always correct. Here are approximate probabilities of positive and negative EIA outcomes when the blood tested does and does not actually contain antibodies to HIV:[9]

	Test Result	
	+	−
Antibodies present	0.9985	0.0015
Antibodies absent	0.006	0.994

Suppose that 1% of a large population carries antibodies to HIV in their blood.

(a) Draw a tree diagram for selecting a person from this population (outcomes: antibodies present or absent) and for testing his or her blood (outcomes: EIA positive or negative).

(b) What is the probability that the EIA is positive for a randomly chosen person from this population?

(c) What is the probability that a person has the antibody, given that the EIA test is positive? (*Comment:* This exercise illustrates a fact that is important when considering proposals for widespread testing for HIV, illegal drugs, or agents of biological warfare: if the condition being tested is uncommon in the population, many positives will be false-positives.)

5.110 Testing for HIV, continued. The previous exercise gives data on the results of EIA tests for the presence of antibodies to HIV. Repeat part (c) of that exercise for two different populations:

(a) Blood donors are prescreened for HIV risk factors, so perhaps only 0.1% (0.001) of this population carries HIV antibodies.

(b) Clients of a drug rehab clinic are a high-risk group, so perhaps 10% of this population carries HIV antibodies.

(c) What general lesson do your calculations illustrate?

5.111 The geometric distributions. You are tossing a balanced die that has probability 1/6 of coming up 1 on each toss. Tosses are independent. We are interested in how long we must wait to get the first 1.

(a) The probability of a 1 on the first toss is 1/6. What is the probability that the first toss is not a 1 and the second toss is a 1?

(b) What is the probability that the first two tosses are not 1s and the third toss is a 1? This is the probability that the first 1 occurs on the third toss.

(c) Now you see the pattern. What is the probability that the first 1 occurs on the fourth toss? On the fifth toss? Give the general result: what is the probability that the first 1 occurs on the kth toss?
(*Comment:* The distribution of the number of trials to the first success is called a ***geometric distribution.*** In this problem you have found geometric distribution probabilities when the probability of a success on each trial is $p = 1/6$. The same idea works for any p.)

5.112 **Teenage drivers.** An insurance company has the following information about drivers aged 16 to 18 years: 20% are involved in accidents each year; 10% in this age group are A students; among those involved in an accident, 5% are A students.

(a) Let A be the event that a young driver is an A student and C the event that a young driver is involved in an accident this year. State the information given in terms of probabilities and conditional probabilities for the events A and C.

(b) What is the probability that a randomly chosen young driver is an A student and is involved in an accident?

5.113 **Race and ethnicity.** The 2000 census allowed each person to choose from a long list of races. That is, in the eyes of the Census Bureau, you belong to whatever race you say you belong to. "Hispanic/Latino" is a separate category; Hispanics may be of any race. If we choose a resident of the United States at random, the 2000 census gives these probabilities:

	Hispanic	Not Hispanic
Asian	0.000	0.036
Black	0.003	0.121
White	0.060	0.691
Other	0.062	0.027

(a) What is the probability that a randomly chosen person is white?

(b) You know that the person chosen is Hispanic. What is the conditional probability that this person is white?

5.114 **More on teenage drivers.** Use your work from Exercise 5.112 to find the percent of A students who are involved in accidents. (Start by expressing this as a conditional probability.)

5.115 **More on race and ethnicity.** Use the information in Exercise 5.113 to answer these questions.

(a) What is the probability that a randomly chosen American is Hispanic?

(b) You know that the person chosen is black. What is the conditional probability that this person is Hispanic?

5.116 **Screening job applicants.** A company retains a psychologist to assess whether job applicants are suited for assembly-line work. The psychologist classifies applicants as A (well suited), B (marginal), or C (not suited). The company is concerned about event D: an employee leaves the company within a year of being hired. Data on all people hired in the past five years give these probabilities:

$$P(A) = 0.4 \qquad P(A \text{ and } D) = 0.1$$
$$P(B) = 0.3 \qquad P(B \text{ and } D) = 0.1$$
$$P(C) = 0.3 \qquad P(C \text{ and } D) = 0.2$$

Sketch a Venn diagram of the events A, B, C, and D and mark on your diagram the probabilities of all combinations of psychological assessment and leaving (or not) within a year. What is $P(D)$, the probability that an employee leaves within a year?

5.117 **Who buys iMacs?** The iMac computer was introduced by Apple Computer in the fall of 1998 and quickly became one of the company's best-selling products. The iMac was particularly aimed at first-time computer buyers. Approximately 5 months after the introduction of the iMac, Apple reported that 32% of iMac buyers were first-time computer buyers. At this same time, approximately 5% of all computer sales were of iMacs.[10] Of buyers who did not purchase an iMac, approximately 40% were first-time computer buyers. Among first-time computer buyers during this time, what percent bought iMacs?

5.118 **Stealing software.** Employees sometimes install on their home computers software that was purchased by their employer for use on their work computers. For most commercial software packages, this is illegal. Suppose that 5% of all employees at a large corporation have illegally installed corporate software on their home computers knowing the act is illegal and an additional 2% have installed corporate software on their home computers not realizing that this is illegal. Of the 5% aware that the home installation is illegal, 80% will deny that they knew the act was illegal if confronted by a "software auditor." If an employee who has illegally installed software at home is confronted and denies knowing it was an illegal act, what is the probability that the employee knew the home installation was illegal?

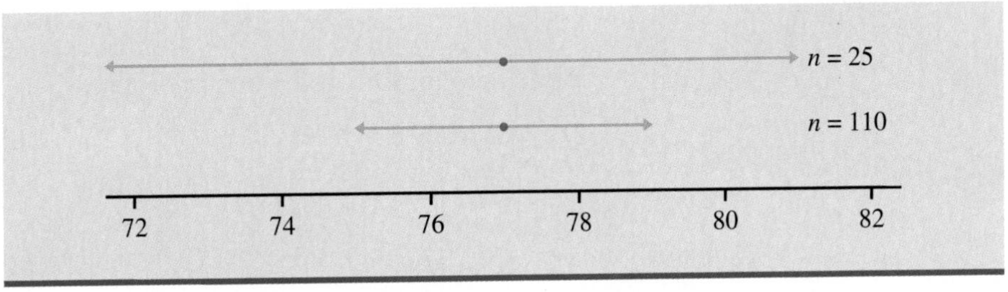

FIGURE 6.7 Confidence intervals for $n = 110$ and $n = 25$, for Example 6.6.

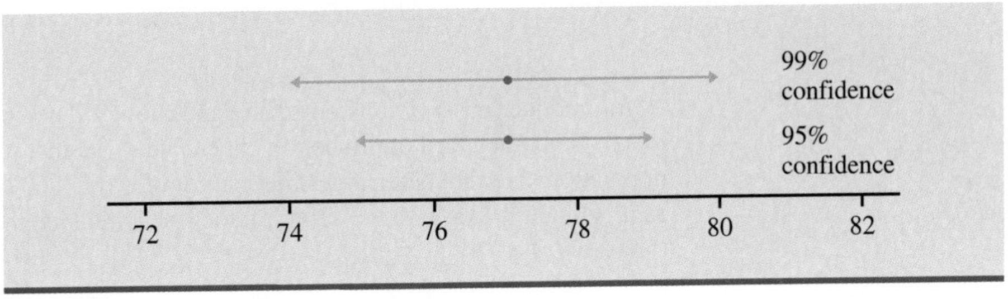

FIGURE 6.8 Confidence intervals for 95% and 99% confidence from the same data, for Example 6.6.

A 95% confidence interval for μ is therefore

$$\begin{aligned}\bar{x} \pm z^* \frac{\sigma}{\sqrt{n}} &= 76.7 \pm 4.8 \\ &= (71.9, 81.5)\end{aligned}$$

Figure 6.7 illustrates how the margin of error increases for the smaller sample.

Suppose next that we demand 99% confidence for the mean LTDR in Example 6.5, rather than 95%. Table D tells us that for 99% confidence, $z^* = 2.576$. The margin of error increases from 2.3 to

$$\begin{aligned}z^* \frac{\sigma}{\sqrt{n}} &= 2.576 \frac{12.3}{\sqrt{110}} \\ &= 3.0\end{aligned}$$

The 99% confidence interval is therefore

$$\begin{aligned}\bar{x} \pm \text{margin of error} &= 76.7 \pm 3.0 \\ &= (73.7, 79.7)\end{aligned}$$

Requiring 99% confidence rather than 95% confidence has increased the margin of error from 2.3 to 3.0. Figure 6.8 compares the two intervals.

Choosing the sample size

A wise user of statistics never plans data collection without at the same time planning the inference. You can arrange to have both high confidence and a small margin of error. The margin of error of the confidence interval $\bar{x} \pm z^*\sigma/\sqrt{n}$ for a Normal mean is

$$z^* \frac{\sigma}{\sqrt{n}}$$

To obtain a desired margin of error m, just set this expression equal to m, substitute the critical value z^* for your desired confidence level, and solve for the sample size n. Here is the result.

Sample Size for Desired Margin of Error

The confidence interval for a population mean will have a specified margin of error m when the sample size is

$$n = \left(\frac{z^*\sigma}{m}\right)^2$$

In practice, observations cost time and money. The sample size you calculate from this formula may turn out to be too expensive. Note that it is the *sample* size and not the population size that determines the margin of error. The size of the *population* (as long as it is much larger than the sample) does not influence the margin of error.

EXAMPLE 6.7 How Many Banks Should We Survey?

CASE 6.1

In Example 6.5 we found that the margin of error was 2.3 for estimating the mean LTDR of community banks with $n = 110$ and 95% confidence. We are willing to settle for a margin of error of 3.0 when we do the survey next year. How many banks should we survey?

For 95% confidence, Table D gives $z^* = 1.960$. We will assume that the standard deviation next year will be approximately the same as the $\sigma = 12.3$ that we obtained this year. For a margin of error of 3.0 we have

$$n = \left(\frac{z^*\sigma}{m}\right)^2 = \left(\frac{1.96 \times 12.3}{3.0}\right)^2 = 64.6$$

Because 64 observations will give a slightly wider interval than desired and 65 observations a slightly narrower interval, we will survey 65 banks. With this choice, our estimate of mean assets will be within 3.0 of the true value with 95% confidence.

Always round *up* to the next higher whole number when using the formula for the sample size n. In practice we often calculate the margins of error corresponding to a range of values of n. We then decide what margin of error we can afford.

APPLY YOUR KNOWLEDGE

6.7 Starting salaries. You are planning a survey of starting salaries for recent business major graduates from your college. From a pilot study you estimate that the standard deviation is about \$9000. What sample size do you need to have a margin of error equal to \$500 with 95% confidence?

6.8 Will the sample size needed be larger or smaller? Suppose that in the setting of the previous exercise you are willing to settle for a margin of error of \$1000. Will the required sample size be larger or smaller? Verify your answer by performing the calculations.

Some cautions

We have already seen that small margins of error and high confidence can require large numbers of observations. You should also be keenly aware that *any formula for inference is correct only in specific circumstances.* If the government required statistical procedures to carry warning labels like those on drugs, most inference methods would have long labels indeed. Our formula $\bar{x} \pm z^*\sigma/\sqrt{n}$ for estimating a Normal mean comes with the following list of warnings for the user:

- The data must be an SRS from the population. We are completely safe if we actually did a randomization and drew an SRS. The ABA survey that lies behind Examples 6.5 to 6.7 is based on a random sample of banks. We are not in great danger if the data can plausibly be thought of as independent observations from a population.
- The formula is not correct for probability sampling designs more complex than an SRS. Correct methods for other designs are available. We will not discuss confidence intervals based on multistage or stratified samples. If you plan such samples, be sure that you (or your statistical consultant) know how to carry out the inference you desire.
- There is no correct method for inference from data haphazardly collected with bias of unknown size. Fancy formulas cannot rescue badly produced data.
- Because $\bar{x}$ is not resistant, outliers can have a large effect on the confidence interval. You should search for outliers and try to correct them or justify their removal before computing the interval. If the outliers cannot be removed, ask your statistical consultant about procedures that are not sensitive to outliers.
- If the sample size is small and the population is not Normal, the true confidence level will be different from the value C used in computing the interval. Examine your data carefully for skewness and other signs of non-Normality. The interval relies only on the distribution of $\bar{x}$, which even for quite small sample sizes is much closer to Normal than that of the individual observations. When $n \geq 15$, the confidence level is not greatly disturbed by non-Normal populations unless extreme outliers or quite strong skewness are present. We will discuss this issue in more detail in the next chapter.
- You must know the standard deviation σ of the population. This unrealistic requirement renders the interval $\bar{x} \pm z^*\sigma/\sqrt{n}$ of little use in statistical practice. We will learn in the next chapter what to do when σ is unknown. If, however, the sample is large, the sample standard deviation s will be close to the unknown σ. The formula $\bar{x} \pm z^*s/\sqrt{n}$ is then an approximate confidence interval for μ.

The most important caution concerning confidence intervals is a consequence of the first of these warnings. *The margin of error in a confidence interval covers only random sampling errors.* The margin of error is obtained from the sampling distribution and indicates how much error can be expected because of chance variation in randomized data production. Practical difficulties such as undercoverage and nonresponse in a sample survey cause additional errors. These errors can be larger than the random sampling error, particularly when the sample size is large. Remember this unpleasant fact when reading the results of an opinion poll. The practical conduct of a survey influences the trustworthiness of its results in ways that are not included in the announced margin of error.

Every inference procedure that we will meet has its own list of warnings. Because many of the warnings are similar to those above, we will not print the full warning label each time. Using the mathematics of probability, it is easy to state conditions under which a method of inference is exactly correct. These conditions are *never* fully met in practice. For example, no population is exactly Normal. Deciding when a statistical procedure should be used in practice often requires judgment assisted by exploratory analysis of the data. Mathematical facts are therefore only a part of statistics. The difference between statistics and mathematics can be stated thus: mathematical theorems are true; statistical methods are often effective when used with skill.

Finally, you should understand what statistical confidence does not say. We are 95% confident that the mean assets of community banks in Case 6.1 lie between \$190 and \$250 million. This says that these numbers were calculated by a method that gives correct results in 95% of all possible samples. It does *not* say that the probability is 95% that the true mean falls between 190 and 250. No randomness remains after we draw a particular sample and get from it a particular interval. The true mean either is or is not between 190 and 250. Probability in its interpretation as long-term relative frequency makes no sense in this situation. The probability calculations of standard statistical inference describe how often the *method* gives correct answers.

APPLY YOUR KNOWLEDGE

6.9 Internet users. A survey of users of the Internet found that males outnumbered females by nearly 2 to 1. This was a surprise, because earlier surveys had put the ratio of men to women closer to 9 to 1. Later in the article we find this information:

> *Detailed surveys were sent to more than 13,000 organizations on the Internet; 1,468 usable responses were received. According to Mr. Quarterman, the margin of error is 2.8 percent, with a confidence level of 95 percent.*[3]

(a) What was the *response rate* for this survey? (The response rate is the percent of the planned sample that responded.)

(b) Do you think that the small margin of error is a good measure of the accuracy of the survey's results? Explain your answer.

BEYOND THE BASICS: THE BOOTSTRAP

Confidence intervals are based on sampling distributions. The interval $\bar{x} \pm z^*s/\sqrt{n}$ follows from the fact that the sampling distribution of $\bar{x}$ is $N(\mu, \sigma/\sqrt{n})$ when the data are an SRS from a $N(\mu, \sigma)$ population. The central limit theorem says that this sampling distribution is also approximately right for large samples from non-Normal populations.

bootstrap

What if the population is clearly non-Normal and we have only a small sample? Then we do not know what the sampling distribution of $\bar{x}$ looks like. The **bootstrap** is a procedure for approximating sampling distributions when theory cannot tell us their shape.[4]

resample

The basic idea is to act as if our sample were the population. We take many samples from it. Each of these is called a **resample.** For each resample, we calculate the mean $\bar{x}$. We get different results from different resamples because we sample *with replacement*. That is, an observation in the original sample can appear more than once in a resample.

The community bank assets data described in Case 6.1 are somewhat skewed toward high values. The mean \$220 million is larger than the median, \$190 million. There are two large banks with assets of \$908 and \$804 million that could be considered outliers.

Because we have no reason to suspect that these banks are qualitatively different from the other community banks in the sample, we are reluctant to discard them. Rather, we will reexamine our inference with a method that is not sensitive to the Normality assumption.

If we had 1000 SRSs from the population of banks, the distribution of the 1000 values of $\overline{x}$ would be close to the sampling distribution of $\overline{x}$. We have only one sample. The bootstrap idea says: take 1000 resamples of size 110 (with replacement) from our one sample of 110 banks. For each resample, compute the mean. Treat the distribution of $\overline{x}$'s from the 1000 resamples as if it were the sampling distribution. Because the sample is like the population, taking resamples from the sample is similar to taking samples from the population.

The bootstrap is practical only when you can use a computer to take 1000 or more resamples quickly. It is an example of how fast and cheap computing has changed the way we do statistics.

EXAMPLE 6.8 Use the Bootstrap to Check the Interval

CASE 6.1

In the discussion of Case 6.1 we found a 95% confidence interval for the mean assets of community banks using the traditional statistical procedure based on the middle 95% of a Normal distribution. The interval was (190, 250). Let's check to see if we made a serious error. The middle 95% of the 1000 $\overline{x}$'s from 1000 resamples runs from 193 to 249. Try it again with 1000 new resamples: we get the interval (191, 252). The two bootstrap estimates are close to each other and also close to the standard interval that assumes Normality. The standard interval is reasonably accurate for these data.

If the bootstrap method applied to this problem gave very different results, we would need to reconsider the analysis. Obtaining similar results from different methods gives us confidence that the answers we seek are coming from the data, not from the particular method that we used.

SECTION 6.1 SUMMARY

- The purpose of a **confidence interval** is to estimate an unknown parameter with an indication of how accurate the estimate is and of how confident we are that the result is correct.

- Any confidence interval has two parts: an interval computed from the data and a confidence level. The interval often has the form

$$\text{estimate} \pm \text{margin of error}$$

- The **confidence level** states the probability that the method will give a correct answer. That is, if you use 95% confidence intervals often, in the long run 95% of your intervals will contain the true parameter value. When you apply the method once, you do not know if your interval gave a correct value (this happens 95% of the time) or not (this happens 5% of the time).

- A level C confidence interval for the mean μ of a Normal population with known standard deviation σ, based on an SRS of size n, is given by

$$\bar{x} \pm z^* \frac{\sigma}{\sqrt{n}}$$

- Here z^* is a **critical value** obtained from the bottom row in Table D. The probability is C that a standard Normal random variable takes a value between $-z^*$ and z^*.

- The **margin of error** in the confidence interval for μ is

$$z^* \frac{\sigma}{\sqrt{n}}$$

- Other things being equal, the margin of error of a confidence interval decreases as
  - the confidence level C decreases,
  - the population standard deviation σ decreases, or
  - the sample size n increases.

- The sample size required to obtain a confidence interval of specified margin of error m for a Normal mean is

$$n = \left(\frac{z^*\sigma}{m}\right)^2$$

where z^* is the critical value for the desired level of confidence.

- A specific confidence interval formula is correct only under specific conditions. The most important conditions concern the method used to produce the data. Other factors such as the form of the population distribution may also be important.

SECTION 6.1 Exercises

For Exercises 6.1 to 6.3, see page 364; for 6.4, see page 365; for 6.5 and 6.6, see page 368; for 6.7 and 6.8, see page 370; and for 6.9, see page 372.

6.10 Margin of error and the confidence interval. A study based on a sample of size 25 reported a mean of 76 with a margin of error of 12 for 95% confidence.

(a) Give the 95% confidence interval.

(b) If you wanted 99% confidence for the same study, would your margin of error be greater than, equal to, or less than 12? Explain your answer.

6.11 Change the sample size. Suppose that the sample mean is 50 and the standard deviation is assumed to be 5. Make a diagram similar to Figure 6.7 (page 369) that illustrates the effect of sample size on the width of a 95% interval. Use the following sample sizes: 10, 20, 40, and 100. Summarize what the diagram shows.

6.12 Change the confidence. A study with 25 observations gave a mean of 70. Assume that the standard deviation is 15. Make a diagram similar to Figure 6.8 (page 369) that illustrates the effect of the confidence level on the width of the interval. Use 80%, 90%, 95%, and 99%. Summarize what the diagram shows.

6.13 Populations sampled and margins of error. Consider the following two scenarios. (A) Take a simple random sample of 100 sophomore students at your college or university. (B) Take a simple random sample 100 sophomore students in your major at your college or university. For each of these samples you will record the amount spent on textbooks used for classes during the fall semester. Which sample should have the smaller margin of error for 95% confidence? Explain your answer.

6.14 Fuel efficiency. Computers in some vehicles calculate various quantities related to performance. One of these is the fuel efficiency, or gas mileage, usually expressed as miles per gallon (MPG). For one vehicle equipped in this way, the MPG were recorded each time the gas tank was filled, and the computer was then reset.[5] Here are the MPG values for a random sample of 20 of these records:

15.8	13.6	15.6	19.1	22.4	15.6	22.5	17.2	19.4	22.6
19.4	18.0	14.6	18.7	21.0	14.8	22.6	21.5	14.3	20.9

Suppose that the standard deviation of the population is known to be $\sigma = 2.9$ MPG.

(a) What is $\sigma_{\overline{x}}$, the standard deviation of $\overline{x}$?

(b) Give a 95% confidence interval for μ, the mean MPG for this vehicle.

6.15 Speed. Refer to the previous exercise. Here are the values of the average speed in miles per hour (MPH) for the same sample:

21.0	19.0	18.7	39.2	45.8	19.8	48.4	21.0	29.1	35.7
31.6	49.0	16.0	34.6	36.3	19.0	43.3	37.5	16.5	34.5

Assume that the standard deviation is 10.3 MPH. Estimate the mean speed at which this vehicle was driven with a margin of error for 95% confidence.

6.16 Convert to metric. In the previous exercise you found an estimate with a margin of error for the average speed expressed in miles per hour. Convert your estimate and margin of error to the metric units kilometers per hour (KPH). To change MPH to KPH, multiply by 1.6.

6.17 What is the cost? In Exercise 6.14 you found an estimate with a margin of error for the fuel efficiency expressed in miles per gallon. Suppose that fuel costs \$3.10 per gallon. Find the estimate and margin of error for fuel efficiency in terms of miles per dollar. To convert miles per gallon to miles per dollar, divide miles per gallon by the cost in dollars per gallon.

6.18 Apartment rental rates. You want to rent an unfurnished one-bedroom apartment for next semester. The mean monthly rent for a random sample of 10 apartments advertised in the local newspaper is \$640. Assume that the standard deviation is \$90. Find a 95% confidence interval for the mean monthly rent for unfurnished one-bedroom apartments available for rent in this community.

6.19 Study habits. A questionnaire about study habits was given to a random sample of students taking a large introductory statistics class. The sample of 35 students reported that they spent an average of 115 minutes per week studying statistics. Assume that the standard deviation is 40 minutes.

(a) Give a 95% confidence interval for the mean time spent studying statistics by students in this class.

(b) Is it true that 95% of the students in the class have weekly study times that lie in the interval you found in part (a)? Explain your answer.

6.20 Clothing for runners. Your company sells exercise clothing and equipment on the Internet. To design the clothing, you collect data on the physical characteristics of your different types of customers. Here are the weights (in kilograms) for a sample of 24 male runners. Assume that these runners can be viewed as a random sample of your potential male customers. Suppose also that the standard deviation of the population is known to be $\sigma = 4.5$ kg.

68.7	61.8	63.2	53.1	62.3	59.7	55.4	58.9
60.9	69.2	63.7	67.8	65.6	65.5	56.0	57.8
66.0	62.9	53.6	65.0	55.8	60.4	69.3	62.1

(a) What is $\sigma_{\overline{x}}$, the standard deviation of $\overline{x}$?

(b) Give a 95% confidence interval for μ, the mean of the population from which the sample is drawn.

(c) Will the interval contain the weights of approximately 95% of similar runners? Explain your answer.

6.21 Pounds versus kilograms. Suppose that the weights of the runners in Exercise 6.20 were recorded in pounds rather than kilograms. Use your answers to Exercise 6.20, and the fact that 1 kilogram equals 2.2 pounds, to answer these questions.

(a) What is the mean weight of these runners?

(b) What is the standard deviation of the mean weight?

(c) Give a 95% confidence interval for the mean weight of the population of runners that these runners represent.

6.22 99% versus 95% confidence interval. Find a 99% confidence interval for the mean weight μ of the population of male runners in Exercise 6.20. Is the 99% confidence interval wider or narrower than the 95% interval found in Exercise 6.20? Explain in plain language why this is true.

6.23 Hotel managers. A study of the career paths of hotel general managers sent questionnaires to an SRS of 160 hotels belonging to major U.S. hotel chains. There were 114 responses. The average time these 114 general managers had spent with their current company was 11.8 years. Give a 99% confidence interval for the mean number of years general managers of major-chain hotels have spent with their current company. (Take it as known that the standard deviation of time with the company for all general managers is 3.2 years.)

6.24 Supermarket shoppers. A marketing consultant observed 50 consecutive shoppers at a supermarket. One variable of interest was how much each shopper spent in the store. Here are the data (in dollars), arranged in increasing order:

4.21	9.15	9.26	10.81	12.69	13.78	15.23	15.62
17.85	18.29	18.36	18.43	19.27	19.50	19.54	20.16
21.68	22.22	23.04	24.07	24.58	25.13	26.24	26.26
27.04	28.06	28.08	28.38	32.03	35.28	36.37	38.64
38.99	41.02	42.97	44.08	44.67	45.40	46.69	49.64
51.30	52.75	54.80	59.07	61.22	70.32	82.70	85.76
88.77	97.85						

Assume that the standard deviation is \$22.00. Find a 95% confidence interval for the mean amount spent by shoppers in similar circumstances.

6.25 Bank workers. We examined the wages of a random sample of National Bank black female hourly workers in Example 1.9 (page 31). Here are the data (in dollars per year):

16,015	17,516	17,274	16,555	20,788
19,312	17,124	18,405	19,090	12,641
17,813	18,206	19,338	15,953	16,904

Find a 95% confidence interval for the mean earnings of all black female hourly workers at National Bank. Use \$1900 for the standard deviation.

6.26 Hotel managers. How large a sample of the hotel managers in Exercise 6.23 would be needed to estimate the mean μ within ± 1 year with 99% confidence?

6.27 Supermarket shoppers. Suppose that you want to perform a study similar to the survey of supermarket shoppers described in Exercise 6.24. If you want the margin of error to be about \$5.00, how many shoppers would you need in your sample? (Use \$22.00 for the standard deviation in your calculations.)

6.28 Bank employees. In Exercise 6.25 we examined the earnings of a random sample of 15 black women who were hourly workers at National Bank. If we wanted to estimate the mean with an interval of the form $\bar{x} \pm 400$, how many observations are required?

6.29 Like your job? A Gallup Poll asked 1001 adult workers about their job satisfaction. One question was "All in all, which best describes how you feel about your job?" The possible answers were "love job," "like job," "dislike job," and "hate job." Fifty-nine percent of the sample responded that they liked their job. Material provided with the results of the poll noted:

Results are based on telephone interviews with 1,001 national adults, aged 18 and older, conducted Aug. 8–11, 2005. For results based on the total sample of national adults, one can say with 95% confidence that the maximum margin of sampling error is 3 percentage points.[6]

The Gallup Poll uses a complex multistage sample design, but the sample percent has approximately a Normal sampling distribution.

(a) The announced poll result was 59% $\pm$ 3%. Can we be certain that the true population percent falls in this interval?

(b) Explain to someone who knows no statistics what the announced result 59% $\pm$ 3% means.

(c) This confidence interval has the same form we have met earlier:

$$\text{estimate} \pm z^* \sigma_{\text{estimate}}$$

What is the standard deviation σ_{estimate} of the estimated percent?

(d) Does the announced margin of error include errors due to practical problems such as undercoverage and nonresponse?

6.30 Like or love your job? Refer to the previous exercise. In the same poll, 32% of the respondents said that they loved their job.

(a) Combine the respondents who like their job with those who love their job. Give the percent who either love their job or like their job.

(b) Assuming that the same margin of error applies to this percent, give the 95% confidence interval.

6.31 Other variables. Refer to the previous two exercises. Gallup polls such as this often present the results for subgroups of respondents such as females and males. Suggest subgroups for this job satisfaction question. Give reasons for your answer.

6.32 More than one confidence interval. As we prepare to take a sample and compute a 95% confidence interval, we know that the probability that the interval we compute will cover the parameter is 0.95. That's the meaning of 95% confidence. If we use several such intervals, however, our confidence that *all* give correct results is less than 95%.

Suppose we are interested in confidence intervals for the median household incomes for three states. We compute a 95% interval for each of the three, based on independent samples in the three states.

(a) What is the probability that all three intervals cover the true median incomes? This probability (expressed as a percent) is our overall confidence level for the three simultaneous statements.

(b) What is the probability that at least two of the three intervals cover the true median incomes?

6.33 An election poll. A newspaper headline describing a poll of registered voters taken two weeks before a recent election reads "Ringel leads with 52%." The accompanying article says that the margin of error is 3% with 95% confidence.

(a) Explain in plain language to someone who knows no statistics what "95% confidence" means.

(b) The poll shows Ringel leading. But the newspaper article says that the election was too close to call. Explain why.

6.34 Manager trainee wages. A newspaper ad for a manager trainee position contained the statement "Our manager trainees have a first-year earnings average of $20,000 to $30,000." Do you think that the ad is describing a confidence interval? Explain your answer.

6.35 Talk show poll. A radio talk show invites listeners to enter a dispute about a proposed pay increase for city council members. "What yearly pay do you think council members should get? Call us with your number." In all, 958 people call. The station calculates the 95% confidence interval for the mean pay μ that all citizens would propose for council members to be $9669 to $9811. Is this result trustworthy? Explain your answer.

6.36 An outlier. Exercise 6.20 gives the weights of a sample of 24 male runners. Suppose that the sample actually contained 25 runners. The extra runner claimed to weigh 92.3 kg.

(a) Compute the 95% confidence interval for the mean with this observation included.

(b) Would you report the interval you calculated in part (a) of this question or the interval you calculated in Exercise 6.20? Explain the reasons for your choice.

6.2 Tests of Significance

Confidence intervals are one of the two most common types of formal statistical inference. They are appropriate when our goal is to estimate a population parameter. The second common type of inference is directed at a different goal: to assess the evidence provided by the data in favor of some claim about the population.

The reasoning of significance tests

A significance test is a formal procedure for comparing observed data with a hypothesis whose truth we want to assess. The hypothesis is a statement about the parameters in a population or model. The results of a test are expressed in terms of a probability that measures how well the data and the hypothesis agree. We use the following example to illustrate these ideas.

EXAMPLE 6.9 Banks' Net Income

CASE 6.1 

The community bank survey described in Case 6.1 also asked about net income and reported the percent change in net income between the first half of last year and the first half of this year. As you might expect, there is considerable bank-to-bank variation in this percent. Some banks report an increase while others report a decrease. The mean change for the 110 banks in the sample is $\bar{x} = 8.1\%$. Because the sample size is large we are willing to use the sample standard deviation $s = 26.4\%$ as if it were the population standard deviation σ. The large sample size also makes it reasonable to assume that $\bar{x}$ is approximately Normal.

Is the 8.1% mean increase in a *sample* good evidence that the net income for *all banks* has changed? After all, the sample result might happen just by chance even if the true mean change for all banks is $\mu = 0\%$. To answer this question, we ask another: Suppose that the truth about the population is that $\mu = 0\%$. This is our hypothesis. *What is the probability of observing a sample mean at least as far from zero as 8.1%?* The answer is 0.001. Because this probability is so small, we see that the sample mean $\bar{x} = 8.1$ is incompatible with a population mean of $\mu = 0$. We conclude that the income of community banks has changed since last year.

What are the key steps in Example 6.9? We want to know if the sample gives good evidence that the mean income for all community banks has changed in the past year. Suppose that there was no change, that is, that $\mu = 0$. Compare the sample outcome $\bar{x} = 8.1$ with the no-change population mean $\mu = 0$. The comparison takes the form of a probability: If $\mu = 0$, then a sample of size 110 will have a mean at least as far from 0 as $\bar{x} = 8.1$ only with probability 0.001.

The fact that the calculated probability is very small leads us to conclude that the average percent change in income is not in fact zero. Here's why. If the true mean is $\mu = 0$, we would see a sample mean $\bar{x}$ as far away as 8.1% only once per 1000 samples. So there are only two possibilities:

1. $\mu = 0$ and we have observed something very unusual, or

2. μ is not zero but has some other value that makes the observed data more probable.

We calculated a probability taking the first of these choices as true. That probability guides our final choice. If the probability is very small, the data don't fit the first possibility and we conclude that the mean is not in fact zero. Here is an example in which the data lead to a different conclusion.

EXAMPLE 6.10 Consider a Different Percent Change

CASE 6.1

Suppose that next year the percent change in net income for a sample of 110 banks is $\bar{x} = 3.5\%$. (We assume that the standard deviation is the same, $\sigma = 26.4\%$.) This sample mean is closer to the value $\mu = 0$ corresponding to no mean change in income. What is the probability that the mean of a sample of size $n = 110$ from a Normal population with mean $\mu = 0$ and standard deviation $\sigma = 26.4$ is as far away or farther away from zero as $\bar{x} = 3.5$? The answer is 0.16. A sample result this far from zero would happen just by chance in 16% of samples from a population having true mean zero. An outcome that could so easily happen just by chance is not good evidence that the population mean is different from zero.

The probabilities in Examples 6.9 and 6.10 measure the compatibility of the outcomes $\bar{x} = 8.1$ and $\bar{x} = 3.5$ with the hypothesis that $\mu = 0$. Figure 6.9 compares the two results graphically. The Normal curve centered at zero is the sampling distribution of $\bar{x}$ when $\mu = 0$. You can see that we are not particularly surprised to observe $\bar{x} = 3.5$, but $\bar{x} = 8.1$ is an extreme outcome. That's the core reasoning of statistical tests: *A sample outcome that would be extreme if a hypothesis were true is evidence that the hypothesis is not true.* Now we proceed to the formal details of tests.

Stating hypotheses

In Example 6.9, we asked whether the bank survey data are plausible if, in fact, the true percent change in net income for all banks (μ) is zero. That is, we ask if the data provide

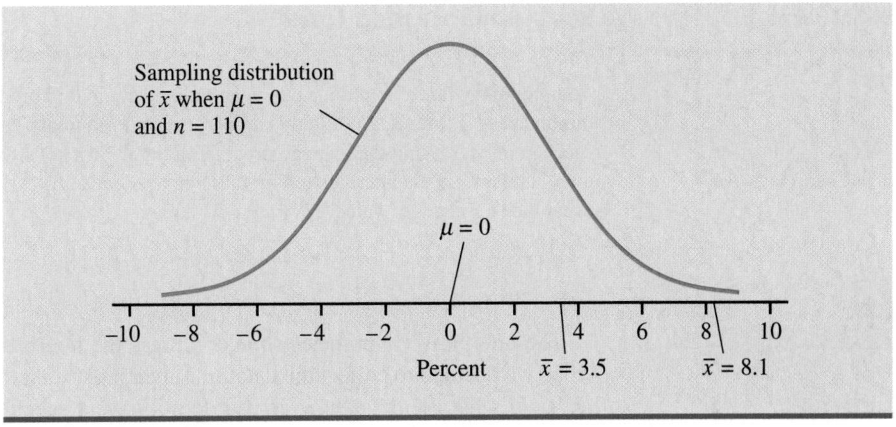

FIGURE 6.9 The mean change in net assets for a sample of 110 banks will have this sampling distribution if the mean for the population of all banks is $\mu = 0$. A sample mean $\bar{x} = 3.5\%$ could easily happen by chance. A sample mean $\bar{x} = 8.1\%$ is so far out on the curve that it would rarely happen just by chance.

evidence *against* the claim that the population mean is zero. The first step in a test of significance is to state a claim that we will try to find evidence against.

Null Hypothesis H_0

The statement being tested in a test of significance is called the **null hypothesis.** The test of significance is designed to assess the strength of the evidence against the null hypothesis. Usually the null hypothesis is a statement of "no effect" or "no difference." We abbreviate "null hypothesis" as H_0.

A null hypothesis is a statement about a population, expressed in terms of some parameter or parameters. The null hypothesis for Example 6.9 is

$$H_0: \mu = 0$$

alternative hypothesis

It is convenient also to give a name to the statement we hope or suspect is true instead of H_0. This is called the **alternative hypothesis** and is abbreviated as H_a. In Example 6.9, the alternative hypothesis states that the percent change in net income is not zero. We write this as

$$H_a: \mu \neq 0$$

Hypotheses always refer to some population or model, not to a particular outcome. For this reason, we always state H_0 and H_a in terms of population parameters.

Because H_a expresses the effect that we hope to find evidence *for,* we often begin with H_a and then set up H_0 as the statement that the hoped-for effect is not present. Stating H_a is not always straightforward. It is not always clear, in particular, whether H_a should be **one-sided** or **two-sided.**

one-sided and two-sided alternatives

The alternative H_a: $\mu \neq 0$ in the bank net income example is two-sided. We simply asked if income had changed. In any given year, income may increase or decrease, so we include both possibilities in the alternative hypothesis. Here is a setting in which a one-sided alternative is appropriate.

EXAMPLE 6.11 Have We Reduced Processing Time?

Your company hopes to reduce the mean time μ required to process customer orders. At present, this mean is 3.8 days. You study the process and eliminate some unnecessary steps. Did you succeed in decreasing the average processing time? You hope to show that the mean is now less than 3.8 days, so the alternative hypothesis is one-sided, H_a: $\mu < 3.8$. The null hypothesis is as usual the "no-change" value, H_0: $\mu = 3.8$ days.

The alternative hypothesis should express the hopes or suspicions we had in mind when we decided to collect the data. It is cheating to first look at the data and then frame H_a to fit what the data show. If you do not have a specific direction firmly in mind in advance, use a two-sided alternative. In fact, some users of statistics argue that we should *always* work with the two-sided alternative.

The choice of the hypotheses in Example 6.11 as

$$H_0: \mu = 3.8$$
$$H_a: \mu < 3.8$$

deserves a final comment. We do not expect that elimination of steps in order processing would actually increase the processing time. However, we can allow for an increase by including this case in the null hypothesis. Then we would write

$$H_0: \mu \geq 3.8$$
$$H_a: \mu < 3.8$$

This statement is logically satisfying because the hypotheses account for all possible values of μ. However, only the parameter value in H_0 that is closest to H_a influences the form of the test in all common significance-testing situations. We will therefore take H_0 to be the simpler statement that the parameter has a specific value, in this case H_0: $\mu = 3.8$.

APPLY YOUR KNOWLEDGE

6.37 Customer feedback. Feedback from your customers shows that many think it takes too long to fill out the online order form for your products. You redesign the form and plan a survey of customers to determine whether or not they think that the new form is actually an improvement. Sampled customers will respond using a five-point scale: -2 if the new form takes much less time than the old form; -1 if the new form takes a little less time; 0 if the new form takes about the same time; $+1$ if the new form takes a little more time; and $+2$ if the new form takes much more time. The mean response from the sample is $\bar{x}$, and the mean response for all of your customers is μ. State null and alternative hypotheses that provide a framework for examining whether or not the new form is an improvement.

6.38 DXA scanners. A dual-energy X-ray absorptiometry (DXA) scanner is used to measure bone mineral density for people who may be at risk for osteoporosis. Customers want assurance that your company's latest-model DXA scanner is accurate. You therefore supply an object called a "phantom" that has known mineral density $\mu = 1.4$ grams per square centimeter. A user scans the phantom 10 times and compares the sample mean reading $\bar{x}$ with the theoretical mean μ using a significance test. State the null and alternative hypotheses for this test.

Test statistics

We will learn the form of significance tests in a number of common situations. Here are some principles that apply to most tests and that help in understanding the form of tests:

- The test is based on a statistic that estimates the parameter appearing in the hypotheses. Usually this is the same estimate we would use in a confidence interval for the parameter. When H_0 is true, we expect the estimate to take a value near the parameter value specified by H_0.
- Values of the estimate far from the parameter value specified by H_0 give evidence against H_0. The alternative hypothesis determines which directions count against H_0.

EXAMPLE 6.12 Banks' Income: The Hypotheses

CASE 6.1

For Example 6.9, the hypotheses are stated in terms of the mean change in net income for all community banks:

$$H_0: \mu = 0$$

$$H_a: \mu \neq 0$$

The estimate of μ is the sample mean $\bar{x}$. Because H_a is two-sided, large positive and negative values of $\bar{x}$ (large increases and decreases of net income in the sample) count as evidence against the null hypothesis.

test statistic

A **test statistic** measures compatibility between the null hypothesis and the data. Many test statistics can be thought of as a distance between a sample estimate of a parameter and the value of the parameter specified by the null hypothesis.

EXAMPLE 6.13 Banks' Income: The Test Statistic

CASE 6.1

For Example 6.9, the null hypothesis is H_0: $\mu = 0$, and a sample gave $\bar{x} = 8.1$. The test statistic for this problem is the standardized version of $\bar{x}$:

$$z = \frac{\bar{x} - \mu}{\sigma/\sqrt{n}}$$

This statistic is the distance between the sample mean and the hypothesized population mean in the standard scale of z-scores. In this example,

$$z = \frac{8.1 - 0}{26.4/\sqrt{110}} = 3.22$$

Even without a formal probability calculation, we know that standard score $z = 3.22$ lies far out on a Normal curve.

The income changes for individual banks do not look Normal, but the central limit theorem assures us that $\bar{x}$ (and therefore z) is approximately Normal because the sample size is large. So if the null hypothesis H_0: $\mu = 0$ is true, the test statistic z is a random variable that has approximately the standard Normal distribution $N(0, 1)$. To move from the test statistic z to a probability, we must do Normal probability calculations. Review Sections 1.3 and 4.4 if you need to refresh your skills.

P-values

A test of significance assesses the evidence against the null hypothesis and provides a numerical summary of this evidence in terms of a probability. The idea is that "surprising" outcomes are evidence against H_0. A surprising outcome is one that is far from what we would expect if H_0 were true. In many cases, including our bank income example, the standard scale of z-scores is one way to measure "far from what we would expect." In Example 6.13, the standardized distance of the sample outcome $\overline{x}$ from the hypothesized population mean $\mu = 0$ was $z = 3.22$. This suggests that the sample is not compatible with the null hypothesis H_0: $\mu = 0$. In fact, the Supreme Court of the United States has said that "two or three standard deviations" ($z = 2$ or 3) is its criterion for rejecting H_0, and this is the criterion used in most applications involving the law.

Because not all test statistics produce z-scores, we translate the values of test statistics into a common language, the language of probability. A test of significance finds the probability of getting an outcome *as extreme or more extreme than the actually observed outcome*. "Extreme" means "far from what we would expect if H_0 were true." The direction or directions that count as "far from what we would expect" are determined by the alternative hypothesis H_a.

P-Value

The probability, computed assuming that H_0 is true, that the test statistic would take a value as extreme or more extreme than that actually observed is called the ***P*-value** of the test. The smaller the P-value, the stronger the evidence against H_0 provided by the data.

To calculate the P-value we must use the sampling distribution of the test statistic. In this chapter, we need only the standard Normal distribution for the test statistic z.

EXAMPLE 6.14 Banks' Income: The P-Value

CASE 6.1

In Example 6.9 the observations are an SRS of size $n = 110$ from a population of community banks with $\sigma = 26.4$. The observed average percent change in net income is $\overline{x} = 8.1$. In Example 6.13, we found that the test statistic for testing H_0: $\mu = 0$ versus H_a: $\mu \neq 0$ is

$$z = \frac{8.1 - 0}{26.4/\sqrt{110}} = 3.22$$

If the null hypothesis is true, we expect z to take a value not too far from 0. Because the alternative is two-sided, values of z far from 0 *in either direction* count as evidence against H_0 and in favor of H_a. So the P-value is

$$P(z \geq 3.22) + P(z \leq -3.22)$$

If H_0 is true, then z has approximately the standard Normal $N(0, 1)$ distribution. Figure 6.10 shows the P-value as a very small area under the standard Normal curve.

FIGURE 6.10 The P-value for Example 6.14. The two-sided P-value is the probability (when H_0 is true) that $\bar{x}$ takes a value at least as far from 0 as the actually observed value.

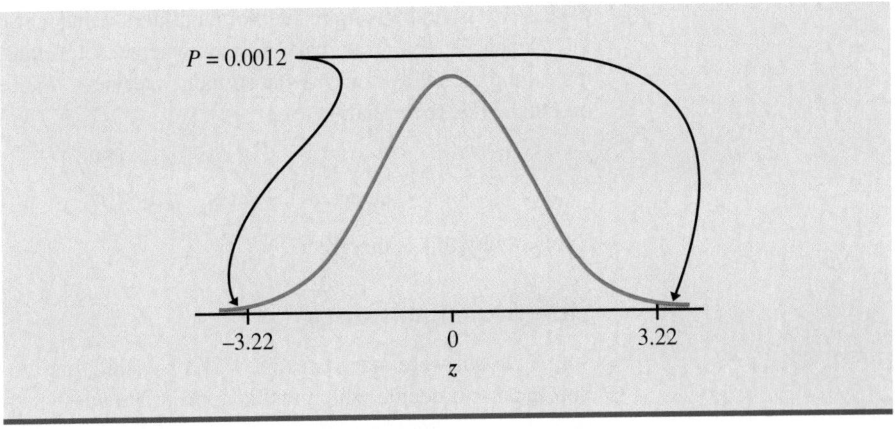

From Table A, we find

$$P(Z \geq 3.22) = 1 - 0.9994 = 0.0006$$

Similarly, from Table A or using the symmetry of the Normal distribution,

$$P(Z \leq -3.22) = 0.0006$$

That is,

$$P = 2P(Z \geq 3.22) = 0.0012$$

In Example 6.9 we rounded this value to 0.001.

APPLY YOUR KNOWLEDGE

6.39 Spending on housing. The Census Bureau reports that households spend an average of 31% of their total spending on housing. A homebuilders association in Cleveland wonders if the national finding applies in their area. They interview a sample of 40 households in the Cleveland metropolitan area to learn what percent of their spending goes toward housing. Take μ to be the mean percent of spending devoted to housing among all Cleveland households. We want to test the hypotheses

$$H_0: \mu = 31\%$$
$$H_a: \mu \neq 31\%$$

The population standard deviation is $\sigma = 9.6\%$.

(a) The study finds $\bar{x} = 28.6\%$ for the 40 households in the sample. What is the value of the test statistic z? Sketch a standard Normal curve and mark z on the axis. Shade the area under the curve that represents the P-value.

(b) Calculate the P-value. Are you convinced that Cleveland differs from the national average?

6.40 State null and alternative hypotheses. In the setting of the previous exercise, suppose that the Cleveland homebuilders were convinced, before interviewing their sample, that residents of Cleveland spend less than the national average on housing. Do the interviews support their conviction? State null and alternative hypotheses. Find the P-value, using the interview results given in the previous problem. Why do the same data give different P-values in these two problems?

6.41 Why is this wrong? The homebuilders wonder if the national finding applies in the Cleveland area. They have no idea whether Cleveland residents spend more or less than the national average. Because their interviews find that $\bar{x} = 28.6\%$, less than the national 31%, their analyst tests

$$H_0\colon \mu = 31\%$$
$$H_a\colon \mu < 31\%$$

Explain why this is incorrect.

Statistical significance

Statistical software automates the task of calculating the test statistic and its P-value. You must still decide which test is appropriate and whether to use a one-sided or two-sided test. You must also decide what conclusion the computer's numbers support. We know that smaller P-values indicate stronger evidence against the null hypothesis. But how strong is strong enough?

One approach is to announce in advance how much evidence against H_0 we will require to reject H_0. We compare the P-value with a level that says "this evidence is strong enough." The decisive level is called the **significance level.** It is denoted by α, the Greek letter alpha. If we choose $\alpha = 0.05$, we are requiring that the data give evidence against H_0 so strong that it would happen no more than 5% of the time (1 time in 20) when H_0 is true. If we choose $\alpha = 0.01$, we are insisting on stronger evidence against H_0, evidence so strong that it would appear only 1% of the time (1 time in 100) if H_0 is in fact true.

significance level

Statistical Significance

If the P-value is as small or smaller than α, we say that the data are **statistically significant at level α.**

"Significant" in the statistical sense does not mean "important." The original meaning of the word is "signifying something." In statistics, the term is used to indicate only that the evidence against the null hypothesis reached the standard set by α. Significance at level 0.01 is often expressed by the statement "The results were significant ($P < 0.01$)." Here P stands for the P-value. The P-value is more informative than a statement of significance because we can then assess significance at any level we choose. For example, a result with $P = 0.03$ is significant at the $\alpha = 0.05$ level but is not significant at the $\alpha = 0.01$ level.

You need not actually find the P-value to assess significance at a fixed level α. You need only compare the observed statistic z with a *critical value* that marks off area α in one or both tails of the standard Normal curve.

EXAMPLE 6.15 Significant?

CASE 6.1 

In Example 6.14, the test statistic took the value $z = 3.22$. Is this significant at the $\alpha = 0.01$ level? Values in the extreme 0.01 area of the standard Normal curve are significant at the 0.01 level. Because the alternative is two-sided, this area is divided equally between the two tails

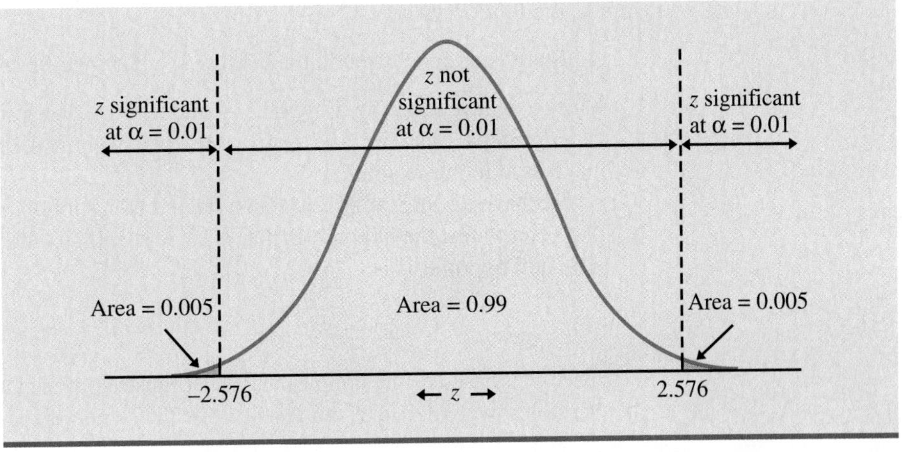

FIGURE 6.11 Values of z in the extreme area 0.01 under a standard Normal curve are significant at $\alpha = 0.01$ (for Example 6.15).

of the curve. So z is significant if it lies in the extreme area 0.005 at either end. Look at the z^* row at the bottom of Table D. The extreme 0.005 in the right tail starts at $z^* = 2.576$. That is, the z-values that are significant at the $\alpha = 0.01$ level are $z > 2.576$ and $z < -2.576$. Figure 6.11 shows why. The bank survey outcome $z = 3.22$ is statistically significant ($P < 0.01$).

APPLY YOUR KNOWLEDGE

6.42 How to show that you are rich. Every society has its own marks of wealth and prestige. In ancient China, it appears that owning pigs was such a mark. Evidence comes from examining burial sites. If the skulls of sacrificed pigs tend to appear along with expensive ornaments, that suggests that the pigs, like the ornaments, signal the wealth and prestige of the person buried. A study of burials from around 3500 B.C. concluded that "there are striking differences in grave goods between burials with pig skulls and burials without them. . . . A test indicates that the two samples of total artifacts are significantly different at the 0.01 level."[7] Explain clearly why "significantly different at the 0.01 level" gives good reason to think that there really is a systematic difference between burials that contain pig skulls and those that lack them.

6.43 Significance. You are testing H_0: $\mu = 0$ against H_a: $\mu \neq 0$ based on an SRS of 30 observations from a Normal population. What values of the z statistic are statistically significant at the $\alpha = 0.005$ level?

6.44 Significance. You are testing H_0: $\mu = 0$ against H_a: $\mu > 0$ based on an SRS of 30 observations from a Normal population. What values of the z statistic are statistically significant at the $\alpha = 0.005$ level?

6.45 The Supreme Court speaks. Court cases in such areas as employment discrimination often involve statistical evidence. The Supreme Court has said that z-scores beyond $z^* = 2$ or 3 are generally convincing statistical evidence. For a two-sided test, what significance level corresponds to $z^* = 2$? To $z^* = 3$?

Tests for a population mean

There are four steps in carrying out a significance test:

1. State the hypotheses.
2. Calculate the test statistic.

3. Find the P-value.

4. State your conclusion in the context of your specific setting.

Once you have stated your hypotheses and identified the proper test, you or your software can do Steps 2 and 3 by following a recipe. We now present the recipe for the test we have used in our examples.

We have an SRS of size n drawn from a Normal population with unknown mean μ. We want to test the hypothesis that μ has a specified value. Call the specified value μ_0. The null hypothesis is

$$H_0: \mu = \mu_0$$

The test is based on the sample mean $\bar{x}$. Because Normal calculations require standardized variables, we will use as our test statistic the standardized sample mean

$$z = \frac{\bar{x} - \mu_0}{\sigma/\sqrt{n}}$$

one-sample z statistic

This **one-sample z statistic** has the standard Normal distribution when H_0 is true. The P-value of the test is the probability that z takes a value at least as extreme as the value for our sample. What counts as extreme is determined by the alternative hypothesis H_a. Here is a summary.

z Test for a Population Mean

To test the hypothesis H_0: $\mu = \mu_0$ based on an SRS of size n from a population with unknown mean μ and known standard deviation σ, compute the **one-sample z statistic**

$$z = \frac{\bar{x} - \mu_0}{\sigma/\sqrt{n}}$$

In terms of a variable Z having the standard Normal distribution, the P-value for a test of H_0 against

H_a: $\mu > \mu_0$ is $P(Z \geq z)$

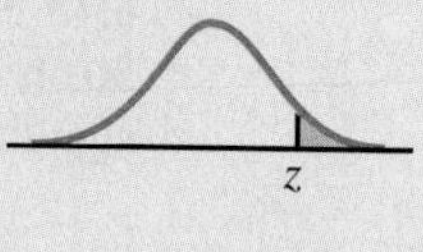

H_a: $\mu < \mu_0$ is $P(Z \leq z)$

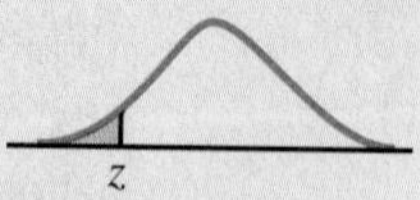

H_a: $\mu \neq \mu_0$ is $2P(Z \geq |z|)$

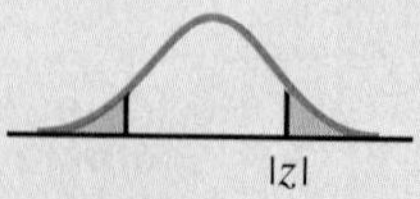

These P-values are exact if the population distribution is Normal and are approximately correct for large n in other cases.

EXAMPLE 6.16 Blood Pressures of Executives

The medical director of a large company is concerned about the effects of stress on the company's younger executives. According to the National Center for Health Statistics, the mean systolic blood pressure for males 35 to 44 years of age is 128 and the standard deviation in this population is 15. The medical director examines the records of 72 executives in this age group and finds that their mean systolic blood pressure is $\bar{x} = 129.93$. Is this evidence that the mean blood pressure for all the company's young male executives is higher than the national average? As usual in this chapter, we make the unrealistic assumption that the population standard deviation is known, in this case that executives have the same $\sigma = 15$ as the general population.

Step 1. **Hypotheses.** The hypotheses about the unknown mean μ of the executive population are

$$H_0: \mu = 128$$
$$H_a: \mu > 128$$

Step 2. **Test statistic.** The z test requires that the 72 executives in the sample are an SRS from the population of the company's young male executives. We must ask how the data were produced. If records are available only for executives with recent medical problems, for example, the data are of little value for our purpose. It turns out that all executives are given a free annual medical exam and that the medical director selected 72 exam results at random. The one-sample z statistic is

$$z = \frac{\bar{x} - \mu_0}{\sigma/\sqrt{n}} = \frac{129.93 - 128}{15/\sqrt{72}}$$
$$= 1.09$$

Step 3. ***P*-value.** Draw a picture to help find the P-value. Figure 6.12 shows that the P-value is the probability that a standard Normal variable Z takes a value of 1.09 or greater. From Table A we find that this probability is

$$P = P(Z \geq 1.09) = 1 - 0.8621 = 0.1379$$

Step 4. **Conclusion.** About 14% of the time an SRS of size 72 from the general male population would have a mean blood pressure as high as that of the executive sample. The observed $\bar{x} = 129.93$ is not significantly higher than the national average at any of the usual significance levels.

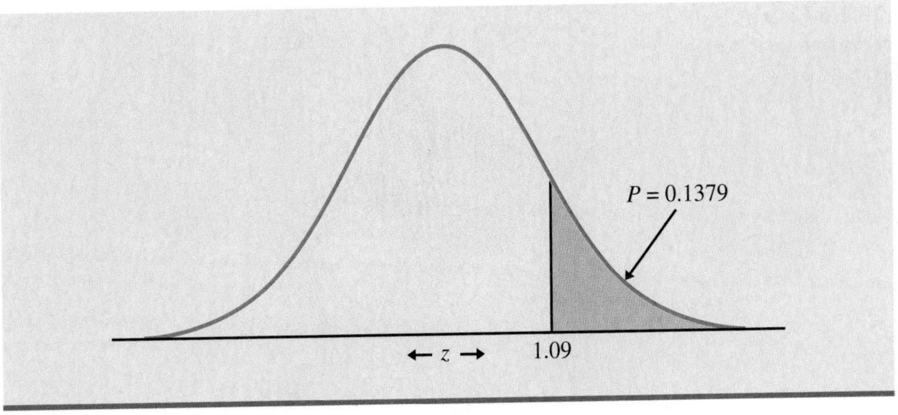

FIGURE 6.12 The P-value for the one-sided test in Example 6.16.

The data in Example 6.16 do *not* establish that the mean blood pressure μ for this company's middle-aged male executives is 128. We sought evidence that μ was higher than 128 and failed to find convincing evidence. That is all we can say. No doubt the mean blood pressure of the entire executive population is not exactly equal to 128. A large enough sample would give evidence of the difference, even if it is very small. Tests of significance assess the evidence *against* H_0. If the evidence is strong, we can confidently reject H_0 in favor of the alternative. Failing to find evidence against H_0 means only that the data are consistent with H_0, not that we have clear evidence that H_0 is true.

EXAMPLE 6.17 A Company-Wide Health Promotion

The company medical director institutes a health promotion campaign to encourage employees to exercise more and eat a healthier diet. One measure of the effectiveness of such a program is a drop in blood pressure. Choose a random sample of 50 employees, and compare their blood pressures from annual physical examinations given before the campaign and again a year later. The mean change in blood pressure for these $n = 50$ employees is $\bar{x} = -6$. We take the population standard deviation to be $\sigma = 20$.

Step 1. **Hypotheses.** We want to know if the health campaign reduced average blood pressure. Taking μ to be the mean change in blood pressure for all employees,

$$H_0\colon \mu = 0$$
$$H_a\colon \mu < 0$$

Step 2. **Test statistic.** The one-sample z test is appropriate:

$$z = \frac{\bar{x} - \mu_0}{\sigma/\sqrt{n}} = \frac{-6 - 0}{20/\sqrt{50}} = -2.12$$

Step 3. ***P*-value.** Because H_a is one-sided on the low side, large negative values of z count against H_0. See Figure 6.13. From Table A, we find that the P-value is

$$P = P(Z \leq -2.12) = 0.0170$$

Step 4. **Conclusion.** A mean change in blood pressure of −6 or better would occur only 17 times in 1000 samples if the campaign had no effect on the blood pressures of the employees. This is convincing evidence that the mean blood pressure in the population of all employees has decreased.

FIGURE 6.13 The P-value for the one-sided test in Example 6.17.

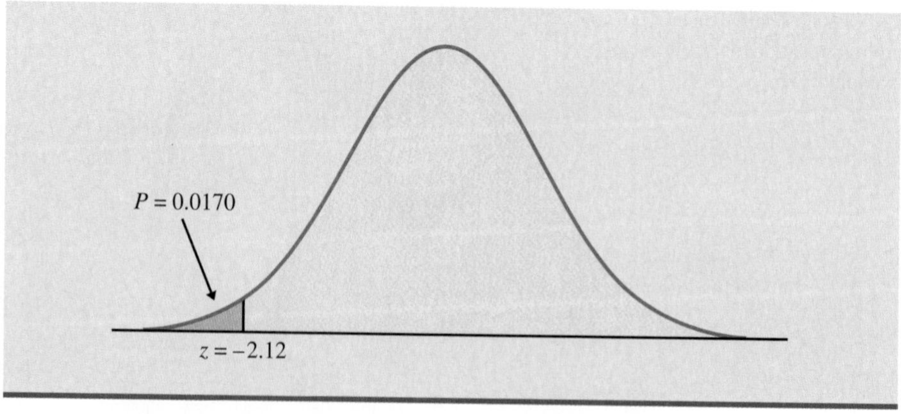

Our conclusion in Example 6.17 is cautious. We would like to conclude that the health campaign *caused* the drop in mean blood pressure. But the data are not protected from confounding. If, for example, the local television station runs a series on the risk of heart attacks and the value of better diet and exercise, many employees may be moved to reform their health habits even without encouragement from the company. Only a randomized comparative experiment protects against such lurking variables. The medical director preferred to launch a company-wide campaign that appealed to all employees. This is no doubt a sound medical decision, but the absence of a control group weakens the statistical conclusion.

APPLY YOUR KNOWLEDGE

6.46 Testing a random number generator. Statistical software has a "random number generator" that is supposed to produce numbers uniformly distributed between 0 to 1. If this is true, the numbers generated come from a population with $\mu = 0.5$. A command to generate 100 random numbers gives outcomes with mean $\bar{x} = 0.522$ and $s = 0.316$. Because the sample is reasonably large, take the population standard deviation also to be $\sigma = 0.316$. Do we have evidence that the mean of all numbers produced by this software is not 0.5?

6.47 The effects of different alternative hypotheses. A test of the null hypothesis H_0: $\mu = \mu_0$ gives test statistic $z = 1.9$.

(a) What is the P-value if the alternative is H_a: $\mu > \mu_0$?

(b) What is the P-value if the alternative is H_a: $\mu < \mu_0$?

(c) What is the P-value if the alternative is H_a: $\mu \neq \mu_0$?

6.48 A new supplier. A new supplier offers a good price on a catalyst used in your production process. You compare the purity of this catalyst with that from your current supplier. The P-value for a test of "no difference" is 0.27. Can you be confident that the purity of the new product is the same as the purity of the product that you have been using? Discuss.

Two-sided significance tests and confidence intervals

A 95% confidence interval captures the true value of μ in 95% of all samples. If we are 95% confident that the true μ lies in our interval, we are also confident that values of μ that fall outside our interval are incompatible with the data. That sounds like the conclusion of a test of significance. In fact, there is an intimate connection between 95% confidence intervals and significance at the 5% level. The same connection holds between 99% confidence intervals and significance at the 1% level, and so on.

Confidence Intervals and Two-Sided Tests

A level α two-sided significance test rejects a hypothesis H_0: $\mu = \mu_0$ exactly when the value μ_0 falls outside a level $1 - \alpha$ confidence interval for μ.

EXAMPLE 6.18 Testing Pharmaceutical Products

The Deely Laboratory analyzes pharmaceutical products to verify the concentration of active ingredients. Such chemical analyses are not perfectly precise. Repeated measurements on the same specimen will give slightly different results. The results of repeated measurements follow a Normal distribution quite closely. The analysis procedure has no bias, so that the mean μ of the population of all measurements is the true concentration in the specimen. The standard deviation of this distribution is a property of the analytical procedure and is known to be $\sigma = 0.0068$ grams per liter. The laboratory analyzes each specimen three times and reports the mean result.

A client sends a specimen for which the concentration of active ingredient is supposed to be 0.86%. Deely's three analyses give concentrations

0.8403 0.8363 0.8447

Is there significant evidence at the 1% level that the true concentration is not 0.86%? This calls for a test of the hypotheses

$$H_0\colon \mu = 0.86$$
$$H_a\colon \mu \neq 0.86$$

We will carry out the test twice, with the usual significance test and then from a 99% confidence interval.

First, the test. The mean of the three analyses is $\bar{x} = 0.8404$. The one-sample z test statistic is therefore

$$z = \frac{\bar{x} - \mu_0}{\sigma/\sqrt{n}} = \frac{0.8404 - 0.86}{0.0068/\sqrt{3}} = -4.99$$

We need not find the exact P-value to assess significance at the $\alpha = 0.01$ level. Look in Table D under tail area 0.005 because the alternative is two-sided. The z-values that are significant at the 1% level are $z > 2.576$ and $z < -2.576$. Our observed $z = -4.99$ is significant ($P < 0.01$).

To compute a 99% confidence interval for the mean concentration, find in Table D the critical value for 99% confidence. It is $z^* = 2.576$, the same critical value that marked off significant z's in our test. The confidence interval is

$$\begin{aligned} \bar{x} \pm z^* \frac{\sigma}{\sqrt{n}} &= 0.8404 \pm 2.576 \frac{0.0068}{\sqrt{3}} \\ &= 0.8404 \pm 0.0101 \\ &= (0.8303, 0.8505) \end{aligned}$$

The hypothesized value $\mu_0 = 0.86$ falls outside this confidence interval. We are therefore 99% confident that μ is *not* equal to 0.86, so we can reject

$$H_0\colon \mu = 0.86$$

at the 1% significance level. On the other hand, we cannot reject

$$H_0\colon \mu = 0.85$$

at the 1% level in favor of the two-sided alternative $H_a\colon \mu \neq 0.85$, because 0.85 lies inside the 99% confidence interval for μ. Figure 6.14 illustrates both cases.

FIGURE 6.14 Values of μ falling outside a 99% confidence interval can be rejected at the 1% significance level. Values falling inside the interval cannot be rejected.

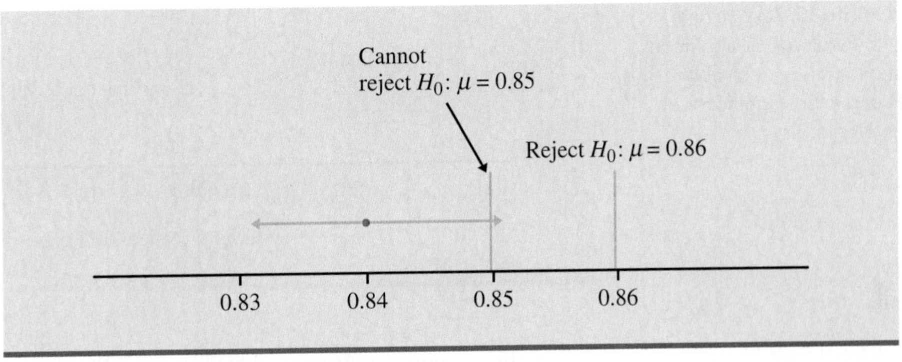

APPLY YOUR KNOWLEDGE

6.49 Does the confidence interval include μ_0? The P-value for a two-sided test of the null hypothesis H_0: $\mu = 15$ is 0.07.

(a) Does the 95% confidence interval include the value 15? Why?

(b) Does the 90% confidence interval include the value 15? Why?

6.50 Can you reject the null hypothesis? A 95% confidence interval for a population mean is (16, 32).

(a) Can you reject the null hypothesis that $\mu = 34$ at the 5% significance level? Why?

(b) Can you reject the null hypothesis that $\mu = 17$ at the 5% significance level? Why?

P-values versus fixed α

In Example 6.18, we concluded that the test statistic $z = -4.99$ is significant at the 1% level. This isn't the whole story. The observed z is far beyond the critical value for $\alpha = 0.01$, and the evidence against H_0 is far stronger than 1% significance suggests. The P-value $P = 0.0000006$ (from software) gives a better sense of how strong the evidence is. *The P-value is the smallest level α at which the data are significant.* Knowing the P-value allows us to assess significance at any level.

EXAMPLE 6.19 How Significant?

In Example 6.17, we tested the hypotheses

$$H_0: \mu = 0$$
$$H_a: \mu < 0$$

to evaluate the effectiveness of a health promotion program on blood pressure. The test had the P-value $P = 0.0170$. This result is not significant at the $\alpha = 0.01$ level, because $0.0170 \geq 0.01$. However, it is significant at the $\alpha = 0.05$ level, because the P-value is less than 0.05. See Figure 6.15.

A P-value is more informative than a reject-or-not finding at a fixed significance level. But assessing significance at a fixed level α is easier, because no probability calculation is required. You need only look up a critical value in a table. Because the practice of statistics

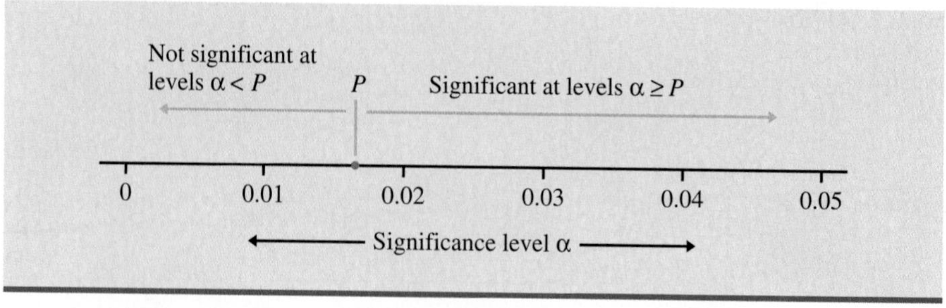

FIGURE 6.15 An outcome with P-value P is significant at all levels α at or above P and is not significant at smaller levels α.

almost always employs software that calculates P-values automatically, tables of critical values are becoming outdated. We include the usual tables of critical values (such as Table D) at the end of the book for learning purposes and to rescue students without good computing facilities. The tables can be used directly to carry out fixed α tests. They also allow us to approximate P-values quickly without a probability calculation. The following example illustrates the use of Table D to find an approximate P-value.

EXAMPLE 6.20 Fill the Bottles

Bottles of a popular cola drink are supposed to contain 300 milliliters (ml) of cola. There is some variation from bottle to bottle because the filling machinery is not perfectly precise. The distribution of the contents is Normal with standard deviation $\sigma = 3$ ml. An inspector who suspects that the bottler is underfilling measures the contents of six bottles. The results are

299.4 297.7 301.0 298.9 300.2 297.0

Is this convincing evidence that the mean contents of cola bottles is less than the advertised 300 ml? The hypotheses are

$$H_0\colon \mu = 300$$
$$H_a\colon \mu < 300$$

The sample mean contents of the six bottles measured is $\bar{x} = 299.03$ ml. The z test statistic is therefore

$$z = \frac{\bar{x} - \mu_0}{\sigma/\sqrt{n}} = \frac{299.03 - 300}{3/\sqrt{6}} = -0.792$$

Small values of z count against H_0 because H_a is one-sided on the low side. The P-value is

$$P(Z \le -0.792)$$

Rather than compute this probability, compare $z = -0.792$ with the critical values in Table D. According to this table, we would

$$\text{reject } H_0 \text{ at level } \alpha = 0.25 \text{ if } z \le -0.674$$
$$\text{reject } H_0 \text{ at level } \alpha = 0.20 \text{ if } z \le -0.841$$

As Figure 6.16 illustrates, the observed $z = -0.792$ lies between these two critical values. We can reject at $\alpha = 0.25$ but not at $\alpha = 0.20$. That is the same as saying that the P-value lies between 0.25 and 0.20. Between 20% and 25% of all samples will have a sample mean at least as small as that observed if the population mean is $\mu = 300$ ml. There is no convincing evidence that the mean is below 300, and there is no need to calculate the P-value more exactly.

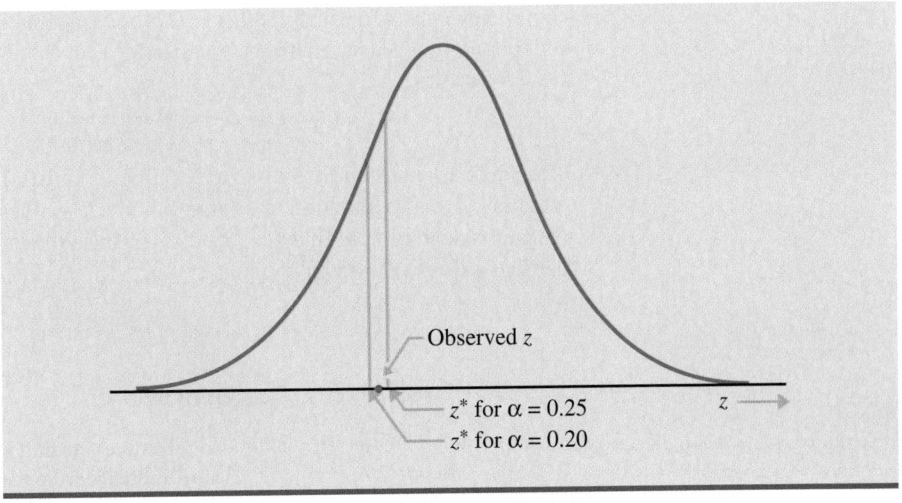

FIGURE 6.16 The P-value of a z statistic can be approximated by noting which levels from Table D it falls between. Here, P lies between 0.20 and 0.25.

APPLY YOUR KNOWLEDGE

6.51 Do you reject the null hypothesis? The P-value for a significance test is 0.049.

(a) Do you reject the null hypothesis at level $\alpha = 0.05$?

(b) Do you reject the null hypothesis at level $\alpha = 0.01$?

(c) Explain your answers.

6.52 Suppose the P-value is a little higher? The P-value for a significance test is 0.051.

(a) Do you reject the null hypothesis at level $\alpha = 0.05$?

(b) Do you reject the null hypothesis at level $\alpha = 0.01$?

(c) Explain your answers.

SECTION 6.2 SUMMARY

- A **test of significance** is intended to assess the evidence provided by data against a **null hypothesis H_0** and in favor of an **alternative hypothesis H_a.** It provides a method for ruling out chance as an explanation for data that deviate from what we expect under H_0.

- The hypotheses are stated in terms of population parameters. Usually, H_0 is a statement that no effect is present, and H_a says that a parameter differs from its null value in a specific direction (**one-sided alternative**) or in either direction (**two-sided alternative**).

- The test is based on a **test statistic.** The **P-value** is the probability, computed assuming that H_0 is true, that the test statistic will take a value at least as extreme as that actually observed. Small P-values indicate strong evidence against H_0. Calculating P-values requires knowledge of the sampling distribution of the test statistic when H_0 is true.

- If the P-value is as small or smaller than a specified value α, the data are **statistically significant** at significance level α.

- Significance tests for the hypothesis H_0: $\mu = \mu_0$ concerning the unknown mean μ of a population are based on the z **statistic:**

$$z = \frac{\overline{x} - \mu_0}{\sigma/\sqrt{n}}$$

- The z test assumes an SRS of size n, known population standard deviation σ, and either a Normal population or a large sample. P-values are computed from the Normal distribution (Table A). Fixed α tests use the table of **standard Normal critical values** (z^* row in Table D).

SECTION 6.2 Exercises

For Exercises 6.37 and 6.38, see page 380; for 6.39 to 6.41, see pages 383–384; for 6.42 to 6.45, see page 385; for 6.46 to 6.48, see page 389; for 6.49 and 6.50, see page 391; and for 6.51 and 6.52, see page 393.

6.53 What's wrong? Here are several situations where there is an incorrect application of the ideas presented in this section. Write a short paragraph explaining what is wrong in each situation and why it is wrong.

(a) A fleet manager for a trucking company wants to test the null hypothesis that the price of diesel fuel will not increase next month.

(b) A random sample of size 30 is taken from a population that is assumed to have a standard deviation of 18. The standard deviation of the sample mean is 18/30.

(c) A researcher tests the following null hypothesis: H_0: $\overline{x} = 20$.

6.54 What's wrong? Here are several situations where there is an incorrect application of the ideas presented in this section. Write a short paragraph explaining what is wrong in each situation and why it is wrong.

(a) A change is made that should improve student satisfaction with the way grades are processed at your college. The null hypothesis, that there is an improvement, is tested versus the alternative, that there is no change.

(b) A significance test rejected the null hypothesis that the sample mean is 35.

(c) A report on a study says that the results are statistically significant and the P-value is 0.85.

6.55 Are the trees randomly distributed? In Example 6.2 we looked at the distribution of longleaf pine trees in the Wade Tract. One way to formulate hypotheses about whether or not the trees are randomly distributed in the tract is to examine the average location in the north-south direction. The values range from 0 to 200, so if the trees are uniformly distributed in this direction, any difference from the middle value (100) should be due to chance variation. The sample mean for the 584 trees in the tract is 99.74. A theoretical calculation based on the assumption that the trees are uniformly distributed gives a standard deviation of 58. Carefully state the null and alternative hypotheses in terms of this variable. Note that this requires that you translate the research question about the random distribution of the trees into specific statements about the mean of a probability distribution. Test your hypotheses, report your results, and write a short summary of what you have found.

6.56 Consider the other direction. Answer the questions in the previous exercise for the east-west direction, where the sample mean is 113.8.

6.57 Compare student loan debt for different groups of students. One purpose of the National Student Loan Survey is to compare the debt of different subgroups of students.[8] For example, the 525 borrowers who last attended a private four-year college had a mean debt of \$21,200, while those who last attended a public four-year college had a mean debt of \$17,100. The difference of \$4100 is fairly large, but we know that these numbers are estimates of the true means. If we took a different sample, we would get different estimates. Can we conclude from these data that the private four-year students have greater debt than public four-year borrowers? We answer this question by computing the probability of obtaining a difference as large or larger than the observed \$4100 assuming that, in fact, there is no difference in the true means. This probability is 0.17. What do you conclude? Illustrate the probability result with a sketch and write a short paragraph explaining your answer.

6.58 Compare student loan debt in two different years. Another purpose of the National Student Loan Survey is to look for changes over time. For example, in 1997, the survey found that the mean debt for undergraduate study was \$11,400. How does this compare with the value of \$18,900 in the 2002 study? The difference is \$7500. To determine if the data provide evidence that there is an increase in borrowing we calculate the probability of observing an increase in mean debt that is \$7500 or more under the assumption that there is no difference in the true means. The calculated probability is 0.00004. What do you conclude? Illustrate the probability result with a sketch and write a short paragraph explaining your answer.

6.59 **Hypotheses.** Each of the following situations requires a significance test about a population mean μ. State the appropriate null hypothesis H_0 and alternative hypothesis H_a in each case.

(a) Larry's car averages 31 miles per gallon on the highway. He now switches to a new motor oil that is advertised as increasing gas mileage. After driving 2500 highway miles with the new oil, he wants to determine if his gas mileage actually has increased.

(b) The diameter of a spindle in a small motor is supposed to be 4 millimeters. If the spindle is either too small or too large, the motor will not perform properly. The manufacturer measures the diameter in a sample of motors to determine whether the mean diameter has moved away from the target.

(c) The mean area of the several thousand apartments in a new development is advertised to be 1400 square feet. A tenant group thinks that the apartments are smaller than advertised. They hire an engineer to measure a sample of apartments to test their suspicion.

6.60 **Hypotheses.** In each of the following situations, a significance test for a population mean μ is called for. State the null hypothesis H_0 and the alternative hypothesis H_a in each case.

(a) A university gives credit in French language courses to students who pass a placement test. The language department wants to know if students who get credit in this way differ in their understanding of spoken French from students who actually take the French courses. Experience has shown that the mean score of students in the courses on a standard listening test is 26. The language department gives the same listening test to a sample of 35 students who passed the credit examination to see if their performance is different.

(b) Experiments on learning in animals sometimes measure how long it takes a mouse to find its way through a maze. The mean time is 22 seconds for one particular maze. A researcher thinks that a loud noise will cause the mice to complete the maze faster. She measures how long each of 12 mice takes with a noise as stimulus.

(c) The examinations in a large accounting class are scaled after grading so that the mean score is 75. A self-confident teaching assistant thinks that his students have a higher mean score than the class as a whole. His students this semester can be considered a sample from the population of all students he might teach, so he compares their mean score with 75.

6.61 **Hypotheses.** In each of the following situations, state an appropriate null hypothesis H_0 and alternative hypothesis H_a. Be sure to identify the parameters that you use to state the hypotheses. (We have not yet learned how to test these hypotheses.)

(a) A sociologist asks a large sample of high school students which academic subject they like best. She suspects that a higher percent of males than of females will name economics as their favorite subject.

(b) An education researcher randomly divides sixth-grade students into two groups for physical education class. He teaches both groups basketball skills, using the same methods of instruction in both classes. He encourages Group A with compliments and other positive behavior but acts cool and neutral toward Group B. He hopes to show that positive teacher attitudes result in a higher mean score on a test of basketball skills than do neutral attitudes.

(c) An economist believes that among employed young adults there is a positive correlation between income and the percent of disposable income that is saved. To test this, she gathers income and savings data from a sample of employed persons in her city aged 25 to 34.

6.62 **Hypotheses.** Translate each of the following research questions into appropriate H_0 and H_a.

(a) Census Bureau data show that the mean household income in the area served by a shopping mall is \$62,500 per year. A market research firm questions shoppers at the mall to find out whether the mean household income of mall shoppers is higher than that of the general population.

(b) Last year, your company's service technicians took an average of 2.6 hours to respond to trouble calls from business customers who had purchased service contracts. Do this year's data show a different average response time?

6.63 **Blood pressure and calcium.** A randomized comparative experiment examined whether a calcium supplement in the diet reduces the blood pressure of healthy men.[9] The subjects received either a calcium supplement or a placebo for 12 weeks. The statistical analysis was quite complex, but one conclusion was that "the calcium group had lower seated systolic blood pressure ($P = 0.008$) compared with the placebo group." Explain this conclusion, especially the P-value, as if you were speaking to a doctor who knows no statistics.

6.64 California brushfires. We often see televised reports of brushfires threatening homes in California. Some people argue that the modern practice of quickly putting out small fires allows fuel to accumulate and so increases the damage done by large fires. A detailed study of historical data suggests that this is wrong—the damage has risen simply because there are more houses in risky areas.[10] As usual, the study report gives statistical information tersely. Here is the summary of a regression of number of fires on decade (9 data points, for the 1910s to the 1990s):

Collectively, since 1910, there has been a highly significant increase ($r^2 = 0.61$, $P < 0.01$) in the number of fires per decade.

How would you explain this statement to someone who knows no statistics? Include an explanation of both the description given by r^2 and the statistical significance.

6.65 Exercise and statistics exams. A study examined whether exercise affects how students perform on their final exam in statistics. The P-value was given as 0.68.

(a) State null and alternative hypotheses that could be used for this study. (Note that there is more than one correct answer.)

(b) Do you reject the null hypothesis? State your conclusion in plain language.

(c) What other facts about the study would you like to know for a proper interpretation of the results?

6.66 Financial aid. The financial aid office of a university asks a sample of students about their employment and earnings. The report says that "for academic year earnings, a significant difference ($P = 0.038$) was found between the sexes, with men earning more on the average. No difference ($P = 0.476$) was found between the earnings of black and white students."[11] Explain both of these conclusions, for the effects of sex and of race on mean earnings, in language understandable to someone who knows no statistics.

6.67 Who is the author? Statistics can help decide the authorship of literary works. Sonnets by a certain Elizabethan poet are known to contain an average of $\mu = 6.9$ new words (words not used in the poet's other works). The standard deviation of the number of new words is $\sigma = 2.7$. Now a manuscript with 5 new sonnets has come to light, and scholars are debating whether it is the poet's work. The new sonnets contain an average of $\bar{x} = 11.2$ words not used in the poet's known works. We expect poems by another author to contain more new words, so to see if we have evidence that the new sonnets are not by our poet we test

$$H_0: \mu = 6.9$$
$$H_a: \mu > 6.9$$

Give the z test statistic and its P-value. What do you conclude about the authorship of the new poems?

6.68 Study habits. The Survey of Study Habits and Attitudes (SSHA) is a psychological test that measures the motivation, attitude toward school, and study habits of students. Scores range from 0 to 200. The mean score for U.S. college students is about 115, and the standard deviation is about 30. A teacher who suspects that older students have better attitudes toward school gives the SSHA to 25 students who are at least 30 years of age. Their mean score is $\bar{x} = 133.2$.

(a) Assuming that $\sigma = 30$ for the population of older students, carry out a test of

$$H_0: \mu = 115$$
$$H_a: \mu > 115$$

Report the P-value of your test, draw a sketch illustrating the P-value, and state your conclusion clearly.

(b) Your test in (a) required two important assumptions in addition to the assumption that the value of σ is known. What are they? Which of these assumptions is most important to the validity of your conclusion in (a)?

6.69 Corn yield. The mean yield of corn in the United States is about 135 bushels per acre. A survey of 50 farmers this year gives a sample mean yield of $\bar{x} = 138.4$ bushels per acre. We want to know whether this is good evidence that the national mean this year is not 135 bushels per acre. Assume that the farmers surveyed are an SRS from the population of all commercial corn growers and that the standard deviation of the yield in this population is $\sigma = 10$ bushels per acre. Report the value of the test statistic z, give a sketch illustrating the P-value, and report the P-value for the test of

$$H_0: \mu = 135$$
$$H_a: \mu \neq 135$$

Are you convinced that the population mean is not 135 bushels per acre? Is your conclusion correct if the distribution of corn yields is somewhat non-Normal? Why?

6.70 Cigarettes. According to data from the Tobacco Institute Testing Laboratory, Camel Lights King Size cigarettes contain an average of 1.4 milligrams of nicotine. An advocacy group commissions an independent test to see if the mean nicotine content is higher than the industry laboratory claims.

(a) What are H_0 and H_a?

(b) Suppose that the test statistic is $z = 2.36$. Is this result significant at the 5% level?

(c) Is the result significant at the 1% level?

6.71 Academic probation and TV watching. There are other z statistics that we have not yet met. We can use Table D to assess the significance of any z statistic. A study compares the habits of students who are on academic probation with students whose grades are satisfactory. One variable measured is the hours spent watching television last week. The null hypothesis is "no difference" between the means for the two populations. The alternative hypothesis is two-sided. The value of the test statistic is $z = -1.27$.

(a) Is the result significant at the 5% level?

(b) Is the result significant at the 1% level?

6.72 Why is it significant at the 5% level? Explain in plain language why a significance test that is significant at the 1% level must always be significant at the 5% level.

6.73 Use Table D. You have performed a two-sided test of significance and obtained a value of $z = 3.1$. Use Table D to find the approximate P-value for this test.

6.74 Find a P-value. You have performed a one-sided test of significance and obtained a value of $z = 0.35$. Use Table D to find the approximate P-value for this test.

6.75 What values will lead to rejection of H_0? You will perform a significance test of H_0: $\mu = 0$ versus H_a: $\mu > 0$.

(a) What values of z would lead you to reject H_0 at the 5% level?

(b) If the alternative hypothesis was H_a: $\mu \neq 0$, what values of z would lead you to reject H_0 at the 5% level?

(c) Explain why your answers to parts (a) and (b) are different.

6.76 Check the P-value. Between what critical values from Table D does the P-value for the outcome $z = -1.27$ in Exercise 6.71 lie? Calculate the P-value using Table A, and verify that it lies between the values you found from Table D.

6.77 Radon. Radon is a colorless, odorless gas that is naturally released by rocks and soils and may concentrate in tightly closed houses. Because radon is slightly radioactive, there is some concern that it may be a health hazard. Radon detectors are sold to homeowners worried about this risk, but the detectors may be inaccurate. University researchers placed 12 detectors in a chamber where they were exposed to 105 picocuries per liter (pCi/l) of radon over 3 days.[12] Here are the readings given by the detectors:

91.9	97.8	111.4	122.3	105.4	95.0
103.8	99.6	96.6	119.3	104.8	101.7

Assume (unrealistically) that you know that the standard deviation of readings for all detectors of this type is $\sigma = 9$.

(a) Give a 95% confidence interval for the mean reading μ for this type of detector.

(b) Is there significant evidence at the 5% level that the mean reading differs from the true value 105? State hypotheses and base a test on your confidence interval from (a).

6.78 Clothing for runners. Your company sells exercise clothing and equipment on the Internet. To design the clothing, you collect data on the physical characteristics of your different types of customers. Here are the weights for a sample of 24 male runners. Assume that these runners can be viewed as a random sample of your potential customers. The weights are expressed in kilograms.

67.8	61.9	63.0	53.1	62.3	59.7	55.4	58.9
60.9	69.2	63.7	68.3	64.7	65.6	56.0	57.8
66.0	62.9	53.6	65.0	55.8	60.4	69.3	61.7

Exercise 6.20 (page 375) asks you to find a 95% confidence interval for the mean weight of the population of all such runners, assuming that the population standard deviation is $\sigma = 4.5$ kg.

(a) Give the confidence interval from that exercise, or calculate the interval if you did not do the exercise.

(b) Based on this confidence interval, does a test of

$$H_0\text{: } \mu = 61.3 \text{ kg}$$
$$H_a\text{: } \mu \neq 61.3 \text{ kg}$$

reject H_0 at the 5% significance level?

(c) Would H_0: $\mu = 63$ be rejected at the 5% level if tested against a two-sided alternative?

6.79 Cockroaches. Your company is developing a better means to eliminate cockroaches from buildings. In the process, your research and development team studies the absorption of sugar by these insects.[13] They feed cockroaches a diet containing measured amounts of a particular sugar. After 10 hours, the cockroaches are killed and the concentration of the sugar in various body parts is determined by a chemical analysis. The paper that reports the research states that a 95% confidence interval for the mean amount (in milligrams) of the sugar in the hindguts of the cockroaches is 4.2 ± 2.3.

(a) Does this paper give evidence that the mean amount of sugar in the hindguts under these conditions is not equal to 7 mg? State H_0 and H_a and base a test on the confidence interval.

(b) Would the hypothesis that $\mu = 5$ mg be rejected at the 5% level in favor of a two-sided alternative?

6.80 Market pioneers. Market pioneers, companies that are among the first to develop a new product or service, tend to have higher market shares than latecomers to the market. What accounts for this advantage? Here is an excerpt from the conclusions of a study of a sample of 1209 manufacturers of industrial goods:

Can patent protection explain pioneer share advantages? Only 21% of the pioneers claim a significant benefit from either a product patent or a trade secret. Though their average share is two points higher than that of pioneers without this benefit, the increase is not statistically significant ($z = 1.13$). Thus, at least in mature industrial markets, product patents and trade secrets have little connection to pioneer share advantages.[14]

Find the P-value for the given z. Then explain to someone who knows no statistics what "not statistically significant" in the study's conclusion means. Why does the author conclude that patents and trade secrets don't help, even though they contributed 2 percentage points to average market share?

6.3 Using Significance Tests

Significance tests are widely used in reporting the results of research in many fields of applied science and in industry. New pharmaceutical products require significant evidence of effectiveness and safety. Courts inquire about statistical significance in hearing class action discrimination cases. Marketers want to know whether a new ad campaign significantly outperforms the old one, and medical researchers want to know whether a new therapy performs significantly better. In all these uses, statistical significance is valued because it points to an effect that is unlikely to occur simply by chance.

Carrying out a test of significance is often quite simple, especially if you get a P-value effortlessly from a calculator or computer. Using tests wisely is not so simple. Here are some points to keep in mind when using or interpreting significance tests.

How small a *P* is convincing?

The purpose of a test of significance is to describe the degree of evidence provided by the sample against the null hypothesis. The P-value does this. But how small a P-value is convincing evidence against the null hypothesis? This depends mainly on two circumstances:

- *How plausible is H_0?* If H_0 represents an assumption that the people you must convince have believed for years, strong evidence (small P) will be needed to persuade them.
- *What are the consequences of rejecting H_0?* If rejecting H_0 in favor of H_a means making an expensive changeover from one type of product packaging to another, you need strong evidence that the new packaging will boost sales.

These criteria are a bit subjective. Different people will often insist on different levels of significance. Giving the P-value allows each of us to decide individually if the evidence is sufficiently strong.

Users of statistics have often emphasized standard levels of significance such as 10%, 5%, and 1%. This emphasis reflects the time when tables of critical values rather than computer software dominated statistical practice. The 5% level ($\alpha = 0.05$) is particularly common. **There is no sharp border between "significant" and "insignificant," only increasingly strong evidence as the P-value decreases.** There is no practical distinction between the P-values 0.049 and 0.051. It makes no sense to treat $P \leq 0.05$ as a universal rule for what is significant.

APPLY YOUR KNOWLEDGE

6.81 Is it significant? More than 200,000 people worldwide take the GMAT examination each year as they apply for MBA programs. Their scores vary Normally with mean about $\mu = 525$ and standard deviation about $\sigma = 100$. One hundred students go through a rigorous training program designed to raise their GMAT scores. Test the hypotheses

$$H_0 : \mu = 525$$
$$H_a : \mu > 525$$

in each of the following situations:

(a) The students' average score is $\bar{x} = 541.4$. Is this result significant at the 5% level?

(b) The average score is $\bar{x} = 541.5$. Is this result significant at the 5% level?

The difference between the two outcomes in (a) and (b) is of no importance. Beware attempts to treat $\alpha = 0.05$ as sacred.

Statistical significance and practical significance

When a null hypothesis ("no effect" or "no difference") can be rejected at the usual levels, $\alpha = 0.05$ or $\alpha = 0.01$, there is good evidence that an effect is present. But that effect may be extremely small. When large samples are available, even tiny deviations from the null hypothesis will be significant.

EXAMPLE 6.21 It's Significant. So What?

We are testing the hypothesis of no correlation between two variables. With 1000 observations, an observed correlation of only $r = 0.08$ is significant evidence at the $\alpha = 0.01$ level that the correlation in the population is not zero but positive. The low significance level does not mean there is a strong association, only that there is strong evidence of some association. The true population correlation is probably quite close to the observed sample value, $r = 0.08$. We might well conclude, however, that for practical purposes we can ignore the association between these variables, even though we are confident (at the 1% level) that the correlation is positive.

Remember the wise saying: *statistical significance is not the same as practical significance.* On the other hand, if we fail to reject the null hypothesis, it may be because H_0 is true or because our sample size is insufficient to detect the alternative. Exercise 6.91 demonstrates in detail the effect on P of increasing the sample size.

The remedy for attaching too much importance to statistical significance is to pay attention to the actual experimental results as well as to the P-value. Plot your data and examine them carefully. Are there outliers or other deviations from a consistent pattern? A few outlying observations can produce highly significant results if you blindly apply common tests of significance. Outliers can also destroy the significance of otherwise-convincing data. The foolish user of statistics who feeds the data to a computer without exploratory analysis will often be embarrassed. Is the effect that you are seeking visible in your plots? If not, ask yourself if the effect is large enough to be of practical importance. It is usually wise to give a confidence interval for the parameter in which you are interested. A confidence interval actually estimates the size of an effect rather than simply asking if it is too large to reasonably occur by chance alone. Confidence intervals are not used as often as they should be, while tests of significance are perhaps overused.

APPLY YOUR KNOWLEDGE

6.82 How far do rich parents take us? How much education children get is strongly associated with the wealth and social status of their parents. In social science jargon, this is "socioeconomic status," or SES. But the SES of parents has little influence on whether children who have graduated from college go on to yet more education. One study looked at whether college graduates took the graduate admissions tests for business, law, and other graduate programs. The effects of the parents' SES on taking the LSAT test for law school were "both statistically insignificant and small."

(a) What does "statistically insignificant" mean?

(b) Why is it important that the effects were small in size as well as insignificant?

Statistical inference is not valid for all sets of data

We know that badly designed surveys or experiments often produce useless results. Formal statistical inference cannot correct basic flaws in the design. A statistical test is valid only in certain circumstances, with properly produced data being particularly important. The z test, for example, should bear the same warning label that we attached on page 371 to the z confidence interval. Similar warnings accompany the other tests that we will learn.

Tests of significance and confidence intervals are based on the laws of probability. Randomization in sampling or experimentation ensures that these laws apply. But we must often analyze data that do not arise from randomized samples or experiments. To apply statistical inference to such data, we must have confidence in a probability model for the data. The diameters of successive holes bored in auto engine blocks during production, for example, may behave like independent observations on a Normal distribution. We can check this probability model by examining the data. If the model appears correct, we can apply the recipes of this chapter to do inference about the process mean diameter μ. Do ask how the data were produced, and don't be too impressed by P-values on a printout until you are confident that the data deserve a formal analysis.

APPLY YOUR KNOWLEDGE

6.83 Give an example. Give an example of a set of data for which statistical inference is not valid.

Beware of searching for significance

Statistical significance ought to mean that you have found an effect that you were looking for. The reasoning behind statistical significance works well if you decide what effect you are seeking, design a study to search for it, and use a test of significance to weigh the evidence you get. In other settings, significance may have little meaning.

EXAMPLE 6.22 Cell Phones and Brain Cancer

Might the radiation from cell phones be harmful to users? Many studies have found little or no connection between using cell phones and various illnesses. Here is part of a news account of one study:

> A hospital study that compared brain cancer patients and a similar group without brain cancer found no statistically significant association between cell phone use and a group of brain cancers known as gliomas. But when 20 types of glioma were considered separately an association was found between phone use and one rare form. Puzzlingly, however, this risk appeared to decrease rather than increase with greater mobile phone use.[15]

Think for a moment: Suppose that the 20 null hypotheses for these 20 significance tests are all true. Then each test has a 5% chance of being significant at the 5% level. That's what $\alpha = 0.05$ means—results this extreme occur only 5% of the time just by chance when the null hypothesis is true. Because 5% is 1/20, we expect about 1 of 20 tests to give a significant result just by chance. Running 1 test and reaching the $\alpha = 0.05$ level is reasonably good evidence that you have found something; running 20 tests and reaching that level only once is not.

The peril of multiple analyses is increased now that a few simple commands will set software to work performing all manner of complicated tests and operations on your data. We will state it as a law that any large set of data—even several pages of a table of random digits—contains some unusual pattern. Sufficient computer time will discover that pattern, and when you test specifically for the pattern that turned up, the result will be significant. That's much like testing for 20 kinds of cancer and finding one test significant. The proper use of significance levels involves choosing one hypothesis before searching your data and then testing that one hypothesis.

Searching data for suggestive patterns is certainly legitimate. Exploratory data analysis is an important part of statistics. But the reasoning of formal inference does not apply when your search for a striking effect in the data is successful. The remedy is clear. Once you have a hypothesis, design a study to search specifically for the effect you now think is there. If the result of this study is statistically significant, you have real evidence.

APPLY YOUR KNOWLEDGE

6.84 Predicting success of trainees. What distinguishes managerial trainees who eventually become executives from those who, after expensive training, don't succeed and leave the company? We have abundant data on past trainees—data on their personalities and goals, their college preparation and performance, even their family backgrounds and their hobbies. Statistical software makes it easy to perform dozens of significance tests on these dozens of variables to see which ones best predict later success. We find that future executives are significantly more likely than washouts to have an urban or suburban upbringing and an undergraduate degree in a technical field.

Explain clearly why using these "significant" variables to select future trainees is not wise. Then suggest a follow-up study using this year's trainees as subjects that should clarify the importance of the variables identified by the first study.

SECTION 6.3 SUMMARY

- P-values are more informative than the reject-or-not result of a fixed level α test. Beware of placing too much weight on traditional values of α, such as $\alpha = 0.05$.

- Very small effects can be highly significant (small P), especially when a test is based on a large sample. A statistically significant effect need not be practically important. Plot the data to display the effect you are seeking, and use confidence intervals to estimate the actual value of parameters.
- On the other hand, lack of significance does not imply that H_0 is true, especially when the test is based on a small sample.
- Significance tests are not always valid. Faulty data collection, outliers in the data, and testing a hypothesis on the same data that suggested the hypothesis can invalidate a test. Many tests run at once will probably produce some significant results by chance alone, even if all the null hypotheses are true.

SECTION 6.3 Exercises

For Exercises 6.81, see page 399; for 6.82, see page 400; for 6.83, see page 400; and for 6.84, see page 401.

6.85 Your role on a team. You are the statistical expert on a team that is planning a study. After you have made a careful presentation of the mechanics of significance testing, one of the team members suggests using $\alpha = 0.50$ for the study because you would be more likely to obtain statistically significant results with this choice. Explain in simple terms why this would not be a good use of statistical methods.

6.86 What do you know? A research report described two results that both achieved statistical significance at the 5% level. The P-value for the first is 0.049; for the second it is 0.00002. Do the P-values add any useful information beyond that conveyed by the statement that both results are statistically significant? Write a short paragraph explaining your views on this question.

6.87 Find some journal articles. Find two journal articles that report results with statistical analyses. For each article, summarize how the results are reported and write a critique of the presentation. Be sure to include details regarding use of significance testing at a particular level of significance, P-values, and confidence intervals.

6.88 Discuss these views. State whether or not you agree with each of the following statements and provide a short summary of the reasons for your answers.

(a) If the P-vlaue is not less than 0.05, the null hypothesis is pfoven.

(b) Practical significance is not the same as statistical significance.

(c) With a sufficiently powerful computer, we can perform a statistical analysis for any set of data.

(d) If you find an interesting pattern in a set of data, it is appropriate to then use a significance test to determine if the pattern is due to chance.

6.89 Significance tests. Which of the following questions does a test of significance answer?

(a) Is the sample or experiment properly designed?

(b) Is the observed effect due to chance?

(c) Is the observed effect important?

6.90 Vitamin C and colds. In a study of the suggestion that taking vitamin C will prevent colds, 400 subjects are assigned at random to one of two groups. The experimental group takes a vitamin C tablet daily, while the control group takes a placebo. At the end of the experiment, the researchers calculate the difference between the percents of subjects in the two groups who were free of colds. This difference is statistically significant ($P = 0.03$) in favor of the vitamin C group. Can we conclude that vitamin C has a strong effect in preventing colds? Explain your answer.

6.91 Coaching for the SAT. Every user of statistics should understand the distinction between statistical significance and practical importance. A sufficiently large sample will declare very small effects statistically significant. Let us suppose that SAT Mathematics (SATM) scores in the absence of coaching vary Normally with mean $\mu = 515$ and $\sigma = 100$. Suppose further that coaching may change μ but does not change σ. An increase in the SATM score from 515 to 518 is of no importance in seeking admission to college, but this unimportant change can be statistically very significant. To see this, calculate the P-value for the test of

$$H_0\colon \mu = 515$$
$$H_a\colon \mu > 515$$

in each of the following situations:

(a) A coaching service coaches 100 students; their SATM scores average $\bar{x} = 518$.

(b) By the next year, the service has coached 1000 students; their SATM scores average $\bar{x} = 518$.

(c) An advertising campaign brings the number of students coached to 10,000; their average score is still $\bar{x} = 518$.

6.92 Coaching for the SAT. Give a 99% confidence interval for the mean SATM score μ after coaching in each part of the previous exercise. For large samples, the confidence interval says, "Yes, the mean score is higher after coaching, but only by a small amount."

6.93 Student loan poll. A local television station announces a question for a call-in opinion poll on the six o'clock news and then gives the response on the eleven o'clock news. Today's question concerns a proposed increase in funds for student loans. Of the 2372 calls received, 1921 oppose the increase. The station, following standard statistical practice, makes a confidence statement: "81% of the Channel 13 Pulse Poll sample oppose the increase. We can be 95% confident that the proportion of all viewers who oppose the increase is within 1.6% of the sample result." Is the station's conclusion justified? Explain your answer.

6.94 Extrasensory perception. A researcher looking for evidence of extrasensory perception (ESP) tests 500 subjects. Four of these subjects do significantly better ($P < 0.01$) than random guessing.

(a) Is it proper to conclude that these four people have ESP? Explain your answer.

(b) What should the researcher now do to test whether any of these four subjects have ESP?

6.95 More than one test. A P-value based on a single test is misleading if you perform several tests. The ***Bonferroni procedure*** gives a significance level for several tests together. Level α then means that if *all* the null hypotheses are true, the probability is α that *any* of the tests rejects its null hypothesis.

If you perform 2 tests and want to use the $\alpha = 5\%$ significance level, Bonferroni says to require a P-value of $0.05/2 = 0.025$ to declare either one of the tests significant. In general, if you perform k tests and want protection at level α, use α/k as your cutoff for statistical significance for each test.

You perform 6 tests and obtain individual P-values of 0.476, 0.032, 0.241, 0.008, 0.010, and 0.001. Which of these are statistically significant using the Bonferroni procedure with $\alpha = 0.05$?

6.96 More than one test. Refer to the previous exercise. A researcher has performed 12 tests of significance and wants to apply the Bonferroni procedure with $\alpha = 0.05$. The calculated P-values are 0.041, 0.569, 0.050, 0.416, 0.001, 0.004, 0.256, 0.041, 0.888, 0.010, 0.002, and 0.433. Which of these tests reject their null hypotheses with this procedure?

6.97 Many tests. Long ago, a group of psychologists carried out 77 separate significance tests and found that 2 were significant at the 5% level. Suppose that these tests are independent of each other. (In fact, they were not independent, because all involved the same subjects.) If all of the null hypotheses are true, each test has probability 0.05 of being significant at the 5% level.

(a) What is the distribution of the number X of tests that are significant?

(b) Find the probability that 2 or more of the tests are significant.

6.4 Power and Inference as a Decision*

Although we prefer to use P-values rather than the reject-or-not view of the fixed α significance test, the latter view is important for planning statistical studies. We will first explain why, then discuss different views of statistical tests.

The power of a statistical test

In examining the usefulness of a confidence interval, we are concerned with both the level of confidence and the margin of error. The confidence level tells us how reliable the method is in repeated use. The margin of error tells us how sensitive the method is, that is, how closely the interval pins down the parameter being estimated. Fixed level

*Although the topics in this section are important in planning and interpreting significance tests, they can be omitted without loss of continuity.

α significance tests are closely related to confidence intervals—in fact, we saw that a two-sided test can be carried out directly from a confidence interval. The significance level, like the confidence level, says how reliable the method is in repeated use. If we use 5% significance tests repeatedly when H_0 is in fact true, we will be wrong (the test will reject H_0) 5% of the time and right (the test will fail to reject H_0) 95% of the time.

High confidence is of little value if the interval is so wide that few values of the parameter are excluded. Similarly, a test with a small level of α is of little value if it almost never rejects H_0 even when the true parameter value is far from the hypothesized value. We must be concerned with the ability of a test to detect that H_0 is false, just as we are concerned with the margin of error of a confidence interval. This ability is measured by the probability that the test will reject H_0 when an alternative is true. The higher this probability is, the more sensitive the test is.

Power

The probability that a fixed level α significance test will reject H_0 when a particular alternative value of the parameter is true is called the **power** of the test.

EXAMPLE 6.23 Exercise and Bones

Can a 6-month exercise program increase the total body bone mineral content (TBBMC) of young women? A team of researchers is planning a study to examine this question. Based on the results of a previous study, they are willing to assume that $\sigma = 2$ for the percent change in TBBMC over the 6-month period. A change in TBBMC of 1% would be considered important, and the researchers would like to have a reasonable chance of detecting a change this large or larger. Are 25 subjects a large enough sample for this project?

We will answer this question by calculating the power of the significance test that will be used to evaluate the data to be collected. The calculation consists of three steps:

1. State H_0, H_a (the particular alternative we want to detect), and the significance level α.
2. Find the values of $\bar{x}$ that will lead us to reject H_0.
3. Calculate the probability of observing these values of $\bar{x}$ when the alternative is true.

Step 1. The null hypothesis is that the exercise program has no effect on TBBMC. In other words, the mean percent change is zero. The alternative is that exercise is beneficial; that is, the mean change is positive. Formally, we have

$$H_0: \mu = 0$$
$$H_a: \mu > 0$$

The alternative of interest is $\mu = 1\%$ increase in TBBMC. A 5% test of significance will be used.

Step 2. The z test rejects H_0 at the $\alpha = 0.05$ level whenever

$$z = \frac{\bar{x} - \mu_0}{\sigma/\sqrt{n}} = \frac{\bar{x} - 0}{2/\sqrt{25}} \geq 1.645$$

Be sure you understand why we use 1.645. Rewrite this in terms of $\bar{x}$:

$$\text{reject } H_0 \text{ when } \bar{x} \geq 1.645\frac{2}{\sqrt{25}}$$

$$\text{reject } H_0 \text{ when } \bar{x} \geq 0.658$$

Because the significance level is $\alpha = 0.05$, this event has probability 0.05 of occurring *when the population mean μ is 0.*

Step 3. The power for the alternative $\mu = 1\%$ increase in TBBMC is the probability that H_0 will be rejected *when in fact $\mu = 1$.* We calculate this probability by standardizing $\bar{x}$, using the value $\mu = 1$, the population standard deviation $\sigma = 2$, and the sample size $n = 25$. The power is

$$P(\bar{x} \geq 0.658 \quad \text{when} \quad \mu = 1) = P\left(\frac{\bar{x} - \mu}{\sigma/\sqrt{n}} \geq \frac{0.658 - 1}{2/\sqrt{25}}\right)$$

$$= P(Z \geq -0.855) = 0.80$$

Figure 6.17 illustrates the power with the sampling distribution of $\bar{x}$ when $\mu = 1$. This significance test rejects the null hypothesis that exercise has no effect on TBBMC 80% of the time if the true effect of exercise is a 1% increase in TBBMC. If the true

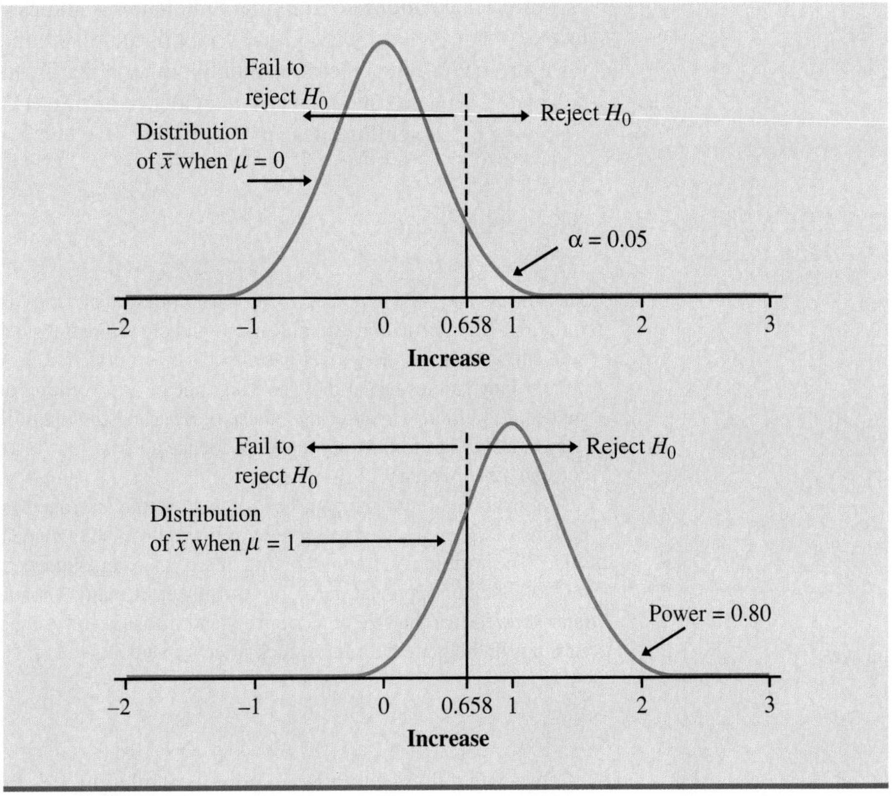

FIGURE 6.17 The sampling distributions of $\bar{x}$ when $\mu = 0$ and when $\mu = 1$ with α and the power. Power is the probability that the test rejects H_0 when the alternative is true.

effect of exercise is greater than a 1% increase, the test will have greater power; it will reject with a higher probability.

High power is desirable. Along with 95% confidence intervals and 5% significance tests, 80% power is becoming a standard. Many U.S. government agencies that provide research funds require that the sample size for the funded studies be sufficient to detect important results 80% of the time using a 5% test of significance.

Increasing the power

Suppose you have performed a power calculation and found that the power is too small. What can you do to increase it? Here are four ways:

- Increase α. A 5% test of significance will have a greater chance of rejecting the alternative than a 1% test because the strength of evidence required for rejection is less.
- Consider a particular alternative that is farther away from μ_0. Values of μ that are in H_a but lie close to the hypothesized value μ_0 are harder to detect (lower power) than values of μ that are far from μ_0.
- Increase the sample size. More data will provide more information about $\bar{x}$ so we have a better chance of distinguishing values of μ.
- Decrease σ. This has the same effect as increasing the sample size: more information about μ. Improving the measurement process and restricting attention to a subpopulation are two common ways to decrease σ.

Power calculations are important in planning studies. Using a significance test with low power makes it unlikely that you will find a significant effect even if the truth is far from the null hypothesis. A null hypothesis that is in fact false can become widely believed if repeated attempts to find evidence against it fail because of low power. The following example illustrates this point.

EXAMPLE 6.24 Are Stock Markets Efficient?

The "efficient market hypothesis" for stock prices says that future stock prices show only random variation. No information available now will help us predict stock prices in the future, because the efficient working of the market has already incorporated all available information in the present price. Many studies tested the claim that one or another kind of information is helpful. In these studies, the efficient market hypothesis is H_0, and the claim that prediction is possible is H_a. Almost all studies failed to find good evidence against H_0. As a result, the efficient market theory became quite popular.

An examination of the significance tests employed found that the power was generally low. Failure to reject H_0 when using tests of low power is not evidence that H_0 is true. As one expert said, "The widespread impression that there is strong evidence for market efficiency may be due just to a lack of appreciation of the low power of many statistical tests."[16] More careful studies later showed that the size of a company and measures of value such as the ratio of stock price to earnings do help predict future stock price movements.

Here is another example of a power calculation, this time for a two-sided z test.

pharmacies. About 45% of consumers make such purchases at pharmacies. What accounts for the popularity of pharmacies, which often charge higher prices?

A study examined consumers' perceptions of overall performance of the three types of store using a long questionnaire that asked about such things as "neat and attractive store," "knowledgeable staff," and "assistance in choosing among various types of nonprescription medication." A performance score was based on 27 such questions. The subjects were 201 people chosen at random from the Indianapolis telephone directory. Here are the means and standard deviations of the performance scores for the sample:[21]

Store type	$\bar{x}$	s
Food stores	18.67	24.95
Mass merchandisers	32.38	33.37
Pharmacies	48.60	35.62

We do not know the population standard deviations, but a sample standard deviation s from so large a sample is usually close to σ. Use s in place of the unknown σ in this exercise.

(a) What population do you think the authors of the study want to draw conclusions about? What population are you certain they can draw conclusions about?

(b) Give 95% confidence intervals for the mean performance for each type of store.

(c) Based on these confidence intervals, are you convinced that consumers think that pharmacies offer higher performance than the other types of stores? In Chapter 12 we will study a statistical method for comparing the means of several groups.

6.122 **CEO pay.** A study of the pay of corporate chief executive officers (CEOs) examined the increase in cash compensation of the CEOs of 104 companies, adjusted for inflation, in a recent year. The mean increase in real compensation was $\bar{x} = 6.9\%$, and the standard deviation of the increases was $s = 55\%$. Is this good evidence that the mean real compensation μ of all CEOs increased that year? The hypotheses are

$$H_0: \mu = 0 \quad \text{(no increase)}$$

$$H_a: \mu > 0 \quad \text{(an increase)}$$

Because the sample size is large, the sample s is close to the population σ, so take $\sigma = 55\%$.

(a) Sketch the Normal curve for the sampling distribution of $\bar{x}$ when H_0 is true. Shade the area that represents the P-value for the observed outcome $\bar{x} = 6.9\%$.

(b) Calculate the P-value.

(c) Is the result significant at the $\alpha = 0.05$ level? Do you think the study gives strong evidence that the mean compensation of all CEOs went up?

6.123 **Large samples.** Statisticians prefer large samples. Describe briefly the effect of increasing the size of a sample (or the number of subjects in an experiment) on each of the following.

(a) The width of a level C confidence interval.

(b) The P-value of a test, when H_0 is false and all facts about the population remain unchanged as n increases.

(c) The power of a fixed level α test, when α, the alternative hypothesis, and all facts about the population remain unchanged.

6.124 **Roulette.** A roulette wheel has 18 red slots among its 38 slots. You observe many spins and record the number of times that red occurs. Now you want to use these data to test whether the probability of a red has the value that is correct for a fair roulette wheel. State the hypotheses H_0 and H_a that you will test. (We will describe the test for this situation in Chapter 8.)

6.125 **Significant.** When asked to explain the meaning of "statistically significant at the $\alpha = 0.05$ level," a student says, "This means there is only probability 0.05 that the null hypothesis is true." Is this a correct explanation of statistical significance? Explain your answer.

6.126 **Significant.** Another student, when asked why statistical significance appears so often in research reports, says, "Because saying that results are significant tells us that they cannot easily be explained by chance variation alone." Do you think that this statement is essentially correct? Explain your answer.

6.127 **Welfare reform.** A study compares two groups of mothers with young children who were on welfare two years ago. One group attended a voluntary training program offered free of charge at a local vocational school and advertised in the local news media. The other group did not choose to attend the training program. The study finds a significant difference ($P < 0.01$) between the proportions of the mothers in the two groups who are still on welfare. The difference is not only significant but quite large. The report says that with 95% confidence the percent of the nonattending group still on welfare is $21\% \pm 4\%$ higher than that of the group who attended the program. You are on the staff of a member of

Congress who is interested in the plight of welfare mothers and who asks you about the report.

(a) Explain briefly and in nontechnical language what "a significant difference ($P < 0.01$)" means.

(b) Explain clearly and briefly what "95% confidence" means.

(c) Is this study good evidence that requiring job training of all welfare mothers would greatly reduce the percent who remain on welfare for several years?

6.128 Simulation. Use a computer to generate $n = 5$ observations from the Normal distribution $N(20, 5)$. Find the 95% confidence interval for μ. Repeat this process 100 times and then count the number of times that the confidence interval includes the value $\mu = 20$. Explain your results.

6.129 Simulation. Use a computer to generate $n = 5$ observations from the Normal distribution $N(20, 5)$. Test H_0: $\mu = 20$ versus H_a: $\mu \neq 20$ at the $\alpha = 0.05$ significance level. Repeat this process 100 times and then count the number of times that you reject H_0. Explain your results.

6.130 Simulation. Use the same procedure for generating data as in the previous exercise. Now test the null hypothesis that $\mu = 22.5$. Explain your results.

6.131 Simulation. Figure 6.5 (page 365) demonstrates the behavior of a confidence interval in repeated sampling by showing the results of 25 samples from the same population. Now you will do a similar demonstration, though in an artificial setting. Suppose that the net assets of a large population of community banks follow the uniform distribution between -20 and 500 (in millions of dollars). Then the mean assets of these banks are $\mu = 240$ and the standard deviation is $\sigma = 150$.

(a) Simulate the drawing of 25 SRSs of size $n = 100$ from this population.

(b) For calculating the confidence intervals, you are willing to assume that the sample means are approximately Normal. Explain why this is a reasonable assumption.

(c) The 50% confidence interval for the population mean μ has the form $\bar{x} \pm m$. What is the margin of error m? (Use 150 for the standard deviation.)

(d) Use your software to calculate the 50% confidence interval for μ for each of your 25 samples. Verify the computer's calculations by checking the interval given for the first sample against your result in (b). Use the $\bar{x}$ reported by the software.

(e) How many of the 25 confidence intervals contain the true mean $\mu = 240$? If you repeated the simulation, would you expect exactly the same number of intervals to contain μ? In a very large number of samples, what percent of the confidence intervals would contain μ?

6.132 Simulation. In the previous exercise you simulated the assets of 25 SRSs of 100 community banks. Now use these samples to demonstrate the behavior of a significance test. We know that the population standard deviation is $\sigma = 150$, and we are willing to assume that the sample means are approximately Normal.

(a) Use your software to carry out a test of

$$H_0: \mu = 240$$
$$H_a: \mu \neq 240$$

for each of the 25 samples.

(b) Verify the computer's calculations by using Table A to find the P-value of the test for the first of your samples. Use the $\bar{x}$ reported by your software.

(c) How many of your 25 tests reject the null hypothesis at the $\alpha = 0.05$ significance level? (That is, how many have P-value 0.05 or smaller?)

(d) Because the simulation was done with $\mu = 240$, samples that lead to rejecting H_0 produce the wrong conclusion. In a very large number of samples, what percent would falsely reject the hypothesis?

CHAPTER 6 Case Study Exercises

CASE STUDY EXERCISE 1: Older customers in restaurants. Persons aged 55 and over represented 21.3% of the U.S. population in the year 2000. This group is expected to increase to 30.5% by 2025. In terms of actual numbers of people, the increase is from 58.6 million to 101.4 million. Restaurateurs have found this market to be important and would like to make their businesses attractive to older customers. One study used a questionnaire to collect data from people aged 50 and over.[22] For one part of the analysis, individuals were classified into two age groups: 50–64 and 65–79. There were 267 people in the first group and 263 in the second. One set of items concerned ambience, menu design, and service. A series of statements were rated on a 1 to 5 scale with 1 representing "strongly disagree" and 5 representing "strongly agree." In some cases the wording of questions has been shortened in the table below. Here are the means:

Question	50–64	65–79
Ambience		
Most restaurants are too dark	2.75	2.93
Most restaurants are too noisy	3.33	3.43
Background music is often too loud	3.27	3.55
Restaurants are too smoky	3.17	3.12
Tables are too small	3.00	3.19
Tables are too close together	3.79	3.81
Menu design		
Print size is not large enough	3.68	3.77
Glare makes menus difficult to read	2.81	3.01
Colors of menus make them difficult to read	2.53	2.72
Service		
It is difficult to hear the service staff	2.65	3.00
I would rather be served than serve myself	4.23	4.14
I would rather pay the server than a cashier	3.88	3.48
Service is too slow	3.13	3.10

First examine the means of the people who are 50 to 64. Order the statements according to the means and describe the results. Then do the same for the older group. For each statement compute the z statistic and the associated P-value for the comparison between the two groups. For these calculations you can assume that the denominator in the test statistic is 0.08, so z is simply the difference in the means divided by 0.08. Note that you are performing 13 significance tests in this exercise. Keep this in mind when you interpret your results. Write a report summarizing your work.

CASE STUDY EXERCISE 2: Accessibility concerns. Refer to the previous question. The questionnaire also asked about accessibility both inside the restaurant and outside. Analyze the following data and write a report.

Question	50–64	65–79
Accessibility and comfort inside		
Most chairs are too small	2.49	2.56
Bench seats are usually too narrow	3.03	3.25
Salad bars and buffets are difficult to reach	3.04	3.09
Serving myself from salad bars and buffets is difficult	2.58	2.75
Floors around salad bars and buffets are often slippery	2.84	3.01
Aisles are too narrow	3.04	3.20
Bathroom stalls are too narrow	2.82	3.10
Outside accessibility		
Doors are too heavy	2.51	3.01
Curbs near entrance are difficult	2.54	3.07
Parking spaces are too narrow	2.83	3.16
Distance from parking lot is too far	2.33	2.64
Parking lots are too dark at night	2.84	3.26

CHAPTER 6 Appendix

Using Minitab and Excel for Inference for the Mean (σ Known)

Confidence Interval

Minitab:

Stat ➤ Basic Statistics ➤ 1-Sample Z

If the sample data are in the worksheet, then choose the **Samples in columns** option and then click-in the column containing the data into the box below. With this option, you can construct confidences intervals for more than one data set simultaneously. Alternatively, if you know the value of the sample mean, you can choose the **Summarized data** option and input the sample mean and sample size in the boxes found below. Since this routine assumes that the population standard deviation (σ) is known, you need to input its value in the **Standard deviation** box. In default mode, Minitab will construct a 95% confidence interval. If you wish to change the level of confidence, click the **Options** button and input your desired confidence level in the **Confidence level** box. Click **OK** to close the pop-up box and then click **OK** to find the confidence interval along with some basic statistics, which are reported in the Session window.

Excel:

Excel does not have a routine for reporting the lower and upper limits of a confidence interval for the mean. However, you can use Excel to compute the margin of error, which can then be subtracted and added to the sample mean to get the confidence interval. To compute the margin of error, click an empty cell in the spreadsheet and then proceed to the **Statistical** function menu as described in the overview section of Chapter 1's Appendix. Scroll down the list of functions and click on the **CONFIDENCE** function choice. In the **Alpha** box, input the value of α (for example, 0.05) to obtain a $(1 - \alpha)$ confidence interval. In the **Standard_dev** box, input the known population standard deviation (σ). In the **Size** box, input the sample size and then click **OK.**

Tests of Significance

Minitab:

Stat ➤ Basic Statistics ➤ 1-Sample Z

This is the same routine described in this Appendix for obtaining the confidence interval for the mean. If you wish to conduct a hypothesis test, select the **Perform hypothesis test** option and input the null hypothesis mean value (μ_0) in the box below. In default mode, Minitab will assume a two-sided alternative. If you wish to have a one-sided alternative, click the **Options** button and choose either the "Less than" or "Greater than" alternative hypothesis choices. Click **OK** to close the pop-up box and then click **OK** to find the test statistic and corresponding P-value, which are reported in the Session window.

Excel:

To conduct a test of the mean with known population standard deviation, Excel provides a statistical function that will report the P-value for a one-sided, greater-than alternative hypothesis. To obtain this P-value, click an empty cell in the spreadsheet and then proceed to the **Statistical** function menu as described in the overview section of Chapter 1's Appendix. Scroll down the list of functions and click on the **ZTEST** function choice. In the **Array** box, input the cell range of the data. In the **X** box, input the null hypothesis mean value (μ_0). In the **Sigma** box, input the known population standard deviation (σ). Click **OK** to find the P-value, which is reported in the selected cell. If your alternative hypothesis is a less-than alternative, subtract the reported P-value from 1 to obtain the appropriate P-value. For a two-sided alternative, if the reported P-value is less than 0.5, you should double it; otherwise, you should double (1 − reported P-value).

Power

Minitab:

Stat ➤ Power and Sample Size ➤ 1-Sample Z

After invoking this routine, you can specify values for any two of the following three dialog boxes: **Sample sizes, Differences,** or **Power values.** Minitab will then compute the item not specified. For example, if you wish to compute the power of a test, input the sample size and the difference between the mean value of the particular alternative of interest (μ) and the null hypothesis mean value (μ_0), that is, $\mu - \mu_0$. In the case of Example 6.25, you would input "3" in the **Sample sizes** box and "-0.015" ($= 0.845 - 0.86$) in the **Differences** box. This routine can also be used to determine what minimal sample size is required to have a desired power in relation to a particular alternative. In addition to providing values for two of the three dialog boxes, you must input the known population standard deviation (σ) in the **Standard deviation** box. In default mode, Minitab will assume a two-sided alternative. If you wish to have a one-sided alternative, click the **Options** button and choose either the "Less than" or the "Greater than" alternative hypothesis choices. In addition, if you wish to change the value of α from the default value of 0.05, then input your desired significance level in the **Significance level** box. Click **OK** to close the pop-up box and then click **OK** to find the results, which are reported in the Session window. Additionally, Minitab will produce a "Power Curve," which is simply a graph of the different power values against a range of difference values.

Excel:

Automated power calculations are not available in standard Excel or the enhanced add-on version of Excel. To compute power in Excel, follow the general steps for computing power described in this chapter and then use Excel's **NORMSDIST** function to compute probabilities from the Normal distribution (refer to Chapter 1's Appendix for details on using the **NORMSDIST** function).

(b) The sample size is 5. Is the test result significant at the 5% level?

(c) Sketch the two t distributions to illustrate your answers.

7.7 Have sales changed? You will have complete sales information for last month in a week, but right now you have data from a random sample of 50 stores. The mean change in sales in the sample is +4.9%, and the standard deviation of the changes is 14%. Are average sales for all stores different from last month?

(a) State appropriate null and alternative hypotheses. Explain how you decided between the one- and two-sided alternatives.

(b) Find the t statistic and its P-value. State your conclusion.

(c) If the test gives strong evidence against the null hypothesis, would you conclude that sales are up in every one of your stores? Explain your answer.

Using software

For small data sets such as the one in Example 7.1 it is easy to perform the computations for confidence intervals and significance tests with an ordinary calculator. For larger data sets, however, software or a statistical calculator eases our work.

EXAMPLE 7.4 Diversify or Be Sued

An investor with a stock portfolio worth several hundred thousand dollars sued his broker and brokerage firm because lack of diversification in his portfolio led to poor performance. Table 7.1 gives the rates of return for the 39 months that the account was managed by the broker.[3] The arbitration panel compared these returns with the average of the S&P 500 for the same period. Consider the 39 monthly returns as a random sample from the population of monthly returns the brokerage would generate if it managed the account forever. Are these returns compatible with a population mean of $\mu = 0.95\%$, the S&P 500 average? Our hypotheses are

$$H_0\colon \mu = 0.95$$

$$H_a\colon \mu \neq 0.95$$

Minitab and SPSS outputs appear in Figure 7.4. Output from other software will look similar.

Here is one way to report the conclusion: the mean monthly return on investment for this client's account was $\bar{x} = -1.1\%$. This differs significantly from the performance of the S&P 500 for the same period ($t = -2.14$, df $= 38$, $P < 0.039$).

The hypothesis test in Example 7.4 leads us to conclude that the mean return on the client's account differs from that of the stock index. Now let's assess the return on the client's account with a confidence interval.

TABLE 7.1 Monthly rates of return on a portfolio (percent)

−8.36	1.63	−2.27	−2.93	−2.70	−2.93	−9.14	−2.64
6.82	−2.35	−3.58	6.13	7.00	−15.25	−8.66	−1.03
−9.16	−1.25	−1.22	−10.27	−5.11	−0.80	−1.44	1.28
−0.65	4.34	12.22	−7.21	−0.09	7.34	5.04	−7.24
−2.14	−1.01	−1.41	12.03	−2.56	4.33	2.35	

FIGURE 7.4 Minitab and SPSS output for Example 7.4.

Minitab

```
Test of mu = 0.95 vs not = 0.95

Variable   N    Mean  StDev  SE Mean        95% CI               T      P
RETURN    39  -1.100  5.991    0.959  (-3.042, 0.842)  -2.14  0.039
```

SPSS

One-Sample Test

	Test Value =0.95					
	t	df	Sig. (2-tailed)	Mean Difference	95% Confidence Interval of the Difference Lower	Upper
RETURN	-2.137	38	.039	-2.0497	-3.9918	-.1077

EXAMPLE 7.5 Estimating Mean Monthly Return

The mean monthly return on the client's portfolio was $\overline{x} = -1.1\%$ and the standard deviation was $s = 5.99\%$. Figure 7.5 gives the Minitab, SPSS, and Excel output for a 95% confidence interval for the population mean μ. Note that Excel gives the margin of error next to the label "Confidence Level(95.0%)" rather than the actual confidence interval. We see that the 95% confidence interval is $(-3.04,\ 0.84)$, or (from Excel) -1.0997 ± 1.9420.

Because the S&P 500 return, 0.95%, falls outside this interval, we know that μ differs significantly from 0.95% at the $\alpha = 0.05$ level. Example 7.4 gave the actual P-value as $P < 0.039$.

The confidence interval suggests that the broker's management of this account had a long-term mean somewhere between a loss of 3.04% and a gain of 0.84% per month. We are interested not in the actual mean but in the difference between the broker's process and the diversified S&P 500 index.

EXAMPLE 7.6 Estimating Difference from a Standard

Following the analysis accepted by the arbitration panel, we are considering the S&P 500 monthly average return as a constant standard. (It is easy to envision scenarios where we would want to treat this type of quantity as random.) The difference between the mean of the investor's account and the S&P 500 is $\overline{x} - \mu = -1.10 - 0.95 = -2.05\%$. In Example 7.5 we found that the 95% confidence interval for the investor's account was $(-3.04,\ 0.84)$. To obtain the corresponding interval for the difference, subtract 0.95 from each of the endpoints. The resulting interval is $(-3.04 - 0.95,\ 0.84 - 0.95)$, or $(-3.99,\ -0.11)$. We conclude with 95% confidence that the underperformance was between -3.99% and -0.11%. This estimate helps to set the compensation owed the investor.

FIGURE 7.5 Minitab, SPSS, and Excel output for Example 7.5.

Minitab

Variable	N	Mean	StDev	SE Mean	95% CI
RETURN	39	-1.100	5.991	0.959	(-3.042, 0.842)

SPSS

Descriptives

			Statistic	Std. Error
RETURN	Mean		-1.0997	0.9593
	95% Confidence Interval for Mean	Lower Bound	-3.0418	
		Upper Bound	0.8423	

RETURN	
Mean	-1.09974359
Standard Error	0.95930991
Median	-1.41
Mode	-2.93
Standard Deviation	5.990888471
Sample Variance	35.89074467
Kurtosis	0.226609438
Skewness	0.158971057
Range	27.47
Minimum	-15.25
Maximum	12.22
Sum	-42.89
Count	39
Confidence Level (95.0%)	1.942021368

APPLY YOUR KNOWLEDGE

7.8 Use software for the vitamin C confidence interval. In Example 7.1 (page 427) we calculated the 95% confidence interval for the mean vitamin C content for a production run of CSB. Use software to compute this interval and verify that you obtain the same interval. Is your software easy to use?

7.9 What does the t distribution look like when n is large? You are using software to calculate t procedures for a large sample, n greater than 5000.

(a) For a two-sided test, how large must the t statistic be to reach significance at the 1% level? (Note that either a large positive number or a large negative number will be significant.)

(b) In which row of Table D did you find your result in part (a)? What general fact about the t distributions does this illustrate?

Matched pairs *t* procedures

The CSB production problem of Case 7.1 concerns only a single population. We know that comparative studies are usually preferred to single-sample investigations because of the protection they offer against confounding. For that reason, inference about a parameter of a single distribution is less common than comparative inference. One common comparative design, however, makes use of single-sample procedures. In a **matched pairs** study, subjects are matched in pairs and the outcomes are compared within each matched pair. The experimenter can toss a coin to assign two treatments to the two subjects in each pair. Matched pairs are also common when randomization is not possible. One situation calling for matched pairs is before-and-after observations on the same subjects, as illustrated in the next example.

matched pairs

EXAMPLE 7.7 The Effects of Language Instruction

A company contracts with a language institute to provide individualized instruction in foreign languages for its executives who will be posted overseas. Is the instruction effective?

Last year, 20 executives studied French. All had some knowledge of French, so they were given the Modern Language Association's listening test of understanding of spoken French before the instruction began. After several weeks of immersion in French, the executives took the listening test again. (The actual French spoken in the two tests was different, so that simply taking the first test should not improve the score on the second test.) Table 7.2 gives the pretest and posttest scores. The maximum possible score on the test is 36.[4] To analyze these data, subtract the pretest score from the posttest score to obtain the improvement for each executive. These 20 differences form a single sample. They appear in the "Gain" columns in Table 7.2. The first executive, for example, improved from 32 to 34, so the gain is $34 - 32 = 2$.

To assess whether the institute significantly improved the executives' comprehension of spoken French, we test

$$H_0: \mu = 0$$
$$H_a: \mu > 0$$

Here μ is the mean improvement that would be achieved if the entire population of executives received similar instruction. The null hypothesis says that no improvement occurs, and H_a says that posttest scores are higher on the average.

TABLE 7.2 French listening scores for executives

Executive	Pretest	Posttest	Gain	Executive	Pretest	Posttest	Gain
1	32	34	2	11	30	36	6
2	31	31	0	12	20	26	6
3	29	35	6	13	24	27	3
4	10	16	6	14	24	24	0
5	30	33	3	15	31	32	1
6	33	36	3	16	30	31	1
7	22	24	2	17	15	15	0
8	25	28	3	18	32	34	2
9	32	26	−6	19	23	26	3
10	20	26	6	20	23	26	3

The 20 differences have

$$\bar{x} = 2.5 \quad \text{and} \quad s = 2.893$$

The one-sample t statistic is therefore

$$t = \frac{\bar{x} - 0}{s/\sqrt{n}} = \frac{2.5}{2.893/\sqrt{20}}$$
$$= 3.86$$

df = 19		
p	0.001	0.0005
t^*	3.579	3.883

The P-value is found from the $t(19)$ distribution. Remember that the degrees of freedom are 1 less than the sample size. Table D shows that 3.86 lies between the upper 0.001 and 0.0005 critical values of the $t(19)$ distribution. The P-value therefore lies between these values. Software gives the value $P = 0.00053$. The improvement in listening scores is very unlikely to be due to chance alone. We have strong evidence that the posttest scores are systematically higher. In scholarly writing it is usual to omit the details of routine statistical procedures; our test would be reported in the form: "The improvement in scores was significant ($t = 3.86$, df = 19, $P = 0.00053$)."

The significance test shows that the mean score has improved. A critic could argue that the test does not show that the instruction *caused* the improvement—for example, the executives might simply be less nervous when taking the test a second time. A more elaborate study with a control group who receive no instruction would be more convincing, but the company is unlikely to assign executives to "no instruction." Also note that the subjects all knew that they would receive overseas assignments. Our conclusions apply only to the population of such executives, not to the larger population of all the company's managers.

A statistically significant but very small improvement in language ability would not justify the expense of the individualized instruction. A confidence interval allows us to estimate the *amount* of the improvement.

EXAMPLE 7.8 The Effects of Language Instruction

Let's compute a 90% confidence interval for the mean improvement in the entire population. The standard error is

$$\text{SE} = \frac{s}{\sqrt{n}} = \frac{2.893}{\sqrt{20}} = 0.6469$$

The margin of error is

$$\text{MOE} = t^*\text{SE} = (1.729)(0.6469) = 1.12$$

where the critical value $t^* = 1.729$ comes from Table D. The confidence interval is

$$\bar{x} \pm \text{MOE} = 2.5 \pm 1.12$$
$$= (1.38,\ 3.62)$$

The estimated average improvement is 2.5 points, with margin of error 1.12 for 90% confidence. Though statistically significant, the effect of the instruction was rather small.

A look at the data discloses one reason for the small average improvement. Several of the executives had pretest scores close to the maximum of 36. They could not improve their scores very much even if their mastery of French increased substantially. This is a weakness in the listening test that is the measuring instrument in this study.

Here are some key points to remember concerning matched pairs:

- A matched pairs analysis is needed when there are two measurements or observations on each individual or experimental unit and our question of interest concerns the difference between the two measurements. Frequently, the observations are "before" and "after" measures in some sense.
- The analysis is based on the difference between the two measures for each individual or experimental unit.
- Analyze the differences using the one-sample confidence interval and significance-testing procedures that we learned in this section.

APPLY YOUR KNOWLEDGE

7.10 Does the product lose value when cooked? CASE 7.1 The researchers studying vitamin C in CSB in Case 7.1 were also interested in a similar commodity called wheat-soy blend (WSB). Both CSB and WSB are mixed with other ingredients and cooked. Cooking can cause loss of vitamin C. In Haiti, gruel ("bouillie" in Creole) is made from WSB, sugar, milk, bananas, and seasonings. The researchers collected specimens of gruel prepared in Haitian households and measured the vitamin C content before and after cooking. Here are the results (milligrams per 100 grams of blend, dry basis):

Household	1	2	3	4	5
Before	73	79	86	88	78
After	20	27	29	36	17

It is not possible for cooking to increase the amount of vitamin C. State appropriate hypotheses and carry out a matched pairs t test for these data.

7.11 How much loss? CASE 7.1 Exercise 7.10 demonstrates that cooking reduces the vitamin C content of food made with wheat-soy blend. This fact is neither new nor surprising. The real question is how much vitamin C is lost. Use the data in Exercise 7.10 to give a 95% confidence interval for the amount of vitamin C lost in preparing and cooking gruel in Haiti.

Robustness of the t procedures

The matched pairs t procedures use one-sample t confidence intervals and significance tests for differences. They are therefore based on an assumption that the population of differences has a Normal distribution. Look carefully at the gain scores in Table 7.2. One executive actually lost 6 points between the pretest and the posttest. This one subject lowered the sample mean from 2.95 for the other 19 subjects to 2.5 for all 20. A Normal quantile plot (Figure 7.6) displays this outlier as well as granularity due to the fact that only whole-number scores are possible. The data do not appear to be Normal. Does this non-Normality suggest that we should not use the t procedures for these data?

The results of one-sample t procedures are exactly correct only when the population is Normal. Real populations are never exactly Normal. All inference procedures are based on some conditions, such as Normality: procedures that are not strongly affected by violations of a condition are called *robust*.

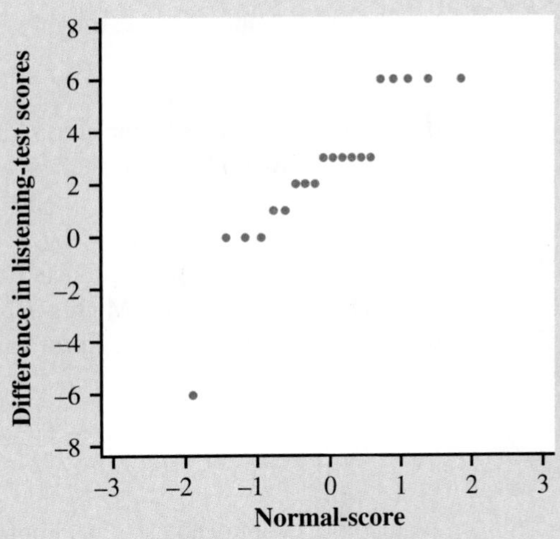

FIGURE 7.6 Normal quantile plot for the change in French listening score.

Robust Procedures

A statistical inference procedure is called **robust** if the probability calculations required are insensitive to violations of the conditions that usually justify the procedure.

The condition that the population be Normal rules out outliers, so the presence of outliers shows that this condition is not fulfilled. The t procedures are not robust against outliers, because $\overline{x}$ and s are not resistant to outliers.

Fortunately, the t procedures are quite robust against non-Normality of the population except when outliers or strong skewness are present, particularly when the sample size is large. The t procedures rely only on the Normality of the sample mean $\overline{x}$. This condition is satisfied when the population is Normal, but the central limit theorem tells us that a mean $\overline{x}$ from a large sample follows a Normal distribution closely even when individual observations are not Normally distributed.

Before using the t procedures for small samples, make a Normal quantile plot, stemplot, or boxplot to check for skewness and outliers. For most purposes, the one-sample t procedures can be safely used when $n \geq 15$ unless an outlier or clearly marked skewness is present. Except in the case of small samples, the condition that the data are an SRS from the population of interest is more crucial than the condition that the population distribution is Normal. Here are practical guidelines for inference on a single mean:[5]

- *Sample size less than 15:* Use t procedures if the data are close to Normal. If the data are clearly non-Normal or if outliers are present, do not use t.
- *Sample size at least 15:* The t procedures can be used except in the presence of outliers or strong skewness.

- *Large samples:* The t procedures can be used even for clearly skewed distributions when the sample is large, roughly $n \geq 40$.

The French instruction data are a borderline case: there are 20 observations, with one clear outlier. The t procedures give approximately correct results, but we would be happier if a good reason, such as illness on the posttest date, justified removing the outlier.

APPLY YOUR KNOWLEDGE

7.12 Oil wells. Data were collected from a sample of oil wells in the Devonian Richmond Dolomite area of the Michigan basin.[6] The variable reported here is the estimated total amount of oil, in thousands of barrels, that could be recovered from each well.

21.7	43.4	79.5	82.2	56.4
36.6	12.0	53.2	204.9	30.5

Would you recommend use of a t confidence interval to estimate the mean amount of oil in the population of all such oil wells? Use a graphical summary to support your answer.

7.13 t is robust. A manufacturer of small appliances employs a market research firm to estimate retail sales of its products. Here are last month's sales of electric can openers from an SRS of 50 stores in the Midwest sales region:

19	19	16	19	25	26	24	63	22	16
13	26	34	10	48	16	20	14	13	24
34	14	25	16	26	25	25	26	11	79
17	25	18	15	13	35	17	15	21	12
19	20	32	19	24	19	17	41	24	27

(a) Make a stemplot of the data. The distribution is skewed to the right and has several high outliers. The *bootstrap* (page 372) is a modern computer-intensive tool for getting accurate confidence intervals without the Normality condition. Three bootstrap simulations, each with 10,000 repetitions, give these 95% confidence intervals for mean sales in the entire region: (20.42, 27.26), (20.40, 27.18), and (20.48, 27.28).

(b) Find the 95% t confidence interval for the mean. It is essentially the same as the bootstrap intervals. The lesson is that for sample sizes as large as $n = 50$, t procedures are very robust.

The power of the t test*

Power calculations are an important part of planning a study. One piece of information that they provide is whether or not our sample size is sufficiently large to answer our research questions.

The power of a statistical test measures its ability to detect deviations from the null hypothesis. Usually, we hope to show that the null hypothesis is false, so high power is important. The power of the one-sample t test against a specific alternative value of the

*This section can be omitted without loss of continuity.

population mean μ is the probability that the test will reject the null hypothesis when this alternative is true. To calculate the power, we assume a fixed level of significance, usually $\alpha = 0.05$.

Calculation of the exact power of the t test takes into account the estimation of σ by s and requires special software. Fortunately, an approximate calculation that is based on assuming that σ is known is generally adequate for planning a study. This calculation is very much like that for the z test, presented in Section 6.4: write the event that the test rejects H_0 in terms of $\overline{x}$, and then find the probability of this event when the population mean has the alternative value.

EXAMPLE 7.9 Is the Sample Size Large Enough?

The company in Example 7.7 is planning to evaluate the next language instruction session. We decide that an improvement of 2 points or more is large enough to be useful in practice. Can we rely on a sample of 20 executives to detect an improvement of this size?

We wish to compute the power of the t test for

$$H_0: \mu = 0$$
$$H_a: \mu > 0$$

against the alternative $\mu = 2$ when $n = 20$. We must have a rough guess of the size of σ in order to compute the power. In planning a large study, a pilot study is often run for this and other purposes. In this case, listening-score improvements in past language instruction programs for similar executives have had sample standard deviations of about 3. We therefore take both $\sigma = 3$ and $s = 3$ in our approximate calculation.

The t test with 20 observations rejects H_0 at the 5% significance level if the t statistic

$$t = \frac{\overline{x} - 0}{s/\sqrt{20}}$$

exceeds the upper 5% point of $t(19)$, which is 1.729. Taking $s = 3$, the event that the test rejects H_0 is therefore

$$t = \frac{\overline{x}}{3/\sqrt{20}} \geq 1.729$$
$$\overline{x} \geq 1.729 \frac{3}{\sqrt{20}}$$
$$\overline{x} \geq 1.160$$

The power is the probability that $\overline{x} \geq 1.160$ when $\mu = 2$. Taking $\sigma = 3$, we find this probability by standardizing $\overline{x}$:

$$\begin{aligned} P(\overline{x} \geq 1.160 \text{ when } \mu = 2) &= P\left(\frac{\overline{x} - 2}{3/\sqrt{20}} \geq \frac{1.160 - 2}{3/\sqrt{20}}\right) \\ &= P(Z \geq -1.252) \\ &= 1 - 0.1056 = 0.8944 \end{aligned}$$

A true difference of 2 points in the population mean scores will produce significance at the 5% level in 89% of all possible samples. We can be reasonably confident of detecting a difference this large.

APPLY YOUR KNOWLEDGE

7.14 If you repeat the calculation in Example 7.9 for values of μ that are larger than 2, would you expect the power to be higher or lower than 0.8944? Why?

7.15 Verify your answer to the previous exercise by doing the calculation for the alternative $\mu = 2.2$.

Inference for non-Normal populations*

We have not discussed how to do inference about the mean of a clearly non-Normal distribution based on a small sample. If you face this problem, you should consult an expert. Three general strategies are available:

- In some cases a distribution other than a Normal distribution describes the data well. There are many non-Normal models for data, and inference procedures for these models are available.
- Because skewness is the chief barrier to the use of t procedures on data without outliers, you can attempt to transform skewed data so that the distribution is symmetric and as close to Normal as possible. Confidence levels and P-values from the t procedures applied to the transformed data will be quite accurate for even moderate sample sizes. Methods are generally available for transforming the results back to the original scale.
- The third strategy is to use a **distribution-free** inference procedure. Such procedures do not assume that the population distribution has any specific form, such as Normal. Distribution-free procedures are often called **nonparametric procedures.** The *bootstrap* (page 372 and Chapter 18) is a modern computer-intensive nonparametric procedure that is especially useful for confidence intervals. Chapter 16 discusses traditional nonparametric procedures, especially significance tests.

distribution-free procedures
nonparametric procedures

Each of these strategies quickly carries us beyond the basic practice of statistics. We emphasize procedures based on Normal distributions because they are the most common in practice, because their robustness makes them widely useful, and (most important) because we are first of all concerned with understanding the principles of inference.

Distribution-free significance tests do not require that the data follow any specific type of distribution such as Normal. The gain in generality isn't free: if the data really are close to Normal, distribution-free tests have less power than t tests. They also don't answer quite the same question. The t tests concern the population *mean.* Distribution-free tests ask about the population *median,* as is natural for distributions that may be skewed.

The sign test

sign test

The simplest distribution-free test, and one of the most useful, is the **sign test.** The following example illustrates this test.

EXAMPLE 7.10 The Effect of Language Instruction

Example 7.7 (page 434) gives data on the improvement in French listening scores after individualized instruction. In that example we used the matched pairs t test on these data, despite granularity

*This section can be omitted without loss of continuity. It requires knowledge of the binomial distributions from the optional Chapter 5.

and an outlier, which make the P-value only roughly correct. The sign test is based on the following simple observation: of the 17 executives whose scores changed, 16 improved and only 1 did more poorly. This is evidence that the instruction improved French listening skills.

To perform a significance test based on the count of executives whose scores improved, let p be the probability that a randomly chosen executive would improve if she attended the institute. The null hypothesis of "no effect" says that the posttest is just a repeat of the pretest with no change in ability, so an executive is equally likely to do better on either test. We therefore want to test

$$H_0: p = 1/2$$
$$H_a: p > 1/2$$

The 17 executives whose scores changed are 17 independent trials, so the number who improve has the binomial distribution $B(17, 1/2)$ if H_0 is true. The P-value for the observed count 16 is therefore $P(X \geq 16)$, where X has the $B(17, 1/2)$ distribution. You can compute this probability with software or from the binomial probability formula (page 325):

$$\begin{aligned} P(X \geq 16) &= P(X = 16) + P(X = 17) \\ &= \binom{17}{16}\left(\frac{1}{2}\right)^{16}\left(\frac{1}{2}\right)^{1} + \binom{17}{17}\left(\frac{1}{2}\right)^{17}\left(\frac{1}{2}\right)^{0} \\ &= (17)\left(\frac{1}{2}\right)^{17} + \left(\frac{1}{2}\right)^{17} \\ &= 0.00014 \end{aligned}$$

As in Example 7.7, there is very strong evidence that participation in the institute has improved performance on the listening test.

There are several varieties of sign test, all based on counts and the binomial distribution. The sign test for matched pairs (Example 7.10) is the most useful. The null hypothesis of "no effect" is then always H_0: $p = 1/2$. The alternative can be one-sided in either direction or two-sided, depending on the type of change we are looking for. The test gets its name from the fact that we look only at the signs of the differences, not their actual values.

The Sign Test for Matched Pairs

Ignore pairs with difference 0; the number of trials n is the count of the remaining pairs. The test statistic is the count X of pairs with a positive difference. P-values for X are based on the binomial $B(n, 1/2)$ distribution.

The matched pairs t test in Example 7.7 tested the hypothesis that the mean of the distribution of differences (score after the instruction minus score before) is 0. The sign test in Example 7.10 is in fact testing the hypothesis that the *median* of the differences is 0. If p is the probability that a difference is positive, then $p = 1/2$ when the median is 0. This is true because the median of the distribution is the point with probability 1/2 lying to its right. As Figure 7.7 illustrates, $p > 1/2$ when the median is greater than 0, again because the probability to the right of the median is always 1/2. The sign test of

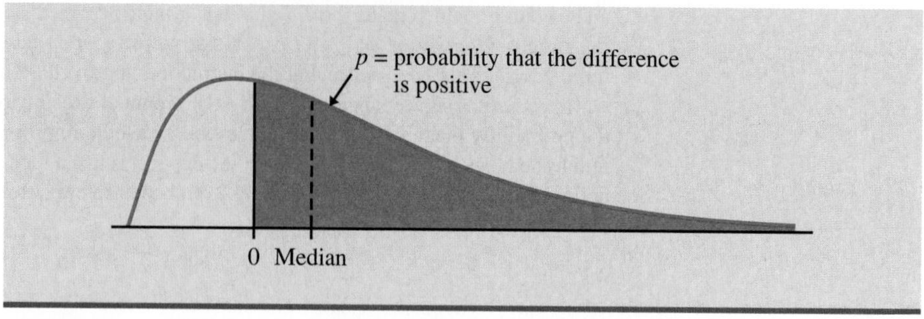

FIGURE 7.7 Why the sign test tests the median difference: when the median is greater than 0, the probability p of a positive difference is greater than 1/2, and vice versa.

H_0: $p = 1/2$ against H_a: $p > 1/2$ is a test of

$$H_0\text{: population median} = 0$$

$$H_a\text{: population median} > 0$$

The sign test in Example 7.10 makes no use of the actual scores—it just counts how many executives improved. The executives whose scores did not change were ignored altogether. Because the sign test uses so little of the available information, it is much less powerful than the t test when the population is close to Normal. Chapter 18 describes other distribution-free tests that are more powerful than the sign test.

APPLY YOUR KNOWLEDGE

7.16 Does the product lose value when cooked? CASE 7.1 Exercise 7.10 (page 436) gives data on the amount of vitamin C in gruel made from wheat-soy blend in 5 Haitian households before and after cooking. Is there evidence that the median amount of vitamin C is less after cooking? State hypotheses, carry out a sign test, and report your conclusion.

SECTION 7.1 SUMMARY

- Significance tests and confidence intervals for the mean μ of a Normal population are based on the sample mean $\bar{x}$ of an SRS. Because of the central limit theorem, the resulting procedures are approximately correct for other population distributions when the sample is large.
- The **standard error** of the sample mean is

$$\text{SE} = \frac{s}{\sqrt{n}}$$

- The standardized sample mean, or **one-sample z statistic,**

$$z = \frac{\bar{x} - \mu}{\sigma/\sqrt{n}}$$

has the $N(0, 1)$ distribution. If the standard deviation $\sigma/\sqrt{n}$ of $\bar{x}$ is replaced by the **standard error** SE $= s/\sqrt{n}$, the **one-sample t statistic**

$$t = \frac{\bar{x} - \mu}{s/\sqrt{n}}$$

has the **t distribution** with $n - 1$ degrees of freedom.

- There is a t distribution for every positive **degrees of freedom** k. All are symmetric distributions similar in shape to Normal distributions. The $t(k)$ distribution approaches the $N(0, 1)$ distribution as k increases.
- The **margin of error** for level C confidence is

$$\text{MOE} = t^*\text{SE} = t^*\frac{s}{\sqrt{n}}$$

  where t^* is the value for the $t(n-1)$ density curve with area C between $-t^*$ and t^*.
- A level C **confidence interval for the mean** μ of a Normal population is

$$\overline{x} \pm \text{MOE}$$

- Significance tests for $H_0\colon \mu = \mu_0$ are based on the t statistic. P-values or fixed significance levels are computed from the $t(n-1)$ distribution.
- These one-sample procedures are used to analyze **matched pairs** data by first taking the differences within the matched pairs to produce a single sample.
- The t procedures are relatively **robust** against lack of Normality, especially for larger sample sizes. The t procedures are useful for non-Normal data when $n \geq 15$ unless the data show outliers or strong skewness.
- The **power** of the t test is calculated like that of the z test, using an approximate value for both σ and s.
- The **sign test** is a **distribution-free test** because it uses probability calculations that are correct for a wide range of population distributions.
- The sign test for "no treatment effect" in matched pairs counts the number of positive differences. The P-value is computed from the $B(n, 1/2)$ distribution, where n is the number of non-0 differences. The sign test is less powerful than the t test in cases where use of the t test is justified.

SECTION 7.1 Exercises

For Exercises 7.1 and 7.2, see page 426; for 7.3 and 7.4, see page 428; for 7.5 to 7.7, see pages 430–431; for 7.8 and 7.9, see pages 432–433; for 7.10 and 7.11, see page 436; for 7.12 and 7.13, see page 438; for 7.14 and 7.15, see page 440; and for 7.16, see page 441.

7.17 What critical value t^* from Table D should be used to calculate the margin of error for a confidence interval for the mean of the population in each of the following situations?

(a) A 95% confidence interval based on $n = 10$ observations.

(b) A 95% confidence interval from an SRS of 25 observations.

(c) A 99% confidence interval from a sample of size 25.

(d) These cases illustrate how the size of the margin of error depends on the confidence level and on the sample size. Summarize the relationships illustrated.

7.18 What critical value t^* from Table D should be used to calculate the margin of error for a confidence interval for the mean of the population in each of the following situations?

(a) A 90% confidence interval based on $n = 14$ observations.

(b) A 90% confidence interval from an SRS of 28 observations.

(c) A 95% confidence interval from a sample of size 28.

(d) These cases illustrate how the size of the margin of error depends on the confidence level and on the sample size. Summarize the relationships illustrated.

7.19 The one-sample t statistic for testing

$$H_0: \mu = 10$$
$$H_a: \mu > 10$$

from a sample of $n = 20$ observations has the value $t = 2.17$.

(a) What are the degrees of freedom for this statistic?

(b) Give the two critical values t^* from Table D that bracket t.

(c) What are the right-tail probabilities p for these two entries?

(d) Between what two values does the P-value of the test fall?

(e) Is the value $t = 2.17$ significant at the 5% level? Is it significant at the 1% level?

(f) If you have software available, find the exact P-value.

7.20 The one-sample t statistic from a sample of $n = 25$ observations for the two-sided test of

$$H_0: \mu = 60$$
$$H_a: \mu \neq 60$$

has the value $t = 0.07$.

(a) What are the degrees of freedom for t?

(b) Locate the two critical values t^* from Table D that bracket t. What are the right-tail probabilities p for these two values?

(c) How would you report the P-value for this test?

(d) Is the value $t = 0.07$ statistically significant at the 5% level? At the 1% level?

(e) If you have software available, find the exact P-value.

7.21 The one-sample t statistic for a test of

$$H_0: \mu = 20$$
$$H_a: \mu < 20$$

based on $n = 120$ observations has the value $t = -4.45$.

(a) What are the degrees of freedom for this statistic?

(b) How would you report the P-value based on Table D?

(c) If you have software available, find the exact P-value.

7.22 LSAT scores. The scores of four roommates on the Law School Admission Test are

529, 593, 655, 503

Find the mean, the standard deviation, and the standard error of the mean. Is it appropriate to calculate a confidence interval based on these data? Explain why or why not.

7.23 Fuel efficiency. Computers in some vehicles calculate various quantities related to performance. One of these is the fuel efficiency, or gas mileage, usually expressed as miles per gallon (MPG). For one vehicle equipped in this way, the MPG were recorded each time the gas tank was filled, and the computer was then reset.[7] Here are the MPG values for a random sample of 20 of these records:

15.8	13.6	15.6	19.1	22.4	15.6	22.5	17.2	19.4	22.6
19.4	18.0	14.6	18.7	21.0	14.8	22.6	21.5	14.3	20.9

Give a 95% confidence interval for μ, the mean MPG for this vehicle.

7.24 Speed. Refer to the previous exercise. Here are the values of the average speed in miles per hour (MPH) for the same sample:

21.0	19.0	18.7	39.2	45.8	19.8	48.4	21.0	29.1	35.7
31.6	49.0	16.0	34.6	36.3	19.0	43.3	37.5	16.5	34.5

Estimate the mean speed at which this vehicle was driven with a margin of error for 95% confidence.

7.25 Clothing for runners. Your company sells exercise clothing and equipment on the Internet. To design the clothing, you collect data on the physical characteristics of your different types of customers. Here are the weights (in kilograms) for a sample of 24 male runners. Assume that these runners can be viewed as a random sample of your potential male customers.

68.7	61.8	63.2	53.1	62.3	59.7	55.4	58.9
60.9	69.2	63.7	67.8	65.6	65.5	56.0	57.8
66.0	62.9	53.6	65.0	55.8	60.4	69.3	62.1

(a) What is $\sigma_{\bar{x}}$, the standard deviation of $\bar{x}$?

(b) Give a 95% confidence interval for μ, the mean of the population from which the sample is drawn.

(c) Will the interval contain the weights of approximately 95% of similar runners? Explain your answer.

7.26 Pounds versus kilograms. Suppose that the weights of the runners in Exercise 7.25 were recorded in pounds rather than kilograms. Use your answers to Exercise 7.25, and the fact that 1 kilogram equals 2.2 pounds, to answer these questions.

(a) What is the mean weight of these runners?

(b) What is the standard deviation of the mean weight?

(c) Give a 95% confidence interval for the mean weight of the population of runners that these runners represent.

7.27 Earnings of bank workers. Here are the annual earnings (dollars) of a random sample of 20 workers from a bank.

28,258	22,029	18,233	29,606	32,346
35,176	29,863	18,904	26,477	21,102
17,002	23,596	28,885	26,780	18,698
23,308	27,576	26,497	22,612	23,757

(a) Display the data in a stemplot and, if your software permits, a Normal quantile plot. The distribution shows no strong departures from Normality.

(b) Give a 95% confidence interval for the mean annual earnings of workers at this bank.

7.28 How large is the pollution problem? Pollution of water resources is a serious problem that can require substantial efforts to improve. To determine the financial resources required, an accurate assessment of the extent of the problem is required. The index of biotic integrity (IBI) is a measure of the water quality in streams. Here are IBI measurements for a sample of streams in the Ozark Highland ecoregion of Arkansas that were collected as part of a study:[8]

47	61	39	59	72	76	85	89	74	89
33	32	46	80	80	53	78	43	88	84
62	55	29	29	54	78	71	55	71	58
33	81	59	71	75	64	41	82	60	83
84	82	82	86	79	67	56	85	91	

(a) Make a stemplot of the data. Also, make a Normal quantile plot if your software permits. Are there outliers present? Is the distribution skewed? If so, in what way? Based on your answers, do you think that t procedures should be used to analyze these data? Explain your answer.

(b) Give a 95% confidence interval for the mean IBI for streams in the Ozark Highland ecoregion of Arkansas that were sampled in this study.

7.29 Earnings of bank workers. Does the sample in Exercise 7.27 give good evidence that the mean annual earnings of workers at this bank are greater than $20,000?

7.30 How large is the pollution problem? When the data for Exercise 7.28 were fed to a statistical package, the output included a t statistic under the label "Test for Location: Mu0 = 0." Explain why this test is meaningless for the IBI water quality data.

7.31 Supermarket shoppers. A marketing consultant observed 40 consecutive shoppers at a supermarket. One variable of interest was how much each shopper spent in the store. Here are the data (in dollars), arranged in increasing order:

4.22	8.88	9.26	10.81	12.69	15.23	15.62	17.00
17.35	18.43	19.50	19.54	20.59	22.22	23.04	24.47
25.13	26.24	26.26	27.65	28.08	28.38	32.03	34.98
37.37	38.64	39.16	41.02	42.97	44.67	45.40	46.69
49.39	52.75	54.80	59.07	61.22	85.76	86.37	93.36

(a) Display the data using a stemplot. Make a Normal quantile plot if your software allows. The data are clearly non-Normal. In what way? Because $n = 40$, the t procedures remain quite accurate.

(b) Calculate the mean, the standard deviation, and the standard error of the mean.

(c) Find a 95% t confidence interval for the mean spending for all shoppers at this store.

7.32 The influence of big shoppers. Eliminate the three largest observations and redo parts (a), (b), and (c) of the previous exercise. Do these observations have a large influence on the results?

7.33 How large is the pollution problem? Refer to the IBI water quality data in Exercise 7.28. Streams with IBI scores of less than 20 are classified as "very poor," while those with scores greater than 20 but less than 40 are classified as "poor."

(a) Count the number of streams in the sample that are classified in these two categories, and use this result to compute an estimate of the proportion of streams that have either very poor or poor IBI scores.

(b) Can you use the confidence interval that you found in Exercise 7.28 to determine a confidence interval for the proportion of Ozark Highland ecoregion streams that have very poor or poor IBI scores? Explain your answer.

7.34 CASE 7.1 **Loss of vitamin C, reconsidered.** Exercise 7.10 gives these data on the amount of vitamin C in gruel made from wheat-soy blend in 5 Haitian households before and after cooking:

Household	1	2	3	4	5
Before	73	79	86	88	78
After	20	27	29	36	17

The units are milligrams per 100 grams of blend, dry basis. In Exercise 7.11, you were asked to give a confidence interval for the amount of vitamin C lost. The result is hard to interpret without some background information. A loss of 50 mg/100 g would be of little concern if we started with 5000 mg/100 g but would be serious if we started with 75 mg/100 g. In fact, the specifications call for the blend to contain 98 mg of vitamin C/100 g. The "before" values differ from the specifications due to variation in manufacturing and in handling the product before it was used to prepare gruel in Haiti. Express the "after" data as percent of specifications and give a 95% confidence interval for the mean percent.

7.35 **Corn prices.** The U.S. Department of Agriculture (USDA) uses sample surveys to obtain important economic estimates. One USDA pilot study estimated the price received by farmers for corn sold in October from a sample of 20 farms. The mean price was reported as \$2.10 per bushel with a standard error of \$0.166 per bushel. Give a 95% confidence interval for the mean price received by farmers for corn sold in October.[9]

7.36 **Health care costs.** The cost of health care is the subject of many studies that use statistical methods. One such study estimated that the average length of service for home health care among people over the age of 65 who use this type of service is 97.0 days with a standard error of 5.2 days. Assuming a large sample, calculate a 90% confidence interval for the mean length of service for all users of home health care.[10]

7.37 **A customer satisfaction survey.** Many organizations do surveys to determine the satisfaction of their customers. Attitudes toward various aspects of campus life were the subject of one such study conducted at Purdue University. Each question was rated on a 1 to 5 scale, with 5 being the highest rating. The mean response of 1406 first-year students to "Feeling welcomed at Purdue" was 3.8 and the standard deviation of the responses was 0.96. Assuming that the respondents are an SRS, give a 99% confidence interval for the mean of all first-year students.

7.38 **Piano lessons.** Do piano lessons improve the spatial-temporal reasoning of preschool children? Neurobiological arguments suggest that this may be true. A study designed to test this hypothesis measured the spatial-temporal reasoning of 34 preschool children before and after six months of piano lessons.[11] (The study also included children who took computer lessons and a control group; but we are not concerned with those here.) The changes in the reasoning scores are

2	5	7	−2	2	7	4	1	0	7	3	4	3	4	9	4	5
2	9	6	0	3	6	−1	3	4	6	7	−2	7	−3	3	4	4

(a) Display the data and summarize the distribution.

(b) Find the mean, the standard deviation, and the standard error of the mean.

(c) Give a 95% confidence interval for the mean improvement in reasoning scores.

7.39 **Are the results statistically significant?** Using the data of the previous exercise, test the null hypothesis that there is no improvement versus the alternative suggested by the neurobiological arguments. State the hypotheses, and give the test statistic with degrees of freedom and the P-value. What do you conclude? From your answer to part (c) of the previous exercise, what can be concluded from this significance test?

7.40 **Credit card fees.** A bank wonders whether omitting the annual credit card fee for customers who charge at least \$4000 in a year would increase the amount charged on its credit card. The bank makes this offer to an SRS of 300 of its existing credit card customers. It then compares how much these customers charge this year with the amount that they charged last year. The mean increase is \$385, and the standard deviation is \$128.

(a) Is there significant evidence at the 1% level that the mean amount charged increases under the no-fee offer? State H_0 and H_a and carry out a t test.

(b) Give a 95% confidence interval for the mean amount of the increase.

(c) The distributions of the amount charged are skewed to the right, but outliers are prevented by the credit limit that the bank enforces on each card. Use of the t procedures is justified in this case even though the population distribution is not Normal. Explain why.

(d) A critic points out that the customers would probably have charged more this year than last even without the new offer because the economy is more prosperous and interest rates are lower. Briefly describe the design of an experiment to study the effect of the no-fee offer that would avoid this criticism.

7.41 **Cockroaches.** Your company is developing a better means to eliminate cockroaches from buildings. In the process, your R&D team studies the absorption of sugar by these insects. They feed cockroaches a diet containing measured amounts of D-glucose. The cockroaches are killed at different times after eating, and the concentration of this sugar in various body parts is determined by a chemical analysis. Five cockroaches dissected after 10 hours had the following amounts (in micrograms) of D-glucose in their hindguts:[12]

55.95 68.24 52.73 21.50 23.78

Find a 95% confidence interval for the mean amount of D-glucose in cockroach hindguts under these conditions.

7.42 **Accuracy of radon detectors.** How accurate are radon detectors of a type sold to homeowners? To answer this question, university researchers placed 12 detectors in a chamber that exposed them to 105 picocuries per liter (pCi/l) of radon. The detector readings were as follows:[13]

91.9	97.8	111.4	122.3	105.4	95.0
103.8	99.6	96.6	119.3	104.8	101.7

(a) Make a stemplot of the data. The distribution is somewhat skewed to the right, but not strongly enough to forbid use of the t procedures.

(b) Is there convincing evidence that the mean reading of all detectors of this type differs from the true value 105? Carry out a test in detail and write a brief conclusion.

7.43 CASE 7.1 **Effect of storage and shipment on a product.** The researchers in the project described in Case 7.1 are also interested in wheat-soy blend (WSB). One question is whether some of the vitamin C content is destroyed as a result of storage and shipment of the product. The researchers marked a sample of bags at the factory and tested each to determine the vitamin C content. Five months later in Haiti they found the marked bags and again tested their contents. The data consist of two vitamin C measures for each bag, one at the time of production in the factory and the other five months later in Haiti. The units are milligrams of vitamin C per 100 grams of WSB. Here are the data:

Factory	Haiti	Factory	Haiti	Factory	Haiti
44	40	45	38	39	43
50	37	32	40	52	38
48	39	47	35	45	38
44	35	40	38	37	38
42	35	38	34	38	41
47	41	41	35	44	40
49	37	43	37	43	35
50	37	40	34	39	38
39	34	37	40	44	36

(a) Set up hypotheses to examine the question of interest to these researchers.

(b) Perform the significance test and summarize your results.

(c) Find 95% confidence intervals for the mean at the factory, for the mean five months later in Haiti, and for the change.

7.44 **Design of controls.** The design of controls and instruments has a large effect on how easily people can use them. A student project investigated this effect by asking 25 right-handed students to turn a knob (with their right hands) that moved an indicator by screw action. There were two identical instruments, one with a right-hand thread (the knob turns clockwise) and the other with a left-hand thread (the knob turns counterclockwise). The table below gives the times required (in seconds) to move the indicator a fixed distance:[14]

Subject	Right thread	Left thread	Subject	Right thread	Left thread
1	113	137	14	107	87
2	105	105	15	118	166
3	130	133	16	103	146
4	101	108	17	111	123
5	138	115	18	104	135
6	118	170	19	111	112
7	87	103	20	89	93
8	116	145	21	78	76
9	75	78	22	100	116
10	96	107	23	89	78
11	122	84	24	85	101
12	103	148	25	88	123
13	116	147			

(a) Each of the 25 students used both instruments. Discuss briefly how the experiment should be arranged and how randomization should be used.

(b) The project hoped to show that right-handed people find right-hand threads easier to use. State the appropriate H_0 and H_a about the mean time required to complete the task.

(c) Carry out a test of your hypotheses. Give the P-value and report your conclusions.

7.45 Is the difference important? Give a 90% confidence interval for the mean time advantage of right-hand over left-hand threads in the setting of the previous exercise. Do you think that the time saved would be of practical importance if the task were performed many times—for example, by an assembly-line worker? To help answer this question, find the mean time for right-hand threads as a percent of the mean time for left-hand threads.

7.46 Executives learn Spanish. The table below gives the pretest and posttest scores on the MLA listening test in Spanish for 20 executives who received intensive training in Spanish.[15] The setting is identical to the one described in Example 7.7.

Subject	Pretest	Posttest	Subject	Pretest	Posttest
1	30	29	11	30	32
2	28	30	12	29	28
3	31	32	13	31	34
4	26	30	14	29	32
5	20	16	15	34	32
6	30	25	16	20	27
7	34	31	17	26	28
8	15	18	18	25	29
9	28	33	19	31	32
10	20	25	20	29	32

(a) We hope to show that the training improves listening skills. State an appropriate H_0 and H_a. Describe in words the parameters that appear in your hypotheses.

(b) Make a graphical check for outliers or strong skewness in the data that you will use in your statistical test, and report your conclusions on the validity of the test.

(c) Carry out a test. Can you reject H_0 at the 5% significance level? At the 1% significance level?

(d) Give a 90% confidence interval for the mean increase in listening score due to the intensive training.

7.47 A field trial. An agricultural field trial compares the yield of two varieties of tomatoes for commercial use. The researchers divide in half each of 10 small plots of land in different locations and plant each tomato variety on one half of each plot. After harvest, they compare the yields in pounds per plant at each location. The 10 differences (Variety A − Variety B) give the following statistics: $\bar{x} = 0.35$ and $s = 0.86$. Is there convincing evidence that Variety A has the higher mean yield? State H_0 and H_a, and give a P-value to answer this question.

7.48 Which design? The following situations all require inference about a mean or means. Identify each as (1) a single sample, (2) matched pairs, or (3) two independent samples. The procedures of this section apply to cases (1) and (2). We will learn procedures for (3) in the next section. Explain your answers.

(a) Your customers are college students who either live in a dorm or live elsewhere. You are interested in comparing the interest of these two groups in a new product that you are developing.

(b) Your customers are college students. You are interested in comparing which of two new products that you are developing would be more attractive to your customers.

7.49 Which design? The following situations all require inference about a mean or means. Identify each as (1) a single sample, (2) matched pairs, or (3) two independent samples. The procedures of this section apply to cases (1) and (2). We will learn procedures for (3) in the next section. Explain your answers.

(a) You want to estimate the average age of your customers.

(b) You do a survey of your customers every year. One of the questions in the survey asks about customer satisfaction on a seven-point scale with the response 1 indicating "very dissatisfied" and 7 indicating "very satisfied." Has the mean customer satisfaction improved from last year to this year?

7.50 Areas of states. While browsing the Internet, you find a site that gives the land area (in square kilometers) for Africa, Antarctica, Asia, Australia, Europe, North America, and South America. You feed the data to your statistical software package and the output produced includes a confidence interval. Is this a valid use of the procedure? Explain your answer.

The following exercises concern the optional material in the sections on the power of the t test and on non-Normal populations.

7.51 Credit card fees. The bank in Exercise 7.40 tested a new idea on a sample of 300 customers. Suppose that the bank wanted to be quite certain of detecting a mean increase of $\mu = \$100$ in the credit card amount charged, at the $\alpha = 0.01$ significance level. Perhaps a sample of only $n = 60$ customers would accomplish this. Find the approximate power of the test with $n = 60$ for the alternative $\mu = \$100$ as follows:

(a) What is the t critical value for the one-sided test with $\alpha = 0.01$ and $n = 60$?

(b) Write the criterion for rejecting H_0: $\mu = 0$ in terms of the t statistic. Then take $s = 112$ and state the rejection criterion in terms of $\bar{x}$.

(c) Assume that $\mu = 100$ (the given alternative) and that $\sigma = 112$. The approximate power is the probability of the event you found in (b), calculated under these assumptions. Find the power. Would you recommend that the bank do a test on 60 customers, or should more customers be included?

7.52 A field trial. The tomato experts who carried out the field trial described in Exercise 7.47 suspect that the relative lack of significance there is due to low power. They would like to be able to detect a mean difference in yields of 0.6 pound per plant at the 0.05 significance level. Based on the previous study, use 0.86 as an estimate of both the population σ and the value of s in future samples.

(a) What is the power of the test from Exercise 7.47 with $n = 10$ for the alternative $\mu = 0.6$?

(b) If the sample size is increased to $n = 25$ plots of land, what will be the power for the same alternative?

7.53 Design of controls. Apply the sign test to the data in Exercise 7.44 to assess whether the subjects can complete a task with a right-hand thread significantly faster than with a left-hand thread.

(a) State the hypotheses two ways, in terms of a population median and in terms of the probability of completing the task faster with a right-hand thread.

(b) Carry out the sign test. Find the approximate P-value using the Normal approximation to the binomial distributions, and report your conclusion.

7.54 Learning Spanish. Use the sign test to assess whether the intensive language training of Exercise 7.46 improves Spanish listening skills. State the hypotheses, give the P-value using the binomial table (Table C), and report your conclusion.

7.2 Comparing Two Means

How do small businesses that fail differ from those that succeed? Business school researchers compare two samples of new firms: one sample of failed businesses and one of firms that are still going after two years. This study *compares two random samples,* one from each of two different populations. Which of two incentive packages will lead to higher use of a bank's credit cards? The bank designs a *randomized comparative experiment to compare two treatments.* Credit card customers are assigned at random to receive one or the other incentive offer. After six months, the bank compares the amounts charged. *Two-sample problems* such as these are among the most common situations encountered in statistical practice.

Two-Sample Problems

- The goal of inference is to compare the responses in two groups.
- Each group is considered to be a sample from a distinct population.
- The responses in each group are independent of those in the other group.

You must carefully distinguish two-sample problems from the matched pairs designs studied earlier. In two-sample problems, there is no matching of the units in the two samples, and the two samples may be of different sizes. Inference procedures for two-sample data differ from those for matched pairs.

We can present two-sample data graphically with a back-to-back stemplot (for small samples) or with side-by-side boxplots (for larger samples). Now we will apply the ideas of formal inference in this setting. When both population distributions are symmetric, and especially when they are at least approximately Normal, a comparison of the mean responses in the two populations is most often the goal of inference.

We have two independent samples, from two distinct populations (such as failed businesses and successful businesses). We measure the same variable (such as initial capital) in both samples. We will call the variable x_1 in the first population and x_2 in the second because the variable may have different distributions in the two populations. Here is the notation that we will use to describe the two populations:

Population	Variable	Mean	Standard deviation
1	x_1	μ_1	σ_1
2	x_2	μ_2	σ_2

We want to compare the two population means, either by giving a confidence interval for $\mu_1 - \mu_2$ or by testing the hypothesis of no difference, H_0: $\mu_1 = \mu_2$. We base inference on two independent SRSs, one from each population. Here is the notation that describes the samples:

Population	Sample size	Sample mean	Sample standard deviation
1	n_1	$\overline{x}_1$	s_1
2	n_2	$\overline{x}_2$	s_2

Throughout this section, the subscripts 1 and 2 show the population to which a parameter or a sample statistic refers.

The two-sample *z* statistic

The natural estimator of the difference $\mu_1 - \mu_2$ is the difference between the sample means, $\overline{x}_1 - \overline{x}_2$. If we are to base inference on this statistic, we must know its sampling distribution. Our knowledge of probability is equal to the task. First, the mean of the difference $\overline{x}_1 - \overline{x}_2$ is the difference of the means $\mu_1 - \mu_2$. This follows from the addition rule for means (page 275) and the fact that the mean of any $\overline{x}$ is the same as the mean of the population. Because the samples are independent, their sample means $\overline{x}_1$ and $\overline{x}_2$ are independent random variables. The addition rule for variances (page 281) says that the variance of the difference $\overline{x}_1 - \overline{x}_2$ is the sum of their variances, which is

$$\frac{\sigma_1^2}{n_1} + \frac{\sigma_2^2}{n_2}$$

We now know the mean and variance of the distribution of $\overline{x}_1 - \overline{x}_2$ in terms of the parameters of the two populations. If the two population distributions are both Normal, then the distribution of $\overline{x}_1 - \overline{x}_2$ is also Normal. This is true because each sample mean alone is Normally distributed and because a difference of independent Normal random variables is also Normal.

Any Normal random variable has the $N(0, 1)$ distribution when standardized. We have arrived at a new z statistic.

Two-Sample z Statistic

Suppose that $\bar{x}_1$ is the mean of an SRS of size n_1 drawn from an $N(\mu_1, \sigma_1)$ population and that $\bar{x}_2$ is the mean of an independent SRS of size n_2 drawn from an $N(\mu_2, \sigma_2)$ population. Then the **two-sample z statistic**

$$z = \frac{(\bar{x}_1 - \bar{x}_2) - (\mu_1 - \mu_2)}{\sqrt{\dfrac{\sigma_1^2}{n_1} + \dfrac{\sigma_2^2}{n_2}}}$$

has the standard Normal $N(0, 1)$ sampling distribution.

In the unlikely event that both population standard deviations are known, the two-sample z statistic is the basis for inference about $\mu_1 - \mu_2$. Exact z procedures are seldom used, however, because σ_1 and σ_2 are rarely known. In Chapter 6, we discussed the one-sample z procedures to introduce the ideas of inference. Now we pass immediately to the more useful t procedures.

The two-sample t procedures

In practice, the two population standard deviations σ_1 and σ_2 are not known. We estimate them by the sample standard deviations s_1 and s_2 from our two samples. Following the pattern of the one-sample case, we substitute the standard errors $s_i/\sqrt{n_i}$ for the standard deviations $\sigma_i/\sqrt{n_i}$ in the two-sample z statistic. The result is the *two-sample t statistic:*

$$t = \frac{(\bar{x}_1 - \bar{x}_2) - (\mu_1 - \mu_2)}{\sqrt{\dfrac{s_1^2}{n_1} + \dfrac{s_2^2}{n_2}}}$$

Unfortunately, this statistic does *not* have a t distribution. A t distribution replaces an $N(0, 1)$ distribution only when a single standard deviation (σ) in a z statistic is replaced by an estimate (s). In this case, we replaced two standard deviations (σ_1 and σ_2) by their estimates (s_1 and s_2), which does not produce a statistic having a t distribution.

Nonetheless, we can approximate the distribution of the two-sample t statistic by using the $t(k)$ distribution with an **approximation for the degrees of freedom k.** We use these approximations to find approximate values of t^* for confidence intervals and to find approximate P-values for significance tests. There are two procedures used in practice:

Satterthwaite approximation

1. Use an approximation known as the **Satterthwaite approximation** to calculate a value of k from the data. In general, this k will not be a whole number.
2. Use degrees of freedom k equal to the smaller of $n_1 - 1$ and $n_2 - 1$.

Most statistical software uses the Satterthwaite approximation for two-sample problems unless the user requests another method. Use of this approximation without software is a bit complicated; we will give the details later in this section. If you are not using software, we recommend the second approximation. This approximation is appealing because it is conservative.[16] That is, margins of error for confidence intervals are a bit larger than they need to be, so the true confidence level is larger than C. For significance testing, the true P-values are a bit smaller than those we obtain from the approximation; for tests at a fixed significance level, we are a little less likely to reject H_0 when it is true. In practice, the choice of approximation almost never makes a difference in our practical conclusion.

The two-sample *t* significance test

We now apply the basic ideas about t procedures to the problem of comparing two means when the standard deviations are unknown. We start with significance tests.

The Two-Sample *t* Significance Test

Draw an SRS of size n_1 from a Normal population with unknown mean μ_1 and an independent SRS of size n_2 from another Normal population with unknown mean μ_2. To test the hypothesis H_0: $\mu_1 = \mu_2$, compute the **two-sample t statistic**

$$t = \frac{(\bar{x}_1 - \bar{x}_2) - (\mu_1 - \mu_2)}{\sqrt{\frac{s_1^2}{n_1} + \frac{s_2^2}{n_2}}}$$

and use P-values or critical values for the $t(k)$ distribution, where the degrees of freedom k are either approximated by software or are the smaller of $n_1 - 1$ and $n_2 - 1$.

EXAMPLE 7.11 Is Our Product Effective?

A company that sells educational materials reports statistical studies to convince customers that its materials improve learning. One new product supplies "directed reading activities" for classroom use. These activities should improve the reading ability of elementary school pupils.

A consultant arranges for a third-grade class of 21 students to take part in these activities for an eight-week period. A control classroom of 23 third-graders follows the same curriculum without the activities. At the end of the eight weeks, all students are given a Degree of Reading Power (DRP) test, which measures the aspects of reading ability that the treatment is designed to improve. The data appear in Table 7.3.[17]

TABLE 7.3 DRP scores for third-graders

Treatment group				Control group			
24	61	59	46	42	33	46	37
43	44	52	43	43	41	10	42
58	67	62	57	55	19	17	55
71	49	54		26	54	60	28
43	53	57		62	20	53	48
49	56	33		37	85	42	

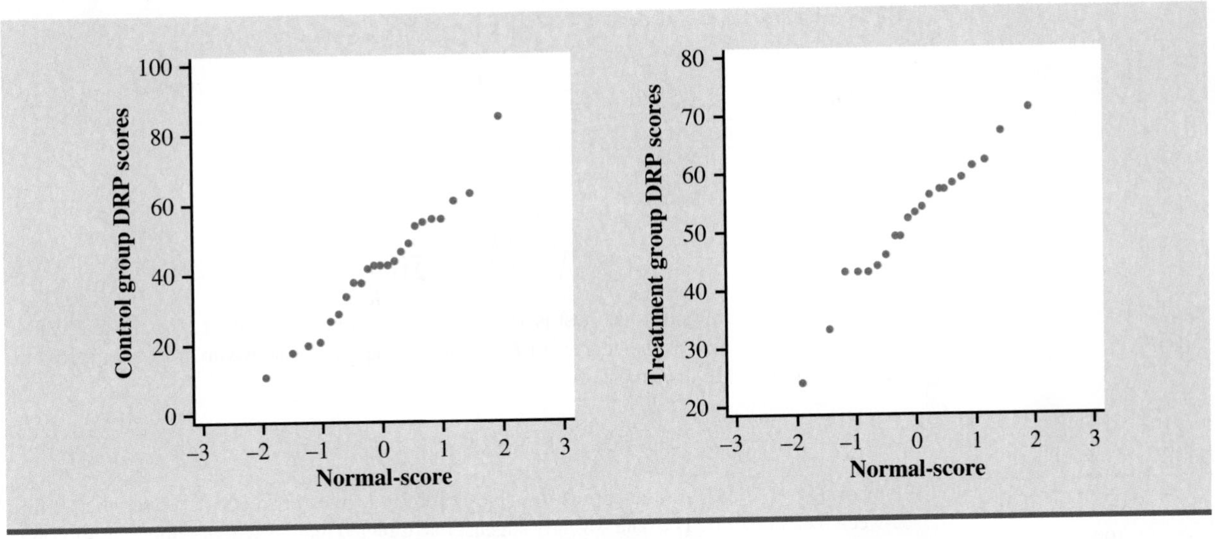

FIGURE 7.8 Normal quantile plots for the DRP scores in Table 7.3.

First examine the data:

Control		Treatment
970	1	
860	2	4
773	3	3
8632221	4	3334699
5543	5	23467789
20	6	127
	7	1
5	8	

A back-to-back stemplot suggests that there is a mild outlier in the control group but no deviation from Normality serious enough to forbid use of t procedures. Separate Normal quantile plots for both groups (Figure 7.8) confirm that both are approximately Normal. The scores of the treatment group appear to be somewhat higher than those of the control group. The summary statistics are

Group	n	$\bar{x}$	s
Treatment	21	51.48	11.01
Control	23	41.52	17.15

Because we hope to show that the treatment (Group 1) is better than the control (Group 2), the hypotheses are

$$H_0: \mu_1 = \mu_2$$
$$H_a: \mu_1 > \mu_2$$

The two-sample t test statistic is

$$t = \frac{\bar{x}_1 - \bar{x}_2}{\sqrt{\frac{s_1^2}{n_1} + \frac{s_2^2}{n_2}}}$$

$$= \frac{51.48 - 41.52}{\sqrt{\frac{11.01^2}{21} + \frac{17.15^2}{23}}} = 2.31$$

The P-value for the one-sided test is $P(T \geq 2.31)$. Software gives the approximate P-value as 0.0132 and uses 37.9 as the degrees of freedom. For the second approximation, the degrees of freedom k are equal to the smaller of

$$n_1 - 1 = 21 - 1 = 20 \text{ and } n_2 - 1 = 23 - 1 = 22$$

df = 20		
p	0.02	0.01
t^*	2.197	2.528

Comparing $t = 2.31$ with the entries in Table D for 20 degrees of freedom, we see that P lies between 0.02 and 0.01. The data strongly suggest that directed reading activity improves the DRP score ($t = 2.31$, df $= 20$, $P < 0.02$).

Some software gives P-values only for the two-sided alternative. In this case, divide the reported value by 2 to get the one-sided P-value. Be sure to check that the means differ in the direction specified by the alternative hypothesis.

APPLY YOUR KNOWLEDGE

7.55 Selling on the Internet. You want to compare the daily sales for two different designs of Web pages for your Internet business. You assign the next 60 days to either Design A or Design B, 30 days to each.

(a) Would you use a one-sided or two-sided significance test for this problem? Explain your choice.

(b) If you use Table D to find the critical value, what are the degrees of freedom?

(c) The t statistic for comparing the mean sales is 3.45. If you use Table D, what P-value would you report? What would you conclude?

7.56 If you perform the significance test in the previous exercise using level $\alpha = 0.05$, how large (positive or negative) must the t statistic be to reject the null hypothesis that the two designs give the same average sales?

7.57 Selling on the Internet. You realize that day of the week may affect online sales. To compare two Web page designs, you choose two successive weeks in the middle of a month. You flip a coin to assign one Monday to the first design and the other Monday to the second. You repeat this for each of the seven days of the week. You now have 7 sales amounts for each design. It is *incorrect* to use the two-sample t test to see if the mean sales differ for the two designs. Carefully explain why.

The two-sample t confidence interval

The same ideas that we used for the two-sample t significance tests also apply to *two-sample t confidence intervals.* We can use either software or the conservative approach with Table D to approximate the value of t^*.

The Two-Sample t Confidence Interval

Draw an SRS of size n_1 from a Normal population with unknown mean μ_1 and an independent SRS of size n_2 from another Normal population with unknown mean μ_2. The **confidence interval for $\mu_1 - \mu_2$** given by

$$(\bar{x}_1 - \bar{x}_2) \pm t^* \sqrt{\frac{s_1^2}{n_1} + \frac{s_2^2}{n_2}}$$

has confidence level at least C no matter what the population standard deviations may be. The margin of error is

$$t^* \sqrt{\frac{s_1^2}{n_1} + \frac{s_2^2}{n_2}}$$

Here, t^* is the value for the $t(k)$ density curve with area C between $-t^*$ and t^*. The value of the degrees of freedom k is approximated by software or we use the smaller of $n_1 - 1$ and $n_2 - 1$.

To complete the analysis of the DRP scores we examined in Example 7.11, we need to describe the size of the treatment effect. We do this with a confidence interval for the difference between the treatment group and the control group means.

EXAMPLE 7.12 How Much Improvement?

We will find a 95% confidence interval for the mean improvement in the entire population of third-graders. The interval is

$$(\bar{x}_1 - \bar{x}_2) \pm t^* \sqrt{\frac{s_1^2}{n_1} + \frac{s_2^2}{n_2}} = (51.48 - 41.52) \pm t^* \sqrt{\frac{11.01^2}{21} + \frac{17.15^2}{23}}$$
$$= 9.96 \pm (t^* \times 4.31)$$

Using software, the degrees of freedom are 37.9 and $t^* = 2.025$. This approximation gives

$$9.96 \pm (2.025 \times 4.31) = 9.96 \pm 8.72 = (1.2,\ 18.7)$$

The conservative approach uses the $t(20)$ distribution. Table D gives $t^* = 2.086$. With this approximation we have

$$9.96 \pm (2.086 \times 4.31) = 9.96 \pm 8.99 = (1.0,\ 18.9)$$

The conservative approach does give a larger interval than the more accurate approximation used by software. However, the difference is rather small.

We estimate the mean improvement in DRP scores to be about 10 points, but with a margin of error of almost 9 points. Although we have good evidence of some improvement, the data do not allow a very precise estimate of the size of the average improvement.

The design of the DRP study is not ideal. Random assignment of students was not possible in a school environment, so existing third-grade classes were used. The effect of the reading programs is therefore confounded with any other differences between the two classes. The classes were chosen to be as similar as possible in variables such as the social and economic status of the students. Pretesting showed that the two classes were on the average quite similar in reading ability at the beginning of the experiment. To avoid the effect of two different teachers, the same teacher taught reading in both classes during the eight-week period of the experiment. We can therefore be somewhat confident that the two-sample test is detecting the effect of the treatment and not some other difference between the classes. This example is typical of many situations in which an experiment is carried out but randomization is not possible.

APPLY YOUR KNOWLEDGE

7.58 New computer monitors? The purchasing department has suggested that all new computer monitors for your company should be a new design. You want data to assure you that employees will like the new monitors. The next 20 employees needing a new computer are the subjects for an experiment.

(a) Label the employees 01 to 20. Randomly choose 10 to receive new monitors. The remaining 10 get standard monitors.

(b) After a month of use, employees express their satisfaction with their new monitors by responding to the statement "I like my new monitor" on a scale from 1 to 5, where 1 represents "strongly disagree," 2 is "disagree," 3 is "neutral," 4 is "agree," and 5 stands for "strongly agree." The employees with the new monitors have average satisfaction 4.4 with standard deviation 0.7. The employees with the standard monitors have average 3.2 with standard deviation 1.5. Give a 95% confidence interval for the difference in the mean satisfaction scores for all employees.

(c) Would you reject the null hypothesis that the mean satisfaction for the two types of monitors is the same versus the two-sided alternative at significance level 0.05? Use your confidence interval to answer this question. Explain why you do not need to calculate the test statistic.

7.59 Why randomize? A coworker suggested that you give the new monitors to the next 10 employees who need new screens and the standard monitor to the following 10. Explain why your randomized design is better.

Robustness of the two-sample procedures

The two-sample t procedures are more robust than the one-sample t methods. When the sizes of the two samples are equal and the distributions of the two populations being compared have similar shapes, probability values from the t table are quite accurate for a broad range of distributions when the sample sizes are as small as $n_1 = n_2 = 5$.[18] When the two population distributions have different shapes, larger samples are needed. The guidelines given on page 437 for the use of one-sample t procedures can be adapted to two-sample procedures by replacing "sample size" with the "sum of the sample sizes" $n_1 + n_2$. These guidelines are rather conservative, especially when the two samples are of equal size. In planning a two-sample study, you should usually choose equal sample sizes. The two-sample t procedures are most robust against non-Normality in this case, and the conservative probability values are most accurate.

EXAMPLE 7.13 Wheat Prices

The U.S. Department of Agriculture (USDA) uses sample surveys to produce important economic estimates. One pilot study estimated wheat prices in July and in September using independent samples of wheat producers in the two months. Here are the summary statistics, in dollars per bushel:[19]

Month	n	$\bar{x}$	s
September	45	\$3.61	\$0.19
July	90	\$2.95	\$0.22

The September prices are higher on the average. But we have data from only a few producers each month. Can we conclude that national average prices in July and September are not the same? Or are these differences merely what we would expect to see due to random variation?

Because we did not specify a direction for the difference before looking at the data, we choose a two-sided alternative. The hypotheses are

$$H_0: \mu_1 = \mu_2$$
$$H_a: \mu_1 \neq \mu_2$$

Because the samples are moderately large, we can confidently use the t procedures even though we lack the detailed data and so cannot verify the Normality condition.

The two-sample t statistic is

$$t = \frac{\bar{x}_1 - \bar{x}_2}{\sqrt{\frac{s_1^2}{n_1} + \frac{s_2^2}{n_2}}} = \frac{3.61 - 2.95}{\sqrt{\frac{0.19^2}{45} + \frac{0.22^2}{90}}} = 135.28$$

df = 40	
p	0.0005
t^*	3.551

The conservative approach finds the P-value by comparing 135.28 to critical values for the $t(44)$ distribution because the smaller sample has 45 observations. We must double the table tail area p because the alternative is two-sided.

Table D does not have entries for 44 degrees of freedom. When this happens, we use the next smaller degrees of freedom. Our calculated value of t is larger than the $p = 0.0005$ entry in the table. Doubling 0.0005, we conclude that the P-value is less than 0.001. The data give conclusive evidence that the mean wheat prices were higher in September than they were in July ($t = 135.28$, df $= 44$, $P < 0.001$).

In this example the exact P-value is very small because $t = 135$ says that the observed mean is 135 standard deviations above the hypothesized mean. This is so unlikely that the probability is zero for all practical purposes. The difference in mean prices is not only highly significant but large enough (66 cents per bushel) to be important to producers.

In this and other examples, we can choose which population to label 1 and which to label 2. After inspecting the data, we chose September as Population 1 because this choice makes the t statistic a positive number. This avoids any possible confusion from reporting a negative value for t. Choosing the population labels is *not* the same as choosing a one-sided alternative after looking at the data. Choosing hypotheses after seeing a result in the data is a violation of sound statistical practice.

Inference for small samples

Small samples require special care. We do not have enough observations to examine the distribution shapes, and only extreme outliers stand out. The power of significance tests tends to be low, and the margins of error of confidence intervals tend to be large. Despite these difficulties, we can often draw important conclusions from studies with small sample sizes. If the size of an effect is as large as it was in the wheat price example, it should still be evident even if the n's are small.

EXAMPLE 7.14 More about Wheat Prices

In the setting of Example 7.13, a quick survey collects prices from only 5 producers each month. The data are

Month	Price of wheat ($/bushel)				
September	$3.5900	$3.6150	$3.5950	$3.5725	$3.5825
July	$2.9200	$2.9675	$2.9175	$2.9250	$2.9325

The prices are reported to the nearest quarter of a cent. First, examine the distributions with a back-to-back stemplot after rounding each price to the nearest cent.

September		July
	2.9	22337
	3.0	
	3.1	
	3.2	
	3.3	
	3.4	
987	3.5	
20	3.6	

The pattern is clear. There is little variation among prices within each month, and the distributions for the two months are far apart relative to the within-month variation.

A significance test can confirm that the difference between months is too large to easily arise just by chance. We test

$$H_0: \mu_1 = \mu_2$$
$$H_a: \mu_1 \neq \mu_2$$

The price is higher in September ($t = 56.99$, df $= 7.55$, $P < 0.0001$). The difference in sample means is 65.9 cents.

Figure 7.9 gives outputs for this analysis from several software systems. Although the formats differ, the basic information is the same. All report the sample sizes, the sample means and standard deviations (or variances), the t statistic, and its P-value. All agree that the P-value is very small, though some give more detail than others. Software often labels the groups in alphabetical order. In this example, July is then the first population and $t = -56.99$, the negative of our result. Always check the means first and report the statistic (you may need to change the sign) in an appropriate way. Be sure to also mention the size of the effect you observed, such as "The mean price for September was 65.9 cents higher than in July."

SPSS and SAS report the results of *two t* procedures: a special procedure that assumes that the two population variances are equal and the general two-sample procedure that we have just studied. We don't recommend the "equal-variances" procedures, but we describe them later, in the section on pooled two-sample t procedures.

FIGURE 7.9 Excel, SPSS, Minitab, and SAS output for Example 7.14.

SPSS

Group Statistics

	MONTH	N	Mean	Std. Deviation	Std. Error Mean
PRICE	JULY	5	2.932500	2.03869E-02	9.11729E-03
	SEPT	5	3.591000	1.58706E-02	7.09753E-03

Independent Samples Test

		t-test for Equality of Means t	df	Sig. (2-tailed)	Mean Difference	Std. Error Difference	95% Confidence Interval of the Difference Lower	Upper
PRICE	Equal variances assumed	–56.99	8	.000	–.6585	1.155E-02	–.685	–.632
	Equal variances not assumed	–56.99	7.546	.000	–.6585	1.155E-02	–.685	–.632

Minitab

Two-Sample T-Test and CI: Price, Month

```
Two-sample T for Price

Month        N      Mean     StDev    SE Mean
July         5    2.9325    0.0204     0.0091
September    5    3.5910    0.0159     0.0071

Difference = mu (July) - mu (September)
Estimate for difference: -0.6585
95% CI for difference: (-0.6858, -0.6312)
T-Test of difference = 0 (vs not =): T-Value = -56.99
P-Value = 0.000 DF = 7
```

SAS

```
                      The TTEST Procedure

                           Statistics
                           Lower CL               Upper CL
Variable    month        N     Mean      Mean       Mean    Std Err

price       july         5   2.9072    2.9325     2.9578     0.0091
price       sept         5   3.5713     3.591     3.6107     0.0071
price       Diff (1-2)        -0.685    -0.659     -0.632     0.0116

                             T-Tests
Variable   Method           Variances      DF    t Value    Pr > |t|
price      Pooled           Equal           8     -56.99    < .0001
price      Satterthwaite    Unequal      7.55     -56.99    < .0001
```

FIGURE 7.9 *(Continued)*

t-Test: Two-Sample Assuming Unequal Variances

	July	September
Mean	2.9325	3.591
Variance	0.000415625	0.000251875
Observations	5	5
Hypothesized Mean Difference	0	
df	8	
t Stat	−56.99216386	
P(T<=t) one-tail	4.98679E-12	
t Critical one-tail	1.859548033	
P(T<=t) two-tail	9.97357E-12	
t Critical two-tail	2.306004133	

Satterthwaite approximation for the degrees of freedom*

We noted earlier that the two-sample t statistic does not have an exact t distribution. Moreover, the exact distribution changes as the unknown population standard deviations σ_1 and σ_2 change. However, the distribution can be approximated by a t distribution with degrees of freedom given by

$$\text{df} = \frac{\left(\dfrac{s_1^2}{n_1} + \dfrac{s_2^2}{n_2}\right)^2}{\dfrac{1}{n_1 - 1}\left(\dfrac{s_1^2}{n_1}\right)^2 + \dfrac{1}{n_2 - 1}\left(\dfrac{s_2^2}{n_2}\right)^2}$$

Most statistical software uses this approximation. It was discovered by a statistician named Satterthwaite, and his name is frequently used to identify the approximation on output. The Satterthwaite approximation is quite accurate when both sample sizes n_1 and n_2 are 5 or larger.

EXAMPLE 7.15 Output for Wheat Prices

Output for the wheat prices example with samples of size 5 appears in Figure 7.9. SPSS and SAS report the degrees of freedom for the Satterthwaite approximation as 7.546 and 7.55. Excel and Minitab round this to a whole number. All of these df's are larger than the conservative df = 4 that we would use in the absence of software. In this example, the t statistic is so large that all choices lead to the same practical conclusion.

*This material can be omitted unless you are using statistical software and wish to understand what the software does.

The number df given by the Satterthwaite approximation is always at least as large as the smaller of $n_1 - 1$ and $n_2 - 1$. On the other hand, df is never larger than the sum $n_1 + n_2 - 2$ of the two individual degrees of freedom. The number of degrees of freedom is generally not a whole number. There is a t distribution with any positive degrees of freedom, even though Table D contains entries only for whole-number degrees of freedom. Because of this and the need to calculate df, we do not recommend using the approximation unless a computer is doing the arithmetic. With software, however, the more accurate procedures are painless.

APPLY YOUR KNOWLEDGE

7.60 Calculating the Satterthwaite df. The SPSS output in Figure 7.9 gives df = 7.546. Use the sample standard deviations in that output and the Satterthwaite formula to verify this value.

7.61 Compare the output. Figure 7.9 gives the output from four software systems for the two-sample t procedures. Make tables to compare the outputs, giving the numerical values reported by the software.

(a) How do they report the means?

(b) How do they report variability for each of the groups?

(c) How do they report the test statistic, degrees of freedom, and the P-value?

(d) Do they give a confidence interval for the mean difference?

(e) Write a short summary comparing the four outputs from the viewpoint of a user of statistics. Which do you like the best? Which do you like the least?

7.62 Can you do better? Design your own output for a two-sample t analysis and illustrate it with the results given in Figure 7.9. Pay particular attention to the use of labels and how numbers are rounded.

The pooled two-sample t procedures*

There is one situation in which a t statistic for comparing two means has exactly a t distribution. Suppose that the two Normal population distributions have the *same* standard deviation. In this case we need substitute only a single standard error in a z statistic, and the resulting t statistic has a t distribution. We will develop the z statistic first, as usual, and from it the t statistic.

Call the common—but still unknown—standard deviation of both populations σ. Both sample variances s_1^2 and s_2^2 estimate σ^2. The best way to combine these two estimates is to average them with weights equal to their degrees of freedom. This gives more weight to the information from the larger sample. The resulting estimator of σ^2 is

$$s_p^2 = \frac{(n_1 - 1)s_1^2 + (n_2 - 1)s_2^2}{n_1 + n_2 - 2}$$

pooled estimator of σ^2

This is called the **pooled estimator of σ^2** because it combines the information in both samples.

When both populations have variance σ^2, the addition rule for variances says that $\bar{x}_1 - \bar{x}_2$ has variance equal to the *sum* of the individual variances, which is

$$\frac{\sigma^2}{n_1} + \frac{\sigma^2}{n_2} = \sigma^2\left(\frac{1}{n_1} + \frac{1}{n_2}\right)$$

*This section is optional, but you should read it if you plan to study Chapters 14 and 15 on analysis of variance.

The standardized difference of means in this equal-variance case is therefore

$$z = \frac{(\bar{x}_1 - \bar{x}_2) - (\mu_1 - \mu_2)}{\sigma\sqrt{\dfrac{1}{n_1} + \dfrac{1}{n_2}}}$$

This is a special two-sample z statistic for the case in which the populations have the same σ. Replacing the unknown σ by the estimate s_p gives a t statistic. The degrees of freedom are $n_1 + n_2 - 2$, the sum of the degrees of freedom of the two sample variances. This statistic is the basis of the pooled two-sample t inference procedures.

The Pooled Two-Sample *t* Procedures

Draw an SRS of size n_1 from a Normal population with unknown mean μ_1 and an independent SRS of size n_2 from another Normal population with unknown mean μ_2. Suppose that the two populations have the same unknown standard deviation. A level C confidence interval for $\mu_1 - \mu_2$ is

$$(\bar{x}_1 - \bar{x}_2) \pm t^* s_p \sqrt{\frac{1}{n_1} + \frac{1}{n_2}}$$

Here t^* is the value for the $t(n_1 + n_2 - 2)$ density curve with area C between $-t^*$ and t^*.

To test the hypothesis H_0: $\mu_1 = \mu_2$, compute the **pooled two-sample *t* statistic**

$$t = \frac{\bar{x}_1 - \bar{x}_2}{s_p\sqrt{\dfrac{1}{n_1} + \dfrac{1}{n_2}}}$$

and use P-values from the $t(n_1 + n_2 - 2)$ distribution.

CASE 7.2 

HEALTHY COMPANIES VERSUS FAILED COMPANIES

In what ways are companies that fail different from those that continue to do business? To answer this question, one study compared various characteristics of 68 healthy and 33 failed firms.[20] One of the variables was the ratio of current assets to current liabilities. Roughly speaking, this is the amount that the firm is worth divided by what it owes. The data appear in Table 7.4.

As usual, we first examine the data. Histograms for the two groups of firms are given in Figure 7.10. Normal curves with mean and standard deviation equal to the sample values are superimposed on the histograms. The distribution for the healthy firms looks more Normal than the distribution for the failed firms. It appears that there may actually be two subgroups of data for the failed firms. This is seen more clearly in the back-to-back stemplot given in Figure 7.11. However, there are no outliers or strong departures from Normality that will prevent us from using the t procedures for these data. Let's compare the mean current assets to current liabilities ratio for the two groups of firms using a significance test.

TABLE 7.4 Ratio of current assets to current liabilities

Healthy firms						Failed firms		
1.50	0.10	1.76	1.14	1.84	2.21	0.82	0.89	1.31
2.08	1.43	0.68	3.15	1.24	2.03	0.05	0.83	0.90
2.23	2.50	2.02	1.44	1.39	1.64	1.68	0.99	0.62
0.89	0.23	1.20	2.16	1.80	1.87	0.91	0.52	1.45
1.91	1.67	1.87	1.21	2.05	1.06	1.16	1.32	1.17
0.93	2.17	2.61	3.05	1.52	1.93	0.42	0.48	0.93
1.95	2.61	1.11	0.95	0.96	2.25	0.88	1.10	0.23
2.73	1.56	2.73	0.90	2.12	1.42	1.11	0.19	0.13
1.62	1.76	2.22	2.80	1.85	0.96	2.03	0.51	1.12
1.71	1.02	2.50	1.55	1.69	1.64	0.92	0.26	1.15
1.03	1.80	0.67	2.44	2.30	2.21	0.13	0.88	0.09
1.96	1.81							

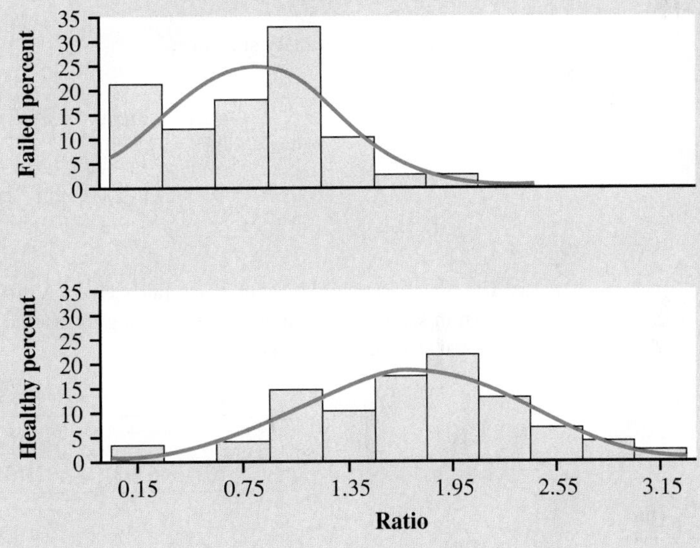

FIGURE 7.10 Histograms for assets to liabilities ratios, for Example 7.16.

EXAMPLE 7.16 Do Mean Asset/Liability Ratios Differ?

CASE 7.2

Take Group 1 to be the firms that were healthy and Group 2 to be those that failed. The question of interest is whether or not the mean ratio of current assets to current liabilities is different for the two groups. We therefore test

$$H_0\colon \mu_1 = \mu_2$$
$$H_a\colon \mu_1 \neq \mu_2$$

FIGURE 7.11 Back-to-back stemplot for assets to liabilities ratios, for Example 7.16.

Failed firms		Healthy firms
1 1 1 0 0	0	1
2 2	0	2
5 5 4 4	0	
6	0	6 6
9 9 9 9 9 8 8 8 8 8	0	8 9 9 9 9 9
1 1 1 1 1 1	1	0 0 0 1 1
3 3	1	2 2 2 3
4	1	4 4 4 5 5 5 5
6	1	6 6 6 6 6 7 7 7
	1	8 8 8 8 8 8 8 9 9 9 9
0	2	0 0 0 0 1 1 1
	2	2 2 2 2 2 3
	2	4 5 5
	2	6 6 7 7
	2	8
	3	0 1

Here are the summary statistics:

Group	Firms	n	$\bar{x}$	s
1	Healthy	68	1.7256	0.6393
2	Failed	33	0.8236	0.4811

The sample standard deviations are fairly close. A difference this large is not particularly unusual even in samples this large. We are willing to assume equal population standard deviations. The pooled sample variance is

$$s_p^2 = \frac{(n_1 - 1)s_1^2 + (n_2 - 1)s_2^2}{n_1 + n_2 - 2}$$

$$= \frac{(67)(0.6393)^2 + (32)(0.4811)^2}{68 + 33 - 2} = 0.35141$$

df = 100	
p	0.0005
t^*	3.300

so that

$$s_p = \sqrt{0.35141} = 0.5928$$

The pooled two-sample t statistic is

$$t = \frac{\bar{x}_1 - \bar{x}_2}{s_p\sqrt{\dfrac{1}{n_1} + \dfrac{1}{n_2}}}$$

$$= \frac{1.7256 - 0.8236}{0.5928\sqrt{\dfrac{1}{68} + \dfrac{1}{33}}} = 7.17$$

The P-value is $P(T \geq 7.17)$, where T has the $t(99)$ distribution. In Table D we have entries for 80 and 100 degrees of freedom. We will use the entries for 100. Our calculated value of t is larger than the $p = 0.0005$ entry in the table. Doubling 0.0005, we conclude that the two-sided P-value is less than 0.001. Statistical software gives a similar result—there is no practical need to report the exact P-value when it is smaller than 0.001.

Of course, a P-value is rarely a complete summary of a statistical analysis. To make a judgment regarding the size of the difference between the two groups of firms, we need a confidence interval.

EXAMPLE 7.17 How Different Are Mean Asset/Liability Ratios?

CASE 7.2

The difference in mean current assets to current liabilities ratios for healthy versus failed firms is

$$\bar{x}_1 - \bar{x}_2 = 1.7256 - 0.8236 = 0.902$$

For a 95% margin of error we will use the critical value $t^* = 1.984$ from the $t(100)$ distribution. The margin of error is

$$t^* s_p \sqrt{\frac{1}{n_1} + \frac{1}{n_2}} = (1.984)(0.5928)\sqrt{\frac{1}{68} + \frac{1}{33}}$$
$$= 0.25$$

We report that the successful firms have current assets to current liabilities ratios that average 0.90 higher than failed firms, with margin of error 0.25 for 95% confidence. Alternatively, we are 95% confident that the difference is between 0.65 and 1.15.

The pooled two-sample t procedures are anchored in statistical theory and have long been the standard version of the two-sample t in textbooks. But they require the condition that the two unknown population standard deviations are equal. As we shall see in Section 7.3, this condition is hard to verify.

The pooled t procedures are therefore a bit risky. They are reasonably robust against both non-Normality and unequal standard deviations when the sample sizes are nearly the same. When the samples are quite different in size, the pooled t procedures become sensitive to unequal standard deviations and should be used with caution unless the samples are large. Unequal standard deviations are quite common. In particular, it is common for the spread of data to increase when the center moves up, as in the data given in Case 7.2. We recommend regular use of the unpooled t procedures, particularly when software automates the Satterthwaite approximation.

APPLY YOUR KNOWLEDGE

7.63 Wheat prices revisited. Example 7.13 (page 456) gives summary statistics for prices received by wheat producers in September and July. The two sample standard deviations are very similar, so we may be willing to assume equal population standard deviations. Calculate the pooled t test statistic and its degrees of freedom from the summary statistics. Use Table D to assess significance. How do your results compare with the unpooled analysis in the example?

7.64 Using software. Figure 7.9 (page 460) gives the outputs from four software systems for comparing prices received by wheat producers in July and September for small samples of 5 producers in each month. Some of the software reports both pooled and unpooled analyses. Which outputs give the pooled results? What are the pooled t and its P-value?

7.65 Pooled equals unpooled? The software outputs in Figure 7.9 give the *same value* for the pooled and unpooled t statistics. Do some simple algebra to show that this is always true when the two sample sizes n_1 and n_2 are the same. In other cases, the two t statistics usually differ.

SECTION 7.2 SUMMARY

- Significance tests and confidence intervals for the difference of the means μ_1 and μ_2 of two Normal populations are based on the difference $\overline{x}_1 - \overline{x}_2$ of the sample means from two independent SRSs. Because of the central limit theorem, the resulting procedures are approximately correct for other population distributions when the sample sizes are large.

- When independent SRSs of sizes n_1 and n_2 are drawn from two Normal populations with parameters μ_1, σ_1 and μ_2, σ_2 the **two-sample z statistic**

$$z = \frac{(\overline{x}_1 - \overline{x}_2) - (\mu_1 - \mu_2)}{\sqrt{\frac{\sigma_1^2}{n_1} + \frac{\sigma_2^2}{n_2}}}$$

  has the $N(0, 1)$ distribution.

- The **two-sample t statistic**

$$t = \frac{(\overline{x}_1 - \overline{x}_2) - (\mu_1 - \mu_2)}{\sqrt{\frac{s_1^2}{n_1} + \frac{s_2^2}{n_2}}}$$

  does *not* have a t distribution. However, software can give accurate P-values and critical values using the **Satterthwaite approximation.**

- **Conservative inference procedures** for comparing μ_1 and μ_2 use the two-sample t statistic and the $t(k)$ distribution with degrees of freedom k equal to the smaller of $n_1 - 1$ and $n_2 - 1$. Use this method unless you are using software.

- An approximate level C **confidence interval** for $\mu_1 - \mu_2$ is given by

$$(\overline{x}_1 - \overline{x}_2) \pm t^* \sqrt{\frac{s_1^2}{n_1} + \frac{s_2^2}{n_2}}$$

  Here, t^* is the value for the $t(k)$ density curve with area C between $-t^*$ and t^*, where k either is found by the Satterthwaite approximation or is the smaller of $n_1 - 1$ and $n_2 - 1$. The **margin of error** is

$$t^* \sqrt{\frac{s_1^2}{n_1} + \frac{s_2^2}{n_2}}$$

- Significance tests for H_0: $\mu_1 = \mu_2$ are based on the **two-sample *t* statistic**

$$t = \frac{\bar{x}_1 - \bar{x}_2}{\sqrt{\frac{s_1^2}{n_1} + \frac{s_2^2}{n_2}}}$$

- The *P*-value is approximated using the $t(k)$ distribution, where k either is found by the Satterthwaite approximation or is the smaller of $n_1 - 1$ and $n_2 - 1$.
- The guidelines for practical use of two-sample *t* procedures are similar to those for one-sample *t* procedures. Equal sample sizes are recommended.
- If we can assume that the two populations have equal variances, **pooled two-sample *t* procedures** can be used. These are based on the **pooled estimator**

$$s_p^2 = \frac{(n_1 - 1)s_1^2 + (n_2 - 1)s_2^2}{n_1 + n_2 - 2}$$

of the unknown common variance and the $t(n_1 + n_2 - 2)$ distribution.

SECTION 7.2 Exercises

For Exercises 7.55 to 7.57, see page 454; for 7.58 and 7.59, see page 456; for 7.60 to 7.62, see page 461; and for 7.63 to 7.65, see pages 465–466.

In exercises that call for two-sample t procedures, you may use either of the two approximations for the degrees of freedom that we have discussed: the value given by your software or the smaller of $n_1 - 1$ and $n_2 - 1$. Be sure to state clearly which approximation you have used.

7.66 A multimedia program designed to change behavior. A multimedia program designed to improve dietary behavior among low-income women was evaluated by comparing women who were randomly assigned to intervention and control groups. The intervention was a 30-minute session in a computer kiosk in the Food Stamp office.[21] One of the outcomes was the score on a knowledge test taken about 2 months after the program. Here is a summary of the data:

Group	n	$\bar{x}$	s
Intervention	165	5.08	1.15
Control	212	4.33	1.16

(a) The test had six multiple-choice items that were scored as correct or incorrect, so the total score was an integer between 0 and 6. Do you think that these data are Normally distributed? Explain why or why not.

(b) Is it appropriate to use the two-sample *t* procedures that we studied in this section to analyze these data? Give reasons for your answer.

(c) Describe appropriate null and alternative hypotheses for evaluating the intervention. Some people would prefer a two-sided alternative in this situation while others would use a one-sided significance test. Give reasons for each point of view.

(d) Carry out the significance test. Report the test statistic with the degrees of freedom and the *P*-value. Write a short summary of your conclusion.

(e) Find a 95% confidence interval for the difference between the two means. Compare the information given by the interval with the information given by the significance test.

(f) The women in this study were all residents of Durham, North Carolina. To what extent do you think the results can be generalized to other populations?

7.67 Self-control and food. Self-efficacy is a general concept that measures how well we think we can control different situations. In the study described in the previous exercise, the participants were asked, "How sure are you that you can eat foods low in fat over the next month?" The response was measured on a five-point scale with 1 corresponding to "not sure at all" and 5 corresponding to "very sure." Here is a summary of the self-efficacy scores obtained about 2 months after the intervention:

Group	n	$\bar{x}$	s
Intervention	165	4.10	1.19
Control	212	3.67	1.12

Analyze the data using the questions in the previous exercise as a guide.

7.68 Dust exposure at work. Exposure to dust at work can lead to lung disease later in life. One study measured the workplace exposure of tunnel construction workers.[22] Part of the study compared 115 drill and blast workers with 220 outdoor concrete workers. Total dust exposure was measured in milligram years per cubic meter (mg.y/m^3). The mean exposure for the drill and blast workers was 18.0 mg.y/m^3 with a standard deviation of 7.8 mg.y/m^3. For the outdoor concrete workers, the corresponding values were 6.5 mg.y/m^3 and 3.4 mg.y/m^3.

(a) The sample included all workers for a tunnel construction company who received medical examinations as part of routine health checkups. Discuss the extent to which you think these results apply to other similar types of workers.

(b) Use a 95% confidence interval to describe the difference in the exposures. Write a sentence that gives the interval and provides the meaning of 95% confidence.

(c) Test the null hypothesis that the exposures for these two types of workers are the same. Justify your choice of a one-sided or two-sided alternative. Report the test statistic, the degrees of freedom, and the P-value. Give a short summary of your conclusion.

(d) The authors of the article describing these results note that the distributions are somewhat skewed. Do you think that this fact makes your analysis invalid? Give reasons for your answer.

7.69 Not all dust is the same. Not all dust particles that are in the air around us cause problems for our lungs. Some particles are too large and stick to other areas of our body before they can get to our lungs. Others are so small that we can breathe them in and out and they will not deposit in our lungs. The researchers in the study described in the previous exercise also measured respirable dust. This is dust that deposits in our lungs when we breathe it. For the drill and blast workers, the mean exposure to respirable dust was 6.3 mg.y/m^3 with a standard deviation of 2.8 mg.y/m^3. The corresponding values for the outdoor concrete workers were 1.4 mg.y/m^3 and 0.7 mg.y/m^3. Analyze these data using the questions in the previous exercise as a guide.

7.70 Change in portion size. A recent study of food portion sizes reported that over a 17-year period, the average size of a soft drink consumed by Americans aged 2 years and older increased from 13.1 ounces (oz) to 19.9 oz. The authors state that the difference is statistically significant with $P < 0.01$.[23] Explain what additional information you would need to compute a confidence interval for the increase and outline the procedure that you would use for the computations. Do you think that a confidence interval would provide useful additional information? Explain why or why not.

7.71 Compare two groups of consumers. The results in the previous exercise were based on two national surveys with a very large number of individuals. Here is a study that also looked at beverage consumption but with much smaller samples. One part of this study compared 20 children who were 7 to 10 years old with 5 who were 11 to 13.[24] The younger children consumed an average of 8.2 oz of sweetened drinks per day, while the older ones averaged 14.5 oz. The standard deviations were 10.7 oz and 8.2 oz respectively.

(a) Do you think that it is reasonable to assume that these data are Normally distributed? Explain why or why not. (*Hint:* Think about the 68–95–99.7 rule.)

(b) Using the methods in this section, test the null hypothesis that the two groups of children consume equal amounts of sweetened drinks versus the two-sided alternative. Report all details of the significance-testing procedure with your conclusion.

(c) Give a 95% confidence interval for the difference in means.

(d) Do you think that the analyses performed in parts (b) and (c) are appropriate for these data? Explain why or why not.

(e) The children in this study were all participants in an intervention study at the Cornell Summer Day Camp at Cornell University. To what extent do you think that these results apply to other groups of children?

7.72 What's wrong? In each of the following situations explain what is wrong and why.

(a) A researcher wants to test $H_0\colon \overline{x}_1 = \overline{x}_2$ versus the two-sided alternative $H_a\colon \overline{x}_1 \neq \overline{x}_2$.

(b) A study recorded the test scores of 20 children who were similar in age. The scores of the 10 boys in the study were compared with the scores of all 20 children using the two-sample methods of this section.

(c) A two-sample t statistic gave a P-value of 0.96. From this you can reject the null hypothesis with 95% confidence.

7.73 Basic concepts. For each of the following, answer the question and give a short explanation of your reasoning.

(a) A 95% confidence interval for the difference between two means is reported as (1.6, 2.3). What can you conclude about the results of a significance test of the null hypothesis that the population means are equal versus the two-sided alternative?

(b) Will larger samples generally give a larger or smaller margin of error for the difference between two sample means?

7.74 Basic concepts. For each of the following, answer the question and give a short explanation of your reasoning.

(a) A significance test for comparing two means gave $t = -3.11$ with 23 degrees of freedom. Can you reject the null hypothesis that the μ's are equal versus the two-sided alternative at the 5% significance level?

(b) Answer part (a) for the one-sided alternative that the difference in means is positive.

7.75 Effect of the confidence level. Assume $\bar{x}_1 = 100$, $\bar{x}_2 = 120$, $s_1 = 10$, $s_2 = 12$, $n_1 = 50$, and $n_2 = 50$. Find a 95% confidence interval for the difference in the corresponding values of μ. Does this interval include more or fewer values than a 99% confidence interval? Explain your answer.

7.76 CASE 7.2 **Healthy companies versus failed companies.** Table 7.4 gives data for 68 healthy firms and 33 comparable firms that failed. The variable recorded is the ratio of a firm's current assets to its current liabilities. We expect healthy firms to have a higher ratio of assets to liabilities on the average. Do the data give good evidence in favor of this expectation? By how much on the average does the ratio for healthy firms exceed that for failed firms (use 99% confidence)? (Examples 7.16 and 7.17 analyze these data under the special assumption that the two populations of firms have the same standard deviation. In practice, we prefer not to make this assumption.)

7.77 How much for an extra bedroom? Tom wants to compare the cost of one- and two-bedroom apartments in the area of your campus. He collects data for a random sample of 10 advertisements of each type. Here are the rents for the two-bedroom apartments (in dollars per month):

605, 510, 580, 650, 675, 675, 750, 500, 495, 675

Here are the rents for the one-bedroom apartments:

520, 645, 600, 505, 450, 550, 515, 495, 650, 385

Find a 95% confidence interval for the additional cost of a second bedroom.

7.78 Is the difference significant? Tom wonders if two-bedroom apartments rent for significantly more than one-bedroom apartments. Use the data in the previous exercise to find out.

(a) State appropriate null and alternative hypotheses.

(b) Report the test statistic, its degrees of freedom, and the P-value. What do you conclude?

(c) Can you conclude that every one-bedroom apartment costs less than every two-bedroom apartment?

(d) In the previous exercise you found a confidence interval. In this exercise you performed a significance test. Which do you think is more useful to someone planning to rent an apartment? Why?

7.79 Effect of storage on a product. Does bread lose vitamins when stored? Researchers prepared loaves of bread with flour fortified with a known amount of vitamins. After baking, they measured the vitamin C content of two loaves. Another two loaves were baked at the same time, stored for three days, and then the vitamin C content was measured. The units are milligrams of vitamin C per hundred grams of flour (mg/100 g). Here are the data:[25]

Immediately after baking:	47.62	49.79
Three days after baking:	21.25	22.34

(a) Does bread lose vitamin C when it is stored for three days? Use a two-sample t test to answer this question. (State the hypotheses, give the test statistic, degrees of freedom, and P-value, and state your conclusion in nontechnical language.)

(b) Give a 90% confidence interval for the amount of vitamin C lost.

7.80 Study design matters! The researchers in Exercise 7.79 might have measured the same two loaves of bread immediately after baking and again after three days. Suppose that the data given had come from this study design. (The values are for first loaf and second loaf from right to left.)

(a) Explain carefully why your analysis from Exercise 7.79 is *not correct* now, even though the data are the same.

(b) Redo the analysis for the design based on measuring the same loaves twice.

7.81 Another ingredient. The researchers of Exercise 7.79 also measured the amount of vitamin E (in mg/100 g of flour) in the same loaves. Here are the data:

Immediately after baking:	94.6	96.0
Three days after baking:	97.4	94.3

(a) Does bread lose vitamin E in short-term storage? State hypotheses for a statistical test, give the test statistic, degrees of freedom, and P-value, and state your conclusion.

(b) Give a 90% confidence interval for the amount of vitamin E lost.

7.82 Are the samples too small? Exercises 7.79 and 7.81 are based on samples of just two loaves of bread. Some people claim that significance tests with very small samples never lead to rejection of the null hypothesis. Discuss this claim using the results of these two exercises.

7.83 Interpreting software output. You use statistical software to perform a significance test of the null hypothesis that two means are equal. The software reports P-values for the two-sided alternative. Your alternative is that the first mean is greater than the second mean.

(a) The software reports $t = -1.88$ with a P-value of 0.07. Would you reject H_0 with $\alpha = 0.05$? Explain your answer.

(b) The software reports $t = 1.88$ with a P-value of 0.07. Would you reject H_0 with $\alpha = 0.05$? Explain your answer.

7.84 Piano lessons. Do piano lessons improve the spatial-temporal reasoning of preschool children? We examined this question in Exercises 7.38 and 7.39 (page 446) by analyzing the change in spatial-temporal reasoning of 34 preschool children after six months of piano lessons. Here we examine the same question by comparing the changes of those students with the changes of 44 children in a control group.[26] Here are the data for the children who took piano lessons:

2	5	7	−2	2	7	4	1	0	7	3	4
3	4	9	4	5	2	9	6	0	3	6	−1
3	4	6	7	−2	7	−3	3	4	4		

The control group scores are

1	−1	0	1	−4	0	0	1	0	−1
0	1	1	−3	−2	4	−1	2	4	2
2	2	−3	−3	0	2	0	−1	3	−1
5	−1	7	0	4	0	2	1	−6	0
2	−1	0	−2						

(a) Display the data and summarize the distributions.

(b) Make a table with the sample size, the mean, the standard deviation, and the standard error of the mean for each of the two groups.

(c) Translate the question of interest into hypotheses, test them, and summarize your conclusions.

7.85 Piano lessons, continued. The previous exercise gives data from a study of the effects of piano lessons. Give a 95% confidence interval that describes the comparison between the children who took piano lessons and the controls.

7.86 Comparing several statistical approaches. Exercises 7.38 and 7.39 (page 446) and Exercises 7.84 and 7.85 all address the effects of piano lessons on spatial-temporal reasoning. Discuss the relative merits of each approach. (You need not actually do all four exercises.)

7.87 Fitness and ego. Employers sometimes seem to prefer executives who appear physically fit, despite the legal troubles that may result. Employers may also favor certain personality characteristics. Fitness and personality are related. In one study, middle-aged college faculty who had volunteered for a fitness program were divided into low-fitness and high-fitness groups based on a physical examination. The subjects then took the Cattell Sixteen Personality Factor Questionnaire.[27] Here are the data for the "ego strength" personality factor:

Low fitness			High fitness		
4.99	5.53	3.12	6.68	5.93	5.71
4.24	4.12	3.77	6.42	7.08	6.20
4.74	5.10	5.09	7.32	6.37	6.04
4.93	4.47	5.40	6.38	6.53	6.51
4.16	5.30		6.16	6.68	

(a) Is the difference in mean ego strength significant at the 5% level? At the 1% level? Be sure to state H_0 and H_a.

(b) Can you generalize these results to the population of all middle-aged men? Give reasons for your answer.

(c) Can you conclude that increasing fitness *causes* an increase in ego strength? Give reasons for your answer.

7.88 Compare the effectiveness of two treatments. In a study of cereal leaf beetle damage to oats, researchers measured the number of beetle larvae per stem in small plots of oats after randomly applying one of two treatments: no pesticide or Malathion at the rate of 0.25 pound per acre. Here are the data:[28]

Control	2	4	3	4	2	3	3	5	3	2	6	3	4
Treatment	0	1	1	2	1	2	1	1	2	1	1	1	

(a) Is there significant evidence at the 1% level that the mean number of larvae per stem is reduced by Malathion? Be sure to state H_0 and H_a.

(b) These data are far from Normal. Why? The researchers nonetheless used t procedures. Although we might prefer a different approach, t procedures are probably reasonably accurate here. Why?

7.89 Study design matters! In Exercise 7.87 you analyzed data on the ego strength of high-fitness and low-fitness participants in an campus fitness program. Suppose that instead you had data on the ego strengths of the *same* men before and after six months in the program. You wonder if the program has affected their ego scores. Explain carefully how the statistical procedures you would use would differ from those you applied in Exercise 7.87.

7.90 Cocaine use and low birth weight. Does cocaine use by pregnant women cause their babies to have low birth weight? To study this question, birth weights of babies of women who tested positive for cocaine during a drug-screening test were compared with the birth weights for women who either tested negative or were not tested, a group we call "other."[29] Here are the summary statistics. The birth weights are measured in grams.

Group	n	$\bar{x}$	s
Positive test	134	2733	599
Other	5974	3118	672

(a) Formulate appropriate hypotheses and carry out the test of significance for these data.

(b) Give a 95% confidence interval for the mean difference in birth weights.

(c) Discuss the limitations of the study design. What do you believe can be concluded from this study?

7.91 Sales of small appliances. A market research firm supplies manufacturers with estimates of the retail sales of their products from samples of retail stores. Marketing managers are prone to look at the estimate and ignore sampling error. Suppose that an SRS of 70 stores this month shows mean sales of 53 units of a small appliance, with standard deviation 12 units. During the same month last year, an SRS of 58 stores gave mean sales of 50 units, with standard deviation 10 units. An increase from 50 to 53 is a rise of 6%. The marketing manager is happy, because sales are up 6%.

(a) Use the two-sample t procedure to give a 95% confidence interval for the difference in mean number of units sold at all retail stores.

(b) Explain in language that the manager can understand why he cannot be confident that sales rose by 6%, and that in fact sales may even have dropped.

7.92 Compare two marketing strategies. A bank compares two proposals to increase the amount that its credit card customers charge on their cards. (The bank earns a percentage of the amount charged, paid by the stores that accept the card.) Proposal A offers to eliminate the annual fee for customers who charge $4000 or more during the year. Proposal B offers a small percent of the total amount charged as a cash rebate at the end of the year. The bank offers each proposal to an SRS of 150 of its existing credit card customers. At the end of the year, the total amount charged by each customer is recorded. Here are the summary statistics:

Group	n	$\bar{x}$	s
A	150	$2185	$368
B	150	$2042	$411

(a) Do the data show a significant difference between the mean amounts charged by customers offered the two plans? Give the null and alternative hypotheses, and calculate the two-sample t statistic. Obtain the P-value (either approximately from Table D or more accurately from software). State your practical conclusions.

(b) The distributions of amounts charged are skewed to the right, but outliers are prevented by the limits that the bank imposes on credit balances. Do you think that skewness threatens the validity of the test that you used in (a)? Explain your answer.

7.93 Study habits. The Survey of Study Habits and Attitudes (SSHA) is a psychological test designed to measure the motivation, study habits, and attitudes toward learning of college students. These factors, along with ability, are important in explaining success in school. Scores on the SSHA range from 0 to 200. A selective private college gives the SSHA to an SRS of both male and female first-year students. The data for the women are as follows:

156	109	137	115	152	140	154	178	111
123	126	126	137	165	165	129	200	150

Here are the scores of the men:

118	140	114	91	180	115	126	92	169	139
121	132	75	88	113	151	70	115	187	114

(a) Examine each sample graphically, with special attention to outliers and skewness. Is use of a t procedure acceptable for these data?

(b) Most studies have found that the mean SSHA score for men is lower than the mean score in a comparable group of women. Test this supposition here. That is, state hypotheses, carry out the test and obtain a P-value, and give your conclusions.

(c) Give a 90% confidence interval for the mean difference between the SSHA scores of male and female first-year students at this college.

7.94 Summer earnings of college students. College financial aid offices expect students to use summer earnings to help pay for college. But how large are these earnings? One college studied this question by asking a sample of students how much they earned.[30] Omitting students who were not employed, 1355 responses were received. Here are the data in summary form:

Group	n	$\overline{x}$	s
Males	680	\$3397.91	\$2494.65
Females	675	\$2480.68	\$1915.55

(a) Use the two-sample t procedures to give a 90% confidence interval for the difference between the mean summer earnings of male and female students.

(b) The distribution of earnings is strongly skewed to the right. Nevertheless, use of t procedures is justified. Why?

(c) Once the sample size was decided, the sample was chosen by taking every kth name from an alphabetical list of undergraduates. Is it reasonable to consider the samples as SRSs chosen from the male and female undergraduate populations?

(d) What other information about the study would you request before accepting the results as describing all undergraduates?

The following exercises concern optional material on the Satterthwaite approximation and the pooled two-sample t procedures.

7.95 Satterthwaite approximation. Example 7.11 (page 452) reports an analysis comparing a new with a traditional method for teaching reading. Starting from the computer's results for $\overline{x}_i$ and s_i, verify that the Satterthwaite approximation for the degrees of freedom is 37.9.

7.96 Pooled procedures. Exercise 7.58 (page 456) compares a new type of computer monitor with a standard design. Reanalyze the data using the pooled procedure. Does the conclusion depend on the choice of the method? The standard deviations are quite different for these data, so we do not recommend use of the pooled procedures in this case.

7.97 The advantage of pooling. The analysis of the loss of vitamin C when bread is stored (Exercise 7.79, page 469) is a rather extreme case. There are only two observations per condition (immediately after baking and three days later). When the samples are so small, we have very little information to make a judgment about whether the population standard deviations are equal. The potential gain from pooling is large when the sample sizes are very small. Assume that we will perform a two-sided test using the 5% significance level.

(a) Find the critical value for the unpooled t test statistic that does not assume equal variances. Use the minimum of $n_1 - 1$ and $n_2 - 1$ for the degrees of freedom.

(b) Find the critical value for the pooled t test statistic.

(c) How does comparing these critical values show an advantage of the pooled test?

7.98 The advantage of pooling. Suppose that in the setting of the previous exercise you are interested in 95% confidence intervals for the difference rather than significance testing. Find the widths of the intervals for the two procedures (assuming or not assuming equal standard deviations). How do they compare?

7.3 Optional Topics in Comparing Distributions*

In this section we discuss two topics that are related to the procedures we have learned for inference about population means. First, it is natural to ask if we can do inference about population spread as well. The answer is yes, but there are many cautions. We also show how to find the power for the two-sample t test. This is a bit technical, but necessary if you plan to design studies.

*This section can be omitted without loss of continuity.

Inference for population spread

The two most basic descriptive features of a distribution are its center and spread. In a Normal population, we measure center and spread by the mean and the standard deviation. We have described procedures for inference about population means for Normal populations and found that these procedures are often useful for non-Normal populations as well. It is natural to turn next to inference about the standard deviations of Normal populations. Our recommendation here is short and clear: Don't do it without expert advice.

There are indeed inference procedures appropriate for the standard deviations of Normal populations. We will describe the most common such procedure, the F test for comparing the spread of two Normal populations. Unlike the t procedures for means, the F test and other procedures for standard deviations are extremely sensitive to non-Normal distributions.[31] This lack of robustness does not improve in large samples. It is difficult in practice to tell whether a significant F-value is evidence of unequal population spreads or simply evidence that the populations are not Normal.

The deeper difficulty that underlies the very poor robustness of Normal population procedures for inference about spread already appeared in our work on describing data. The standard deviation is a natural measure of spread for Normal distributions but not for distributions in general. In fact, because skewed distributions have unequally spread tails, no single numerical measure is adequate to describe the spread of a skewed distribution. Thus, the standard deviation is not always a useful parameter, and even when it is, the results of inference about it are not trustworthy. Consequently, we do not recommend use of inference about population standard deviations in basic statistical practice.[32]

It was once common to test equality of standard deviations as a preliminary to performing the pooled two-sample t test for equality of two population means. It is better practice to check the distributions graphically, with special attention to skewness and outliers, and to use the more general two-sample t that does not require equal standard deviations.

Chapters 14 and 15 discuss procedures called "analysis of variance" for comparing several means. These procedures are extensions of the pooled t test and require that the populations have a common standard deviation. Fortunately, like the t test, analysis of variance comparisons of means are quite robust. (Analysis of variance uses F statistics, but these are not the same as the F statistic for comparing two population standard deviations.) Formal tests for the equality of two standard deviations are not very robust and will often give misleading results. In the words of one distinguished statistician, "To make a preliminary test on variances is rather like putting to sea in a rowing boat to find out whether conditions are sufficiently calm for an ocean liner to leave port!"[33]

The F test for equality of spread

Because of the limited usefulness of procedures for inference about the standard deviations of Normal distributions, we will present only one such procedure. Suppose that we have independent SRSs from two Normal populations, a sample of size n_1 from $N(\mu_1, \sigma_1)$ and a sample of size n_2 from $N(\mu_2, \sigma_2)$. The population means and standard deviations are all unknown. The hypothesis of equal spread,

$$H_0: \sigma_1 = \sigma_2$$
$$H_a: \sigma_1 \neq \sigma_2$$

is tested by a simple statistic, the ratio of the two sample variances.

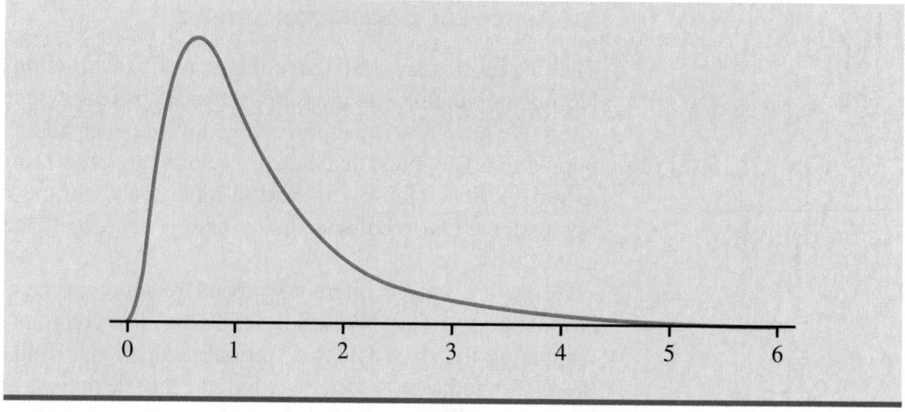

FIGURE 7.12 The density curve for the $F(9, 10)$ distribution. The F distributions are skewed to the right.

The F Statistic and F Distributions

When s_1^2 and s_2^2 are sample variances from independent SRSs of sizes n_1 and n_2 drawn from Normal populations, the ***F* statistic**

$$F = \frac{s_1^2}{s_2^2}$$

has the ***F* distribution** with $n_1 - 1$ and $n_2 - 1$ degrees of freedom when H_0: $\sigma_1 = \sigma_2$ is true.

F distributions

The ***F* distributions** are a family of distributions with two parameters, the degrees of freedom of the sample variances in the numerator and denominator of the F statistic.* The numerator degrees of freedom are always mentioned first. Interchanging the degrees of freedom changes the distribution, so the order is important. Our brief notation will be $F(j, k)$ for the F distribution with j degrees of freedom in the numerator and k in the denominator. The F distributions are not symmetric but are right-skewed. The density curve in Figure 7.12 illustrates the shape. Because sample variances cannot be negative, the F statistic takes only positive values and the F distribution has no probability below 0. The peak of the F density curve is near 1; values far from 1 in either direction provide evidence against the hypothesis of equal standard deviations.

Tables of F critical values are awkward, because a separate table is needed for every pair of degrees of freedom j and k. Table E in the back of the book gives upper p critical values of the F distributions for $p = 0.10, 0.05, 0.025, 0.01$, and 0.001. For example, these critical values for the $F(9, 10)$ distribution shown in Figure 7.12 are

p	0.10	0.05	0.025	0.01	0.001
F^*	2.35	3.02	3.78	4.94	8.96

The skewness of the F distributions causes additional complications. In the symmetric Normal and t distributions, the point with probability 0.05 below it is just the negative of

*The F distributions are another of R. A. Fisher's contributions to statistics and are called F in his honor. Fisher introduced F statistics for comparing several means. We will meet these useful statistics in Chapters 14 and 15.

the point with probability 0.05 above it. This is not true for F distributions. We therefore require either tables of both the upper and lower tails or some way of getting by without lower-tail critical values. Statistical software that eliminates the need for tables is plainly very convenient. If you do not use statistical software, arrange the F test as follows:

1. Take the test statistic to be

$$F = \frac{\text{larger } s^2}{\text{smaller } s^2}$$

This amounts to naming the populations so that s_1^2 is the larger of the observed sample variances. The resulting F is always 1 or greater.

2. Compare the value of F with critical values from Table E. Then *double* the significance levels from the table to obtain the significance level for the two-sided F test.

The idea is that we calculate the probability in the upper tail and double to obtain the probability of all ratios on either side of 1 that are at least as improbable as that observed. Remember that the order of the degrees of freedom is important in using Table E.

EXAMPLE 7.18 Comparing Healthy and Failed Firms

CASE 7.2

Case 7.2 (page 462) recounts a study that compared the mean ratios of current assets to current liabilities for successful and failed firms. There we used the pooled two-sample t procedures. Because these procedures require equal population standard deviations, it is tempting to first test

$$H_0: \sigma_1 = \sigma_2$$
$$H_a: \sigma_1 \neq \sigma_2$$

The 68 healthy firms had a standard deviation of $s = 0.6393$, while the 33 failed firms had a standard deviation of $s = 0.4811$. The F test statistic is therefore

$$F = \frac{\text{larger } s^2}{\text{smaller } s^2} = \frac{0.6393^2}{0.4811^2} = 1.77$$

We compare the calculated value $F = 1.77$ with critical points for the $F(67, 32)$ distribution. One set of entries in Table E that is close to this distribution is the $F(60, 30)$ distribution. Our observed value $F = 1.77$ falls between the critical values $F^* = 1.74$ and $F^* = 1.94$, corresponding to tail areas 0.05 and 0.025. The two-sided P-value therefore lies between 0.10 and 0.05. The standard deviations are significantly different at the 10% level but not at the 5% level.

In most significance tests, we insist on quite strong evidence before we abandon a null hypothesis. That's because we are trying to convince ourselves and others that the effect described by the alternative hypothesis really is present in the population. In this example, however, the null hypothesis H_0: $\sigma_1 = \sigma_2$ is a requirement for using the pooled t to compare two means. Evidence much weaker than the usual significance levels of 5% or 1% should lead you to question H_0 and abandon the pooled t for the more general t that we have recommended.

Statistical output often includes the results of this test with the output for the two-sample t test. Here is the output from SAS:

Equality of Variances

Variable	Method	Num DF	Den DF	F Value	Pr > F
ratio	Folded F	67	32	1.77	0.0792

We see that the exact P-value, *if* the populations are Normal, is 0.0792. When we examined the histograms and the stemplot (Figures 7.10 and 7.11) for these data, we noted that the data for the failed firms did not look particularly Normal, but we were not concerned about that fact because we were interested in comparing the means. For the question of equality of variances, we are not in the same situation. To the extent that our populations are not Normal, we are less confident in our conclusion that the standard deviations are not significantly different.

The power of the two-sample t test

The two-sample t test is one of the most used statistical procedures. Unfortunately, because of inadequate planning, users frequently fail to find evidence for the effects that they believe to be present. Power calculations should be part of the planning of any statistical study.

In an optional part of Section 7.1, we learned how to approximate the power of the one-sample t test. The basic idea is the same for the two-sample case, but we give the exact method rather than an approximation. The exact power calculation involves a new distribution, the **noncentral t distribution.** This calculation is not practical by hand but is easy with software that calculates probabilities for this new distribution.

noncentral t distribution

We consider only the common case where the null hypothesis is "no difference," $\mu_1 - \mu_2 = 0$. We illustrate the calculation for the pooled two-sample t test. A simple modification is needed when we do not pool. The unknown parameters in the pooled t setting are μ_1, μ_2, and a single common standard deviation σ. To find the power for the pooled two-sample t test, follow these steps.

Step 1. Specify these quantities:

(a) an alternative that you consider important to detect; that is, a value for $\mu_1 - \mu_2$;

(b) the sample sizes, n_1 and n_2;

(c) a fixed significance level α, often $\alpha = 0.05$; and

(d) an estimate of the standard deviation σ from a pilot study or previous studies under similar conditions.

Step 2. Find the degrees of freedom $\text{df} = n_1 + n_2 - 2$ and the value of t^* that will lead to rejecting H_0 at your chosen level α.

noncentrality parameter

Step 3. Calculate the **noncentrality parameter**

$$\delta = \frac{|\mu_1 - \mu_2|}{\sigma\sqrt{\dfrac{1}{n_1} + \dfrac{1}{n_2}}}$$

Step 4. The power is the probability that a noncentral t random variable with degrees of freedom df and noncentrality parameter δ will be less than t^*. Use software to calculate this probability. In SAS, the command is `1-PROBT(tstar,df,delta)`. If you do not have software that can perform this calculation, you can approximate the power as the probability that a standard Normal random variable is greater than $t^* - \delta$, that is, $P(Z > t^* - \delta)$. Use Table A or software for standard Normal probabilities.

Note that the denominator in the noncentrality parameter,

$$\sigma\sqrt{\frac{1}{n_1}+\frac{1}{n_2}}$$

is our guess at the standard error for the difference in the sample means. Therefore, if we wanted to assess a possible study in terms of the margin of error for the estimated difference, we would examine t^* times this quantity.

If we do not assume that the standard deviations are equal, we need to guess both standard deviations and then combine these to get an estimate of the standard error:

$$\sqrt{\frac{\sigma_1^2}{n_1}+\frac{\sigma_2^2}{n_2}}$$

This guess is then used in the denominator of the noncentrality parameter. Use the conservative value, the smaller of $n_1 - 1$ and $n_2 - 1$, for the degrees of freedom.

EXAMPLE 7.19 Healthy versus Failed Firms

CASE 7.2 

In Case 7.2 we compared the ratio of current assets to current liabilities for 68 successful and 33 failed firms. Using the pooled two-sample procedure, the difference was statistically significant ($t = 7.71$, df $= 99$, $P < 0.001$). Now that this study is several years old, we are planning a similar study to determine if the finding continues to hold.

Should our new sample have similar numbers of firms? Or could we save resources by using smaller samples and still be able to declare that the successful and failed firms are different? To answer this question, we do a power calculation.

Step 1. We want to be able to detect a difference in the means that is about the same as the value that we observed in our previous study. So in our calculations we will use $\mu_1 - \mu_2 = 1.15$. We are willing to assume that the standard deviations will be about the same as in the earlier study, so we take the standard deviation for each of the two groups of firms to be the pooled value from our previous study, $\sigma = 0.5928$.

We need only two pieces of additional information: a significance level α and the sample sizes n_1 and n_2. For the first, we will choose the standard value $\alpha = 0.05$. For the sample sizes we want to try several different values. Let's start with $n_1 = 15$ and $n_2 = 15$.

Step 2. The degrees of freedom are $n_1 + n_2 - 2 = 28$. The critical value is $t^* = 2.048$, the value from Table D for a two-sided $\alpha = 0.05$ significance test based on 28 degrees of freedom.

Step 3. The noncentrality parameter is

$$\delta = \frac{1.15}{0.5928\sqrt{\frac{1}{15}+\frac{1}{15}}} = \frac{1.15}{0.2165} = 5.31$$

Step 4. Software gives the power as 0.99922, over 99.9%. The Normal approximation is very accurate:

$$P(Z > t^* - \delta) = P(Z > -3.262) = 0.99945$$

If we repeat the calculation with $n_1 = 10$ and $n_2 = 10$, we still have power greater than 0.98. A difference of means as large as that found in the earlier study can be detected with quite small samples.

A different, and perhaps more important, issue is the margin of error for the estimated difference. For $n_1 = 15$ and $n_2 = 15$, it is

$$t^* \times 0.5928\sqrt{\frac{1}{15} + \frac{1}{15}} = 2.048 \times 5.31 = 0.44$$

Repeating the calculation for $n_1 = 10$ and $n_2 = 10$ gives 0.56. If we want to reduce the margin of error for the difference in the means of asset/liability ratios, we will need larger sample sizes.

SECTION 7.3 SUMMARY

- Inference procedures for comparing the standard deviations of two Normal populations are based on the ***F* statistic,** which is the ratio of sample variances:

$$F = \frac{s_1^2}{s_2^2}$$

- When an SRS of size n_1 is drawn from the x_1 population and an independent SRS of size n_2 is drawn from the x_2 population, the F statistic has the ***F* distribution** $F(n_1 - 1, n_2 - 1)$ if the two population standard deviations σ_1 and σ_2 are in fact equal.

- The ***F* test for equality of standard deviations** tests H_0: $\sigma_1 = \sigma_2$ versus H_a: $\sigma_1 \neq \sigma_2$ using the statistic

$$F = \frac{\text{larger } s^2}{\text{smaller } s^2}$$

and doubles the upper-tail probability to obtain the P-value.

- The t procedures are quite **robust** when the distributions are not Normal. The F tests and other procedures for inference about the spread of one or more Normal distributions are not robust. They are so strongly affected by non-Normality that we do not recommend them for regular use.

- The **power** of the two-sample t test is found by first finding the critical value for the significance test, the degrees of freedom, and the **noncentrality parameter** for the alternative of interest. These are used to calculate the power from a **noncentral *t* distribution.** A Normal approximation works quite well. Calculating margins of error for various study designs and conditions is an alternative procedure for evaluating designs.

SECTION 7.3 Exercises

In all exercises calling for use of the F test, assume that both population distributions are very close to Normal. The actual data are not always sufficiently Normal to justify use of the F test.

7.99 The F statistic $F = s_1^2/s_2^2$ is calculated from samples of size $n_1 = 16$ and $n_2 = 21$. (Remember that n_1 is the numerator sample size.)

(a) What is the upper 5% critical value for this F?

(b) In a test of equality of standard deviations against the two-sided alternative, this statistic has the value $F = 2.45$. Is this value significant at the 10% level? Is it significant at the 5% level?

7.100 The F statistic for equality of standard deviations based on samples of sizes $n_1 = 10$ and $n_2 = 17$ takes the value $F = 3.12$.

(a) Is this significant evidence of unequal population standard deviations at the 5% level?

(b) Use Table E to give an upper and a lower bound for the P-value.

7.101 **Piano lessons.** In Exercise 7.84 (page 470) we examined the effect of piano lessons on spatial-temporal reasoning. Do the data provide evidence that would cause us to suspect that the standard deviation of the children who took piano lessons is different from that of the controls? Set up the hypotheses, perform the significance test, and summarize the results.

7.102 **Wheat prices.** Example 7.14 (page 458) describes a USDA survey used to estimate wheat prices in July and September. Calculate the two sample standard deviations. Perform the test for equality of standard deviations and summarize your conclusion.

7.103 **Vitamin C loss in storage.** Exercise 7.79 (page 469) presents data on the loss of vitamin C when bread is stored. Two loaves were measured immediately after baking and another two loaves were measured after three days of storage. These are very small sample sizes.

(a) Use Table E to find the value that the ratio of variances would have to exceed for us to reject (at the 5% level) the null hypothesis that the standard deviations are equal. What does this suggest about the power of the test?

(b) Perform the test and state your conclusion.

7.104 **Vitamin E loss in storage.** Exercise 7.81 (page 469) gives data on the loss of vitamin E when bread is stored. Two loaves were measured immediately after baking and another two loaves were measured after three days of storage. These are very small sample sizes.

(a) Use Table E to find the value that the ratio of variances would have to exceed for us to reject (at the 5% level) the null hypothesis that the standard deviations are equal. What does this suggest about the power of the test?

(b) Perform the test and state your conclusion.

7.105 **Study habits of men and women.** Return to the SSHA data in Exercise 7.93 (page 471). SSHA scores are generally less variable among women than among men. We want to know whether this is true for this college.

(a) State H_0 and H_a. Note that H_a is one-sided.

(b) Because Table E contains only upper critical values for F, a one-sided test requires the numerator s^2 in the F statistic to belong to the group that H_a claims to have the larger σ. Calculate this F.

(c) Compare F to the entries in Table E (no doubling of p) to obtain the P-value. Be sure the degrees of freedom are in the proper order. What do you conclude about the variation in SSHA scores?

7.106 **Cocaine use and birth weight: power.** Exercise 7.90 (page 471) summarizes data on cocaine use and birth weight. The study has been criticized because of several design problems. Suppose that you are designing a new study. Based on the results in Exercise 7.90, you think that the true difference in mean birth weights may be about 300 grams (g). A difference this large is clinically important. For planning purposes assume that you will have 100 women in each group and that the common standard deviation is 650 g, a guess that is between the two standard deviations in Exercise 7.90. If you use a pooled two-sample t test with significance level 0.05, what is the power of the test for this design?

7.107 **Power, continued.** Repeat the power calculation in the previous exercise, for 25, 50, 75, and 125 women in each group. Summarize your power study, including the results for 100 women per group that you found in the previous exercise. A graph of power against sample size will help.

7.108 **Margins of error.** For each of the sample sizes considered in the previous two exercises, estimate the margin of error for the 95% confidence interval for the difference in mean weights. Display these results with a graph or a sketch.

7.109 **Ego strength: power.** You want to compare the ego strengths of MBA students who plan to seek work at consulting firms and those who favor manufacturing firms. Based on the data from Exercise 7.87, you will use $\sigma = 0.7$ for planning purposes. The pooled two-sample t test with $\alpha = 0.01$ will be used to make the comparison. You judge a difference of 0.5 points to be of interest.

(a) Find the power for the design with 20 MBA students in each group.

(b) The power in part (a) is not acceptable. Redo the calculations for 30 students in each group and $\alpha = 0.05$.

STATISTICS IN SUMMARY

This chapter presents t tests and confidence intervals for inference about the mean of a single population and for comparing the means of two populations. The one-sample t procedures do inference about one mean, and the two-sample t procedures compare two means. Matched pairs studies use one-sample procedures because you first create a single sample by taking the differences in the responses within each pair. These t procedures are among the most common methods of statistical inference.

The t procedures require that the data be random samples and that the distribution of the population or populations be Normal. One reason for the wide use of t procedures is that they are not very strongly affected by lack of Normality. If you can't regard your data as a random sample, however, the results of inference may be of little value.

The chapter exercises are important in this and later chapters. You must now recognize problem settings and decide which of the methods presented in the chapter fits. In this chapter, you must recognize one-sample studies, matched pairs studies, and two-sample studies. Here are the most important skills you should have after reading this chapter.

A. Recognition

1. Recognize when a problem requires inference about a mean or comparing two means.
2. Recognize from the design of a study whether one-sample, matched pairs, or two-sample procedures are needed.

B. One-Sample t Procedures

1. Recognize when the t procedures are appropriate in practice, in particular that they are quite robust against lack of Normality but are influenced by outliers.
2. Also recognize when the design of the study, outliers, or a small sample from a skewed distribution make the t procedures risky.
3. Use t to obtain a confidence interval at a stated level of confidence for the mean μ of a population.
4. Carry out a t test for the hypothesis that a population mean μ has a specified value against either a one-sided or a two-sided alternative. Use Table D of t distribution critical values to approximate the P-value or carry out a fixed α test.
5. Recognize matched pairs data and use the t procedures to obtain confidence intervals and to perform tests of significance for such data.

C. Two-Sample t Procedures

1. Recognize when the two-sample t procedures are appropriate in practice.
2. Give a confidence interval for the difference between two means. Use the two-sample t statistic with conservative degrees of freedom if you do not have statistical software. Use software if you have it.
3. Test the hypothesis that two populations have equal means against either a one-sided or a two-sided alternative. Use the two-sample t test with conservative degrees of freedom if you do not have statistical software. Use software if you have it.
4. Know that procedures for comparing the standard deviations of two Normal populations are available, but that these procedures are risky because they are not at all robust against non-Normal distributions.

CHAPTER 7 Review Exercises

7.110 Does dress affect competence and intelligence ratings? Researchers performed a study to examine whether or not women are perceived as less competent and less intelligent when they dress in a sexy manner versus a business-like manner. Competence was rated from 1 (not at all) to 7 (extremely), and a 1 to 5 scale was used for intelligence. Under each condition, 17 subjects provided data. Here are summary statistics:[34]

	Sexy		Business-like	
Rating	Mean	SD	Mean	SD
Competence	4.13	0.99	5.42	0.85
Intelligence	2.91	0.74	3.50	0.71

Analyze the two variables and write a report summarizing your work. Be sure to include details regarding the statistical methods you used, your assumptions, and your conclusions.

7.111 Perceived quality of high- and low-performing restaurants. A study classified 394 quick-service restaurants (QSR) into high-performing and low-performing groups based on their total sales. Each restaurant was rated on a collection of perceived measures of quality by a large number of diners using a 1 to 7 scale. In this study we view the diners as a measuring instrument, and our major interest is in comparing the 170 high-sales restaurants with the 224 low-sales restaurants. Here are summary statistics:[35]

	High Sales		Low Sales	
Perceived quality	Mean	SD	Mean	SD
Food served in promised time	4.60	1.35	4.15	1.38
Quickly corrects mistakes	3.59	1.25	3.43	1.19
Well-dressed staff	4.25	1.31	3.86	1.38
Visually attractive menu	4.54	1.45	4.33	1.35
Ordered food served accurately	4.22	1.26	3.85	1.13
Well-trained personnel	4.01	1.27	3.95	1.18
Clean dining area and restrooms	4.05	1.26	3.97	1.24
Employees adjust to needs	3.94	1.19	3.80	1.24
Employees know menu	4.17	1.19	3.88	1.15
Convenient operating hours	4.83	1.32	4.59	1.19

Use this information to compare the two groups of restaurants and write a report summarizing your work. Be sure to include details regarding the statistical methods you used, your assumptions, and your conclusions.

7.112 Evaluate the dress study. Refer to Exercise 7.110. Participants in the study viewed a videotape of a woman described as a 28-year-old senior manager for a Chicago advertising firm who had been working for this firm for 7 years. The same woman was used for each of the two conditions, but she wore different clothing each time. For the business-like condition, the woman wore little makeup, black slacks, a turtleneck, a business jacket, and flat shoes. For the sexy condition, the same woman wore a tight knee-length skirt, a low-cut shirt with a cardigan over it, high-heeled shoes, and more makeup, and her hair was tousled. The subjects who evaluated the videotape were male and female undergraduate students who were predominantly Caucasian, from middle- to upper-class backgrounds, and between the ages of 18 and 24. The content of the videotape was identical in both conditions. The woman described her general background, life in college, and hobbies.

(a) Write a critique of this study with particular emphasis on its limitations and how you would take these into account when drawing conclusions based on the study.

(b) Propose an alternative study that would address a similar question. Be sure to provide details about how your study would be run.

7.113 Evaluate the restaurant study. Refer to Exercise 7.111. Subjects who provided the evaluation data were shoppers who entered a mall between the hours of 1:00 P.M. 6:00 P.M., on Monday, Wednesday, and Saturday during two weeks, at a single location in Seoul, South Korea. A total of 950 questionnaires were distributed, and 394 provided data that could be used in the study. Seven QSRs were studied: McDonald's, Burger King, Hardee's, Jakob's, KFC, Lotteria, and Popeye's. Jakob's and Lotteria are two major domestic QSR brands. To account for size differences, total sales were divided by the number of units in operation during the survey period to determine sales per unit. This was the variable used to classify the QSR brands. Age, education, number of visits to QSRs per month, and average amount spent per visit for the sample were compared with other surveys of QSR customers. No statistically significant differences in these variables were found.

(a) Write a critique of this study with particular emphasis on its limitations and how you would take these into account when drawing conclusions based on the study.

(b) Propose an alternative study that would address a similar question. Be sure to provide details about how your study would be run.

7.114 Air in poultry-processing plants. The air in poultry-processing plants often contains fungus spores. If the ventilation is inadequate, this can affect the health of the workers. The problem is most serious during the summer. To measure the presence of spores, air samples are pumped to an agar plate and "colony-forming units (CFUs)" are counted after an incubation period. Here are data from two locations in a plant that processes 37,000 turkeys per day, taken on four days in the summer. The units are CFUs per cubic meter of air.[36]

	Day 1	Day 2	Day 3	Day 4
Kill room	3175	2526	1763	1090
Processing	529	141	362	224

(a) Explain carefully why these are matched pairs data.

(b) The spore count is clearly higher in the kill room. Give sample means and a 90% confidence interval to estimate how much higher. Be sure to state your conclusion in plain English.

7.115 Personalities of hotel managers. Successful hotel managers must have personality characteristics often thought of as feminine (such as "compassionate") as well as those often thought of as masculine (such as "forceful"). The Bem Sex-Role Inventory (BSRI) is a personality test that gives separate ratings for female and male stereotypes, both on a scale of 1 to 7. Here are summary statistics for a sample of 148 male general mangers of three-star and four-star hotels.[37] The data come from a comprehensive mailing to these hotels. The response rate was 48%, which is good for mail surveys of this kind. Although nonresponse remains an issue, users of statistics usually act as if they have an SRS when the response rate is "good enough."

	Masculinity score	Femininity score
Mean	$\bar{x} = 5.91$	$\bar{x} = 5.29$
Standard deviation	$s = 0.57$	$s = 0.75$

The mean BSRI masculinity score for the general male population is $\mu = 4.88$. Is there evidence that hotel managers on the average score higher in masculinity than the general male population?

7.116 Another personality trait of hotel managers. Continue your study from the previous exercise. The mean BSRI femininity score in the general male population is $\mu = 5.19$. (It does seem odd that the mean femininity score is higher than the mean masculinity score, but such is the world of personality tests. The two scales are separate.) Is there evidence that hotel managers on the average score higher in femininity than the general male population?

7.117 Alcohol content of wine. The alcohol content of wine depends on the grape variety, the way in which the wine is produced from the grapes, the weather, and other influences. Here are data on the percent of alcohol in wine produced from the same grape variety in the same year by 48 winemakers in the same region of Italy:[38]

12.86	12.88	12.81	12.70	12.51
12.60	12.25	12.53	13.49	12.84
12.93	13.36	13.52	13.62	12.25
13.16	13.88	12.87	13.32	13.08
13.50	12.79	13.11	13.23	12.58
13.17	13.84	12.45	14.34	13.48
12.36	13.69	12.85	12.96	13.78
13.73	13.45	12.82	13.58	13.40
12.20	12.77	14.16	13.71	13.40
13.27	13.17	14.13		

(a) Make a stemplot of the data. The distribution is a bit irregular, but there is no reason to avoid use of t procedures for $n = 48$.

(b) Give a 95% confidence interval for the mean alcohol content of wine of this type.

7.118 Air in poultry-processing plants: summer versus winter. The air in poultry-processing plants often contains fungus spores. If the ventilation is inadequate, this can affect the health of the workers. The problem is most serious during the summer and least serious during the winter. To measure the presence of spores, air samples are pumped to an agar plate and "colony-forming units (CFUs)" are counted after an incubation period. Here are data from the "kill room" of a plant that processes 37,000 turkeys per day, taken on four separate days in the summer and in the winter. The units are CFUs per cubic meter of air.[39]

Summer	3175	2526	1763	1090
Winter	384	104	251	97

The counts are clearly much higher in the summer. Give a 90% confidence interval to estimate how much higher the mean count is during the summer. Be sure to write a conclusion in plain English.

7.119 **The manufacture of dyed clothing fabrics.** Different fabrics respond differently when dyed. This matters to clothing manufacturers, who want the color of the fabric to be just right. Fabrics made of cotton and of ramie are dyed with the same "procion blue" dye applied in the same way. A colorimeter is used to measure the lightness of the color on a scale in which black is 0 and white is 100. Here are the data for 8 pieces of each fabric:[40]

Cotton	48.82	48.88	48.98	49.04
	48.68	49.34	48.75	49.12
Ramie	41.72	41.83	42.05	41.44
	41.27	42.27	41.12	41.49

Which fabric is darker when dyed in this way? Write an answer to this question that includes summary statistics and a test of significance.

7.120 **Durable press and breaking strength.** "Durable press" cotton fabrics are treated to improve their recovery from wrinkles after washing. Unfortunately, the treatment also reduces the strength of the fabric. A study compared the breaking strength of fabric treated by two commercial durable press processes. Five specimens of the same fabric were assigned at random to each process. Here are the data, in pounds of pull needed to tear the fabric:[41]

Permafresh 55	29.9	30.7	30.0	29.5	27.6
Hylite LF	28.8	23.9	27.0	22.1	24.2

Is there good evidence that the two processes result in different mean breaking strengths?

7.121 **Find a confidence interval.** Continue your work from the previous exercise. A fabric manufacturer wants to know how large a strength advantage fabrics treated by the Permafresh method have over fabrics treated by the Hylite process. Give a 95% confidence interval for the difference in mean breaking strengths.

7.122 **Recovery from wrinkles.** Of course, the reason for durable press treatment is to reduce wrinkling. "Wrinkle recovery angle" measures how well a fabric recovers from wrinkles. Higher is better. Here are data on the wrinkle recovery angle (in degrees) for the same fabric specimens discussed in the previous two exercises:

Permafresh 55	136	135	132	137	134
Hylite LF	143	141	146	141	145

Which process has better wrinkle resistance? Is the difference statistically significant?

7.123 **Insulation failures.** A manufacturer of electric motors tests insulation at a high temperature (250°C) and records the number of hours until the insulation fails. The data for 5 specimens are[42]

300 324 372 372 444

The small sample size makes judgment difficult, but engineering experience suggests that the logarithm of the failure time will have a Normal distribution. Take the logarithms of the 5 observations, and use t procedures to give a 90% confidence interval for the mean of the log failure time for insulation of this type.

7.124 **Comparing earnings of bank employees.** Banks employ many workers paid by the hour as tellers and data clerks and in other capacities. Table 1.10 (page 30) presents the annual earnings for a random sample of hourly workers at National Bank. Data on the population of all such workers are in the file *hourly.dat,* described in detail in the Data Appendix. Suppose that we are interested only in the question of whether or not there is an apparent difference in the salaries of men and women. We will therefore combine the sample data for the two genders. Use the data in Table 1.10 for an analysis that compares the earnings of men and women. Include a graphical summary, the results of a significance test, and a confidence interval. Summarize your conclusions. Does the finding of a statistically significant difference mean that the bank discriminates?

7.125 **Competitive prices?** A retailer entered into an exclusive agreement with a supplier who guaranteed to provide all products at competitive prices. The retailer eventually began to purchase supplies from other vendors who offered better prices. The original supplier filed a legal action claiming violation of the agreement. In defense, the retailer had an audit performed on a random sample of invoices. For each audited invoice, all purchases made from other suppliers were examined and the prices were compared with those offered by the original supplier. For each invoice, the percent of purchases for which the alternate supplier offered a lower price than the original supplier was recorded. Here are the data:[43]

100	0	0	100	33	45	100	34	78
100	77	33	100	69	100	89	100	100
100	100	100	100	100	100	100		

Report the average of the percents with a 95% margin of error. Do the sample invoices suggest that the original supplier's prices are not competitive on the average?

7.126 Behavior of pet owners. On the morning of March 5, 1996, a train with 14 tankers of propane derailed near the center of the small Wisconsin town of Weyauwega. Six of the tankers were ruptured and burning when the 1700 residents were ordered to evacuate the town. Researchers study disasters like this so that effective relief efforts can be designed for future disasters. About half of the households with pets did not evacuate all of their pets. A study conducted after the derailment focused on problems associated with retrieval of the pets after the evacuation and characteristics of the pet owners. One of the scales measured "commitment to adult animals." The people who evacuated some or all of their pets were compared with those who did not evacuate any of their pets. Higher scores indicate that the pet owner is more likely to take actions that benefit the pet. Here are the data summaries:[44]

Group	n	$\bar{x}$	s
Evacuated all or some pets	116	7.95	3.62
Did not evacuate any pets	125	6.26	3.56

Analyze the data and prepare a short report describing the results.

7.127 Weight-loss programs. In a study of the effectiveness of weight-loss programs, 47 subjects who were at least 20% overweight took part in a group support program for 10 weeks. Private weighings determined each subject's weight at the beginning of the program and 6 months after the program's end. A t test was used to assess the significance of the average weight loss. The paper reporting the study said, "The subjects lost a significant amount of weight over time, $t(46) = 4.68$, $p < 0.01$."[45] It is common to report the results of statistical tests in this abbreviated style.

(a) Which t test did the study use?

(b) Explain to someone who knows no statistics but is interested in weight-loss programs what the practical conclusion is.

(c) The paper follows the tradition of reporting significance only at fixed levels such as $\alpha = 0.01$. In fact, the results are more significant than "$p < 0.01$" suggests. What can you say about the P-value of the test?

7.128 Preservatives in meat products. Nitrites are often added to meat products as preservatives. In a study of the effect of these chemicals on bacteria, the rate of uptake of a radiolabeled amino acid was measured for a number of cultures of bacteria, some growing in a medium to which nitrites had been added. Here are the summary statistics from this study:

Group	n	$\bar{x}$	s
Nitrite	30	7880	1115
Control	30	8112	1250

Carry out a test of the research hypothesis that nitrites decrease amino acid uptake, and report your results.

7.129 Testing job applicants. The one-hole test is used to test the manipulative skill of job applicants. This test requires subjects to grasp a pin, move it to a hole, insert it, and return for another pin. The score on the test is the number of pins inserted in a fixed time interval. One study compared male college students with experienced female industrial workers. Here are the data for the first minute of the test:[46]

Group	n	$\bar{x}$	s
Students	750	35.12	4.31
Workers	412	37.32	3.83

(a) We expect that the experienced workers will outperform the students, at least during the first minute, before learning occurs. State the hypotheses for a statistical test of this expectation and perform the test. Give a P-value and state your conclusions.

(b) The distribution of scores is slightly skewed to the left. Explain why the procedure you used in (a) is nonetheless acceptable.

(c) One purpose of the study was to develop performance norms for job applicants. Based on the data above, what is the range that covers the middle 95% of experienced workers? (Be careful! This is not the same as a 95% confidence interval for the mean score of experienced workers.)

(d) The five-number summary of the distribution of scores among the workers is

23 33.5 37 40.5 46

for the first minute and

32 39 44 49 59

for the fifteenth minute of the test. Display these summaries graphically, and describe briefly the differences between the distributions of scores in the first and fifteenth minutes.

7.130 Occupation and diet. Do various occupational groups differ in their diets? A British study of this question compared 98 drivers and 83 conductors of London double-decker buses. The conductors' jobs require more physical activity. The article reporting the study gives the data as "mean daily consumption (± se)."[47] Some of the study results appear below:

	Drivers	Conductors
Total calories	2821 ± 44	2844 ± 48
Alcohol (grams)	0.24 ± 0.06	0.39 ± 0.11

(a) What does "se" stand for? Give $\bar{x}$ and s for each of the four sets of measurements.

(b) Is there significant evidence at the 5% level that conductors consume more calories per day than do drivers? Use a t test to give a P-value, and then assess significance.

(c) How significant is the observed difference in mean alcohol consumption? Use a t test to obtain the P-value.

7.131 Occupation and diet, continued. Use the data in the previous exercise to give two confidence intervals:

(a) A 90% confidence interval for the mean daily alcohol consumption of London double-decker bus conductors.

(b) An 80% confidence interval for the difference in mean daily alcohol consumption between drivers and conductors.

7.132 The pooled test. Use of the pooled two-sample t test is justified in part (b) of Exercise 7.130. Explain why. Find the P-value for the pooled t statistic and compare with your result in Exercise 7.130.

7.133 Conditions for inference. The report cited in Exercise 7.130 says that the distributions of alcohol consumption among the individuals studied are "grossly skew."

(a) Do you think that this skewness prevents the use of the two-sample t test for equality of means? Explain your answer.

(b) (Optional) Do you think that the skewness of the distributions prevents the use of the F test for equality of standard deviations? Explain your answer.

7.134 Conditions for inference. Table 1.15 (page 81) gives the populations of all 58 counties in the state of California. Is it proper to apply the one-sample t method to these data to give a 95% confidence interval for the mean population of a California county? Explain your answer.

7.135 Male and female CS students (Optional). Is there a difference between the average SAT scores of male and female computer science students? The CSDATA data set, described in the Data Appendix, gives the Math (SATM) and Verbal (SATV) scores for a group of 224 computer science majors. The variable SEX indicates whether each individual is male or female.

(a) Compare the two distributions graphically, and then use software to compare the average SATM scores of males and females. Is it appropriate to use the pooled t test for this comparison? Write a brief summary of your results and conclusions. Refer to both versions of the t test and also to the F test for equality of standard deviations. Include a 99% confidence interval for the difference in the means.

(b) The students in the CSDATA data set are all computer science majors who entered a major university during a particular year. To what extent do you think that your results would generalize to (i) computer science students entering in different years, (ii) computer science majors at other colleges and universities, and (iii) college students in general?

7.136 Ego strengths of MBA graduates: power. In Exercise 7.109 (page 479) you found the power for a study designed to compare the "ego strengths" of two groups of MBA students. Now you must design a study to compare MBA graduates who reached partner in a large consulting firm with those who joined the firm but failed to become partners.

Assume the same value of $\sigma = 0.07$ and use $\alpha = 0.05$. You are planning to have 20 subjects in each group. Calculate the power of the pooled two-sample t test that compares the mean ego strengths of these two groups of MBA graduates for several values of the true difference. Include values that have a very small chance of being detected and some that are virtually certain to be seen in your sample. Plot the power versus the true difference and write a short summary of what you have found.

7.137 *t* approaches *z*. As the degrees of freedom increase, the t distributions get closer and closer to the $N(0, 1)$, or z, distribution. One way to see this is to look at how the critical value t^* for a 95% confidence interval changes with the degrees of freedom. Make a plot with degrees of freedom from 2 to 100 on the x axis and t^* on the y axis. Draw a horizontal line on the plot corresponding to the value of $z^* = 1.96$. Summarize the main features of the plot.

7.138 Sample size and margin of error. The margin of error for the one-sample t confidence interval depends on the confidence level, the standard deviation, and the sample size. Fix the confidence level at 95% and the standard error at $s = 1$ to examine the effect of the sample size n. Find the margin of error for sample sizes of 5 to 100 by 5s. That is, let $n = 5, 10, 15, \ldots, 100$. Plot the margins of error versus the sample size and summarize the relationship.

CHAPTER 7 Case Study Exercises

CASE STUDY 1: Architectural firms. The data file *ARCH* described in the Data Appendix gives characteristics of 25 large Indianapolis-area architectural firms. Make a table giving the mean, the standard deviation, the 95% confidence interval, and the five-number summary for the variables 1998 billings, 1997 billings, the number of licensed architects employed, the number of licensed engineers employed, and the number of full-time equivalent staff.

Classify each firm as "old" or "new" based on whether or not they began doing business in the area before 1970. Compare the means of the old and new firms for the variables 1998 billings, 1997 billings, the number of licensed architects employed, the number of licensed engineers employed, and the number of full-time equivalent staff. Be sure to state whether or not you use the pooled procedures and why. Give your results with graphical and numerical summaries. Then write a short paragraph explaining any differences that you have found.

CASE STUDY 2: Three or four bedrooms. How much more would you expect to pay for a home that has four bedrooms than for a home that has three? Here are data for West Lafayette, Indiana.[48] These are the selling prices (in dollars) that the owners of the homes are asking.

Four-bedroom homes:

121,900	139,900	157,000	159,900	176,900
224,900	235,000	245,000	294,000	

Three-bedroom homes:

65,500	79,900	79,900	79,900	82,900
87,900	94,000	97,500	105,000	111,900
116,900	117,900	119,900	122,900	124,000
125,000	126,900	127,900	127,900	127,900
132,900	145,000	145,500	157,500	194,000
205,900	259,900	265,000		

Plot the selling prices for the two sets of homes and describe the two distributions. Test the null hypothesis that the mean asking prices for the two sets of homes are equal versus the two-sided alternative. Give the test statistic with degrees of freedom, the P-value, and your conclusion. Would you consider using a one-sided alternative for this analysis? Explain why or why not. Give a 95% confidence interval for the difference in mean selling prices. These data are not SRSs from a population. Give a justification for use of the two-sample t procedures in this case.

Go to the Website `www.realtor.com` and select two geographical areas of interest to you. You will compare the prices of similar types of homes in these two areas. State clearly how you define the areas and the type of homes. For example, you can use city names or zip codes to define the area and you can select single-family homes or condominiums. We view these homes as representative of the asking prices of homes for these areas at the time of your search. If the search gives a large number of homes, select a random sample. Be sure to explain exactly how you do this. Use the methods you have learned in this chapter to compare the selling prices. Be sure to include a graphical summary.

CHAPTER 7 Appendix

Using Minitab and Excel for Inference for Distributions

Confidence Interval for Mean (σ Unknown)

Minitab:

Stat ➤ Basic Statistics ➤ 1-Sample t

If the data are in the worksheet, then choose the **Samples in columns** option and click the column containing the data into the box below. With this option, you can construct confidence intervals for more than one data set simultaneously. Alternatively, if you know the values of the sample mean and sample standard deviation, you can choose the **Summarized data** option and then input the sample size, sample mean, and sample standard deviation in the boxes found below. In default mode, Minitab will construct a 95% confidence interval. If you wish to change the level of confidence, click the **Options** button and input your desired confidence level in the **Confidence level** box. Click **OK** to close the pop-up box and then click **OK** to find the confidence interval along with some basic statistics, which are reported in the Session window.

Excel:

Excel does not have a routine for reporting the lower and upper limits of a confidence interval for the mean. However, you can use Excel to compute the margin of error, which can then be subtracted from and added to the sample mean to get the confidence interval. To find the margin of error, select "Descriptive Statistics" in the **Data Analysis** menu box and click **OK.** Enter the cell range of the data into the **Input Range** box. Place a checkmark next to the **Confidence Level for Mean** option. If you wish to change the level of confidence, input your desired confidence level in the adjacent box. Since you will need the sample mean value to ultimately construct the confidence interval, place a checkmark next to the **Summary statistics** option. Click **OK** and you will find the margin of error reported in a spreadsheet next to a cell labeled "Confidence Level."

Test for Population Mean (σ Unknown)

Minitab:

Stat ➤ Basic Statistics ➤ 1-Sample t

This is the same routine described in this Appendix for obtaining the confidence interval for the mean. If you wish to conduct a hypothesis test, select the **Perform hypothesis test** option and input the null hypothesis mean value (μ_0) in the box below. In default mode, Minitab will assume a two-sided alternative. If you wish to have a one-sided alternative, click the **Options** button and choose either the "less than" or the "greater than" alternative hypothesis choice. Click **OK** to close the pop-up box and then click **OK** to find the test statistic and corresponding P-value, which are reported in the Session window.

Excel:

Interestingly, even though Excel provides a statistical function for conducting a test of the mean with known population standard deviation, Excel does not provide a dedicated statistical function or routine for testing the mean when the population standard deviation is unknown. The one-sample t test is available in the enhanced add-on version of Excel.

Even though there is no dedicated routine in standard Excel, there is a way to utilize the software. First, compute the value of the one-sample t statistic. The values of the sample mean and sample standard deviation needed for this computation can be obtained from the "Descriptive Statistics" option found in the **Data Analysis** menu box. At this point, we can use Excel to compute areas under the t distribution density curve to obtain the P-value for the observed one-sample t statistic. To do so, click an empty cell in the spreadsheet and then proceed to the **Statistical** function menu as described in the overview section of Chapter 1's appendix. Scroll down the list of functions and click on the **TDIST** function choice. This function will find the area to the right of only a positive t-value. Enter the magnitude of the observed t statistic in the **X** box. In the **Deg_freedom** box, enter the appropriate degrees of freedom. In the **Tails** box, enter "1" if you have a one-sided alternative and "2" if you have a two-sided alternative. Click **OK** to find a probability reported in the selected cell. If the observed t statistic is negative and you have a greater-than alternative, then subtract the reported probability from 1 to obtain the appropriate P-value. If the observed t statistic is positive and you have a less-than alternative, then subtract the reported probability from 1 to obtain the appropriate P-value. In all other cases, the reported probability is the appropriate P-value.

Matched Pairs *t* Test

Minitab:

Stat ➤ Basic Statistics ➤ Paired t

If the data are in the worksheet, then choose the **Samples in columns** option and click the two columns containing the data into the boxes below. Alternatively, if you know the values of the sample mean and sample standard deviation, you can choose the **Summarized data (differences)** option and input the sample size, sample mean of the differences, and sample standard deviation of the differences in the boxes found below. In default mode, Minitab will construct a 95% confidence interval for the mean of the differences. If you wish to change the level of confidence, click the **Options** button and input your desired confidence level in the **Confidence level** box. In addition to reporting a confidence interval, this routine will conduct a test for the mean difference. In default mode, Minitab will assume a two-sided alternative. If you wish to have a one-sided alternative, click the **Options** button and choose either the "less than" or the "greater than" alternative hypothesis choice. It is important to realize that your choice of an appropriate one-sided alternative hypothesis should take into account the fact that Minitab obtains the differences by subtracting the second sample from the first sample. If you wish to test against a mean difference other than 0, input the null hypothesis value in **Test mean** box. Click **OK** to close the pop-up box and then click **OK** to find the confidence interval along with the test statistic and corresponding P-value, which are reported in the Session window.

Excel:

Select "t-Test: Paired Two Sample for Means" in the **Data Analysis** menu box and click **OK.** Enter the cell range of the data for the two samples into the **Variable 1 Range** and **Variable 2 Range** boxes. Excel obtains the differences by subtracting the second sample from the first sample. If you wish to test against a mean difference other than 0, input the null hypothesis value in the **Hypothesized Mean Difference** box. Click **OK** to find descriptive statistics on the samples reported along with a t statistic and both a one-sided P-value and a two-sided P-value. The one-sided P-value is computed as the probability that the t statistic is more negative if the observed statistic is negative or as the probability that the t statistic is more positive if the observed statistic is positive. No regard to the alternative hypothesis is given. If you are testing a greater-than alternative hypothesis and the observed t statistic is negative, then subtract the reported one-sided P-value from 1 to obtain the appropriate P-value. Similarly, if you are testing a less-than alternative hypothesis and the observed t statistic is positive, then subtract the reported one-sided P-value from 1 to obtain the appropriate P-value. In all other cases, the reported probability is the appropriate P-value.

Power (One-Sample t)

Minitab:

Stat ➤ Power and Sample Size ➤ 1-Sample t

This routine is nearly identical to the routine for finding the power of a one-sample z test discussed in Chapter 6's Appendix. The only difference is that, in the **Standard deviation** box, you need to enter an estimate of the population standard deviation (σ). For a matched pairs study, enter the estimated standard deviation of the differences between the pairs.

Excel:

Automated power calculations are not available in standard Excel or the enhanced add-on version of Excel. As done in Example 7.9, the Normal distribution can be used to compute the approximate power. Accordingly, you can use Excel's **NORMSDIST** function to compute probabilities from the Normal distribution (refer to Chapter 1's Appendix for details on using the **NORMSDIST** function).

Sign Test

Minitab:

Stat ➤ Nonparametrics ➤ 1-Sample Sign

The sign test can be used to test against any general median value. In this chapter, we focused on testing the differences of matched pairs against a median value of 0. For such an application, click the column containing the differences into the **Variables** box. Select the **Test median** option and keep the default test median value at 0. Choose the appropriate alternative hypothesis from the **Alternative** menu box. Click **OK** to find the P-value for the test reported in the Session window.

Excel:

The sign test is not available in standard Excel but is available in the enhanced add-on version of Excel.

Comparing Two Means

Minitab:

Stat ➤ Basic Statistics ➤ 2-Sample t

There are three ways to enter the data with this routine. If the data for the two samples are in two separate columns, then choose the **Samples in different columns** option and click the columns containing the data into the two boxes below. You can also have the data for the two samples all in one column with a group label in second column. If the data are stored in this manner, choose the **Samples in one columns** option and then click the data column into the **Samples** box and click the column of labels into the **Subscripts** box. As a third option, if you know the values of the sample means and sample standard deviations, you can choose the **Summarized data** option and input the sample sizes, sample means, and sample standard deviations in the boxes found below. The default for this routine is not to assume equal population variances. If you wish to assume equal population variances, select the **Assume equal variances** option.

In default mode, Minitab will construct a 95% confidence interval for the difference between the two population means. If you wish to change the level of confidence, click the **Options** button and input your desired confidence level in the **Confidence level** box. In addition to reporting a confidence interval, this routine will conduct a test for the difference between the means. In default mode, Minitab will assume a two-sided alternative. If you wish to have a one-sided alternative, then click the **Options** button and choose either the "less than" or the "greater than" alternative hypothesis choice. Your choice of the appropriate one-sided alternative hypothesis should take into account what you specified as the first and second samples. If you wish to test against a difference between means other than 0, input the null hypothesis value in the **Test difference** box. Click **OK** to close the pop-up box and then click **OK** to find the confidence interval along with the test statistic and corresponding P-value, which are reported in the Session window.

Excel:

If you do not want to assume equal population variances, select "t-Test: Two-Sample Assuming Unequal Variances" in the **Data Analysis** menu box and click **OK.** If you wish to assume equal population variances, select "t-Test: Two-Sample Assuming Equal Variances" in the **Data Analysis** menu box and click **OK.** Enter the cell range of the data for the two samples into the **Variable 1 Range** and **Variable 2 Range** boxes. If you wish to test against a difference between means other than 0, input the null hypothesis value in **Hypothesized Mean Difference** box. Click **OK** to find descriptive statistics on the samples reported along with a t statistic and both a one-sided P-value and a two-sided P-value. The one-sided P-value is computed as the probability that the t statistic is more negative if the observed statistic is negative or as the probability that the t statistic is more positive if the observed statistic is positive. No regard to the alternative hypothesis is given. If you are testing a greater-than alternative hypothesis and the observed t statistic is negative, then subtract the reported one-sided P-value from 1 to obtain the appropriate P-value. Similarly, if you are testing a less-than alternative hypothesis and the observed t statistic is positive, then subtract the reported one-sided P-value from 1 to obtain the appropriate P-value. In all other cases, the reported probability is the appropriate P-value.

F Test for Equality of Spread

Minitab:

Stat ➤ Basic Statistics ➤ 2 Variances

There are three ways to enter the data with this routine. If the data for the two samples are in two separate columns, then choose the **Samples in different columns** option and click the columns containing the data into the two boxes below. You can also have the data for the two samples all in one column with a group label in a second column. If the data are stored in this manner, choose the Samples **in one columns** option and then click the data column into the **Samples** box and click the column of labels into the **Subscripts** box. As a third option, if you know the values of the sample variances, then you can choose the **Summarized data** option and input the sample sizes and sample variances in the boxes found below. Click **OK** to find F test statistic and corresponding P-value, which are reported in the Session window. Minitab will also produce a plot showing the confidence intervals for the population standard deviations along with a boxplot for each of the samples. Finally, you will notice that Minitab also reports a Levene's test statistic along with a corresponding P-value. The Levene's test is an alternative to the F test when we cannot safely assume Normality for the two populations.

Excel:

Select "F Test Two-Sample for Variances" in the **Data Analysis** menu box and click **OK.** Enter the cell range of the data for the two samples into the **Variable 1 Range** and **Variable 2 Range** boxes. If you wish to test against a difference between means other than 0, input the null hypothesis value in the **Hypothesized Mean Difference** box. Click **OK** to find descriptive statistics on the samples reported along with the F statistic and corresponding P-value.

Power (Two-Sample *t*)

Minitab:

Stat ➤ Power and Sample Size ➤ 2-Sample t

This routine is essentially identical to the routine for finding the power of a one-sample t test discussed earlier in this Appendix. This routine assumes that the two sample sizes (n_1 and n_2) are equal. Thus, you need to enter only one sample size in the **Sample sizes** box. Furthermore, as done in Example 7.19, Minitab assumes that the standard deviations of the two populations are equal. The estimated standard deviation should be entered in the **Standard deviation** box.

Excel:

Automated power calculations are not available in standard Excel or the enhanced add-on version of Excel. As done in Example 7.19, the Normal distribution can be used to compute the approximate power. Accordingly, you can use Excel's **NORMSDIST** function to compute probabilities from the Normal distribution (refer to Chapter 1's Appendix for details on using the **NORMSDIST** function).

CHAPTER 8

Inference for Proportions

8.1 Inference for a Single Proportion

8.2 Comparing Two Proportions

PRELUDE: JURY SELECTION

In a small border county in Texas, a so-called key man system was used to select citizens to serve on juries. Under this procedure, lists of persons in the county were compiled by jury commissioners and these were interviewed under oath by the county judge, who determined whether or not they were qualified. Qualifications included literacy and "good moral character." This system was challenged in a case called *Castaneda v. Partida* on the basis that it reduced the proportion of Hispanic citizens serving on juries. A statistical comparison was at the heart of the case: 79% of the county's adult population had Spanish surnames, but only 39% of the grand jurors did. This comparison gave a z statistic of 29 with an extremely small P-value. The United States Supreme Court concluded that this disparity established a prima facie case.[1] Procedures such as the key man system are no longer used to select juries in the United States. The Court interpreted the z statistic as the number of standard deviations by which the two percents differed: 79% differed from 39% by 29 standard deviations. The decision stated that a difference *greater than 2 or 3 standard deviations* is sufficient. This criterion is sometimes called the *Castaneda rule*. These values of z correspond to P-values of 0.0456 and 0.0026.

Introduction

Many studies collect data on *categorical variables,* such as the race or occupation of a person, the make of a car, or the type of complaint received from a customer. When we record categorical variables, our data consist of *counts* or of *percents* obtained from counts.

The parameters we want to do inference about in these settings are *population proportions*. Just as in the case of inference about population means, we may be concerned with a single population or with comparing two populations. Inference about one or two proportions is very similar to inference about means, which we discussed in Chapter 7. In particular, inference for both means and proportions is based on sampling distributions that are approximately Normal.

We begin in Section 8.1 with inference about a single population proportion. Section 8.2 concerns methods for comparing two proportions.

8.1 Inference for a Single Proportion

CASE 8.1

WORK STRESS AND PERSONAL LIFE

"The nature of work is changing at whirlwind speed. Perhaps now more than ever before, job stress poses a threat to the health of workers and, in turn, to the health of organizations."[2] So says the National Institute for Occupational Safety and Health. Employers are concerned about the effect of stress on their employees. Stress can lower morale and efficiency and increase medical costs. A national survey of restaurant employees found that 75% reported that work stress had a negative impact on their personal lives.[3]

The human resources manager of a chain of restaurants is concerned that work stress may be affecting the chain's employees. She asks a random sample of 100 employees to respond Yes or No to the question "Does work stress have a negative impact on your personal life?" Of these, 68 say "Yes." The *parameter* of interest is the proportion of the chain's employees who would answer "Yes" if asked. This is a **population proportion,** which we call p. The *statistic* used to estimate this unknown parameter is the **sample proportion**

population proportion

sample proportion

$$\hat{p} = \frac{68}{100} = 0.68$$

The *count* of "Yes" answers in the sample of Case 8.1 is $X = 68$. We will regularly use X to stand for sample counts and $\hat{p} = X/n$ to denote sample proportions. The sample proportion $\hat{p}$ in Case 8.1 is a discrete random variable that can take the values 0, $1/100, 2/100, \dots, 99/100$, or 1.* If the sample size n is very small, we must base tests and confidence intervals for p on the discrete distribution of $\hat{p}$. Discrete distributions are a bit awkward to work with.[4] Fortunately, we can approximate the distribution of $\hat{p}$ by a Normal distribution when the sample size n is large.

*In many cases, a probability model for $\hat{p}$ can be based on the binomial distributions for counts, discussed in the optional Chapter 5.

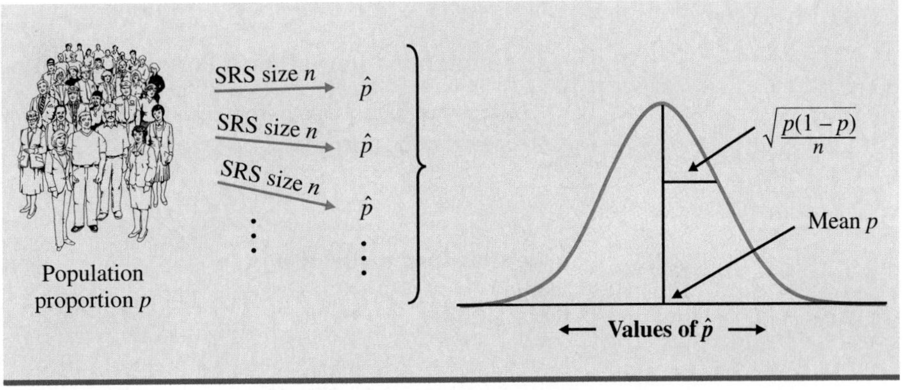

FIGURE 8.1 Draw a large SRS from a population in which the proportion p are successes. The sampling distribution of the sample proportion $\hat{p}$ of successes has approximately a Normal distribution.

Sampling Distribution of a Sample Proportion

Choose an SRS of size n from a large population that contains population proportion p of "successes." Let $\hat{p}$ be the **sample proportion** of successes,

$$\hat{p} = \frac{\text{count of successes in the sample}}{n} = \frac{X}{n}$$

Then:

- For large sample sizes, the distribution of $\hat{p}$ is **approximately Normal.**
- The **mean** of the distribution of $\hat{p}$ is p.
- The **standard deviation** of $\hat{p}$ is

$$\sqrt{\frac{p(1-p)}{n}}$$

Figure 8.1 summarizes these facts in a form that recalls the idea of sampling distributions. We will consider only inference procedures based on this Normal approximation. These procedures are similar to those for inference about the mean of a Normal distribution. We will see, however, that there are a few extra details involved, caused by the added difficulty in approximating the discrete distribution of $\hat{p}$ by a continuous Normal distribution.

Large-sample confidence interval for a single proportion

The sample proportion $\hat{p} = X/n$ is the natural estimator of the population proportion p. Notice that $\sqrt{\frac{p(1-p)}{n}}$, the standard deviation of $\hat{p}$, depends upon the unknown parameter p. In our calculations, we estimate it by replacing the population parameter p with the sample estimate $\hat{p}$. Therefore, our estimated standard error is $SE_{\hat{p}} = \sqrt{\frac{\hat{p}(1-\hat{p})}{n}}$. If the sample size is large, the distribution of $\hat{p}$ will be approximately Normal with mean p and standard deviation $SE_{\hat{p}}$. It follows that $\hat{p}$ will be within two standard deviations ($2SE_{\hat{p}}$) of the unknown parameter p about 95% of the time. This is how we use the Normal approximation to construct the large-sample confidence interval for p. Here are the details.

z Confidence Interval for a Population Proportion

Choose an SRS of size n from a large population with unknown proportion p of successes. The **sample proportion** is

$$\hat{p} = \frac{X}{n}$$

The **standard error of $\hat{p}$** is

$$\text{SE}_{\hat{p}} = \sqrt{\frac{\hat{p}(1-\hat{p})}{n}}$$

and the **margin of error** for confidence level C is

$$m = z^* \text{SE}_{\hat{p}}$$

where z^* is the value for the standard Normal density curve with area C between $-z^*$ and z^*. The **large-sample level C confidence interval** for p is

$$\hat{p} \pm m$$

You can use this interval for 90%, 95%, or 99% confidence when the number of successes and the number of failures are both at least 15.

EXAMPLE 8.1 Estimating the Effect of Work Stress

CASE 8.1

The sample survey in Case 8.1 found that 68 of a sample of 100 employees agreed that work stress had a negative impact on their personal lives. That is, the sample size is $n = 100$ and the count of successes is $X = 68$. The sample proportion of employees affected by work stress is

$$\hat{p} = \frac{X}{n} = \frac{68}{100} = 0.6731$$

The standard error is

$$\text{SE}_{\hat{p}} = \sqrt{\frac{\hat{p}(1-\hat{p})}{n}} = \sqrt{\frac{0.68(1-0.68)}{100}} = 0.04665$$

The z critical value for 95% confidence is $z^* = 1.96$, so the margin of error is

$$m = 1.96\text{SE}_{\hat{p}} = (1.96)(0.04665) = 0.09143$$

The confidence interval is

$$\hat{p} \pm m = 0.68 \pm 0.09143$$

We are 95% confident that between 58.9% and 77.1% of the restaurant chain's employees feel that work stress is damaging their personal lives.

Remember that the margin of error in any confidence interval includes only random sampling error. If employees hesitate to respond honestly, for example, your estimate is likely to miss by more than the margin of error.

Because the calculations for statistical inference for a single proportion are relatively straightforward, many software packages do not include them. Figure 8.2 gives output from Minitab and SAS for the data in Case 8.1. As usual, the output reports more digits than are useful. When you use software, be sure to think about how many digits are meaningful for your purposes. SAS gives the standard error next to the label ASE, which stands for asymptotic standard error. The SAS output also includes an alternative interval based on an "exact" method, which matches the Minitab interval and our calculations.

APPLY YOUR KNOWLEDGE

8.1 Will the upgrade be profitable? To profitably produce a planned upgrade of a software product you make, you must charge customers \$100. Are your customers willing to pay this much? You contact a random sample of 50 customers and find that 17 would pay \$100 for the upgrade. Find a 95% confidence interval for the proportion of all of your customers (the population) who would be willing to buy the upgrade for \$100.

8.2 Holiday shopping. A poll of 811 adults aged 18 or older asked about purchases that they intended to make for the upcoming holiday season.[5] One of the questions asked about what kind of gift they intended to buy for the person on whom they would spend the most. Clothing was the first choice of 487 people. Give a 95% confidence interval for the proportion of people in this population who intend to buy clothing as their first choice.

FIGURE 8.2 Minitab and SAS output for the confidence interval in Example 8.1.

Minitab

```
Sample     X     N    Sample p          95% CI
1         68   100    0.680000   (0.588572, 0.771428)

Using the normal approximation.
```

SAS

Binomial Proportion for y = 0

Proportion	0.6800
ASE	0.0466
95% Lower Conf Limit	0.5886
95% Upper Conf Limit	0.7714

Exact Conf Limits	
95% Lower Conf Limit	0.5792
95% Upper Conf Limit	0.7698

Sample Size = 100

Plus four confidence interval for a single proportion*

Modern computer studies reveal that the large-sample confidence intervals can be quite inaccurate. We can get a hint of the difficulties by asking what we would do if the sample survey in Case 8.1 found that *none* of the 100 employees in the sample said job stress hurt their personal lives. Then, because $\hat{p} = 0$, the standard error and the margin of error based on this estimate will both be 0. As a result, the large-sample method suggests that we are certain that no employees in the entire restaurant chain are bothered by work stress. This isn't plausible.

Both computer studies and careful mathematics show that we can do better by moving the sample proportion $\hat{p}$ slightly away from 0 and 1.[6] There are several ways to do this. Here is a simple adjustment that works very well in practice.

The adjustment is based on the following idea: act as if we have 4 additional observations, 2 of which are successes and 2 of which are failures. The new sample size is $n + 4$ and the count of successes is $X + 2$. Because this estimate was first suggested by Edwin Bidwell Wilson in 1927 (though rarely used in practice until recently), we call it the **Wilson estimate.**

Wilson estimate

To compute a confidence interval based on the Wilson estimate, first replace the value of X by $X + 2$ and the value of n by $n + 4$. Then use the values in the formulas for the z confidence interval. In Example 8.1, we had $X = 68$ and $n = 100$. To apply the plus four approach we use the z procedure with $X = 70$ and $n = 104$. You can use this interval when the sample size is at least $n = 10$ and the confidence level is 90%, 95%, or 99%.

APPLY YOUR KNOWLEDGE

8.3 Will the upgrade be profitable? Refer to Exercise 8.1. Compute the plus four 95% confidence interval and compare this interval with the one that you obtained in that exercise.

8.4 New-product sales. Yesterday, your top salesperson called on 5 customers and obtained orders for your new product from all 5. Suppose that it is reasonable to view these 5 customers as a random sample of all of her customers.

(a) Give the plus four estimate of the proportion of her customers who would buy the new product. Notice that we don't estimate that all customers will buy, even though all 5 in the sample did.

(b) Give the margin of error for 95% confidence. (You may see that the upper endpoint of the confidence interval is greater than 1. In that case, take the upper endpoint to be 1.)

(c) Do the results apply to all of your sales force? Explain why or why not.

8.5 Construct an example. Make up an example where the large-sample method and the plus four method give very different intervals. Do not use a case where either $\hat{p} = 0$ or $\hat{p} = 1$.

Significance test for a single proportion

We know that the sample proportion $\hat{p} = X/n$ is approximately Normal, with mean $\mu_{\hat{p}} = p$ and standard deviation $\sigma_{\hat{p}} = \sqrt{p(1-p)/n}$. To construct confidence intervals, we need to use an estimate of the standard deviation based on the data because the standard deviation depends upon the unknown parameter p. When performing a significance test, however, the null hypothesis specifies a value for p, which we will call p_0. When we

*The material on the plus four confidence interval is optional and can be omitted without loss of continuity.

calculate P-values, we act as if the hypothesized p were actually true. When we test H_0: $p = p_0$, we substitute p_0 for p in the expression for $\sigma_{\hat{p}}$ and then standardize $\hat{p}$. Here are the details.

z Significance Test for a Population Proportion

Choose an SRS of size n from a large population with unknown proportion p of successes. To test the hypothesis H_0: $p = p_0$, compute the z **statistic**

$$z = \frac{\hat{p} - p_0}{\sqrt{\dfrac{p_0(1 - p_0)}{n}}}$$

In terms of a standard Normal random variable Z, the approximate P-value for a test of H_0 against

H_a: $p > p_0$ is $P(Z \geq z)$

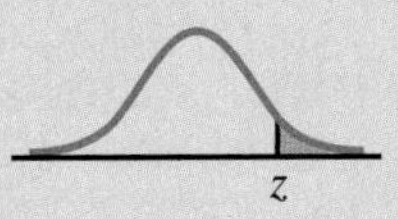

H_a: $p < p_0$ is $P(Z \leq z)$

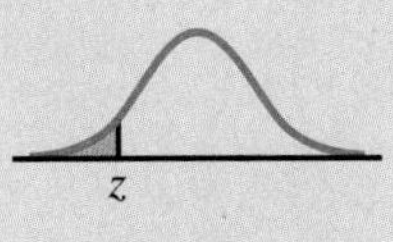

H_a: $p \neq p_0$ is $2P(Z \geq |z|)$

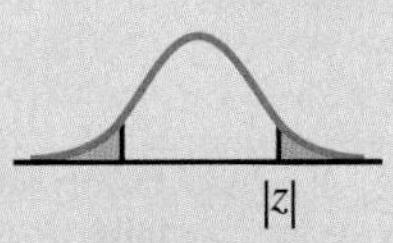

Use this test when the expected number of successes np_0 and the expected number of failures $n(1 - p_0)$ are both at least 10.

We call this z test a "large-sample test" because it is based on a Normal approximation to the sampling distribution of $\hat{p}$ that becomes more accurate as the sample size increases. For small samples, or if the population is less than 10 times as large as the sample, consult an expert for other procedures.

EXAMPLE 8.2 Work Stress

CASE 8.1

A national survey of restaurant employees found that 75% said that work stress had a negative impact on their personal lives. A sample of 100 employees of a restaurant chain finds that 68 answer "Yes" when asked, "Does work stress have a negative impact on your personal life?" Is this good reason to think that the proportion of all employees of this chain who would say "Yes" differs from the national proportion $p_0 = 0.75$?

To answer this question, we test

$$H_0: p = 0.75$$
$$H_a: p \neq 0.75$$

FIGURE 8.3 The P-value for Example 8.2.

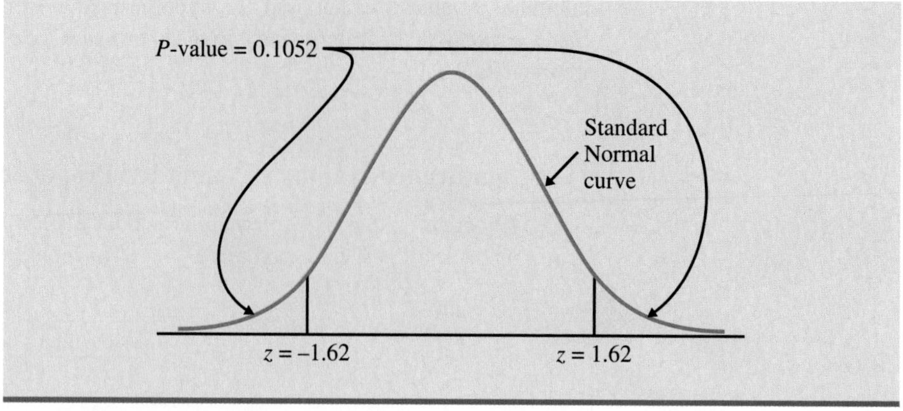

The expected numbers of "Yes" and "No" responses are $100 \times 0.75 = 75$ and $100 \times 0.25 = 25$. Both are greater than 10, so we can use the z test. The test statistic is

$$z = \frac{\hat{p} - p_0}{\sqrt{\dfrac{p_0(1-p_0)}{n}}}$$

$$= \frac{0.68 - 0.75}{\sqrt{\dfrac{(0.75)(0.25)}{100}}} = 1.62$$

From Table A we find $P(Z \geq 1.62) = 1 - 0.9474$, or 0.0526. The P-value is the area in both tails, $P = 2 \times 0.0526 = 0.1052$. Figure 8.3 displays the P-value as an area under the standard Normal curve. We conclude that the chain restaurant data are compatible with the survey results ($\hat{p} = 0.68$, $z = 1.62$, $P = 0.11$).

Minitab and SAS outputs for the analysis in Example 8.2 appear in Figure 8.4. (Example 8.2 finds a slightly different P-value because we rounded the z statistic to two decimal places to use Table A.)

In Example 8.2, we counted "Yes" responses. Would we get the same results if we instead counted the people who said "No"? We would. If we count No's as successes, both the sample and the population proportions are proportions of No's. The null hypothesis is then the claim that the population proportion is 0.25 rather than the 0.75 used for Yes's in Example 8.2. You will find that the z test statistic is unchanged except for its sign and that the P-value remains the same.

As usual, the confidence interval in Example 8.1 is more informative than the significance test in Example 8.2. The confidence interval gives the range of population proportions p that are consistent with the sample data. Because the 95% confidence interval is (0.589, 0.771), we would not be surprised if the truth were 60% or 75%. The test simply says that we don't have good evidence against the single value 75% that served as p_0. Significance tests for a single population proportion are not common in practice, because we rarely want to compare data with a precise value p_0. The confidence interval, however, is used quite often.

FIGURE 8.4 Minitab and SAS output for the significance test in Example 8.2.

Minitab

```
Test of p = 0.75 vs p not = 0.75

Sample   X    N  Sample p               95% CI              Z-Value  P-Value
1       68  100  0.680000  (0.588572, 0.771428)    -1.62    0.106

Using the normal approximation.
```

SAS

```
Test of H0: Proportion = 0.75

ASE under H0          0.0433
Z                    -1.6166
One-sided Pr < Z      0.0530
Two-sided Pr > |Z|    0.1060

Sample Size = 100
```

APPLY YOUR KNOWLEDGE

8.6 A profitable upgrade? In Exercise 8.1 we found that 17 customers from a random sample of 50 would be willing to buy a software upgrade that costs \$100. If the upgrade is to be profitable, you will need to sell it to more than 20% of your customers. Do the sample data give good evidence that more than 20% are willing to buy?

(a) Formulate this problem as a hypothesis test. Give the null and alternative hypotheses. Will you use a one-sided or a two-sided alternative? Why?

(b) Carry out the significance test. Report the test statistic and the P-value.

(c) Should you proceed with plans to produce and market the upgrade?

8.7 Yes or no? Case 8.1 describes a survey of 100 employees, 68 of whom answered "Yes" to a question on work stress. That is, 32 of the sample of 100 answered "No."

CASE 8.1

(a) Example 8.1 gives a 95% confidence interval for the proportion of all employees who would answer "Yes." Give the 95% confidence interval for the proportion who would answer "No." Explain carefully why your result agrees with that of Example 8.1.

(b) Example 8.2 tests the null hypothesis that the proportion of "Yes" among all employees is 0.75. Carry out a two-sided test of the null hypothesis that the proportion of "No" is 0.25. Explain carefully why your result agrees with that of Example 8.2.

Choosing a sample size

In Chapter 6, we showed how to choose the sample size n to obtain a confidence interval with specified margin of error m for a Normal mean. Because we are using a Normal approximation for inference about a population proportion, sample size selection proceeds in much the same way.

Recall that the margin of error for the large-sample confidence interval for a population proportion is

$$m = z^*\text{SE}_{\hat{p}} = z^*\sqrt{\frac{\hat{p}(1-\hat{p})}{n}}$$

Choosing a confidence level C fixes the critical value z^*. The margin of error also depends on the value of $\hat{p}$ and the sample size n. Because we don't know the value of $\hat{p}$ until we gather the data, we must guess a value to use in the calculations. We will call the guessed value p^*. Here are two ways to get p^*:

- Use the sample estimate from a pilot study or from similar studies done earlier.
- Use $p^* = 0.5$. Because the margin of error is largest when $\hat{p} = 0.5$, this choice gives a sample size that is somewhat larger than we really need for the confidence level we choose. It is a safe choice no matter what the data later show.

Once we have chosen p^* and the margin of error m that we want, we can find the n we need to achieve this margin of error. Here is the result.

Sample Size for Desired Margin of Error

The level C confidence interval for a proportion p will have a margin of error approximately equal to a specified value m when the sample size is

$$n = \left(\frac{z^*}{m}\right)^2 p^*(1-p^*)$$

Here z^* is the critical value for confidence C, and p^* is a guessed value for the proportion of successes in the future sample.

The margin of error will be less than or equal to m if p^* is chosen to be 0.5. The sample size required is then given by

$$n = \left(\frac{z^*}{2m}\right)^2$$

The value of n obtained by this method is not particularly sensitive to the choice of p^* as long as p^* is not too far from 0.5. However, if your actual sample turns out to have $\hat{p}$ smaller than about 0.3 or larger than about 0.7, the sample size based on $p^* = 0.5$ may be much larger than needed.

EXAMPLE 8.3 Planning a Sample of Customers

Your company has received complaints about its customer support service. You intend to hire a consulting company to carry out a sample survey of customers. Before contacting the consultant, you want some idea of the sample size you will have to pay for. One critical question is the degree of satisfaction with your customer service, measured on a five-point scale. You want to estimate the proportion p of your customers who are satisfied (that is, who choose either "satisfied" or "very satisfied," the two highest levels on the five-point scale).

You want to estimate p with 95% confidence and a margin of error less than or equal to 3%, or 0.03. For planning purposes, you are willing to use $p^* = 0.5$. To find the sample size required,

$$n = \left(\frac{z^*}{2m}\right)^2 = \left[\frac{1.96}{(2)(0.03)}\right]^2 = 1067.1$$

Round up to get $n = 1068$. (Always round up. Rounding down would give a margin of error slightly greater than 0.03.)

Similarly, for a 2.5% margin of error we have (after rounding up)

$$n = \left[\frac{1.96}{(2)(0.025)}\right]^2 = 1537$$

and for a 2% margin of error,

$$n = \left[\frac{1.96}{(2)(0.02)}\right]^2 = 2401$$

News reports frequently describe the results of surveys with sample sizes between 1000 and 1500 and a margin of error of about 3%. These surveys generally use sampling procedures more complicated than simple random sampling, so the calculation of confidence intervals is more involved than what we have studied in this section. The calculations in Example 8.3 nonetheless show in principle how such surveys are planned.

In practice, many factors influence the choice of a sample size. The following Case Study illustrates one set of factors.

CASE 8.2 

MARKETING CHRISTMAS TREES

An association of Christmas tree growers in Indiana sponsored a sample survey of Indiana households to help improve the marketing of Christmas trees.[7] The researchers decided to use a telephone survey and estimated that each telephone interview would take about 2 minutes. Nine trained students in agribusiness marketing were to make the phone calls between 1:00 P.M. and 8:00 P.M. on a Sunday. After discussing problems related to people not being at home or being unwilling to answer the questions, the survey team proposed a sample size of 500. Several of the questions asked demographic information about the household. The key questions of interest had responses of "Yes" or "No," for example, "Did you have a Christmas tree last year?" The primary purpose of the survey was to estimate various sample proportions for Indiana households. An important issue in designing the survey was therefore whether the proposed sample size of $n = 500$ would be adequate to provide the sponsors of the survey with the information they required.

To address this question, we calculate the margins of error of 95% confidence intervals for various values of $\hat{p}$.

EXAMPLE 8.4 Margins of Error

CASE 8.2

In the Christmas tree market survey, the margin of error of a 95% confidence interval for any value of $\hat{p}$ and $n = 500$ is

$$m = z^* \mathrm{SE}_{\hat{p}} = 1.96\sqrt{\frac{\hat{p}(1-\hat{p})}{500}}$$

The results for various values of $\hat{p}$ are

$\hat{p}$	m	$\hat{p}$	m
0.05	0.019	0.60	0.043
0.10	0.026	0.70	0.040
0.20	0.035	0.80	0.035
0.30	0.040	0.90	0.026
0.40	0.043	0.95	0.019
0.50	0.044		

The survey team judged these margins of error to be acceptable, and they used a sample size of 500 in their survey.

The table in Example 8.4 illustrates two points. First, the margins of error for $\hat{p} = 0.05$ and $\hat{p} = 0.95$ are the same. The margins of error will always be the same for $\hat{p}$ and $1 - \hat{p}$. This is a direct consequence of the form of the confidence interval. Second, the margin of error varies only between 0.040 and 0.044 as $\hat{p}$ varies from 0.3 to 0.7, and the margin of error is greatest when $\hat{p} = 0.5$, as we claimed earlier. It is true in general that the margin of error will vary relatively little for values of $\hat{p}$ between 0.3 and 0.7. Therefore, when planning a study, it is not necessary to have a very precise guess for p. If $p^* = 0.5$ is used and the observed $\hat{p}$ is between 0.3 and 0.7, the actual interval will be a little shorter than needed, but the difference will be quite small.

APPLY YOUR KNOWLEDGE

8.8 Is there interest in a new product? One of your employees has suggested that your company develop a new product. You decide to take a random sample of your customers and ask whether or not there is interest in the new product. The response is on a 1 to 5 scale, with 1 indicating "definitely would not purchase"; 2, "probably would not purchase"; 3, "not sure"; 4, "probably would purchase"; and 5, "definitely would purchase." For an initial analysis, you will record the responses 1, 2, and 3 as "No" and 4 and 5 as "Yes." What sample size would you use if you wanted the 95% margin of error to be 0.08 or less?

8.9 More information is needed. Refer to the previous exercise. Suppose that, after reviewing the results of the previous survey, you proceeded with preliminary development of the product. Now you are at the stage where you need to decide whether or not to make a major investment to produce and market the product. You will use another random sample of your customers, but now you want the margin of error to be smaller. What sample size would you use if you wanted the 95% margin of error to be 0.04 or less?

SECTION 8.1 SUMMARY

- Inference about a population proportion is based on an SRS of size n. When n is large, the distribution of the **sample proportion** $\hat{p} = X/n$ is approximately Normal with mean p and standard deviation $\sqrt{p(1-p)/n}$.

- The **standard error of $\hat{p}$** is

$$\text{SE}_{\hat{p}} = \sqrt{\frac{\hat{p}(1-\hat{p})}{n}}$$

- The z **margin of error** for confidence level C is

$$m = z^*\text{SE}_{\hat{p}}$$

where z^* is the value for the standard Normal density curve with area C between $-z^*$ and z^*.

- The z **large-sample level C confidence interval** for p is

$$\hat{p} \pm m$$

We recommend using this method when the number of successes and the number of failures are both at least 15.

- The **plus four estimate of a population proportion** is obtained by adding two successes and two failures to the sample and then using the z procedure. We recommend using this method when the sample size is at least 10 and the confidence level is 90%, 95%, or 99%.

- The **sample size** required to obtain a confidence interval of approximate margin of error m for a proportion is found from

$$n = \left(\frac{z^*}{m}\right)^2 p^*(1-p^*)$$

where p^* is a guessed value for the proportion and z^* is the standard Normal critical value for the desired level of confidence. To ensure that the margin of error of the interval is less than or equal to m no matter what $\hat{p}$ may be, use

$$n = \left(\frac{z^*}{2m}\right)^2$$

- Tests of H_0: $p = p_0$ are based on the z **statistic**

$$z = \frac{\hat{p} - p_0}{\sqrt{\frac{p_0(1-p_0)}{n}}}$$

with P-values calculated from the $N(0, 1)$ distribution. Use this test when the expected number of successes np_0 and the expected number of failures $n(1-p_0)$ are both at least 10.

SECTION 8.1 Exercises

For Exercises 8.1 and 8.2, see page 497; for 8.3 to 8.5, see page 498; for 8.6 and 8.7, see page 501; and for 8.8 and 8.9, see page 504.

8.10 What's wrong? Explain what is wrong with each of the following:

(a) A student project used a confidence interval to describe the results in a final report. The confidence level was 110%.

(b) The margin of error for a confidence interval used for an opinion poll takes into account the fact that people who did not answer the poll questions may have had different responses from those who did answer the questions.

(c) If the P-value for a significance test is 0.35, we can conclude that the null hypothesis has a 35% chance of being true.

8.11 What's wrong? Explain what is wrong with each of the following:

(a) An approximate 95% confidence interval for an unknown proportion p is $\hat{p}$ plus or minus its standard error.

(b) You can use a significance test to evaluate the hypothesis H_0: $\hat{p} = 0.3$ versus the two-sided alternative.

(c) The large-sample significance test for a population proportion is based on a t statistic.

8.12 Draw some pictures (optional). Consider the binomial setting with $n = 60$ and $p = 0.4$.

(a) The sample proportion $\hat{p}$ will have a distribution that is approximately Normal. Give the mean and the standard deviation of this Normal distribution.

(b) Draw a sketch of this Normal distribution. Mark the location of the mean.

(c) Find a value p^* for which the probability is 95% that $\hat{p}$ will be between $\pm p^*$. Mark these two values on your sketch.

8.13 Gambling and college athletics. Gambling is an issue of great concern to those involved in intercollegiate athletics. Because of this, the National Collegiate Athletic Association (NCAA) surveyed student-athletes concerning their gambling-related behaviors.[8] There were 5594 Division I male athletes in the survey. Of these, 3547 reported participation in some gambling behavior. This includes playing cards, betting on games of skill, buying lottery tickets, betting on sports, and similar activities.

(a) Find the sample proportion and the large-sample margin of error for 95% confidence. Explain in simple terms the meaning of the 95%.

(b) Because of the way that the study was designed to protect the anonymity of the student-athletes who responded, it was not possible to calculate the number of students who were asked to respond but did not. Does this fact affect the way that you interpret the results? Write a short paragraph explaining your answer.

8.14 Women athletes and gambling. In the study described in the previous exercise, 1447 out of a total of 3469 female student-athletes reported participation in some gambling activity.

(a) Use the large-sample methods to find an estimate of the true proportion with a 95% confidence interval.

(b) The margin of error for this sample is not the same as the margin of error calculated for the previous exercise. Explain why.

8.15 Do students report Internet sources? The National Survey of Student Engagement found that 87% of students report that their peers at least "sometimes" copy information from the Internet in their papers without crediting the source.[9] Assume that the sample size is 430,000.

(a) Find the margin of error for 99% confidence.

(b) Here are some facts from the report that summarizes the survey. More than 430,000 students from 730 four-year colleges and universities participated. The average response rate was 43% and ranged from 15% to 89%. Institutions paid a participation fee of between $3000 and $7500 based on the size of their undergraduate enrollment. Discuss these as sources of error in this study. How do you think these errors would compare with the error that you calculated in part (a)?

8.16 Dogs or rats to find cocaine (optional). Dogs are big and expensive. Rats are small and cheap. Can rats be trained to replace dogs in sniffing out illegal drugs? One study trained six male albino Sprague-Dawley rats to rear up on their hind legs in response to the smell of cocaine.[10] After training, each rat was tested 80 times. In the test a rat was presented with a large number of cups, one of which smelled like cocaine. A success was recorded if the rat correctly identified the cup containing cocaine by rearing up in front of it. The numbers of successes for the six rats were 80, 80, 73, 80, 74, and 80. You want to estimate the success rate in the future for each of the six rats. Compare the large-sample estimates with the plus four estimates for this problem and make a recommendation concerning which is better. Write a short summary giving reasons for your recommendation.

8.17 Long sermons. The National Congregations Study collected data in a one-hour interview with a key informant—that is, a minister, priest, rabbi, or other staff person or leader.[11] One question concerned the length of the typical sermon. For 390 out of 1191 congregations, the typical sermon lasted more than 30 minutes.

(a) Use the large-sample inference procedures to estimate the true proportion for this question with a 95% confidence interval.

(b) (Optional) Compute the interval using the plus four method. Compare these results with those from part (a) and summarize what the comparison tells you about the two methods.

(c) There were 1236 congregations surveyed in this study. Calculate the nonresponse rate for this question. Does this influence how you interpret the results? Write a short discussion of this issue.

(d) The respondents to this question were not asked to use a stopwatch to record the lengths of a random sample of sermons at their congregations. They responded based on their impressions of the sermons. Do you think that ministers, priests, rabbis, or other staff persons or leaders might perceive sermon lengths differently from the people listening to the sermons? Discuss how your ideas influence your interpretation of the results of this study.

8.18 Are the congregations conservative? The study described in the previous exercise also asked each respondent to classify his or her congregation according to theological orientation. For this question, 707 out of 1191 congregations were classified as "more conservative." Using the questions in the previous exercise as a guide, analyze and interpret these data. Compare your answers to parts (c) and (d) in the two exercises and discuss reasons why you think the answers should be similar or different.

8.19 Student loans. A survey of 1280 student loan borrowers found that 448 had loans totaling more than \$20,000 for their undergraduate education.[12] Give a 95% confidence interval for the proportion of all student loan borrowers who have loans of \$20,000 or more for their undergraduate education.

8.20 Did the borrowers get a degree? In the survey described in the previous exercise, there were 1050 borrowers whose total debt was \$10,000 or more. Of these, 192 left school without completing a degree. Consider the population to be borrowers whose total debt was \$10,000 or more. Find a 95% confidence interval for the proportion of borrowers who left school without completing a degree in this population.

8.21 How would the confidence interval change? Refer to Exercise 8.19. Would a 99% confidence interval be wider or narrower than the one that you found in that exercise? Verify your results by computing the interval.

8.22 How would the confidence interval change? Refer to Exercise 8.20. Would a 90% confidence interval be wider or narrower than the one that you found in that exercise? Verify your results by computing the interval.

8.23 College students and diets. For a study of unhealthy eating behaviors, 267 college women aged 18 to 25 years were surveyed.[13] Of these, 69% reported that they were on a diet sometime during the past year. Give a 95% confidence interval for the true proportion of college women aged 18 to 25 years in this population who dieted last year.

8.24 High school students and diets. In the study described in the previous exercise, the researchers also surveyed 266 high school students who were 18 years old. In this sample 58.3% reported that they had dieted sometime in the past year. Give a 95% confidence interval for the true proportion of 18-year-old high school students in this population who were on a diet sometime during the past year.

8.25 Marketing pet care products to older adults. You have been asked to investigate the possibility of a marketing campaign to promote your company's pet care products to older adults. Your report will include information about your potential market. In a study of the relationship between pet ownership and physical activity in older adults, 594 subjects reported that they owned a pet, while 1939 reported that they did not.[14] Give a 95% confidence interval for the proportion of older adults in this population who are pet owners.

8.26 Income of your potential customers. In the study described in the previous exercise, 1434 subjects out of a total of 2533 reported that their annual income was \$25,000 or more.

(a) Give a 95% confidence interval for the true proportion of subjects in this population with incomes above \$25,000.

(b) Do you think that some respondents might not give truthful answers to a question about their income? Discuss the possible effects on your estimate and confidence interval.

(c) In the previous exercise, the question analyzed concerned pet ownership. Compare this question with the income question with respect to the possibility that the respondents were not truthful.

8.27 Should young people have credit cards? In a survey of teens aged 12 to 19 years, 38% said that they thought that credit cards should be limited to adult use.[15]

(a) The survey summary stated that approximately 2000 teens were surveyed. Use this information to construct a 95% confidence interval for the population proportion who think that credit card use should be limited in this way.

(b) Comment on the age range for the survey. Do you think that there might be considerable variation in the responses based on age? Discuss and propose an alternative way to conduct the survey or to report the results.

8.28 Do job applicants lie? When trying to hire managers and executives, companies sometimes verify the academic credentials described by the applicants. One company that performs these checks summarized its findings for a six-month period. Of the 84 applicants whose credentials were checked, 15 lied about having a degree.[16]

(a) Find the sample proportion of applicants who lie about having a degree and the standard error of this estimate.

(b) Consider these data to be a random sample of credentials from a large collection of similar applicants. Give a 95% confidence interval for the true proportion of applicants who lie about having a degree.

8.29 Can you make this inference? Suppose that 9 of the 84 applicants checked in the previous exercise lied about their major. Can we conclude that a total of $24 = 15 + 9$ applicants lied about having a degree or about their major? Explain your answer.

8.30 CASE 8.2 **Christmas tree marketing.** One question in the Christmas tree market survey described in Case 8.2 was "Did you have a Christmas tree last year?" Of the 500 respondents, 421 answered "Yes."

(a) What proportion of the sampled households responded "Yes"?

(b) Give the standard error for your estimate in part (a).

(c) Find a 95% confidence interval for the proportion of Indiana households that had a Christmas tree last year.

8.31 Shipping the orders on time. As part of a quality improvement program, your mail-order company is studying the process of filling customer orders. According to company standards, an order is shipped on time if it is sent within 2 working days of the time it is received. You select an SRS of 100 of the 5000 orders received in the past month for an audit. The audit reveals that 84 of these orders were shipped on time. Find a 95% confidence interval for the true proportion of the month's orders that were shipped on time.

8.32 Power companies and trimming trees. Large trees growing near power lines can cause power failures during storms when their branches fall on the lines. Power companies spend a great deal of time and money trimming and removing trees to prevent this problem. Researchers are developing hormone and chemical treatments that will stunt or slow tree growth. If the treatment is too severe, however, the tree will die. In one series of laboratory experiments on 216 sycamore trees, 41 trees died. Give a 90% confidence interval for the proportion of sycamore trees that would be expected to die from this particular treatment.

8.33 Financial goals of college students. In recent years over 70% of first-year college students responding to a national survey have identified "being well-off financially" as an important personal goal. A state university finds that 141 of an SRS of 200 of its first-year students say that this goal is important. Give a 95% confidence interval for the proportion of all first-year students at the university who would identify being well-off as an important personal goal.

8.34 Alcohol abuse on campus. College presidents have described alcohol abuse as the number one problem on campus. How common is it? A survey of 17,096 students in U.S. four-year colleges collected information on drinking behavior and alcohol-related problems.[17] The researchers defined "frequent binge drinking" as having five or more drinks in a row three or more times in the past two weeks. According to this definition, 3314 students were classified as frequent binge drinkers. Find a 99% confidence interval for the proportion of frequent binge drinkers in this population.

8.35 Bicycle accidents and alcohol. In the United States approximately 900 people die in bicycle accidents each year. One study examined the records of 1711 bicyclists aged 15 or older who were fatally injured in bicycle accidents between 1987 and 1991 and were tested for alcohol.[18] Of these, 542 tested positive for alcohol (blood alcohol concentration of 0.01% or higher).

(a) Summarize the data with appropriate descriptive statistics.

(b) To do statistical inference for these data, we think of p as the probability that a tested bicycle rider is positive for alcohol. Find a 95% confidence interval for p.

(c) Can you conclude from your statistical analysis of this study that alcohol causes fatal bicycle accidents?

8.36 What proportion were legally drunk? The study mentioned in the previous exercise found that 386 bicyclists had blood alcohol levels above 0.10%, a level defined as legally drunk in all states. Give a 95% confidence interval for the proportion who were legally drunk according to this criterion.

8.37 Can we use the *z* test? In each of the following cases, is the sample large enough to permit safe use of the *z* test? (The population is very large.)

(a) $n = 12$ and H_0: $p = 0.6$.

(b) $n = 100$ and H_0: $p = 0.4$.

(c) $n = 1000$ and H_0: $p = 0.98$.

(d) $n = 500$ and H_0: $p = 0.3$.

8.38 CASE 8.2 **Checking the demographics of a sample.** Of the 500 households that responded to the Christmas tree marketing survey, 38% were from rural areas (including small towns), and the other 62% were from urban areas (including suburbs). According to the census, 36% of Indiana households are in rural areas, and the remaining 64% are in urban areas. Let p be the proportion of rural respondents. Set up hypotheses about p_0 and perform a test of significance to examine how well the sample represents the state in regard to rural versus urban residence. Summarize your results.

8.39 More on demographics. In the previous exercise we arbitrarily chose to state the hypotheses in terms of the proportion of rural respondents. We could as easily have used the proportion of *urban* respondents.

(a) Write hypotheses in terms of the proportion of urban residents to examine how well the sample represents the state in regard to rural versus urban residence.

(b) Perform the test of significance and summarize the results.

(c) Compare your results with the results of the previous exercise. Summarize and generalize your conclusion.

8.40 Vouchers for schools? A national opinion poll found that 42% of all American adults agree that parents should be given vouchers good for education at any public or private school of their choice. The result was based on a small sample. How large an SRS is required to obtain a margin of error of ± 0.035 (that is, $\pm 3.5\%$) in a 95% confidence interval? (Use the previous poll's result to obtain the guessed value p^*.)

8.41 Insect infestations. An entomologist samples a field for egg masses of a harmful insect by placing a yard-square frame at random locations and carefully examining the ground within the frame. An SRS of 70 locations selected from a county's pastureland found egg masses in 14 locations. Give a 95% confidence interval for the proportion of all possible locations that are infested.

8.42 CASE 8.2 **Profile of the survey respondents.** Of the 500 respondents in the Christmas tree market survey of Case 8.2, 44% had no children at home and 56% had at least one child at home. The corresponding census figures are 48% with no children and 52% with at least one child. Test the null hypothesis that the telephone survey technique has a probability of selecting a household with no children that is equal to the value obtained by the census. Give the *z* statistic and the *P*-value. What do you conclude?

8.43 Mathematician tosses coin 10,000 times! The South African mathematician John Kerrich, while a prisoner of war during World War II, tossed a coin 10,000 times and obtained 5067 heads.

(a) Is this significant evidence at the 5% level that the probability that Kerrich's coin comes up heads is not 0.5?

(b) Give a 95% confidence interval to see what probabilities of heads are roughly consistent with Kerrich's result.

8.44 Instant versus fresh-brewed coffee. A matched pairs experiment compares the taste of instant coffee with fresh-brewed coffee. Each subject tastes two unmarked cups of coffee, one of each type, in random order and states which he or she prefers. Of the 60 subjects who participate in the study, 24 prefer the instant coffee and the other 36 prefer fresh-brewed. Take p to be the proportion of the population that prefers fresh-brewed coffee.

(a) Test the claim that a majority of people prefer the taste of fresh-brewed coffee. Report the *z* statistic and its *P*-value. Is your result significant at the 5% level? What is your practical conclusion?

(b) Find a 90% confidence interval for p.

8.45 High-income households on a mailing list. Land's Beginning sells merchandise through the mail. It is considering buying a list of addresses from a magazine. The magazine claims that at least 25% of its subscribers have high incomes (that is, household income in excess of $100,000). Land's Beginning would like to estimate the proportion of high-income people on the list. Verifying income is difficult, but another company offers this service. Land's Beginning will pay to verify the incomes of an SRS of people on the magazine's list.

They would like the margin of error of the 95% confidence interval for the proportion to be 0.04 or less. Use the guessed value $p^* = 0.25$ to find the required sample size.

8.46 Change the specs. Refer to the previous exercise. For each of the following variations on the design specifications, state whether the required sample size will be higher, lower, or the same as that found above.

(a) Use a 99% confidence interval.

(b) Change the allowable margin of error to 0.01.

(c) Use a planning value of $p^* = 0.15$.

(d) Use a different company to do the income verification.

8.47 Start a student nightclub? A student organization wants to start a nightclub for students under the age of 21. To assess support for this proposal, the organization will select an SRS of students and ask each respondent if he or she would patronize this type of establishment. About 75% of the student body are expected to respond favorably. What sample size is required to obtain a 95% confidence interval with an approximate margin of error of 0.06? Suppose that 50% of the sample respond favorably. Calculate the margin of error of the 95% confidence interval.

8.48 Are the customers dissatisfied? A cell phone manufacturer would like to know what proportion of its customers are dissatisfied with the service received from their local distributor. The customer relations department will survey a random sample of customers and compute a 99% confidence interval for the proportion that are dissatisfied. From past studies, they believe that this proportion will be about 0.1. Find the sample size needed if the margin of error of the confidence interval is to be about 0.015. Suppose 15% of the sample say that they are dissatisfied. What is the margin of error of the 99% confidence interval?

8.49 Increase student fees? You have been asked to survey students at a large college to determine the proportion that favor an increase in student fees to support an expansion of the student newspaper. Each student will be asked whether he or she is in favor of the proposed increase. Using records provided by the registrar you can select a random sample of students from the college. After careful consideration of your resources, you decide that it is reasonable to conduct a study with a sample of 120 students. Construct a table of the margins of error for 95% confidence when $\hat{p}$ takes the values 0.1, 0.2, 0.3, 0.4, 0.5, 0.6, 0.7, 0.8, and 0.9.

8.50 Justify the cost of the survey. A former editor of the student newspaper agrees to underwrite the study in the previous exercise because she believes the results will demonstrate that most students support an increase in fees. She is willing to provide funds for a sample of size 500. Write a short summary for your benefactor of why the increased sample size will provide better results.

8.2 Comparing Two Proportions

Because comparative studies are so common, we often want to compare the proportions of two groups (such as men and women) that have some characteristic. We call the two groups being compared Population 1 and Population 2, and the two population proportions of "successes" p_1 and p_2. The data consist of two independent SRSs. The sample sizes are n_1 for Population 1 and n_2 for Population 2. The proportion of successes in each sample estimates the corresponding population proportion. Here is the notation we will use in this section:

Population	Population proportion	Sample size	Count of successes	Sample proportion
1	p_1	n_1	X_1	$\hat{p}_1 = X_1/n_1$
2	p_2	n_2	X_2	$\hat{p}_2 = X_2/n_2$

To compare the two unknown population proportions, start with the observed difference between the two sample proportions,

$$D = \hat{p}_1 - \hat{p}_2$$

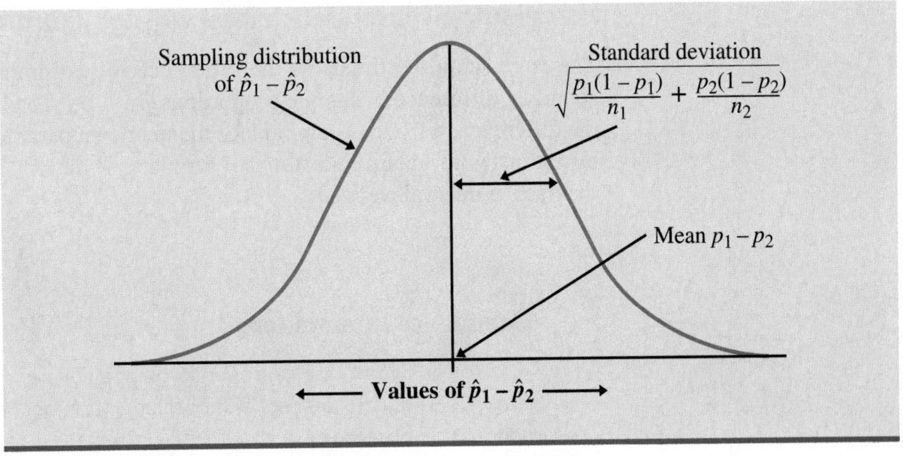

FIGURE 8.5 The sampling distribution of the difference of two sample proportions is approximately Normal. The mean and standard deviation are found from the two population proportions of successes, p_1 and p_2.

When both sample sizes are sufficiently large, the sampling distribution of the difference D is approximately Normal. What are the mean and the standard deviation of D? Each of the two $\hat{p}$'s has the mean and standard deviation given in the box on page 495. Because the two samples are independent, the two $\hat{p}$'s are also independent. We can apply the rules for means and variances of sums of random variables. Here is the result, which is summarized in Figure 8.5.

Sampling Distribution of $\hat{p}_1 - \hat{p}_2$

Choose independent SRSs of sizes n_1 and n_2 from two populations with proportions p_1 and p_2 of successes. Let $D = \hat{p}_1 - \hat{p}_2$ be the difference between the two sample proportions of successes. Then

- As both sample sizes increase, the sampling distribution of D becomes **approximately Normal.**
- The **mean** of the sampling distribution is $p_1 - p_2$.
- The **standard deviation** of the sampling distribution is

$$\sigma_D = \sqrt{\frac{p_1(1-p_1)}{n_1} + \frac{p_2(1-p_2)}{n_2}}$$

APPLY YOUR KNOWLEDGE

8.51 Rules for means and variances. It is quite easy to verify the mean and standard deviation of the difference D.

(a) What are the means and standard deviations of the two sample proportions $\hat{p}_1$ and $\hat{p}_2$? (Look at the box on page 495 if you need to review this.)

(b) Use the addition rule for means of random variables: what is the mean of $D = \hat{p}_1 - \hat{p}_2$?

(c) The two samples are independent. Use the addition rule for variances of random variables: what is the variance of D?

Large-sample confidence intervals for a difference in proportions

The large-sample estimate of the difference in two proportions $p_1 - p_2$ is the corresponding difference in sample proportions $\hat{p}_1 - \hat{p}_2$. To obtain a confidence interval for the difference, we once again replace the unknown parameters in the standard deviation by estimates to obtain an estimated standard deviation, or standard error. Here is the confidence interval we want.

z Confidence Interval for Comparing Two Proportions

Choose an SRS of size n_1 from a large population having proportion p_1 of successes and an independent SRS of size n_2 from another population having proportion p_2 of successes.

The large-sample estimate of the difference in proportions is

$$D = \hat{p}_1 - \hat{p}_2 = \frac{X_1}{n_1} - \frac{X_2}{n_2}$$

The **standard error of the difference** is

$$\mathrm{SE}_D = \sqrt{\frac{\hat{p}_1(1-\hat{p}_1)}{n_1} + \frac{\hat{p}_2(1-\hat{p}_2)}{n_2}}$$

and the **margin of error for confidence level C** is

$$m = z^*\mathrm{SE}_D$$

where z^* is the value for the standard Normal density curve with area C between $-z^*$ and z^*. The **large-sample level C confidence interval** for $p_1 - p_2$ is

$$(\hat{p}_1 - \hat{p}_2) \pm m$$

Use this method when the number of successes and the number of failures in both samples are at least 10.

CASE 8.3 "NO SWEAT" GARMENT LABELS

Following complaints about the working conditions in some apparel factories both in the United States and abroad, a joint government and industry commission recommended that companies that monitor and enforce proper standards be allowed to display a "No Sweat" label on their products. Does the presence of these labels influence consumer behavior?

A survey of U.S. residents aged 18 or older asked a series of questions about how likely they would be to purchase a garment under various conditions. For some conditions, it was stated that the garment had a "No Sweat" label; for others, there was no mention of such a label. On the basis of the responses, each person was classified as a "label user" or a "label nonuser."[19] About 16.5% of those surveyed were label users. One purpose of the study was to describe the demographic characteristics of users and nonusers.

EXAMPLE 8.5 Gender Differences in Label Use

CASE 8.3 

The study in Case 8.3 suggested that there is a gender difference in the proportion of label users. Here is a summary of the data. We let X denote the number of label users.

Population	n	X	$\hat{p} = X/n$
1 (women)	296	63	0.213
2 (men)	251	27	0.108

First, we find the estimate of the difference:

$$\begin{aligned} D &= \hat{p}_1 - \hat{p}_2 \\ &= \frac{X_1}{n_1} - \frac{X_2}{n_2} \\ &= 0.213 - 0.108 \\ &= 0.105 \end{aligned}$$

Next, we calculate the standard error:

$$\begin{aligned} \text{SE}_D &= \sqrt{\frac{0.213(1-0.213)}{63} + \frac{0.108(1-0.108)}{27}} \\ &= 0.0308 \end{aligned}$$

For 95% confidence, we use $z^* = 1.96$, so the margin of error is

$$\begin{aligned} m &= z^* \text{SE}_D \\ &= (1.96)(0.0308) \\ &= 0.060 \end{aligned}$$

The large-sample 95% confidence interval is

$$\begin{aligned} D \pm m &= 0.105 \pm 0.060 \\ &= (0.04,\ 0.16) \end{aligned}$$

With 95% confidence we can say that the difference in the proportions is between 0.04 and 0.16. Alternatively, we can report that the gender difference is about 10% in favor of women, with a 95% margin of error of 6%.

Minitab and SAS output for Example 8.5 appear in Figure 8.6. Other statistical packages provide output that is similar.

In surveys such as this, men and women are typically not sampled separately. The respondents to a single sample are divided after the fact into men and women. The sample sizes are then random and reflect the characteristics of the population sampled. Two-sample significance tests and confidence intervals are still approximately correct in this situation, even though the two sample sizes were not fixed in advance.

In Example 8.5 we chose women to be the first population. Had we chosen men as the first population, the estimate of the difference would be negative (−0.104). Because it is easier to discuss positive numbers, we generally choose the first population to be the one with the higher proportion. The choice doesn't affect the substance of the analysis.

FIGURE 8.6 Minitab and SAS output for Example 8.5.

Minitab

```
Sample    X     N    Sample p
1        63   296    0.212838
2        27   251    0.107570

Difference = p (1) - p (2)
Estimate for difference: 0.105268
95% CI for difference: (0.0449066, 0.165630)
```

SAS

	Risk	ASE	(Asymptotic) 95% Confidence	Limits
Row 1	0.2128	0.0238	0.1662	0.2595
Row 2	0.1076	0.0196	0.0692	0.1459
Total	0.1645	0.0159	0.1335	0.1956
Difference	0.1053	0.0308	0.0449	0.1656

APPLY YOUR KNOWLEDGE

8.52 Who gets stock options? Different kinds of companies compensate their key employees in different ways. Established companies may pay higher salaries, while new companies may offer stock options that will be valuable if the company succeeds. Do high-tech companies tend to offer stock options more often than other companies? One study looked at a random sample of 200 companies. Of these, 91 were listed in the *Directory of Public High Technology Corporations* and 109 were not listed. Treat these two groups as SRSs of high-tech and non-high-tech companies. Seventy-three of the high-tech companies and 75 of the non-high-tech companies offered incentive stock options to key employees.[20] Give a 95% confidence interval for the difference in the proportions of the two types of companies that offer stock options.

8.53 Unhappy HMO customers. A study was designed to find reasons why patients leave a health maintenance organization (HMO).[21] Patients were classified as to whether or not they had filed a complaint with the HMO. We want to compare the proportion of complainers who leave the HMO with the proportion of those who do not file complaints. In the year of the study, 639 patients filed complaints, and 54 of these patients left the HMO voluntarily. For comparison, the HMO chose an SRS of 743 patients who had not filed complaints. Twenty-two of these patients left voluntarily. Give an estimate of the difference in the two proportions with a 95% confidence interval.

Plus four confidence intervals for a difference in proportions*

Just as in the case of estimating a single proportion, a small modification of the sample proportions greatly improves the accuracy of confidence intervals.[22] As before, we first

*The material on the plus four confidence interval for a difference in proportions is optional and can be omitted without loss of continuity.

add 2 successes and 2 failures to the actual data, dividing them equally between the two samples. That is, *add 1 success and 1 failure to each sample.* Note that each sample size is increased by 2. We then perform the calculations for the z procedure with the modified data. As in the case of a single sample, we use the term **Wilson estimates** for the estimates produced in this way. We recommend using this method when both sample sizes are at least 5 and the confidence level is 90%, 95%, or 99%.

Wilson estimates

In Example 8.5, we had $X_1 = 63$, $n_1 = 296$, $X_2 = 27$, and $n_2 = 251$. For the plus four procedure, we would use $X_1 = 64$, $n_1 = 298$, $X_2 = 28$, and $n_2 = 253$.

APPLY YOUR KNOWLEDGE

8.54 Gender and labels using plus four. Refer to Example 8.5 (page 513), where we computed a 95% confidence interval for the difference in the proportions of men and women who were likely to use "No Sweat" labels when deciding to purchase clothing. Redo the computations using the plus four method and compare your results with those obtained in Example 8.5.

8.55 Plus four with smaller sample sizes. Refer to the previous exercise and to Example 8.5. Suppose that the sample sizes were smaller but that the proportions remained approximately the same. Specifically, assume that 6 out of 30 women were label users and 3 out of 25 men were label users. Compute the plus four interval for 95% confidence. Then, compute the corresponding z interval and compare the results.

Significance tests

Although we prefer to compare two proportions by giving a confidence interval for the difference between the two population proportions, it is sometimes useful to test the null hypothesis that the two population proportions are the same.

We standardize $D = \hat{p}_1 - \hat{p}_2$ by subtracting its mean $p_1 - p_2$ and then dividing by its standard deviation

$$\sigma_D = \sqrt{\frac{p_1(1 - p_1)}{n_1} + \frac{p_2(1 - p_2)}{n_2}}$$

If n_1 and n_2 are large, the standardized difference is approximately $N(0, 1)$. To get a confidence interval, we used sample estimates in place of the unknown population proportions p_1 and p_2 in the expression for σ_D. Although this approach would lead to a valid significance test, we follow the more common practice of replacing the unknown σ_D with an estimate that takes into account the null hypothesis that $p_1 = p_2$. If these two proportions are equal, we can view all of the data as coming from a single population. Let p denote the common value of p_1 and p_2. The standard deviation of $D = \hat{p}_1 - \hat{p}_2$ is then

$$\sigma_{Dp} = \sqrt{\frac{p(1 - p)}{n_1} + \frac{p(1 - p)}{n_2}}$$

$$= \sqrt{p(1 - p)\left(\frac{1}{n_1} + \frac{1}{n_2}\right)}$$

The subscript on σ_{Dp} reminds us that this is the standard deviation under the special condition that the two populations share a common proportion p of successes.

We estimate the common value of p by the overall proportion of successes in the two samples:

$$\hat{p} = \frac{\text{number of successes in both samples}}{\text{number of observations in both samples}} = \frac{X_1 + X_2}{n_1 + n_2}$$

pooled estimate of p

This estimate of p is called the **pooled estimate** because it combines, or pools, the information from both samples.

To estimate the standard deviation of D, substitute $\hat{p}$ for p in the expression for σ_{Dp}. The result is a standard error for D under the condition that the null hypothesis H_0: $p_1 = p_2$ is true. The test statistic uses this standard error to standardize the difference between the two sample proportions.

Significance Tests for Comparing Two Proportions

Choose an SRS of size n_1 from a large population having proportion p_1 of successes and an independent SRS of size n_2 from another population having proportion p_2 of successes. To test the hypothesis

$$H_0\text{: } p_1 = p_2$$

compute the z **statistic**

$$z = \frac{\hat{p}_1 - \hat{p}_2}{\text{SE}_{Dp}}$$

where the **pooled standard error** is

$$\text{SE}_{Dp} = \sqrt{\hat{p}(1-\hat{p})\left(\frac{1}{n_1} + \frac{1}{n_2}\right)}$$

based on the **pooled estimate** of the common proportion of successes

$$\hat{p} = \frac{X_1 + X_2}{n_1 + n_2}$$

In terms of a standard Normal random variable Z, the P-value for a test of H_0 against

H_a: $p_1 > p_2$ is $P(Z \geq z)$

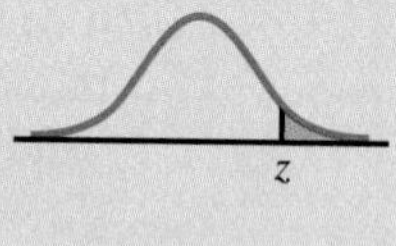

H_a: $p_1 < p_2$ is $P(Z \leq z)$

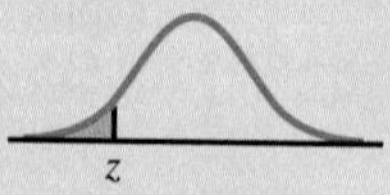

H_a: $p_1 \neq p_2$ is $2P(Z \geq |z|)$

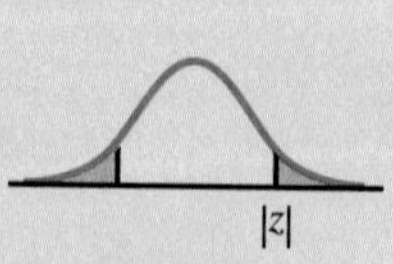

Use this test when the number of successes and the number of failures in each of the samples is at least 5.

EXAMPLE 8.6 Men, Women, and Garment Labels

CASE 8.3

Example 8.5 (page 513) presents survey data on whether consumers are "label users" who pay attention to label details when buying a garment. Are men and women equally likely to be label users? Here is the data summary:

Population	n	X	$\hat{p} = X/n$
1 (women)	296	63	0.213
2 (men)	251	27	0.108

The sample proportions are certainly quite different, but we need a significance test to verify that the difference is too large to easily result from the play of chance in choosing the sample. Formally, we compare the proportions of label users in the two populations (women and men) by testing the hypotheses

$$H_0\colon p_1 = p_2$$

$$H_a\colon p_1 \neq p_2$$

The pooled estimate of the common value of p is

$$\hat{p} = \frac{63 + 27}{296 + 251} = \frac{90}{547} = 0.1645$$

This is just the proportion of label users in the entire sample.

The test statistic is calculated as follows:

$$\mathrm{SE}_{Dp} = \sqrt{(0.1645)(0.8355)\left(\frac{1}{296} + \frac{1}{251}\right)} = 0.03181$$

$$z = \frac{\hat{p}_1 - \hat{p}_2}{\mathrm{SE}_{Dp}} = \frac{0.213 - 0.108}{0.03181}$$

$$= 3.30$$

That is, the observed difference is more than 3 standard deviations away from zero. The P-value is $2P(Z \geq 3.30)$. From Table A we have $P = 2 \times 0.0005 = 0.0010$. Software gives $P = 0.0009$. We report: 21% of women are label users versus only 11% of men; the difference is statistically significant ($z = 3.30$, $P < 0.001$).

Figure 8.7 gives the Minitab and SAS outputs for Example 8.6. Carefully examine the output to find all of the important pieces that you would need to report the results of the analysis and to draw a conclusion.

Many market researchers would expect the proportion of label users to be higher among women than among men. That is, we might choose the one-sided alternative $H_a\colon p_1 > p_2$. The P-value would be half of the value obtained for the two-sided test. Because the z statistic is so large, this distinction is of no practical importance.

APPLY YOUR KNOWLEDGE

8.56 Are the high-techs different? In Exercise 8.52 we looked at whether or not companies offered stock options to their employees. There, we compared high-tech companies with other companies using a 95% confidence interval. Let's now test the

FIGURE 8.7 Minitab and SAS output for Example 8.6.

Minitab

```
Sample     X     N    Sample p
1         63   296    0.212838
2         27   251    0.107570

Difference = p(1) - p(2)
Estimate for difference: 0.105268
Test for difference = 0 (vs not = 0): z = 3.31 P-Value = 0.001
```

SAS

Two Sample Test of Equality of Proportions

Sample Statistics

– Frequencies of x for gen –

Value	1	2
0	233	224
1	63	27

Hypothesis Test

Null hypothesis:

Proportion of x(gen=1) – Proportion of x(gen=2) = 0

Alternative:

Proportion of x(gen=1) – Proportion of x(gen=2) ^= 0

– Proportions of x for gen –

Value	1	2	Z	Prob > z
1	0.2128	0.1076	3.31	0.0009

null hypothesis that the two types of companies are equally likely to offer this kind of benefit to their employees. In the sample, 73 of the 91 high-tech companies and 75 of the 109 other companies offered incentive stock options to key employees. State appropriate null and alternative hypotheses, compute the test statistic, and report the P-value. Give a brief statement of your conclusion.

8.57 Are the unhappy HMO customers likely to leave? In Exercise 8.53 we examined data from a study designed to find reasons why patients leave a health maintenance organization (HMO). There we compared the proportion of complainers who leave the HMO with the proportion of noncomplainers who leave. In the year of the study, 639 patients filed complaints and 54 of these patients left the HMO voluntarily. For comparison, the HMO chose an SRS of 743 patients who had not filed complaints. Twenty-two of those patients left voluntarily. We expect a higher proportion of complainers to leave. Do the data support this expectation? State hypotheses, find the test statistic and its P-value, and state your conclusion.

BEYOND THE BASICS: RELATIVE RISK

In Example 8.5 (page 513) we compared the proportions of women and men who are "label users" when they shop for clothing by giving a confidence interval for the *difference* of proportions. We might alternatively choose to make this comparison by giving the

relative risk

ratio of the two proportions. This ratio is often called the **relative risk** (RR). A relative risk of 1 means that the proportions $\hat{p}_1$ and $\hat{p}_2$ are equal. Confidence intervals for relative risk apply the principles that we have studied, but the details are somewhat complicated. Fortunately, we can leave the details to software and concentrate on interpreting and communicating the results.

EXAMPLE 8.7 Relative Risk for Use of Labels

CASE 8.3

The following table summarizes the data on the proportions of men and women who use labels when buying clothing:

Population	n	X	$\hat{p} = X/n$
1 (women)	296	63	0.2128
2 (men)	251	27	0.1076

The relative risk for this sample is

$$\text{RR} = \frac{\hat{p}_1}{\hat{p}_2} = \frac{0.2128}{0.1076} = 1.98$$

Confidence intervals for the relative risk in the entire population of shoppers are based on this sample relative risk. Software (for example, PROC FREQ with the MEASURES option in SAS) gives a 95% confidence interval as 1.30 to 3.01. Our summary: Women are about twice as likely as men to use labels; the 95% confidence interval is (1.30, 3.01).

In Example 8.7 the confidence interval is clearly not symmetric about the estimate: that is, 1.98 is not the midpoint of 1.30 and 3.01. This is true in general for confidence intervals for relative risk.

Relative risk—that is, comparing proportions by a ratio rather than by a difference—is particularly useful when the proportions are small. This is often the case in epidemiology and medical statistics. Here is a typical epidemiological example.

EXAMPLE 8.8 Blood Pressure and Heart Disease

There is much evidence that high blood pressure is associated with increased risk of death from cardiovascular disease. A major study of this association examined 3338 men with high blood pressure and 2676 men with low blood pressure. During the period of the study, 21 men in the low-blood-pressure and 55 in the high-blood-pressure group died from cardiovascular disease.[23]

As usual, we choose the group with the higher proportion to be Population 1. The proportion of the high-blood-pressure group who died is $\hat{p}_1 = 0.0165$. For men with low blood pressure, the proportion is $\hat{p}_2 = 0.0078$. The difference is statistically significant ($z = 2.98$, $P = 0.0014$), and the 95% confidence interval for the difference in population proportions is (0.0032, 0.0141).

Because the proportions of men who died are both small, relative risk communicates the results of this study more effectively. The relative risk for the sample is

$$\text{RR} = \frac{\hat{p}_1}{\hat{p}_2} = \frac{0.0165}{0.0078} = 2.1$$

Software gives the 95% confidence interval for the population as 1.3 to 3.5. That is, the risk of dying from cardiovascular disease is doubled for men with high blood pressure compared with men who have low blood pressure (RR = 2.1, 95% confidence interval = 1.3 to 3.5).

SECTION 8.2 SUMMARY

- The **estimate of the difference in two population proportions** is

$$D = \hat{p}_1 - \hat{p}_2$$

where

$$\hat{p}_1 = \frac{X_1}{n_1} \quad \text{and} \quad \hat{p}_2 = \frac{X_2}{n_2}$$

- The **standard error of the difference** is

$$\text{SE}_D = \sqrt{\frac{\hat{p}_1(1-\hat{p}_1)}{n_1} + \frac{\hat{p}_2(1-\hat{p}_2)}{n_2}}$$

and the **margin of error for confidence level C** is

$$m = z^* \text{SE}_D$$

where z^* is the value for the standard Normal density curve with area C between $-z^*$ and z^*.

- The **z large-sample level C confidence interval** for the difference in two proportions $p_1 - p_2$ is

$$(\hat{p}_1 - \hat{p}_2) \pm m$$

We recommend using this method when the number of successes and the number of failures in both samples are at least 10.

- The **plus four confidence interval for comparing two proportions** is obtained by adding one success and one failure to each sample and then using the z procedure. We recommend using this method when both sample sizes are at least 5 and the confidence level is 90%, 95%, or 99%.

- Significance tests of H_0: $p_1 = p_2$ use the **z statistic**

$$z = \frac{\hat{p}_1 - \hat{p}_2}{\text{SE}_{Dp}}$$

with P-values from the $N(0, 1)$ distribution. In this statistic,

$$\text{SE}_{Dp} = \sqrt{\hat{p}(1-\hat{p})\left(\frac{1}{n_1} + \frac{1}{n_2}\right)}$$

where $\hat{p}$ is the **pooled estimate** of the common value of p_1 and p_2,

$$\hat{p} = \frac{X_1 + X_2}{n_1 + n_2}$$

- **Relative risk** is the ratio of two sample proportions:

$$RR = \frac{\hat{p}_1}{\hat{p}_2}$$

Confidence intervals for relative risk are an alternative to confidence intervals for the difference when we want to compare two proportions.

SECTION 8.2 Exercises

For Exercises 8.51, see page 511; for 8.52 and 8.53, see page 514; for 8.54 and 8.55, see page 515; and for 8.56 and 8.57, see pages 517–518.

8.58 What's wrong? For each of the following, explain what is wrong and why.

(a) A z statistic is used to test the null hypothesis that $\hat{p}_1 = \hat{p}_2$.

(b) If two sample proportions are equal, then the sample counts are equal.

(c) A 95% confidence interval for the difference in two proportions includes errors due to nonresponse.

8.59 Draw a picture (optional). Suppose there are two binomial populations. For the first, the true proportion of successes is 0.4; for the second, it is 0.5. Consider taking independent samples from these populations, 50 from the first and 60 from the second.

(a) Find the mean and the standard deviation of the distribution of $\hat{p}_1 - \hat{p}_2$.

(b) This distribution is approximately Normal. Sketch this Normal distribution and mark the location of the mean.

(c) Find a value d for which the probability is 0.95 that the difference in sample proportions is within $\pm d$. Mark these values on your sketch.

8.60 College student summer employment. Suppose (as is roughly true) that 85% of college men and 83% of college women were employed last summer. A sample survey interviews SRSs of 400 college men and 400 college women. The two samples are of course independent.

(a) What is the approximate distribution of the proportion $\hat{p}_F$ of women who worked last summer? What is the approximate distribution of the proportion $\hat{p}_M$ of men who worked?

(b) The survey wants to compare men and women. What is the approximate distribution of the difference in the proportions who worked, $\hat{p}_M - \hat{p}_F$?

8.61 Credit cards and impulse shopping. We might expect that shoppers are more likely to use credit cards for "impulse purchases" (that is, those they decide to make on the spot), as opposed to purchases they had in mind when they went to the store. Stop every third person leaving a department store with a purchase. (This is in effect a random sample of people who buy at that store.) A few questions allow us to classify the purchase as impulse or not. Here are the data on how the customer paid:[24]

	Credit Card?	
	Yes	No
Impulse purchases	13	18
Planned purchases	35	31

(a) Is the difference in credit card use between impulse and planned purchases statistically significant?

(b) Give a 95% confidence interval for the difference.

8.62 Brand loyalty. It's hard to persuade consumers to abandon a product with which they are familiar. One experiment gave consumers free samples of a new laundry detergent and also of a standard detergent. After some time, ask the subjects which detergent they prefer.[25] Among the 48 customers who normally used the standard product, 19 preferred the new product; among the 56 customers who did not use the standard product, 29 preferred the new product. Are current users of the standard detergent less likely than nonusers to prefer the new detergent? Summarize the data and do a test of significance.

8.63 Consider other factors. The reaction of nonusers to the new detergent, reported in the previous exercise, looks promising. Let's consider only people who don't currently use the standard detergent and look at other factors that might influence which detergent they prefer. There were 116 customers who used soft water and 110 customers who used hard water. In the soft-water group, 53 customers preferred the new product, while 42 customers in the hard-water group expressed this preference.

	Soft water	Hard water
Prefer standard product	63	68
Prefer new product	53	42

Compare the preferences of people with hard water and soft water, including a test of significance. Did you learn anything that might be used in advertising the new detergent?

8.64 A corporate liability trial. A major court case on liability for contamination of groundwater took place in the town of Woburn, Massachusetts. A town well in Woburn was contaminated by industrial chemicals. During the period that residents drank water from this well, there were 16 birth defects among 414 births. In years when the contaminated well was shut off and water was supplied from other wells, there were 3 birth defects among 228 births. The plaintiffs suing the firms responsible for the contamination claimed that these data show that the rate of birth defects was higher when the contaminated well was in use.[26] How statistically significant is the evidence? Be sure to state what assumptions your analysis requires and to what extent these assumptions seem reasonable in this case.

8.65 Support for a marketing program. Many states have "corn checkoff" programs that divert a small part of the sale price of corn (typically one-half cent per bushel). These funds are used to develop new markets, to promote renewable fuels and new technologies that use corn, and to access federal government money for these activities. Some checkoff programs are voluntary and some are mandatory. The Indiana Department of Agriculture asked random samples of corn producers in each county whether they favored a mandatory program. In Tippecanoe County, 263 farmers were in favor of the program and 252 were not. In neighboring Benton County, 260 were in favor and 377 were not.

(a) Find the proportions of farmers in favor of the program in each of the two counties.

(b) Find the standard error needed to compute a confidence interval for the difference in the proportions.

(c) Compute a 99% confidence interval for the difference between the proportions of farmers favoring the program in Tippecanoe County and in Benton County. Do you think opinions differed in the two counties?

8.66 Perform a significance test. Refer to the survey of farmers described in the previous exercise.

(a) Formulate null and alternative hypotheses for comparing the proportions of farmers in the two counties who favor mandatory checkoff.

(b) Combine the two samples and find the overall proportion of farmers who favor the corn checkoff program.

(c) Find the standard error needed for testing the hypotheses you stated in (a).

(d) Compute the z statistic and its P-value. What conclusion do you draw?

8.67 CASE 8.2 **Natural versus artificial Christmas trees.** In the Christmas tree survey introduced in Case 8.2 (page 503), respondents who had a tree during the holiday season were asked whether the tree was natural or artificial. Respondents were also asked if they lived in an urban area or in a rural area. Of the 421 households displaying a Christmas tree, 160 lived in rural areas and 261 were urban residents. The tree growers want to know if there is a difference in preference for natural trees versus artificial trees between urban and rural households. Here are the data:

Population	n	X(natural)
1 (rural)	160	64
2 (urban)	261	89

(a) Give the null and alternative hypotheses that are appropriate for this problem assuming that we have no prior information suggesting that one population would have a higher preference than the other.

(b) Test the null hypothesis. Give the test statistic and the P-value, and summarize the results.

(c) Give a 90% confidence interval for the difference in proportions.

8.68 Summer employment of college students. A university financial aid office polled an SRS of undergraduate students to study their summer employment. Not all students were employed the previous summer. Here are the results for men and women:

	Men	Women
Employed	712	623
Not employed	68	92
Total	780	715

(a) Is there evidence that the proportion of male students employed during the summer differs from the

CHAPTER 9

Inference for Two-Way Tables

PRELUDE: MUSIC AND MARKETING

Music influences our mood and behavior. Compare, for instance, the music we hear during car chases with that played during love scenes in films and on television. Marketers try to choose background music that will influence consumers. Does the type of music we hear have an effect on the purchases we make? One study of this question varied the type of background music and observed the effect on wine sales. You see that this is a comparative experiment. The percent of French wine among all bottles sold was 52% when French music was playing and 36% when other types of music were playing.[1] The researchers used the methods of this chapter to determine that their results were statistically significant.

9.1 Analysis of Two-Way Tables

When we compared two proportions in Section 8.2, we started by summarizing the raw data by giving the number of observations in each group (n) and how many of these were classified as "successes" (X).

EXAMPLE 9.1 No Sweat Labels

Case 8.3 concerned the response of men and women to "No Sweat" labels on a garment. These labels supposedly guarantee fair working conditions for the workers who made the garment. Here is the data summary from Example 8.5 (page 513). The table gives the number n of subjects in each gender. The count X is the number who were classified as No Sweat label users.

Population	n	X
1 (women)	296	63
2 (men)	251	27
Total	547	90

To compare men and women, we calculated sample proportions from these counts.

Two-way tables

two-way table

In this chapter we start with a different summary of the same data. Rather than recording just the count of label users, we record counts for all outcomes in a **two-way table.**

EXAMPLE 9.2 No Sweat Labels

Here is the two-way table classifying customers by gender and whether or not they are label users:

	Gender		
Label user	**Women**	**Men**	**Total**
Yes	63	27	90
No	233	224	457
Total	296	251	547

Check that this table simply rearranges the information in Example 9.1.

Because we are interested in how gender influences label use, we view gender as an explanatory variable and label use as a response variable. This is why we put gender in the columns (like the x axis in a regression) and label use in the rows (like the y axis in a regression). Be sure that you understand how this table is obtained from the table in Example 9.1. Most errors in the use of categorical-data methods come from a misunderstanding of how these tables are constructed.

We call this particular two-way table a 2×2 table because there are two rows (Yes and No for label use) and two columns (Women and Men). The advantage of two-way tables is that they can present data for variables having more than two categories by simply increasing the number of rows or columns. Suppose, for example, that we recorded the influence of No Sweat labels on a consumer using a 5-point scale rather than simply "Yes" and "No." The response variable would then have 5 levels, so our table would be 5×2, with 5 rows and 2 columns. We studied two-way tables in Section 2.5 (page 150). Now would be a good time to briefly review that material.

In this section we advance from describing data to inference in the setting of two-way tables. Our data are counts of observations, classified according to two categorical variables. The question of interest is whether there is a relation between the row variable and the column variable. For example, is there a relation between gender and label use? In Example 8.5 we found that there was a relation: women are more likely than men to use the No Sweat labels. Now we will assess the statistical significance of this relationship.

We introduce inference for two-way tables with data that form a 2×2 table. The methodology applies to tables in general and we will discuss a 3×3 table (two categorical variables, each with three categories) in the next section.

CASE 9.1 

EXCLUSIVE TERRITORIES AND THE SUCCESS OF NEW FRANCHISE CHAINS

Many popular businesses are franchises—think of McDonald's. The owner of a local franchise benefits from the brand recognition, national advertising, and detailed guidelines provided by the franchise chain. In return, he or she pays fees to the franchise firm and agrees to follow its policies. The relationship between the local entrepreneur and the franchise firm is spelled out in a detailed contract.

One clause that the contract may or may not contain is the entrepreneur's right to an exclusive territory. This means that the new outlet will be the only representative of the franchise in a specified territory and will not have to compete with other outlets of the same chain. How does the presence of an exclusive-territory clause in the contract relate to the survival of the business? A study designed to address this question collected data from a sample of 170 new franchise firms.[2]

Two categorical variables were measured for each firm. First, the firm was classified as successful or not based on whether or not it was still franchising as of a certain date. Second, the contract of each firm was classified according to whether or not there was an exclusive-territory clause. Here are the data:

Observed numbers of firms

	Exclusive territory		
Success	Yes	No	Total
Yes	108	15	123
No	34	13	47
Total	142	28	170

The entries in the two-way table in Case 9.1 are the observed, or sample, counts of the numbers of firms in each category. For example, 108 successful firms with an exclusive-territory contract while 15 successful firms did not. The table includes the marginal totals, calculated by summing over the rows or columns. The grand total, 170, is the sum of the row totals and is also the sum of the column totals. It is the total number of firms in the study.

The rows and columns of a two-way table represent values of two categorical variables. These are called "Success" and "Exclusive territory" in Case 9.1. We are interested in the influence of exclusive territories on success, so Exclusive territory is the explanatory variable (the column variable) and Success is the response (row) variable. Each combination of values for these two variables defines a **cell.** A two-way table with r rows and c columns contains $r \times c$ cells. The 2×2 table in Case 9.1 has 4 cells. In this study, we have data on two variables for a single sample of 170 firms. The same table might also have arisen from two separate samples, one from successful firms and the other from unsuccessful firms. Fortunately, the same inference applies in both cases. Not all two-way tables have a response variable and an explanatory variable. They can be used to display the relationship between any two categorical variables.

cell

APPLY YOUR KNOWLEDGE

9.1 Wine and music. The Prelude to this chapter describes a study of the effect of music on purchases of French wine.

(a) Write down the outline of a two-way table in which you would record the data for this study. Your outline will show the number of rows and columns and their labels but no actual data in the cells.

(b) Would you view one variable as a response variable and the other as an explanatory variable? Give a reason for your answer. How did this influence the form of your table outline?

9.2 A reduction in force. A human resources manager wants to assess the impact of a planned reduction in force (RIF) on employees over the age of 40. (Various laws state that discrimination against this group is illegal.) The company has 750 employees over 40 and 550 who are 40 years of age or less. The current plan for the RIF will terminate 120 employees: 85 who are over 40, and 35 who are 40 or less. Display these data in a two-way table. (Be careful. Remember that each employee should be counted in exactly one cell.)

Describing relations in two-way tables

Analysis of two-way tables in practice uses statistical software to carry out the considerable arithmetic required. We will use output from some typical software packages for the data of Case 9.1 to describe inference for two-way tables. In Section 9.2 we will give more detail, so that you can do the work with a calculator if software is not available.

To describe relations between categorical variables, we compute and compare percents. The count in each cell can be viewed as a percent of the grand total, of the row total, or of the column total. In the first case, we are describing the **joint distribution** of the two variables; in the other two cases, we are examining the **conditional distributions.** You must decide which percents are most appropriate. Software usually prints out all three, but not all are of interest in a specific problem.

joint distribution
conditional distribution

EXAMPLE 9.3 Software Output

CASE 9.1

Figure 9.1 shows the output from Minitab, SPSS, and SAS for the data of Case 9.1. We named the variables SUCCESS and EXCL.

The two-way table appears in the output in expanded form. Each cell contains four entries. They appear in different orders or with different

FIGURE 9.1 Minitab, SPSS, and SAS output for Example 9.3.

Minitab

Tabulated statistics: success, excl

```
Rows: success    Columns: excl

             1        2      All

1          108       15      123
         87.80    12.20   100.00
         76.06    53.57    72.35
        102.74    20.26   123.00

2           34       13       47
         72.34    27.66   100.00
         23.94    46.43    27.65
         39.26     7.74    47.00

All        142       28      170
         83.53    16.47   100.00
        100.00   100.00   100.00
        142.00    28.00   170.00

Cell Contents:          Count
                        % of Row
                        % of Column
                        Expected count

Pearson Chi-Square = 5.911, DF = 1, P-Value = 0.015
```

SPSS

SUCCESS * EXCL Crosstabulation

			EXCL		Total
			1	2	
SUCCESS	1	Count	108	15	123
		Expected Count	102.7	20.3	123.0
		% within SUCCESS	87.8%	12.2%	100.0%
		% within EXCL	76.1%	53.6%	72.4%
	2	Count	34	13	47
		Expected Count	39.3	7.7	47.0
		% within SUCCESS	72.3%	27.7%	100.0%
		% within EXCL	23.9%	46.4%	27.6%
Total		Count	142	28	170
		Expected Count	142.0	28.0	170.0
		% within SUCCESS	83.5%	16.5%	100.0%
		% within EXCL	100.0%	100.0%	100.0%

Chi-Square Tests

	Value	df	Asymp. Sig. (2-sided)
Pearson Chi-Square	5.911	1	.015
N of Valid Cases	170		

SAS

success excl

Frequency Expected Row Pct Col Pct	1_YES	2_NO	Total
1_YES	108 102.74 87.80 76.06	15 20.259 12.20 53.57	123
2_NO	34 39.259 72.34 23.94	13 7.7412 27.66 46.43	47
Total	142	28	170

Statistics for Table of success by excl

Statistic	DF	Value	Prob
Chi-Square	1	5.9112	0.0150

labels, but all three outputs contain the same information. The frequency or count is the first entry in SPSS and SAS. The row and column totals appear in the margins, just as in Case 9.1. The cell count as a percent of the row total is variously labeled as "% of Row" or "% within SUCCESS" or "Row Pct." For the first cell, this is 108/123, or 87.8%. The cell count as a percent of the column total is also given. You can request yet another entry, cell count divided by the total number of observations (the joint distribution). This is often not very useful and tends to clutter up the output.

In Case 9.1 we are interested in the effect of having an exclusive territory on the success of the firm. To compare successful and unsuccessful firms, we examine column percents. Here they are, rounded from the output for clarity:

Column percents for firms

	Exclusive territory	
Success	**Yes**	**No**
Yes	76%	54%
No	24%	46%
Total	100%	100%

The "Total" row reminds us that 100% of each type of firm have been classified as successful or not. (The sums sometimes differ slightly from 100% because of roundoff error.) The bar graph in Figure 9.2 compares the percents. The data reveal a clear relationship: 76% of firms with exclusive territories are successful, as opposed to only 54% of firms that did not have an exclusive-territory contract.

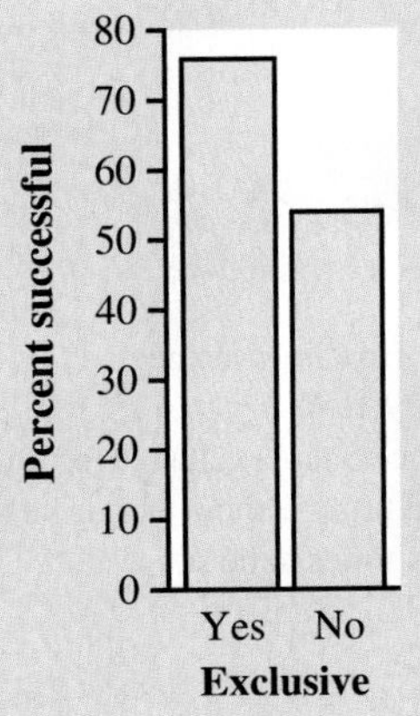

FIGURE 9.2 Bar graph of the percents of successful firms, for Example 9.3.

APPLY YOUR KNOWLEDGE

9.3 Reading software output. Look at Figure 9.1. What percent of successful firms had an exclusive-territory contracts? What percent of unsuccessful firms had an exclusive-territory contracts?

9.4 Reading software output. Look at Figure 9.1. What percent of firms are successful? What percent of firms had an exclusive-territory contract?

The hypothesis: no association

The difference between the percents of successes among the two types of firms is quite large. A statistical test will tell us whether or not these differences can be plausibly attributed to chance. Specifically, if there is no association between success and having an exclusive territory, how likely is it that a sample would show differences as large or larger than those displayed in Figure 9.2?

The null hypothesis H_0 of interest in a two-way table is: There is *no association* between the row variable and the column variable. In Example 9.3, this null hypothesis says that success and having an exclusive territory are not related. The alternative hypothesis H_a is that there is an association between these two variables. The alternative H_a does not specify any particular direction for the association. For $r \times c$ tables in general, the alternative includes many different possibilities. Because it includes all of the many kinds of association that are possible, we cannot describe H_a as either one-sided or two-sided.

In our example, the hypothesis H_0 that there is no association between success and having an exclusive territory is equivalent to the statement that the distributions of the success variable are the same among firms with and without exclusive territories. For $r \times c$ tables like that in Example 9.2, there are c distributions for the row variable, one for each population. The null hypothesis then says that the c distributions of the row variable are identical. The alternative hypothesis is that the distributions are not all the same.

Expected cell counts

expected cell counts

To test the null hypothesis in $r \times c$ tables, we compare the observed cell counts with **expected cell counts** calculated under the assumption that the null hypothesis is true. Our test statistic is a numerical measure of the distance between the observed and expected cell counts.

EXAMPLE 9.4 Expected Counts from Software

CASE 9.1

The expected counts for the successful-firms example appear in the computer output shown in Figure 9.1. They are labeled Exp Freq or Expected Count or Expected. For example, the expected count for the first cell is 102.74.

How is this expected count obtained? Look at the percents in the right margin of the table in Figure 9.1. We see that 72.35% of all firms are successful. If the null hypothesis of no relation between success and exclusive territories is true, we expect this overall percent to apply to both firms with and firms without exclusive territories. In particular, we expect 72.35% of the firms with exclusive territories to be successful. Since there are 142 firms with exclusive territories, the expected count is 72.35% of 142, or 102.74. The other expected counts are calculated in the same way.

The reasoning of Example 9.4 leads to a simple formula for calculating expected cell counts. To compute the expected count for successful firms with exclusive territories, we multiplied the proportion of successful firms (123/170) by the number of firms with exclusive territories (142). From Figure 9.1 we see that the numbers 123 and 142 are the row and column totals for the cell of interest and that 170 is n, the total number of observations for the table. The expected cell count is therefore the product of the row and column totals divided by the table total.

Expected Cell Counts

The **expected count** in any cell of a two-way table when the null hypothesis of no association is true is

$$\text{expected count} = \frac{\text{row total} \times \text{column total}}{n}$$

APPLY YOUR KNOWLEDGE

9.5 Expected counts. We want to calculate the expected count of unsuccessful firms that do not have an exclusive territory. From Figure 9.1, how many firms lack exclusive territories? What percent of all firms are unsuccessful? Explain in words why, if there is no association between success and exclusive territories, the expected count we want is the product of these two numbers. Verify that the formula gives the same answer.

9.6 An alternative view. Refer to Figure 9.1. Verify that you can obtain the expected count for the first cell by multiplying the number of successful firms by the percent of firms that have exclusive territories. Explain your calculations in words.

The chi-square test

To test the H_0 that there is no association between the row and column classifications, we use a statistic that compares the entire set of observed counts with the set of expected counts. First, take the difference between each observed count and its corresponding

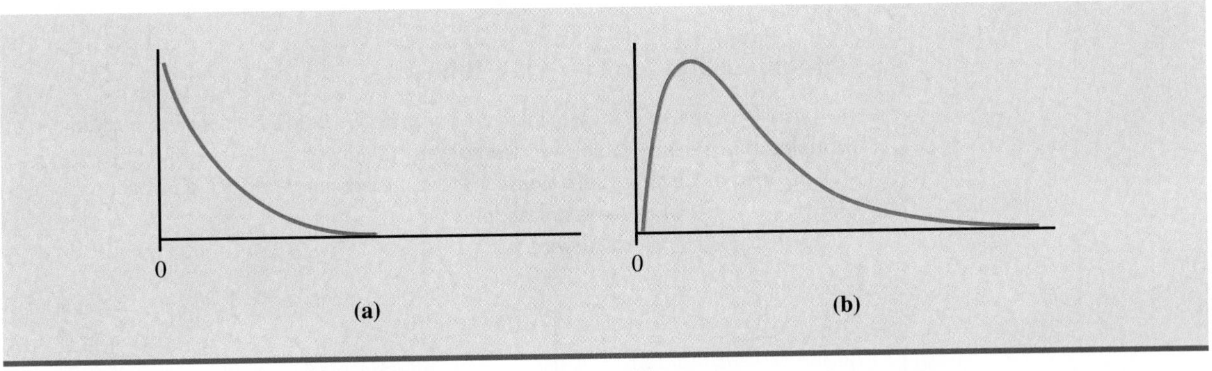

FIGURE 9.3 (a) The $\chi^2(2)$ density curve. (b) The $\chi^2(4)$ density curve.

expected count, and then square these values so that they are all 0 or positive. A large difference means less if it comes from a cell that we think will have a large count, so divide each squared difference by the expected count, a kind of standardization. Finally, sum over all cells. The result is called the *chi-square statistic* X^2.*

Chi-Square Statistic

The **chi-square statistic** is a measure of how much the observed cell counts in a two-way table diverge from the expected cell counts. The recipe for the statistic is

$$X^2 = \sum \frac{(\text{observed count} - \text{expected count})^2}{\text{expected count}}$$

where "observed" represents an observed sample count, "expected" represents the expected count for the same cell, and the sum is over all $r \times c$ cells in the table.

If the expected counts and the observed counts are very different, a large value of X^2 will result. Therefore, large values of X^2 provide evidence against the null hypothesis. To obtain a P-value for the test, we need the sampling distribution of X^2 under the assumption that H_0 (no association between the row and column variables) is true. We once again use an approximation, related to the Normal approximations that we employed in Chapter 8. The result is a new distribution, the **chi-square distribution,** which we denote by χ^2 (χ is the lowercase form of the Greek letter chi).

chi-square distribution

Like the t distributions, the χ^2 distributions form a family described by a single parameter, the degrees of freedom. We use $\chi^2(\text{df})$ to indicate a particular member of this family. Figure 9.3 displays the density curves of the $\chi^2(2)$ and $\chi^2(4)$ distributions. As the figure suggests, χ^2 distributions take only positive values and are skewed to the right. Table F in the back of the book gives upper critical values for the χ^2 distributions.

*The chi-square statistic was invented by the English statistician Karl Pearson (1857–1936) in 1900, for purposes slightly different from ours. It is the oldest inference procedure still used in its original form. With the work of Pearson and his contemporaries at the beginning of the twentieth century, statistics first emerges as a separate discipline.

Chi-Square Test for Two-Way Tables

The null hypothesis H_0 is that there is no association between the row and column variables in a two-way table. The alternative is that these variables are related.

If H_0 is true, the chi-square statistic X^2 has approximately a χ^2 distribution with $(r - 1)(c - 1)$ degrees of freedom.

The P-value for the chi-square test is

$$P(\chi^2 \geq X^2)$$

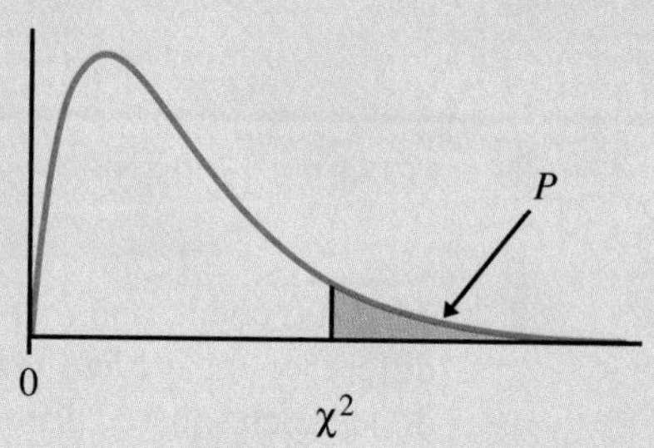

where χ^2 is a random variable having the $\chi^2(\text{df})$ distribution with df = $(r - 1)(c - 1)$.

The chi-square test always uses the upper tail of the χ^2 distribution, because any deviation from the null hypothesis makes the statistic larger. The approximation of the distribution of X^2 by χ^2 becomes more accurate as the cell counts increase. Moreover, it is more accurate for tables larger than 2×2 tables. For tables larger than 2×2, we will use this approximation whenever the average of the expected counts is 5 or more and the smallest expected count is 1 or more. For 2×2 tables, we require that all four expected cell counts be 5 or more.[3]

EXAMPLE 9.5 Exclusive Territories and Franchise Firm Success

CASE 9.1

The results of the chi-square significance test for the successful-firms example appear in the lower parts of the computer outputs in Figure 9.1, labeled Chi-Square or Pearson Chi-Square. Because all the expected cell counts are moderately large, the χ^2 distribution provides accurate P-values. We see that $X^2 = 5.91$ and df = 1, and the P-value is given as 0.015 under the various headings P-Value, Asymp. Sig. (2-sided), or Prob. As a check we verify that the degrees of freedom are correct for a 2×2 table:

$$\text{df} = (r - 1)(c - 1) = (2 - 1)(2 - 1) = 1$$

The chi-square test confirms that the data contain clear evidence against the null hypothesis that there is no relationship between success and exclusive territories. Under H_0, the chance of obtaining a value of X^2 greater than or equal to the calculated value of 5.91 is small—less than 15 times in 1000. The test does not tell us what kind of relationship is present. It is up to us to see that the data show that firms with exclusive territories are more likely to be successful. You should always accompany a chi-square test by percents such as those in Example 9.3 and Figure 9.2 and by a description of the nature of the relationship.

The observational study of Case 9.1 cannot tell us whether having exclusive territories is a *cause* of success in a franchise firm. The association may be explained by confounding of contract terms with other variables such as type of business. Our data don't allow us to investigate possible confounding variables. A randomized comparative experiment that assigns firms to have or not have exclusive territories would settle the issue of causation. As is often the case, however, an experiment isn't practical. The authors of this study supplemented the data we used with interviews of founders of franchises and a theoretical framework for the results. Still, they limit their conclusion to stating that the firms with exclusive territories are more likely to survive.

APPLY YOUR KNOWLEDGE

9.7 Degrees of freedom. A chi-square significance test is performed to examine the association between two categorical variables in a 6×3 table. What are the degrees of freedom associated with the test statistic?

9.8 The *P*-value. A test for association gives $X^2 = 27.41$ with df $= 12$. How would you report the P-value for this problem? Use Table F in the back of the book.

The chi-square test and the *z* test

We began this chapter by converting a "compare two proportions" setting (Example 9.1) into a 2×2 table. We now have two ways to test the hypothesis of equality of two population proportions: the chi-square test and the two-sample z test from Section 8.2. In fact, *these tests always give exactly the same result,* because the chi-square statistic is equal to the square of the z statistic, and $\chi^2(1)$ critical values are equal to the squares of the corresponding $N(0, 1)$ critical values. Exercise 9.9 asks you to verify this for Example 9.1. The advantage of the z test is that we can test either one-sided or two-sided alternatives and add confidence intervals to the significance test. The chi-square test always tests the two-sided alternative for a 2×2 table. The advantage of the chi-square test is that it is much more general: we can compare more than two population proportions or, more generally yet, ask about relations in two-way tables of any size.

APPLY YOUR KNOWLEDGE

9.9 No Sweat labels. Sample proportions from Example 9.1 and the two-way table in Example 9.2 (page 536) report the same information in different ways. We saw in Chapter 8 (page 517) that the z statistic for the hypothesis of equal population proportions is $z = 3.30$ with $P < 0.001$.

(a) Find the chi-square statistic X^2 for this two-way table and verify that it is equal (up to roundoff error) to z^2.

(b) Verify that the 0.001 critical value for chi-square with df $= 1$ (Table F) is the square of the 0.0005 critical value for the standard Normal distribution (Table D). The 0.0005 critical value corresponds to a P-value of 0.001 for the two-sided z test.

(c) Explain carefully why the two hypotheses

H_0: $p_1 \neq p_2$ (z test)

H_0: no relation between gender and label use (X^2 test)

say the same thing about the population.

BEYOND THE BASICS: META-ANALYSIS

Policymakers wanting to make decisions based on research are sometimes faced with the problem of summarizing the results of many studies. These studies may show effects of different magnitudes, some highly significant and some not significant. What *overall conclusion* can we draw? **Meta-analysis** is a collection of statistical techniques designed to combine information from different but similar studies. Each individual study must be examined with care to ensure that its design and data quality are adequate. The basic idea is to compute a measure of the effect of interest for each study. These are then combined, usually by taking some sort of weighted average, to produce a summary measure for all of the studies. Of course, a confidence interval for the summary is included in the results. Here is an example.

meta-analysis

EXAMPLE 9.6 Vitamin A Saves Lives of Young Children

Vitamin A is often given to young children in developing countries to prevent night blindness. It was observed that children receiving vitamin A appear to have reduced death rates. To investigate the possible relationship between vitamin A supplementation and death, a large field trial with over 25,000 children was undertaken in Aceh Province of Indonesia. About half of the children were given large doses of vitamin A, and the other half were controls. The researchers reported a 34% reduction in mortality (deaths) for the treated children who were 1 to 6 years old compared with the controls. Several additional studies were then undertaken. Most of the results confirmed the association: treatment of young children in developing countries with vitamin A reduces the death rate; but the size of the effect varied quite a bit.

How can we use the results of these studies to guide policy decisions? To address this question, a meta-analysis was performed on data from eight studies.[4] Although the designs varied, each study provided a two-way table of counts. Here is the table for the study conducted in Aceh Province. A total of $n = 25{,}200$ children were enrolled in the study. Approximately half received vitamin A supplements. One year after the start of the study, the number of children who had died was determined.

	Vitamin A	Control
Dead	101	130
Alive	12,890	12,079
Total	12,991	12,209

relative risk

The summary measure chosen was the **relative risk:** the ratio formed by dividing the proportion of children who died in the vitamin A group by the proportion of children who died in the control group. For Aceh, the proportion who died in the vitamin A group was

$$\frac{101}{12{,}991} = 0.00777$$

or 7.7 per thousand. For the control group, the proportion who died was

$$\frac{130}{12{,}209} = 0.01065$$

or 10.6 per thousand. The relative risk is therefore

$$\frac{0.00777}{0.01065} = 0.73$$

Relative risk less than 1 means that the vitamin A group has the lower mortality rate.

The relative risks for the eight studies were

0.73 0.50 0.94 0.71 0.70 1.04 0.74 0.80

A meta-analysis combined these eight results to produce a relative risk estimate of 0.77 with a 95% confidence interval of (0.68, 0.88). That is, vitamin A supplementation reduced the mortality rate to 77% of its value in an untreated group. The confidence interval does not include 1, so we can reject the null hypothesis of no effect (a relative risk of 1). The researchers examined many variations of this meta-analysis, such as using different weights and leaving out one study at a time. These variations had little effect on the final estimate.

After these findings were published, large-scale programs to distribute high-potency vitamin A supplements were started. These programs have saved hundreds of thousands of lives since the meta-analysis was conducted and the arguments and uncertainties were resolved.

SECTION 9.1 SUMMARY

- The **null hypothesis** for $r \times c$ tables of count data is that there is no relationship between the row variable and the column variable.
- **Expected cell counts** under the null hypothesis are computed using the formula

$$\text{expected count} = \frac{\text{row total} \times \text{column total}}{n}$$

- The null hypothesis is tested by the **chi-square statistic,** which compares the observed counts with the expected counts:

$$X^2 = \sum \frac{(\text{observed} - \text{expected})^2}{\text{expected}}$$

- Under the null hypothesis, X^2 has approximately the **chi-square distribution** with $(r-1)(c-1)$ degrees of freedom. The P-value for the test is

$$P(\chi^2 \geq X^2)$$

where χ^2 is a random variable having the $\chi^2(\text{df})$ distribution with df = $(r-1)(c-1)$.

- The chi-square approximation is adequate for practical use when the average expected cell count is 5 or greater and all individual expected counts are 1 or greater, except in the case of 2×2 tables. All four expected counts in a 2×2 table should be 5 or greater.

The section we just completed assumed that you have access to software or a statistical calculator. If you do, you can now work the exercises that appear at the end of the chapter. If not, you should read the part of the optional Section 9.2 that illustrates the details of chi-square calculations before attempting the exercises.

9.2 Formulas and Models for Two-Way Tables*

The calculations required to analyze a two-way table are straightforward but tedious. In practice, we recommend using software, but it is possible to do the work with a calculator, and some insight can be gained by examining the details. Here is an outline of the steps required.

Computations for Two-Way Tables

1. Calculate descriptive statistics that convey the important information in the table. Usually these will be column or row percents.
2. Find the expected counts and use these to compute the X^2 statistic.
3. Use chi-square critical values from Table F to find the approximate P-value.
4. Draw a conclusion about the association between the row and column variables.

The following example illustrates these steps.

CASE 9.2 BACKGROUND MUSIC AND CONSUMER BEHAVIOR

Market researchers know that background music can influence the mood and purchasing behavior of customers. One study in a supermarket in Northern Ireland compared three treatments: no music, French accordion music, and Italian string music. Under each condition, the researchers recorded the numbers of bottles of French, Italian and other wine purchased.[5] Here is the two-way table that summarizes the data:

Counts for wine and music

	Music			
Wine	None	French	Italian	Total
French	30	39	30	99
Italian	11	1	19	31
Other	43	35	35	113
Total	84	75	84	243

This is a 3×3 table, to which we have added the marginal totals obtained by summing across rows and columns. For example, the first-row total is $30 + 39 + 30 = 99$. The

*The analysis of two-way tables is based on computations that are a bit messy and on statistical models that require a fair amount of notation to describe. This section gives the details. By studying this material you will deepen your understanding of the methods described in this chapter, but this section is optional.

grand total, the number of bottles of wine in the study, can be computed by summing the row totals, $99 + 31 + 113 = 243$, or the column totals, $84 + 75 + 84 = 243$. It is a good idea to do both as a check on your arithmetic.

Conditional distributions

First, we summarize the observed relation between the music being played and the type of wine purchased. The researchers expected that music would influence sales, so music type is the explanatory variable and the type of wine purchased is the response variable. In general, the clearest way to describe this kind of relationship is to compare the conditional distributions of the response variable for each value of the explanatory variable. So we will compare the column percents that give the conditional distribution of purchases for each type of music played.

EXAMPLE 9.7 Wine Sales, Given Music Type

CASE 9.2

When no music was played, there were 84 bottles of wine sold. Of these, 30 were French wine. Therefore, the column proportion for this cell is

$$\frac{30}{84} = 0.357$$

That is, 35.7% of the wine sold was French when no music was played. Similarly, 11 bottles of Italian wine were sold under this condition, and this is 13.1% of the sales.

$$\frac{11}{84} = 0.131$$

In all, we calculate nine percents. Here are the results:

Column percents for wine and music

	Music			
Wine	**None**	**French**	**Italian**	**Total**
French	35.7	52.0	35.7	40.7
Italian	13.1	1.3	22.6	12.8
Other	51.9	46.7	41.7	46.5
Total	100.0	100.0	100.0	100.0

In addition to the conditional distributions of types of wine sold for each kind of music being played, the table also gives the marginal distribution of the types of wine sold. These percents appear in the rightmost column, labeled "Total."

The sum of the percents in each column should be 100, except for possible small roundoff errors. It is good practice to calculate each percent separately and then sum each column as a check. In this way we can find arithmetic errors that would not be uncovered if, for example, we calculated the column percent for the "Other" row by subtracting the sum of the percents for "French" and "Italian" from 100.

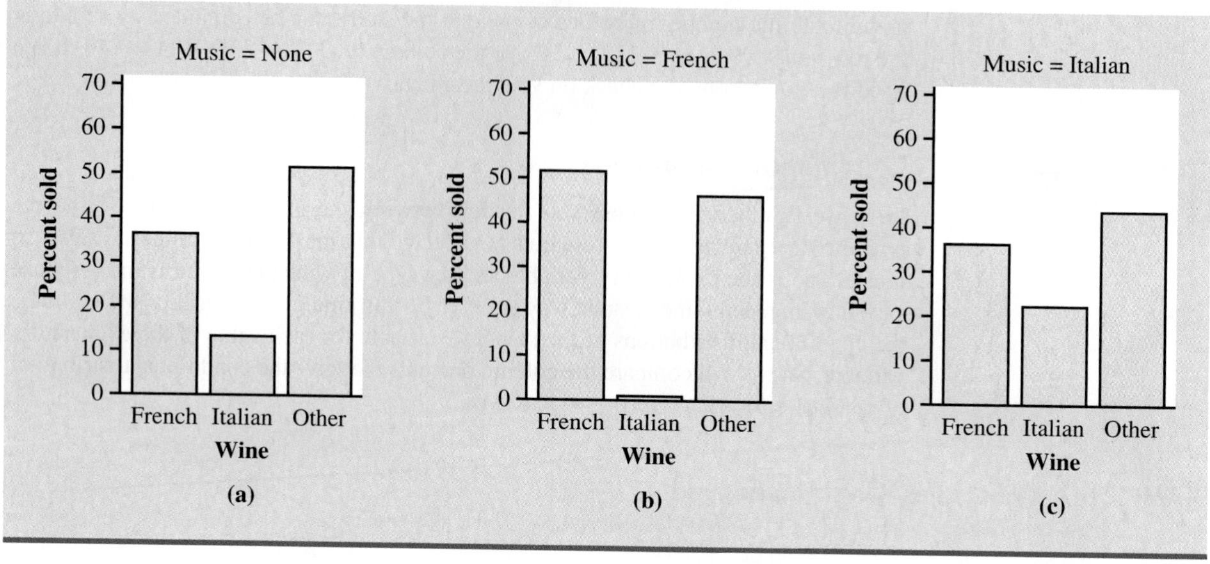

FIGURE 9.4 Comparison of the percents of different types of wine sold for different music conditions, for Example 9.7.

Figure 9.4 compares the distributions of types of wine sold for each of the three music conditions. There appears to be an association between the music played and the type of wine that customers buy. Sales of Italian wine are very low when French music is playing but are higher when Italian music or no music is playing. French wine is popular in this market, selling well under all music conditions but notably better when French music is playing.

Another way to look at these data is to examine the row percents. These fix a type of wine and compare its sales when different types of music are playing. Figure 9.5

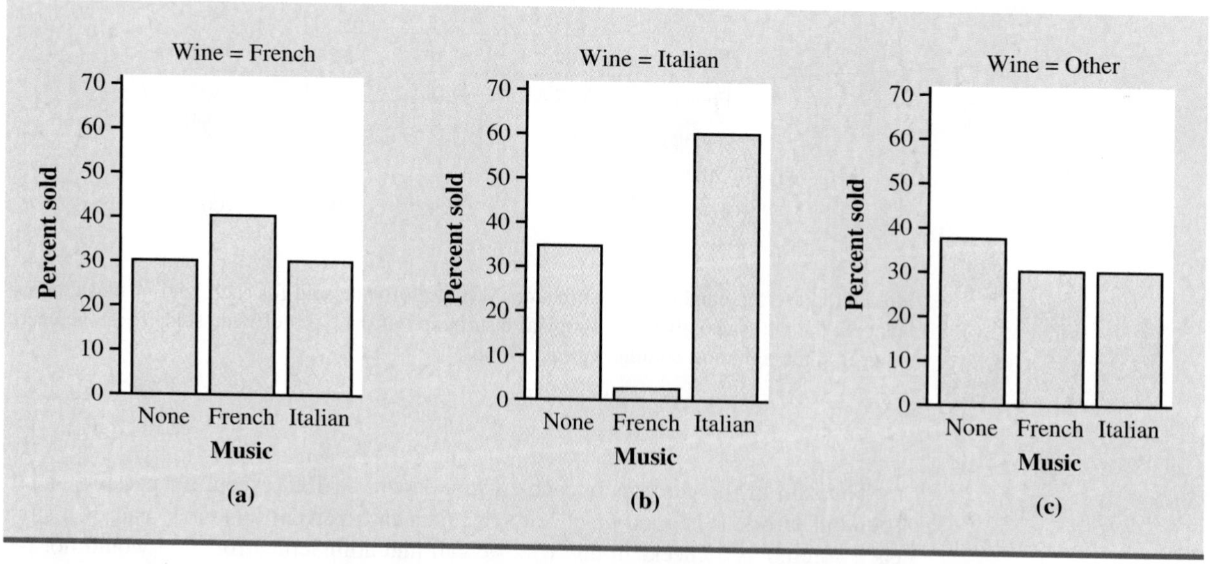

FIGURE 9.5 Comparison of the percents of different types of wine sold for different music conditions, for Example 9.7.

displays these results. We see that more French wine is sold when French music is playing. Similarly for Italian wine. The negative effect of French music on sales of Italian wine is dramatic.

We observe a clear relationship between music type and wine sales for the 243 bottles sold during the study. The chi-square test assesses whether this observed association is statistically significant, that is, too strong to occur often just by chance. The test only confirms that there is some relationship. The percents we have compared describe the nature of the relationship. What is more, the chi-square test does not in itself tell us what population our conclusion describes. If the study was done in one market on a Saturday, the results may apply only to Saturday shoppers at this market. The researchers may invoke their understanding of consumer behavior to argue that their findings apply more generally, but that is beyond the scope of the statistical analysis.

Expected cell counts

The null hypothesis is that there is no relationship between music and wine sales. The alternative is that these two variables are related. We know that under this hypothesis the expected cell counts are

$$\text{expected count} = \frac{\text{row total} \times \text{column total}}{n}$$

EXAMPLE 9.8 Expected Cell Counts

CASE 9.2 

What is the expected count in the upper-left cell in the table for Case 9.2, bottles of French wine sold when no music is playing, under the null hypothesis that music and wine sales are independent?

The column total, the number of bottles of wine sold when no music is playing, is 84. The row total shows that 99 bottles of French wine were sold during the study. The total sales were 243. The expected cell count is therefore

$$\frac{(84)(99)}{243} = 34.222$$

Note that although any count of bottles sold must be a whole number, an expected count need not be. The expected count is the mean over many repetitions of the study, assuming no relationship.

Nine similar calculations produce this table of expected counts:

Expected counts for wine and music

	Music			
Wine	**None**	**French**	**Italian**	**Total**
French	34.222	30.556	34.222	99.000
Italian	10.716	9.568	10.716	31.000
Other	39.062	34.877	39.062	113.001
Total	84.000	75.001	84.000	243.001

We can check our work by adding the expected counts to obtain the row and column totals, as in the table. These should be the same as those in the table of observed counts, except for small roundoff errors, such as 113.001 rather than 113 for the total number of bottles of other wine sold.

The X^2 statistic and its *P*-value

The expected counts are all large, so we proceed with the chi-square test. We compare the table of observed counts with the table of expected counts using the X^2 statistic.[6] We must calculate the term for each cell, then sum over all nine cells. For French wine with no music, the observed count is 30 bottles and the expected count is 34.222. The contribution to the X^2 statistic for this cell is therefore

$$\frac{(30 - 34.222)^2}{34.222} = 0.5209$$

The X^2 statistic is the sum of nine such terms:

$$\begin{aligned} X^2 &= \sum \frac{(\text{observed} - \text{expected})^2}{\text{expected}} \\ &= \frac{(30 - 34.222)^2}{34.222} + \frac{(39 - 30.556)^2}{30.556} + \frac{(30 - 34.222)^2}{34.222} \\ &\quad + \frac{(11 - 10.716)^2}{10.716} + \frac{(1 - 9.568)^2}{9.568} + \frac{(19 - 10.716)^2}{10.716} \\ &\quad + \frac{(43 - 39.062)^2}{39.062} + \frac{(35 - 34.877)^2}{34.877} + \frac{(35 - 39.062)^2}{39.062} \\ &= 0.5209 + 2.3337 + 0.5209 + 0.0075 + 7.6724 + 6.4038 \\ &\quad + 0.3971 + 0.0004 + 0.4223 \\ &= 18.28 \end{aligned}$$

Because there are $r = 3$ types of wine and $c = 3$ music conditions, the degrees of freedom for this statistic are

$$\text{df} = (r - 1)(c - 1) = (3 - 1)(3 - 1) = 4$$

df = 4		
p	0.0025	0.001
χ^2	16.42	18.47

Under the null hypothesis that music and wine sales are independent, the test statistic X^2 has a $\chi^2(4)$ distribution. To obtain the P-value, look at the df = 4 row in Table F. The calculated value $X^2 = 18.28$ lies between the critical points for probabilities 0.0025 and 0.001. The P-value is therefore between 0.0025 and 0.001. Because the expected cell counts are all large, the P-value from Table F will be quite accurate. There is strong evidence ($X^2 = 18.28$, df = 4, $P < 0.0025$) that the type of music being played has an effect on wine sales.

The size and nature of the relationship between music and wine sales are described by row and column percents. These are displayed in Figures 9.4 and 9.5. Here is another way to look at the data: we see that just two of the nine terms that make up the chi-square sum contribute about 14 of the total $X^2 = 18.28$. Comparing the observed and expected counts in these two cells, we see that sales of Italian wine are much below expectation when French music is playing and much above expectation when Italian music is playing. We are led to a specific conclusion: sales of Italian wine are strongly affected by Italian and French music. Figure 9.5(b) displays this effect.

Models for two-way tables

The chi-square test for the presence of a relationship between the two directions in a two-way table is valid for data produced from several different study designs. The precise statement of the null hypothesis "no relationship" in terms of population parameters is different for different designs.

The entries in a two-way table count the individuals studied—franchise firms in Case 9.1, bottles of wine sold in Case 9.2. Each individual counts in only one cell of the table. The two cases differ in design. The data in Case 9.1 concern a single sample of franchise firms, each classified in two ways: whether or not they were successful (rows) and whether or not they had exclusive-territory contracts (columns). In Case 9.2, the market researchers changed the background music and took three samples of wine sales in three distinct environments. Each column in the table represents one of these samples, and each row a type of wine.

The first model: comparing several populations

Case 9.2 (wine sales in three environments) is an example of *separate and independent random samples* from each of c populations. The c columns of the two-way table represent the populations. There is a single categorical response variable, wine type. The r rows of the table correspond to the values of the response variable.

We know that the z test for comparing the two proportions of successes and the chi-square test for the 2×2 table are equivalent. The $r \times c$ table allows us to compare more than two populations or more than two categories of response, or both. In this setting, the null hypothesis "no relationship between column variable and row variable" becomes

H_0: The distribution of the response variable is the same in all c populations.

Because the response variable is categorical, its distribution just consists of the probabilities of its r values. The null hypothesis says that these probabilities (or population proportions) are the same in all c populations.

EXAMPLE 9.9 Music and Wine Sales

CASE 9.2

In the market research study of Case 9.2, we compare three populations:

Population 1: bottles of wine sold when no music is playing

Population 2: bottles of wine sold when French music is playing

Population 3: bottles of wine sold when Italian music is playing

We have three samples, of sizes 84, 75, and 84, a separate sample from each population. The null hypothesis for the chi-square test is

H_0: The proportions of each wine type sold are the same in all three populations.

The parameters of the model are the proportions of the three types of wine that would be sold in each of the three environments. There are three proportions (for French wine, Italian wine, and other wine) for each environment.

Model for Comparing Several Populations Using Two-Way Tables

Select independent SRSs from each of c populations, of sizes $n_1, n_2, \ldots, n_c$. Classify each individual in a sample according to a categorical response variable with r possible values. There are c different probability distributions, one for each population.

The null hypothesis is that the distributions of the response variable are the same in all c populations. The alternative hypothesis says that these c distributions are not all the same.

The second model: testing independence

A second model for which our analysis of $r \times c$ tables is valid is illustrated by the exclusive-territory study of Case 9.1. There, a *single* sample from a *single* population was classified according to two categorical variables.

EXAMPLE 9.10 Exclusive Territories and Franchise Success

CASE 9.2

The single population studied is

Population: recently established franchise firms

The researchers had a sample of 170 such firms. They measured two categorical variables for each firm:

Column variable: Exclusive territory? (Yes/No)

Row variable: Firm successful? (Yes/No)

The null hypothesis for the chi-square test is

H_0: The row variable and the column variable are independent.

The parameters of the model are the probabilities for each of the four possible combinations of values of the row and column variables. If the null hypothesis is true, the multiplication rule for independent events (page 314) says that these can be found as the products of outcome probabilities for each variable alone.

Model for Examining Independence in Two-Way Tables

Select an SRS of size n from a population. Measure two categorical variables for each individual.

The null hypothesis is that the row and column variables are independent. The alternative hypothesis is that the row and column variables are dependent.

Concluding remarks

You can distinguish between the two models by examining the design of the study. In the independence model, there is a single sample. The column totals and row totals are random variables. The total sample size n is set by the researcher; the column and row sums are known only after the data are collected. For the comparison-of-populations model, on the other hand, there is a sample from each of two or more populations. The column sums are the sample sizes selected at the design phase of the research. The null hypothesis in both models says that there is no relationship between the column variable and the row variable. The precise statement of the hypothesis differs, depending on the sampling design. Fortunately, *the test of the hypothesis of "no relationship" is the same for both models:* it is the chi-square test. There are yet other statistical models for two-way tables that justify the chi-square test of the null hypothesis "no relation," made precise in ways suitable for these models. Statistical methods related to the chi-square test also allow the analysis of three-way and higher-way tables of count data. You can find a discussion of these topics in texts on analysis of categorical data.[7]

Both models require that the data can be viewed as random samples from well-defined populations. When you use the chi-square test (and other inference procedures), you are acting as if the data come from random samples or randomized experiments. In practice, there are often some weaknesses in study design. Case 9.2, in counting bottles of wine sold, ignores the fact that some customers buy one bottle and others buy several bottles. If a single customer buys many bottles during the study period, the data may not be a random sample of bottles sold because they give too much weight to this one customer's taste. The franchising study in Case 9.1 took place at a specific time and therefore under business conditions that no doubt differ from later conditions. Fortunately, our results in these two examples are sufficiently clear that we are still comfortable with our conclusions.

SECTION 9.2 SUMMARY

- To analyze a two-way table, first **compute percents or proportions** that describe the relationship between the row and column variables. Then calculate **expected counts,** the **chi-square statistic,** and the ***P*-value.**
- Two different models for generating $r \times c$ tables lead to the chi-square test. In the first model, independent SRSs are drawn from each of c populations, and each observation is classified according to a categorical variable with r possible values. The null hypothesis is that the distributions of the row categorical variable are the same for all c populations. In the second model, a single SRS is drawn from a population, and observations are classified according to two categorical variables having r and c possible values. In this model, H_0 states that the row and column variables are independent.

STATISTICS IN SUMMARY

The chi-square test is one of the most common statistical procedures because two-way tables of counts are frequently constructed in practice. The central idea is always to ask if there is some relationship between the column categories and the row categories. The chi-square test assesses the statistical significance of the column-row relationship but does not by itself tell us the nature or size of the relationship. Here are the things you now should be able to do.

A. Two-Way Tables

1. Arrange data on two categorical variables measured on the same group of individuals in a two-way table of counts for the possible outcomes.
2. Use percents to describe the relationship between two categorical variables, starting from the counts in a two-way table.

B. Interpreting Chi-Square Tests

1. Locate expected cell counts, the X^2 statistic, and its P-value in output from your software or calculator.
2. Explain what null hypothesis the X^2 statistic tests in a specific two-way table.
3. If the test is significant, use percents or comparison of expected and observed counts to see what deviations from the null hypothesis are most important.

C. Doing Chi-Square Tests (Optional)

1. Calculate the expected count for any cell from the observed counts in a two-way table.
2. Calculate the component of the X^2 statistic for any cell, as well as the overall statistic. Make a quick assessment of the significance of the statistic by comparing the observed and expected counts.
3. Give the degrees of freedom of a X^2 statistic.
4. Use the X^2 critical values in Table F to approximate the P-value of a chi-square test.

CHAPTER 9 Review Exercises

For Exercises 9.1 and 9.2, see page 538; for 9.3 and 9.4, see page 541; for 9.5 and 9.6, see page 542; for 9.7 and 9.8, see page 545; and for 9.9, see page 545.

9.10 What's wrong? Explain what is wrong with each of the following:

(a) A chi-square test was used to test the null hypothesis that there is an association between two categorical variables.

(b) The P-value for a chi-square significance test was 1.05.

(c) Expected cell counts are computed under the assumption that the alternative hypothesis is true.

9.11 Construct a table. Construct a 3×3 table of counts where there is no apparent association between the row and column variables.

9.12 Find the P-value. For each of the following situations give the degrees of freedom and an appropriate bound on the P-value (give the exact value if you have software available) for the X^2 statistic for testing the null hypothesis of no association between the row and column variables.

(a) A 4 by 5 table with $X^2 = 26.23$.

(b) A 4 by 3 table with $X^2 = 26.23$.

(c) A 5 by 4 table with $X^2 = 26.23$.

(d) A 7 by 6 table with $X^2 = 26.23$.

9.13 Admission to business and law school. Mountain View University has professional schools in business and law. Here is a three-way table of applicants to these professional schools, categorized by gender, school, and admission decision.[8]

Business		
	Admit	
Gender	Yes	No
Male	400	200
Female	200	100

Law		
	Admit	
Gender	Yes	No
Male	90	110
Female	200	200

(a) Make a two-way table of gender by admission decision for the combined professional schools by summing entries in the three-way table.

(b) From your two-way table, compute separately the percents of male and female applicants admitted. Male applicants are admitted to Mountain View's professional schools at a higher rate than female applicants.

(c) Perform the significance test for the combined two-way table. We justify the use of a significance test in this setting by viewing the admissions process that generated these data as the object of our study.

(d) Now compute separately the percents of male and female applicants admitted by the business school and by the law school.

(e) Perform a significance test for the business school data. Do the same for the law school data.

(f) Explain carefully, as if speaking to a skeptical reporter, how it can happen that Mountain View appears to favor males when this is not true within each of the professional schools.

9.14 Construct a similar table. Refer to the previous exercise. Make up a similar table for a hypothetical university having four different schools that illustrates the same point. Carefully summarize your table with the appropriate percents.

9.15 Class size and departments. A university classifies its classes as either "small" (fewer than 40 students) or "large." A dean sees that 62% of Department A's classes are small, while Department B has only 40% small classes. She wonders if she should cut Department A's budget and insist on larger classes. Department A responds to the dean by pointing out that classes for third- and fourth-year students tend to be smaller than classes for first- and second-year students. The three-way table below gives the counts of classes by department, size, and student audience. Write a short report for the dean that summarizes these data. Start by computing the percents of small classes in the two departments, and include other numerical and graphical comparisons as needed. (Do not perform any statistical significance tests.) Here are the numbers of classes to be analyzed:

	Department A			Department B		
Year	Large	Small	Total	Large	Small	Total
First	2	0	2	18	2	20
Second	9	1	10	40	10	50
Third	5	15	20	4	16	20
Fourth	4	16	20	2	14	16

9.16 Sexual imagery in magazine ads. In what ways do advertisers in magazines use sexual imagery to appeal to youth? One study classified each of 1509 full-page or larger ads as "not sexual" or "sexual," according to the amount and style of the dress of the male or female model in the ad. The ads were also classified according to the target readership of the magazine.[9] Here is the two-way table of counts:

	Magazine readership			
Model dress	Women	Men	General interest	Total
Not sexual	351	514	248	1113
Sexual	225	105	66	396
Total	576	619	314	1509

(a) Summarize the data numerically and graphically.

(b) Perform the significance test that compares the model dress for the three categories of magazine readership. Summarize the results of your test and give your conclusion.

(c) All of the ads were taken from the March, July, and November issues of six magazines in one year. Discuss this fact from the viewpoint of the validity of the significance test and the interpretation of the results.

9.17 Intended readership of ads with sexual imagery. The ads in the study described in the previous exercise were also classified according to the age group of the intended readership. Here is a summary of the data:

	Magazine readership age group	
Model dress	Young adult	Mature adult
Not sexual (percent)	72.3%	76.1%
Sexual (percent)	27.7%	23.9%
Number of ads	1006	503

Using parts (a) and (b) in the previous exercise as a guide, analyze these data and write a report summarizing your work.

9.18 Identity theft and college students. A study of identity theft looked at how well consumers protect themselves from this increasingly prevalent crime. The behaviors of 61 college students were compared with the behaviors of 59 nonstudents.[10] One of the questions was "When asked to create a password, I have used either my mother's maiden name, or my pet's name, or my birth date, or the last four digits of my social security number, or a series of consecutive numbers." For the students, 22 agreed with this statement while 30 of the nonstudents agreed.

(a) Display the data in a two-way table and perform the chi-square test. Summarize the results.

(b) Reanalyze the data using the methods for comparing two proportions that we studied in the previous chapter. Compare the results and verify that the chi-square statistic is the square of the z statistic.

(c) The students in this study were junior and senior college students from two sections of a course in Internet marketing at a large northeastern university. The nonstudents were a group of individuals who were recruited to attend commercial focus groups on the West Coast conducted by a lifestyle marketing organization. Discuss how the method of selecting the subjects in this study relates to the conclusions that can be drawn from it.

9.19 Student athletes and gambling. A survey of student athletes that asked questions about gambling behavior classified students according to the National Collegiate Athletic Association (NCAA) division.[11] For male student athletes, the percent who reported wagering on collegiate sports are given here along with the numbers of respondents in each division:

Division	I	II	III
Percent	17.2%	21.0%	24.4%
Number	5619	2957	4089

(a) Use a significance test to compare the percents for the three NCAA divisions. Give details and a short summary of your conclusion.

(b) The percents in the table above are given in the NCAA report, but the numbers of male student athletes in each division who responded to the survey question are estimated based on other information in the report. To what extent do you think this has an effect on the results? (*Hint:* Rerun your analysis a few times, with slightly different numbers of students but the same percents.)

(c) Some student athletes may be reluctant to provide this kind of information, even in a survey where there is no possibility that they can be identified. Discuss how this fact may affect your conclusions.

(d) The chi-square test for this set of data assumes that the responses of the student athletes are independent. However, some of the students are at the same school and even on the same team. Discuss how you think this might affect the results.

9.20 Air pollution from a steel mill. One possible effect of air pollution is genetic damage. A study designed to examine this problem exposed one group of mice to air near a steel mill and another group to air in a rural area and compared the numbers of mutations in each group.[12] Here are the data for a mutation at the *Hm-2* gene locus:

	Location	
Mutation	Steel mill air	Rural air
Yes	30	23
No		
Total	96	150

(a) Fill in the missing entries in the table.

(b) Summarize the data numerically and graphically.

(c) Is there evidence to conclude that the location is related to the occurrence of mutations? Perform the significance test and summarize the results.

9.21 Hummingbirds in Santa Lucia. *E. jugularis* is a type of hummingbird that lives in the forest preserves of the Caribbean island of Santa Lucia. The males and the females of this species have bills that are shaped somewhat differently. Researchers who study these birds thought that the bill shape might be related to the shape of the flowers that they visit for food. The researchers observed 49 females and 21 males. Of the females, 20 visited the flowers of *H. bihai,* while none of the males visited these flowers.[13] Display the data in a two-way table and perform the chi-square test. Summarize the results and give a brief statement of your conclusion. Your two-way table has a count of zero in one cell. Does this invalidate your significance test? Explain why or why not.

9.22 Internet references in prominent journals. The World Wide Web (WWW) has led to an enormous increase in the amount of information that is easily available to anyone with Internet access. References to Internet pages are becoming quite common in the scientific literature. One study examined Internet references in articles in three prominent journals: the *New England Journal of Medicine* (*NEJM*), the *Journal of the American Medical Association* (*JAMA*), and

Science.[14] In one part of the study, Internet references were classified according to the top-level domain. Here are the data:

	Journal		
Top-level domain	*NEJM*	*JAMA*	*Science*
.gov	41	103	111
.org	37	46	162
.com	6	17	14
.edu	4	8	47
Other	9	15	52

Analyze the data. Include numerical and graphical summaries as well as a significance test. Summarize your results and conclusions.

9.23 Students change majors. A task force set up to examine retention of students in the majors that they chose when starting college examined data on transfers to other majors.[15] Here are some data giving counts of students classified by initial major and the area that they transferred to:

	Area transferred to				
Initial major	Engineering	Management	Liberal arts	Other	Total
Biology	13	25	158		398
Chemistry	16	15	19		114
Mathematics	3	11	20		72
Physics	9	5	14		61

Complete the table by computing the values for the "Other" column. Write a short paragraph explaining what conclusions you can draw about the relationship between initial major and area transferred to. Be sure to include numerical and graphical summaries as well as the details of your significance test.

9.24 A reduction in force. In economic downturns or to improve their competitiveness, corporations may undertake a "reduction in force" (RIF), in which substantial numbers of employees are laid off. Federal and state laws require that employees be treated equally regardless of their age. In particular, employees over the age of 40 years are a "protected class." Many allegations of discrimination focus on comparing employees over 40 with their younger coworkers. Here are the data for a recent RIF:

	Over 40	
Released	No	Yes
Yes	7	41
No	504	765

(a) Complete this two-way table by adding marginal and table totals. What percent of each employee age group (over 40 or not) were laid off? Does there appear to be a relationship between age and being laid off?

(b) Perform the chi-square test. Give the test statistic, the degrees of freedom, the P-value, and your conclusion.

9.25 Performance appraisal. A major issue that arises in RIFs like that in the previous exercise is the extent to which employees in various groups are similar. If, for example, employees over 40 receive generally lower performance ratings than younger workers, that might explain why more older employees were laid off. We have data on the last performance appraisal. The possible values are "partially meets expectations," "fully meets expectations," "usually exceeds expectations," and "continually exceeds expectations." Because there were very few employees who partially met expectations, we combine the first two categories. Here are the data:

	Over 40	
Performance appraisal	No	Yes
Partially or fully meets expectations	82	230
Usually exceeds expectations	353	496
Continually exceeds expectations	61	32

Note that the total number of employees in this table is less than the number in the previous exercise because some employees do not have a performance appraisal. Analyze the data. Do the older employees appear to have lower performance evaluations?

9.26 Majors for men and women in business. A study of the career plans of young women and men sent questionnaires to all 722 members of the senior class in the College of Business Administration at the University of Illinois. One question asked which major within the business program the student had chosen. Here are the data from the students who responded:[16]

	Female	Male
Accounting	68	56
Administration	91	40
Economics	5	6
Finance	61	59

(a) Test the null hypothesis that there is no relation between the gender of students and their choice of major. Give a P-value and state your conclusion.

(b) Describe the differences between the distributions of majors for women and men with percents, with a graph, and in words.

(c) Which two cells have the largest terms in the sum that makes up the X^2 statistic? How do the observed and expected counts differ in these cells? (This should strengthen your conclusions in (b).)

(d) Two of the observed cell counts are small. Do the study data satisfy our guidelines for safe use of the chi-square test?

(e) What percent of the students did not respond to the questionnaire? The nonresponse weakens conclusions drawn from these data.

9.27 Survey response rates. To study the export activity of manufacturing firms, researchers mailed questionnaires to an SRS of firms in each of five industries that export many of their products. The response rate was only 12.5%, because private companies don't like to fill out long questionnaires from academic researchers. Here are data on the planned sample sizes and the actual number of responses received from each industry:[17]

	Sample size	Responses
Metal products	185	17
Machinery	301	35
Electrical equipment	552	75
Transportation equipment	100	15
Precision instruments	90	12

If the response rates differ greatly, comparisons among the industries may be difficult. Is there good evidence of unequal response rates among the five industries? (Start by creating a two-way table of response or nonresponse by industry.)

9.28 Secondhand stores. Shopping at secondhand stores is becoming more popular and has even attracted the attention of business schools. A study of customers' attitudes toward secondhand stores interviewed samples of shoppers at two secondhand stores of the same chain in two cities. The breakdown of the respondents by gender is as follows:[18]

	City 1	City 2
Men	38	68
Women	203	150
Total	241	218

Is there a significant difference between the proportions of women customers in the two cities?

(a) State the null hypothesis, find the sample proportions of women in both cities, do a two-sided z test, and give a P-value using Table A.

(b) Calculate the X^2 statistic and show that it is the square of the z statistic. Show that the P-value from Table F agrees (up to the accuracy of the table) with your result from (a).

(c) Give a 95% confidence interval for the difference between the proportions of women customers in the two cities.

9.29 More secondhand stores. The study of shoppers in secondhand stores cited in the previous exercise also compared the income distributions of shoppers in the two stores. Here is the two-way table of counts:

Income	City 1	City 2
Under \$10,000	70	62
\$10,000 to \$19,999	52	63
\$20,000 to \$24,999	69	50
\$25,000 to \$34,999	22	19
\$35,000 or more	28	24

A statistical calculator gives the chi-square statistic for this table as $X^2 = 3.955$. Is there good evidence that customers at the two stores have different income distributions? (Give the degrees of freedom, the P-value, and your conclusion.)

9.30 Child care workers. A large study of child care used samples from the data tapes of the Current Population Survey over a period of several years. The result is close to an SRS of child care workers. The Current Population Survey has three classes of child care workers: private household, nonhousehold, and preschool teacher. Here are data on the number of blacks among women workers in these three classes:[19]

	Total	Black
Household	2455	172
Nonhousehold	1191	167
Teachers	659	86

(a) What percent of each class of child care workers is black?

(b) Make a two-way table of class of worker by race (black or other).

(c) Can we safely use the chi-square test? What null and alternative hypotheses does X^2 test?

(d) The chi-square statistic for this table is $X^2 = 53.194$. What are its degrees of freedom? Use Table F to approximate the P-value.

(e) What do you conclude from these data?

9.31 Mail survey response rate. Can you increase the response rate for a mail survey by contacting the respondents before they receive the survey? A study designed to address this question compared three groups of subjects.[20] The first group received a preliminary letter about the survey, the second group was phoned, and the third received no preliminary contact. A positive response was defined as returning the survey within two weeks. Here are the counts:

	Intervention		
Response	**Letter**	**Phone call**	**None**
Yes	171	146	118
No	220	68	455
Total	391	214	573

(a) For each intervention find the proportion of positive responses.

(b) Translate the question of interest into appropriate null and alternative hypotheses for this problem.

(c) Give the test statistic, degrees of freedom, and the P-value for the significance test. What do you conclude?

9.32 Nonresponse among physicians. Does a prenotification letter affect the response rate of physicians chosen for a sample survey? A study response rate of those who received the letters was compared with that of a control group who did not.[21] Here are the data:

Response	Letter	No letter
Yes	2570	2645
No	2448	2384
Total	5018	5029

(a) Give the percents of positive responses for those who received letters and those who did not.

(b) Analyze the two-way table. State the hypotheses and give the test statistic, degrees of freedom, P-value, and your conclusion.

9.33 Planning a study. The survey in Exercise 9.31 was conducted in 1966 on subjects who were college students in Houston, Texas, and asked about clothing preferences. The data in Exercise 9.32 were collected in 1989, and the survey questions concerned pregnancy among resident physicians. You are planning a study to be conducted next month to assess the needs in your community for a new Internet access provider. Discuss whether and how you would use the results of these two surveys to design your study.

9.34 Persistence of fund performance. If the performance of a stock fund is due to the skill of the manager, then we would expect a fund that does well this year to perform well next year also. This is called persistence of fund performance. One study classified funds as losers or winners depending on whether their rate of return was less than or greater than the median of all funds.[22] To examine the question of interest, we form a two-way table that classifies each fund as a loser or winner in each of two successive years. Here is one such table:

	Next year	
This year	**Winner**	**Loser**
Winner	85	35
Loser	37	83

Is there evidence in favor of persistence of fund performance in this table? Support your conclusion with a complete analysis of the data.

9.35 Rerun comparing proportions. Rerun the analysis in the previous exercise using the method for comparing two proportions of Section 8.2. Verify that the X^2 statistic is the square of the z statistic and that the P-values for both analyses are the same.

9.36 Retrospective and prospective studies. We have already remarked that the chi-square analysis does not depend on the study design that led to a particular two-way table. Let's verify that this is also true for the "compare two proportions" analysis of 2×2 tables.

Return to the data in Exercise 9.34. These data might result from either of two designs. If we draw separate random samples of winners and losers this year and record the outcome next year, this is a ***prospective study*** (forward looking). We would compare the percents of winners and losers next year for the two "this year" groups. You did this in Exercise 9.34. On the other hand, if we draw separate random samples of winners and losers "next year" and look back to see if they were winners or losers in the previous year, we have a ***retrospective study*** (backward looking). You would now compare the percents of winners and losers this year for the two "next year" groups. Thus, the two designs lead to two different sets of sample proportions. Verify that you nonetheless get the same value of z (and therefore the same P-value) using either the prospective or the retrospective approach.

9.37 Do conclusions generalize? If we find evidence in favor of an effect in one set of circumstances, it is natural to want to conclude that it holds in others. Unfortunately, this is not always true. For example, here is another table from the study described in Exercise 9.34:

	Next year	
This year	**Winner**	**Loser**
Winner	96	148
Loser	145	99

Analyze these data as in Exercise 9.34. What do you conclude? This set of data is for 1987 to 1988; in Exercise 9.34 the years were 1977 to 1978. Many things change with time, as we learned in Chapter 2.

9.38 Retention of graduate students. Are there gender differences in the progress of students in doctoral programs? A major university classified all students entering PhD programs in a given year by their status six years later. The categories used were as follows: completed the degree, still enrolled, and dropped out. Here are the data:

Status	Men	Women
Completed	423	98
Still enrolled	134	33
Dropped out	238	98

Assume that these data can be viewed as a random sample giving us information on student progress. Describe the data using whatever percents are appropriate. State and test a null hypothesis and alternative that address the question of gender differences. Summarize your conclusions. What factors not given might be relevant to this study?

9.39 Simpson's paradox and flight arrival times. Example 2.24 (page 156) presents data that illustrate Simpson's paradox. The data concern the frequency of on-time arrivals for two airlines.

(a) Apply the chi-square test to the data for all flights combined and summarize the results.

(b) Run separate chi-square analyses for each departure city and summarize these results.

(c) Are the effects that illustrate Simpson's paradox in this example statistically significant?

9.40 Student loans. A study of 865 college students found that 42.5% had student loans. The students were randomly selected from the approximately 30,000 undergraduates enrolled in a large public university. The overall purpose of the study was to examine the effects of student-loan burdens on the choice of a career.[23] A student with a large debt may be more likely to choose a field where starting salaries are high so that the loan can more easily be repaid. The following table classifies the students by field of study and whether or not they have a loan.

	Student loan	
Field of study	**Yes**	**No**
Agriculture	32	35
Child development and family studies	37	50
Engineering	98	137
Liberal arts and education	89	124
Management	24	51
Science	31	29
Technology	57	71

Carry out a complete analysis of the association between having a loan and field of study, including a description of the association and an assessment of its statistical significance.

9.41 Compare fields of study on the PEOPLE score. In the study described in the previous exercise, students were asked to respond to some questions regarding their interests and attitudes. Some of these questions form a scale called PEOPLE that measures altruism, or an interest in the welfare of others. Each student was classified as low, medium, or high on this scale. Is there an association between PEOPLE score and field of study? Here are the data:

	PEOPLE score		
Field of study	**Low**	**Medium**	**High**
Agriculture	5	27	35
Child development and family studies	1	32	54
Engineering	12	129	94
Liberal arts and education	7	77	129
Management	3	44	28
Science	7	29	24
Technology	2	62	64

Analyze the data and summarize your results. Are there some fields of study that have very large or very small proportions of students in the high-PEOPLE category?

9.42 Women pharmacy students. The proportion of women entering many professions has undergone considerable change in recent years. A study of students enrolled in pharmacy programs describes the changes in this field. A random sample of 700 students in their third or higher year of study at colleges of pharmacy was taken in each of nine years. The following table gives the numbers of women in each of these samples:[24]

Year	1970	1972	1974	1976	1978	1980	1982	1984	1986
Women	164	195	226	283	302	342	369	385	412

Use the chi-square test to assess the change in the percent of women pharmacy students over time, and summarize your results. (You will need to calculate the number of male students for each year using the fact that the sample size each year was 700.) Plot the percent of women versus year. Describe the plot. Is it roughly linear? Find the least-squares line that summarizes the relation between time and the percent of women pharmacy students.

9.43 Does the trend continue? Refer to the previous exercise. Here are the actual percents of women pharmacy students for the years 1987 to 2000:[25]

Year	1987	1988	1989	1990	1991	1992	1993
Women	60.0%	60.6%	61.6%	62.4%	63.0%	63.4%	63.2%
Year	1994	1995	1996	1997	1998	1999	2000
Women	63.3%	63.4%	63.8%	64.2%	64.4%	64.9%	65.9%

Plot these percents versus year and summarize the pattern. Using your analysis of the data in this and the previous exercise, write a report summarizing the changes that have occurred in the percent of women pharmacy students from 1970 to 2000. Include an estimate of the percent for the year 2004 with an explanation of why you chose this estimate.

9.44 Jury selection. Exercise 8.107 (page 529) concerns *Castaneda v. Partida,* the case in which the Supreme Court decision used the phrase "two or three standard deviations" as a criterion for statistical significance. There were 181,535 persons eligible for jury duty, of whom 143,611 were Mexican Americans. Of the 870 people selected for jury duty, 339 were Mexican Americans. We are interested in finding out if there is an association between being a Mexican American and being selected as a juror. Formulate this problem using a two-way table of counts. Construct the 2×2 table using the variables "Mexican American or not" and "juror or not." Find the X^2 statistic and its P-value. Square the z statistic that you obtained in Exercise 8.107 and verify that the result is equal to the X^2 statistic.

9.45 Dissatisfied customers. Customers who are dissatisfied with a product often discard it. Marketers need to understand factors related to dissatisfaction. Unfortunately, many pet owners are dissatisfied customers. Euthanasia of healthy but unwanted pets by animal shelters is believed to be the leading cause of death for cats and dogs. A study designed to find factors associated with bringing a cat to an animal shelter compared data on cats that were brought to the Humane Society of Saint Joseph County in Mishawaka, Indiana, with controls, cats from the same county that were not brought in.[26] One of the factors examined was the source of the cat; the categories were private owner or breeder, pet store, and other (includes born in home, stray, and obtained from a shelter). This kind of study is called a ***case-control study*** by epidemiologists. Here are the data:

	Source		
Group	**Private**	**Pet store**	**Other**
Cases (brought to shelter)	124	16	76
Controls (not brought)	219	24	203

(a) Should you use row or column percents to describe these data? Give reasons for your answer and summarize the pattern that you see in these percents.

(b) Use a significance test to examine the association between the two variables. Summarize the results.

9.46 What about dogs? The investigators responsible for the study of cats in the previous exercise did a similar study for dogs.[27] Here are the data:

	Source		
Group	**Private**	**Pet store**	**Other**
Cases	188	7	90
Controls	518	68	142

Analyze the data and write a short report explaining your conclusions.

9.47 Compare the sources of dogs and cats. The studies described in the previous two exercises contain data on where people got their pets. The control group data (but not the "cases") were obtained by a random digit dialing telephone survey and can be considered an SRS of households with a cat or a dog in this geographic area. Compare the sources of cats and of dogs. Write a short report on your analysis; include appropriate descriptive statistics, the results of a significance test, and your conclusion.

9.48 More categories from the same data. The "Other" category for the source of the pet in Exercises 9.45 and 9.46 includes born in home, stray, and obtained from a shelter. The following two-way table lists these categories separately for cats:

	Source				
Group	**Private**	**Pet store**	**Home**	**Stray**	**Shelter**
Cases	124	16	20	38	18
Controls	219	24	38	116	49

Here are the results for dogs:

	Source				
Group	**Private**	**Pet store**	**Home**	**Stray**	**Shelter**
Cases	188	7	11	23	56
Controls	518	68	20	55	67

Analyze these 2×5 tables and compare the significance of the chi-square test with your results for the 2×3 tables in Exercises 9.45 and 9.46. With a large number of cells, the chi-square test sometimes does not have very much power.

9.49 Which model? This exercise concerns the optional material in Section 9.2 on models for two-way tables. Look at Exercises 9.26, 9.27, 9.28, and 9.30. For each exercise, state whether you are comparing several populations based on separate samples from each population (the first model for two-way tables) or testing independence between two categorical variables based on a single sample (the second model).

9.50 *Titanic!* In 1912 the luxury liner *Titanic*, on its first voyage, struck an iceberg and sank. Some passengers got off the ship in lifeboats, but many died. Think of the *Titanic* disaster as an experiment in how the people of that time behaved when faced with death in a situation where only some can escape. The passengers are a sample from the population of their peers. Here is information about who lived and who died, by gender and economic status. (The data leave out a few passengers whose economic status is unknown.)[28]

Men		
Status	**Died**	**Survived**
Highest	111	61
Middle	150	22
Lowest	419	85
Total	680	168

Women		
Status	**Died**	**Survived**
Highest	6	126
Middle	13	90
Lowest	107	101
Total	126	317

(a) Compare the percents of men and of women who died. Is there strong evidence that a higher proportion of men die in such situations? Why do you think this happened?

(b) Look only at the women. Describe how the three economic classes differ in the percent of women who died. Are these differences statistically significant?

(c) Now look only at the men and answer the same questions.

9.51 Sports goals. Knowing why different groups of customers participate in an activity or purchase a product can be very useful information in designing a marketing strategy. One study looked at why students participate in recreational sports and compared the profiles of men and women participants.[29] One goal of people who participate in sports is social comparison—the desire to win or to do better than other people. Another is mastery—the desire to improve one's skills or to try one's best. Data were collected from 67 male and 67 female undergraduates at a large university. Each student was classified into one of four categories based on his or her responses to a questionnaire about sports goals. The four categories were high social comparison–high mastery (HSC-HM), high social comparison–low mastery (HSC-LM), low social comparison–high mastery (LSC-HM), and low social comparison–low mastery (LSC-LM). Here are the data displayed in a two-way table:

Observed counts for sports goals

	Sex		
Goal	**Female**	**Male**	**Total**
HSC-HM	14	31	45
HSC-LM	7	18	25
LSC-HM	21	5	26
LSC-LM	25	13	38
Total	67	67	134

(a) Analyze this 4×2 table and summarize your conclusions.

(b) Construct a 2×2 table by summing over the mastery variable. (For example, there will be $14 + 7 = 21$ females in the HSC group.) Analyze this table and summarize your results.

(c) Perform a similar analysis by summing over the social comparison variable.

(d) Write a report summarizing your conclusions.

9.52 Credit cards and household income. A Gallup Poll used telephone interviews to ask 1025 adults aged 18 and over about credit-card ownership.[30] A report based on the poll described the relationship between ownership of a credit card and income. The report states that 54% of people with incomes less than $20,000 have no credit cards. The percents for other income levels are 24% for $20,000 to $30,000, 18% for $30,000 to $50,000, and 7% for over $50,000.

(a) Make a graph that describes the relationship between credit card ownership and income.

(b) Describe the relationship in a short paragraph.

(c) If possible, perform the statistical significance test that addresses the question of whether or not there is a relationship. If it is not possible to do this, explain what additional information you would need to perform the test.

CHAPTER 9 Case Study Exercises

CASE STUDY EXERCISE 1: Web users. To design effective marketing strategies, you need to know your customers. What are the characteristics of people who use the World Wide Web to collect information on travel, and how do they differ from those who use other sources? A survey that collected data to address this question examined the responses of 1401 Web users (WWW) and 1080 people who used other sources for this information (Other).[31] The following tables give counts of WWW and Other for various demographic characteristics. Note that the marginal sums are sometimes less than 1401 and 1080 because of missing data. Use the methods of this chapter to compare the two groups. Include graphical and numerical summaries along with the results of your significance tests. In some cases you may want to combine some categories for the demographic variables. Be sure to include a discussion of missing values. Write a report summarizing your work.

Age in years

	WWW	Other
Under 18	22	24
18–25	160	161
26–35	328	184
36–45	277	189
46–55	224	164
Over 55	101	109

Gender

	WWW	Other
Female	709	561
Male	423	291

Education

	WWW	Other
Grammar school	4	15
High school	85	125
Vocational training	54	53
Some college	336	293
College	357	218
Postgraduate	259	114
Professional	27	17
Other	10	17

Occupational category

	WWW	Other
Management	167	87
Professional	264	156
Educator/student	175	164
Computer related	309	164
Other	217	281

Household income (U.S. $)

	WWW	Other
Less than 10,000	43	65
10,000–19,999	58	78
20,000–29,999	116	102
30,000–39,999	149	127
40,000–49,999	127	105
50,000–74,999	259	129
75,000–99,999	119	71
Over 100,000	134	47
Rather not say	127	128

Race

	WWW	Other
Caucasian/white	1001	772
African American	20	16
Asian/Pacific Islander	35	16
Hispanic/Latino	20	15
Other	56	33

CASE STUDY EXERCISE 2: Start-up businesses in the United States and Korea. What are the characteristics of successful start-up businesses in the United States, and how do they differ from similar businesses in Korea? A study designed to address these questions examined characteristics of 62 U.S. firms and 53 Korean counterparts.[32] The tables below give counts for various characteristics. Analyze these data using the methods of this chapter, and write a report summarizing your findings. Include numerical as well as graphical summaries with the results of your significance tests.

Gender of owner/manager

	U.S.	Korea
Female	19	14
Male	43	39

Age of owner/manager (in years)

	U.S.	Korea
Under 30	2	2
31–40	12	7
41–50	17	33
Over 50	31	11

Major of owner/manager in college

	U.S.	Korea
Business/economics	12	12
Engineering	12	29
Other	38	12

Education of owner/manager

	U.S.	Korea
High school	3	3
Undergraduate degree	26	37
Master's degree	20	6
Doctoral degree	13	7

Previous area of work of owner/manager

	U.S.	Korea
Technical	4	4
Administrative	14	12
Marketing	11	14
Research and development	6	6
Other	27	17

Previous job position of owner/manager

	U.S.	Korea
Owner	4	3
CEO	8	11
Department manager	16	10
Department director	14	14
Employee	20	15

Years of experience of owner/manager in current business

	U.S.	Korea
Less than 1	1	31
1–2	5	14
3–4	14	2
5 or more	42	6

Type of business

	U.S.	Korea
General (opportunistic)	33	30
Technical (craftsman)	29	23

Ownership type

	U.S.	Korea
Sole proprietorship	1	10
Partnership	4	2
Corporation	56	36
Other	1	5

Type of site

	U.S.	Korea
General (free) location	30	43
Industrial complex	17	2
Other	15	8

CHAPTER 9 Appendix

Using Minitab and Excel for Analysis of Two-Way Tables

Analysis of Two-Way Tables

Minitab:

Stat ➤ Tables ➤ Cross Tabulation and Chi-Square

With this pull-down sequence, you can have Minitab tabulate the occurrences of one variable against another variable to ultimately create a two-way table. To create a two-way table with r rows and c columns, you should have two columns of data in the worksheet. One column must have r distinct labels (numeric or text), and the other column must have c distinct labels (numeric or text). Any given row will then reflect the simultaneous occurrence of one of the r categories with one of the c categories. For example, if you open the Minitab file for Case 9.1 (*ca09_001.MTW*), you will find two columns named "success" and "excl" in which there are two distinct values, namely, "1" and "2," which represent the categories of "Yes" and "No," respectively. In the first row, the data entry for success is "2" and the data entry for "excl" is "2"; this row then represents 1 of the 13 unsuccessful firms that did not have an exclusive-territory contract; see Case 9.1 (page 537). In general, to implement this Minitab routine, click the column with the r categories into the **For rows** box and click the column with the c categories into the **For columns** box. In addition to reporting counts, you can request percents (row, column, and total) to be reported by making selections in the **Display** option section. If the counts have been pre-tabulated for each combination of categories, then click the column having these counts in the optional **Frequencies are in** dialog box. To conduct a chi-square analysis, click the **Chi-Square** button and then select the **Chi-Square analysis** option and, if you wish, the **Expected cell counts** option. Click **OK** to close the pop-up box and then click **OK** to find the two-way table along with the chi-square analysis reported in the Session window. It should be noted that Minitab will report two chi-square statistics (each with a P-value). The Pearson chi-square statistic is the test statistic discussed in this chapter.

If the cell counts for the two-way table have been pre-tabulated and the counts are laid out as a two-way table in the worksheet, then consider the following pull-down sequence:

Stat ➤ Tables ➤ Chi-Square Test (Two-Way Table in Worksheet)

In general, the worksheet should have c columns and each column should have r rows. The entries in the worksheet cells are the two-way table cell counts. For example, if you open the Minitab file for Case 9.2 (*ca09_002.MTW*), you will find data in three rows of three columns. In the first row of column one (c1), the data entry is "30," which represents the 30 bottles of French wine purchased when no background music was played; see Case 9.2 (page 548). In general, to implement this routine, click all the data columns into the **Columns containing the table** box and then click **OK** to find the two-way table along with the chi-square analysis reported in the Session window.

Excel:

Excel provides a statistical function that will perform a chi-square analysis. This function requires as inputs the two-way table cell counts and the expect counts. Excel does not automatically calculate the expected counts. As a first step, we need to create the two-way table. You should have two adjacent columns of data in the spreadsheet, where one column has r distinct labels (numeric or text) and the other column has c distinct labels (numeric or text). For each of these columns, there should be a column name in the top row of each column. Now click any cell in the data range. Then click the **Insert** tab, click **PivotTable** in the **Tables** group, and finally click **PivotTable**. The cell range that includes the two column names and the data will be inputted into the **Table/Range** box. Click **OK** and Excel will produce a **PivotTable Field List** box. You will find the column name(s) that you highlighted listed as field(s). Select the field(s) presented to you by clicking a checkmark next to the name(s). Now, click and hold the field name containing the r distinct labels and drag the field from the field section to the **Row Labels** section. Similarly, click and hold the field name containing the c distinct labels and drag the field from the field section to the **Column Labels** section. At this stage, drag one of the fields (not both) into the **Σ Values** section. To have counts reported, click the field name found in the **Σ Values** section, select the **Value Field Setting** option, click the **Summarize by** tab, select "Count" from the menu, and then click **OK** to find the two-way table in the spreadsheet. If the cell counts for the two-way table have been pretabulated, simply put the cell counts directly into the spreadsheet to construct the two-way table. It is then useful to sum the counts to obtain row and column totals, which can be placed in the margins of the table.

With the two-way table created, you now need to create a two-way table of expected counts in a separate area of the spreadsheet. This is done by inserting in a given cell the formula of row total times column total divided by the total sample size. To calculate the chi-square statistic, click an empty cell in the spreadsheet, and then proceed to the **Statistical** function menu as described in the overview section of Chapter 1's Appendix. Scroll down the list of functions and click on the **CHITEST** function choice. In the **Actual_range** box, input the cell range of the observed cell counts. In the **Expected_range** box, input the cell range of the expected cell counts. Click **OK** to find the P-value for the chi-square test reported in the selected cell.

CHAPTER 10

Inference for Regression

10.1 Inference about the Regression Model

10.2 Using the Regression Line

10.3 Some Details of Regression Inference

PRELUDE: WILL STOCKS GO UP OR DOWN?

Predicting the course of the stock market could make you rich. No wonder lots of people use lots of computer power to pore over market data looking for patterns. Some popular patterns are a bit bizarre. The "Super Bowl Indicator" says that the football Super Bowl, played in January, predicts how stocks will behave each year. The current National Football League (NFL) was formed by merging the original NFL with the American Football League (AFL). The indicator claims that stocks go up in years when a team from the old NFL wins and down when an AFL team wins.

The Super Bowl Indicator was right in 28 of 31 years between the first Super Bowl in 1967 and 1997. Sounds impressive. But stocks went down only 6 times in those 31 years, so just predicting "up" every year would have been right 25 times. Original NFL teams won most Super Bowls for good reasons: there are 17 of them against only 11 old AFL teams, and the NFL was the established and stronger league. So "NFL wins" was pretty much the same as "up every year." The indicator is now fading fast: the great 1990s boom in stocks roared on unhindered by AFL wins in 1998 and 1999, while stocks fell after NFL wins in 2000 and 2001.

The Super Bowl predictor is simple-minded. There are statistical methods to predict one variable from others that go well beyond just counting ups and downs. *Regression,* which we return to in this chapter, is the starting point for these methods. But, alas, even the fanciest statistical tools can't predict stock prices.

Introduction

simple linear regression

One of the most common uses of statistical methods is to predict a response based on one or several explanatory variables. Prediction is most straightforward when there is a straight-line relationship between a quantitative response variable and a single quantitative explanatory variable. This is **simple linear regression,** the topic of this chapter. The following chapter expands the discussion to *multiple regression,* which allows more than one explanatory variable. Here are some regression problems we will consider:

- How do wages increase with length of service in a sample of women who work in banks? How can we generalize this from the sample to the population of all such women?
- A scatterplot shows a straight-line relationship between the sizes (square feet) of houses sold in a community and their selling prices. How accurately can we predict a house's selling price from its size?
- How is a company's reputation (a subjective measure) related to objective performance measures such as profitability?

As we saw in Chapter 2, when a scatterplot shows a linear relationship between a quantitative explanatory variable x and a quantitative response variable y, we can use the least-squares line fitted to the data to predict y for a given value of x. Now we want to do tests and confidence intervals in this setting.

We think of the least-squares line we calculate from a sample as an estimate of a regression line for the population, just as the sample mean $\overline{x}$ is an estimate of the population mean μ. We will write the population regression line as $\beta_0 + \beta_1 x$. The numbers β_0 and β_1 are *parameters* that describe the population. From now on we will write the least-squares line fitted to sample data as $b_0 + b_1 x$. This notation reminds us that the intercept b_0 of the fitted line estimates the intercept β_0 of the population line, and the slope b_1 estimates the slope β_1. The numbers b_0 and b_1 are *statistics* calculated from a sample.

We can give confidence intervals and significance tests for inference about the slope β_1 and the intercept β_0. Because regression lines are often used for prediction, we also consider inference about either the mean response or an individual future observation on y for a given value of the explanatory variable x. Finally, we discuss statistical inference about the correlation between two variables x and y.

10.1 Inference about the Regression Model

Simple linear regression studies the relationship between a response variable y and an explanatory variable x. We expect that different values of x will produce different mean responses. We encountered a similar but simpler situation in Chapter 7 when we discussed methods for comparing two population means. Figure 10.1 illustrates the statistical model for comparing the items per hour entered in a day by two groups of financial clerks using new software to enter data. Group 2 received some training in the software and Group 1 was not trained. Entries per hour is the response variable. The treatment (training or not) is the explanatory variable. The model has two important parts:

- The mean entries per hour may be different in the two populations. These means are μ_1 and μ_2 in Figure 10.1.

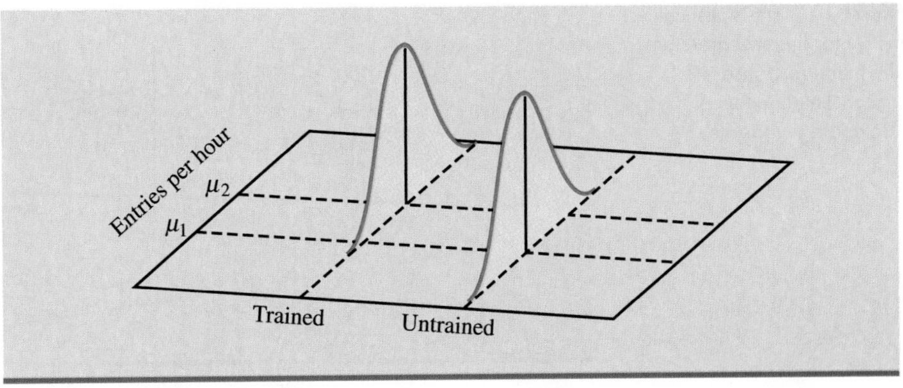

FIGURE 10.1 The statistical model for comparing the responses to two treatments. The mean response depends on the treatment.

- Individual subjects' entries per hour vary within each population according to a Normal distribution. The two Normal curves in Figure 10.1 describe the individual responses. These Normal distributions have the same standard deviation.

Statistical model for simple linear regression

subpopulation

Now imagine giving different lengths x of training to different groups of subjects. The values of x define different groups of subjects. We think of these groups as belonging to **subpopulations,** one for each possible value of x. Each subpopulation consists of all individuals in the population having the same value of x. If you gave $x = 15$ hours of training to some subjects and $x = 30$ hours of training to some others, these two groups are samples from the corresponding subpopulations.

The statistical model for simple linear regression also has two important parts:

- The mean entries per hour μ_y changes as the number of hours of training x changes. The means all lie on a straight line. That is, $\mu_y = \beta_0 + \beta_1 x$.
- Individual entries per hour y for subjects with the same amount of training x vary according to a Normal distribution. These Normal distributions all have the same standard deviation.

population regression line

Compare Figure 10.1 for two groups with Figure 10.2, which pictures the regression model in which the explanatory variable x can take many values. Rather than just two means μ_1 and μ_2, we are interested in how the many means μ_y change as x changes. In general, the means μ_y might follow any sort of pattern as x changes. In simple linear regression we assume that all these means lie on a line when plotted against x. The equation of the line is $\mu_y = \beta_0 + \beta_1 x$, with intercept β_0 and slope β_1. This is the **population regression line;** it describes how the mean response changes with x. The line in Figure 10.2 is the population regression line. The three Normal curves show how responses y will vary when we fix x for three different values of x. Each curve is centered at the mean response, that is, at the μ_y given by the population regression line for a specific x. All three curves have the same spread, measured by their common standard deviation σ.

From data analysis to inference

The data for a regression problem are observed values of x and y. The model takes each x to be a fixed known quantity, like the hours of training a worker has received.[1] The response y to a given x is a random variable that can take different values if we have

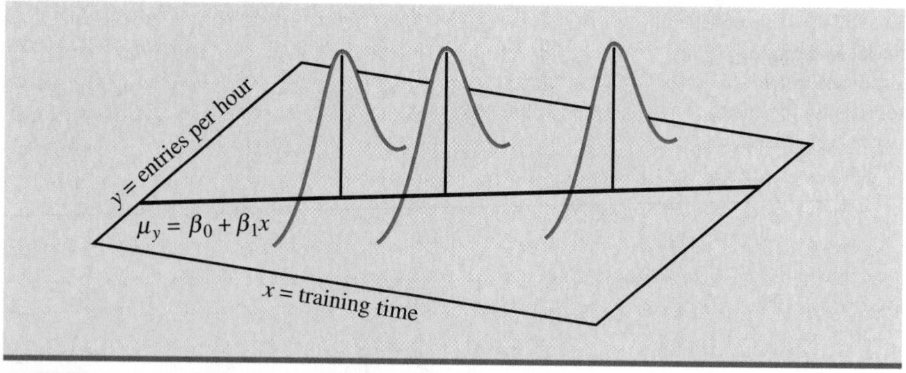

FIGURE 10.2 The statistical model for linear regression. The mean response is a straight-line function of the explanatory variable.

several observations with the same x-value. The model describes the mean and standard deviation of the random variable y.

We will use the following Case Study to explain the fundamentals of simple linear regression. Because regression calculations in practice are always done by software, we will rely on computer output for the arithmetic for the Case Study. Later in the chapter, we show formulas for doing the calculations. These are useful in understanding multiple regression and analysis of variance, to be taken up in later chapters.

CASE 10.1 DO WAGES RISE WITH EXPERIENCE?

Many factors affect the wages of workers: the industry they work in, their type of job, their education and other experience, and changes in general levels of wages. We will look at a random sample of 59 married women who hold customer service jobs in Indiana banks. Table 10.1 gives their weekly wages at a specific point in time and also their length of service with their employer, in months.[2] The size of the place of work is recorded simply as "Large" (100 or more workers) or "Small." Because industry, job type, and the time of measurement are the same for all 59 subjects, we expect to see a clear relationship between wages and length of service. Let's do a preliminary analysis.

Figure 10.3 is a scatterplot of the data. The explanatory variable x is length of service (LOS) in months. The response variable y is the weekly wage earned, which we call WAGES.

Let's briefly review some of the ideas from Chapter 2 regarding least-squares regression. We start with a plot of the data, as in Figure 10.3, and verify that the relationship is approximately linear with no outliers. We then apply the least-squares method to find the *least-squares regression line.*

Least-Squares Regression Line

The **least-squares regression line** is the line that makes the sum of the squares of the vertical distances of the data points from the line as small as possible.

The idea is illustrated in Figure 10.4, which includes only the data points for the employees with the three highest values of length of service. The middle point corresponds to an individual with length of service (x) equal to 222 months. In Table 10.1 the data

TABLE 10.1 Bank wages and length of service in months

Wages	LOS	Size	Wages	LOS	Size	Wages	LOS	Size
$389	94	Large	$443	222	Small	$547	228	Small
395	48	Small	353	58	Large	347	27	Large
329	102	Small	349	41	Small	328	48	Small
295	20	Small	499	153	Large	327	7	Large
377	60	Large	322	16	Small	320	74	Small
479	78	Small	408	43	Small	404	204	Large
315	45	Large	393	96	Large	443	24	Large
316	39	Large	277	98	Large	261	13	Small
324	20	Large	649	150	Large	417	30	Large
307	65	Small	272	124	Small	450	95	Large
403	76	Large	486	60	Large	443	104	Large
378	48	Small	393	7	Large	566	34	Large
348	61	Small	311	22	Small	461	184	Small
488	30	Large	316	57	Large	436	156	Small
391	108	Large	384	78	Large	321	25	Large
541	61	Large	360	36	Large	221	43	Small
312	10	Small	369	83	Small	547	36	Large
418	68	Large	529	66	Large	362	60	Small
417	54	Large	270	47	Small	415	102	Large
516	24	Large	332	97	Small			

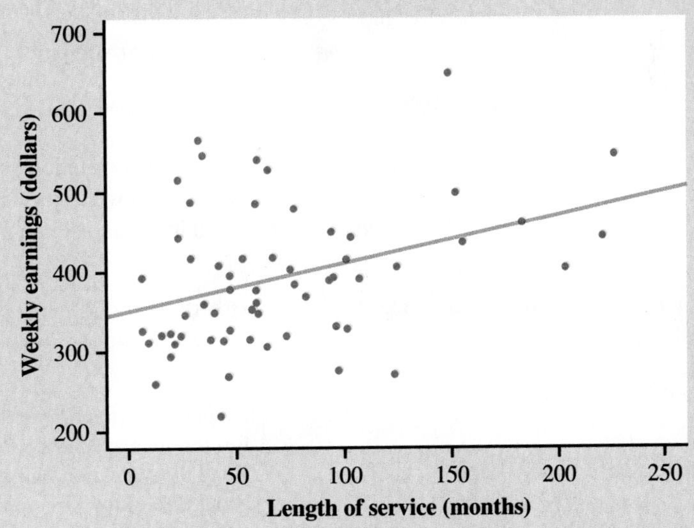

FIGURE 10.3 Scatterplot, with regression line, of weekly earnings versus length of service for a sample of bank employees.

for this individual appear as the first entry in the second column. The actual or observed value of weekly earnings (y) is $443. A part of the least-squares line appears with the three data points in Figure 10.4. For a length of service equal to 222 months, the value of weekly earnings on the least-squares line is $480. This is the predicted value of wages ($\hat{y}$) for an individual who has 222 months of service. The difference between the observed (y)

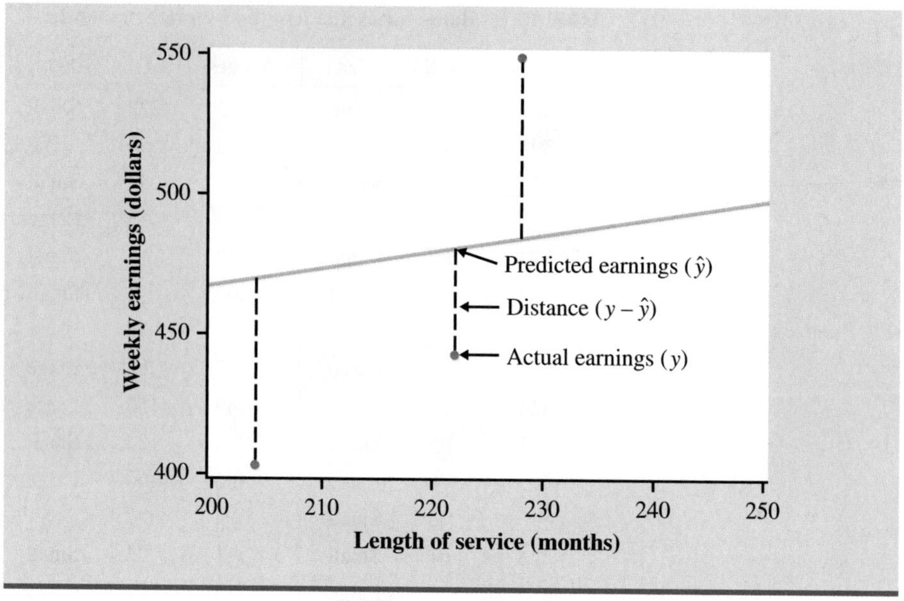

FIGURE 10.4 The least-squares idea. For each observation, find the vertical distance between each point and a regression line. The least-squares regression line makes the sum of the squares of these distances as small as possible.

and predicted ($\hat{y}$) values of wages is the residual ($y - \hat{y}$). The least-squares regression line is the line that minimizes the sum of the squares of the residuals.

EXAMPLE 10.1 Prediction of Wages from Length of Service

CASE 10.1

The line in Figure 10.4 is the least-squares regression line for predicting WAGES from LOS. The equation of this line is

$$\text{PREDICTED WAGES} = 349.4 + 0.5905 \times \text{LOS}$$

In Section 2.2 we discussed the correlation as a measure of association between two quantitative variables. In Section 2.3 we learned to interpret the square of the correlation as the fraction of the variation in y that is explained by x in a simple linear regression.

EXAMPLE 10.2 Correlation for Wages and Length of Service

CASE 10.1

For our Case, the correlation between LOS and WAGES is $r = 0.3535$. Because the squared correlation $r^2 = 0.1249$, the change in wages along the regression line as length of service increases explains only about 12% of the variation. The remaining 88% is due to other differences among these women. For example, they do not all work the same number of hours per week.

We can use the least-squares regression equation to find predicted wages corresponding to a given value of length of service. The difference between the observed and predicted values is the residual.

EXAMPLE 10.3 Predicted Values and Residuals for Wages

CASE 10.1

Suppose a woman has been with her bank for 125 months. We predict that she will earn

$$349.4 + (0.5905)(125) = \$423 \text{ per week}$$

If her actual wages are \$433, then her residual would be

$$y - \hat{y} = \$433 - \$423 = \$10$$

APPLY YOUR KNOWLEDGE

10.1 Predict the wages. In Table 10.1 the first entry corresponds to a woman who earns \$389 and has 94 months of service. Find the predicted wages and the residual for this individual.

CASE 10.1

10.2 Predicted wages for other values of length of service. Suppose you wanted to use the least-squares regression equation from Example 10.1 to examine the wages for four women bank employees who work in similar jobs under similar conditions. The values of length of service for these women are 1 month, 100 months, 200 months, and 400 months. For each, calculate the predicted wages and discuss the appropriateness of using the equation to predict wages for each of these women.

CASE 10.1

Having reviewed the basics of least-squares regression, we are now ready to proceed with a discussion of inference for regression. Here's what is new in this chapter:

- We regard the 59 women for whom we have data as a simple random sample from the population of all married women who work in customer service at Indiana banks.
- We use the regression line calculated from this sample as a basis for inference about the population. For example, we want to give not simply a prediction (\$423) but a prediction with a margin of error and a level of confidence for the wages of a woman not in our sample who has 125 months of service.

The population regression line $\mu_y = \beta_0 + \beta_1 x$ describes the relationship between mean wages μ_y and length of service x in the population. The slope β_1 is the mean increase in weekly earnings for each additional month of service. The intercept β_0 is also meaningful in this example. It is the mean "starting wage," the mean earnings when the length of service is $x = 0$.

We cannot observe the population regression line, because the observed responses y vary about their means. In Figure 10.3 we see the least-squares regression line that describes the overall pattern of the data, along with the scatter of individual points about this line. The statistical model for regression makes the same distinction. The population regression line describes only the on-the-average relationship. Think of the model in the form

$$\text{DATA} = \text{FIT} + \text{RESIDUAL}$$

The FIT part of the model consists of the subpopulation means, given by the expression $\beta_0 + \beta_1 x$. The RESIDUAL part represents deviations of the data from the line of population means. The model assumes that these deviations are Normally distributed with standard deviation σ. We use ϵ (the Greek letter epsilon) to stand for the RESIDUAL part of the statistical model. A response y is the sum of its mean and a chance deviation ϵ from the mean. The deviations ϵ represent "noise"—that is, variation in y due to other causes that prevent the observed (x, y)-values from forming a perfectly straight line on the scatterplot.

Simple Linear Regression Model

The data are n observations on an explanatory variable x and a response variable y,

$$(x_1, y_1),\quad (x_2, y_2),\quad \ldots,\quad (x_n, y_n)$$

The **statistical model for simple linear regression** states that the observed response y_i when the explanatory variable takes the value x_i is

$$y_i = \beta_0 + \beta_1 x_i + \epsilon_i$$

Here $\mu_y = \beta_0 + \beta_1 x_i$ is the mean response when $x = x_i$. The deviations ϵ_i are independent and Normally distributed with mean 0 and standard deviation σ.

The parameters of the model are the intercept β_0 and slope β_1 of the population regression line and the variability σ of the response y about this line.

The simple linear regression model can be justified in a wide variety of circumstances. Sometimes we observe the values of two variables and we formulate a model with one of these as the response variable and the other as the explanatory variable. This was the setting for Case 10.1, where the response variable was wages and the explanatory variable was length of service. In other settings the values of the explanatory variable are chosen by the persons designing the study. The scenario illustrated by Figure 10.2 is an example of this setting. Here the explanatory variable is training time, which is set at a few carefully selected values. The response variable is the number of entries per hour.

For the simple linear regression model to be valid, one essential assumption is that the relationship between the response variable and the explanatory variable is approximately linear. This is the fit part of the model. Another essential assumption concerns the residual part of the model. The assumption states that the residuals are approximately Normal with mean zero and standard deviation σ. If the data are collected through some sort of random sampling, this assumption is often easy to justify. This is the case in the two scenarios described above, in which both variables are observed in a random sample from a population or the response variable is measured at predetermined values of the explanatory variable. In many other settings, particularly in business applications, we analyze all of the data available and there is no random sampling. Here we often justify the use of inference for simple linear regression by viewing the data as coming from some sort of process. The line gives a good description of the relationship, the fit, and we model the deviations from the fit, the residuals, as coming from a Normal probability distribution.

EXAMPLE 10.4 Retail Sales and Floor Space

It is customary in retail operations to assess the performance of stores partly in terms of their annual sales relative to their floor area (square feet). We might expect sales to increase linearly as stores get larger, with, of course, individual variation among stores of the same size. The regression model for a population of stores says that

$$\text{SALES} = \beta_0 + \beta_1 \times \text{AREA} + \epsilon$$

The slope β_1 is, as usual, a rate of change: it is the expected increase in annual sales associated with each additional square foot of floor space. The intercept β_0 is needed to describe the line but has no statistical importance because no stores have area close to zero. Floor space does not completely determine sales. The ϵ term in the model accounts for differences among individual stores with the same floor space. A store's location, for example, is important.

APPLY YOUR KNOWLEDGE

10.3 Domestic and foreign stock markets. Returns on common stocks in the United States and overseas appear to be growing more closely correlated as economies become more interdependent. Suppose that this population regression line connects the total annual returns (in percent) on two indexes of stock prices:

$$\text{MEAN OVERSEAS RETURN} = 4.6 + 0.67 \times \text{U.S. RETURN}$$

(a) What is β_0 in this line? What does this number say about overseas returns when the U.S. market is flat (0% return)?

(b) What is β_1 in this line? What does this number say about the relationship between U.S. and overseas returns?

(c) We know that overseas returns will vary in years having the same return on U.S. common stocks. Write the regression model based on the population regression line given above. What part of this model allows overseas returns to vary when U.S. returns remain the same?

10.4 Fixed and variable costs. In some mass production settings there is a linear relationship between the number x of units of a product in a production run and the total cost y of making these x units. Write a population regression model to describe this relationship.

(a) Which parameter in your model is the fixed cost (for example, the cost of setting up the production line) that does not change as x increases?

(b) Which parameter in your model shows how total cost changes as more units are produced? Do you expect this number to be greater than 0 or less than 0?

(c) Actual data from several production runs will not fit a straight line exactly. What term in your model allows variation among runs of the same size x?

Estimating the regression parameters

The method of least squares presented in Chapter 2 fits the least-squares line to summarize a relationship between the observed values of an explanatory variable and a response variable. Now we want to use this line as a basis for inference about a population from which our observations are a sample. We can do this when the statistical model for regression holds. In that setting, the slope b_1 and intercept b_0 of the least-squares line

$$\hat{y} = b_0 + b_1 x$$

estimate the slope β_1 and the intercept β_0 of the population regression line.

Using the formulas from Chapter 2 with our new notation, the slope of the least-squares line is

$$b_1 = r\frac{s_y}{s_x}$$

and the intercept is

$$b_0 = \bar{y} - b_1\bar{x}$$

Here, r is the correlation between the observed values of y and x, s_y is the standard deviation of the sample of y's, and s_x is the standard deviation of the sample of x's.

The remaining parameter to be estimated is σ, which measures the variation of y about the population regression line. More precisely, σ is the standard deviation of the Normal distribution of the deviations ϵ_i in the regression model. It should come as no surprise that we use the deviations of the observed responses from the fitted line to estimate σ. Recall that the vertical deviations of the points in a scatterplot from the fitted regression line are the **residuals.** We will use e_i for the residual of the ith observation:

residuals

$$\begin{aligned} e_i &= \text{observed response} - \text{predicted response} \\ &= y_i - \hat{y}_i \\ &= y_i - b_0 - b_1 x_i \end{aligned}$$

The residuals e_i are the sample quantities that correspond to the model deviations ϵ_i. The e_i sum to 0, and the ϵ_i come from a population with mean 0.

To estimate σ, we work first with the variance and take the square root to obtain the standard deviation. For simple linear regression the estimate of σ^2 is the average squared residual

$$\begin{aligned} s^2 &= \frac{1}{n-2} \sum e_i^2 \\ &= \frac{1}{n-2} \sum (y_i - \hat{y}_i)^2 \end{aligned}$$

We average by dividing the sum by $n - 2$ in order to make s^2 an unbiased estimator of σ^2. Recall that the sample variance of n observations uses the divisor $n - 1$ because the n deviations $x_i - \overline{x}$ are not n separate quantities but rather must sum to 0. Similarly, the residuals e_i are not n separate quantities. When any $n - 2$ residuals are known, we can find the other two. We say that the residuals and s^2 have $n - 2$ **degrees of freedom.** To estimate σ, use

degrees of freedom

$$s = \sqrt{s^2}$$

We call s the *regression standard error.*

Estimating the Regression Parameters

In the simple linear regression setting, we use the slope b_1 and intercept b_0 of the **least-squares regression line** to estimate the slope β_1 and intercept β_0 of the population regression line.

The standard deviation σ in the model is estimated by the **regression standard error**

$$s = \sqrt{\frac{1}{n-2} \sum (y_i - \hat{y}_i)^2}$$

In practice, we use software to calculate b_1, b_0, and s from data on x and y. Here are the results for the bank wages example of Case 10.1.

FIGURE 10.5 Excel output for the regression of bank employee wages on their length of service, for Example 10.5.

SUMMARY OUTPUT

Regression Statistics	
Multiple R	0.3535
R Square	0.1249
Adjusted R Square	0.1096
Standard Error	82.2335
Observations	59

ANOVA

	df	*SS*	*MS*	*F*	*Significance F*
Regression	1	55034.36	55034.36	8.1384	0.0060
Residual	57	385453.64	6762.345		
Total	58	440488			

	Coefficients	*Standard Error*	*t Stat*	*P-value*	*Lower 95%*	*Upper 95%*
Intercept	349.3781	18.09649	19.306	1.12E-26	313.140	385.616
LOS	0.5905	0.20697	2.853	0.006029	0.176	1.005

EXAMPLE 10.5 Do Wages Rise with Experience?

CASE 10.1

Figure 10.5 displays Excel output for the regression of bank workers' weekly wages (WAGES) on their length of service (LOS) for our sample of 59 married female customer service workers. We find there the correlation $r = 0.3535$ and the squared correlation that we used in Example 10.2, along with the intercept and slope of the least-squares line. The regression standard error s is labeled simply "Standard Error."

The three parameter estimates are

$$b_0 = 349.3781 \quad b_1 = 0.5905 \quad s = 82.2335$$

After rounding, the fitted regression line is therefore

$$\hat{y} = 349 + 0.59x$$

As usual, we ignore the parts of the output that we do not yet need. We will return to the output for additional information later.

Figure 10.6 shows the regression output from two other software packages. Although the formats differ, you can easily find the results you need. Once you know what to look for, you can understand statistical output from almost any software.

APPLY YOUR KNOWLEDGE

10.5 Research and development spending. The National Science Foundation collects data on the research and development spending by universities and colleges in the United States.[3] Here are the data for the years 1995 to 1999:

Year	1995	1996	1997	1998	1999
Spending (billions of dollars)	22.2	23.0	24.4	25.8	27.5

(a) Make a scatterplot that shows the increase in research and development spending over time. Does the pattern suggest that the spending is increasing linearly over time?

FIGURE 10.6 Minitab and SPSS outputs for the regression of bank employee wages on their length of service. The data are the same as in Figure 10.5.

Minitab

```
The regression equation is
WAGES = 349 + 0.590 LOS

Predictor        Coef   SE Coef       T       P
Constant       349.38     18.10   19.31   0.000
LOS            0.5905    0.2070    2.85   0.006

S = 82.2335     R-Sq = 12.5%     R-Sq(adj) = 11.0%

Analysis of Variance

Source           DF       SS       MS      F       P
Regression        1    55034    55034   8.14   0.006
Residual Error   57   385454     6762
Total            58   440488
```

SPSS

Model Summary

Model	R	R Square	Adjusted R Square	Std. Error of the Estimate
1	0.353[a]	0.125	0.110	82.2335

a. Predictors: (Constant), LOS

ANOVA[b]

Model		Sum of Squares	df	Mean Square	F	Sig.
1	Regression	55034.359	1	55034.359	8.138	0.006[a]
	Residual	385453.64	57	6762.345		
	Total	440488.00	58			

a. Predictors: (Constant), LOS
b. Dependent Variable: WAGES

Coefficients[a]

Model		Unstandardized Coefficients		Standardized Coefficients		
		B	Std. Error	Beta	t	Sig.
1	(Constant)	349.378	18.096		19.306	0.000
	LOS	0.590	0.207	0.353	2.853	0.006

a. Dependent Variable: WAGES

(b) Find the equation of the least-squares regression line for predicting spending from year. Add this line to your scatterplot.

(c) For each of the five years find the residual. Use these residuals to calculate the standard error s. (Do these calculations with a calculator.)

(d) Write the regression model for this setting. What are your estimates of the unknown parameters in this model?

(e) Use your least-squares equation to predict research and development spending for the year 2001. The actual spending for that year was \$32.7 billion. Add this point to your plot and comment on why your equation performed so poorly.

(*Comment:* These are *time series data*. Simple regression is often a good fit to time series data over a limited span of time. See Chapter 13 for methods designed specifically for use with time series.)

Conditions for regression inference

You can fit a least-squares line to any set of explanatory-response data when both variables are quantitative. If the scatterplot doesn't show a roughly linear pattern, the fitted line may be almost useless. But it is still the line that fits the data best in the least-squares sense. The simple linear regression model, which is the basis for inference, imposes several conditions. We should verify these conditions before proceeding to inference. The conditions concern the population, but we can observe only our sample. In doing inference, we act as if **the sample is an SRS from the population.** The 59 workers in Case 10.1 are in fact a multistage random sample from the population of married women who work in customer service in Indiana banks. The resulting data are close to an SRS, and we will treat them as an SRS.

The next condition is that **there is a linear relationship in the population,** described by the population regression line. We can't observe the population line, so we check this condition by asking if the sample data show a roughly linear pattern in a scatterplot. The model also says that **the standard deviation of the responses about the population line is the same for all values of the explanatory variable.** In practice, the spread of observations above and below the least-squares line should be roughly uniform as x varies.

Plotting the residuals against the explanatory variable is helpful in checking these conditions because a residual plot magnifies patterns. The residual plot in Figure 10.7 for the data of Case 10.1 looks satisfactory. There is no curved pattern, and whatever narrowing there is for large values of LOS can be explained by the fact that there are fewer observations there.

The final condition is that **the response varies Normally about the population regression line.** In that case, we expect the residuals e_i to also be Normally distributed.[4] A Normal quantile plot of the residuals (Figure 10.8) shows some right-skewness but

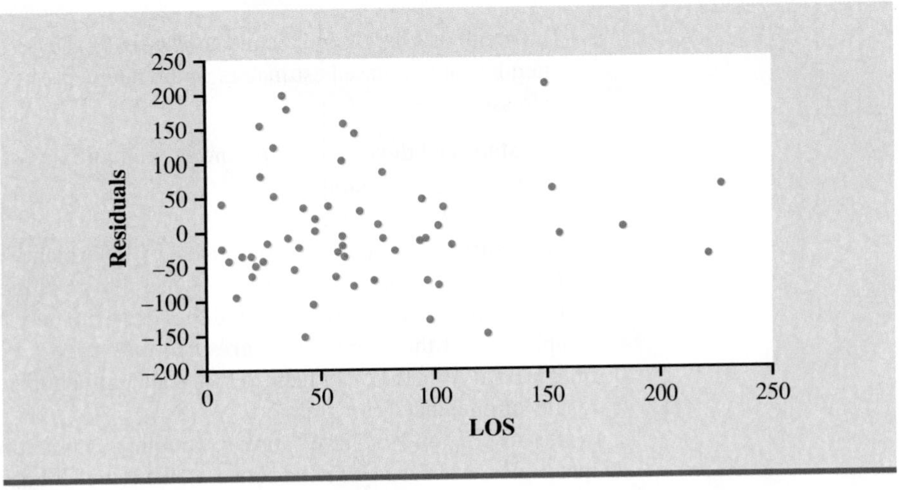

FIGURE 10.7 Plot of the regression residuals against the explanatory variable for the bank worker data.

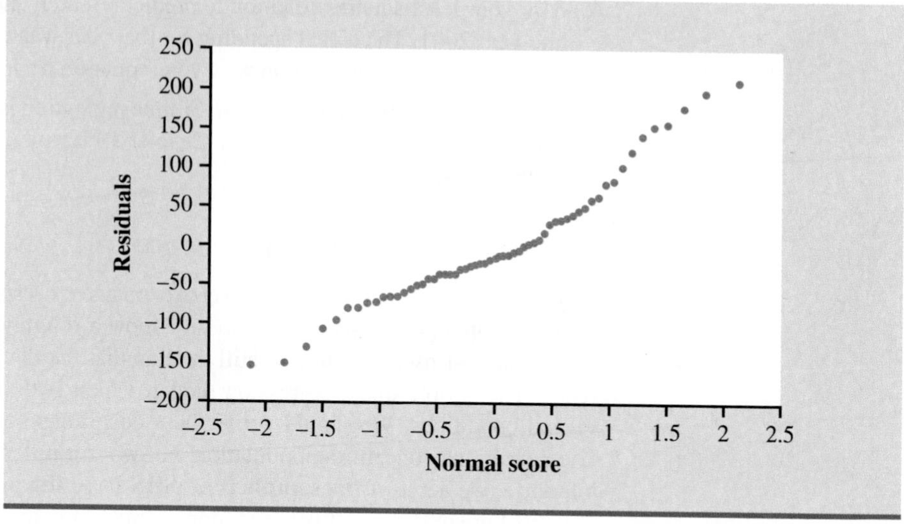

FIGURE 10.8 Normal quantile plot of the regression residuals for the bank worker data.

no serious deviations from a Normal distribution. The data give no reason to doubt the simple linear regression model, so we proceed to inference.

Confidence intervals and significance tests

Chapter 7 presented confidence intervals and significance tests for means and differences in means. In each case, inference rested on the standard errors of estimates and on t distributions. Inference for the slope and intercept in linear regression is similar in principle, although the recipes are more complicated. All of the confidence intervals, for example, have the form

$$\text{estimate} \pm t^* \text{SE}_{\text{estimate}}$$

where t^* is a critical value of a t distribution.

Confidence intervals and tests for the slope and intercept are based on the sampling distributions of the estimates b_1 and b_0. Here are the facts:

- When the simple linear regression model is true, each of b_0 and b_1 has a **Normal distribution.**
- The **mean** of b_0 is β_0 and the mean of b_1 is β_1. That is, the intercept and slope of the fitted line are unbiased estimators of the intercept and slope of the population regression line.
- The **standard deviations** of b_0 and b_1 are multiples of the model standard deviation σ. (We will give details later.)

Normality of b_0 and b_1 is a consequence of Normality of the individual deviations ϵ_i in the regression model. Fortunately, a general form of the central limit theorem tells us that the distributions of b_0 and b_1 will be approximately Normal when we have a large sample, even if the ϵ_i are not. **Regression inference is robust against moderate lack of Normality.** On the other hand, outliers and influential observations can invalidate the results of inference for regression.

Because b_0 and b_1 have Normal sampling distributions, standardizing these estimates gives standard Normal z statistics. The standard deviations of these estimates are multiples of σ, the model parameter that describes the variability about the population regression line. Because we do not know σ, we estimate it by s, the variability of the data about the least-squares line. When we do this, we get t distributions with degrees of freedom $n-2$, the degrees of freedom of s. We give formulas for the standard errors SE_{b_1} and SE_{b_0} later. For now we will concentrate on the basic ideas and let software do the calculations.

Inference for Regression Slope

A **level C confidence interval** for the slope β_1 of the population regression line is

$$b_1 \pm t^* SE_{b_1}$$

In this expression t^* is the value for the $t(n-2)$ density curve with area C between $-t^*$ and t^*. The **margin of error** is $t^* SE_{b_1}$.

To test the hypothesis $H_0\colon \beta_1 = 0$, compute the **t statistic**

$$t = \frac{b_1}{SE_{b_1}}$$

The **degrees of freedom** are $n-2$. In terms of a random variable T having the $t(n-2)$ distribution, the P-value for a test of H_0 against

$H_a\colon \beta_1 > 0$ is $P(T \ge t)$

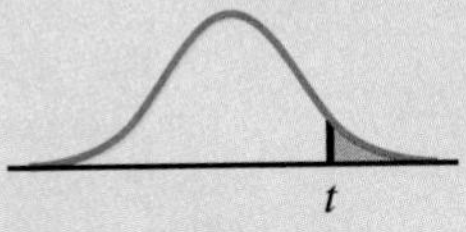

$H_a\colon \beta_1 < 0$ is $P(T \le t)$

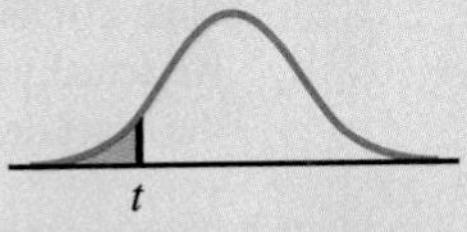

$H_a\colon \beta_1 \ne 0$ is $2P(T \ge |t|)$

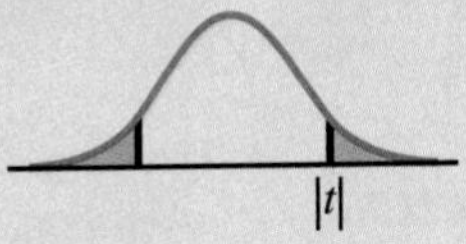

Confidence intervals and significance tests for the intercept β_0 are exactly the same, replacing b_1 and SE_{b_1} by b_0 and its standard error SE_{b_0}. Although computer outputs often include a test of $H_0\colon \beta_0 = 0$, this information usually has little practical value. From the equation for the population regression line, $\mu_y = \beta_0 + \beta_1 x$, we see that β_0 is the mean response corresponding to $x = 0$. In many practical situations, this subpopulation does not exist or is not interesting.

On the other hand, the test of $H_0\colon \beta_1 = 0$ is quite useful. When we substitute $\beta_1 = 0$ in the model, the x term drops out and we are left with

$$\mu_y = \beta_0$$

This model says that the mean of y does not vary with x. All of the y's come from a single population with mean β_0, which we would estimate by $\bar{y}$. The hypothesis $H_0\colon \beta_1 = 0$ therefore says that there is no straight-line relationship between y and x and that linear regression of y on x is of no value for predicting y. The t test for this hypothesis asks whether the data provide sufficient evidence to conclude that the slope is not zero.

EXAMPLE 10.6 Do Wages Rise with Experience?

CASE 10.1 

The Excel regression output in Figure 10.5 for the bank wages problem contains the information needed for inference about the regression coefficients. You can see that the slope of the least-squares line is $b_1 = 0.5905$ and that the standard error of this statistic is $SE_{b_1} = 0.20697$.

The t statistic and P-value for the test of H_0: $\beta_1 = 0$ against the two-sided alternative H_a: $\beta_1 \neq 0$ appear in the columns labeled "t Stat" and "P-value." The t statistic for the significance of the regression is

$$t = \frac{b_1}{SE_{b_1}} = \frac{0.5905}{0.20697} = 2.85$$

We expect that wages will rise with length of service, so our alternative hypothesis is one-sided, H_a: $\beta_1 > 0$. The P-value for this H_a is one-half the two-sided value given by Excel; that is, $P = 0.0030$. There is strong evidence that mean wages increase as length of service increases.

A 95% confidence interval for the slope β_1 of the regression line in the population of all married female customer service workers in Indiana banks is

$$\begin{aligned} b_1 \pm t^* SE_{b_1} &= 0.5905 \pm (2.009)(0.20697) \\ &= 0.5905 \pm 0.4158 \\ &= 0.175 \text{ to } 1.006 \end{aligned}$$

The t distributions for this problem have $n - 2 = 57$ degrees of freedom. Table D has no entry for 57 degrees of freedom, so we used the table entry $t^* = 2.009$ for 50 degrees of freedom. As a result, our confidence interval agrees only approximately with the more accurate software result. Note that using the next *lower* degrees of freedom in Table D makes our interval a bit wider than we actually need for 95% confidence. Use this conservative approach when you don't know t^* for the exact degrees of freedom.

APPLY YOUR KNOWLEDGE

Treasury bills and inflation. *When inflation is high, lenders require higher interest rates to make up for the loss of purchasing power of their money while it is loaned out. Table 10.2 displays the return (almost entirely interest rate) of one-year Treasury bills and the rate of inflation as measured by the change in the government's Consumer Price Index in the same year.*[5] *An inflation rate of 5% means that the same set of goods and services costs 5% more. The data cover 51 years, from 1950 to 2000. Figure 10.9 is a scatterplot of these data. Figure 10.10 shows Excel regression output for predicting T-bill return from inflation rate. The following problems ask you to use this information.*

10.6 Look at the data. Give a brief description of the form, direction, and strength of the relationship between the inflation rate and the return on Treasury bills. What is the equation of the least-squares regression line for predicting T-bill return?

10.7 Is there a relationship? What are the slope b_1 of the fitted line and its standard error? Use these numbers to calculate by hand the t statistic for testing the hypothesis that there is no straight-line relationship between inflation rate and T-bill return against the alternative that the return on T-bills increases as the rate of inflation increases. (State hypotheses, give both t and its degrees of freedom, and use Table D to approximate the P-value. Then compare your results with those given by Excel. Excel's P-value 7.563E-08 is shorthand for 0.00000007563. We would report this as "< 0.0001.")

TABLE 10.2 **Returns on Treasury bills and rate of inflation**

Year	T-bill percent	Inflation percent	Year	T-bill percent	Inflation percent	Year	T-bill percent	Inflation percent
1950	1.22	5.93	1967	4.21	3.04	1984	9.84	3.95
1951	1.49	6.00	1968	5.22	4.72	1985	7.72	3.80
1952	1.65	0.75	1969	6.57	6.20	1986	6.16	1.10
1953	1.83	0.75	1970	6.52	5.57	1987	5.47	4.43
1954	0.86	−0.74	1971	4.39	3.27	1988	6.36	4.42
1955	1.57	0.37	1972	3.84	3.41	1989	8.38	4.65
1956	2.47	2.99	1973	6.93	8.71	1990	7.84	6.11
1957	3.15	2.90	1974	8.01	12.34	1991	5.60	3.06
1958	1.53	1.76	1975	5.80	6.94	1992	3.50	2.90
1959	2.98	1.73	1976	5.08	4.86	1993	2.90	2.75
1960	2.67	1.36	1977	5.13	6.70	1994	3.91	2.67
1961	2.12	0.67	1978	7.19	9.02	1995	5.60	2.54
1962	2.73	1.33	1979	10.38	13.20	1996	5.20	3.32
1963	3.11	1.64	1980	11.26	12.50	1997	5.25	1.70
1964	3.53	0.97	1981	14.72	8.92	1998	4.85	1.61
1965	3.92	1.92	1982	10.53	3.83	1999	4.69	2.68
1966	4.75	3.46	1983	8.80	3.79	2000	5.69	3.39

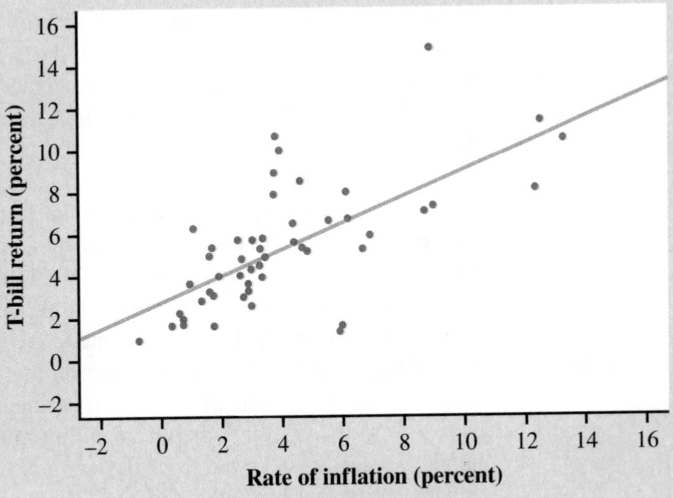

FIGURE 10.9 Scatterplot of the percent return on Treasury bills against the rate of inflation the same year, for Exercises 10.6 to 10.8.

10.8 Estimating the slope. Using Excel's values for b_1 and its standard error, find a 95% confidence interval for the slope β_1 of the population regression line. Compare your result with Excel's 95% confidence interval.

The word "regression"

To "regress" means to go backward. Why are statistical methods for predicting a response from an explanatory variable called "regression"? Sir Francis Galton (1822–1911), who

FIGURE 10.10 Excel output for the regression of the percent return on Treasury bills against the rate of inflation the same year, for Exercises 10.6 to 10.8.

SUMMARY OUTPUT

Regression Statistics	
Multiple R	0.6700
R Square	0.4489
Adjusted R Square	0.4377
Standard Error	2.1801
Observations	51

ANOVA

	df	SS	MS	F	Significance F
Regression	1	189.705	189.705	39.914	7.56289E-08
Residual	49	232.890	4.753		
Total	50	422.596			

	Coefficients	Standard Error	t Stat	P-value	Lower 95%	Upper 95%
Intercept	2.6660	0.5039	5.2912	2.830E-06	1.653	3.679
INFLATION	0.6270	0.0992	6.3177	7.563E-08	0.428	0.826

was the first to apply regression to biological and psychological data, looked at examples such as the heights of children versus the heights of their parents. He found that the taller-than-average parents tended to have children who were also taller than average, but not as tall as their parents. Galton called this fact "regression toward mediocrity," and the name came to be applied to the statistical method. Galton also invented the correlation coefficient r and named it "correlation."

The regression fallacy. Why are the children of tall parents shorter on the average than their parents? The parents are tall in part because of their genes. But they are also tall in part by chance. Looking at tall parents selects those in whom chance produced height. Their children inherit their genes, but not their good luck. As a group, the children are taller than average (genes) but their heights vary by chance about the average, some upward and some downward. The children, unlike the parents, were not selected because they were tall. In the same way, children of short parents tend to be taller than their parents.

Here's another example. Students who score at the top on the first exam in a course are likely to do less well on the second exam. Does this show that they stopped working? No—they scored high in part because they knew the material but also in part because they were lucky. On the second exam they may still know the material but be less lucky. As a group, they will do better than average but not as well as they did on the first exam. The students at the bottom on the first exam will tend to move up on the second, for the same reason.

regression fallacy

The **regression fallacy** is the assertion that regression toward the mean shows that there is some systematic effect at work: students with top scores now work less hard; or managers of last year's best-performing mutual funds lose their touch this year; or heights get less variable with each passing generation as tall parents have shorter children and short parents have taller children. The Nobel economist Milton Friedman says, "I suspect that the regression fallacy is the most common fallacy in the statistical analysis of economic data."[6] Beware.

APPLY YOUR KNOWLEDGE

10.9 Hot funds? Explain carefully to a naive investor why the mutual funds that had the highest returns last year will as a group probably do less well relative to other funds this year.

10.10 Mediocrity triumphant? In the early 1930s a man named Horace Secrist wrote a book titled *The Triumph of Mediocrity in Business*. Secrist found that businesses that did unusually well or unusually poorly in one year tended to be nearer the average in profitability at a later year. Why is it a fallacy to say that this fact demonstrates an overall movement toward "mediocrity"?

Inference about correlation

The correlation between wages and length of service for the 59 bank workers in Table 10.1 is $r = 0.3535$. This value appears in the Excel output in Figure 10.5 (page 579), where it is labeled "Multiple R."[7] We expect a positive correlation between length of service and wages in the population of all married female bank workers. Is the sample result convincing evidence that this is true?

population correlation ρ

This question concerns a new population parameter, the **population correlation.** This is the correlation between length of service and wages when we measure these variables for every member of the population. We will call the population correlation ρ, the Greek letter rho. To assess the evidence that $\rho > 0$ in the bank worker population, we must test the hypotheses

$$H_0: \rho = 0$$
$$H_a: \rho > 0$$

It is natural to base the test on the sample correlation $r = 0.3535$. Table G in the back of the book shows the one-sided critical values of r. To use software for the test, we exploit the close link between correlation and regression slope. In fact, the population correlation ρ is zero, positive, or negative exactly when the slope β_1 of the population regression line is zero, positive, or negative. So the t statistic for testing H_0: $\beta_1 = 0$ also tests H_0: $\rho = 0$. What is more, this t statistic can be written in terms of the sample correlation r.

Test for Zero Population Correlation

To test the hypothesis H_0: $\rho = 0$ that the population correlation is 0, compare the sample correlation r with critical values in Table G or use the t statistic for regression slope.

The t statistic for the slope can be calculated from the sample correlation r:

$$t = \frac{r\sqrt{n-2}}{\sqrt{1-r^2}}$$

This t statistic has $n - 2$ degrees of freedom.

EXAMPLE 10.7 Wages and Length of Service

CASE 10.1

The sample correlation between wages and length of service is $r = 0.3535$ from a sample of size $n = 59$. We can use Table G to test

$$H_0: \rho = 0$$
$$H_a: \rho > 0$$

The table has no entry for $n = 59$. If we follow the conservative practice of using the next smaller entry, for $n = 50$, we find that the P-value for $r = 0.3535$ lies between 0.005 and 0.01.

We can get a more accurate result from the Excel output in Figure 10.5 (page 579). In the "LOS" line we see that $t = 2.853$ with two-sided P-value 0.006029. That is, $P = 0.0030$ for our one-sided alternative.

Finally, we can calculate t directly from r as follows:

$$t = \frac{r\sqrt{n-2}}{\sqrt{1-r^2}}$$
$$= \frac{0.3535\sqrt{59-2}}{\sqrt{1-(0.3535)^2}}$$
$$= \frac{2.6689}{0.9354} = 2.853$$

If we are not using software, we can compare $t = 2.853$ with critical values from the t table (Table D) with $n - 2 = 57$ degrees of freedom.

The alternative formula for the test statistic is convenient because it uses only the sample correlation r and the sample size n. Remember that correlation, unlike regression, does not require the distinction between explanatory and response variables. For variables x and y, there are two regressions (y on x and x on y) but just one correlation. Both regressions produce the same t statistic.

The distinction between the regression setting and correlation is important only for understanding the conditions under which the test for 0 population correlation makes sense. In the regression model, we take the values of the explanatory variable x as given. The values of the response y are Normal random variables, with means that are a straight-line function of x. In the model for testing correlation, we think of the setting where we obtain a random sample from a population and measure both x and y. Both are assumed to be Normal random variables. In fact, they are taken to be **jointly Normal.** This implies that the conditional distribution of y for each possible value of x is Normal, just as in the regression model.

jointly Normal

APPLY YOUR KNOWLEDGE

10.11 T-bills and inflation. We expect the interest rates on Treasury bills to rise when the rate of inflation rises and fall when inflation falls. That is, we expect a positive correlation between the return on T-bills and the inflation rate.

(a) Find the sample correlation r for the 51 years in Table 10.2 in the Excel output in Figure 10.10. Use Table G to get an approximate P-value. What do you conclude?

(b) From r, calculate the t statistic for testing correlation. What are its degrees of freedom? Use Table D to give an approximate P-value. Compare your result with the P-value from (a).

(c) Verify that your t for correlation calculated in (b) has the same value as the t for slope in the Excel output.

10.12 Two regressions. We have regressed wages of bank workers on their length of service, with the results appearing in the output in Figure 10.5. Use software to regress length of service on wages for the same data (Table 10.1).

(a) What is the equation of the least-squares line for predicting length of service from wages? It is a different line than the regression line from Figure 10.5.

(b) Verify that the two lines cross at the mean values of the two variables. That is, substitute the mean length of service into the line from Figure 10.5 and show that the predicted wage equals the mean of the wages of the 59 subjects. Then substitute the mean wage into your new line and show that the predicted length of service equals the mean length of service for the subjects.

(c) Verify that the two regressions give the same value of the t statistic for testing the hypothesis of zero population slope. You could use either regression to test the hypothesis of zero population correlation.

SECTION 10.1 SUMMARY

- **Least-squares regression** fits a straight line to data in order to predict a response variable y from an explanatory variable x. Inference about regression requires additional conditions.
- The **regression model** says that there is a **population regression line** $\mu_y = \beta_0 + \beta_1 x$ that describes how the mean response in an entire population varies as x changes. The observed response y for any x has a Normal distribution with mean given by the population regression line and with the same standard deviation σ for any value of x. The parameters of the regression model are the intercept β_0, the slope β_1, and the standard deviation σ.
- The slope b_0 and intercept b_1 of the least-squares line estimate the slope β_0 and intercept β_1 of the population regression line. To estimate σ, use the **regression standard error s.**
- The standard error s has $n - 2$ **degrees of freedom.** Inference about β_0 and β_1 uses t distributions with $n - 2$ degrees of freedom.
- **Confidence intervals for the slope** of the population regression line have the form $b_1 \pm t^* \mathrm{SE}_{b_1}$. In practice, use software to find the slope b_1 of the least-squares line and its standard error SE_{b_1}.
- To test the hypothesis that the population slope is zero, use the ***t* statistic** $t = b_1/\mathrm{SE}_{b_1}$, also given by software. This null hypothesis says that straight-line dependence on x has no value for predicting y.
- The t test for zero population slope also tests the null hypothesis that the **population correlation** is zero. This t statistic can be expressed in terms of the sample correlation, $t = r\sqrt{n-2}/\sqrt{1-r^2}$.

SECTION 10.1 Exercises

For Exercises 10.1 and 10.2, see page 575; for 10.3 and 10.4, see page 577; for 10.5, see page 579; for 10.6 to 10.8, see pages 584–585; for 10.9 and 10.10, see page 586; and for 10.11 and 10.12, see page 588.

10.13 Predicting water quality. Pollution of water resources is a serious problem that can require substantial efforts to improve. To determine the financial resources required, an accurate assessment of the extent of the problem is required. The index of biotic integrity (IBI) is a measure of the water quality in streams that is fairly expensive to measure. Land use measures, on the other hand, are relatively inexpensive to obtain. IBI and land use measures for a collection of streams in the Ozark Highland ecoregion of Arkansas were collected as part of a study.[8] Table 10.3 gives the data for IBI and the area of the watershed in square kilometers for streams in the original sample with area less than or equal to 70 km^2.

(a) Use numerical and graphical methods to describe the variable IBI. Do the same for area. Summarize your results.

(b) Plot the data and describe the relationship. Are there any outliers or unusual patterns?

(c) Give the statistical model for simple linear regression for this problem.

TABLE 10.3 Watershed area (square kilometers) and index of biotic integrity

Area	IBI	Area	IBI	Area	IBI	Area	IBI	Area	IBI
21	47	29	61	31	39	32	59	34	72
34	76	49	85	52	89	2	74	70	89
6	33	28	46	21	32	59	80	69	80
47	78	8	53	8	43	58	88	54	84
10	62	57	55	18	29	19	29	39	54
49	78	9	71	5	55	14	58	9	71
23	33	31	59	18	81	16	71	21	75
32	64	10	41	26	82	9	60	54	84
12	83	21	82	27	82	23	86	26	79
16	67	26	56	26	85	28	91		

TABLE 10.4 Percent forest and index of biotic integrity

Forest	IBI	Forest	IBI	Forest	IBI	Forest	IBI	Forest	IBI
0	47	0	61	0	39	0	59	0	72
0	76	3	85	3	89	7	74	8	89
9	33	10	46	10	32	11	80	14	80
17	78	17	53	18	43	21	88	22	84
25	62	31	55	32	29	33	29	33	54
33	78	39	71	41	55	43	58	43	71
47	33	49	59	49	81	52	71	52	75
59	64	63	41	68	82	75	60	79	84
79	83	80	82	86	82	89	86	90	79
95	67	95	56	100	85	100	91		

(d) State the null and alternative hypotheses for examining the relationship between IBI and area.

(e) Run the simple linear regression and summarize the results.

(f) Obtain the residuals and plot them versus area. Is there anything unusual in the plot?

(g) Do the residuals appear to be approximately Normal? Give reasons for your answer.

(h) Do the assumptions for the analysis of these data using the model you gave in part (c) appear to be reasonable? Explain your answer.

10.14 Predicting water quality using a different explanatory variable. The researchers who conducted the study described in the previous exercise also recorded the percent of the watershed area that was forest for each of the streams. The data are given in Table 10.4. Analyze these data using the questions in the previous exercise as a guide.

10.15 Comparing the analyses. In Exercises 10.13 and 10.14, you used two different explanatory variables to predict IBI. Summarize the two analyses and compare the results. If you had to choose between the two, which one would you prefer? Give reasons for your answer.

10.16 Using the correlation to describe the results. Refer to Exercise 10.13. Find the correlation and test the null hypothesis that the corresponding population correlation is zero versus the two-sided alternative. Is the correlation a good numerical measure to describe these data? Compare the results of your significance test with those of the test you performed in Exercise 10.13 and explain the relationship.

10.17 Using the other explanatory variable. Refer to Exercise 10.14. Using the questions in the previous exercise as a guide, use the correlation to analyze the relationship between IBI and percent of watershed area that was forest.

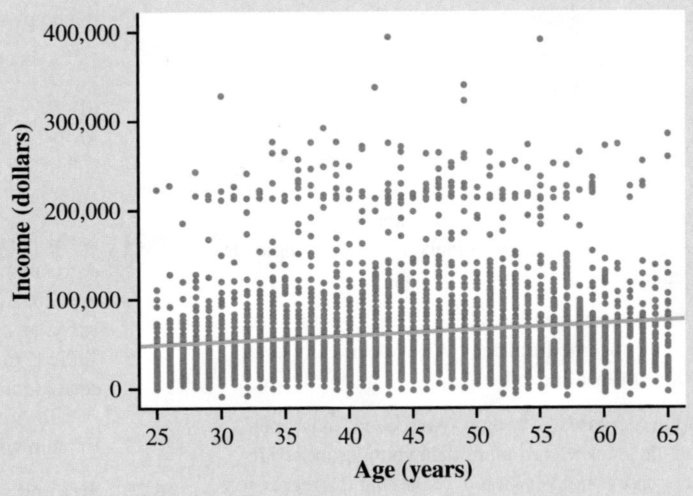

FIGURE 10.11 Scatterplot of income against age for a random sample of 5712 men aged 25 to 65, for Exercises 10.19 to 10.21.

FIGURE 10.12 Excel output for the regression of income on age, for Exercises 10.19 to 10.21.

SUMMARY OUTPUT

Regression Statistics	
Multiple R	0.18775
R Square	0.03525
Adjusted R Square	0.03508
Standard Error	47620.29
Observations	5712

ANOVA

	df	*SS*	*MS*	*F*	*Significance F*
Regression	1	4.7310E+11	4.73E+11	208.6271	1.7913E-46
Residual	5710	1.2949E+13	2.27E+09		
Total	5711	1.3422E+13			

	Coefficients	*Standard Error*	*t Stat*	*P-value*	*Lower 95%*	*Upper 95%*
Intercept	24874.3745	2637.4198	9.4313	5.75E-21	19704.031	30044.718
AGE	892.1135	61.7639	14.4439	1.79E-46	771.033	1013.194

10.18 An outlier can destroy statistical significance. Consider the data in Table 10.4 and the relationship between IBI and watershed area. The relationship between these two variables is statistically significant. Demonstrate the potential effect of an outlier on statistical significance by changing the IBI value of one of the observations in such a way that the relationship between the two variables is no longer statistically significant. The relationship between these two variables is positive. Can you change the data in such a way that the apparent relationship is more positive, that is, by raising the value of IBI for an observation with a large watershed area? Write a short summary of what you have learned from this exercise.

Age and income. *How do the incomes of working-age people change with age? Because many older women have been out of the labor force for much of their lives, we look only at men between the ages of 25 and 65. Because education strongly influences income, we look only at men who have a bachelor's degree but no higher degree. The data file for the following exercise contains the age and income of a random sample of 5712 such men. (These are all such men in the government sample of 55,899 people in the data set* INDIVIDUALS, *described in the Data Appendix.) Figure 10.11 is a scatterplot of these data. Figure 10.12 displays Excel output for regressing income on age. The line in the scatterplot is the least-squares regression line. Exercises 10.19 to 10.21 ask you to interpret this information.*

10.19 Looking at age and income. The scatterplot in Figure 10.11 has a distinctive form.

(a) Age is recorded as of the last birthday. How does this explain the vertical stacks in the scatterplot?

(b) Give some reasons why older men in this population might earn more than younger men. Give some reasons why younger men might earn more than older men. What do the data show about the relationship between age and income in the sample? Is the relationship very strong?

(c) What is the equation of the least-squares line for predicting income from age? What specifically does the slope of this line tell us?

10.20 Income increases with age. We see that older men do on the average earn more than younger men, but the increase is not very rapid. (Note that the regression line describes many men of different ages—data on the same men over time might show a different pattern.)

(a) We know even without looking at the Excel output that there is highly significant evidence that the slope of the population regression line is greater than 0. Why do we know this?

(b) Excel gives a 95% confidence interval for the slope of the population regression line. What is this interval?

(c) Give a 99% confidence interval for the slope of the population regression line.

10.21 Was inference justified? You see from Figure 10.11 that the incomes of men at each age are (as expected) not Normal but right-skewed.

(a) How is this apparent on the plot?

(b) Nonetheless, your confidence interval in the previous exercise will be quite accurate even though it is based on Normal distributions. Why?

10.22 The average starting wage. The intercept β_0 of the population regression line of wages of bank workers on months of service measures the starting wage, the average earnings with no prior service at this employer. Use the Excel output in Figure 10.5 (page 579) to give a 90% confidence interval for β_0.

10.23 T-bills and inflation. Exercises 10.6 to 10.8 interpret the part of the Excel output in Figure 10.10 (page 586) that concerns the slope, the rate at which T-bill returns increase as the rate of inflation increases. Use this output to answer questions about the intercept.

(a) The intercept β_0 in the regression model is meaningful in this example. Explain what β_0 represents. Why should we expect β_0 to be greater than 0?

(b) What values does Excel give for the estimated intercept b_0 and its standard error SE_{b_0}?

(c) Is there good evidence that β_0 is greater than 0?

(d) Write the formula for a 95% confidence interval for β_0. Verify that hand calculation (using the Excel values for b_0 and SE_{b_0}) agrees approximately with the output in Figure 10.10.

10.24 Is the correlation significant? A study reports correlation $r = -0.5$ based on a sample of size $n = 20$. Another study reports the same correlation based on a sample of size $n = 10$. For each, use Table G to test the null hypothesis that the population correlation $\rho = 0$ against the one-sided alternative $\rho < 0$. Are the results significant at the 5% level? Explain why the conclusions of the two studies differ.

10.25 Size and selling price of houses. Table 10.5 describes a random sample of 30 houses sold in a Midwest city during a recent year.[9] We will examine the relationship between size and price.

(a) Plot the selling price versus the number of square feet. Describe the pattern. Does r^2 suggest that size is quite helpful for predicting selling price?

(b) Do a linear regression analysis. Give the least-squares line and the results of the significance test for the slope. What does your test tell you about the relationship between size and selling price?

TABLE 10.5 Selling price and size of homes

Price ($1000)	Size (sq ft)	Price ($1000)	Size (sq ft)	Price ($1000)	Size (sq ft)
268	1897	142	1329	83	1378
131	1157	107	1040	125	1668
112	1024	110	951	60	1248
112	935	187	1628	85	1229
122	1236	94	816	117	1308
128	1248	99	1060	57	892
158	1620	78	800	110	1981
135	1124	56	492	127	1098
146	1248	70	792	119	1858
126	1139	54	980	172	2010

10.26 Stocks and bonds. How is the flow of investors' money into stock mutual funds related to the flow of money into bond mutual funds? Here are data on the net new money flowing into stock and bond mutual funds in the years 1985 to 2000, in billions of dollars.[10] "Net" means that funds flowing out are subtracted from those flowing in. If more money

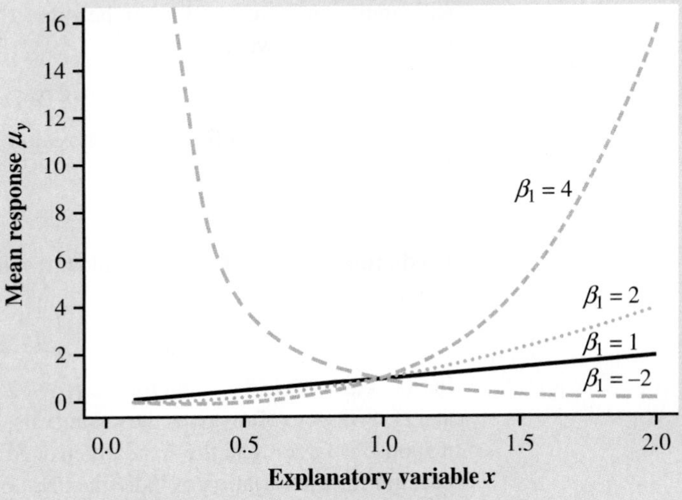

FIGURE 10.17 The nonlinear model $\mu_y = \beta_0 x^{\beta_1}$ includes these and other relationships between the explanatory variable x and the mean response.

BEYOND THE BASICS: NONLINEAR REGRESSION

The simple linear regression model assumes that the relationship between the response variable and the explanatory variable can be summarized with a straight line. When the relationship is not linear, we can sometimes transform one or both of the variables so that the relationship becomes linear. Exercise 10.31 is an example in which the relationship of log y with x is linear. In other circumstances, we use models that directly express a curved relationship using parameters that are not just intercepts and slopes. These are **nonlinear models.**

nonlinear models

Here is a typical example of a model that involves parameters β_0 and β_1 in a nonlinear way:

$$y_i = \beta_0 x_i^{\beta_1} + \epsilon_i$$

This nonlinear model still has the form

$$\text{DATA} = \text{FIT} + \text{RESIDUAL}$$

The FIT term describes how the mean response μ_y depends on x. Figure 10.17 shows the form of the mean response for several values of β_1 when $\beta_0 = 1$. Choosing $\beta_1 = 1$ produces a straight line, but other values of β_1 result in a variety of curved relationships.

We cannot write simple formulas for the estimates of the parameters β_0 and β_1, but software can calculate both estimates and approximate standard errors for the estimates. If the deviations ϵ_i follow a Normal distribution, we can do inference both on the model parameters and for prediction. The details become more complex, but the ideas remain the same as those we have studied.

SECTION 10.2 SUMMARY

- The **estimated mean response** for the subpopulation corresponding to the value x^* of the explanatory variable is found by substituting $x = x^*$ in the equation of the least-squares regression line:

$$\text{estimated mean response} = \hat{y} = b_0 + b_1 x^*$$

- The **predicted value of the response** y for a single observation from the subpopulation corresponding to the value x^* of the explanatory variable is found in exactly the same way:

$$\text{predicted individual response} = \hat{y} = b_0 + b_1x^*$$

- **Confidence intervals for the mean response** μ_y when x has the value x^* have the form

$$\hat{y} \pm t^*\text{SE}_{\hat{\mu}}$$

- **Prediction intervals** for an individual response y have a similar form with a larger standard error:

$$\hat{y} \pm t^*\text{SE}_{\hat{y}}$$

In both cases, t^* is the value for the $t(n-2)$ density curve with area C between $-t^*$ and t^*. Software often gives these intervals. The standard error $\text{SE}_{\hat{y}}$ for an individual response is larger than the standard error $\text{SE}_{\hat{\mu}}$ for a mean response because it must account for the variation of individual responses around their mean.

SECTION 10.2 Exercises

For Exercises 10.33 and 10.34, see page 598.

10.35 Predicting water quality from watershed area. Refer to Exercise 10.13 (page 589).

(a) Find a 95% confidence interval for mean response (index of biotic integrity) corresponding to an area of 31 km^2.

(b) Find a 95% prediction interval for a future response.

(c) Write a short paragraph interpreting the meaning of the intervals in terms of Ozark Highland streams.

(d) Do you think that these results can be applied to other streams in Arkansas or in other states? Explain why or why not.

10.36 Predicting water quality from the percent of forested area. Refer to Exercise 10.14 (page 590).

(a) Find a 95% confidence interval for mean response (index of biotic integrity) corresponding to 49% forest.

(b) Find a 95% prediction interval for a future response.

(c) Write a short paragraph interpreting the meaning of the intervals in terms of Ozark Highland streams.

(d) Do you think that these results can be applied to other streams in Arkansas or in other states? Explain why or why not.

10.37 Compare the estimates. Case 17 in Table 10.3 and Table 10.4 corresponds to the same watershed area. For this case the area is 31 km^2 and the percent forest is 49%. A predicted index of biotic integrity based on area was computed in Exercise 10.35, while one based on percent forest was computed in Exercise 10.36. Compare these two estimates and explain why they differ. Use the idea of a prediction interval to interpret these results.

10.38 Is the price right? Refer to Exercise 10.27 (page 593), where the relationship between the size of a home and its selling price is examined.

(a) Suppose that you have a client who is thinking about purchasing a home in this area that is 1600 square feet in size. The asking price is \$180,000. What advice would you give this client?

(b) Answer the same question for a client who is looking at a 1200-square-foot home that is selling for \$80,000.

10.39 Predicting income from age. Figures 10.11 and 10.12 (page 591) analyze data on the age and income of 5712 men between the ages of 25 and 65. Minitab output predicting the income for ages 30, 40, 50, and 60 years is given at the top of the next page.

(a) Use the regression line from Figure 10.11 to verify the "Fit" for age 30 years.

(b) Give a 95% confidence interval for the income of all 30-year-old men.

(c) Rabi is 30 years old. You don't know his income, so give a 95% prediction interval based on his age alone. How useful do you think this interval is?

```
Predicted Values
 Fit SE Fit          95.0% CI              95.0% PI
51638    948    (   49780,   53496)    (   -41735,   145010)
60559    637    (   59311,   61807)    (   -32803,   153921)
69480    822    (   67870,   71091)    (   -23888,   162848)
78401   1307    (   75840,   80963)    (   -14988,   171790)
```

10.40 Predict what? The two 95% intervals for the income of 30-year-olds given in Exercise 10.39 are very different. Explain briefly to someone who knows no statistics why the second interval is so much wider than the first. Start by looking at 30-year-olds in Figure 10.11.

10.41 Predicting income from age, continued. Use the computer outputs in Figure 10.12 and Exercise 10.39 to give a 99% confidence interval for the mean income of all 40-year-old men.

10.42 T-bills and inflation. Figure 10.10 (page 586) gives part of a regression analysis of the data in Table 10.2 relating the return on Treasury bills to the rate of inflation. The output includes prediction of the T-bill return when the inflation rate is 3.7%.

(a) Use the output to give a 90% confidence interval for the mean return on T-bills in all years having 3.7% inflation.

(b) You think next year's inflation rate will be 3.7%. It isn't possible, without complicated arithmetic, to give a 90% prediction interval for next year's T-bill return based on the output displayed. Why not?

10.43 Two confidence intervals. The data used for Exercise 10.39 include 195 men 30 years old. The mean income of these men is $\overline{y} = \$49,880$ and the standard deviation of these 195 incomes is $s_y = \$38,250$.

(a) Use the one-sample t procedure to give a 95% confidence interval for the mean income μ_y of 30-year-old men.

(b) Why is this interval different from the 95% confidence interval for μ_y in the regression output? (*Hint:* What data are used by each method?)

The following exercises require use of software that will calculate the intervals required for predicting mean response and individual response.

10.44 Size and selling price of houses. Table 10.5 (page 579) gives data on the size in square feet of a random sample of houses sold in a Midwest city along with their selling prices.

(a) Find the mean size $\overline{x}$ of these houses and also their mean selling price $\overline{y}$. Give the equation of the least-squares regression line for predicting price from size, and use it to predict the selling price of a house of mean size. (You knew the answer, right?)

(b) Jasmine and Woodie are selling a house whose size is equal to the mean of our sample. Give an interval that predicts the price they will receive with 95% confidence.

10.45 Beer and blood alcohol. Exercise 10.30 (page 593) gives data from measuring the blood alcohol content (BAC) of students 30 minutes after they drank an assigned number of cans of beer. Steve thinks he can drive legally 30 minutes after he drinks 5 beers. The legal limit is BAC = 0.08. Give a 90% confidence interval for Steve's BAC. Can he be confident he won't be arrested if he drives and is stopped?

10.46 Selling a large house. Among the houses for which we have data in Table 10.5, just 3 have floor areas of 1800 square feet or more. Give a 90% confidence interval for the mean selling price of houses with floor areas of 1800 square feet or more.

10.3 Some Details of Regression Inference*

We have assumed that you will use software to handle regression in practice. If you do, it is much more important to understand what the standard error of the slope SE_{b_1} means than it is to know the formula your software uses to find its numerical value.

*This section is optional. You may want to read parts of it if you are not using statistical software or if you plan to read Chapter 11 on multiple regression.

For that reason, we have not yet given formulas for the standard errors. We have also not explained the block of output from software that is labeled ANOVA or Analysis of Variance. This section remedies both of these omissions.

Standard errors

We will give the formulas for all the standard errors we have met, for two reasons. First, you may want to see how these formulas can be obtained from facts you already know. The second reason is more practical: some software (in particular, spreadsheet programs) does not automate inference for prediction. We will see that the hard work lies in calculating the regression standard error s, which almost any regression software will do for you. With s in hand, the rest is easy, but only if you know more details.

Tests and confidence intervals for the slope of a population regression line start with the slope b_1 of the least-squares line and with its standard error SE_{b_1}. If you are willing to skip some messy algebra, it is easy to see where SE_{b_1} and the similar standard error SE_{b_0} of the intercept come from.

1. The regression model takes the explanatory values x_i to be fixed numbers and the response values y_i to be independent random variables all having the same standard deviation σ.

2. The least-squares slope is $b_1 = rs_y/s_x$. Here is the first bit of messy algebra that we skip: it is possible to write the slope b_1 as a linear function of the responses, $b_1 = \sum a_i y_i$. The coefficients a_i depend on the x_i.

3. Because the a_i are constants, we can find the variance of b_1 by applying the rule for the variance of a sum of independent random variables (page 281). It is just $\sigma^2 \sum a_i^2$. A second piece of messy algebra shows that this simplifies to

$$\sigma_{b_1}^2 = \frac{\sigma^2}{\sum(x_i - \bar{x})^2}$$

The standard deviation σ about the population regression line is of course not known. If we estimate it by the regression standard error s based on the residuals from the least-squares line, we get the standard error of b_1. Here are the results for both slope and intercept.

Standard Errors for Slope and Intercept

The standard error of the slope b_1 of the least-squares regression line is

$$SE_{b_1} = \frac{s}{\sqrt{\sum(x_i - \bar{x})^2}}$$

The standard error of the intercept b_0 is

$$SE_{b_0} = s\sqrt{\frac{1}{n} + \frac{\bar{x}^2}{\sum(x_i - \bar{x})^2}}$$

The critical fact is that both standard errors are multiples of the regression standard error s. In a similar manner, accepting the results of yet more messy algebra, we get the standard errors for the two uses of the regression line that we have studied.

Standard Errors for Two Uses of the Regression Line

The standard error for estimating the mean response when the explanatory variable x takes the value x^* is

$$\text{SE}_{\hat{\mu}} = s\sqrt{\frac{1}{n} + \frac{(x^* - \bar{x})^2}{\sum(x_i - \bar{x})^2}}$$

The standard error for predicting an individual response when $x = x^*$ is

$$\text{SE}_{\hat{y}} = s\sqrt{1 + \frac{1}{n} + \frac{(x^* - \bar{x})^2}{\sum(x_i - \bar{x})^2}}$$

Once again both standard errors are multiples of s. The only difference between the two prediction standard errors is the extra 1 under the square root sign in the standard error for predicting an individual response. This added term reflects the additional variation in individual responses. It means that, as we have said earlier, $\text{SE}_{\hat{y}}$ is always greater than $\text{SE}_{\hat{\mu}}$.

EXAMPLE 10.12 Prediction Intervals from a Spreadsheet

CASE 10.1

In Example 10.8, we used statistical software to predict the earnings of Tonya, who has worked 125 months in customer service in an Indiana bank. Suppose that we have only the Excel spreadsheet. The prediction interval then requires some additional work.

Step 1. From the Excel output in Figure 10.5, we know that $s = 82.2335$. Excel can easily find the mean and variance of the lengths of service x for the 59 workers in Table 10.1. They are $\bar{x} = 70.4915$ and $s_x^2 = 2721.668$.

Step 2. We need the value of $\sum(x_i - \bar{x})^2$. Recalling the definition of the variance, we see that this is just

$$\begin{aligned}\sum(x_i - \bar{x})^2 &= (n-1)s_x^2\\ &= (58)(2721.668) = 157{,}856.744\end{aligned}$$

Step 3. The standard error for predicting Tonya's wages from her length of service, $x^* = 125$, is

$$\begin{aligned}\text{SE}_{\hat{y}} &= s\sqrt{1 + \frac{1}{n} + \frac{(x^* - \bar{x})^2}{\sum(x_i - \bar{x})^2}}\\ &= 82.2335\sqrt{1 + \frac{1}{59} + \frac{(125 - 70.4915)^2}{157{,}856.744}}\\ &= 82.2335\sqrt{1 + \frac{1}{59} + \frac{2971.1765}{157{,}856.755}}\\ &= (82.2335)(1.01773) = 83.6914\end{aligned}$$

Step 4. We predict Tonya's wages from the least-squares line (Figure 10.5 again):

$$\hat{y} = 349.3781 + (0.5905)(125) = 423.19$$

This agrees with the "Fit" from software in Example 10.8. The 95% prediction interval requires the 95% critical value for $t(57)$. For hand calculation we use $t^* = 2.009$ from Table D with df = 50. The interval is

$$\begin{aligned}\hat{y} \pm t^* \text{SE}_{\hat{y}} &= 423.19 \pm (2.009)(83.6914)\\ &= 423.19 \pm 168.14\\ &= 255.1 \text{ to } 591.3\end{aligned}$$

This agrees with the software result in Example 10.8, with a small difference due to roundoff and especially to not having the exact t^*.

The formulas for the standard errors for prediction show us one more thing about prediction. They both contain the term $(x^* - \overline{x})^2$, the squared distance of the value x^* for which we want to do prediction from the mean $\overline{x}$ of the x-values in our data. We see that prediction is most accurate (smallest margin of error) near the mean and grows less accurate as we move away from the mean of the explanatory variable. If you know what values of x you want to do prediction for, try to collect data centered near these values.

APPLY YOUR KNOWLEDGE

10.47 T-bills and inflation. Figure 10.10 gives the Excel output for regressing the annual return on Treasury bills on the annual rate of inflation. The data appear in Table 10.2 (page 586). Starting with the regression standard error $s = 2.1801$ from the output and the variance of the inflation rates in Table 10.2 (use your calculator), find the standard error of the regression slope, SE_{b_1}. Check your result against the Excel output.

10.48 Predicting T-bill return. Figure 10.16 uses statistical software to predict the return on Treasury bills in a year when the inflation rate is 3.7%. Let's do this without specialized software. Figure 10.16 contains Excel regression output. Use a calculator or software to find the variance s_x^2 of the annual inflation rates in Table 10.2. From this information, find the 95% prediction interval for one year's T-bill return. Check your result against the software output in Figure 10.15.

Analysis of variance for regression

Software output for regression problems, such as those in Figures 10.5, 10.6, and 10.10, reports values under the heading of ANOVA or Analysis of Variance. You can ignore this part of the output for simple linear regression, but it becomes useful in *multiple regression,* where several explanatory variables are used together to predict a response.

analysis of variance

Analysis of variance is the term for statistical analyses that break down the variation in data into separate pieces that correspond to different sources of variation. In the regression setting, the observed variation in the responses y_i comes from two sources:

- As the explanatory variable x moves, it pulls the response with it along the regression line. In Figure 10.3, for example, workers with around 150 months of service have generally higher wages than workers with around 50 months of service. The least-squares line drawn on the scatterplot describes this tie between x and y.
- When x is held fixed, y still varies because not all individuals who share a common x have the same response y. There are several workers with around 50 months of service, and their wage values are scattered above and below the least-squares line.

We discussed these sources of variation in Chapter 2 (page 124), where the main point was that the squared correlation r^2 is the proportion of the total variation in the responses that comes from the first source, the straight-line tie between x and y.

ANOVA equation

Analysis of variance for regression expresses these two sources of variation in algebraic form so that we can calculate the breakdown of overall variation into two parts. Skipping quite a bit of messy algebra, we just state that this **analysis of variance equation** always holds:

$$\text{Total variation in } y = \text{Variation along the line} + \text{Variation about the line}$$

$$\sum (y_i - \overline{y})^2 = \sum (\hat{y}_i - \overline{y})^2 + \sum (y_i - \hat{y}_i)^2$$

Understanding the ANOVA equation requires some thought. The "Total variation" in the responses y_i is expressed by the sum of the squares of the deviations $y_i - \overline{y}$. If all responses were the same, all would equal the mean response $\overline{y}$ and the total variation would be zero. The total variation term is just $n - 1$ times the variance of the responses. The "Variation along the line" term has the same form: it is the variation among the *predicted* responses $\hat{y}_i$. The predicted responses lie on the least-squares line—they show how y moves in response to x. The "Variation about the line" term is the sum of squares of the *residuals* $y_i - \hat{y}_i$. It measures the size of the scatter of the observed responses above and below the line. If all the responses fell exactly on a straight line, the residuals would all be 0 and there would be no variation about the line. The total variation would equal the variation along the line.

EXAMPLE 10.13 ANOVA for Bank Workers' Wages

CASE 10.1

sum of squares

Figure 10.18 repeats Figure 10.5. It is the Excel output for the regression of bank workers' wages on their length of service (Case 10.1). The three terms in the analysis of variance equation appear under the "SS" heading. SS stands for **sum of squares,** reflecting the fact that

FIGURE 10.18 Excel output for the regression of bank employee wages on their length of service, for Example 10.13. We now concentrate on the analysis of variance part of the output.

SUMMARY OUTPUT

Regression Statistics	
Multiple R	0.3535
R Square	0.1249
Adjusted R Square	0.1096
Standard Error	82.2335
Observations	59

ANOVA

	df	*SS*	*MS*	*F*	*Significance F*
Regression	1	55034.36	55034.36	8.1384	0.0060
Residual	57	385453.64	6762.345		
Total	58	440488			

	Coefficients	*Standard Error*	*t Stat*	*P-value*	*Lower 95%*	*Upper 95%*
Intercept	349.3781	18.09649	19.306	1.12E-26	313.140	385.616
LOS	0.5905	0.20697	2.853	0.006029	0.176	1.005

each of the three terms is a sum of squared quantities. You can read the output as follows:

$$\begin{array}{ccccc} \text{Total variation in } y & = & \text{Variation along the line} & + & \text{Variation about the line} \\ \text{Total SS} & = & \text{Regression SS} & + & \text{Residual SS} \\ 440{,}488.00 & = & 55{,}034.36 & + & 385{,}453.64 \end{array}$$

The proportion of variation in wages explained by regressing wages on length of service is

$$\begin{aligned} r^2 &= \frac{\text{Regression SS}}{\text{Total SS}} \\ &= \frac{55{,}034.36}{440{,}488.00} = 0.1249 \end{aligned}$$

This agrees with the "R Square" value in the output. Only about 12.5% of the variation in wages is explained by the linear relationship between wages and length of service. The rest is variation in wages among workers with similar lengths of service.

degrees of freedom

There is more to the ANOVA table in Figure 10.18. Each sum of squares has a **degrees of freedom.** The total degrees of freedom is $n - 1 = 58$, the degrees of freedom for the variance of $n = 59$ observations. This matches the total sum of squares, which is the sum of squares that appears in the definition of the variance. We know that the degrees of freedom for the residuals and for t statistics in simple linear regression is $n - 2$. It is therefore no surprise that the degrees of freedom for the residual sum of squares is also $n - 2 = 57$. That leaves just 1 degree of freedom for regression, because degrees of freedom in ANOVA also add:

$$\begin{array}{ccccc} \text{Total df} & = & \text{Regression df} & + & \text{Residual df} \\ n-1 & = & 1 & + & n-2 \end{array}$$

mean square

Dividing a sum of squares by its degrees of freedom gives a **mean square (MS).** The total mean square (not given in the output) is just the variance of the responses y_i. The residual mean square is the square of our old friend the regression standard error:

$$\begin{aligned} \text{Residual mean square} &= \frac{\text{Residual SS}}{\text{Residual df}} \\ &= \frac{\sum(y_i - \hat{y}_i)^2}{n-2} \\ &= s^2 \end{aligned}$$

You see that the analysis of variance table reports in a different way quantities such as r^2 and s that are needed in regression analysis. It also reports in a different way the test for the overall significance of the regression. If regression on x has no value for predicting y, we expect the slope of the population regression line to be close to zero. That is, the null hypothesis of "no linear relationship" is H_0: $\beta_1 = 0$. To test H_0, we standardize the slope of the least-squares line to get a t statistic. The ANOVA approach starts instead with sums of squares. If regression on x has no value for predicting y, we expect the regression SS to be only a small part of the total SS, most of which will be made up of the residual SS. It turns out that the proper way to standardize this comparison is to use the ratio

$$F = \frac{\text{Regression MS}}{\text{Residual MS}}$$

ANOVA F statistic

This **ANOVA F statistic** appears in the second column from the right in the ANOVA table in Figure 10.18. If H_0 is true, we expect F to be small. For simple linear regression, the ANOVA F statistic always equals the square of the t statistic for testing H_0: $\beta_1 = 0$. That is, the two tests amount to the same thing.

EXAMPLE 10.14 ANOVA for Bank Workers' Wages, Continued

CASE 10.1

The Excel output in Figure 10.18 contains the analysis of variance equation for sums of squares and also the corresponding equation for their degrees of freedom. The residual mean square is

$$\begin{aligned}\text{Residual MS} &= \frac{\text{Residual SS}}{\text{Residual df}} \\ &= \frac{385{,}453.64}{57} = 6762.345\end{aligned}$$

The square root of the residual MS is $\sqrt{6762.345} = 82.2335$. This is the regression standard error s, as claimed. The ANOVA F statistic is

$$\begin{aligned}F &= \frac{\text{Regression MS}}{\text{Residual MS}} \\ &= \frac{55{,}034.36}{6762.345} = 8.1384\end{aligned}$$

The square root of F is $\sqrt{8.1384} = 2.853$. Sure enough, this is the value of the t statistic for testing the significance of the regression, which also appears in the Excel output. The P-value for F, $P = 0.0060$, is the same as the two-sided P-value for t.

We have now explained almost all of the results that appear in a typical regression output such as Figure 10.18. ANOVA shows exactly what r^2 means in regression. Aside from this, ANOVA seems redundant; it repeats in less clear form information that is found elsewhere in the output. This is true—that's why this section is optional. ANOVA comes into its own in *multiple regression,* the topic of the next chapter.

APPLY YOUR KNOWLEDGE

T-bills and inflation. *Figure 10.10 (page 586) gives Excel output for the regression of the rate of return on Treasury bills against the rate of inflation during the same year. Exercises 10.49 to 10.51 use this output.*

10.49 A significant relationship? The output reports *two* tests of the null hypothesis that regressing on inflation does not help to explain the return on T-bills. State the hypotheses carefully, give the two test statistics, show how they are related, and give the common P-value.

10.50 The ANOVA table. Use the numerical results in the Excel output to verify each of these relationships.

(a) The ANOVA equation for sums of squares.

(b) How to obtain the total degrees of freedom and the residual degrees of freedom from the number of observations.

(c) How to obtain each mean square from a sum of squares and its degrees of freedom.

(d) How to obtain the F statistic from the mean squares.

10.51 ANOVA by-products.

(a) The output gives $r^2 = 0.4489$. How can you obtain this from the ANOVA table?

(b) The output gives the regression standard error as $s = 2.1801$. How can you obtain this from the ANOVA table?

SECTION 10.3 SUMMARY

- The **analysis of variance equation** for simple linear regression expresses the total variation in the responses as the sum of two sources: the linear relationship of y with x and the residual variation in responses for the same x. The equation is expressed in terms of **sums of squares.**
- Each sum of squares has a **degrees of freedom.** A sum of squares divided by its degrees of freedom is a **mean square.** The residual mean square is the square of the regression standard error.
- The **ANOVA table** gives the degrees of freedom, sums of squares, and mean squares for total, regression, and residual variation. The **ANOVA F statistic** is the ratio F = Regression MS/Residual MS. In simple linear regression, F is the square of the t statistic for the hypothesis that regression on x does not help explain y.

SECTION 10.3 Exercises

For Exercises 10.47 and 10.48, see page 604; and for 10.49 to 10.51, see page 607.

U.S. versus overseas stock returns. *How are returns on common stocks in overseas markets related to returns in U.S. markets? Measure U.S. returns by the annual rate of return on the Standard & Poor's 500 stock index and overseas returns by the annual rate of return on the Morgan Stanley Europe, Australasia, Far East (EAFE) index. Both are recorded in percents. Regress the EAFE returns on the S&P 500 returns for the 30 years 1971 to 2000. Here is part of the Minitab output for this regression:*

```
The regression equation is
EAFE = 4.76 + 0.663 S&P

Analysis of Variance
Source            DF         SS         MS
Regression         1     3445.9     3445.9
Residual Error
Total             29    13598.3
```

Exercises 10.52 to 10.54 use this output.

10.52 The ANOVA table. Complete the analysis of variance table by filling in the "Residual Error" row.

10.53 s and r^2. What are the values of the regression standard error s and the squared correlation r^2?

10.54 Estimating the slope. The standard deviation of the S&P 500 returns for these years is 16.45%. From this and your work in the previous exercise, find the standard error for the least-squares slope b_1. Give a 90% confidence interval for the slope β_1 of the population regression line.

Corporate reputation and profitability. *Is a company's reputation, a subjective assessment, related to objective measures of corporate performance such as its profitability? One study of this relationship examined the records of 154 Fortune 500 firms.*[13] *Corporate reputation was measured on a scale of 1 to 10 by a* Fortune *magazine survey. Profitability was defined as the rate of return on invested capital. Figure 10.19 contains SAS output for the regression of profitability (PROFIT) on reputation score (REPUTAT). The format is very similar to the Excel and Minitab output we have seen, with minor differences in labels. Exercises 10.55 to 10.62 concern this study. You can take it as given that examination of the data shows no serious violations of the conditions required for regression inference.*

10.55 Significance in two senses.

(a) Is there good evidence that reputation helps explain profitability? (State hypotheses, give a test statistic and P-value, and state a conclusion.)

(b) What percent of the variation in profitability among these companies is explained by regression on reputation?

(c) Use your findings in (a) and (b) as the basis for a short description of the distinction between statistical significance and practical significance.

10.56 Estimating the slope. Explain clearly what the slope β_1 of the population regression line tells us in this setting. Give a 99% confidence interval for this slope.

10.57 Predicting profitability. An additional calculation shows that the variance of the reputation scores for these 154 firms is $s_x^2 = 0.8101$. SAS labels the regression standard error s as "Root MSE." Starting from these facts, give a 95% confidence interval for

FIGURE 10.19 SAS output for the regression of the profitability of 154 companies on their reputation scores, for Exercises 10.55 to 10.62.

```
Dependent Variable: PROFIT

                 Analysis of Variance

                          Sum of          Mean
Source          DF       Squares        Square        F Value        Prob>F

Model            1       0.18957       0.18957         36.492        0.0001
Error          152       0.78963       0.00519
C Total        153       0.97920

    Root MSE        0.07208        R-Square        0.1936
    Dep Mean        0.10000        Adj R-sq        0.1883
    C.V.           72.07575

                 Parameter Estimates

                    Parameter        Standard      T for H0:
Variable   DF        Estimate           Error    Parameter=0    Prob > |T|

INTERCEP    1       -0.147573      0.04139259         -3.565        0.0005
REPUTAT     1        0.039111      0.00647442          6.041        0.0001
```

the mean profitability (return on investment) for all companies with reputation score $x = 7$.

10.58 **Predicting profitability.** A company not covered by the *Fortune* survey has reputation score $x = 7$. Will a 95% prediction interval for this company's profitability be wider or narrower than the confidence interval found in the previous exercise? Explain why we should expect this. Then give the 95% prediction interval.

10.59 ***F* versus *t*.** How do the ANOVA F statistic and its P-value relate to the t statistic for the slope and its P-value? Identify these results on the output and verify their relationship (up to roundoff error).

10.60 **The regression standard error.** SAS labels the regression standard error s as "Root MSE." How can you obtain s from the ANOVA table? Do this, and verify that your result agrees with Root MSE.

10.61 **Squared correlation.** SAS gives the squared correlation r^2 as "R-Square." How can you obtain r^2 from the ANOVA table? Do this, and verify that your result agrees with R-Square.

10.62 **Correlation.** The regression in Figure 10.19 takes reputation as explaining profitability. We could as well take reputation as in part explained by profitability. We would then reverse the roles of the variables, regressing REPUTAT on PROFIT. Both regressions lead to the same conclusions about the correlation between PROFIT and REPUTAT. What is this correlation r? Is there good evidence that it is positive?

STATISTICS IN SUMMARY

The methods of data analysis apply to any set of data. We can make a scatterplot and calculate the correlation and the least-squares regression line whenever we have data on two quantitative variables. Statistical inference makes sense only in more restrictive circumstances. The regression model describes the circumstances in which we can do inference about regression. The regression model includes a new parameter, the standard deviation σ that describes how much variation there is in responses y when x is held fixed. Estimating σ is the key to inference about regression. We use the regression standard error s (roughly, the sample standard deviation of the residuals) to estimate σ. Here are the skills you should develop from studying this chapter.

A. Preliminaries

1. Make a scatterplot to show the relationship between an explanatory and a response variable.

2. Use a calculator or software to find the correlation and the equation of the least-squares regression line.

B. Recognition

1. Recognize the regression setting: a straight-line relationship between an explanatory variable x and a response variable y.
2. Recognize which type of inference you need in a particular regression setting.
3. Inspect the data to recognize situations in which inference isn't safe: a nonlinear relationship, influential observations, strongly skewed residuals in a small sample, or nonconstant variation of the data points about the regression line.

C. Do Inference Using Software Output

1. Explain in any specific regression setting the meaning of the slope β_1 of the population regression line.
2. Understand software output for regression. Find in the output the slope and intercept of the least-squares line, their standard errors, the regression standard error s, and the squared correlation r^2.
3. Carry out tests and calculate confidence intervals for the slope β_1 of the population regression line.
4. Explain the distinction between a confidence interval for the mean response when x has a specific value and a prediction interval for an individual response for the same value of x.
5. If software gives output for prediction, use that output to give either confidence or prediction intervals.

D. Details of Regression (Optional)

1. Give either type of interval for prediction starting with basic regression output and descriptive statistics for the explanatory variable x.
2. Find the regression standard deviation s and the squared correlation r^2 from an ANOVA table.
3. Use the ANOVA F statistic to test the significance of regression. Find the t statistic for this test from F.

CHAPTER 10 Review Exercises

10.63 Plot indicates model assumptions. Construct a plot with data and a regression line that would fit the simple linear regression model framework. Then construct another plot that would have the same slope and intercept but a much smaller value of the regression standard error s.

10.64 Significance tests and confidence intervals. The significance test for the slope in a simple linear regression gave a value $t = 5.31$ with 50 degrees of freedom. Would the 95% confidence interval for the slope include the value zero? Give a reason for your answer.

10.65 Bias in Medicare payments. Payments to hospitals for pharmaceuticals under Medicare's Outpatient Prospective Payment System (OPPS) are based on estimates of costs. These are determined by multiplying the cost of the pharmaceutical to the hospital by a department-specific average markup. Some evidence suggests, however, that when hospitals set charges for the pharmaceuticals sold through their pharmacies, they do not simply add a fixed percent of the cost to each item to cover the expense of operating the pharmacy. It has been suggested that hospitals apply below-average markups for pharmaceutical products with above-average costs. This is the "charge compression" hypothesis. If it is true, then the system for reimbursing hospitals for pharmaceutical costs is based on biased estimates that underestimate true costs. A study designed to test the charge compression hypothesis used Medicare OPPS data on 139 different drugs.[14] One analysis presented the results of a simple linear regression analysis using (log of) cost to predict (log of) markup.

(a) A negative coefficient for cost in this model would be consistent with support for the charge compression hypothesis. Explain why.

(b) The researchers who conducted the study reported that the constant was 2.885 and the coefficient for (log) cost was −0.295. Give the equation of the fitted regression line.

(c) A t statistic is given for the coefficient of (log) cost. The value is −12.26. Interpret this statistic and what it means in terms of the charge compression hypothesis.

10.66 Correlations for restaurant spending. A study of spending by customers in restaurants examined 1413 transactions.[15] Five of the variables measured were check (total check amount divided by the number of customers at the table), minutes (the amount of time spent dining), table (the size of the table), party (the number of people in the party), and SPM (spending per minute, check divided by minutes). Here is a table of the correlations for these variables:

	Check	Minutes	Table	Party
Minutes	0.251			
Table	0.045	0.083		
Party	−0.306	0.137	0.379	
SPM	0.689	−0.397	−0.031	−0.400

(a) Perform a significance test for each of these correlations and summarize the results.

(b) Discuss the pattern in the correlations, paying particular attention to the sign, the size, and the results of the significance test.

(c) You performed nine significance tests in this exercise. Suppose that you wanted to do a Bonferroni correction to take into account this fact and to keep the overall false rejection rate at 5%. In that case, you would declare a correlation to be statistically significant only if the P-value is $0.05/9$ or less. Perform the significance tests using the Bonferroni correction. Summarize the results and compare them with the results you obtained in part (a).

10.67 What can we infer? The study described in the previous exercise analyzed data that were collected from a Chevys Freshmex Restaurant in suburban Phoenix during busy times at the restaurant on Fridays, Saturdays, and Sundays.

(a) To what extent do you think that the results that you obtained in the previous exercise apply to other restaurants in other cities? Give reasons for you answers.

(b) Design a similar study for a different restaurant. Give details regarding what data you will collect and how you will collect it.

10.68 Brand equity and sales. Brand equity is one of the most important assets of a business. It includes brand loyalty, brand awareness, perceived quality, and brand image. One study examined the relationship between brand equity and sales using simple linear regression analysis.[16] The correlation between brand equity and sales was reported to be 0.757 with a significance level of 0.001.

(a) Explain in simple language the meaning of these results.

(b) The study examined quick-service restaurants in Korea and was based on 394 usable surveys from a total of 950 that were distributed to shoppers at a mall. Write a short narrative commenting on the design of the study and how well you think the results would apply to other settings.

10.69 Hotel sizes and numbers of employees. A human resources study of hotels collected data on the size, measured by number of rooms, and the number of employees for 14 hotels in Canada.[17] Here are the data:

Employees	Rooms	Employees	Rooms
1200	1388	275	424
180	348	105	240
350	294	435	601
250	413	585	1590
415	346	560	380
139	353	166	297
121	191	228	108

(a) To what extent can the number of employees be predicted by the size of the hotel? Plot the data and summarize the relationship.

(b) Is this the type of relationship that you would expect to see before examining the data? Explain why or why not.

(c) Calculate the least-squares regression line and add it to the plot.

(d) Give the results of the significance test for the regression slope with your conclusion.

(e) Find a 95% confidence interval for the slope.

10.70 How can we use the results? Refer to the previous exercise.

(a) If one hotel had 100 more rooms than another, how many additional employees would you expect that hotel to have?

(b) Give a 95% confidence interval for your answer in part (a).

(c) The study collected these data from 14 hotels in Toronto. Discuss how well you think the results can be generalized to other hotels in Toronto, to hotels in Canada, and to hotels in other countries.

10.71 Check the outliers. The plot that you generated in Exercise 10.69 has two observations that appear to be outliers.

(a) Identify these points on a plot of the data.

(b) Rerun the analysis with the other 12 hotels and summarize the effect of these hotels on the results that you gave in Exercise 10.69.

10.72 Growth in grocery store size. Here are data giving the median store size (in square feet) by year for grocery stores:[18]

Year	Store size	Year	Store size	Year	Store size
1993	33.0	1997	39.3	2001	44.0
1994	35.1	1998	40.5	2002	44.0
1995	37.2	1999	44.8		
1996	38.6	2000	44.6		

(a) Use a simple linear regression and a prediction interval to give an estimate, along with a measure of uncertainty, for the median grocery store size in 2003.

(b) Plot the data with the regression line. Based on what you see, do you think that the answer that you computed in part (a) is a good prediction? Explain why or why not.

10.73 Expenditures of school districts. There are 315 school corporations in the state of Indiana. Various information about these corporations is available on the Internet.[19] Here are data on the numbers of students (NStu), expressed in thousands, and the total yearly expenditures (Exp), expressed in millions of dollars, for a simple random sample of 30 of these school corporations:

NStu	Exp	NStu	Exp	NStu	Exp
9	5.3	3	3.7	45	24.5
32	17.8	37	19.5	18	9.8
62	35.2	68	35.1	17	10.0
14	8.2	8	5.1	16	9.4
90	42.6	17	9.5	17	9.2
14	9.7	5	3.1	8	4.6
16	9.3	34	17.7	11	6.8
5	3.2	16	9.1	24	12.5
16	8.3	23	10.7	4	2.8
32	17.2	102	60.1	11	5.8

Use these data to explain how the number of students in a school corporation can be used to predict the total yearly expenditures. Write a report summarizing your work and conclusions.

10.74 Some unusual observations. Refer to the previous exercise. Two corporations that were not included in the simple random sample are the School System of Hammond and the Northwest Indiana Special Education Cooperative. Hammond is a very large corporation with 137 thousand students and 83 million dollars in expenditures. On the other hand, Northwest Indiana is listed as having 39 students (which would be rounded to 0 thousand students) and expenditures of 13.9 million dollars. We assume that this school corporation provides services to others with special education needs within the state. Reanalyze the data from the previous exercise with each of these corporations added to the data set (31 observations) and with both added (32 observations). Use graphical and numerical summaries to describe how the results and inferences change for these altered data sets.

Workers at large and small banks. *Table 10.1 gives the wages and months of service for a sample of 59 married women who hold customer service jobs in Indiana banks. The table also notes whether each woman worked at a large bank (100 or more workers) or at a smaller bank. We have not yet used the bank size information. Exercises 10.75 to 10.77 ask you to refine the analysis of these data.*

10.75 The effect of bank size. Figure 10.3 is a scatterplot of wages against length of service for all 59 women. Make a new scatterplot of these variables using different symbols for the 34 women who work in large banks and the 25 women who work in small banks. Which group appears to have generally higher wages? For which group does it appear that regressing wages on length of service will do a better job of explaining wages?

10.76 Verifying the effect of bank size. Do a two-sample t test comparing the mean wages at small and large banks. Wages are significantly higher at large banks. Do another two-sample t test comparing the mean length of service at small and large banks. These means do not differ significantly.

10.77 Separate regressions. The plot and tests of the previous exercises seem to confirm that bank size does influence the relationship between wages and length of service. Do separate regressions of wages on length of service for large banks ($n = 34$) and for small banks ($n = 25$). Report the tests for significance of regression in both cases. Write a careful summary of your findings. In particular, for which of the two groups of banks might we use length of service to predict wages?

The Leaning Tower of Pisa. *The Leaning Tower of Pisa was reopened to the public late in 2001 after being closed for almost 12 years while engineers took steps to prevent the tower from collapsing. Data on the lean of the tower over time show why it was in danger of collapse. The following table gives measurements for the years 1975 to 1987. The variable "lean" represents the difference between where a point near the top of the tower would be if the tower were straight and where it actually is. The data are coded as tenths of a millimeter in excess of 2.9 meters, so that the 1975 lean, which was 2.9642 meters, appears in the table as 642. Only the last two digits of the year were entered into the computer.*[20]

Year	Lean	Year	Lean	Year	Lean
75	642	80	688	84	717
76	644	81	696	85	725
77	656	82	698	86	742
78	667	83	713	87	757
79	673				

Exercises 10.78 to 10.80 ask you to analyze these data.

10.78 The lean of the Leaning Tower.

(a) Plot the lean of the tower against time. Is the trend linear? That is, is the tower's lean increasing at a fixed rate?

(b) What is the equation of the least-squares line for predicting lean? What percent of the variation in lean is explained by this line?

(c) Give a 95% confidence interval for the average rate of change (tenths of a millimeter per year) of the lean.

10.79 Looking into the past.

(a) In 1918 the lean was 2.9071 meters. (The coded value is 71.) Using the least-squares equation for the years 1975 to 1987, calculate a predicted value for the lean in 1918. (Note that you must use the coded value 18 for year.)

(b) Although the least-squares line gives an excellent fit to the data for 1975 to 1987, this pattern does not extrapolate to 1918. Write a short statement explaining why this conclusion follows from the information available. Use numerical and graphical summaries to support your explanation.

10.80 Looking to the future.

(a) The engineers working on the tower were most interested in how much the tower would lean if no corrective action was taken. Use the least-squares equation to predict the tower's lean in the year 2000 if no corrective action had been taken.

(b) To give a margin of error for the lean in 2000, would you use a confidence interval for a mean response or a prediction interval? Explain your choice.

10.81 Predicting success in a statistics course. Can a pretest on mathematics skills predict success in a statisticscourse? The 55 students in an introductory statistics class took a pretest at the beginning of the semester. The least-squares regression line for predicting the score y on the final exam from the pretest score x was $\hat{y} = 10.5 + 0.82x$. The standard error of b_1 was 0.38. Test the null hypothesis that there is no linear relationship between the pretest score and the score on the final exam against the two-sided alternative.

CHAPTER 10 Case Study Exercises

CASE STUDY 1: **Agricultural productivity.** Few sectors of the economy have increased their productivity as rapidly as agriculture. Productivity is defined as output per unit input. "Total factor productivity" (TFP) takes all inputs (labor, capital, fuels, and so on) into account. Table 10.6 gives the total factor productivity of U.S. farms from 1948 to 1994.[21] The entries are index numbers. That is, they give each year's TFP as a percent of the value for 1948. Your assignment is to describe in some detail how U.S. farm productivity has increased.

(a) Plot TFP against year. It appears that around 1980 the rate of increase in TFP changed. How is this apparent from the plot? What was the nature of the change?

TABLE 10.6 Total factor productivity of U.S. farms, 1948–1994

Year	TFP	Year	TFP	Year	TFP	Year	TFP	Year	TFP
1948	100	1958	111	1968	138	1978	158	1988	193
1949	95	1959	111	1969	139	1979	164	1989	212
1950	94	1960	114	1970	138	1980	156	1990	219
1951	98	1961	120	1971	149	1981	175	1991	218
1952	100	1962	121	1972	149	1982	180	1992	235
1953	102	1963	124	1973	151	1983	162	1993	220
1954	106	1964	125	1974	143	1984	184	1994	245
1955	104	1965	129	1975	155	1985	197		
1956	106	1966	128	1976	152	1986	199		
1957	106	1967	134	1977	164	1987	205		

(b) Regress TFP on year using only the data for the years 1948 to 1980. Add the least-squares line to your scatterplot. The line makes the finding in (a) clearer.

(c) Give a 95% confidence interval for the annual rate of change in TFP during the period 1948 to 1980.

(d) Regress TFP on year for the years 1981 to 1994. Add this line to your plot. Give a 95% confidence interval for the annual rate of improvement in TFP during these years.

(e) Write a brief report on trends in U.S. farm productivity since 1948, making use of your analysis in parts (a) to (d).

CASE STUDY 2: Philip Morris versus the market. Table 10.7 shows the monthly returns on the common stock of Philip Morris (MO), as the company was then named, and the returns on the Standard & Poor's 500 stock index for the same months. Return is measured in percent. The data are for 83 consecutive months running from mid-1990 to mid-1997, a period chosen to avoid the stock market bubble of the late 1990s. (The time order runs down the columns, but we will ignore trends over time.)

We expect a stock to move in concert with the market to some extent, but the strength of the relationship varies greatly

TABLE 10.7 Monthly percent returns on Philip Morris (MO) stock and the S&P 500-stock index

MO	S&P	MO	S&P	MO	S&P	MO	S&P	MO	S&P
−5.7	−9.0	−0.5	0.5	−7.1	−2.7	4.2	4.4	−4.8	−0.2
1.2	−5.5	−4.5	−2.1	−8.4	−5.0	4.0	0.7	17.2	2.1
4.1	−0.4	8.7	4.0	7.7	2.0	2.8	3.4	−3.7	3.3
3.2	6.4	2.7	−2.1	−9.6	1.6	6.7	0.9	3.5	6.0
7.3	0.5	4.1	0.6	6.0	−2.9	−10.4	0.5	0.5	1.2
7.5	6.5	−10.3	0.3	6.8	3.8	2.7	1.5	4.2	−1.0
18.6	7.1	4.8	3.4	10.9	4.1	10.3	2.5	4.2	0.3
3.7	1.7	−2.3	0.6	1.6	−2.9	5.7	0.0	11.7	6.1
−1.8	0.9	−3.1	1.5	0.2	2.2	0.6	−4.4	−0.6	−2.5
2.4	4.3	−10.2	1.4	−2.4	−3.7	−14.2	2.1	0.5	0.2
−6.5	−5.0	−3.7	1.5	−2.4	0.0	1.3	5.2	13.2	3.8
6.7	5.1	−26.6	−1.8	3.9	4.0	2.9	2.8	1.3	5.8
9.4	2.3	7.2	2.7	1.7	3.9	11.8	7.6	2.8	3.5
−2.0	−2.1	−2.9	−0.3	9.0	2.5	10.6	−3.1	8.3	4.4
−2.8	1.3	−2.3	0.1	3.6	3.4	5.2	6.2	0.9	0.0
−3.4	−4.0	3.5	3.8	7.6	4.0	13.8	0.8		
19.2	9.5	−4.6	−1.3	3.2	1.9	−14.7	−4.5		

among different stocks. We will examine the relationship between MO and market returns in detail.

(a) Regress the MO returns on the market returns. Make a scatterplot and draw the least-squares line on the plot. Explain carefully what the slope and intercept of this line mean, in terms understandable to an investor. Also give a measure of the strength of the relationship and explain its meaning to an investor.

(b) Suppose an investor is willing to take these data as a sample of future returns. Explain why we cannot expect future returns (the population) to have exactly the same slope as the least-squares line. Then give a 90% confidence interval for the slope of the population regression line.

(c) Find the residuals from your regression. (Most software will do this for you.) Are any of the residuals outliers by the $1.5 \times IQR$ criterion (page 45)? If so, circle the corresponding points on your scatterplot. Is it likely that these points strongly influence the regression? Why? Verify your answer by redoing the regression without the outlier(s) and adding the new line to your plot for easy comparison with the original line.

(d) If your software allows, make a Normal quantile plot of the residuals. Aside from any outliers detected in (c) is the distribution approximately Normal?

(e) An investor believes that a market rally is imminent and that the S&P 500 will rise 7.5% in the next month. Give a 90% confidence interval for the return on MO next month.

CHAPTER 10 Appendix

Using Minitab and Excel for Inference for Regression

Regression was introduced in Chapter 2, and you can refer to its Appendix for guidance on creating scatterplots, computing correlation, getting simple regression output, and obtaining residual plots. In this Appendix, we will provide more details on the software in relation to the topic of inference.

Simple Regression—Confidence and Prediction Limits

Minitab:

Stat ➤ Regression ➤ Regression

Minitab does not compute confidence intervals for the regression coefficients (β_0 and β_1). However, for a given value of the explanatory variable, Minitab can compute confidence intervals for the mean and prediction intervals. Once you have clicked-in the response and explanatory data columns, then click the **Options** button. Now input the value of the explanatory variable (x^*) in the **Prediction intervals for new observations** box. If you wish, you can change the confidence level from the default value of "95" as seen in the **Confidence level** box. Click **OK** to close the pop-up box and then click **OK** to get the regression output along with the confidence and prediction intervals reported at the bottom of the output.

Excel:

Excel does not compute confidence intervals for the mean or prediction intervals based on an estimated regression model. These intervals are available in the enhanced add-on version of Excel. Interestingly, unlike Minitab, Excel can report confidence intervals for the regression coefficients (β_0 and β_1). To obtain these confidence intervals, place a checkmark next to the **Confidence Level** option. If you wish, you can change the confidence level from the default value of "95" as seen in the box to the right of the **Confidence Level** option.

Correlation—Inference

Minitab:

Stat ➤ Basic Statistics ➤ Correlation

Obtaining correlation output was described in the Appendix of Chapter 2. In the correlation output, a P-value is reported only for the two-sided test of H_0: $\rho = 0$ versus H_a: $\rho \neq 0$.

Excel:

Testing of the correlation parameter is not available in standard Excel, but one-sided and two-sided tests of the correlation parameter are available in the enhanced add-on version of Excel.

CHAPTER 11

Multiple Regression

PRELUDE: EXECUTIVE ORDER 11246

Executive Order 11246, signed by President Lyndon B. Johnson in 1965, prohibits discrimination in hiring and employment decisions on the basis of race, color, gender, religion, and national origin. It applies to contractors doing business in excess of $10,000 with the U.S. government. The Office of Federal Contract Compliance Programs (OFCCP) is responsible for monitoring compliance with this Executive Order. Setting employees' pay is an important employment decision, and the OFCCP frequently examines the salary data of government contractors. Statistical methods are very useful for this purpose. We can construct a statistical model for the determination of salary and ask about discrimination within the context of this model.[1]

Consider gender, for example. Should we use a two-sample t test (Section 7.2) to compare the average salaries of men and women? The t test is appropriate if all employees do similar jobs and have similar qualifications and experience. More typically, however, employees do different jobs and have different qualifications and different lengths of service. Salary, the response variable, then depends on several explanatory variables. These include variables that describe the job and others that describe the employee's qualifications for the job and performance on the job. Finally, we would also consider gender as an explanatory variable.

Multiple regression allows us to construct a model that explains salary. We can then use the model to ask whether there is a systematic difference between the salaries of men and women when salaries are adjusted for the other explanatory variables. If the model shows men are paid more than women and the salary gap is statistically significant, we have a finding consistent with a claim of discrimination. The company must find a nondiscriminatory explanation for the disparity or take corrective action.

Introduction

In Chapters 2 and 10 we studied the relationship between one explanatory variable and one response variable. In this chapter we look at situations where several explanatory variables work together to explain the response. We build on the descriptive tools we learned in Chapter 2—scatterplots, least-squares regression, and correlation—and on the basics of regression inference from Chapter 10. Many of these ideas carry over. For example, we continue to use scatterplots and correlation for pairs of variables. However, the presence of several explanatory variables that may assist or substitute for each other in predicting the response leads to several new ideas. We start by exploring some of these ideas with an example.

EXAMPLE 11.1 A Space Model

Allocation of space or other resources within an organization is often done using quantitative methods. Characteristics for a subunit of the organization are determined, and then a mathematical formula is used to decide the required needs.

A university has used this approach to determine space needs in square feet (ft^2) for each department.[2] The formula for office space allocates 210 ft^2 for the department head (HEAD), 160 ft^2 for each faculty member (FAC), 160 ft^2 for each manager (MGR), 150 ft^2 for each administrator and lecturer (LECT), 65 ft^2 for each graduate student (GRAD), and 120 ft^2 for each clerical and service worker (CLSV).

The Chemistry Department in a university has 1 department head, 45.24 faculty, 17.00 managers, 38.00 lecturers, 315.00 graduate students, and 43.25 clerical and service workers. Note that fractions of people are possible in these calculations because individuals may have appointments in more than one department. For example, a person with an even split between two departments would be counted as 0.50 in each.

EXAMPLE 11.2 Office Space Needs for the Chemistry Department

Let's calculate the office space needs for the Chemistry Department based on these personnel. We start with 210 ft^2 for the department head. We have 45.24 faculty, each needing 160 ft^2. Therefore, the total office space needed for faculty is 45.24×160 ft^2, which is 7238.4 ft^2. We do the same type of calculation for each personnel category and then sum the results.

Here are the calculations in a table:

Category	Number of employees	Ft^2 per employee	Number times ft^2 per employee
HEAD	1.00	210	210.0
FAC	45.24	160	7,238.4
MGR	17.00	160	2,720.0
LECT	38.00	150	5,700.0
GRAD	315.00	65	20,475.0
CLSV	43.25	120	5,190.0
Total			41,533.4

The calculations that we just performed use a set of predictors, HEAD, FAC, MGR, LECT, GRAD, and CLSV, to find the office space needs for the Chemistry Department. Given values of these predictors for any other department in the university, we can perform the same calculations to find the office space needs. We organized our calculations for the Chemistry Department in the table given above. Another way to organize calculations of this type is to give a formula.

EXAMPLE 11.3 The Formula

Let's assume that each department has exactly one head. So the first term in our equation will be the space need for this position, 210 ft^2. To this we add the space needs for the faculty, 160 ft^2 for each, or 160FAC. Similarly, we add the number of square feet for each category of personnel times the number of employees in the category. The result is the office space needs predicted by the space model. Here is the formula:

$$\text{PredSpace} = 210 + 160\text{FAC} + 160\text{MGR} + 150\text{LECT} + 65\text{GRAD} + 120\text{CLSV}$$

The formula combines information from the predictor variables and computes the space needs for any department. This prediction generally will not match the actual space being used by a department. The difference between the value predicted by the model and the actual space being used is of interest to the people who assign space to departments.

EXAMPLE 11.4 Compare Predicted Space with Actual Space

The Chemistry Department currently uses 51,232 ft^2 of office space. On the other hand, the model predicts an office space need of 41,533.4 ft^2. The difference between these two quantities is a residual:

$$\begin{aligned}\text{Residual} &= \text{ActualSpace} - \text{PredSpace}\\ &= 51{,}232 - 41{,}533.4\\ &= 9698.6\end{aligned}$$

According to the university space model, the Chemistry Department has about 10,000 ft^2 more of office space than it needs. The university director of space management is considering the possibility of giving some of this excess space to a department that has actual space less than what the model predicts.

Of course, the Chemistry Department does not think that it has excess space. In negotiations with the space management office, they will explain that they need all of the space that they currently have and that their needs are not fully captured by the model.

APPLY YOUR KNOWLEDGE

11.1 Check the formula. The table that appears before Example 11.3 shows that the predicted office space needed by the Chemistry Department is 41,533.4 ft^2. Verify that the formula given in Example 11.3 gives the same predicted value.

11.2 Needs of the Department of Mathematics. The Department of Mathematics has 1 department head, 55 faculty, 3 managers, 46 administrators and lecturers, 205 graduate students, and 23 clerical and service workers.

(a) Find the office needs for the Mathematics Department that are predicted by the model.

(b) The actual office space for this department is 23,039 ft^2. Find the residual and explain what it means in a few sentences.

Our space model examples illustrate many of the key ideas that we need for multiple regression. We have several variables that are combined in a prediction equation. Residuals are the differences between the actual values and the predicted values. We now illustrate both the techniques of multiple regression (always using software) and the new ideas with a series of case studies.

CASE 11.1  **ASSETS, SALES, AND PROFITS**

Table 11.1 shows some characteristics of the 30 stocks in the Dow Jones Industrial Average (DJIA).[3] Included are the stock symbol, company name, assets (in billions of dollars) as of December 31, 1999, and sales and profits (in billions of dollars) for the year 1999.[4] How are profits related to sales and assets? In this case, profits represents the response variable and sales and assets are two explanatory variables.

11.1 Data Analysis for Multiple Regression

As with any statistical analysis, we begin our multiple regression analysis with a careful examination of the data.

Data for multiple regression

The data for a simple linear regression problem consist of observations on an explanatory variable x and a response variable y. We use n for the number of cases, or individuals. The major difference in the data for multiple regression is that we have more than one explanatory variable.

EXAMPLE 11.5 Data for Assets, Sales, and Profits

CASE 11.1 

In Case 11.1, the cases are the 30 firms. Each observation consists of a value for a response variable (profits) and values for the two explanatory variables (assets and sales).

TABLE 11.1 Dow Jones 30 industrials: assets, sales, and profits

Symbol	Firm	Assets ($ billions)	Sales ($ billions)	Profits ($ billions)
AA	Alcoa	17.07	16.45	1.05
AXP	American Express	148.52	21.28	2.48
T	AT&T	169.41	62.39	3.43
BA	Boeing	36.15	57.99	2.31
CAT	Caterpillar	26.64	19.70	0.95
C	Citigroup	716.94	82.01	9.87
KO	Coca-Cola	21.62	19.81	2.43
DD	DuPont	40.78	16.91	7.69
EK	Eastman Kodak	14.37	14.09	1.39
XOM	Exxon Mobil	144.52	130.97	7.91
GE	General Electric	405.20	110.83	10.72
GM	General Motors	274.73	167.37	6.00
HWP	Hewlett-Packard	23.53	23.74	1.54
HD	Home Depot	35.30	42.11	3.49
HON	Honeywell	13.47	38.43	2.32
INTC	Intel	87.50	87.55	7.71
IBM	International Business Machines	43.85	29.39	7.31
IP	International Paper	30.27	24.94	0.18
JPM	J. P. Morgan Chase	29.16	27.47	4.17
JNJ	Johnson & Johnson	20.98	13.26	1.95
MCD	McDonald's	35.63	32.71	5.89
MRK	Merck	37.16	21.86	7.79
MSFT	Microsoft	13.90	15.66	1.76
MMM	Minnesota Mining & Manufacturing	260.90	18.07	2.06
MO	Philip Morris	61.38	61.75	7.68
PG	Procter & Gamble	32.11	39.19	3.76
SBC	SBC Communications	83.21	49.49	8.16
UTX	United Technologies	24.37	23.84	1.53
WMT	Wal-Mart	70.25	165.01	5.38
DIS	Walt Disney	43.68	23.75	1.30

In general, we have data on n cases and we use p for the number of explanatory variables. Data are often entered into spreadsheets and computer regression programs in a format where each row describes an individual and each column corresponds to a different variable.

EXAMPLE 11.6 Spreadsheet Data for Assets, Sales, and Profits

CASE 11.1

In Case 11.1, there are 30 firms; assets and sales are the explanatory variables. Therefore, $n = 30$ and $p = 2$. Figure 11.1 shows the part of an Excel spreadsheet with the first 10 cases.

FIGURE 11.1 First 10 cases of data in spreadsheet for Example 11.6.

	A	B	C	D	E
1	symbol	firm	assets	sales	profits
2	AA	Alcoa	17.07	16.45	1.05
3	AXP	American Express	148.52	21.28	2.48
4	T	AT&T	169.41	62.39	3.43
5	BA	Boeing	36.15	57.99	2.31
6	CAT	Caterpillar	26.64	19.7	0.95
7	C	Citigroup	716.94	82.01	9.87
8	KO	Coca-Cola	21.62	19.81	2.43
9	DIS	WaltDisney	43.68	23.75	1.3
10	DD	DuPont	40.78	16.91	7.69
11	EK	Eastman Kodak	14.37	14.09	1.39

APPLY YOUR KNOWLEDGE

11.3 Deposits, assets, and number of banks. Table 11.2 gives data for insured commercial banks, by state or other area.[5] The cases are the 50 states, the District of Columbia, Puerto Rico, Guam, and the Virgin Islands. Bank assets and deposits are given in billions of dollars. We are interested in describing how assets are explained by deposits and the number of banks.

(a) What is the response variable?

(b) What are the explanatory variables?

(c) What is p, the number of explanatory variables?

(d) What is n, the sample size?

11.4 Look at the data. Examine the data for deposits, assets, and number of banks given in Table 11.2. That is, use graphs to display the distribution of each variable and the relationship between each pair of variables. Based on your examination, how would you describe the data? Are there any states or other areas that you consider to be outliers or unusual in any way?

Preliminary data analysis for multiple regression

Following our principles of data analysis, we look first at each variable separately, then at relationships among the variables. We again combine plots and numerical description.

EXAMPLE 11.7 Describing Assets, Sales, and Profits

CASE 11.1

Figure 11.2 shows descriptive statistics from Excel for the 30 stocks in the DJIA. Figure 11.3 presents stemplots for each variable.

Consider assets. The stemplot shows a strongly skewed distribution with two high outliers. The outliers are Citigroup and General Electric. Numerical measures reflect the skewness. The mean assets of all 30 firms are \$99 billion with a standard deviation of \$149 billion. The median is \$37 billion, much less than the mean. The minimum, \$13 billion, is much closer to the median than the maximum, \$717 billion.

TABLE 11.2 Insured commercial banks by state or other area

State or area	Number	Assets ($ billions)	Deposits ($ billions)	State or area	Number	Assets ($ billions)	Deposits ($ billions)
Alabama	175	101.2	72.7	Montana	96	9.0	7.5
Alaska	6	4.8	3.5	Nebraska	326	25.9	21.6
Arizona	41	39.3	22.8	Nevada	25	25.9	8.1
Arkansas	226	101.2	72.7	New Hampshire	21	11.7	8.5
California	336	474.7	361.4	New Jersey	71	79.9	62.4
Colorado	216	33.9	29.3	New Mexico	58	11.3	9.0
Connecticut	26	4.8	4.0	New York	153	1119.2	630.7
Delaware	34	127.9	50.8	North Carolina	60	433.1	270.9
District of Columbia	6	1.2	0.9	North Dakota	117	8.9	7.6
Florida	266	116.9	92.1	Ohio	235	230.6	154.4
Georgia	353	69.2	46.9	Oklahoma	320	34.1	28.0
Guam	2	0.8	0.7	Oregon	41	5.8	4.7
Hawaii	14	22.9	15.7	Pennsylvania	212	267.6	194.8
Idaho	16	1.4	1.2	Puerto Rico	13	33.7	21.6
Illinois	784	265.4	194.8	Rhode Island	9	77.3	54.8
Indiana	185	66.5	50.9	South Carolina	80	17.5	14.5
Iowa	453	43.3	36.0	South Dakota	106	30.3	11.8
Kansas	403	31.3	26.7	Tennessee	232	75.1	56.3
Kentucky	271	51.0	38.2	Texas	839	235.1	191.8
Louisiana	158	46.7	37.6	Utah	49	39.6	20.1
Maine	17	4.9	3.7	Vermont	21	7.1	5.9
Maryland	83	35.2	26.9	Virginia	151	77.8	55.9
Massachusetts	46	123.4	84.2	Virgin Islands	2	0.1	0.1
Michigan	163	118.8	85.3	Washington	80	11.7	9.9
Minnesota	520	131.9	97.9	West Virginia	100	21.6	17.5
Mississippi	107	34.4	27.8	Wisconsin	361	72.5	55.4
Missouri	404	63.4	53.5	Wyoming	52	8.3	7.2

FIGURE 11.2 Descriptive statistics for Example 11.7

assets		*sales*		*profits*	
Mean	98.7533333	Mean	48.6006667	Mean	4.34033333
Standard Error	27.1485377	Standard Error	7.93154625	Standard Error	0.55441229
Median	36.655	Median	28.43	Median	3.46
Standard Deviation	148.698665	Standard Deviation	43.442868	Standard Deviation	3.03664116
Minimum	13.47	Minimum	13.26	Minimum	0.18
Maximum	716.94	Maximum	167.37	Maximum	10.72
Count	30	Count	30	Count	30

FIGURE 11.3 Stemplots for Example 11.7

```
 0 | 1112222233334444446789
 1 | 457
 2 | 67
 3 |
 4 | 1
 5 |
 6 |
 7 | 1
```

Assets

```
 0 | 834667                 0 | 2
 2 | 0012444579389          1 | 0034558
 4 | 298                    2 | 013345
 6 | 22                     3 | 458
 8 | 28                     4 | 2
10 | 1                      5 | 49
12 | 1                      6 | 0
14 |                        7 | 377789
16 | 57                     8 | 2
                            9 | 9
                           10 | 7
```

Sales | Profits

Will the skewness affect our analysis? Later in this chapter, we will describe a statistical model that is the basis for inference in multiple regression. This model does not require Normality for the distributions of the response and explanatory variables. The Normality assumption applies to the distribution of the residuals, as was the case for inference in simple linear regression. We look at the distribution of each variable to be used in a multiple regression to determine if there are any unusual patterns that may be important in building our regression analysis.

APPLY YOUR KNOWLEDGE

11.5 Sales of the DJIA firms. Based on Figures 11.2 and 11.3, describe the distribution of the sales of the DJIA companies. Are the companies that are outliers in assets also outliers in sales? Why are you not surprised that Wal-Mart has high sales relative to its assets?

CASE 11.1

11.6 Profits of the DJIA firms. Based on Figures 11.2 and 11.3, describe the distribution of the profits of the DJIA companies. This distribution has a shape distinctly different from that of the explanatory variables. What aspect of the distribution do Excel's descriptive statistics fail to capture?

CASE 11.1

Now that we know something about the distributions of the individual variables, we look at the relations between pairs of variables. We need to proceed with caution, however, knowing that we may have outliers and influential observations.

EXAMPLE 11.8 Assets, Sales, and Profits in Pairs

CASE 11.1

With three variables, we also have three pairs of variables to examine. Figure 11.4 gives the three correlations and Figure 11.5 displays the corresponding scatterplots. We used a scatterplot smoother (page 131) to help us see the overall pattern of each scatterplot.

FIGURE 11.4 Correlations for Example 11.8.

	assets	*sales*	*profits*
assets	1		
sales	0.454876	1	
profits	0.532522	0.538364	1

FIGURE 11.5 Plots of pairs of variables for Example 11.8.

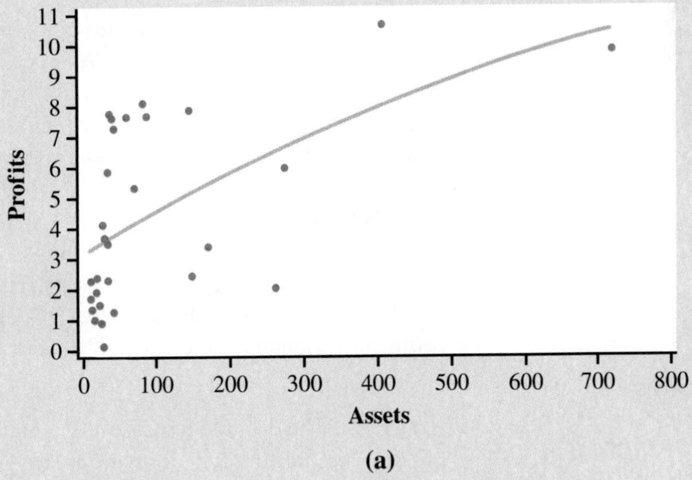

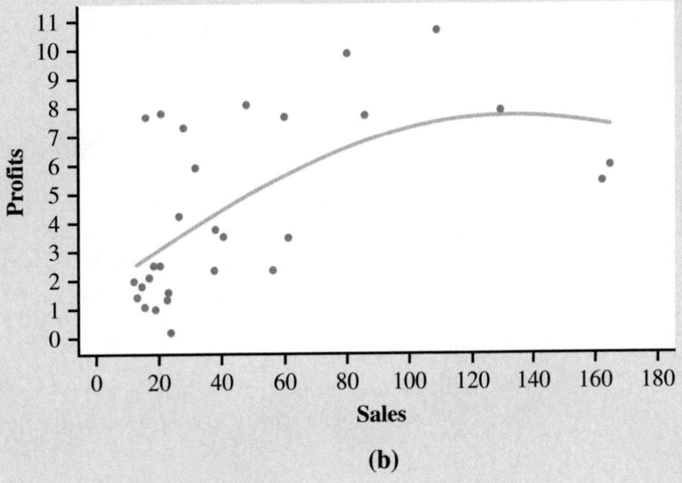

FIGURE 11.5 *(Continued)*

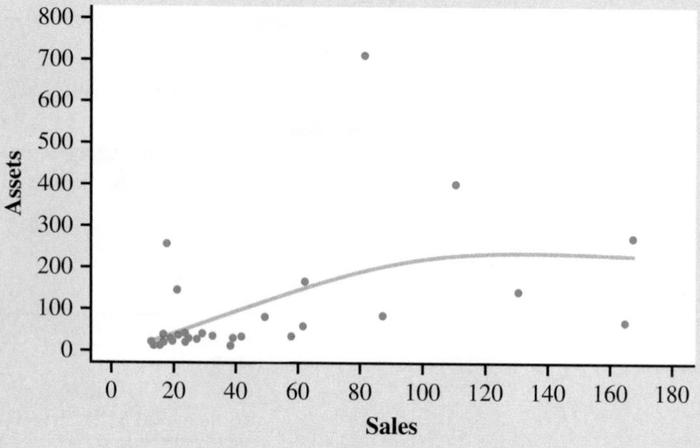

(c)

Both assets and sales have moderate positive correlations with profits. These variables may be useful in explaining profits. Assets and sales are also moderately positively correlated ($r = 0.45$). Because we will use both assets and sales to explain profits, we are happy that this correlation is not very high. Two highly correlated variables contain about the same information, so that both together may explain profits little better than either alone.

The plots are more revealing. The relationship between profits and assets is approximately linear, but the relationship is dominated by the two companies, Citigroup and General Electric, that have very large assets. The relationship between profits and sales, on the other hand, is somewhat curved. This appears to be due to the influence of the two companies, General Motors and Wal-Mart, that have the largest sales.

APPLY YOUR KNOWLEDGE

11.7 Try logs. The data file for Case 11.1 contains the logarithms of each variable. The logarithm transformation pulls in the long tail of a skewed distribution. It is common to use logarithms to make economic and financial data more symmetric before doing inference. Find the correlations and generate scatterplots for each pair of transformed variables. Interpret the results and compare with our analysis of the original variables.

CASE 11.1

Estimating the multiple regression coefficients

Simple linear regression with a response variable y and one explanatory variable x begins by using the least-squares idea (Section 2.3) to fit a straight line $\hat{y} = b_0 + b_1 x$ to data on the two variables. Although we now have p explanatory variables, the principle is the same: we use the least-squares idea to fit a linear function

$$\hat{y} = b_0 + b_1 x_1 + b_2 x_2 + \cdots + b_p x_p$$

to the data.

We use a subscript i to distinguish different cases. For the ith case the predicted response is

$$\hat{y}_i = b_0 + b_1 x_{i1} + b_2 x_{i2} + \cdots + b_p x_{ip}$$

As usual, the residual is the difference between the observed value of the response variable and the value predicted by the model:

$$e = \text{observed response} - \text{predicted response}$$

residual

For the ith case, the **residual** is

$$e_i = y_i - \hat{y}_i$$

method of least squares

The **method of least squares** chooses the b's that make the sum of squares of the residuals as small as possible. In other words, the *least-squares estimates* are the values that minimize the quantity

$$\sum (y_i - \hat{y}_i)^2$$

As in the simple linear regression case, it is possible to give formulas for the least-squares estimates. Because the formulas are complicated and hand calculation is out of the question, we are content to understand the least-squares principle and to let software do the computations.

EXAMPLE 11.9 Predicting Profits from Sales and Assets

CASE 11.1

Our examination of explanatory and response variables separately and then in pairs suggests that we have skewed distributions with some outliers and possibly some influential observations. We can find the least-squares fit for any set of data, but we must examine the results with caution. Output for the multiple regression analysis from Excel, SPSS, Minitab, and SAS appears in Figure 11.6. Rounding the results to three significant digits gives the least-squares equation

$$\widehat{\text{Profits}} = 2.34 + 0.00741 \times \text{Assets} + 0.0261 \times \text{Sales}$$

In Example 11.9 we rounded off the coefficients to *three significant digits*. Significant digits do not include any zeros before the first nonzero digit. So the three significant digits for the coefficient of Assets are 741. The SPSS output in Figure 11.6 gives the results in *scientific notation* that emphasizes the significant digits. The coefficient of assets, 0.007406, appears in the form 7.406E-03. The number after the "E" tells us how many places to move the decimal point. Move it to the right if the number is positive and to the left if it is negative. For example, 3.65E+02 is 365 and 4.651E-03 is 0.004651.

APPLY YOUR KNOWLEDGE

11.8 Reading software output. Examine the outputs from the four different software packages in Figure 11.6. Find the multiple regression coefficients in each. Report the numbers as given, without rounding off.

CASE 11.1

11.9 Regression after transforming. In Exercise 11.7 we considered using the logarithm transformation for all variables in Case 11.1. Run the regression and report the least-squares equation for the log variables. Note that the units differ from those in Example 11.9 so the results cannot be directly compared.

CASE 11.1

Regression residuals

The residuals are the errors in predicting the sample responses from the multiple regression equation. Recall that the residuals are the differences between the observed and

FIGURE 11.6 Excel, SPSS, Minitab, and SAS output, for Example 11.9.

SUMMARY OUTPUT

Regression Statistics	
Multiple R	0.6278164
R Square	0.39415343
Adjusted R Square	0.34927591
Standard Error	2.44958163
Observations	30

ANOVA

	df	*SS*	*MS*	*F*	*Significance F*
Regression	2	105.402342	52.7011708	8.78286949	0.00115318
Residual	27	162.012155	6.00045018		
Total	29	267.414497			

	Coefficients	*Standard Error*	*t Stat*	*P-value*	*Lower 95%*	*Upper 95%*
Intercept	2.3404548	0.6821015	3.43124127	0.00194848	0.94089815	3.74001145
assets	0.00740634	0.00343499	2.15614689	0.04014324	0.00035833	0.01445435
sales	0.02610001	0.01175747	2.21986724	0.03501518	0.00197569	0.05022434

SPSS

Regression

Model Summary

Model	R	R Square	Adjusted R Square	Std. Error of the Estimate
	.628	.394	.349	2.44958

a Predictors: (Constant), SALES, ASSETS

ANOVA

Model		Sum of Squares	df	Mean Square	F	Sig.
1	Regression	105.402	2	52.701	8.783	.001
	Residual	162.012	27	6.000		
	Total	267.414	29			

a Predictors: (Constant), SALES, ASSETS
b Dependent Variable: PROFITS

Coefficients

Model		Unstandardized Coefficients		Standardized Coefficients	t	Sig.	95% Confidence Interval for B	
		B	Std. Error	Beta			Lower Bound	Upper Bound
1	(Constant)	2.340	.682		3.431	.002	.941	3.740
	ASSETS	7.406E-03	.003	.363	2.156	.040	.000	.014
	SALES	2.610E-02	.0 12	.373	2.220	.035	.002	.050

a Dependent Variable: PROFITS

Minitab

Regression Analysis: profits versus assets, sales

```
The regression equation is
profits = 2.34 + 0.00741 assets + 0.0261 sales

Predictor          Coef      SE Coef       T       P
Constant         2.3405       0.6821    3.43   0.002
assets         0.007406     0.003435    2.16   0.040
sales           0.02610      0.01176    2.22   0.035

S = 2.44958        R-Sq = 39.4%        R-Sq(adj) = 34.9%

Analysis of Variance

Source            DF         SS        MS       F       P
Regression         2    105.402    52.701    8.78   0.001
Residual Error    27    162.012     6.000
Total             29    267.414
```

SAS

The REG Procedure
Model: MODEL1
Dependent Variable: profits

Analysis of Variance

Source	DF	Sum of Squares	Mean Square	F Value	Pr > F
Model	2	105.40234	52.70117	8.78	0.0012
Error	27	162.01215	6.00045		
Corrected Total	29	267.41450			

Root MSE	2.44958	R-Square	0.3942
Dependent Mean	4.34033	Adj R-Sq	0.3493
Coeff Var	56.43764		

Parameter Estimates

Variable	DF	Parameter Estimate	Standard Error	t Value	Pr > |t|	95% Confidence Limits	
Intercept	1	2.34045	0.68210	3.43	0.0019	0.94090	3.74001
sales	1	0.02610	0.01176	2.22	0.0350	0.00198	0.05022
assets	1	0.00741	0.00343	2.16	0.0401	0.00035833	0.01445

predicted values of the response variable.

$$e = \text{observed response} - \text{predicted response}$$
$$= y - \hat{y}$$

As with simple linear regression, the residuals sum to zero and the best way to examine them is to use plots.

We first examine the distribution of the residuals using stemplots or histograms. To see if the residuals appear to be approximately Normal, we use a Normal quantile plot.

EXAMPLE 11.10 Distribution of the Residuals

CASE 11.1

Figure 11.7 is a stemplot of the residuals. The units for the stems are billions of dollars. There is a peak at -1 and the distribution looks somewhat skewed to the right. The Normal quantile plot in Figure 11.8 indicates that the residuals do not have a Normal distribution, because the plot deviates substantially from a straight line. The right-skewness causes the plot to bend upward starting roughly at z-score 0.

FIGURE 11.7 Stemplot of residuals for Example 11.10.

−3	0
−2	7710
−1	8888665411
−0	962
0	129
1	1
2	445
3	399
4	66

FIGURE 11.8 Normal quantile plot of residuals for Example 11.10.

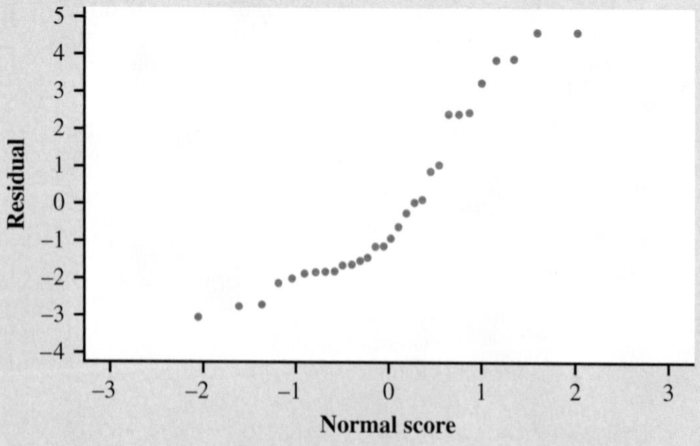

Another important aspect of examining the residuals is to plot them against each explanatory variable. Sometimes we can detect unusual patterns when we examine the data in this way.

EXAMPLE 11.11 Residual Plots

CASE 11.1

The residuals are plotted versus assets in Figure 11.9 and versus sales in Figure 11.10. Note the point corresponding to Citigroup in the plot versus assets. It is the company with assets of $716.94 billion. We noted this outlier in the stemplot for assets (Figure 11.3) and in the plot of profits versus assets (Figure 11.5(a)). We see in Figure 11.9 that its residual is close to zero. It is possible that this observation is distorting the regression equation by exerting a great deal of influence. On the other hand, it is possible that the point is extreme but fits the pattern of the other observations. The plot with the smoothed function appears to support the latter view. However, the

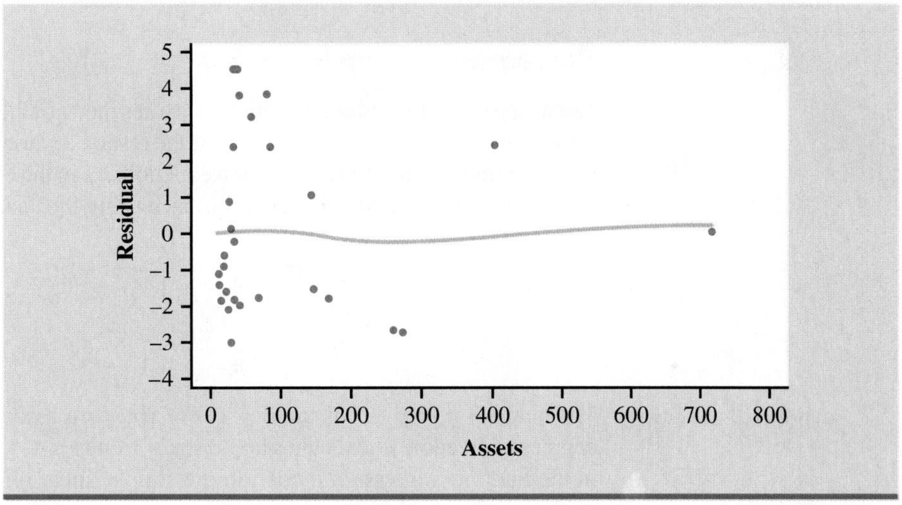

FIGURE 11.9 Plot of residuals versus assets for Example 11.11.

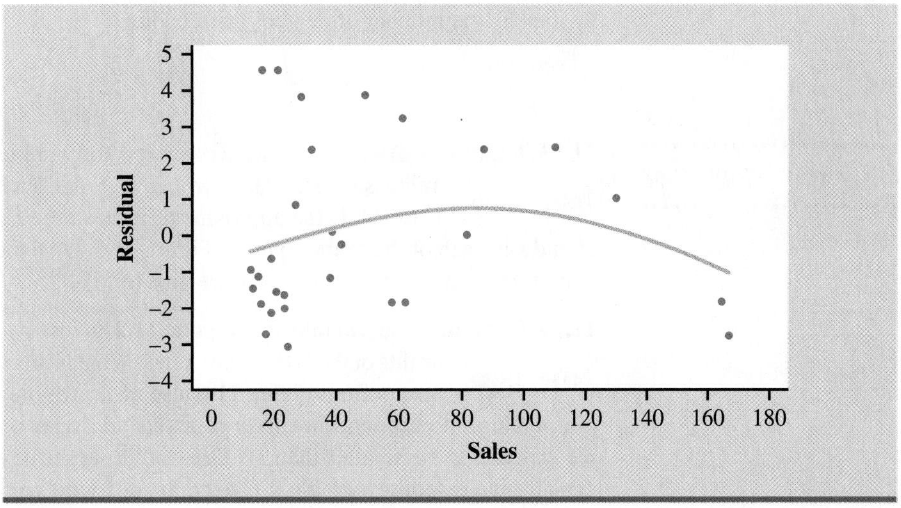

FIGURE 11.10 Plot of residuals versus sales for Example 11.11.

two observations with the large sales appear to be pulling the regression function down relative to the slight upward trend for the data with lower values of sales. This is very similar to the pattern that we saw Figure 11.5(b), where we plotted profits versus sales.

APPLY YOUR KNOWLEDGE

11.10 Examine the effect of Citigroup, large assets. Delete Citigroup from the data set and rerun the multiple regression. Describe how the regression coefficients change.

CASE 11.1

11.11 Examine the effect of General Motors and Wal-Mart, large sales. Delete General Motors and Wal-Mart from the data set and rerun the multiple regression. Describe how the regression coefficients have changed.

CASE 11.1

11.12 Residuals for the log analysis. In Exercise 11.9, you carried out multiple regression using the logarithms of all variables in Table 11.1. Obtain the residuals from this regression and examine them using a stemplot. If you have suitable software, make a Normal quantile plot. Summarize your conclusions and compare your plots with the plots for the original variables.

CASE 11.1

The regression standard error

Just as the sample standard deviation measures the variability of observations about their mean, we can quantify the variability of the response variable about the predicted values obtained from the multiple regression equation. As in the case of simple linear regression (see page 578), we first calculate a variance using the squared residuals:

$$s^2 = \frac{1}{n-p-1}\sum e_i^2$$

$$= \frac{1}{n-p-1}\sum (y_i - \hat{y}_i)^2$$

degrees of freedom

The quantity $n - p - 1$ is the **degrees of freedom** associated with s^2. The number of degrees of freedom equals the sample size n minus $p + 1$, the number of coefficients b_i in the multiple regression model. In the simple linear regression case there is just one explanatory variable, so $p = 1$ and the number of degrees of freedom for s^2 is $n - 2$. The **regression standard error** s is the square root of the sum of squares of residuals divided by the number of degrees of freedom:

regression standard error

$$s = \sqrt{s^2}$$

APPLY YOUR KNOWLEDGE

11.13 Reading software output. Regression software usually reports both s^2 and the regression standard error s. For the assets, sales, and profits data of Case 11.1, the approximate values are $s^2 = 6.00$ and $s = 2.45$. Locate s^2 and s in each of the four outputs in Figure 11.6. Give the unrounded values from each output. What name does each software give to s?

CASE 11.1

11.14 Compare the variability. Figure 11.2 gives the standard deviation s_y of the profits of the DJIA companies. What is this value? The regression standard error s from Figure 11.6 also measures the variability of profits, this time after taking into account the effect of assets and sales on profits. Explain briefly why we expect s to be smaller than s_y. One way to describe how well multiple regression explains the response variable y is to compare s with s_y.

CASE 11.1

Case 11.1 uses data on the assets, sales, and profits of the 30 companies included in the Dow Jones Industrial Average. These are not an SRS from any population. They are selected by the editors of the *Wall Street Journal* and change over time as the economic importance of different industries changes. General Electric is the only survivor from the group originally chosen in 1896. Intel and Microsoft were added only in 1999.

Data analysis does not require that the cases be a random sample from a larger population. Our analysis of Case 11.1 tells us something about the DJIA companies, not about all publicly traded companies or any other larger group. Inference, as opposed to data analysis, draws conclusions about a population or process from which our data are a sample. Inference is most easily understood when we have an SRS from a clearly defined population. The INDIVIDUALS data set in the Data Appendix, for example, is a random sample from the population of all American residents between ages 25 and 65 who have worked but whose main work experience is not in agriculture.

Applications of statistics in business settings frequently involve data that are not random samples. We often justify inference by saying that we are studying an underlying process that generates the data. In salary-discrimination studies, we have data on all employees in a particular group. The salaries of these current employees reflect the process by which the company sets salaries. Multiple regression builds a model of this process, and inference tells us whether gender, for example, has a statistically significant effect in the context of this model.

Whether inference from a multiple regression model not based on a random sample is trustworthy is a matter for judgment. In a discrimination case, we start with data on *all* employees in some group.

SECTION 11.1 SUMMARY

- **Data for multiple linear regression** consist of the values of a response variable y and p explanatory variables $x_1, x_2, \ldots, x_p$ for n cases. We write the data and enter them into software in the form

	Variables				
Case	x_1	x_2	$\ldots$	x_p	y
1	x_{11}	x_{12}	$\ldots$	x_{1p}	y_1
2	x_{21}	x_{22}	$\ldots$	x_{2p}	y_2
$\vdots$					
n	x_{n1}	x_{n2}	$\ldots$	x_{np}	y_n

- **Data analysis for multiple regression** starts with an examination of the distribution of each of the variables and scatterplots to display the relations between the variables.

- The **multiple regression equation** predicts the response variable by a linear relationship with all the explanatory variables:

$$\hat{y} = b_0 + b_1x_1 + b_2x_2 + \cdots + b_px_p$$

- The coefficients b_i in this equation are estimated using the **principle of least squares.**

- The **residuals** for multiple linear regression are

$$e_i = y_i - \hat{y}_i$$

- Always examine the **distribution of the residuals** and plot them against the explanatory variables.
- The variability of the responses about the multiple regression equation is measured by the **regression standard error s**, where s is the square root of

$$s^2 = \frac{\sum e_i^2}{n - p - 1}$$

SECTION 11.1 Exercises

For Exercises 11.1 and 11.2, see page 620; for 11.3 and 11.4, see page 622; for 11.5 and 11.6, see page 624; for 11.7, see page 626; for 11.8 and 11.9, see page 627; for 11.10 to 11.12, see page 632, and for 11.13 and 11.14, see page 632.

11.15 Data analysis: individual variables. The following table gives the price (in dollars), weight (in pounds), amps, and maximum cutting depth (in inches) for a collection of 19 circular saws.[6]

(a) Make a table giving the mean, the standard deviation, and the five-number summary for each variable.

(b) Use stemplots to make graphical summaries of each distribution.

(c) Describe the distributions. Are there any unusual observations?

Price	Weight	Amps	Depth
150	11	15	2.4
110	12	15	2.2
130	11	15	2.4
150	11	15	2.3
140	12	15	2.4
100	11	15	2.4
150	13	15	2.5
90	9	10	2.5
140	11	15	2.4
110	12	15	2.4
70	12	14	2.4
30	10	10	2.5
80	12	13	2.4
50	11	13	2.4
80	13	14	2.4
30	10	12	2.5
50	11	12	2.5
45	11	12	2.5
40	10	12	2.4

11.16 Data analysis: pairs of variables. Refer to the circular saw data in Exercise 11.15. Examine the relationship between each pair of variables.

(a) Use graphical summaries. Summarize what you have learned from looking at these graphs.

(b) Now, use numerical summaries to examine the relationship between each pair of variables. Summarize what you have learned from looking at these numbers and compare this information with what you learned from the graphical summaries.

(c) Are there any unusual observations or outliers?

(d) If you were interested in predicting price, which variables appear to be most promising from this analysis?

11.17 Multiple regression equation. Refer to the circular saw data in Exercise 11.15. Run a multiple regression to predict price using weight, amps, and depth as explanatory variables.

(a) Give the equation for predicted price.

(b) What is the value of the regression standard error s? Verify that this value is the square root of the sum of squares of residuals divided by the degrees of freedom for the residuals.

11.18 Predict some values. Use the multiple regression analysis that you performed in the previous exercise to answer the following questions.

(a) Predict the price of a circular saw that weighs 10 pounds, uses 12 amps of current, and has a maximum cutting depth of 2.5 inches.

(b) Predict the price of a circular saw that weighs 12 pounds, uses 15 amps of current, and has a maximum cutting depth of 2.5 inches.

(c) Predict the price of a circular saw that weighs 20 pounds, uses 12 amps of current, and has a maximum cutting depth of 2.5 inches.

(d) Which of the three predictions that you found in parts (a), (b), and (c) do you think would be very unreliable? Give a reason for your answer.

11.19 Residuals. Refer to Exercise 11.17. Find the residuals for the multiple regression used to predict price using weight, amps, and depth as explanatory variables.

(a) Give a graphical summary of the distribution of the residuals. Are there any outliers in this distribution?

(b) Plot the residuals versus each of the explanatory variables. Describe the plots and any unusual cases.

11.20 Rankings. Overall scores based on cutting speed, power, ease of use, and construction were computed and the saws were ranked on the basis of these scores. The data displayed in Exercise 11.15 list the saws in this order. The top-rated saw is the first entry in the table, and the first column contains the top 10 in order, followed by the saws listed in the second column.

(a) Plot the residuals from the multiple regression analysis versus this rank and describe the pattern.

(b) Do these results suggest that there is information in the ranks that is not contained in the explanatory variables used for the multiple regression analysis? Explain your answer.

(c) Rerun the multiple regression analysis with rank as an additional explanatory variable and describe the results.

11.21 Best Buys. The report on the saws described in Exercise 11.15 lists saws with Ranks 2, 6, 8, and 11 as "Best Buys." A saw that has a negative residual has a price that is less than the price that is predicted by the regression equation. Find the residuals from the multiple regression analysis that you performed in part (c) of the previous exercise. Does there appear to be a relationship between the indication that a saw is a "Best Buy" and these residuals? Explain your answer.

11.22 Predicted values. The fitted regression equation for a multiple regression is

$$\hat{y} = -2.6 + 4.1x_1 - 3.2x_2$$

(a) If $x_1 = 5$ and $x_2 = 3$, what is the predicted value of y?

(b) For the answer to part (a) to be valid, is it necessary that the values $x_1 = 5$ and $x_2 = 3$ correspond to a case in the data set? Explain why or why not.

(c) If you hold x_1 at a fixed value, what is the effect of an increase of one unit in x_2 on the predicted value of y?

11.23 Data analysis: individual variables. The following table gives data on market share, number of accounts, and assets held by the 10 largest online stock brokerages.[7] Market share is expressed in percents, based on the number of trades per day. The number of accounts is given in thousands, and assets are given in billions of dollars.

Consider the three variables market share, number of accounts, and assets.

(a) Make a table giving the mean, the standard deviation, and the five-number summary for each of these variables.

(b) Use stemplots to make graphical summaries of the three distributions.

(c) Describe the distributions. Are there any unusual observations?

Brokerage	Market share	Accounts	Assets
Charles Schwab	27.5	2500	219.0
E*Trade	12.9	909	21.1
TD Waterhouse	11.6	615	38.8
Datek	10.0	205	5.5
Fidelity	9.3	2300	160.0
Ameritrade	8.4	428	19.5
DLJ Direct	3.6	590	11.2
Discover	2.8	134	5.9
Suretrade	2.2	130	1.3
National Discount Brokers	1.3	125	6.8

11.24 Data analysis: pairs of variables. Refer to the previous exercise.

(a) Plot market share versus number of accounts, market share versus assets, and number of accounts versus assets.

(b) Summarize these relationships. Are there any influential observations?

(c) Find the correlation between each pair of variables.

11.25 Multiple regression equation. Refer to the brokerage data in Exercise 11.23. Run a multiple regression to predict market share using number of accounts and assets as explanatory variables.

(a) Give the equation for predicted market share.

(b) What is the value of the regression standard error s?

11.26 Residuals. Refer to the brokerage data in Exercise 11.23. Find the residuals for the multiple regression used to predict market share with number of accounts and assets as explanatory variables.

(a) Give a graphical summary of the distribution of the residuals. Are there any outliers in this distribution?

(b) Plot the residuals versus the number of accounts. Describe the plot and any unusual cases.

(c) Repeat part (b) with assets in place of number of accounts.

Your analyses in Exercises 11.23 to 11.26 point to two firms, Charles Schwab and Fidelity, as unusual in several respects. How influential are these firms? The following four exercises provide answers.

11.27 Rerun Exercise 11.23 without the data for Schwab and Fidelity. Compare your results with what you obtained in that exercise.

11.28 Rerun Exercise 11.24 without the data for Schwab and Fidelity. Compare your results with what you obtained in that exercise.

11.29 Rerun Exercise 11.25 without the data for Schwab and Fidelity. Compare your results with what you obtained in that exercise.

11.30 Rerun Exercise 11.26 without the data for Schwab and Fidelity. Compare your results with what you obtained in that exercise.

11.31 **Retail sales.** Table 2.1 (page 96) gives data on daily sales at a secondhand shop for 25 days. The data are described in Case 2.1 (page 96). We expect that cash items, check items, and credit card items together will predict gross sales.

(a) Describe the distribution of each of these variables using both graphical and numerical summaries. Briefly summarize what you find and note any unusual observations.

(b) Use plots and the correlations to describe the relationships between each pair of variables. Summarize your results.

11.32 **Predict retail sales.** Continue your analysis of the data of Table 2.1. Use cash items, check items, and credit card items to predict gross sales.

(a) Give the prediction equation.

(b) What is the value of the regression standard error s?

11.33 **Residuals.** Analyze the residuals from the multiple regression in the previous exercise.

11.34 **Architectural firms.** Table 1.3 (page 13) contains data describing firms engaged in commercial architecture in the Indianapolis, Indiana, area. Consider the variables total billings, architects, engineers, and staff.

(a) Using numerical and graphical summaries, describe the distribution of each of these variables.

(b) For each of the 6 pairs of variables, use graphical and numerical summaries to describe the relationships.

11.35 **Predict total billings.** We expect that employee counts in the three categories given will help predict total billings. Carry out a multiple regression using the data in Table 1.3.

(a) Report the fitted regression equation.

(b) Give the value of the regression standard error s.

11.36 **Residuals.** Analyze the residuals from the multiple regression in the previous exercise.

11.2 Inference for Multiple Regression

To move from using multiple regression for data analysis to inference in the multiple regression setting, we need to make some assumptions about our data. These assumptions are summarized in the form of a statistical model. As with all of the models that we have studied, we do not require that the model be exactly correct. We only require that it be approximately true and that the data do not severely violate the assumptions.

Recall that the *simple linear regression model* assumes that the mean of the response variable y depends on the explanatory variable x according to a linear equation

$$\mu_y = \beta_0 + \beta_1 x$$

For any fixed value of x, the response y varies Normally around this mean and has a standard deviation σ that is the same for all values of x.

In the *multiple regression* setting, the response variable y depends on not one but p explanatory variables, denoted by $x_1, x_2, \ldots, x_p$. The mean response is a linear function of the explanatory variables:

$$\mu_y = \beta_0 + \beta_1 x_1 + \beta_2 x_2 + \cdots + \beta_p x_p$$

population regression equation

This expression is the **population regression equation.** We do not observe the mean response, because the observed values of y vary about their means. We can think of subpopulations of responses, each corresponding to a particular set of values for *all* of the explanatory variables $x_1, x_2, \ldots, x_p$. In each subpopulation, y varies Normally with a mean given by the population regression equation. The regression model assumes that the standard deviation σ of the responses is the same in all subpopulations.

Multiple linear regression model

To form the multiple regression model, we combine the population regression equation with assumptions about the form of the *variation* of the observations about their mean. We again think of the model in the form

$$\text{DATA} = \text{FIT} + \text{RESIDUAL}$$

The FIT part of the model consists of the subpopulation mean μ_y. The RESIDUAL part represents the variation of the response y around its subpopulation mean. That is, the model is

$$y = \mu_y + \epsilon$$

The symbol ϵ represents the deviation of an individual observation from its subpopulation mean. We assume that these deviations are Normally distributed with mean 0 and an unknown standard deviation σ that does not depend on the values of the x variables.

Multiple Linear Regression Model

The **statistical model for multiple linear regression** is

$$y_i = \beta_0 + \beta_1 x_{i1} + \beta_2 x_{i2} + \cdots + \beta_p x_{ip} + \epsilon_i$$

for $i = 1, 2, \ldots, n$.

The **mean response** μ_y is a linear function of the explanatory variables:

$$\mu_y = \beta_0 + \beta_1 x_1 + \beta_2 x_2 + \cdots + \beta_p x_p$$

The **deviations** ϵ_i are independent and Normally distributed with mean 0 and standard deviation σ. That is, they are an SRS from the $N(0, \sigma)$ distribution.

The parameters of the model are $\beta_0, \beta_1, \beta_2, \ldots, \beta_p$, and σ.

The assumption that the subpopulation means are related to the regression coefficients β by the equation

$$\mu_y = \beta_0 + \beta_1 x_1 + \beta_2 x_2 + \cdots + \beta_p x_p$$

implies that we can estimate all subpopulation means from estimates of the β's. To the extent that this equation is accurate, we have a useful tool for describing how the mean of y varies with the x's.

CASE 11.2 PREDICTING COLLEGE GPA

The CSDATA data set described in the Data Appendix contains information about all 224 students who entered a university in a particular year and were planning to major in computer science.[8] The data were collected to see if information available before students enroll can predict success in the early university years. The response variable is a student's cumulative grade point average (GPA) after three semesters. Among the explanatory variables are average high school grades in mathematics (HSM), science (HSS), and English (HSE). Data are also available on each student's SAT Math (SATM) and Verbal (SATV) scores.

EXAMPLE 11.12 A Model for Predicting GPA

CASE 11.2

We expect that high school grades will help predict college GPA. The multiple regression model then has $p = 3$ explanatory variables: $x_1 =$ HSM, $x_2 =$ HSS, and $x_3 =$ HSE. The high school grades are coded on a scale from 1 to 10, with 10 corresponding to A, 9 to A−, 8 to B+, and so on. These grades define the subpopulations. For example, the straight-C students are the subpopulation defined by HSM = 4, HSS = 4, and HSE = 4.

The multiple regression model for the subpopulation mean GPAs is

$$\mu_{\text{GPA}} = \beta_0 + \beta_1\text{HSM} + \beta_2\text{HSS} + \beta_3\text{HSE}$$

For the straight-C subpopulation of students, the model gives the subpopulation mean as

$$\mu_{\text{GPA}} = \beta_0 + 4\beta_1 + 4\beta_2 + 4\beta_3$$

Estimating the parameters of the model

To estimate mean GPA in Example 11.12, we must estimate the coefficients β_0, β_1, β_2, and β_3. Inference requires that we also estimate the variability of the responses about their mean, represented in the model by the standard deviation σ. In any multiple regression model, the parameters to be estimated from the data are $\beta_0, \beta_1, \ldots, \beta_p$, and σ. We estimate these parameters by applying least-squares multiple regression as in Section 11.1. That is, we view the coefficients b_j in the multiple regression equation

$$\hat{y} = b_0 + b_1x_1 + b_2x_2 + \cdots + b_px_p$$

as estimates of the population parameters β_j.

The observed variability of the responses about this fitted model is measured by the variance

$$s^2 = \frac{1}{n-p-1}\sum e_i^2$$

and the regression standard error

$$s = \sqrt{s^2}$$

In the model, the parameters σ^2 and σ measure the variability of the responses about the population regression equation. It is natural to estimate σ^2 by s^2 and σ by s.

Estimating the Regression Parameters

In the multiple linear regression setting, we use the **method of least-squares regression** to estimate the population regression parameters.

The standard deviation σ in the model is estimated by the **regression standard error**

$$s = \sqrt{\frac{1}{n-p-1}\sum(y_i - \hat{y}_i)^2}$$

Inference about the regression coefficients

Confidence intervals and significance tests for each of the regression coefficients β_j have the same form as in simple linear regression. The standard errors of the b's have more complicated formulas, but all are again multiples of s. Statistical software does the calculations.

Confidence Intervals and Significance Tests for β_j

A **level C confidence interval** for β_j is

$$b_j \pm t^* \mathrm{SE}_{b_j}$$

where SE_{b_j} is the standard error of b_j and t^* is the value for the $t(n-p-1)$ density curve with area C between $-t^*$ and t^*.

To test the hypothesis H_0: $\beta_j = 0$, compute the ***t* statistic**

$$t = \frac{b_j}{\mathrm{SE}_{b_j}}$$

In terms of a random variable T having the $t(n-p-1)$ distribution, the P-value for a test of H_0 against

H_a: $\beta_j > 0$ is $P(T \geq t)$

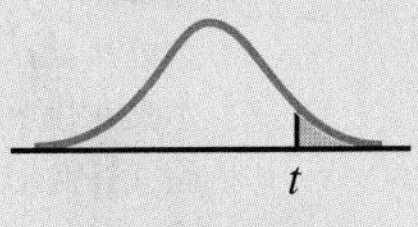

H_a: $\beta_j < 0$ is $P(T \leq t)$

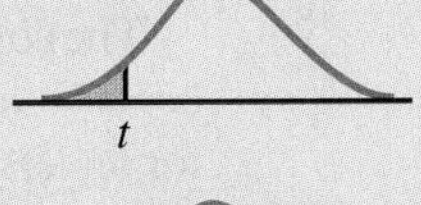

H_a: $\beta_j \neq 0$ is $2P(T \geq |t|)$

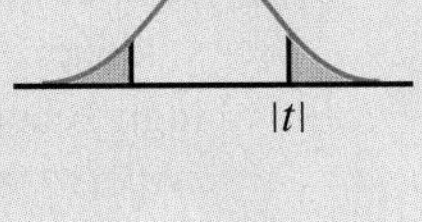

EXAMPLE 11.13 Predicting GPA from High School Grades

CASE 11.2

In Example 11.12, there are $p = 3$ explanatory variables: high school grades HSM, HSS, and HSE in three subjects. We have data on $n = 224$ students. The degrees of freedom for multiple regression are therefore

$$n - p - 1 = 224 - 3 - 1 = 220$$

Figure 11.11 shows multiple regression output from Excel, SPSS, Minitab, and SAS. You see that the regression equation is

$$\widehat{\text{GPA}} = 0.690 + 0.169\text{HSM} + 0.0343\text{HSS} + 0.045\text{HSE}$$

and that the regression standard error is $s = 0.70$.

The outputs also present the t statistic for each regression coefficient and its two-sided P-value. For example, the t statistic for the coefficient of HSM is 4.75 with a very small P-value. The data give strong evidence against the null hypothesis

$$H_0\colon \beta_1 = 0$$

that the population coefficient for high school math grades is zero. We would report this result as $t = 4.75$, $\text{df} = 220$, $P < 0.001$. Three of the four outputs also give the 95% confidence interval for the coefficient β_1. It is $(0.099, 0.239)$. The confidence interval does not include 0, consistent with the fact that the test rejects the null hypothesis at the 5% significance level.

Be very careful in your interpretation of the t tests and confidence intervals for individual regression coefficients. In *simple linear regression,* the model says that $\mu_y = \beta_0 + \beta_1 x$. The null hypothesis $H_0\colon \beta_1 = 0$ says that regression on x is of no value for predicting the response y, or alternatively, that there is no straight-line relationship between x and y. The corresponding hypothesis for the *multiple regression* model $\mu_y = \beta_0 + \beta_1 x_1 + \beta_2 x_2 + \beta_3 x_3$ of Example 11.13 says that x_1 is of no value for predicting y, *given that x_2 and x_3 are also in the model.* That's a very important difference. The outputs in Figure 11.11 show, for example, that the P-value for high school science grades HSS is about $P = 0.36$. That is, HSS does not help us predict GPA, *given that math and English grades are available to use for prediction.* This does *not* mean that science grades cannot help predict college GPA. In a simple linear regression of GPA on HSS, without HSM and HSE present, the regression slope may be highly significant.

The conclusions of inference about any one explanatory variable in multiple regression depend on what other explanatory variables are also in the model. This is a basic principle for understanding multiple regression. The t tests in Figure 11.11 show that high school science grades do not significantly aid prediction of the college GPA of computer science students *if high school math and English grades are also in the model.* On the other hand, high school math grades are highly significant *even when science and English grades are also in the model.*

FIGURE 11.11 Multiple regression output from Excel, SPSS, Minitab, and SAS, for Examples 11.13, 11.14, and 11.15.

SUMMARY OUTPUT

Regression Statistics	
Multiple R	0.45229993
R Square	0.20457523
Adjusted R Square	0.19372853
Standard Error	0.69983913
Observations	224

ANOVA

	df	*SS*	*MS*	*F*	*Significance F*
Regression	3	27.7123313	9.23744377	18.860594	6.3588E-11
Residual	220	107.750458	0.48977481		
Total	223	135.462789			

	Coefficients	*Standard Error*	*t Stat*	*P-value*	*Lower 95%*	*Upper 95%*
Intercept	0.58987662	0.29424324	2.00472446	0.04621816	0.00998041	1.16977282
hsm	0.16856664	0.03549214	4.74940781	3.6784E-06	0.09861854	0.23851475
hss	0.03431557	0.03755888	0.91364725	0.36190243	−0.03970568	0.10833682
hse	0.04510182	0.03869585	1.16554668	0.24505989	−0.03116018	0.12136383

SPSS

Regression

Model Summary

Model	R	R Square	Adjusted R Square	Std. Error of the Estimate
1	.452	.205	.194	.69984

a Predictors: (Constant), HSE, HSM, HSS

ANOVA

Model		Sum of Squares	df	Mean Square	F	Sig.
1	Regression	27.712	3	9.237	18.861	.000
	Residual	107.750	220	.490		
	Total	135.463	223			

a Predictors: (Constant), HSE, HSM, HSS
b Dependent Variable: GPA

Coefficients

		Unstandardized Coefficients		Standardized Coefficients	t	Sig.	95% Confidence Interval for B	
Model		B	Std. Error	Beta			Lower Bound	Upper Bound
1	(Constant)	.590	.294		2.005	.046	.010	1.170
	HSM	.169	.035	.354	4.749	.000	.099	.239
	HSS	3.432E-02	.038	.075	.914	.362	−.040	.108
	HSE	4.510E-02	.039	.087	1.166	.245	−.031	.121

a Dependent Variable: GPA

Minitab

Regression Analysis: gpa versus hsm, hss, hse

```
The regression equation is
gpa = 0.590 + 0.169 hsm + 0.0343 hss + 0.0451 hse

Predictor        Coef     SE Coef        T        P
Constant       0.5899      0.2942     2.00    0.046
hsm           0.16857     0.03549     4.75    0.000
hss           0.03432     0.03756     0.91    0.362
hse           0.04510     0.03870     1.17    0.245

S = 0.699839       R-Sq = 20.5%       R-Sq(adj) = 19.4%

Analysis of Variance

Source            DF        SS       MS       F        P
Regression         3   27.7123   9.2374   18.86    0.000
Residual Error   220  107.7505   0.4898
Total            223  135.4628
```

SAS

The REG Procedure
Model: MODEL1
Dependent Variable: gpa

Analysis of Variance

Source	DF	Sum of Squares	Mean Square	F Value	Pr > F
Model	3	27.71233	9.23744	18.86	< .0001
Error	220	107.75046	0.48977		
Corrected Total	223	135.46279			

Root MSE	0.69984	R-Square	0.2046
Dependent Mean	2.63522	Adj R-Sq	0.1937
Coeff Var	26.55711		

Parameter Estimates

Variable	Label	DF	Parameter Estimate	Standard Error	t Value	Pr > |t|	95% Confidence Limits	
Intercept	Intercept	1	0.58988	0.29424	2.00	0.0462	0.00998	1.16977
hsm	hsm	1	0.16857	0.03549	4.75	< .0001	0.09862	0.23851
hss	hss	1	0.03432	0.03756	0.91	0.3619	–0.03971	0.10834
hse	hse	1	0.04510	0.03870	1.17	0.2451	–0.03116	0.12136

APPLY YOUR KNOWLEDGE

11.37 Read the outputs. CASE 11.2 Carefully examine the outputs from the four software packages given in Figure 11.11. Make a table giving the estimated regression coefficient for high school science, the standard error, the t statistic with its degrees of freedom, and the P-value as reported by each of the packages. What do you conclude about this coefficient?

11.38 The model matters. CASE 11.2 Carry out the simple linear regression of college GPA on high school science grades, HSS. What is the P-value of the t test for the hypothesis that HSS does not help predict GPA? Explain carefully to someone who knows no statistics why the conclusions about HSS here and in the previous exercise differ so greatly.

11.39 A simpler model. CASE 11.2 In the multiple regression analysis using all of HSM, HSS, and HSE, high school science, HSS, appears to be the least helpful (given that the other two explanatory variables are in the model). Do a new analysis using only high school math and high school English to predict college GPA. Give the estimated regression equation for this analysis and compare it with the analysis using all three high school variables as predictors. Summarize the inference results for the coefficients.

Inference about prediction

confidence interval for mean response

prediction interval

Inference about the regression coefficients looks much the same in simple and multiple regression, but there are important differences in interpretation. Inference about prediction also looks much the same, and in this case the interpretation is also the same. We may wish to give a **confidence interval for the mean response** for some specific set of values of the explanatory variables. Or we may want a **prediction interval** for an individual responsefor the same set of specific values.

The distinction between predicting mean and individual response is exactly as in simple regression. The prediction interval is again wider because it must allow for the variation of individual responses about the mean. In most software, the commands for prediction inference are the same for multiple and simple regression. The details of the arithmetic performed by the software are of course more complicated for multiple regression, but this does not affect interpretation of the output.

What about changes in the model, which we saw can greatly influence inference about the regression coefficients? It is often the case that different models give similar predictions. We expect, for example, the predictions of college GPA from HSM and HSE alone will be about the same as predictions based on all of HSM, HSS, and HSE.

APPLY YOUR KNOWLEDGE

11.40 GPA for C+ students. CASE 11.2 Straight-C+ students in high school have HSM $= 5$, HSS $= 5$, and HSE $= 5$. Use your software to give predictions based on all three variables.

(a) Give a 95% confidence interval for the mean college GPA of all straight-C+ computer science students.

(b) Ashlee was a straight-C+ student in high school and is now entering this university planning to major in computer science. Give a 95% prediction interval for Ashlee's GPA after three semesters of college.

11.41 A simpler model. CASE 11.2 Find the two intervals of the previous exercise using the simpler model with just HSM and HSE as explanatory variables. Compare the intervals with those from the previous exercise. Do the two models give similar predictions?

ANOVA table for multiple regression

The basic ideas of the regression ANOVA table are the same in simple and multiple regression. ANOVA expresses variation in the form of sums of squares. It breaks the total variation into two parts, the sum of squares explained by the regression equation and the sum of squares of the residuals. The ANOVA table has the same form except for the degrees of freedom, which reflect the number p of explanatory variables. Here is the ANOVA table for multiple regression:

Source	Degrees of freedom	Sum of squares	Mean square	F
Regression	DFR $= p$	SSR $= \sum(\hat{y}_i - \bar{y})^2$	MSR = SSR/DFR	MSR/MSE
Residual	DFE $= n - p - 1$	SSE $= \sum(y_i - \hat{y}_i)^2$	MSE = SSE/DFE	
Total	DFT $= n - 1$	SST $= \sum(y_i - \bar{y})^2$		

The brief notation introduced in the table uses, for example, MSE for the residual mean square. This is common notation; the "E" stands for "error." Of course, no error has been made. "Error" in this context is just a synonym for "residual."

The degrees of freedom and sums of squares add, just as in simple regression:

$$\text{SST} = \text{SSR} + \text{SSE}$$
$$\text{DFT} = \text{DFR} + \text{DFE}$$

The estimate of the variance σ^2 for our model is again given by the MSE in the ANOVA table. That is, $s^2 = \text{MSE}$.

ANOVA F test

The ratio MSR/MSE is again the statistic for the **ANOVA *F* test.** In simple linear regression the F test from the ANOVA table is equivalent to the two-sided t test of the hypothesis that the slope of the regression line is 0. In the multiple regression setting, the null hypothesis for the F test states that *all* of the regression coefficients (with the exception of the intercept) are 0. One way to write this is

$$H_0\colon \beta_1 = 0 \text{ and } \beta_2 = 0 \text{ and } \cdots \text{ and } \beta_p = 0$$

A shorter way to express this hypothesis is

$$H_0\colon \beta_1 = \beta_2 = \cdots = \beta_p = 0$$

The alternative hypothesis is

$$H_a\colon \text{at least one of the } \beta_j \text{ is not } 0$$

The null hypothesis says that none of the explanatory variables helps explain the response, at least when used in the form expressed by the multiple regression equation. The alternative states that at least one of them is linearly related to the response. As in simple linear regression, large values of F give evidence against H_0. When H_0 is true, F has the $F(p,\ n - p - 1)$ distribution. The degrees of freedom for the F distribution are those associated with the regression and residual terms in the ANOVA table.

Analysis of Variance *F* Test

In the multiple regression model, the hypothesis

$$H_0: \beta_1 = \beta_2 = \cdots = \beta_p = 0$$

versus

$$H_a: \text{at least one of these coefficients is not zero}$$

is tested by the analysis of variance F statistic

$$F = \frac{\text{MSR}}{\text{MSE}}$$

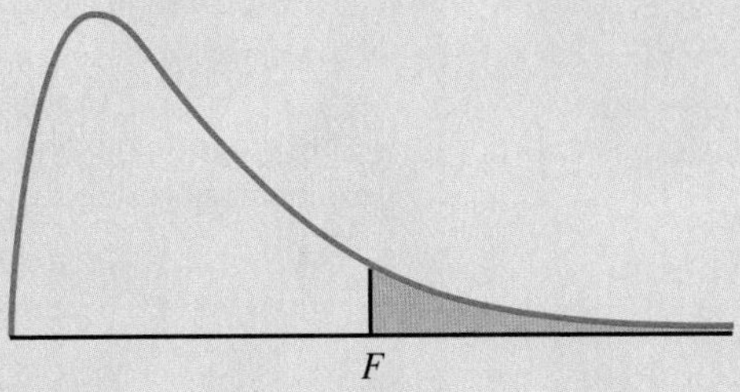

The P-value is the probability that a random variable having the $F(p,\ n-p-1)$ distribution is greater than or equal to the calculated value of the F statistic.

EXAMPLE 11.14 *F* Test for High School Grades

CASE 11.2

Figure 11.11 gives the results of multiple regression analysis using the three high school grade variables to predict GPA. The F statistic is 18.86. The degrees of freedom appear in the ANOVA table. They are 3 and 220. The software packages report the P-value in different forms: Excel, 6.35877E-11; SPSS, .000; Minitab, 0.000; and SAS, <.0001. We would report the results as follows. The three high school grade variables contain information that can be used to predict grade point average ($F = 18.86$, df $= 3$ and 220, $P < 0.0001$).

A significant F test does not tell us which explanatory variables explain the response. It simply allows us to conclude that at least one of the coefficients is not zero. We may want to refine the model by eliminating some variables that do not appear to be useful. On the other hand, if we fail to reject the null hypothesis, we have found no evidence that *any* of the coefficients are not zero. In this case, there is little point in attempting to refine the model.

APPLY YOUR KNOWLEDGE

11.42 *F* test for the model without HSS. Rerun the multiple regression for Case 11.2 using high school math and high school English to predict grade point average. Report the F statistic, the associated degrees of freedom, and the P-value. How do these differ from the corresponding values for the model with the three high school grade predictors? What do you conclude?

CASE 11.2

Squared multiple correlation R^2

For simple linear regression the square r^2 of the sample correlation can be written as the ratio of SSR to SST. We interpret r^2 as the proportion of variation in y explained by linear regression on x. A similar statistic is important in multiple regression.

The Squared Multiple Regression Correlation

The statistic

$$R^2 = \frac{\text{SSR}}{\text{SST}} = \frac{\sum(\hat{y}_i - \bar{y})^2}{\sum(y_i - \bar{y})^2}$$

is the proportion of the variation of the response variable y that is explained by the explanatory variables $x_1, x_2, \ldots, x_p$ in a multiple linear regression.

multiple regression correlation coefficient

Often, R^2 is multiplied by 100 and expressed as a percent. The square root of R^2, called the **multiple regression correlation coefficient,** is the correlation between the observations y_i and the predicted values $\hat{y}_i$.

EXAMPLE 11.15 R^2 for High School Grades

CASE 11.2

Figure 11.11 gives the results of multiple regression analysis using the three high school grade variables to predict GPA. The value of the R^2 statistic is given as 0.205 or 20.5%. Be sure that you can find this statistic on each of the four outputs. We conclude that about 20% of the variation in grade point average can be explained by the high school grades.

The F statistic for the multiple regression of college GPA on HSM, HSS, and HSE is highly significant, $P < 0.0001$. There is strong evidence of a relationship between high school grades and success in college. The squared multiple correlation, however, gives us a different picture. High school grades explain only about 20% of the variability in GPA. The other 80% is represented by the RESIDUAL term in our model and is due to differences among the students that are not measured by their high school grades. These may include attending class regularly, doing homework carefully and on time, and staying sober. Once again, we have an illustration of the familiar and important distinction between the *statistical significance* of an effect and its *size*.

APPLY YOUR KNOWLEDGE

11.43 R^2 for different models. Use each of the following sets of explanatory variables to predict GPA: (a) HSM, HSS, HSE; (b) HSM, HSE; (c) HSM, HSS; (d) HSS, HSE; (e) HSM. Make a table giving the model and the value of R^2 for each. Summarize what you have found.

CASE 11.2

Inference for a collection of regression coefficients

We have studied two different types of significance tests for multiple regression. The F test examines the hypothesis that the coefficients for *all* of the explanatory variables are zero. On the other hand, we used t tests to examine *individual* coefficients. (For simple linear regression with one explanatory variable, these are two different ways to examine the same question.) Often we are interested in an intermediate setting: does a set of explanatory variables contribute to explaining the response, given that another set of explanatory variables is also available? We formulate such questions as follows: start with the multiple regression model that contains all the explanatory variables and test the hypothesis that a set of the coefficients are all zero.

F Test for a Collection of Regression Coefficients

In the multiple regression model with p explanatory variables, the hypothesis

$$H_0\text{: } q \text{ specific explanatory variables all have zero coefficients}$$

versus

$$H_a\text{: at least one of these coefficients is not zero}$$

is tested by an F statistic. The degrees of freedom are q and $n - p - 1$. The P-value is the probability that a random variable having the $F(q,\ n - p - 1)$ distribution is greater than or equal to the calculated value of the F statistic.

Some software allows you to directly state and test hypotheses of this form. Here is a way to find the F statistic by doing two regression runs.

1. Regress y on all p explanatory variables. Read the R^2-value from the output and call it R_1^2.
2. Then regress y on just the $p - q$ variables that remain after you remove the q variables from the model. Again read the R^2-value and call it R_2^2. This will be smaller than R_1^2 because removing variables can only decrease R^2.
3. The test statistic is

$$F = \left(\frac{n - p - 1}{q}\right)\left(\frac{R_1^2 - R_2^2}{1 - R_1^2}\right)$$

with q and $n - p - 1$ degrees of freedom.

EXAMPLE 11.16 Do SAT Scores Add Predictive Ability?

CASE 11.2

We have to this point used only high school grades to predict college GPA. The data also include the students' SAT scores. We can ask

Do SAT scores help predict GPA, given that high school grades are included in the model?

The same question in another form is

> If we start with a model containing both high school grades and SAT scores, does removing SAT scores reduce our ability to predict GPA?

The first regression run includes $p = 5$ explanatory variables: HSM, HSS, HSE, SATM, and SATV. The R^2 for this model is $R_1^2 = 0.2115$.

Now remove the $q = 2$ variables SATM and SATV and redo the regression with just HSM, HSS, and HSE as explanatory variables. We have seen that for this model we get $R_2^2 = 0.2046$.

The test statistic is

$$F = \left(\frac{n-p-1}{q}\right)\left(\frac{R_1^2 - R_2^2}{1 - R_1^2}\right)$$

$$= \left(\frac{224-5-1}{2}\right)\left(\frac{0.2115 - 0.2046}{1 - 0.2115}\right) = 0.95$$

The degrees of freedom are $q = 2$ and $n - p - 1 = 224 - 5 - 1 = 218$.

The closest entry in Table E has 2 and 200 degrees of freedom. For this distribution we would need $F = 3.04$ or larger for significance at the 5% level. Thus, $P > 0.05$. Software gives $P = 0.39$. SAT scores do not contribute significantly to explaining GPA when high school grades are already in the model.

The hypothesis test in Example 11.16 asks about the coefficients of the SAT scores in a model that also contains the high school grades as explanatory variables. If we start with a different model, we may get a different answer. For example, we would not be surprised to find that SAT scores help explain GPA in a model with only the two SAT scores as explanatory variables. *Individual regression coefficients, their standard errors, and significance tests are meaningful only when interpreted in the context of the other explanatory variables in the model.*

APPLY YOUR KNOWLEDGE

11.44 Are SAT scores useful predictors of GPA? CASE 11.2 Run the multiple regression to predict GPA using the three high school variables and the two SAT scores as explanatory variables. Then run the model using only the SAT scores.

(a) Example 11.16 claims that R^2 for the first model is 0.2115. Does your work confirm this?

(b) Make a table giving the SAT coefficients and their standard errors, t statistics, and P-values for both models. Explain carefully how your assessment of the value of SAT scores as predictors of GPA depends on whether or not the high school scores are in the model.

11.45 Are grades useful when SAT scores are available? CASE 11.2 We saw that the SAT scores are not useful in a model that contains the high school grade variables. Now, let's examine the other version of this question. Do the three high school grade variables help explain GPA in a model that contains the two SAT variables? Run the models with all five predictors and with only the SAT scores. Compare the values of R^2. Perform the F test and give its degrees of freedom and P-value. Carefully state a conclusion about the usefulness of high school grades when SAT scores are available.

SECTION 11.2 SUMMARY

- The statistical model for **multiple linear regression** with response variable y and p explanatory variables $x_1, x_2, \ldots, x_p$ is

$$y_i = \beta_0 + \beta_1 x_{i1} + \beta_2 x_{i2} + \cdots + \beta_p x_{ip} + \epsilon_i$$

where $i = 1, 2, \ldots, n$. The deviations ϵ_i are independent Normal random variables with mean 0 and a common standard deviation σ. The **parameters** of the model are $\beta_0, \beta_1, \beta_2, \ldots, \beta_p$, and σ.

- The β's are estimated by the coefficients $b_0, b_1, b_2, \ldots, b_p$ of the multiple regression equation fitted to the data by **the method of least squares.** The parameter σ is estimated by the **regression standard error**

$$s = \sqrt{\text{MSE}} = \sqrt{\frac{\sum e_i^2}{n - p - 1}}$$

where the e_i are the **residuals,**

$$e_i = y_i - \hat{y}_i$$

- A **level C confidence interval for the regression coefficient** β_j is

$$b_j \pm t^* \text{SE}_{b_j}$$

where t^* is the value for the $t(n - p - 1)$ density curve with area C between $-t^*$ and t^*.

- Tests of the hypothesis H_0: $\beta_j = 0$ are based on the **individual t statistic:**

$$t = \frac{b_j}{\text{SE}_{b_j}}$$

and the $t(n - p - 1)$ distribution.

- The estimate b_j of β_j and the test and confidence interval for β_j are all based on a specific multiple linear regression model. The results of all of these procedures change if other explanatory variables are added to or deleted from the model.

- The **ANOVA table** for a multiple linear regression gives the degrees of freedom, sum of squares, and mean squares for the regression and residual sources of variation. The **ANOVA F statistic** is the ratio MSR/MSE and is used to test the null hypothesis

$$H_0\text{: } \beta_1 = \beta_2 = \cdots = \beta_p = 0$$

If H_0 is true, this statistic has the $F(p,\ n - p - 1)$ distribution.

- The **squared multiple correlation** is given by the expression

$$R^2 = \frac{\text{SSR}}{\text{SST}}$$

and is interpreted as the proportion of the variability in the response variable y that is explained by the explanatory variables $x_1, x_2, \ldots, x_p$ in the multiple linear regression.

- The null hypothesis that a **collection of q explanatory variables** all have coefficients equal to zero is tested by an **F statistic** with q degrees of freedom in the numerator and $n - p - 1$ degrees of freedom in the denominator. This statistic can be computed from the squared multiple correlations for the model with all of the explanatory variables included (R_1^2) and the model with the q variables deleted (R_2^2):

$$F = \left(\frac{n-p-1}{q}\right)\left(\frac{R_1^2 - R_2^2}{1 - R_1^2}\right)$$

SECTION 11.2 Exercises

For Exercises 11.37 to 11.39, see page 643; for 11.40 and 11.41, see page 643; for 11.42, see page 645; for 11.43, see page 646; and for 11.44 and 11.45, see page 648.

11.46 Pension benefits. The defined-benefit (DB) pension plan guarantees a certain income to employees when they retire. In contrast, a defined-contribution (DC) plan specifies that a regular contribution will be made to an investment account. Upon retirement, the employee receives the income from the investment. The DB has been the traditional plan but in recent years there has been a shift toward DC plans. One study examined the change in the proportion of DC-covered employees in 40 different industries.[9]

The researchers who conducted the study used multiple regression methods to examine the effects of various explanatory variables on the change in the proportion of individuals covered by DC plans over a 20-year period. One set of variables included in the models were classified as "supply-side" factors that relate to changes in firm characteristics. One of these focused on quantifying shorter-term employment relationships using the change in the proportion of workers with fewer than 5 years with the company. They called this variable P5. Variables such as age, gender, and region of residence were included in the model to control for these factors. A total of 30 variables were included.

(a) In a model to predict the change in the proportion of DC plans, the regression coefficient for P5 is 0.625 with a standard error of 0.189. Construct the t statistic for testing the null hypothesis that the coefficient for P5 is zero. Carry out the test and summarize the result.

(b) Give a 95% confidence interval for the coefficient for P5. From your calculations in part (a) of this exercise, would you expect the interval to include zero? Explain your answer.

11.47 Decreases in DB plans. Refer to the previous exercise. A model for the change in DB plans was also analyzed. The coefficient for P5 in this model was -1.186 with a standard error of 0.133. Answer the questions in parts (a) and (b) of the previous exercise for this analysis.

11.48 Do the defined-contribution results and the defined-benefit results agree? Refer to the previous two exercises. Summarize the results and interpret the signs for the coefficient for P5 in the two models. Do the results appear to be consistent? Explain your answer.

11.49 Interpret the "demand-side" explanatory variables. Refer to the previous three exercises. Another set of variables included in the model were classified as "demand-side" factors that relate to the changing needs of individuals in the labor force. One of these was the change in the proportion of dual-earner couples. The coefficient in the DC model was -0.986 with a standard error of 0.118, while the coefficient in the DB model was 0.466 with a standard error of 0.167. Using the previous three exercises as a guide, write a short report summarizing these results.

11.50 Confidence intervals and significance tests. In each of the following settings, give a 95% confidence interval for the coefficients of x_1 and x_2.

(a) $n = 25$, $\hat{y} = 10.6 + 12.1x_1 + 17.3x_2$, $SE_{b_1} = 7.2$, and $SE_{b_2} = 4.1$.

(b) $n = 103$, $\hat{y} = 15.6 + 12.1x_1 + 7.3x_2$, $SE_{b_1} = 7.2$, and $SE_{b_2} = 4.1$.

(c) For each of the settings in parts (a) and (b), test the null hypotheses that each of the two coefficients is zero versus the two-sided alternative.

11.51 What's wrong? In each of the following situations, explain what is wrong and why.

(a) The multiple correlation gives the proportion of the variation in the response variable that is explained by the explanatory variables.

(b) In a multiple regression with a sample size of 50 and 4 explanatory variables, the test statistic for the null hypothesis H_0: $b_2 = 0$ is a t statistic that follows the $t(45)$ distribution when the null hypothesis is true.

(c) One of the assumptions for multiple regression is that the distribution of each explanatory variable is Normal.

11.52 Inference basics. You run a multiple regression with 66 cases and 5 explanatory variables.

(a) What are the degrees of freedom for the F statistic for testing the null hypothesis that all five of the regression coefficients for the explanatory variables are zero?

(b) Software output gives MSE = 36. What is the estimate of the standard deviation σ of the model?

(c) The output gives the estimate of the regression coefficient for the first explanatory variable as 12.5 with a standard error of 2.4. Find a 95% confidence interval for the true value of this coefficient.

(d) Test the null hypothesis that the regression coefficient for the first explanatory variable is zero. Give the test statistic, the degrees of freedom, the P-value, and your conclusion.

11.53 Inference basics. You run a multiple regression with 63 cases and 2 explanatory variables. The ANOVA table includes the sums of squares SSR = 16 and SSE = 120.

(a) Find the F statistic for testing the null hypothesis that the regression coefficients for the 2 explanatory variables are all zero. Carry out the significance test and report the results.

(b) What is the value of R^2 for this model? Explain what this number tells us.

11.54 Bank auto loans. Banks charge different interest rates for different loans. A random sample of 2229 loans made by banks for the purchase of new automobiles was studied to identify variables that explain the interest rate charged. A multiple regression was run with interest rate as the response variable and 13 explanatory variables.[10]

(a) The F statistic reported is 71.34. State the null and alternative hypotheses for this statistic. Give the degrees of freedom and the P-value for this test. What do you conclude?

(b) The value of R^2 is 0.297. What percent of the variation in interest rates is explained by the 13 explanatory variables?

11.55 Bank auto loans, continued. Table 11.3 gives the coefficients for the fitted model and the individual t statistic for each explanatory variable in the study described in the previous exercise. The t-values are given without the sign, assuming that all tests are two-sided.

TABLE 11.3 Regression coefficients and t statistics for Exercise 11.55

Variable	b	t
Intercept	15.47	
Loan size (in dollars)	−0.0015	10.30
Length of loan (in months)	−0.906	4.20
Percent down payment	−0.522	8.35
Cosigner (0 = no, 1 = yes)	−0.009	3.02
Unsecured loan (0 = no, 1 = yes)	0.034	2.19
Total payments (borrower's monthly installment debt)	0.100	1.37
Total income (borrower's total monthly income)	−0.170	2.37
Bad credit report (0 = no, 1 = yes)	0.012	1.99
Young borrower (0 = older than 25, 1 = 25 or younger)	0.027	2.85
Male borrower (0 = female, 1 = male)	−0.001	0.89
Married (0 = no, 1 = yes)	−0.023	1.91
Own home (0 = no, 1 = yes)	−0.011	2.73
Years at current address	−0.124	4.21

(a) State the null and alternative hypotheses tested by an individual t statistic. What are the degrees of freedom for these t statistics? What values of t will lead to rejection of the null hypothesis at the 5% level?

(b) Which of the explanatory variables are significantly different from zero in this model? Explain carefully what you conclude when an individual t statistic is not significant.

(c) The signs of many of the coefficients are what we might expect before looking at the data. For example, the negative coefficient for loan size means that larger loans get a smaller interest rate. This is reasonable. Examine the signs of each of the statistically significant coefficients and give a short explanation of what they tell us.

11.56 Auto dealer loans. The previous two exercises describe auto loans made directly by a bank. The researchers also looked at 5664 loans made indirectly, that is, through an auto dealer. They again used multiple regression to predict the interest rate using the same set of 13 explanatory variables.

(a) The F statistic reported is 27.97. State the null and alternative hypotheses for this statistic. Give the degrees of freedom and the P-value for this test. What do you conclude?

(b) The value of R^2 is 0.141. What percent of the variation in interest rates is explained by the 13 explanatory variables? Compare this value with the percent explained for direct loans in Exercise 11.54.

11.57 Auto dealer loans, continued. Table 11.4 gives the estimated regression coefficient and individual t statistic for each explanatory variable in the setting of the previous exercise. The t-values are given without the sign, assuming that all tests are two-sided.

(a) What are the degrees of freedom of any individual t statistic for this model? What values of t are significant at the 5% level? Explain carefully what significance tells us about an explanatory variable.

(b) Which of the explanatory variables are significantly different from zero in this model?

(c) The signs of many of these coefficients are what we might expect before looking at the data. For example, the negative coefficient for loan size means that larger loans get a smaller interest rate. This is reasonable. Examine the signs of each of the statistically significant coefficients and give a short explanation of what they tell us.

11.58 Direct versus indirect loans. The previous four exercises describe a study of loans for buying new cars. The authors conclude that banks take higher risks with indirect loans because they do not take into account borrower characteristics when setting the loan rate. Explain how the results of the multiple regressions lead to this conclusion.

TABLE 11.4 Regression coefficients and t statistics for Exercise 11.57

Variable	b	t
Intercept	15.89	
Loan size (in dollars)	−0.0029	17.40
Length of loan (in months)	−1.098	5.63
Percent down payment	−0.308	4.92
Cosigner (0 = no, 1 = yes)	−0.001	1.41
Unsecured loan (0 = no, 1 = yes)	0.028	2.83
Total payments (borrower's monthly installment debt)	−0.513	1.37
Total income (borrower's total monthly income)	0.078	0.75
Bad credit report (0 = no, 1 = yes)	0.039	1.76
Young borrower (0 = older than 25, 1 = 25 or younger)	−0.036	1.33
Male borrower (0 = female, 1 = male)	−0.179	1.03
Married (0 = no, 1 = yes)	−0.043	1.61
Own home (0 = no, 1 = yes)	−0.047	1.59
Years at current address	−0.086	1.73

11.59 Model for a subpopulation. In Example 11.12 we discussed the model

$$\mu_{\text{GPA}} = \beta_0 + \beta_1\text{HSM} + \beta_2\text{HSS} + \beta_3\text{HSE}$$

for predicting grade point average using high school grades.

(a) Give the model for the subpopulation mean GPA for students having high school grade scores HSM = 8(B+), HSS = 9 (A−), and HSE = 7(B).

(b) Using the parameter estimates given in Figure 11.11 (page 641), estimate the mean GPA for this subpopulation of students. Briefly explain what your numerical answer means.

11.60 CASE 11.2 **Another subpopulation.** Answer parts (a) and (b) of the previous exercise for the subpopulation of students having high school grade scores HSM = 7 (B), HSS = 6 (B−), and HSE = 9 (A−).

11.61 Faculty salaries. Data on the salaries of full professors in an engineering department at a large midwestern university are given below. The salaries are for the academic years 2002–2003 and 2005–2006. The data also include years in rank as a full professor.

Years in rank	2002 salary ($)	2005 salary ($)
3	95,600	113,400
4	93,800	114,500
5	104,200	113,300
6	119,000	134,000
6	100,600	115,000
7	108,200	128,000
7	92,100	100,800
8	106,700	115,700
10	102,300	144,200
10	112,500	133,100
11	113,100	131,100
13	122,500	134,400
15	121,100	130,000
15	124,000	133,700
35	153,300	172,800
36	138,500	144,500

(a) Write the model that you would use for a multiple regression to predict salary in 2005 from salary in 2002 and years in rank.

(b) What are the parameters of your model?

(c) Run the multiple regression and give the estimates of the model parameters.

(d) Test the hypothesis that the coefficients for salary in 2002 and years in rank are both zero. Give the test statistic with degrees of freedom and the P-value. What do you conclude?

(e) What is the value of R^2?

(f) Give the results of the hypothesis test for the coefficient for salary in 2002. Include the test statistic, degrees of freedom, and the P-value. Do the same for years in rank. Summarize your conclusions from these two tests.

11.62 Examine the assumptions. We now ask whether the data of the previous exercise meet the requirements of the multiple regression model. Find the residuals.

(a) Examine the distribution of the residuals. Summarize what you have found.

(b) Plot the residuals versus each of the explanatory variables. Describe the plots. Does your analysis suggest that the model assumptions may not be reasonable for this problem? Why?

11.63 Compare regression coefficients. Using the faculty salary data in Exercise 11.61, do the regression to predict salary in 2005 using only years in rank.

(a) Give the fitted regression equation.

(b) Summarize the results of the significance test for the coefficient for years in rank.

(c) In Exercise 11.61 you found a coefficient for years in rank and reported the results of a significance test for this coefficient. Give those results here and explain why they differ from what you found in parts (a) and (b) of this exercise.

11.64 Compensation and human capital. A study of bank branch manager compensation collected data on the salaries of 82 managers at branches of a large eastern U.S. bank.[11] Multiple regression models were used to predict how much these branch managers were paid. The researchers examined two sets of explanatory variables. The first set were variables that measured characteristics of the branch and the position of the branch manager. These were number of branch employees, a variable constructed to represent how much competition the branch faced, market share, return on assets, an efficiency ranking, and the rank of the manager. A second set of variables were called human capital variables and measured characteristics of the manager. These were experience in industry, gender, years of schooling, and age. For the multiple regression using all of the explanatory variables, the value of R^2 was 0.77. When the human capital variables were deleted, R^2 fell to 0.06. Test the null hypothesis that the coefficients for the human capital variables are all zero in the model that includes all of the explanatory variables. Give the test statistic with its degrees of freedom and P-value, and give a short summary of your conclusion in nontechnical language.

11.3 Multiple Regression Model Building

In Case 11.2 we examined how high school grades and SAT scores could be used to predict the college grade point averages of a group of students. We saw that both sets of variables contain information that can be used for predicting GPA. However, when we add the SAT scores to a model containing the high school grades, our ability to predict improves very little.

model building

Often we have many explanatory variables, and our goal is to use these to explain the variation in the response variable. A model using just a few of the variables often predicts about as well as the model using all the explanatory variables. We may also find that the reciprocal of a variable is a better choice than the variable itself, or that including the square of an explanatory variable improves prediction. How can we find a good model? That is the **model building** issue. A complete discussion would be quite lengthy, so we will be content to illustrate some of the basic ideas with a Case Study.

CASE 11.3 PRICES OF HOMES

People wanting to buy a home can find information on the Internet about homes for sale in their community. We will work with online data for homes for sale in Lafayette and West Lafayette, Indiana.[12] The response variable is Price, the asking price of a home. The online data contain the following explanatory variables: (a) SqFt, the number of square feet for the home, (b) BedRooms, the number of bedrooms, (c) Baths, the number of bathrooms, (d) Garage, the number of cars that can fit in the garage, and (e) Zip, the postal zip code for the address. There are 504 homes in the data set.

The analysis starts with understanding the variables and with initial data analysis. Here is a short summary of this work.

Price, as we expect, has a right-skewed distribution. The mean (in thousands of dollars) is \$158 and the median is \$130. There is one high outlier at \$830, which we will delete as unusual in this location. Remember that a skewed distribution for Price does not itself violate the conditions for multiple regression. The model requires that the *residuals* from the fitted regression equation be approximately Normal. We will have to examine how well this condition is satisfied when we build our regression model.

BedRooms ranges from 1 to 5. The Web site uses 5 for all homes with 5 or more bedrooms. The data contain just one home with 1 bedroom. **Baths** includes both full baths (with showers or bathtubs) and half baths (which lack bathing facilities). Typical values are 1, 1.5, 2, and 2.5. **Garage** has values of 0, 1, 2, and 3. The Web site uses the value 3 when 3 or more vehicles can fit in the garage. There are 50 homes that can fit 3 or more vehicles into their garage (or possibly garages). The data set has begun a process of combining some values of these variables, such as 5 or more bedrooms and garages that hold 3 or more vehicles. We will continue this process as we build models for predicting Price.

Zip describes location, traditionally the most important explanatory variable for house prices, but Zip is a quite crude description because a single zip code covers a broad area. All of the postal zip codes in this community have 4790 as the first four digits. The fifth digit is coded as the variable Zip. The possible values are 1, 4, 5, 6, and 9. There is only one home with zip code 47901. We will treat this home as a special case and will not analyze it with the rest of the data.

SqFt, the number of square feet for the home, is a quantitative variable that we expect to strongly influence Price. We will start our analysis by examining the relationship between Price and this explanatory variable. To control for location, we start by examining only the homes in zip code 47904, corresponding to Zip = 4. Most homes for sale in this area are moderately priced.

EXAMPLE 11.17 Price and Square Feet

CASE 11.3

Table 11.5 gives data for the 44 homes for sale in zip code 47904. Preliminary examination of Price reveals that there are a few homes with prices that are somewhat high relative to the others. Similarly, some values for SqFt are relatively high. Because we do not want our analysis to be overly influenced by these homes, we exclude any home with Price greater than

TABLE 11.5 Homes for sale in zip code 47904

Id	Price ($)	SqFt	BedRooms	Baths	Garage	Id	Price ($)	SqFt	BedRooms	Baths	Garage
01	52,900	932	1	1.0	0	23	75,000	2188	4	1.5	2
02	62,900	760	2	1.0	0	24	76,900	1400	3	1.5	2
03	64,900	900	2	1.0	0	25	81,900	796	2	1.0	2
04	69,900	1504	3	1.0	0	26	84,500	864	2	1.0	2
05	76,900	1030	3	2.0	0	27	84,900	1350	3	1.0	2
06	87,900	1092	3	1.0	0	28	89,600	1504	3	1.0	2
07	94,900	1288	4	2.0	0	29	87,000	1200	2	1.0	2
08	52,000	1370	3	1.0	1	30	89,000	876	2	1.0	2
09	72,500	698	2	1.0	1	31	89,000	1112	3	2.0	2
10	72,900	766	2	1.0	1	32	93,900	1230	3	1.5	2
11	73,900	777	2	1.0	1	33	96,000	1350	3	1.5	2
12	73,900	912	2	1.0	1	34	99,900	1292	3	2.0	2
13	81,500	925	3	1.0	1	35	104,900	1600	3	1.5	2
14	82,900	941	2	1.0	1	36	114,900	1630	3	1.5	2
15	84,900	1108	3	1.5	1	37	124,900	1620	3	2.5	2
16	84,900	1040	2	1.0	1	38	124,900	1923	3	3.0	2
17	89,900	1300	3	2.0	1	39	129,000	2090	3	1.5	2
18	92,800	1026	3	1.0	1	40	173,900	1608	2	2.0	2
19	94,900	1560	3	1.0	1	41	179,900	2250	5	2.5	2
20	114,900	1581	3	1.5	1	42	199,500	1855	2	2.0	2
21	119,900	1576	3	2.5	1	43	80,000	1600	3	1.0	3
22	65,000	853	3	1.0	2	44	129,000	2296	3	2.5	3

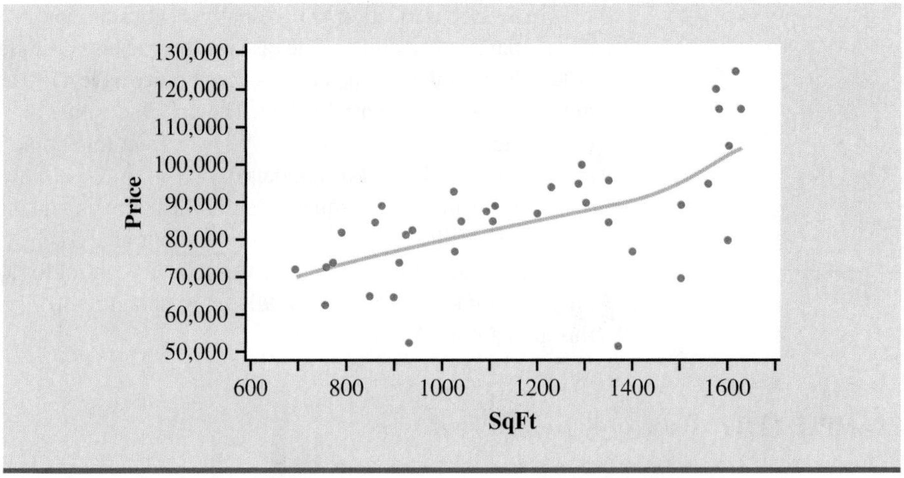

FIGURE 11.12 Plot of price versus square feet for Example 11.17.

\$150,000 and any home with SqFt greater than 1800 ft^2. Seven homes were excluded by these criteria.

Figure 11.12 displays the relationship between SqFt and Price. We have added a "smooth" fit to help us see the pattern. The relationship is approximately linear but curves up somewhat for the higher-priced homes.

Because the relationship is approximately linear and we expect SqFt to be an important explanatory variable, let's start by examining the simple linear regression of Price on SqFt.

EXAMPLE 11.18 Regression of Price on Square Feet

CASE 11.3

Figure 11.13 gives the regression output. The number of degrees of freedom in the "Corrected Total" line in the ANOVA table is 36. This is correct for the $n = 37$ homes that remain after we excluded 7 of the original 44. The fitted model is

$$\widehat{\text{Price}} = 45{,}298 + 34.32\ \text{SqFt}$$

The coefficient for SqFt is statistically significant ($t = 4.57$, df $= 35$, $P < 0.0001$). Each additional square foot of area raises selling prices by \$34.32 on the average. From the R^2 we see that 37.3% of the variation in the home prices is explained by a linear relationship with square feet. We hope that multiple regression will allow us to improve on this first attempt to explain selling price.

APPLY YOUR KNOWLEDGE

11.65 Distributions. Make stemplots of the prices and of the square feet for the 44 homes in Table 11.5. Do the 7 homes excluded in Example 11.17 appear unusual for this location?

CASE 11.3

11.66 Plot the residuals. Obtain the residuals from the simple linear regression in the above example and plot them versus SqFt. Describe the plot. Does it suggest that the relationship might be curved?

CASE 11.3

FIGURE 11.13 Linear regression output for predicting price using square feet, for Example 11.18.

Analysis of Variance

Source	DF	Sum of Squares	Mean Square	F Value	Pr > F
Model	1	3780229462	3780229462	20.86	<.0001
Error	35	6343998647	181257104		
Corrected Total	36	10124228108			

Root MSE	13463	R-Square	0.3734
Dependent Mean	85524	Adj R-Sq	0.3555
Coeff Var	15.74193		

Parameter Estimates

Variable	Label	DF	Parameter Estimate	Standard Error	t Value	Pr > |t|
Intercept	Intercept	1	45298	9082.26322	4.99	<.0001
SqFt	SqFt	1	34.32362	7.51591	4.57	<.0001

11.67 Predicted values. CASE 11.3 Use the simple linear regression equation to obtain the predicted price for a home that has 1000 ft^2. Do the same for a home that has 1500 ft^2.

Models for curved relationships

Figure 11.12 suggests that the relationship between SqFt and Price may be slightly curved. One simple kind of curved relationship is a quadratic function. To model a quadratic function with multiple regression, create a new variable that is the square of the explanatory variable and include it in the regression model. There are now $p = 2$ explanatory variables, x and x^2. The model is

$$y = \beta_0 + \beta_1 x + \beta_2 x^2 + \epsilon$$

with the usual conditions on the ϵ_i.

EXAMPLE 11.19 Quadratic Regression of Price on Square Feet

CASE 11.3

To predict price using a quadratic function of square feet, first create a new variable by squaring each value of SqFt. Call this variable SqFt2. Figure 11.14 displays the output for multiple regression of Price on SqFt and SqFt2. The fitted model is

$$\widehat{\text{Price}} = 81{,}273 - 30.14\,\text{SqFt} + 0.0271\,\text{SqFt2}$$

This model explains 38.6% of the variation in Price, little more than the 37.3% explained by simple linear regression of Price on SqFt. The coefficient of SqFt2 is not significant ($t = 0.84$, df $= 34$, $P = 0.41$). That is, the squared term does not significantly improve the fit when the SqFt term is present. We conclude that adding SqFt2 to our model is not helpful.

FIGURE 11.14 Quadratic regression output for predicting price using square feet, for Example 11.19.

Analysis of Variance

Source	DF	Sum of Squares	Mean Square	F Value	Pr > F
Model	2	3910030335	1955015167	10.70	0.0002
Error	34	6214197773	182770523		
Corrected Total	36	10124228108			

Root MSE	13519	R-Square	0.3862
Dependent Mean	85524	Adj R-Sq	0.3501
Coeff Var	15.80751		

Parameter Estimates

Variable	Label	DF	Parameter Estimate	Standard Error	t Value	Pr > |t|
Intercept	Intercept	1	81273	43653	1.86	0.0713
SqFt	SqFt	1	–30.13753	76.86278	–0.39	0.6974
SqFt2		1	0.02710	0.03216	0.84	0.4053

The output in Figure 11.14 is a good example of the need for care in interpreting multiple regression. The individual t tests for *both* SqFt and SqFt2 are not significant. Yet the overall F test for the null hypothesis that both coefficients are zero *is* significant ($F = 10.70$, df $= 2$ and 34, $P < 0.0002$). To resolve this apparent contradiction, remember that a t test assesses the contribution of a single variable, *given that the other variables are present in the model.* Once either SqFt or SqFt2 is present, the other contributes very little. This is a consequence of the fact that these two variables are highly correlated. This phenomenon is called **collinearity** or **multicollinearity.** In extreme cases collinearity can cause numerical instabilities, and the results of the regression calculations can become very inaccurate. Although we can dispense with either one of the two explanatory variables, the F test tells us that we cannot drop both of them. It is natural to keep SqFt and drop its square, SqFt2.

collinearity
multicollinearity

Multiple regression can fit a *polynomial* model of any degree:

$$y = \beta_0 + \beta_1 x + \beta_2 x^2 + \cdots + \beta_k x^k + \epsilon$$

In general, we include all powers up to the highest power in the model. A relationship that curves first up and then down, for example, might be described by a cubic model with explanatory variables x, x^2, and x^3. Other transformations of the explanatory variable, such as the square root and the logarithm, can also be used to model curved relationships.

APPLY YOUR KNOWLEDGE

11.68 The relationship between SqFt and SqFt2. Using the data set for Example 11.19, plot SqFt2 versus SqFt. Describe the relationship. We know that it is not linear, but is it approximately linear? What is the correlation between SqFt and SqFt2? The plot and correlation demonstrate that these variables are collinear and explain why neither of them contributes much to a multiple regression once the other is present. CASE 11.3

11.69 Predicted values. Use the quadratic regression equation in Example 11.19 to predict the price of a home that has 1000 ft^2. Do the same for a home that has 1500 ft^2. Compare these predictions with the ones from an analysis that uses only SqFt as an explanatory variable.

CASE 11.3

Models with categorical explanatory variables

Although adding the square of SqFt failed to improve our model significantly, Figure 11.12 does suggest that the price rises a bit more steeply for larger homes. Perhaps some of these homes have other desirable characteristics that increase the price. Let's examine another explanatory variable.

EXAMPLE 11.20 Price and the Number of Bedrooms

CASE 11.3

Figure 11.15 gives a plot of Price versus BedRooms. We see that there appears to be a curved relationship. However, all but two of the homes have either two or three bedrooms. One home has one bedroom and another has four. These two cases are why the relationship appears to be curved. To avoid this situation we will group the four-bedroom home with those that have three bedrooms (BedRooms = 3) and the one-bedroom home with the homes that have two bedrooms.

The price of the four-bedroom home is in the middle of the distribution of the prices for the three-bedroom homes. On the other hand, the one-bedroom home has the lowest price of all the homes in the data set. This observation may require special attention later.

"Number of bedrooms" is now a *categorical variable* that places homes in two groups: one/two bedrooms and three/four bedrooms. Software often allows you to simply declare that a variable is categorical. Then the values for the two groups don't matter. We could use the values 2 and 3 for the two groups. If you work directly with the variable, however, it is better to indicate whether or not the home has three or more bedrooms. We will take the "number of bedrooms" categorical variable to be Bed3 = 1 if the home has three or more bedrooms and Bed3 = 0 if it does not. Bed3 is called an *indicator variable*.

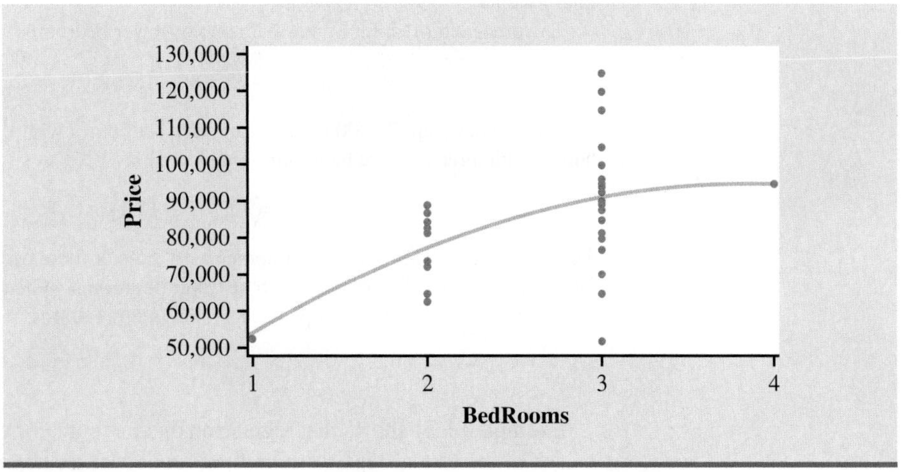

FIGURE 11.15 Plot of price versus the number of bedrooms, for Example 11.20.

Indicator Variables

An indicator variable is a variable with the values 0 and 1. To use a categorical variable that has I possible values in a multiple regression, create $K = I - 1$ indicator variables to use as the explanatory variables. This can be done in many different ways. Here is one common choice:

$$X1 = \begin{cases} 1 & \text{if the categorical variable has the first value} \\ 0 & \text{otherwise} \end{cases}$$

$$X2 = \begin{cases} 1 & \text{if the categorical variable has the second value} \\ 0 & \text{otherwise} \end{cases}$$

$$\vdots$$

$$XK = \begin{cases} 1 & \text{if the categorical variable has the next to last value} \\ 0 & \text{otherwise} \end{cases}$$

We need only $I - 1$ variables to code I different values because the last value is identified by "all $I - 1$ indicator variables are 0."

EXAMPLE 11.21 Price and the Number of Bedrooms

CASE 11.3

Figure 11.16 displays the output for the regression of Price on the indicator variable Bed3. This model explains 19% of the variation in price. This is about one-half of the 37.3% explained by SqFt, but it suggests that Bed3 may be a useful explanatory variable.

The fitted equation is

$$\widehat{\text{Price}} = 75{,}700 + 15{,}146\text{Bed3}$$

The coefficient for Bed3 is significantly different from 0 ($t = 2.88$, df $= 35$, $P = 0.0068$). This coefficient is the slope of the least-squares line. That is, it is the increase in the average price when Bed3 increases by 1. The indicator variable Bed3 has only two values, so we can clarify the interpretation.

The predicted price for homes with two or fewer bedrooms (Bed3 $= 0$) is

$$\widehat{\text{Price}} = 75{,}700 + 15{,}146(0) = 75{,}700$$

That is, the intercept 75,700 is the mean price for homes with Bed3 $= 0$. The predicted price for homes with three or more bedrooms (Bed3 $= 1$) is

$$\widehat{\text{Price}} = 75{,}700 + 15{,}146(1) = 90{,}846$$

That is, the slope 15,146 says that homes with three or more bedrooms are priced \$15,146 higher on the average than homes with two or fewer bedrooms. When we regress on a single indicator variable, both intercept and slope have simple interpretations.

Example 11.21 shows that regression on one indicator variable essentially models the means of the two groups. A regression model for a categorical variable with I possible

FIGURE 11.16 Output for predicting price using whether or not there are three or more bedrooms, for Example 11.21.

Analysis of Variance

Source	DF	Sum of Squares	Mean Square	F Value	Pr > F
Model	1	1934368525	1934368525	8.27	0.0068
Error	35	8189859583	233995988		
Corrected Total	36	10124228108			

Root MSE	15297	R-Square	0.1911
Dependent Mean	85524	Adj R-Sq	0.1680
Coeff Var	17.88605		

Parameter Estimates

Variable	Label	DF	Parameter Estimate	Standard Error	t Value	Pr > |t|
Intercept	Intercept	1	75700	4242.60432	17.84	<.0001
Bed3		1	15146	5267.78172	2.88	0.0068

values requires $I - 1$ indicator variables and therefore I regression coefficients (including the intercept) to model the I category means. Here is an example of a categorical explanatory variable with four possible values.

EXAMPLE 11.22 Price and the Number of Bathrooms

CASE 11.3

The homes in our data set have 1, 1.5, 2, or 2.5 bathrooms. Figure 11.17 gives a plot of price versus the number of bathrooms with a "smooth" fit. The relationship does not appear to be linear so we will start by treating the number of bathrooms as a categorical variable. We require three indicator variables for the four values. To use the homes that have 1 bath as the basis for comparisons, we let this correspond to "all indicator variables equal to 0." The indicator variables are

$$\text{Baths 15} = \begin{cases} 1 \text{ if the home has 1.5 baths} \\ 0 \text{ otherwise} \end{cases}$$

$$\text{Baths 2} = \begin{cases} 1 \text{ if the home has 2 baths} \\ 0 \text{ otherwise} \end{cases}$$

$$\text{Baths 25} = \begin{cases} 1 \text{ if the home has 2.5 baths} \\ 0 \text{ otherwise} \end{cases}$$

Multiple regression using these three explanatory variables gives the output in Figure 11.18. The overall model is statistically significant ($F = 12.59$, $df = 3$ and 33, $P < 0.0001$), and it explains 53.3% of the variation in price. This is somewhat more than the 37.3% explained by

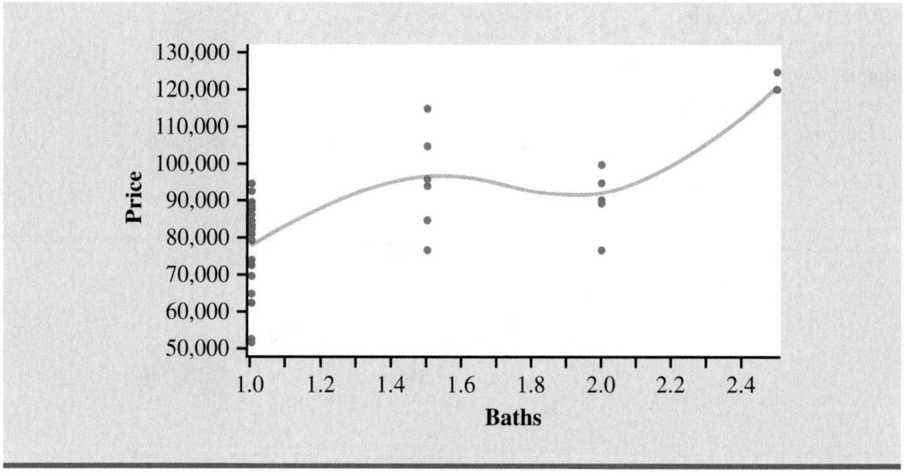

FIGURE 11.17 Plot of price versus the number of bathrooms, for Example 11.22.

square feet. The fitted model is

$$\widehat{\text{Price}} = 77{,}504 + 20{,}533 \text{ Baths } 15 + 12{,}616 \text{ Baths } 2 + 44{,}896 \text{ Baths } 25$$

The coefficients of all the indicator variables are statistically significant, indicating that each additional bathroom is associated with higher prices.

FIGURE 11.18 Output for predicting price using indicator variables for the number of bathrooms, for Example 11.22.

Analysis of Variance

Source	DF	Sum of Squares	Mean Square	F Value	Pr > F
Model	3	5404093400	1801364467	12.59	<.0001
Error	33	4720134708	143034385		
Corrected Total	36	10124228108			

Root MSE	11960	R-Square	0.5338
Dependent Mean	85524	Adj R-Sq	0.4914
Coeff Var	13.98397		

Parameter Estimates

Variable	Label	DF	Parameter Estimate	Standard Error	t Value	Pr > |t|
Intercept	Intercept	1	77504	2493.76950	31.08	<.0001
Baths15		1	20553	5162.59333	3.98	0.0004
Baths2		1	12616	5901.33572	2.14	0.0400
Baths25		1	44896	8816.80661	5.09	<.0001

APPLY YOUR KNOWLEDGE

11.70 Find the means. Using the data set for Example 11.21, find the mean price for the homes that have three or more bedrooms and the mean price for those that do not.

CASE 11.3

(a) Compare these sample means with the predicted values given in Example 11.21.

(b) What is the difference between the mean price of the homes in the sample that have three or more bedrooms and the mean price of those that do not? Verify that this difference is the coefficient for the indicator variable Bed3 in the regression in Example 11.21.

11.71 Compare the means. Regression on a single indicator variable compares the mean responses in two groups. It is in fact equivalent to the pooled t test for comparing two means (Chapter 7, page 462). Use the pooled t test to compare the mean price of the homes that have three or more bedrooms with the mean price of those that do not. Verify that the test statistic, degrees of freedom, and P-value agree with the t test for the coefficient of Bed3 in Example 11.21.

CASE 11.3

11.72 Modeling the means. Following the pattern in Example 11.21, use the output in Figure 11.18 to write the equations for the predicted mean price for

CASE 11.3

(a) homes with 1 bathroom.

(b) homes with 1.5 bathrooms.

(c) homes with 2 bathrooms.

(d) homes with 2.5 bathrooms.

(e) How can we interpret the coefficient for one of the indicator variables, say Baths2, in language understandable to house shoppers?

More elaborate models

We now suspect that a model that uses square feet, number of bedrooms, and number of bathrooms may explain price reasonably well. Before examining such a model, we use an insight based on careful data analysis to improve the treatment of number of baths.

Figure 11.17 reminds us that the data describe only two homes with 2.5 bathrooms. Our model with three indicator variables fits a mean for these two observations. The pattern of Figure 11.17 reveals an interesting feature: adding a half bath to either 1 or 2 baths raises the predicted price by a similar, quite substantial amount. If we use this information to construct a model, we can avoid the problem of fitting one parameter to just two houses.

EXAMPLE 11.23 An Alternative Bath Model

CASE 11.3

Starting again with 1-bath homes as the base (all indicator variables 0), let B2 be an indicator variable for an extra full bath and let Bh be an indicator variable for an extra half bath. Thus, a home with 2 baths has Bh = 0 and B2 = 1. A home with 2.5 baths has Bh = 1 and B2 = 1. Regressing Price on Bh and B2 gives the output in Figure 11.19.

The overall model is statistically significant ($F = 18.30$, df = 2 and 34, $P < 0.0001$), and it explains 51.8% of the variation in price. This compares favorably with the 53.3% explained by the model with three indicator variables for bathrooms. The fitted model is

$$\widehat{\text{Price}} = 76{,}929 + 15{,}837\text{B2} + 23{,}018\text{Bh}$$

FIGURE 11.19 Output for predicting price using the alternative coding for bathrooms, for Example 11.23.

Analysis of Variance

Source	DF	Sum of Squares	Mean Square	F Value	Pr > F
Model	2	5248929412	2624464706	18.30	<.0001
Error	34	4875298697	143391138		
Corrected Total	36	10124228108			

Root MSE	11975	R-Square	0.5185
Dependent Mean	85524	Adj R-Sq	0.4901
Coeff Var	14.00140		

Parameter Estimates

Variable	Label	DF	Parameter Estimate	Standard Error	t Value	Pr > |t|
Intercept	Intercept	1	76929	2434.86662	31.59	<.0001
B2		1	15837	5032.10205	3.15	0.0034
Bh		1	23018	4593.65967	5.01	<.0001

That is, an extra full bath adds \$15,837 to the mean price and an extra half bath adds \$23,018. The t statistics show that both regression coefficients are significantly different from zero ($t = 3.15$, df $= 34$, $P = 0.0034$; and $t = 5.01$, df $= 34$, $P < 0.0001$).

So far we have learned that the price of a home is related to the number of square feet, whether or not there are three or more bedrooms, whether or not there is an additional full bathroom, and whether or not there is an additional half bathroom. Let's try a model including all of these explanatory variables.

EXAMPLE 11.24 Square Feet, Bedrooms, and Bathrooms

CASE 11.3

Figure 11.20 gives the output for predicting price using SqFt, Bed3, B2, and Bh. The overall model is statistically significant ($F = 11.48$, df $=$ 4 and 32, $P < 0.0001$), and it explains 58.9% of the variation in price. The individual t for Bed3 is not statistically significant ($t = -0.97$, df $= 32$, $P = 0.3374$). That is, in a model that contains square feet and information about the bathrooms, there is no additional information in the number of bedrooms that is useful for predicting price. This happens because the explanatory variables are related to each other: houses with more bedrooms tend to also have more square feet and more baths.

We therefore redo the regression without Bed3. The output appears in Figure 11.21. The value of R^2 has decreased slightly to 57.7%, but now all of the coefficients for the explanatory variables are statistically significant. The fitted regression equation is

$$\widehat{\text{Price}} = 59,268 + 16.78\text{SqFt} + 13,161\text{B2} + 16,859\text{Bh}$$

FIGURE 11.20 Output for predicting price using square feet, bedroom, and bathroom information, for Example 11.24.

Analysis of Variance

Source	DF	Sum of Squares	Mean Square	F Value	Pr > F
Model	4	5966829910	1491707478	11.48	<.0001
Error	32	4157398198	129918694		
Corrected Total	36	10124228108			

Root MSE	11398	R-Square	0.5894
Dependent Mean	85524	Adj R-Sq	0.5380
Coeff Var	13.32742		

Parameter Estimates

Variable	Label	DF	Parameter Estimate	Standard Error	t Value	Pr > |t|
Intercept	Intercept	1	55539	9390.30284	5.91	<.0001
SqFt	SqFt	1	22.86649	10.02864	2.28	0.0294
Bed3		1	−5788.52568	5943.78386	−0.97	0.3374
B2		1	14564	5155.65595	2.82	0.0081
Bh		1	17209	5247.38676	3.28	0.0025

FIGURE 11.21 Output for predicting price using square feet and bathroom information, for Example 11.24.

Analysis of Variance

Source	DF	Sum of Squares	Mean Square	F Value	Pr > F
Model	3	5843609810	1947869937	15.02	<.0001
Error	33	4280618298	129715706		
Corrected Total	36	10124228108			

Root MSE	11389	R-Square	0.5772
Dependent Mean	85524	Adj R-Sq	0.5388
Coeff Var	13.31701		

Parameter Estimates

Variable	Label	DF	Parameter Estimate	Standard Error	t Value	Pr > |t|
Intercept	Intercept	1	59268	8567.44638	6.92	<.0001
SqFt	SqFt	1	16.77989	7.83689	2.14	0.0397
B2		1	13161	4946.59620	2.66	0.0119
Bh		1	16859	5230.97932	3.22	0.0029

APPLY YOUR KNOWLEDGE

11.73 What about garages? CASE 11.3 We have not yet examined the number of garage spaces as a possible explanatory variable for price. Make a scatterplot of price versus garage spaces. Describe the pattern. Use a "smooth" fit if your software has this capability. Otherwise, find the mean price for each possible value of Garage, plot the means on your scatterplot, and connect the means with lines. Is the relationship approximately linear?

11.74 The home with three garages. CASE 11.3 There is only one home with 3 garage spaces. We might either place this house in the Garage = 2 group or remove it as unusual. Either decision leaves Garage with values 0, 1, and 2. Based on your plot in the previous exercise, which choice do you recommend?

Variable selection methods

We have arrived at a reasonably satisfactory model for predicting the asking price of houses. But it is clear that there are many other models we might consider. We have not used the Garage variable, for example. What is more, the explanatory variables can *interact* with each other. This means that the effect of one explanatory variable depends upon the value of another explanatory variable. We account for this situation in a regression model by including **interaction terms.** The simplest way to construct an interaction term is to multiply the two explanatory variables together. Thus, if we wanted to allow the effect of an additional half bath to depend upon whether or not there is an additional full bath, we would create a new explanatory variable by taking the product B2 × Bh.

interaction terms

Considering interactions increases the number of possible explanatory variables. If we start with the 5 explanatory variables SqFt, Bed3, B2, Bh, and Garage, there are 10 interactions between pairs of variables. That is, there are now 15 possible explanatory variables in all. From 15 explanatory variables it is possible to build 32,727 different models for predicting price. We need to automate the process of examining possible models. Modern regression software offers *variable selection methods* that examine, for example, the R^2-values for all possible multiple regression models. The software then presents us with the models having the highest R^2 for each number of explanatory variables.

EXAMPLE 11.25 Predicting Asking Price

CASE 11.3

Software tells us that the highest available R^2 increases as we increase the number of explanatory variables as follows:

Variables	R^2
1	0.44
2	0.57
3	0.62
4	0.66
5	0.72
⋮	
13	0.77

Because of collinearity problems, models with 14 or all 15 explanatory variables cannot be used. The highest possible R^2 is 77%, using 13 explanatory variables. There are only 37 houses in the data set. A model with too many explanatory variables will fit the accidental wiggles in the prices of these specific houses and may do a poor job of predicting prices for other houses. This is called **overfitting.**

overfitting

There is no formula for choosing the "best" multiple regression model. We want to avoid overfitting, and we prefer smaller models to larger models. We want a model that makes intuitive sense. For example, the best single predictor ($R^2 = 0.44$) is SqFtBh, the interaction between square feet and having an extra half bath. In general, we would not use a model that has interaction terms unless the explanatory variables involved in the interaction are also included. The variable selection output does suggest that we include SqFtBh, and therefore SqFt and Bh.

EXAMPLE 11.26 One More Model

CASE 11.3 

Figure 11.22 gives the output for the multiple regression of Price on SqFt, Bh, and the interaction between these variables. This model explains 55.7% of the variation in price. The coefficients for SqFt and Bh are significant at the 10% level but not at the 5% level ($t = 1.82$, $df = 33$, $P = 0.0777$; and $t = -1.79$, $df = 33$, $P = 0.0825$). However, the interaction is significantly different from zero ($t = 2.29$, $df = 33$, $P = 0.0284$). Because the interaction

FIGURE 11.22 Output for predicting price using square feet, extra half bathroom, and the interaction, for Example 11.26.

Analysis of Variance

Source	DF	Sum of Squares	Mean Square	F Value	Pr > F
Model	3	5639442004	1879814001	13.83	<.0001
Error	33	4484786104	135902609		
Corrected Total	36	10124228108			

Root MSE	11658	R-Square	0.5570
Dependent Mean	85524	Adj R-Sq	0.5168
Coeff Var	13.63089		

Parameter Estimates

Variable	Label	DF	Parameter Estimate	Standard Error	t Value	Pr > |t|
Intercept	Intercept	1	63375	9263.60218	6.84	<.0001
SqFt	SqFt	1	15.15440	8.32360	1.82	0.0777
Bh		1	−58800	32832	−1.79	0.0825
SqFtBh		1	52.81209	23.03886	2.29	0.0284

is significant, we will keep the terms SqFt and Bh in the model even though their P-values do not quite pass the 0.05 standard. The fitted regression equation is

$$\widehat{\text{Price}} = 63{,}375 + 15.15\,\text{SqFt} - 58{,}800\,\text{Bh} + 52.81\,\text{SqFtBh}$$

The negative coefficient for Bh seems odd. We expect an extra half bath to increase price. A plot will help us to understand what this model says about the prices of homes.

EXAMPLE 11.27 Interpretation of the Fit

CASE 11.3

Figure 11.23 plots Price against SqFt, using different plot symbols to show the values of the categorical variable Bh. Homes without an extra half bath are plotted as circles, and homes with an extra half bath are plotted as squares. Look carefully: none of the smaller homes have an extra half bath.

The lines on the plot graph the model from Example 11.26. The presence of the categorical variable Bh and the interaction Bh × SqFt account for the *two* lines. That is, the model expresses the fact that the relationship between price and square feet depends on whether or not there is an additional half bath.

We can determine the equations of the two lines from the fitted regression equation. Homes that lack an extra half bath have Bh = 0. When we set Bh = 0 in the regression equation

$$\widehat{\text{Price}} = 63{,}375 + 15.15\text{SqFt} - 58{,}800\text{Bh} + 52.81\text{SqFtBh}$$

we get

$$\widehat{\text{Price}} = 63{,}375 + 15.15\text{SqFt}$$

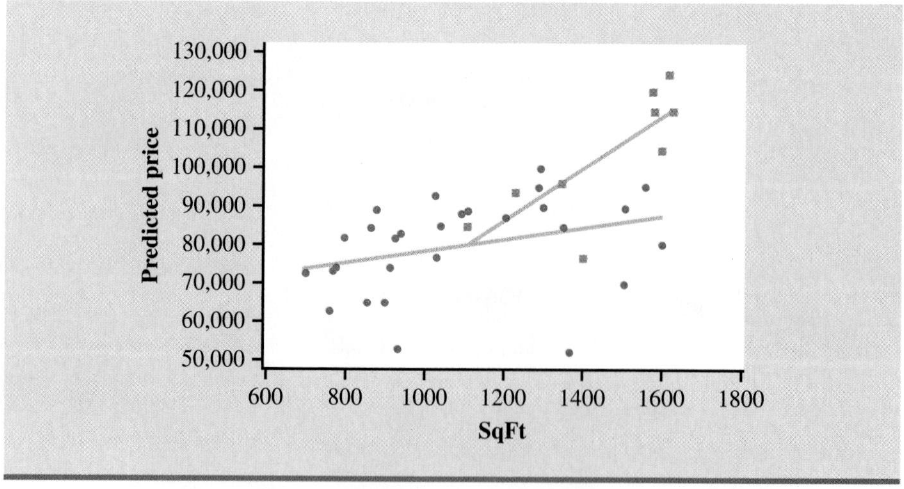

FIGURE 11.23 Plot of the data and model for price predicted by square feet, extra half bathroom, and the interaction, for Example 11.27.

For homes that have an extra half bath, Bh = 1 and the regression equation becomes

$$\begin{aligned}\widehat{\text{Price}} &= 63{,}375 + 15.15\text{SqFt} - 58{,}800 + 52.81\text{SqFt} \\ &= (63{,}375 - 58{,}800) + (15.15 + 52.81)\text{SqFt} \\ &= 4575 + 67.96\text{SqFt}\end{aligned}$$

In Figure 11.23, we graphed this line starting at the price of the least-expensive home with an extra half bath. These two equations tell us that an additional square foot increases asking price by \$15.15 for homes without an extra half bath and by \$67.96 for homes that do have an extra half bath.

APPLY YOUR KNOWLEDGE

11.75 Comparing some predicted values. CASE 11.3 Consider two homes, both with 1400 ft^2. Suppose the first has an extra half bath and the second does not. Find the predicted price for each home and then find the difference.

11.76 Suppose the homes are larger? CASE 11.3 Consider two additional homes, both with 1600 ft^2, one with an extra half bath and one without. Find the predicted prices and the difference. How does this difference compare with the difference you obtained in the previous exercise? Explain what you have found.

11.77 How about the smaller homes? CASE 11.3 Would it make sense to do the same calculations as in the previous two exercises for homes that have 700 ft^2? Explain why or why not.

11.78 Residuals. CASE 11.3 Once we have chosen a model, we must examine the residuals for violations of the conditions of the multiple regression model. Examine the residuals from the model in Example 11.26.

(a) Plot the residuals against SqFt. Do the residuals show a random scatter, or is there some systematic pattern?

(b) The residual plot shows three somewhat low residuals, between −\$20,000 and −\$40,000. Which homes are these? Is there anything unusual about these homes?

(c) Make a Normal quantile plot of the residuals. (Make a histogram if your software does not make Normal quantile plots.) Is the distribution roughly Normal?

BEYOND THE BASICS: MULTIPLE LOGISTIC REGRESSION

Many studies have yes/no or success/failure response variables. A surgery patient lives or dies; a consumer does or does not purchase a product after viewing an advertisement. Because the response variable in a multiple regression is assumed to have a Normal distribution, this methodology is not suitable for predicting yes/no responses. However, there are models that apply the ideas of regression to response variables with only two possible outcomes.

logistic regression

The most common technique is called **logistic regression.** The starting point is that if each response is 0 or 1 (for failure or success), then the mean response is the probability p of a success. Logistic regression tries to explain p in terms of one or more explanatory variables. Details are even more complicated than those for multiple regression, but the fundamental ideas are very much the same and software handles most details. Here is an example.

EXAMPLE 11.28 Mail-Order Sales

A company uses many different mailed catalogs to sell different types of merchandise. One catalog that features home goods, such as bedspreads and pillows, was mailed to 200,000 people who were not current customers.[13] The response variable is whether or not the person places an order. We use logistic regression to model the probability p of a purchase as a function of five explanatory variables.[14] These are x_1, number of purchases within the last 24 months from a home gift catalog; x_2, the proportion of single people in the zip code area based on census data; x_3, number of credit cards; x_4, a variable that distinguishes apartment dwellers from those who live in single-family homes; and x_5, an indicator of whether or not the customer has ever made a purchase from a similar type of catalog.

Similar to the F test in multiple regression, there is a chi-square test for multiple logistic regression that tests the null hypothesis that *all* coefficients of the explanatory variables are zero. For our example, the value is $X^2 = 141.34$, and the degrees of freedom are the number of explanatory variables, 5 in this case. (Recall that we studied the chi-square distribution in Chapter 9, where we analyzed two-way tables of counts.) The P-value is reported by software as $P = 0.0001$. (You can verify that it is less than 0.0005 using Table F.) We conclude that not all of the explanatory variables have zero coefficients.

Interpretation of the coefficients is a little more difficult in multiple logistic regression because of the form of the model. For our example, the fitted model is

$$\log\left(\frac{p}{1-p}\right) = -4.80 + 0.11x_1 - 0.11x_2 + 0.14x_3 - 0.43x_4 + 0.22x_5$$

The expression $p/(1-p)$ is the odds of a successful outcome. Logistic regression models the "log odds" as a linear combination of the explanatory variables.

In place of the t tests for individual coefficients in multiple regression, chi-square tests, each with 1 degree of freedom, are used to test whether individual coefficients are zero. The P-values for each of these tests are very small, ranging from 0.0067 to 0.0001. We conclude that all the coefficients are nonzero. The signs of the coefficients tell us whether the explanatory variable is positively or negatively related to the response in the context of the model. We see that having made purchases in the past and having more credit cards are associated with a higher chance of buying from this catalog, whereas people who live in an apartment and in a neighborhood with a high proportion of single people are less likely to purchase these home goods.

The predicted value for this model allows us to estimate the probability p that a customer will make a purchase from the catalog. In the future, this model will be applied to mail the catalog only to consumers whose estimated probability of making a purchase is above some cutoff value.

SECTION 11.3 SUMMARY

- Start the model-building process by performing **data analysis** for multiple linear regression. Examine the distribution of the variables and the form of relationships among them.
- Note any **categorical explanatory variables** that have very few cases for some values. If it is reasonable, combine these values with other values. If not, delete these cases and examine them separately.
- For **curved relationships,** consider transformations or additional explanatory variables that will account for the curvature. Sometimes adding a **quadratic term** improves the fit.

- Examine the possibility that the effect of one explanatory variable depends upon the value of another explanatory variable. **Interactions** can be used to model this situation.
- Examine software outputs from modern **variable selection methods** to see what models of each subset size have the highest R^2.

SECTION 11.3 Exercises

For Exercises 11.65 to 11.67, see page 656; for 11.68 and 11.69, see pages 658–659; for 11.70 to 11.72, see page 663; for 11.73 and 11.74, see page 666; and for 11.75 to 11.78, see page 669.

11.79 Quadratic models. Sketch each of the following quadratic equations for values of x between 0 and 12. Then describe the relationship between μ_y and x in your own words.

(a) $\mu_y = 8 + 3x + 3x^2$

(b) $\mu_y = 12 - 25x + 3x^2$

(c) $\mu_y = 50 - 28x - 3x^2$

11.80 Models with indicator variables. Suppose that x is an indicator variable with the value 0 for Group A and 1 for Group B. The following equations describe relationships between the value of μ_y and membership in Group A or B. For each equation, give the value of the mean response μ_y for Group A and for Group B.

(a) $\mu_y = 10 + 3x$

(b) $\mu_y = 10 + 30x$

(c) $\mu_y = 10 + 300x$

11.81 Differences in means. Verify that the coefficient of x in each part of the previous exercise is equal to the mean for Group B minus the mean for Group A. Do you think that this will be true in general? Explain your answer.

11.82 Models with interactions. Suppose that x_1 is an indicator variable with the value 0 for Group A and 1 for Group B, and x_2 is a quantitative variable. Each of the models below describes a relationship between μ_y and the explanatory variables x_1 and x_2. For each model, substitute the value 0 for x_1 and write the resulting equation for μ_y in terms of x_2 for Group A. Then substitute $x_1 = 1$ to obtain the equation for Group B and sketch the two equations on the same graph. Describe in words the difference in the relationship for the two groups.

(a) $\mu_y = 80 + 40x_1 + 7x_2 + 12x_1x_2$

(b) $\mu_y = 60 - 8x_1 + 7x_2 - 8x_1x_2$

(c) $\mu_y = 200 + 3x_1 + 7x_2 - 14x_1x_2$

11.83 Differences in slopes and intercepts. Refer to the previous exercise. Verify that the coefficient of x_1x_2 is equal to the slope for Group B minus the slope for Group A in each of these cases. Also, verify that the coefficient of x_1 is equal to the intercept for Group B minus the intercept for Group A in each of these cases. Do you think these two results will be true in general? Explain your answer.

11.84 Write the model. For each of the following situations write a model for μ_y of the form

$$\mu_y = \beta_0 + \beta_1 x_1 + \beta_2 x_2 + \cdots + \beta_p x_p$$

where p is the number of explanatory variables. Be sure to give the value of p and, if necessary, explain how each of the x's is coded.

(a) A model where the explanatory variable is a categorical variable with five possible values.

(b) A model where there are three explanatory variables. One of these is categorical with two possible values; another is categorical with three possible values. Include a term that would model an interaction of the first categorical variable and the third (quantitative) explanatory variable.

(c) A quartic regression, where terms up to and including the fourth power of an explanatory variable are included in the model.

11.85 Online stock brokerages. Refer to the online stock brokerage data in Exercise 11.23 (page 635). Plot assets versus the number of accounts. Investigate the possibility that the relationship is curved by running a multiple regression to predict assets using the number of accounts and the square of the number of accounts as explanatory variables. (Note that to use statistical inference for these data, we need to assume that there is some underlying model that generated the data and that it is the properties of this model that are of interest.)

(a) Give the fitted regression equation.

(b) Find a 95% confidence interval for the coefficient of the squared term.

(c) Give the results of the significance test for the coefficient of the squared term. Report the test statistic with its degrees of freedom and P-value, and summarize your conclusion.

(d) Rerun the analysis without the quadratic term. Explain why the coefficient of the number of accounts is not the same as you found for part (a).

11.86 Professors' salaries. Refer to the data on salaries of a collection of engineering full professors given in Exercise 11.61 (page 653). A plot of salary for 2005 versus years in rank suggests that the relationship may be slightly curved. Examine this question by running a regression to predict the 2005 salary using years in rank and the square of years in rank. Report the relevant test statistic with its degrees of freedom and P-value, and summarize your conclusion.

11.87 Compare the models. Refer to the previous exercise. We can view this analysis in the framework of testing a hypothesis about a collection of regression coefficients that we studied in Section 11.2 (page 647). The first model includes years in rank and the square of years in rank, while the second includes only years in rank.

(a) Run both regressions and find the value of R^2 for each.

(b) Find the F statistic for comparing the models based on the difference in the values of R^2. Carry out the test and report your conclusion.

(c) Verify that the square of the t statistic that you found in the previous exercise for testing the coefficient of the quadratic term is equal to the F statistic that you found for this exercise.

11.88 Predict the quality of a product. Refer to the CHEESE data set in the Data Appendix. Here the measure of quality is a variable called Taste and the explanatory variables are the concentrations of three chemicals found in cheese. These are acetic acid, hydrogen sulfide, and lactic acid. With three explanatory variables, there are three models that have a single explanatory variable, three that have two explanatory variables, and one with all three included. Run these 7 regressions and make a table giving the regression coefficients and the value of R^2 for each regression. (If an explanatory variable is not included in a particular regression, enter a value of 0 for its coefficient in the table.) Mark coefficients that are statistically significant at the 5% level with an asterisk (*). Summarize your results and state which model you prefer.

STATISTICS IN SUMMARY

Multiple regression uses more than one explanatory variable to explain the variation in a response variable. In particular, multiple regression allows *categorical explanatory variables, polynomial functions* of a quantitative explanatory variable, and *interactions* among explanatory variables. As in the case of simple linear regression, we can fit a multiple regression equation by the *least-squares* method to any set of data. Inference requires more restrictive conditions that are summarized in the *multiple regression model.* To do inference, we must estimate not only the coefficients of the regression equation but also the standard deviation σ that describes how much variation there is in responses y when the x's are held fixed. We use the *regression standard error* s (roughly, the sample standard deviation of the residuals) to estimate σ. Here are the skills you should develop from studying this chapter.

A. Preliminaries

1. Write a suitable regression model for your situation. Choose a response variable and promising explanatory variables. Recognize categorical explanatory variables and use indicator functions to include them in the model.
2. Examine the distribution of each explanatory variable and the response variable.
3. Make scatterplots to show the relationship between explanatory variables and the response variable. Decide whether, for example, a quadratic term may be needed.
4. Use software to find by least squares the regression equation that fits your chosen model to the data.

5. Inspect the data to recognize situations in which inference isn't safe: influential observations, strongly skewed residuals in a small sample, or nonconstant variation of the data points about the fitted equation.

B. Inference Using Software Output

1. Explain in any specific regression setting the meaning of the coefficients (β's) of the population regression equation.
2. Understand software output for multiple regression. Find in the output the intercept and the coefficients for the fitted regression equation, their standard errors and individual t statistics, and the regression standard error.
3. Use software output to carry out tests and calculate confidence intervals for the β's. Recognize clearly that conclusions about one explanatory variable depend on what other variables are also present in the model.
4. Use software output to carry out the F test for the significance of the model as a whole. Understand why F can be significant even though all individual t's are not significant.
5. Explain the distinction between a confidence interval for the mean response and a prediction interval for an individual response. If software gives output for prediction, use that output to give either confidence or prediction intervals.
6. Know how to test a null hypothesis concerning the β's for a subset of variables.

CHAPTER 11 Review Exercises

The following four exercises use price promotion data given in Table 11.6.

11.89 Discount promotions at a supermarket. How does the frequency that a supermarket product is promoted at a discount affect the price that customers expect to pay for the product? Does the percent reduction also affect this expectation? These questions were examined by researchers in a study that used 160 subjects. The treatment conditions corresponded to the number of promotions (1, 3, 5, or 7) that were described during a 10-week period and the percent that the product was discounted (10%, 20%, 30%, and 40%). Ten students were randomly assigned to each of the $4 \times 4 = 16$ treatments.[15]

(a) Plot the expected price versus the number of promotions. Do the same for expected price versus discount. Summarize the results.

(b) These data come from a designed experiment with an equal number of observations for each promotion by discount combination. Find the means and standard deviations for expected price for each of these combinations. Describe any patterns that are evident in these summaries.

(c) Using your summaries from part (b), make a plot of the mean expected price versus the number of promotions for the 10% discount condition. Connect these means with straight lines. On the same plot add the means for the other discount conditions. Summarize the major features of this plot.

11.90 Run the multiple regression. Refer to the previous exercise. Run a multiple regression using promotions and discount to predict expected price. Write a summary of your results.

11.91 Residuals and other models. Refer to the previous exercise. Analyze the residuals from your analysis and investigate the possibility of using quadratic and interaction terms as predictors. Write a report recommending a final model for this problem with a justification for your recommendation.

11.92 Can we generalize the results? The subjects in this experiment were college students at a large midwestern university who were enrolled in an introductory management course. They received the information about the promotions during a 10-week period during their course. Do you think that these facts about the data would influence how you would interpret and generalize the results? Write a summary of your ideas regarding this issue.

11.93 Predicting water quality. Pollution of water resources is a serious problem that can require

TABLE 11.6 Expected price data

Number of promotions	Percent discount	Expected price ($)									
1	40	4.10	4.50	4.47	4.42	4.56	4.69	4.42	4.17	4.31	4.59
1	30	3.57	3.77	3.90	4.49	4.00	4.66	4.48	4.64	4.31	4.43
1	20	4.94	4.59	4.58	4.48	4.55	4.53	4.59	4.66	4.73	5.24
1	10	5.19	4.88	4.78	4.89	4.69	4.96	5.00	4.93	5.10	4.78
3	40	4.07	4.13	4.25	4.23	4.57	4.33	4.17	4.47	4.60	4.02
3	30	4.20	3.94	4.20	3.88	4.35	3.99	4.01	4.22	3.70	4.48
3	20	4.88	4.80	4.46	4.73	3.96	4.42	4.30	4.68	4.45	4.56
3	10	4.90	5.15	4.68	4.98	4.66	4.46	4.70	4.37	4.69	4.97
5	40	3.89	4.18	3.82	4.09	3.94	4.41	4.14	4.15	4.06	3.90
5	30	3.90	3.77	3.86	4.10	4.10	3.81	3.97	3.67	4.05	3.67
5	20	4.11	4.35	4.17	4.11	4.02	4.41	4.48	3.76	4.66	4.44
5	10	4.31	4.36	4.75	4.62	3.74	4.34	4.52	4.37	4.40	4.52
7	40	3.56	3.91	4.05	3.91	4.11	3.61	3.72	3.69	3.79	3.45
7	30	3.45	4.06	3.35	3.67	3.74	3.80	3.90	4.08	3.52	4.03
7	20	3.89	4.45	3.80	4.15	4.41	3.75	3.98	4.07	4.21	4.23
7	10	4.04	4.22	4.39	3.89	4.26	4.41	4.39	4.52	3.87	4.70

substantial efforts to improve. To determine the financial resources required, an accurate assessment of the extent of the problem is necessary. The index of biotic integrity (IBI) is a measure of the water quality in streams that is fairly expensive to determine. Land use measures, on the other hand, are relatively inexpensive to obtain. IBI and land use measures for a collection of streams in the Ozark Highland ecoregion of Arkansas were collected as part of a study.[16] Table 11.7 gives the data for IBI and the area of the watershed in square kilometers (Area) and the percent of the watershed area that is forest (Forest) for streams in the original sample with area less than or equal to 70 km^2.

(a) Use numerical and graphical methods to describe each of the three variables in this data set. Summarize your results.

(b) Plot the data and describe the relationships between each pair of variables. Are there any outliers or unusual patterns?

(c) Give the statistical model for a multiple regression that would use Area and Forest to predict IBI.

(d) State the null and alternative hypotheses for all of the significance tests associated with this analysis.

(e) Run the multiple regression and summarize the results.

(f) Obtain the residuals and plot them versus Area and versus Forest. Is there anything unusual in these plots?

(g) Do the residuals appear to be approximately Normal? Give reasons for your answer.

(h) Do the assumptions for the analysis of these data using the model you gave in part (c) appear to be reasonable? Explain your answer.

11.94 More complicated analyses. Refer to the previous exercise. Investigate the possibility that quadratic terms and interactions would improve the estimation of IBI. Write a summary of your results.

The following 11 exercises use the PCB data set described in the Data Appendix.

11.95 PCBs and fish. Production of polychlorinated biphenyls (PCBs) was banned in the United States in 1977, but because of their widespread use, these compounds are found in many species of fish. As a result, 38 states have issued advisories about limiting consumption of certain species caught in some areas. Specific advisories are targeted toward pregnant and lactating women and all women who

TABLE 11.7 Watershed area, percent forest, and index of biotic integrity

Area	Forest	IBI	Area	Forest	IBI	Area	Forest	IBI
21	0	47	29	0	61	31	0	39
32	0	59	34	0	72	34	0	76
49	3	85	52	3	89	2	7	74
70	8	89	6	9	33	21	10	32
28	10	46	59	11	80	69	14	80
8	17	53	47	17	78	8	18	43
58	21	88	54	22	84	10	25	62
57	31	55	18	32	29	19	33	29
39	33	54	49	33	78	9	39	71
5	41	55	9	43	71	14	43	58
23	47	33	18	49	81	31	49	59
16	52	71	21	52	75	32	59	64
10	63	41	26	68	82	9	75	60
12	79	83	54	79	84	21	80	82
27	86	82	23	89	86	26	90	79
16	95	67	26	95	56	26	100	85
28	100	91						

are of childbearing age. Unfortunately, there are 209 different varieties, called congeners, of PCBs. Measurement of all of these congeners in a fish specimen is an expensive and time-consuming process. If the total amount of PCBs in a specimen can be estimated with data collected on a few congeners, costs can be reduced and more specimens can be measured. Consider the following variables: PCB (the total amount of PCB) and four congeners: PCB52, PCB118, PCB138, and PCB180.

(a) Using numerical and graphical summaries, describe the distribution of each of these variables.

(b) Using numerical and graphical summaries, describe the relationship between each pair of variables in this set.

11.96 Predict total PCB. Use the four congeners, PCB52, PCB118, PCB138, and PCB180, in a multiple regression to predict PCB.

(a) Write the statistical model for this analysis. Include all assumptions.

(b) Run the regression and summarize the results.

(c) Examine the residuals. Do they appear to be approximately Normal? When you plot them versus each of the explanatory variables, are any patterns evident?

11.97 Check the outliers. The examination of the residuals in part (c) of the previous exercise suggests that there may be two outliers, one with a high residual and one with a low residual.

(a) Because of safety issues, we are more concerned about underestimating PCB in a specimen than about overestimating. Give the specimen number for each of the two suspected outliers. Which one corresponds to an overestimate of PCB?

(b) Rerun the analysis with the two suspected outliers deleted, summarize these results, and compare them with those you obtained in the previous exercise.

11.98 Run a new model and compare the results. Run a regression to predict PCB using the variables PCB52, PCB118, and PCB138. Note that this is similar to the analysis that you did in Exercise 11.96 with the change that PCB180 is not included as an explanatory variable.

(a) Summarize the results.

(b) In this analysis, the regression coefficient for PCB118 is not statistically significant. Give the estimate of the coefficient and the associated P-value.

(c) Find the estimate of the coefficient for PCB118 and the associated P-value for the model analyzed in Exercise 11.96.

(d) Using the results in parts (b) and (c), write a short paragraph explaining how the inclusion of other variables in a multiple regression can have an effect on the estimate of a particular coefficient and the results of the associated significance test.

11.99 Dioxins and furans. Dioxins and furans are other classes of chemicals that can cause undesirable health effects similar to those caused by PCBs. The three types of chemicals are combined using toxic equivalent scores (TEQs), which attempt to measure the health effects on a common scale. The PCB data set contains TEQs for PCBs, dioxins, and furans. The variables are called TEQPCB, TEQDIOXIN, and TEQFURAN. The data set also includes the total TEQ, defined to be the sum of these three variables.

(a) Consider using a multiple regression to predict TEQ using the three components TEQPCB, TEQDIOXIN, and TEQFURAN as explanatory variables. Write the multiple regression model in the form

$$\text{TEQ} = \beta_0 + \beta_1\text{TEQPCB} + \beta_2\text{TEQDIOXIN} + \beta_3\text{TEQFURAN} + \epsilon$$

Give numerical values for the parameters β_0, β_1, β_2, and β_3.

(b) The multiple regression model assumes that the ϵ's are Normal with mean zero and standard deviation σ. What is the numerical value of σ?

(c) Use software to run this regression and summarize the results.

11.100 Predict toxic equivalents. The information summarized in TEQ is used to assess and manage risks from these chemicals. For example, the World Health Organization (WHO) has established the tolerable daily intake (TDI) as 1 to 4 TEQs per kilogram of body weight per day. Therefore, it would be very useful to have a procedure for estimating TEQ using just a few variables that can be measured cheaply. Use the four PCB congeners, PCB52, PCB118, PCB138, and PCB180, in a multiple regression to predict TEQ. Give a description of the model and assumptions, summarize the results, examine the residuals, and write a summary of what you have found.

11.101 Try logs. Because distributions of variables such as PCB, the PCB congeners, and TEQ tend to be skewed, researchers frequently analyze the logarithms of the measured variables. Create a data set that has the logs of each of the variables in the PCB data set. Note that zero is a possible value for PCB126; most software packages will eliminate these cases when you request a log transformation.

(a) If you do not do anything about the 16 zero values of PCB126, what does your software do with these cases? Is there an error message of some kind?

(b) If you attempt to run a regression to predict the log of PCB using the log of PCB126 and the log of PCB52, are the cases with the zero values of PCB126 eliminated? Do you think that is a good way to handle this situation?

(c) The smallest nonzero value of PCB126 is 0.0052. One common practice when taking logarithms of measured values is to replace the zeros by one-half of the smallest observed value. Create a logarithm data set using this procedure; that is, replace the 16 zero values of PCB126 by 0.0026 before taking logarithms. Use numerical and graphical summaries to describe the distributions of the log variables.

11.102 Compare the results. Refer to the previous exercise.

(a) Use numerical and graphical summaries to describe the relationships between each pair of log variables.

(b) Compare these summaries with the summaries that you produced in Exercise 11.95 for the measured variables.

11.103 Find a good model for log PCB. Use the log data set that you created in Exercise 11.101 to find a good multiple regression model for predicting the log of PCB. Use only log PCB variables for this analysis. Write a report summarizing your results.

11.104 Find a good model for log TEQ. Use the log data set that you created in Exercise 11.101 to find a good multiple regression model for predicting the log of TEQ. Use only log TEQ variables for this analysis. Write a report summarizing your results and comparing them with the results that you obtained in Exercise 11.99.

11.105 Explain why the coefficients change. Use the results of your analysis of the log PCB data in Exercise 11.103 to write an explanation of how regression coefficients, standard errors of regression coefficients, and tests of significance for explanatory variables can change depending on what other explanatory variables are included in the multiple regression analysis.

11.106 Correlations may not be a good way to screen for multiple regression predictors. Data set A given

TABLE 11.8 Data set A

Y	X_1	X_2	Y	X_1	X_2	Y	X_1	X_2
3.4	28.2	−4.3	3.0	12.0	8.4	3.4	23.7	−0.5
2.9	5.0	14.9	3.2	−5.7	26.8	2.9	1.7	16.6
2.9	14.7	4.9	2.8	0.8	18.8	2.9	26.7	−7.5
3.0	14.4	6.1	2.7	11.1	7.3	2.8	6.4	11.7
3.1	3.6	16.6	3.0	2.9	16.7	2.9	16.4	2.5
3.2	7.4	14.4	3.2	34.3	−11.7	2.9	20.9	−1.8
3.3	−1.2	23.7	3.2	31.3	−8.7	3.1	14.3	7.0
2.9	16.3	3.2	3.2	−4.0	26.8	3.2	18.3	4.3
3.2	7.8	14.4	3.2	22.6	−1.0	3.2	1.3	20.0
3.1	15.4	5.6	3.0	1.2	18.8	3.0	11.3	8.8

in Table 11.8 was constructed to illustrate this point.

(a) Find the correlations between the response variable Y and each of the explanatory variables X_1 and X_2. Plot the data and run the two simple linear regressions to verify that no evidence of a relationship is found by this approach. Some researchers would conclude at this point that there is no point in further exploring the possibility that X_1 and X_2 could be useful in predicting Y.

(b) Analyze the data using X_1 and X_2 in a multiple regression to predict Y. The fit is quite good. Summarize the results of this analysis.

(c) What do you conclude about an analytical strategy that first looks at one candidate predictor at a time and selects from these candidates for a multiple regression based on some threshold level of significance?

11.107 The multiple regression results do not tell the whole story. Data set B given in Table 11.9 was constructed to illustrate this point.

(a) Run the multiple regression using X_1 and X_2 to predict Y. The F test and the significance tests for the coefficients of the explanatory variables fail to reach the 5% level of significance. Summarize these results.

(b) Now run the two simple linear regressions using each of the explanatory variables in separate analyses. The coefficients of the explanatory variables are statistically significant at the 5% level in each of these analyses. Verify these conclusions with plots and correlations.

(c) What do you conclude about an analytical strategy that looks only at multiple regression results?

TABLE 11.9 Data set B

Y	X_1	X_2	Y	X_1	X_2	Y	X_1	X_2
−0.4	7.0	1.0	−1.5	−0.3	0.5	1.4	6.8	0.5
2.9	15.4	1.5	1.0	9.8	−1.3	1.6	15.4	1.2
0.1	−1.7	−0.9	2.3	−4.5	0.7	0.5	16.1	1.4
1.4	−0.7	0.8	2.7	4.6	−1.0	1.0	20.5	1.6
2.4	4.1	−1.1	2.0	18.4	2.5	2.2	11.3	1.8
1.3	29.9	3.2	−0.3	−1.4	−1.8	1.2	11.4	−1.2
1.2	19.4	2.3	2.4	25.8	1.4	2.3	7.3	3.0
1.1	10.4	1.7	−0.8	2.0	−1.4	2.4	31.1	3.1
0.2	5.8	−0.6	3.6	9.2	0.5	1.1	7.2	0.8
3.6	22.0	3.4	1.9	18.2	1.3	1.4	19.3	2.6

11.108 Price-fixing litigation. Multiple regression is sometimes used in litigation. In the case of *Cargill, Inc. v. Hardin,* the prosecution charged that the cash price of wheat was manipulated in violation of the Commodity Exchange Act. In a statistical study conducted for this case, a multiple regression model was constructed to predict the price of wheat using three supply-and-demand explanatory variables.[17] Data for 14 years were used to construct the regression equation, and a prediction for the suspect period was computed from this equation. The value of R^2 was 0.989.

(a) The fitted model gave the predicted value \$2.136 with standard error \$0.013. Express the prediction as an interval. (The degrees of freedom were large for this analysis, so use 100 as the df to determine t^*.)

(b) The actual price for the period in question was \$2.13. The judge decided that the analysis provided evidence that the price was not artificially depressed, and the opinion was sustained by the court of appeals. Write a short summary of the results of the analysis that relate to the decision and explain why you agree or disagree with it.

11.109 Vitamin-enriched bread. Does bread lose its vitamins when stored? Small loaves of bread were prepared with flour that was fortified with a fixed amount of vitamins. After baking, the vitamin C content of two loaves was measured. Another two loaves were baked at the same time, stored for one day, and then the vitamin C content was measured. In a similar manner, two loaves were stored for three, five, and seven days before measurements were taken. The units are milligrams per hundred grams of flour (mg/100 g).[18] Here are the data:

Condition	Vitamin C (mg/100 g)	
Immediately after baking	47.62	49.79
One day after baking	40.45	43.46
Three days after baking	21.25	22.34
Five days after baking	13.18	11.65
Seven days after baking	8.51	8.13

We will use some regression models to examine the relationship between the vitamin C concentration (VitC) and days after baking (Days) using these data.

(a) Run a linear regression to predict VitC using Days. Report the regression equation and the test statistic for the coefficient of Days with its degrees of freedom and P-value, and summarize your conclusion.

(b) Plot VitC versus Days. Also plot the residuals from your model in part (a) versus Days. Interpret these plots.

(c) Run a multiple regression using Days and the square of Days to predict VitC. Summarize the results of all of the relevant significance tests associated with this analysis.

(d) Write a short summary comparing the results of parts (a) and (c) of this exercise. Be sure to mention the values of R^2 for both regressions.

11.110 What about vitamins A and E? Refer to the previous exercise. Measurements of the amounts of vitamin A (beta-carotene) and vitamin E in each loaf are given below. Using the parts of the previous exercise as a guide, analyze the data for each of these vitamins. Write a report summarizing what happens to the three vitamins in bread when it is stored. Be sure to note similarities and differences in the three sets of results.

Condition	Vitamin A (mg/100 g)		Vitamin E (mg/100 g)	
Immediately after baking	3.36	3.34	94.6	96.0
One day after baking	3.28	3.20	95.7	93.2
Three days after baking	3.26	3.16	97.4	94.3
Five days after baking	3.25	3.36	95.0	97.7
Seven days after baking	3.01	2.92	92.3	95.1

Exercises 11.111 to 11.113 use the bank wages data given in Table 10.1 (page 573). For these exercises we code the size of the bank as 1 if it is large and 0 if it is small. There is one outlier in this data set. Delete it and use the remaining 59 observations in these exercises.

11.111 Length of service and wages. Use length of service (LOS) to predict wages with a simple linear regression. Write a short summary of your results and conclusions.

11.112 Size of the bank and wages. Predict wages using the size of the bank as the explanatory variable. Use the coded values 0 and 1 for this model.

(a) Summarize the results of your analysis. Include a statement of all hypotheses, test statistics with degrees of freedom, P-values, and conclusions.

(b) Calculate the t statistic for comparing the mean wages for the large and the small banks assuming equal standard deviations. Give the degrees of freedom. Verify that this t is the same as the t statistic for the coefficient of size in the regression. Explain why this makes sense.

TABLE 11.10 U.S. corn yield

Year	Yield	Year	Yield	Year	Yield	Year	Yield
1957	48.3	1968	79.5	1979	109.5	1990	118.5
1958	52.8	1969	85.9	1980	91.0	1991	108.6
1959	53.1	1970	72.4	1981	108.9	1992	131.5
1960	54.7	1971	88.1	1982	113.2	1993	100.7
1961	62.4	1972	97.0	1983	81.1	1994	138.6
1962	64.7	1973	91.3	1984	106.7	1995	113.5
1963	67.9	1974	71.9	1985	118.0	1996	127.1
1964	62.9	1975	86.4	1986	119.4	1997	126.7
1965	74.1	1976	88.0	1987	119.8	1998	134.4
1966	73.1	1977	90.8	1988	84.6	1999	133.8
1967	80.1	1978	101.0	1989	116.3	2000	136.9

(c) Plot the residuals versus LOS. What do you conclude?

11.113 Use both variables to predict wages. Use a multiple linear regression to predict wages from LOS and the size of the bank. Include an interaction term in your model. Write a report summarizing your work. Include graphs and the results of significance tests.

Exercises 11.114 to 11.120 use the corn and soybean yield data given in Tables 11.10 and 11.11.

11.114 Corn yield varies over time. Run the simple linear regression using year to predict corn yield.

(a) Summarize the results of your analysis, including the significance test results for the slope and R^2 for this model.

(b) Analyze the residuals with a Normal quantile plot. Is there any indication in the plot that the residuals are not Normal?

(c) Plot the residuals versus soybean yield. Does the plot indicate that soybean yield might be useful in a multiple linear regression with year to predict corn yield?

11.115 Can soybean yield predict corn yield? Run the simple linear regression using soybean yield to predict corn yield.

(a) Summarize the results of your analysis, including the significance test results for the slope and R^2 for this model.

(b) Analyze the residuals with a Normal quantile plot. Is there any indication in the plot that the residuals are not Normal?

TABLE 11.11 U.S. soybean yield

Year	Yield	Year	Yield	Year	Yield	Year	Yield
1957	23.2	1968	26.7	1979	32.1	1990	34.1
1958	24.2	1969	27.4	1980	26.5	1991	34.2
1959	23.5	1970	26.7	1981	30.1	1992	37.6
1960	23.5	1971	27.5	1982	31.5	1993	32.6
1961	25.1	1972	27.8	1983	26.2	1994	41.4
1962	24.2	1973	27.8	1984	28.1	1995	35.3
1963	24.4	1974	23.7	1985	34.1	1996	37.6
1964	22.8	1975	28.9	1986	33.3	1997	38.9
1965	24.5	1976	26.1	1987	33.9	1998	38.9
1966	25.4	1977	30.6	1988	27.0	1999	36.6
1967	24.5	1978	29.4	1989	32.3	2000	38.1

(c) Plot the residuals versus year. Does the plot indicate that year might be useful in a multiple linear regression with soybean yield to predict corn yield?

11.116 Use both predictors. From the previous two exercises, we conclude that year *and* soybean yield may be useful together in a model for predicting corn yield. Run this multiple regression.

(a) Explain the results of the ANOVA F test. Give the null and alternative hypotheses, the test statistic with degrees of freedom, and the P-value. What do you conclude?

(b) What percent of the variation in corn yield is explained by these two variables? Compare it with the percent explained in the simple linear regression models of the previous two exercises.

(c) Give the fitted model. Why do the coefficients for year and soybean yield differ from those in the previous two exercises?

(d) Summarize the significance test results for the regression coefficients for year and soybean yield.

(e) Give a 95% confidence interval for each of these coefficients.

(f) Plot the residuals versus year and versus soybean yield. What do you conclude?

11.117 Try a quadratic. We need a new variable to model the curved relation that we see between corn yield and year in the residual plot of the last exercise. Let year2 = $(\text{year} - 1978.5)^2$. (When adding a squared term to a multiple regression model, we sometimes subtract the mean of the variable being squared before squaring. This eliminates the correlation between the linear and quadratic terms in the model and thereby reduces collinearity.)

(a) Run the multiple linear regression using year, year2, and soybean yield to predict corn yield. Give the fitted regression equation.

(b) Give the null and alternative hypotheses for the ANOVA F test. Report the results of this test, giving the test statistic, degrees of freedom, P-value, and conclusion.

(c) What percent of the variation in corn yield is explained by this multiple regression? Compare this with the model in the previous exercise.

(d) Summarize the results of the significance tests for the individual regression coefficients.

(e) Analyze the residuals and summarize your conclusions.

11.118 Compare models. Run the model to predict corn yield using year and the squared term year 2 defined in the previous exercise.

(a) Summarize the significance test results.

(b) The coefficient for year2 is not statistically significant in this run, but it was highly significant in the model analyzed in the previous exercise. Explain how this can happen.

(c) Obtain the fitted values for each year in the data set and use these to sketch the curve on a plot of the data. Plot the least-squares line on this graph for comparison. Describe the differences between the two regression functions. For what years do they give very similar fitted values? For what years are the differences between the two relatively large?

11.119 Do a prediction. Use the simple linear regression model with corn yield as the response variable and year as the explanatory variable to predict the corn yield for the year 2001, and give the 95% prediction interval. Also, use the multiple regression model where year and year2 are both explanatory variables to find another predicted value with the 95% interval. Explain why these two predicted values are so different. The actual yield for 2001 was 138.2 bushels per acre. How well did your models predict this value?

11.120 Predict the yield for another year. Repeat the previous exercise doing the prediction for 2002. Compare the results of this exercise with the previous one. Why are they different?

Exercises 11.121 to 11.129 use the CSDATA data set described in the Data Appendix. Case 11.2 (page 638) also concerned this study of predicting college GPA.

11.121 SAT scores and GPA. Use software to make a plot of GPA versus SATM. Do the same for GPA versus SATV. Describe the general patterns. Are there any unusual values?

11.122 High school grades and GPA. Make a plot of GPA versus HSM. Do the same for the other two high school grade variables. Describe the three plots. Are there any outliers or influential points?

11.123 Predict GPA from high school grades. Regress GPA on the three high school grade variables. Calculate and store the residuals from this regression. Plot the residuals versus each of the three predictors and versus the predicted value of GPA. Are there any unusual points or patterns in these four plots?

11.124 Predict GPA from SAT scores. Use the two SAT scores in a multiple regression to predict GPA. Calculate and store the residuals. Plot the residuals versus each of the explanatory variables and versus the predicted GPA. Describe the plots.

11.125 Use the math explanatory variables. It appears that the mathematics explanatory variables are strong predictors of GPA for computer science students. Run a multiple regression using HSM and SATM to predict GPA.

(a) Give the fitted regression equation.

(b) State the H_0 and H_a tested by the ANOVA F statistic, and explain their meaning in plain language. Report the value of the F statistic, its P-value, and your conclusion.

(c) Give 95% confidence intervals for the regression coefficients of HSM and SATM. Do either of these include the point 0?

(d) Report the t statistics and P-values for the tests of the regression coefficients for HSM and SATM. What conclusions do you draw from these tests?

(e) What is the value of s, the estimate of σ?

(f) What percent of the variation in GPA is explained by HSM and SATM in your model?

11.126 Use the verbal explanatory variables. How well do verbal variables predict the performance of computer science students? Perform a multiple regression analysis to predict GPA from HSE and SATV. Summarize the results and compare them with those obtained in the previous exercise. In what ways do the regression results indicate that the mathematics variables are better predictors?

11.127 Analyze the males. The variable Sex has the value 1 for males and 2 for females. Create a data set containing the values for males only. Run a multiple regression analysis for predicting GPA from the three high school grade variables for this group. Interpret the results and state what conclusions can be drawn from this analysis. In what way (if any) do the results for males alone differ from those for all students?

11.128 Analyze the females and compare. Refer to the previous exercise. Perform the analysis using the data for females only. Are there any important differences between female and male students in predicting GPA?

11.129 The effect of gender. In the previous two exercises, you analyzed the males and females using separate multiple regressions with the high school grades as explanatory variables. Here we will run the analyses together. Recode the variable Sex into a new variable Gender that is an indicator variable. (You can do this by setting Gender equal to Sex minus 1.) Construct three interaction variables that model the interaction between gender and each of the high school grade variables. Then run a multiple regression using seven explanatory variables: the three high school grade variables, gender, and the three interaction variables.

(a) Report the fitted equation and the results of the significance tests for the regression coefficients.

(b) Substitute the value 0 for Gender and simplify the fitted model. This is the model for males. Verify that this is the same fitted model that you obtained in Exercise 11.127.

(c) Repeat part (b) to obtain the results for females and verify that this is the same fitted model that you obtained in Exercise 11.128.

(d) Use software or the method for comparing the coefficients of a collection of q explanatory variables using the values of R^2 (page 647) to test the null hypothesis that the three interaction terms are all zero.

CHAPTER 11 Case Study Exercises

CASE STUDY 1: Predict the quality of a product. This Case Study uses the CHEESE data set described in the Data Appendix. The quality of the cheese is assessed by a panel of tasters whose scores are summarized in a single variable called Taste. This is the response variable for this Case Study. The explanatory variables are three chemicals that are present in the cheese: acetic acid, hydrogen sulfide, and lactic acid. There are 30 cases in this data set. Analyze these data using multiple regression methods and write a report summarizing your results. Be sure to include appropriate graphical displays.

CASE STUDY 2: Self-concept and grade point average of seventh-grade students. This Case Study uses the CONCEPT data set described in the Data Appendix. There are 78 cases, and the response variable is grade point average. Explanatory variables include age, sex, an IQ score, an overall self-concept score, and 6 subscale scores. Use the methods you learned in this chapter to examine models for predicting grade point average from these explanatory variables. Be sure to examine the assumptions needed for the multiple regressions. If there are outliers, be sure to assess their effect on your final results by rerunning the analyses without them.

CASE STUDY 3: Is gender related to salary for hourly employees? This Case Study uses the HOURLY data set described in the Data Appendix. The response variable is annual salary, and the primary explanatory variable of interest is gender. If there is a statistically significant relationship between salary and gender, the company may face litigation.[19] These employees are called "nonexempt" employees because they are subject to the regulations of the Fair Labor Standards Act of 1938, which control things such as overtime pay. Some of the employees work part-time, and this should be taken into consideration when examining the question of gender differences. Analyze the data and write a report summarizing your conclusions. Be sure to include concise numerical summaries and graphical displays that will explain what you have found.

CASE STUDY 4: Is gender related to salary for salaried employees? This Case Study uses the SALARY data set described in the Data Appendix. These data are similar to those in Case Study 3, but here we will look at the salaried employees. These employees are exempt from the Fair Labor Standards Act of 1938. This means, for example, that they do not receive overtime pay. Again, the response variable is annual salary, and the primary explanatory variable of interest is gender. For these employees a major determinant of salary is job level. This variable should be used as an explanatory variable in models where you examine the gender question. Note that the values are integers between 7 and 14. You will need to decide whether or not to treat job level as a categorical variable. Analyze the data and prepare a report summarizing your findings.

CASE STUDY 5: Prices of homes. This Case Study uses the HOMES data set described in the Data Appendix. The file includes the data that we used for Case 11.3 (page 654), as well as data for several other zip codes. Pick a different zip code and analyze the data. Compare your results with what we found for zip code 47904 in Section 11.3.

CHAPTER 11 Appendix

Using Minitab and Excel for Multiple Regression

Scatterplots—Multiple X'S

Minitab:

Graph ➤ Scatterplot

As discussed in the chapter, a preliminary step in the data analysis of multiple variables is to plot the response variable against each of the explanatory variables and, in addition, to plot the explanatory variables against each other. You can do this by creating separate scatterplots for all the pairs of variables (refer to the Appendix of Chapter 2 for guidance on producing individual scatterplots). Alternatively, an option exists to create and present the scatterplots simultaneously. To do this, click the data column for the response variable into row 1 of the **Y variables** box, and click the data column for the first explanatory variable into row 1 of the **X variables** box. Then click the data column for the response variable into row 2 of the **Y variables** box, and click the data column for the second explanatory variable into row 2 of the **X variables** box. Continue this process for as many explanatory variables you have. Thereafter, you can click all the pairs of explanatory variables against each other into the subsequent rows. To have all these scatterplots presented simultaneously, click the **Multiple Graphs** button and then select the **In separate panels of the same graph** option. Click **OK** to close the pop-up box and click **OK** to produce the plots.

Excel:

Excel does not offer an option of presenting multiple scatterplots simultaneously. You will need to create a scatterplot for each pair of variables (refer to the Appendix of Chapter 2 for guidance on producing individual scatterplots).

Multiple Regression—Estimation, Confidence, and Prediction Limits

Minitab:

Stat ➤ Regression ➤ Regression

The only difference from the steps explained for the simple regression model in the Appendices of Chapters 2 and 10 is that you need to click more than one explanatory variable into the **Predictors** box. To obtain confidence intervals for means and prediction intervals, enter the values for each of the p explanatory variables in the **Prediction intervals for new observations** box. (*Note:* The values for the explanatory variables should be inputted in the same order that they have been clicked into the **Predictors** box.)

Excel:

The only difference from the steps explained for the simple regression model in the Appendices of Chapters 2 and 10 is that you need to input a cell range of multiple columns for the multiple explanatory variables. In the spreadsheet, the data for the multiple explanatory variables must be placed in adjacent columns ranging over the same rows. Once the data for explanatory variables have been set up in this fashion, you can then enter the cell range of the explanatory variables into the **Input X Range** box.

Variable Selection

Minitab:

Stat ➤ Regression ➤ Best Subsets

Minitab offers a number of automated variable selection methods to help you find a good subset of explanatory variables without requiring the estimation of all possible subset regressions. As noted in the chapter, one such method is based on examining the R^2-values for all the possible subset regressions and then presenting the models having the highest R^2 for a given number of explanatory variables. In Minitab, this method is known as "Best Subsets Regression" and is invoked by following the above-listed pull-down sequence. In the **Best Subsets Regression** pop-up box click-in the response variable data column into the **Response** box, and click the explanatory variable data column into the **Free predictors** box. Normally, you would input all the explanatory variables into the **Free predictors** box. However, there is a caveat. Explanatory variables that are fully explained by one or more of the other explanatory variables are regarded as "not free" and should not be inputted into the **Free predictors** box. Such a situation is typically encountered when dealing with indicator variables. As mentioned in Section 11.3, if we have I indicator variables for I categories, then only $I - 1$ indicator variables are needed. So, for best subsets regression, you should input all but one of the indicator variables. In default mode, Minitab reports the top two models based on one explanatory variable, then the top two models based on two explanatory variables, and so on. If you click the **Options** button, you can change the number of models that can be reported in the **Models of each size to print** box. Minitab will allow you to report up to five best models. Click **OK** to close the pop-up box, and click **OK** to produce the best subsets regression output.

Excel:

Variable selection methods are not available in standard Excel, but they are available in the enhanced add-on version of Excel.

CHAPTER 12

Statistics for Quality: Control and Capability

PRELUDE: REDUCING HOSPITAL LOSSES

Both nonprofit and for-profit hospitals are financially pressed by restrictions on reimbursement by insurers and the government. Statistical analysis can help identify the sources of losses in a hospital's complex operations and perhaps suggest ways to reduce these losses.

Analysis at one hospital first looked at losses broken down by diagnosis. The leading source, accounting for 15% of the total dollar losses, was joint replacement surgery, mostly hip and knee replacement. *Control charts* based on hospital records showed that these losses were stable over time. That is, the losses are not due to unusual events and will continue at the same rate unless changes are made. Study of bills for joint replacement showed that charges for the actual surgery, for use of the operating room, and for the implant used in joint replacement made up most of the total.

The next step was to analyze costs broken down by the surgeon in charge. There was much variation among surgeons in two key areas. About one-third of surgeons regularly used more than the standard operating room time, thus incurring extra cost that is not reimbursed. The surgeons also chose different brands of implants, some more expensive than others. If implants were standardized, the supplier would offer a lower price. The analysis showed that much of the loss comes from *variation* in the joint replacement process. If the hospital can *reduce variation* by persuading doctors to agree on standard implants and by helping the slow surgeons improve their technique by learning from their peers, losses will come down with no change in patient satisfaction. This chapter presents statistical tools for monitoring the variation in processes of all kinds.[1]

Introduction

Beginning in the 1980s, the marketplace signals were becoming clear: poor quality in products and services would not be tolerated by customers. Organizations increasingly recognized that what they didn't know about the quality of their products could have devastating results: customers often simply left when encountering poor quality, rather than making complaints and hoping that the organization makes changes. To make matters worse, customers would voice their discontent to other customers, resulting in a spiraling negative effect on the organization in question. The twenty-first century's competitive marketplace is pressuring organizations to leave no room for error in the delivery of products and services.

To meet these marketplace challenges, organizations have recognized that a shift to a different paradigm of management thought and action is necessary. The new paradigm calls for developing an organizational system dedicated to customer responsiveness and continuous improvement in quickly developing innovative products and services that at once combine exceptional quality, fast and on-time delivery, and low prices and costs. In the pursuit of developing such an organizational system, there has been an onslaught of recommended management approaches, including Total Quality Management (TQM), Continuous Quality Improvement (CQI), Business Process Engineering (BPR), Business Process Improvement (BPI), and, most recently, Six-Sigma (6σ). In addition, the work of numerous individuals has helped shape contemporary quality thinking. These individuals include W. Edwards Deming, Joseph Juran, Armand Feigenbaum, Kaoru Ishikawa, and Genichi Taguchi.[2]

Since no approach or philosophy is one-size-fits-all, organizations are learning to develop their own personalized versions of a quality management system that integrates the aspects of these approaches and philosophies that best suit the challenges of their competitive environments. However, in the end, it is universally accepted that any effective quality management approach must integrate certain basic themes. Three particular themes are particularly pertinent to our discussions in this chapter. First, as will be discussed in more detail, the modern approach to management views work as a process. Second, a key to maintaining and improving quality is the systematic use of data in place of intuition or anecdotes. Finally, it needs to be recognized that variation is present in all processes and the goal of an organization is to understand and respond wisely to variation.

EXAMPLE 12.1 Using Data to Improve Quality

(a) Sometimes data that are routinely produced make a quality problem obvious. The internal financial statements of a professional society showed that hiring temporary employees to enter membership data was causing expenditures above budgeted levels each year during the several months when memberships were renewed. Investigation led to two actions.

Membership renewal dates were staggered across the year to spread the workload more evenly. More important, outdated and inflexible data entry software was replaced by a modern system that was much easier to use. Result: permanent employees can now process renewals quickly, eliminating the need for temps and also reducing member complaints.

(b) Systematic collection of data helps an organization to move beyond dealing with obvious problems. Motorola places a corporate-wide emphasis on measuring the performance of its services as well as of its manufactured products. Behind the counter of every local service center, for example, is a chart showing the average time from a customer's call until a service person reaches the customer's location, month by month. The trend should be steadily downward as ways are found to speed response.

Because using data is a key to improving quality, statistical methods have much to contribute. Simple tools are often the most effective. Motorola's service centers calculate mean response times each month and make a time plot (Chapter 1). A scatterplot and perhaps a regression line (Chapter 2) can show how the time to answer telephone calls to a corporate call center influences the percent of callers who hang up before their calls are answered. In this chapter, we will introduce you to another simple statistical tool, known as a control chart, which is used extensively to monitor and control processes.

Beyond the application of simple tools, there is an increasing use of more sophisticated statistical tools in the pursuit of quality. For example, the design of a new product as simple as a multivitamin tablet may involve interviewing samples of consumers to learn what vitamins and minerals they want included and using randomized comparative experiments in designing the manufacturing process (Chapter 3). An experiment might discover, for example, what combination of moisture level in the raw vitamin powder and pressure in the tablet-forming press produces the right tablet hardness.

As we proceed to the primary focus of this chapter, it should be underscored that quality is a broad concept with many dimensions. You may feel, for example, that a restaurant serving filet mignon is a higher-quality establishment than a fast-food outlet that serves hamburgers. However, from a standards-based perspective, the fast-food outlet, for example, may be viewed as high quality while the restaurant serving filet mignon is viewed as low quality. This is because, unlike the filet mignons, the hamburgers are freshly grilled, served at the right temperature, and are the same every time you visit. Statistically minded management can assess quality by sampling hamburgers and measuring the time from order to being served, the temperature of the burgers, and their tenderness. In this chapter, we will direct our attention to this dimension of quality associated with process consistency.

This chapter focuses on one particular aspect of statistics for improving quality: *statistical process control.* The techniques are simple and are based on sampling distributions (Chapter 4), but the underlying ideas are important and a bit subtle.

Processes

In thinking about statistical inference, we distinguish between the *sample* data we have in hand and the wider *population* that the data represent. We hope to use the sample to draw conclusions about the population. In thinking about quality improvement, it is often more natural to speak of *processes* rather than populations. This is because work is organized in processes. Here are some examples:

- Processing an application for admission to a university and deciding whether or not to admit the student.

- Reviewing an employee's expense report for a business trip and issuing a reimbursement check.
- Hot forging to shape a billet of titanium into a blank that, after machining, will become part of a medical implant for hip, knee, or shoulder replacement.

Each of these processes is made up of several successive operations that eventually produce the output—an admission decision, reimbursement check, or metal component.

Process

A **process** is a chain of activities that turns inputs into outputs.

We can accommodate processes in our sample-versus-population framework: think of the population as containing all the outputs that would be produced by the process if it ran forever in its present state. The outputs produced today or this week are a sample from this population. Because the population doesn't actually exist now, it is simpler to speak of a process and of recent output as a sample from the process in its present state.

Systematic approach to process improvement

Management by intuition, slogans, or exhortation does not provide an environment or strategy conducive to process improvement. One of the key lessons of quality management is that process improvement should be based on an approach that is systematic, scientific, and fact (data) based.

The systematic steps of process improvement involve identifying the key processes to improve, process understanding/description, root cause analysis, assessment of attempted improvement efforts, and implementation of successful improvements. The systematic steps for process improvement are captured in the Plan-Do-Check-Act (PDCA) cycle. This cycle calls for one to *plan* the intended work, which includes identifying the process to improve, describing the current process, and coming up with solutions for improving the process. One must then *do,* which involves the implementation of the solution or change to the process; typically, improvements are made on a small scale so as not to disrupt the routine activities of the organization. Next, one must *check* to see if the improvement efforts have indeed been successful. Finally, if the process improvement efforts were successful, the organization will *act* by implementing the changes as part of the organization's routine activities. Completion of these general steps represents one PDCA cycle. By continually initiating the PDCA cycle, continuous process improvement is accomplished, as depicted in Figure 12.1.

Advocates of the Six-Sigma approach emphasize that the Six-Sigma improvement model distinguishes itself from other process improvement models in that it calls for projects to be selected only if they are clearly linked to business priorities. This means that not only must projects be linked to customers' needs but they must have a significant financial impact seen in the bottom line. Organizations pursuing process improvement as part of a Six-Sigma effort use a tailored version of the generic PDCA improvement model known as Define-Measure-Analyze-Improve-Control (DMAIC). In the *Define* phase, the goal is to clearly identify an improvement opportunity in measurable terms and establish project goals. In the *Measure* phase, data are gathered to establish the current process

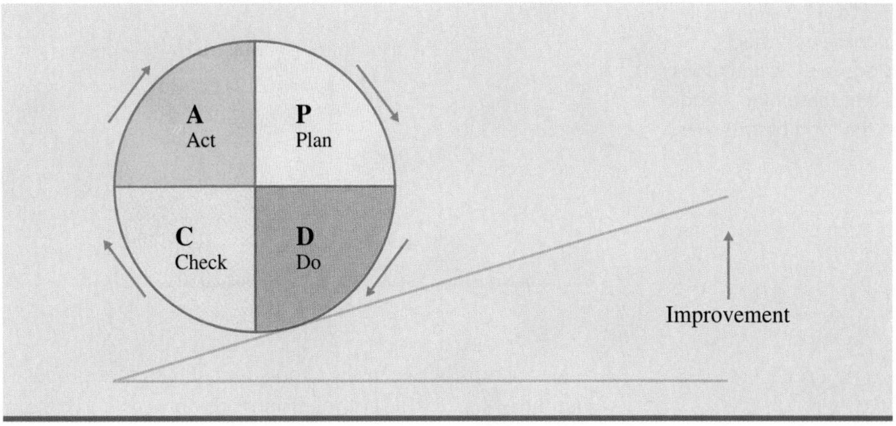

FIGURE 12.1 The PDCA cycle.

performance. In the *Analyze* phase, efforts are made to find the sources (root causes) for less-than-desirable process performance. In many applications, root cause analysis relies on performing appropriately designed experiments and analyzing the resulting data using statistical techniques such as analysis of variance (Chapter 14) and multiple regression (Chapter 11). In the *Improve* phase, solutions are developed and implemented to attack the root causes. Finally, in the *Control* phase, process improvements are institutionalized, and procedures and methods are put into place to hold the process in control so as to maintain the gains from the improvement efforts. One of the most commonly used statistical tools used in the Control phase is the control chart, which is the focus of this chapter.

Process improvement toolkit

Each of the steps of the PDCA and DMAIC improvement models can potentially make use of a variety of tools. The quality literature is rich with examples of tools useful for process improvement. Indeed, a number of statistical tools that we have already introduced in earlier chapters frequently play a key role in process improvement efforts. For example, the Pareto chart (Chapter 1) is used to rank data about the frequency of process problems or causes. The histogram (Chapter 1) allows us to visualize the process behavior in terms of location, variability, and distribution. The scatterplot (Chapter 2) can be used to investigate whether two variables are related, which might help in identifying potential root causes of problems.

Two nonstatistical tools for process improvement efforts are particularly worthy of mention. One of the first steps in improving a process is to understand it. If the process is at all complex, even the people involved with it may not have a full picture of how their work interacts with other steps in ways that influence process quality. A brainstorming session is in order: bring people together to gain an understanding of the process. This understanding is often presented graphically using a **flowchart.** A flowchart is a picture of the stages of a process. Many organizations have formal standards for making flowcharts. Because flowcharts are not statistical graphics, we will informally illustrate their use in a case study and not insist on a specific format. A flowchart can often provide a jump start to the process improvement effort in that it can expose unexpected complexities (for example, unnecessary loops) or non-value-added activities (for example, waiting points that increase overall cycle time). Another useful tool for helping understand the intricacies of a process is a **cause-and-effect diagram.** This diagram organizes the logical

flowchart

cause-and-effect diagram

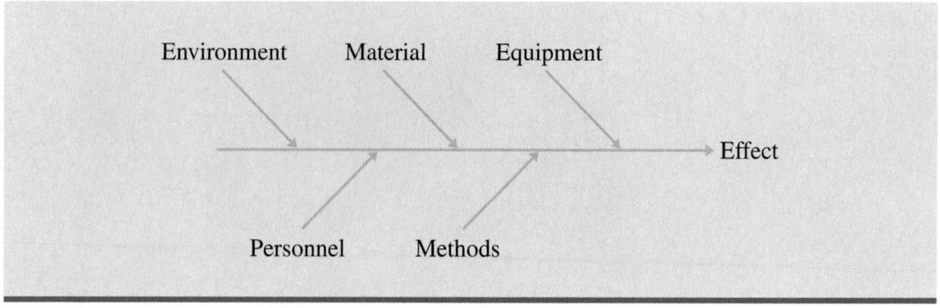

FIGURE 12.2 An outline for a cause-and-effect diagram. Group causes under these main headings in the form of branches.

relationships between the inputs and stages of a process and an output. Sometimes the output is successful completion of the process task; sometimes it is a quality problem that we hope to solve. A good starting outline for a cause-and-effect diagram appears in Figure 12.2. The main branches organize the causes and serve as a skeleton for detailed entries. You can see why these are sometimes called fishbone diagrams. Once again we will illustrate the diagram by a case study rather than insist on a specific format.[3]

CASE 12.1 HOT FORGING

Hot forging involves heating metal to a plastic state and then shaping it by applying thousands of pounds of pressure to force the metal into a die (a kind of mold). Figure 12.3 is a flowchart of a typical hot-forging process.[4]

A process improvement team, after making and discussing this flowchart, came to several conclusions:

- Inspecting the billets of metal received from the supplier adds no value. We should insist that the supplier be responsible for the quality of the material. The supplier should put in place good statistical process control (see Section 12.2) and routinely measure process capability (see Section 12.3). We can then eliminate the inspection step.
- Can we buy the metal billets already cut to rough length and deburred by the supplier, thus eliminating the cost of preparing the raw material ourselves?
- Heating the metal billet and forging (pressing the hot metal into the die) are the heart of the process. We should concentrate our attention here.

The team then prepared a cause-and-effect diagram (Figure 12.4) for the heating and forging part of the process. The team members shared their specialist knowledge of the causes in their area, resulting in a more complete picture than any one person could produce. Figure 12.4 is a simplified version of the actual diagram. We have given some added detail for the "hammer stroke" branch under "equipment" to illustrate the next level of branches. Even this requires some knowledge of hot forging to understand. Based on detailed discussion of the diagram, the team decided what variables to measure and at what stages of the process to measure them. Producing well-chosen data is the key to improving the process.

We will apply statistical methods to a series of measurements made on a process. Deciding what specific variables to measure is an important step in quality improvement. Often we use a "performance measure" that describes an output of a process. A company's financial office might record the percent of errors that outside auditors find in expense account reports or the number of data entry errors per week. The personnel department

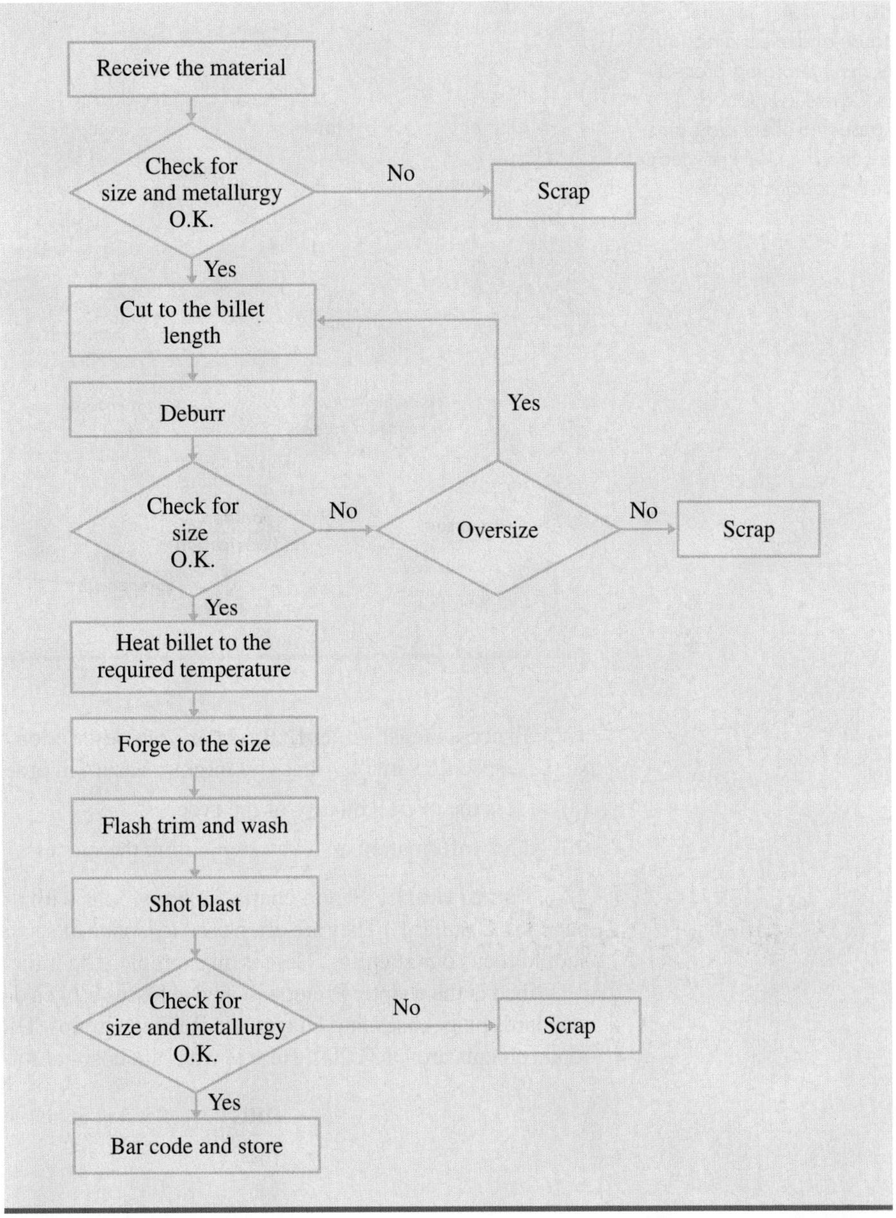

FIGURE 12.3 Flowchart of the hot-forging process in Case 12.1. Use this as a model for flowcharts: decision points appear as diamonds, and other steps in the process appear as rectangles. Arrows represent flow from step to step.

may measure the time to process employee insurance claims or the percent of job offers that are accepted. In the case of complex processes, it is wise to measure key steps within the process rather than just final outputs. The process team in Case 12.1 might recommend that the temperature of the die and of the billet be measured just before forging.

APPLY YOUR KNOWLEDGE

12.1 Describe a process. Choose a process that you know well. If you lack experience with actual business processes, choose a personal process such as cooking scrambled eggs or balancing your checkbook. Make a flowchart of the process. Make a cause-and-effect diagram that presents the factors that lead to successful completion of the process.

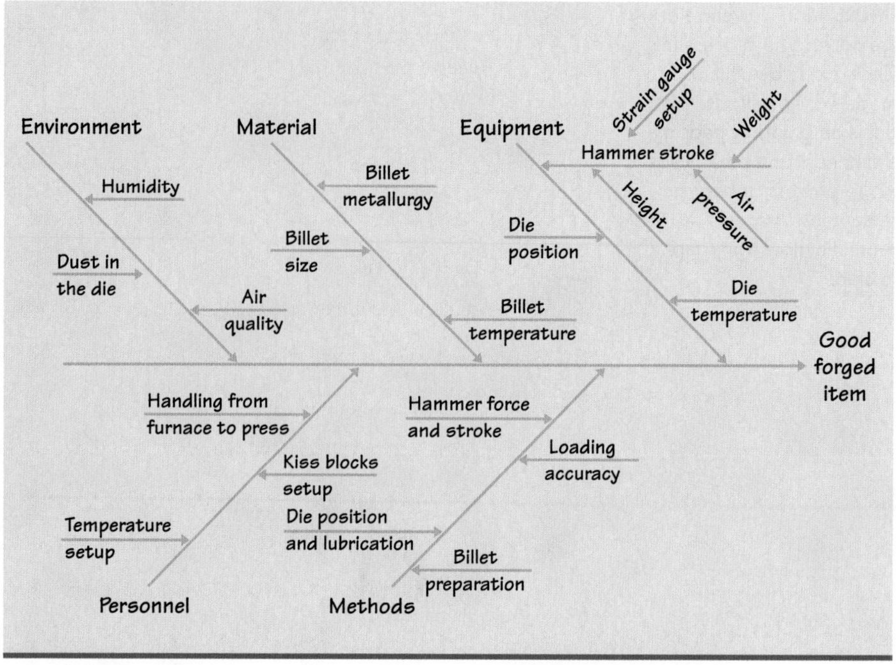

FIGURE 12.4 Simplified cause-and-effect diagram of the hot-forging process in Case 12.1. Good cause-and-effect diagrams require detailed knowledge of the specific process.

12.2 Process measurement. Based on your description of the process in Exercise 12.1, suggest specific variables that you might measure in order to

(a) assess the overall quality of the process.

(b) gather information on a key step within the process.

12.3 Pareto charts. Pareto charts are bar graphs with the bars ordered by height. (See page 8 in Chapter 1.) They are often used to isolate the "vital few" categories on which we should focus our attention. Here is an example. The initial study of losses at the hospital described in the chapter Prelude looked at losses broken down by diagnosis. Government standards place cases into Diagnostic Related Groups (DRGs). For example, major joint replacements are DRG 209. Here is what the hospital found:

DRG	Percent of losses
104	5.2
107	10.1
109	7.7
116	13.7
148	6.8
209	15.2
403	5.6
430	6.8
462	9.4

What percent of total losses do these 9 DRGs account for? Make a Pareto chart of losses by DRG. Which DRGs should the hospital study first when attempting to reduce its losses?

12.1 Statistical Process Control

The goal of statistical process control is to make a process stable over time and then keep it stable unless planned changes are made. You might want, for example, to keep your weight constant over time. A manufacturer of machine parts wants the critical dimensions to be the same for all parts. "Constant over time" and "the same for all" are not realistic requirements. They ignore the fact that *all processes have variation.* Your weight fluctuates from day to day, the critical dimension of a machined part varies a bit from item to item, the time to process a college admission application is not the same for all applications. Variation occurs in even the most precisely made product due to small changes in the raw material, the adjustment of the machine, the behavior of the operator, and even the temperature in the plant. Because variation is always present, we can't expect to hold a variable exactly constant over time. The statistical description of stability over time requires that the *pattern of variation* remain stable, not that there be no variation in the variable measured.

Statistical Control

A process that continues to be described by the same distribution when observed over time is said to be in statistical control, or simply **in control.**

Control charts are statistical tools that monitor a process and alert us when the process has been changed so that it is now **out of control.** This is a signal to find and respond to the cause of the change.

common cause

In the language of statistical quality control, a process that is in control has only common cause variation. **Common cause** variation is the inherent variability of the system, due to many small causes that are always present. Since it is assumed that these many underlying small causes result in small *random* perturbations to which all process outcomes are exposed, their cumulative effect is by definition assumed to be random by nature. Thus, an in-control process is a random process that generates random or independent process outcomes over time.

special cause

When the normal functioning of the process has changed, we say that **special cause** variation is added to the common cause variation. A special cause can be viewed as any factor impinging on the process and resulting in variation not consistent with common cause variation. In contrast to common causes, special causes can often be traced to some clear and identifiable event. Examples might include an operator error, a jammed machine, or a bad batch of raw material. These are classic manufacturing examples where the special cause variation has negative implications on the process. In particular, when dealing with manufacturing processes where the goal is to produce parts as close to targets or specifications as possible, any added variation is undesirable. In such situations, we hope to be able to discover what lies behind special cause variation and eliminate that cause to restore the stable functioning of the process.

Historically, statistical process control (SPC) methods were devised for the monitoring of manufactured parts with the intention of detecting unwanted special cause variation. However, one of the great contributions of the quality revolution is the recognition that any process, not just classical manufacturing processes, has the potential to be improved. In the business arena, SPC methods are routinely used for monitoring services processes, for example, patient waiting time in a hospital clinic. These same methods, however, can be used to monitor the ratings of a television show, daily stock returns, the level of ozone in the atmosphere, or even your golf scores. With this broader perspective, process change due to a special cause might be viewed favorably: for example, a decrease in waiting times or an increase in monthly customer satisfaction ratings. In such situations, our intention should not be to eliminate the special cause but rather to learn about the special cause and promote its effects.

EXAMPLE 12.2 Common Cause, Special Cause

Imagine yourself doing the same task repeatedly, say folding an advertising flyer, stuffing it into an envelope, and sealing the envelope. The time to complete the task will vary a bit, and it is hard to point to any one reason for the variation. Your completion time shows only common cause variation.

Now the telephone rings. You answer, and though you continue folding and stuffing while talking, your completion time rises beyond the level expected from common causes alone. Answering the telephone adds special cause variation to the common cause variation that is always present. The process has been disturbed and is no longer in its normal and stable state.

If you are paying temporary employees to fold and stuff advertising flyers, you avoid this special cause by not having telephones present and by asking your employees to turn off their cell phones while they are working.

The idea underlying control charts is simple but ingenious. By setting limits upon the natural variability of a process, control charts work by distinguishing the always-present common cause variation in a process from the additional variation that suggests that the process has been changed by a special cause. A control chart sounds an alarm when it sees too much variation. Control charts combine graphical and numerical descriptions of data with use of sampling distributions.*

APPLY YOUR KNOWLEDGE

12.4 Special causes. Jeannine participates in bicycle road races. She regularly rides 25 kilometers over the same course in training. Her time varies a bit from day to day but is generally stable. Give several examples of special causes that might raise or lower Jeannine's time on a particular day.

12.5 Common causes and special causes. In Exercise 12.1, you described a process that you know well. What are some sources of common cause variation in this process? What are some special causes that might at times drive the process out of control (unfavorably or favorably)?

$\bar{x}$ charts for process monitoring

When first applying control charts to a process, the process behavior is not fully understood. The process may not be in control. Without stability of the process, any numerical descriptions of the data used to construct the control chart will not serve as reliable guides for monitoring the process into the future. Upon collecting initial data on the process, it is important to assess the stability of the process and bring it into control if it is not. This may mean uncovering and removing the unwanted effects of special causes. Or it may mean incorporating the favorable effects of the special causes and stabilizing the

*Control charts were invented in the 1920s by Walter Shewhart at the Bell Telephone Laboratories. Shewhart's classic book, *Economic Control of Quality of Manufactured Product* (Van Nostrand, New York, 1931), organized the application of statistics to improving quality.

chart setup

process monitoring

process at a more favorable position. We call this the **chart setup** stage. Later, when the process has been operating in control for some time and you understand its usual behavior, control charts are used to monitor the process and alert you to any process changes that occur in the future. We will call this **process monitoring.**[5]

Although in practice chart setup precedes process monitoring, the big ideas of control charts are more easily understood in the process-monitoring setting. We will start there, then discuss the more complex process improvement setting.

Choose a quantitative variable x that is an important measure of quality. The variable might be the diameter of a part, the number of envelopes stuffed in an hour, or the time to respond to a customer call. Here are the conditions for process monitoring.

Process-Monitoring Conditions

Measure a quantitative variable x that has a **Normal distribution.** The process has been operating in control for a long period, so that we know the **process mean** μ and the **process standard deviation** σ that describe the distribution of x as long as the process remains in control.

In practice, we must of course estimate the process mean and standard deviation from past data on the process. Under the process-monitoring conditions, we have very many observations and the process has remained in control. The law of large numbers tells us that estimates from past data will be very close to the truth about the process. That is, at the process-monitoring stage we can act as if we know the true values of μ and σ. Note carefully that μ and σ describe the center and spread of our variable x *only as long as the process remains in control.* A special cause may at any time affect the process and change the mean, the standard deviation, or both.

To make control charts, begin by taking small samples from the process at regular intervals. For example, we might measure 4 or 5 consecutive parts or time the responses to 4 or 5 consecutive customer calls. There is an important idea here: *the observations in a sample are so close together that we can assume that the process is stable during this short period of time.* Variation within the same sample gives us a benchmark for the common cause variation in the process. *The process standard deviation σ refers to the standard deviation within the time period spanned by one sample.* If the process remains in control, the same σ describes the standard deviation of observations across any time period. Control charts help us decide whether this is the case.

$\bar{x}$ chart

We start with the **$\bar{x}$ chart,** which is based on plotting the means of the successive samples. Here is the outline:

1. **Take samples** of size n from the process at regular intervals. **Plot the means** $\bar{x}$ of these samples against the order in which the samples were taken.

2. We know that the sampling distribution of $\bar{x}$ under the process-monitoring conditions is Normal with mean μ and standard deviation $\sigma/\sqrt{n}$ (see page xx). Draw a solid **center line** on the chart at height μ.

center line

3. The 99.7 part of the 68–95–99.7 rule for Normal distributions (page 56) says that, as long as the process remains in control, 99.7% of the values of $\bar{x}$ will fall between $\mu - 3\sigma/\sqrt{n}$ and $\mu + 3\sigma/\sqrt{n}$. Draw dashed **control limits** on the chart at these heights. The control limits mark off the range of variation in sample means that we expect to see when the process remains in control.

control limits

If the process remains in control and the process mean and standard deviation do not change, we will rarely observe an $\overline{x}$ outside the control limits. Such an $\overline{x}$ is therefore a signal that the underlying conditions of the process may have changed.

CASE 12.2 MANUFACTURING COMPUTER MONITORS

A manufacturer of computer monitors must control the tension on the mesh of fine vertical wires that lies behind the surface of the viewing screen. Too much tension will tear the mesh, and too little will allow wrinkles. Tension is measured by an electrical device with output readings in millivolts (mV). The manufacturing process has been stable with mean tension $\mu = 275$ mV and process standard deviation $\sigma = 43$ mV.

The mean 275 mV and the common cause variation measured by the standard deviation 43 mV describe the stable state of the process. If these values are not satisfactory—for example, if there is too much variation among the monitors—the manufacturer must make some fundamental change in the process. This might involve buying new equipment or changing the alloy used in the wires of the mesh. One advantage of statistical control is that we know how the process will behave and can decide whether its behavior is satisfactory. In fact, the common cause variation in mesh tension does not affect the performance of the monitors. We want to watch the process and maintain its current condition.

The operator measures the tension on a sample of 4 monitors each hour. Table 12.1 gives the last 20 samples. The table also gives the mean $\overline{x}$ and the standard deviation s for each sample. The operator did not have to calculate these—modern measuring equipment often comes equipped with software that automatically records $\overline{x}$ and s and even produces control charts.

TABLE 12.1 Twenty control chart samples of mesh tension

Sample	Tension measurements				Sample mean	Standard deviation
1	234.5	272.3	234.5	272.3	253.4	21.8
2	311.1	305.8	238.5	286.2	285.4	33.0
3	247.1	205.3	252.6	316.1	255.3	45.7
4	215.4	296.8	274.2	256.8	260.8	34.4
5	327.9	247.2	283.3	232.6	272.7	42.5
6	304.3	236.3	201.8	238.5	245.2	42.8
7	268.9	276.2	275.6	240.2	265.2	17.0
8	282.1	247.7	259.8	272.8	265.6	15.0
9	260.8	259.9	247.9	345.3	278.5	44.9
10	329.3	231.8	307.2	273.4	285.4	42.5
11	266.4	249.7	231.5	265.2	253.2	16.3
12	168.8	330.9	333.6	318.3	287.9	79.7
13	349.9	334.2	292.3	301.5	319.5	27.1
14	235.2	283.1	245.9	263.1	256.8	21.0
15	257.3	218.4	296.2	275.2	261.8	33.0
16	235.1	252.7	300.6	297.6	271.5	32.7
17	286.3	293.8	236.2	275.3	272.9	25.6
18	328.1	272.6	329.7	260.1	297.6	36.5
19	316.4	287.4	373.0	286.0	315.7	40.7
20	296.8	350.5	280.6	259.8	296.9	38.8

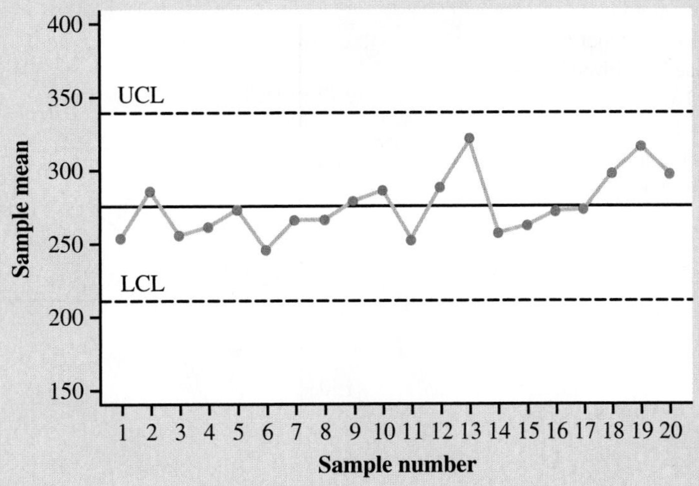

FIGURE 12.5 $\overline{x}$ chart for the mesh tension data of Table 12.1. No points lie outside the control limits.

Figure 12.5 is an $\overline{x}$ control chart for the 20 mesh tension samples in Table 12.1. We have plotted each sample mean from the table against its sample number. For example, the mean of the first sample was 253.4 mV, and this is the value plotted for sample 1. The center line is at $\mu = 275$ mV. The upper and lower control limits are

$$\mu + 3\frac{\sigma}{\sqrt{n}} = 275 + 3\frac{43}{\sqrt{4}} = 275 + 64.5 = 339.5 \text{ mV} \qquad \text{(UCL)}$$

$$\mu - 3\frac{\sigma}{\sqrt{n}} = 275 - 3\frac{43}{\sqrt{4}} = 275 - 64.5 = 210.5 \text{ mV} \qquad \text{(LCL)}$$

As is common, we have labeled the control limits UCL for upper control limit and LCL for lower control limit.

EXAMPLE 12.3 Interpreting $\overline{x}$ Charts

CASE 12.2 

Figure 12.5 is a typical $\overline{x}$ chart for a process in control. The means of the 20 samples do vary, but all lie within the range of variation marked out by the control limits. We are seeing the common cause variation of a stable process. There is an important management implication here. As long as the process continues to behave in this way, any adjustments to in-control process outcomes are a waste of time and resources. In fact, tampering with an in-control process can have the adverse effect of increasing process variation. Short of fundamental changes to the process, no action is the best action. Control charts were devised not only to signal when to respond but also to protect the process from counterproductive interventions.*

*In the classic book by W. Edwards Deming, *Out of the Crisis* (MIT Center for Advanced Engineering Study, Cambridge, MA, 1986), Deming demonstrates the effects of counterproductive adjustment to an in-control process by means of a physical experiment based on dropping marbles through a funnel onto a tabletop. Participants of the experiment learn that the least scatter on the tabletop is obtained by not moving the funnel, that is, by means of "no action."

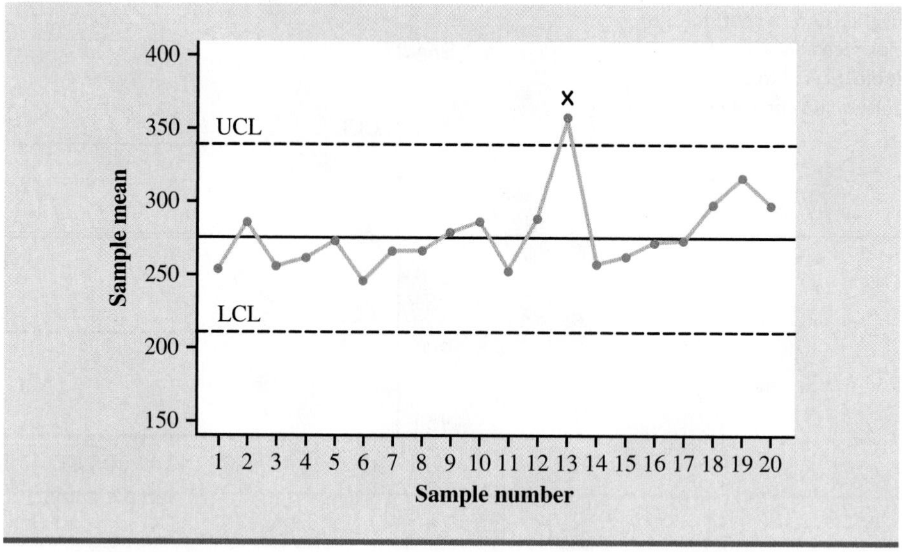

FIGURE 12.6 This $\bar{x}$ chart is identical to that in Figure 12.5 except that a special cause has driven $\bar{x}$ for sample 13 above the upper control limit. The out-of-control point is marked with an x.

Figures 12.6 and 12.7 illustrate two ways in which the process can go out of control. In Figure 12.6, the process was disturbed by a special cause sometime between sample 12 and sample 13. As a result, the mean tension for sample 13 falls above the upper control limit. It is common practice to mark all out-of-control points with an "x" to call attention to them. A search for the cause begins as soon as we see a point out of control. Investigation finds that the mounting of the tension-measuring device has slipped, resulting in readings that are too high. When the problem is corrected, samples 14 to 20 are again in control.

Figure 12.7 shows the effect of a steady upward drift in the process center, starting at sample 11. You see that some time elapses before the $\bar{x}$ for sample 18 is out of control. The one-point-out signal works better for detecting sudden large disturbances than for detecting slow drifts in a process.

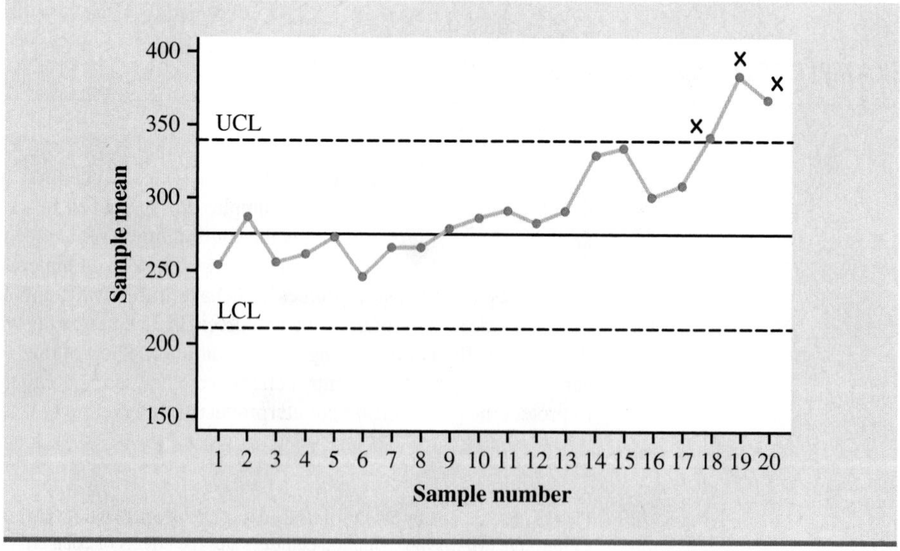

FIGURE 12.7 The first 10 points on this $\bar{x}$ chart are as in Figure 12.5. The process mean drifts upward after sample 10, and the sample means $\bar{x}$ reflect this drift. The points for samples 18, 19, and 20 are out of control.

We have learned that the control chart was originally designed to detect disturbances to common cause variability, reflecting special causes, which are unexpected and unwanted. However, as noted, modern applications of control charts recognize situations where special cause effects may be desirable. Unexpected changes with favorable implications might be described as serendipitous discoveries. Such discoveries should be studied by the organization so that the knowledge gained can result in a sustained process improvement.

However, control charts are not just useful for detecting unexpected changes. Control charts can be used to judge whether a planned attempt to improve a process has resulted in a successful change or not. Checking for successful change is a critical aspect of the "Check" phase of PDCA and the "Improve" phase of DMAIC. Figure 12.8(a) shows a case where the control chart demonstrates a successful attempt to decrease the time (in hours) needed to obtain lab results in a hospital (sample means based on samples of

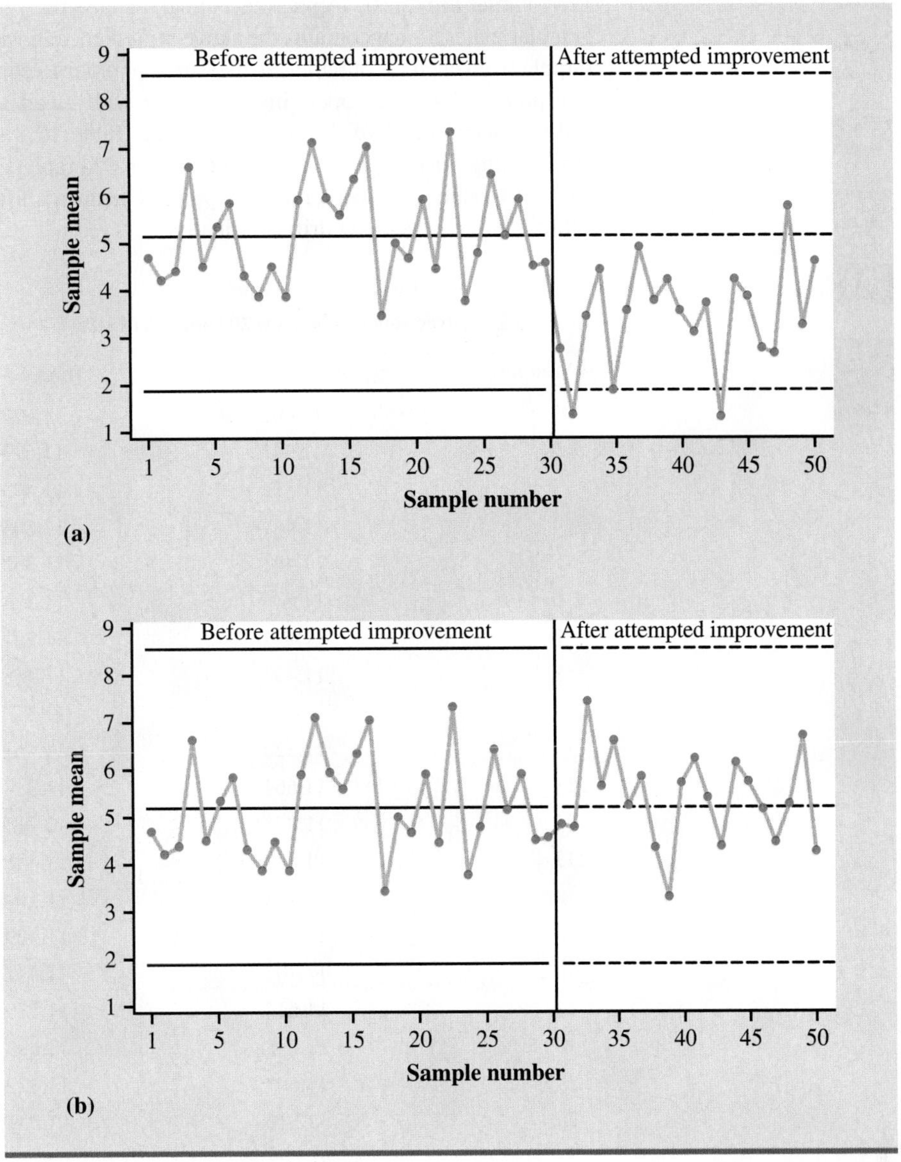

FIGURE 12.8 Using control charts to assess improvement efforts.

patients taken each shift). In this case, control chart limits should be revised, and the new process should be monitored to maintain the gains, as called for in the "Control" phase of the DMAIC improvement model. However, if sample means are as seen Figure 12.8(b), then the control chart indicates no impact from the attempted process improvement; the organization should then seek alternative improvement ideas.

APPLY YOUR KNOWLEDGE

12.6 Auto thermostats. A maker of auto air conditioners checks a sample of 4 thermostatic controls from each hour's production. The thermostats are set at 75°F and then placed in a chamber where the temperature is raised gradually. The temperature at which the thermostat turns on the air conditioner is recorded. The process mean should be $\mu = 75°$. Past experience indicates that the response temperature of properly adjusted thermostats varies with $\sigma = 0.5°$. The mean response temperature $\bar{x}$ for each hour's sample is plotted on an $\bar{x}$ control chart. Calculate the center line and control limits for this chart.

12.7 Tablet hardness. A pharmaceutical manufacturer forms tablets by compressing a granular material that contains the active ingredient and various fillers. The hardness of a sample from each lot of tablets is measured in order to control the compression process. The process has been operating in control with mean at the target value $\mu = 11.5$ and estimated standard deviation $\sigma = 0.2$. Table 12.2 gives three sets of data, each representing $\bar{x}$ for 20 successive samples of $n = 4$ tablets. One set remains in control at the target value. In a second set, the process mean μ shifts suddenly to a new value. In a third, the process mean drifts gradually.

TABLE 12.2 Three sets of $\bar{x}$'s from 20 samples of size 4

Sample	Data set A	Data set B	Data set C
1	11.602	11.627	11.495
2	11.547	11.613	11.475
3	11.312	11.493	11.465
4	11.449	11.602	11.497
5	11.401	11.360	11.573
6	11.608	11.374	11.563
7	11.471	11.592	11.321
8	11.453	11.458	11.533
9	11.446	11.552	11.486
10	11.522	11.463	11.502
11	11.664	11.383	11.534
12	11.823	11.715	11.624
13	11.629	11.485	11.629
14	11.602	11.509	11.575
15	11.756	11.429	11.730
16	11.707	11.477	11.680
17	11.612	11.570	11.729
18	11.628	11.623	11.704
19	11.603	11.472	11.052
20	11.816	11.531	11.905

(a) What are the center line and control limits for an $\bar{x}$ chart for this process?

(b) Draw a separate $\bar{x}$ chart for each of the three data sets. Mark any points that are beyond the control limits.

(c) Based on your work in (b) and the appearance of the control charts, which set of data comes from a process that is in control? In which case does the process mean shift suddenly and at about which sample do you think that the mean changed? Finally, in which case does the mean drift gradually?

s charts for process monitoring

The $\bar{x}$ charts in Figures 12.5, 12.6, and 12.7 were easy to interpret because the process standard deviation remained fixed at 43 mV. The effects of moving the process mean away from its in-control value (275 mV) are then clear to see. We know that even the simplest description of a distribution should give both a measure of center and a measure of spread. So it is with control charts. We must monitor both the process center, using an $\bar{x}$ chart, and the process spread, using a control chart for the sample standard deviation s.

The standard deviation s does not have a Normal distribution, even approximately. Under the process-monitoring conditions, the sampling distribution of s is skewed to the right. Nonetheless, control charts for any statistic are based on the "plus or minus three standard deviations" idea motivated by the 68–95–99.7 rule for Normal distributions. Control charts are intended to be practical tools that are easy to use. Standard practice in process control therefore ignores such details as the effect of non-Normal sampling distributions. Here is the general control chart setup for a sample statistic Q (short for "quality characteristic").

Three-Sigma Control Charts

To make a **three-sigma control chart** for any statistic Q:

1. Take samples from the process at regular intervals and plot the values of the statistic Q against the order in which the samples were taken.
2. Draw a **center line** on the chart at height μ_Q, the mean of the statistic when the process is in control.
3. Draw upper and lower **control limits** on the chart three standard deviations of Q below and above the mean. That is,

$$\text{UCL} = \mu_Q + 3\sigma_Q$$

$$\text{LCL} = \mu_Q - 3\sigma_Q$$

   Here σ_Q is the standard deviation of the sampling distribution of the statistic Q when the process is in control.

4. The chart produces an **out-of-control signal** when a plotted point lies outside the control limits.

We have applied this general idea to $\bar{x}$ charts. If μ and σ are the process mean and standard deviation, the statistic $\bar{x}$ has mean $\mu_{\bar{x}} = \mu$ and standard deviation $\sigma_{\bar{x}} = \sigma/\sqrt{n}$. The center line and control limits for $\bar{x}$ charts follow from these facts.

What are the corresponding facts for the sample standard deviation s? Study of the sampling distribution of s for samples from a Normally distributed process characteristic gives these facts:

1. The *mean* of s is a constant times the process standard deviation σ, $\mu_s = c_4\sigma$.
2. The *standard deviation* of s is also a constant times the process standard deviation, $\sigma_s = c_5\sigma$.

The constants are called c_4 and c_5 for historical reasons. Their values depend on the size of the samples. For large samples, c_4 is close to 1. That is, the sample standard deviation s has little bias as an estimator of the process standard deviation σ. Because statistical process control often uses small samples, we pay attention to the value of c_4. Following the general pattern for three-sigma control charts:

1. The *center line* of an s chart is at $c_4\sigma$.
2. The *control limits* for an s chart are at

$$\text{UCL} = \mu_s + 3\sigma_s = c_4\sigma + 3c_5\sigma = (c_4 + 3c_5)\sigma$$
$$\text{LCL} = \mu_s - 3\sigma_s = c_4\sigma - 3c_5\sigma = (c_4 - 3c_5)\sigma$$

That is, the control limits LCL and UCL are also constants times the process standard deviation. These constants are called (again for historical reasons) B_6 and B_5. We don't need to remember that $B_6 = c_4 + 3c_5$ and $B_5 = c_4 - 3c_5$, because tables give us the numerical values of B_6 and B_5.

$\bar{x}$ and s Control Charts for Process Monitoring[6]

Take regular samples of size n from a process that has been in control with process mean μ and process standard deviation σ. The center line and control limits for an $\bar{x}$ **chart** are

$$\text{UCL} = \mu + 3\frac{\sigma}{\sqrt{n}}$$
$$\text{CL} = \mu$$
$$\text{LCL} = \mu - 3\frac{\sigma}{\sqrt{n}}$$

The center line and control limits for an s **chart** are

$$\text{UCL} = B_6\sigma$$
$$\text{CL} = c_4\sigma$$
$$\text{LCL} = B_5\sigma$$

The **control chart constants** c_4, B_5, and B_6 depend on the sample size n.

Table 12.3 gives the values of the control chart constants c_4, c_5, B_5, and B_6 for samples of sizes 2 to 10. This table makes it easy to draw s charts. The table has no B_5 entries for samples of size smaller than $n = 6$. The lower control limit for an s chart is zero for samples of sizes 2 to 5. This is a consequence of the fact that s has a right-skewed distribution and takes only values greater than zero. Three standard deviations above the

TABLE 12.3 **Control chart constants**

Sample size n	c_4	c_5	B_5	B_6
2	0.7979	0.6028		2.606
3	0.8862	0.4633		2.276
4	0.9213	0.3889		2.088
5	0.9400	0.3412		1.964
6	0.9515	0.3076	0.029	1.874
7	0.9594	0.2820	0.113	1.806
8	0.9650	0.2622	0.179	1.751
9	0.9693	0.2459	0.232	1.707
10	0.9727	0.2321	0.276	1.669

mean (UCL) lies on the long right side of the distribution. Three standard deviations below the mean (LCL) on the short left side is below zero, so we say that LCL = 0.

EXAMPLE 12.4 $\bar{x}$ and s Charts for Mesh Tension

CASE 12.2

Figure 12.9 is the s chart for the computer monitor mesh tension data in Table 12.1. The samples are of size $n = 4$ and the process standard deviation in control is $\sigma = 43$ mV. The center line is therefore

$$\text{CL} = c_4\sigma = (0.9213)(43) = 39.6 \text{ mV}$$

The control limits are

$$\text{UCL} = B_6\sigma = (2.088)(43) = 89.8$$

$$\text{LCL} = B_5\sigma = (0)(43) = 0$$

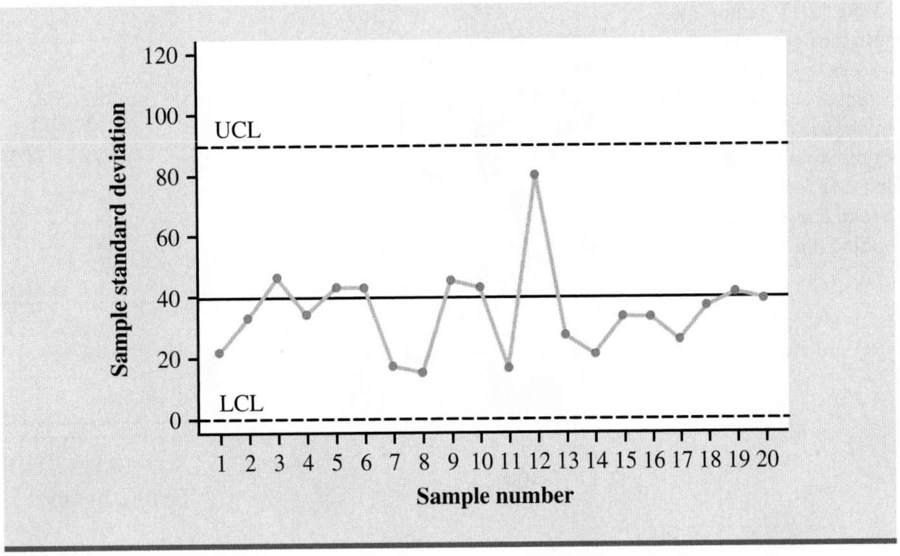

FIGURE 12.9 s chart for the mesh tension data of Table 12.1. Both the s chart and the $\bar{x}$ chart (Figure 12.5) are in control.

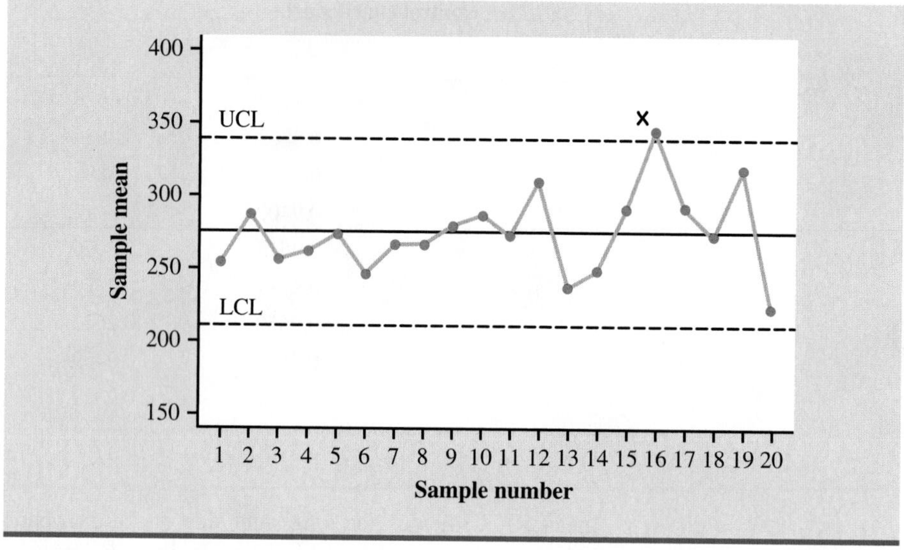

FIGURE 12.10 $\bar{x}$ chart for mesh tension when the process variability increases after sample 10. The $\bar{x}$ chart does show the increased variability, but the s chart is clearer and should be read first.

Figures 12.5 and 12.9 go together: they are $\bar{x}$ and s charts for monitoring the mesh-tensioning process. Both charts are in control, showing only common cause variation within the bounds set by the control limits.

Figures 12.10 and 12.11 are $\bar{x}$ and s charts for the mesh-tensioning process when a new and poorly trained operator takes over between samples 10 and 11. The new operator introduces added variation into the process, increasing the process standard deviation from its in-control value of 43 mV to 60 mV. The $\bar{x}$ chart in Figure 12.10 shows one point out of control. Only on closer inspection do we see that the spread of the $\bar{x}$'s increases after sample 10. In fact, the process mean has remained unchanged at 275 mV. The apparent lack of control in the $\bar{x}$ chart is entirely due to the larger process variation. There is a lesson here: *it is difficult to interpret an* $\bar{x}$ *chart unless* s *is in control.* When you look at $\bar{x}$ and s charts, always start with the s chart.

The s chart in Figure 12.11 shows lack of control starting at sample 11. As usual, we mark the out-of-control points by an "x." The points for samples 13 and 15 also lie above the UCL, and the

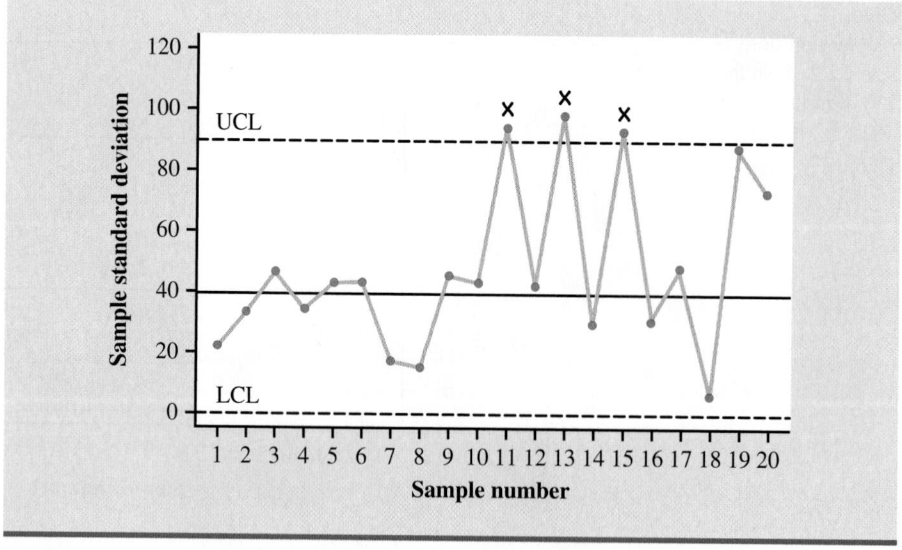

FIGURE 12.11 s chart for mesh tension when the process variability increases after sample 10. Increased within-sample variability is clearly visible. Find and remove the s-type special cause before reading the $\bar{x}$ chart.

overall spread of the sample points is much greater than for the first 10 samples. In practice, the s chart would call for action after sample 11. We would ignore the $\bar{x}$ chart until the special cause (the new operator) for the lack of control in the s chart has been found and removed by training the operator.

Example 12.4 suggests a strategy for using $\bar{x}$ and s charts in practice. First examine the s chart. Lack of control on an s chart is due to special causes that affect the observations *within a sample* differently. New and nonuniform raw material, a new and poorly trained operator, and mixing results from several machines or several operators are typical "s-type" special causes.

Once the s chart is in control, the stable value of the process standard deviation σ means that the variation within samples serves as a benchmark for detecting variation in the level of the process over the longer time periods between samples. The $\bar{x}$ chart, with control limits that depend on σ, does this. The $\bar{x}$ chart, as we saw in Example 12.4, responds to s-type causes as well as to longer-range changes in the process, so it is important to eliminate s-type special causes first. Then the $\bar{x}$ chart will alert us to, for example, a change in process level caused by new raw material that differs from that used in the past or a gradual drift in the process level caused by wear in a cutting tool.

EXAMPLE 12.5 s-Type and $\bar{x}$-Type Special Causes

A large health maintenance organization (HMO) uses control charts to monitor the process of directing patient calls to the proper department or doctor's receptionist. Each day at a random time, 5 consecutive calls are recorded electronically. The first call today is handled quickly by an experienced operator, but the next goes to a newly hired operator who must ask a supervisor for help. The sample has a large s, and lack of control signals the need to train new hires more thoroughly.

The same HMO monitors the time required to receive orders from its main supplier of pharmaceutical products. After a long period in control, the $\bar{x}$ chart shows a systematic shift downward in the mean time because the supplier has changed to a more efficient delivery service. This is a desirable special cause, but it is nonetheless a systematic change in the process. The HMO will have to establish new control limits that describe the new state of the process, with smaller process mean μ.

The second setting in Example 12.5 reminds us that a major change in the process returns us to the chart setup stage. In the absence of deliberate changes in the process, process monitoring uses the same values of μ and σ for long periods of time. One exception is common: careful monitoring and removal of special causes as they occur can permanently reduce the process σ. Because for small sample sizes the lower control limit of the s chart is 0, any reductions in the process standard deviation cannot be flagged with a point below the control limit. Reductions in the process standard deviation are recognized if the points on the s chart trend downward or remain near or below the center line for a long period of time. If this is the case, it is wise to update the value of σ to the new, smaller value.

APPLY YOUR KNOWLEDGE

12.8 Responding to applicants. The personnel department of a large company records a number of performance measures. Among them is the time required to respond to an application for employment, measured from the time the application arrives. Suggest some plausible examples of each of the following.

(a) Reasons for common cause variation in response time.

(b) s-type special causes.

(c) $\bar{x}$-type special causes.

12.9 Auto thermostats. In Exercise 12.6 you gave the center line and control limits for an $\bar{x}$ chart. What are the center line and control limits for an s chart for this process?

12.10 Tablet hardness. Exercise 12.7 concerns process control data on the hardness of tablets for a pharmaceutical product. Table 12.4 gives data for 20 new samples of size 4, with the $\bar{x}$ and s for each sample. The process has been in control with mean at the target value $\mu = 11.5$ and standard deviation $\sigma = 0.2$.

(a) Make both $\bar{x}$ and s charts for these data based on the information given about the process.

(b) At some point, the within-sample process variation increased from $\sigma = 0.2$ to $\sigma = 0.4$. About where in the 20 samples did this happen? What is the effect on the s chart? On the $\bar{x}$ chart?

(c) At that same point, the process mean changed from $\mu = 11.5$ to $\mu = 11.7$. What is the effect of this change on the s chart? On the $\bar{x}$ chart?

TABLE 12.4 Twenty samples of size 4, with $\bar{x}$ and s

Sample	Hardness				$\bar{x}$	s
1	11.432	11.350	11.582	11.184	11.387	0.1660
2	11.791	11.323	11.734	11.512	11.590	0.2149
3	11.373	11.807	11.651	11.651	11.620	0.1806
4	11.787	11.585	11.386	11.245	11.501	0.2364
5	11.633	11.212	11.568	11.469	11.470	0.1851
6	11.648	11.653	11.618	11.314	11.558	0.1636
7	11.456	11.270	11.817	11.402	11.486	0.2339
8	11.394	11.754	11.867	11.003	11.504	0.3905
9	11.349	11.764	11.402	12.085	11.650	0.3437
10	11.478	11.761	11.907	12.091	11.809	0.2588
11	11.657	12.524	11.468	10.946	11.649	0.6564
12	11.820	11.872	11.829	11.344	11.716	0.2492
13	12.187	11.647	11.751	12.026	11.903	0.2479
14	11.478	11.222	11.609	11.271	11.395	0.1807
15	11.750	11.520	11.389	11.803	11.616	0.1947
16	12.137	12.056	11.255	11.497	11.736	0.4288
17	12.055	11.730	11.856	11.357	11.750	0.2939
18	12.107	11.624	11.727	12.207	11.916	0.2841
19	11.933	10.658	11.708	11.278	11.394	0.5610
20	12.512	12.315	11.671	11.296	11.948	0.5641

SECTION 12.1 SUMMARY

- Work is organized in **processes,** chains of activities that lead to some result. We use **flowcharts** and **cause-and-effect diagrams** to describe processes.
- All processes have variation. If the pattern of variation is stable over time, the process is **in statistical control. Control charts** are statistical plots intended to warn when a process is **out of control.**
- Standard **3σ control charts** plot the values of some statistic Q for regular samples from the process against the time order of the samples. The **center line** is at the mean of Q. The **control limits** lie three standard deviations of Q above and below the center line. A point outside the control limits is an **out-of-control signal.** For **process monitoring** of a process that has been in control, the mean and standard deviation are based on past data from the process and are updated regularly.
- When we measure some quantitative characteristic of the process, we use **$\bar{x}$ and s charts** for process control. The s chart monitors variation within individual samples. If the s chart is in control, the $\bar{x}$ chart monitors variation from sample to sample. To interpret the charts, always look first at the s chart.

SECTION 12.1 Exercises

For Exercises 12.1 to 12.3, see pages 691–692; for 12.4 and 12.5, see page 694; for 12.6 and 12.7, see page 700; and for 12.8 to 12.10, see pages 705–706.

12.11 Describe a process. Each weekday morning, you must get to work or to your first class on time. Make a flowchart of your daily process for doing this, starting when you wake. Be sure to include the time at which you plan to start each step.

12.12 Common cause, special cause. Each weekday morning, you must get to work or to your first class on time. The time at which you reach work or class varies from day to day, and your planning must allow for this variation. List several common causes of variation in your arrival time. Then list several special causes that might result in unusual variation, such as being late to work or class.

12.13 Pareto charts. Continue the study of the process of getting to work or class on time. If you kept good records, you could make a Pareto chart of the reasons (special causes) for late arrivals at work or class. Make a Pareto chart that you think roughly describes your own reasons for lateness. That is, list the reasons from your experience and chart your estimates of the percent of late arrivals each reason explains.

12.14 Pareto charts. Painting new auto bodies is a multistep process. There is an "electrocoat" that resists corrosion, a primer, a color coat, and a gloss coat. A quality study for one paint shop produced this breakdown of the primary problem type for those autos whose paint did not meet the manufacturer's standards:

Problem	Percent
Electrocoat uneven—redone	4%
Poor adherence of color to primer	5%
Lack of clarity in color	2%
"Orange peel" texture in color	32%
"Orange peel" texture in gloss	1%
Ripples in color coat	28%
Ripples in gloss coat	4%
Uneven color thickness	19%
Uneven gloss thickness	5%
Total	100%

Make a Pareto chart. Which stage of the painting process should we look at first?

12.15 Milling. The width of a slot cut by a milling machine is important to the proper functioning of a hydraulic system for large tractors. The manufacturer checks the control of the milling process by measuring a sample of 5 consecutive items during each hour's production.

The target width for the slot is $\mu = 0.8750$ inch. The process has been operating in control with center close to the target and $\sigma = 0.0012$ inch. What center line and control limits should be drawn on the s chart? On the $\bar{x}$ chart?

12.16 Dyeing yarn. The unique colors of the cashmere sweaters your firm makes result from heating undyed yarn in a kettle with a dye liquor. The pH (acidity) of the liquor is critical for regulating dye uptake and hence the final color. There are 5 kettles, all of which receive dye liquor from a common source. Twice each day, the pH of the liquor in each kettle is measured, giving a sample of size 5. The process has been operating in control with $\mu = 4.22$ and $\sigma = 0.127$.

(a) Give the center line and control limits for the s chart.

(b) Give the center line and control limits for the $\bar{x}$ chart.

12.17 Mounting-hole distances. Figure 12.12 reproduces a data sheet from the floor of a factory that makes electrical meters.[7] The sheet shows measurements on the distance between two mounting holes for 18 samples of size 5. The heading informs us that the measurements are in multiples of 0.0001 inch above 0.6000 inch. That is, the first measurement 44 stands for 0.6044 inch. All the measurements end in 4. Although we don't know why this is true, it is clear that in effect the measurements were made to the nearest 0.001 inch, not to the nearest 0.0001 inch.

Calculate $\bar{x}$ and s for the first two samples. The data file *ex12_17* contains $\bar{x}$ and s for all 18 samples. Based on long experience with this process, you are keeping control charts based on $\mu = 43$ and $\sigma = 12.74$. Make s and $\bar{x}$ charts for the data in Figure 12.12 and describe the state of the process.

12.18 Dyeing yarn: special causes. The process described in Exercise 12.16 goes out of control. Investigation finds that a new type of yarn was recently introduced. The pH in the kettles is influenced by both the dye liquor and the yarn. Moreover, on a few occasions a faulty valve on one of the kettles had allowed water to enter that kettle; as a result, the yarn in that kettle had to be discarded. Which of these special causes appears on the s chart and which on the $\bar{x}$ chart? Explain your answer.

12.19 Probability out? An $\bar{x}$ chart plots the means of samples of size 4 against center line CL = 700 and control limits LCL = 687 and UCL = 713. The process has been in control. Now the process is disrupted in a way that changes the mean to $\mu = 693$ and the standard deviation to $\sigma = 12$. What is the probability that the first sample after the disruption gives a point beyond the control limits of the $\bar{x}$ chart?

12.20 Alternative control limits. American and Japanese practice uses 3σ control charts. That is, the control limits are 3 standard deviations on either side of the mean. When the statistic being plotted has a Normal distribution, the probability of a point outside the limits

VARIABLES CONTROL CHART ($\bar{X}$ & R)

Part No. 32506	Chart No. 1

Part name (project)	Operation (process)	Specification limits
Metal frame	Distance between mounting holes	0.6054" ± 0.0010"

Operator	Machine	Gage	Unit of measure	Zero equals
	R-5		0.0001"	0.6000"

Date		3/7				3/8						3/9							
Time		8:30	10:30	11:45	1:30	8:15	10:15	11:45	2:00	3:00	4:00	8:30	10:00	11:45	1:30	2:30	3:30	4:30	5:30
Sample measurements	1	44	64	34	44	34	34	54	64	24	34	34	54	44	24	54	54	54	54
	2	44	44	44	54	14	64	64	34	54	44	44	44	24	24	24	34	34	24
	3	44	34	54	54	84	34	34	54	44	44	34	24	34	54	54	24	74	64
	4	44	34	44	34	54	44	44	44	34	34	64	54	34	44	44	44	44	34
	5	64	54	54	44	44	44	34	44	34	34	34	24	44	44	44	54	54	44
Average, $\bar{X}$																			
Range, R		20	30	20	20	70	30	30	30	30	10	30	30	20	30	40	30	40	40

FIGURE 12.12 A process control record sheet kept by operators. This is typical of records kept by hand when measurements are not automated. We will see in the next section why such records mention $\bar{x}$ and R control charts rather than $\bar{x}$ and s charts.

is about 0.003 (or about 0.0015 in each direction) by the 68–95–99.7 rule. European practice uses control limits placed so that the probability of a point out is 0.001 in each direction. For a Normally distributed statistic, how many standard deviations on either side of the mean do these alternative control limits lie?

12.21 **2σ control charts.** Some special situations call for 2σ control charts. That is, the control limits for a statistic Q will be $\mu_Q \pm 2\sigma_Q$. Suppose that you know the process mean μ and standard deviation σ and will plot $\bar{x}$ and s from samples of size n.

(a) What are the 2σ control limits for an $\bar{x}$ chart?

(b) Find expressions for the upper and lower 2σ control limits for an s chart in terms of the control chart constants c_4 and c_5 introduced on page 703.

12.2 Using Control Charts

We are now familiar with the ideas that undergird all control charts and also with the details of making $\bar{x}$ and s charts. This section discusses a variety of topics related to using control charts in practice.

$\bar{x}$ and *R* charts

We have seen that it is essential to monitor both the center and the spread of a process. Control charts were originally intended to be used by factory workers with limited knowledge of statistics in the era before even calculators, let alone software, were common. In that environment, the standard deviation is too difficult to calculate. The $\bar{x}$ chart for center was therefore combined with a control chart for spread based on the **sample range** rather than the sample standard deviation. The range R of a sample is just the difference between the largest and smallest observations. It is easy to find R without a calculator. Using R rather than s to measure the spread of samples replaces the s chart with an ***R* chart.** It also changes the $\bar{x}$ chart because the control limits for $\bar{x}$ use the estimated process spread. So both R charts and the $\bar{x}$ charts used with them differ in their details from s charts and their $\bar{x}$ charts.

sample range

R chart

Because the range R uses only the largest and smallest observations in a sample, it is less informative than the standard deviation s calculated from all the observations. For this reason, $\bar{x}$ and s charts are now preferred to $\bar{x}$ and R charts. R charts remain common, because tradition dies hard and also because it is easier for workers to understand R than s. In this short introduction, we concentrate on the principles of control charts, so we won't give the details of constructing $\bar{x}$ and R charts. These details appear in any text on quality control.[8] If you meet a set of $\bar{x}$ and R charts, remember that the interpretation of these charts is just like the interpretation of $\bar{x}$ and s charts.

EXAMPLE 12.6 $\bar{x}$ and *R* Charts for Pen Diameter

Figure 12.13 is a display produced by custom process control software attached to a laser micrometer. In this demonstration prepared by the software maker, the micrometer is measuring the diameter in millimeters of samples of pens shipped by an office supply company. The software controls the laser, records measurements, makes the control charts, and sounds an alarm when a point is out of control. This is typical of process control technology in modern manufacturing settings.

Despite the advanced technology involved, the software presents $\bar{x}$ and R charts rather than $\bar{x}$ and s charts, no doubt because R is easier to explain. The R chart monitors within-sample variation

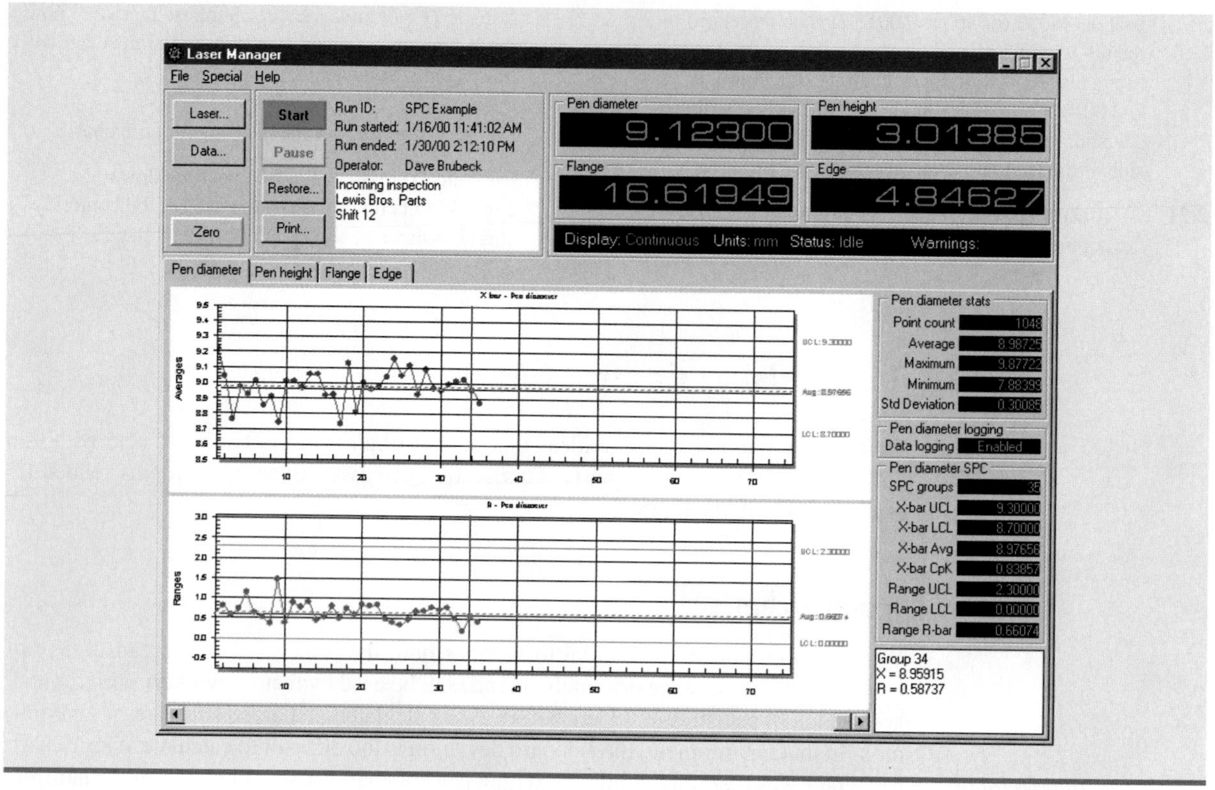

FIGURE 12.13 Output for operators from the Laser Manager software by System Dynamics, Inc. The software prepares control charts directly from measurements made by a laser micrometer. (Image provided by Gordon A. Feingold, System Dynamics, Inc. Used by permission.)

(just like an s chart), so we look at it first. We see that the process spread is stable and well within the control limits. Just as in the case of s, the LCL for R is 0 for the samples of size $n = 5$ used here. The $\bar{x}$ chart is also in control, so process monitoring will continue. The software will sound an alarm if either chart goes out of control.

Additional out-of-control signals

Up to this point we have used only the basic "one point beyond the control limits" criterion to signal that a process may have gone out of control. We would like a quick signal when the process moves out of control, but we also want to avoid "false alarms," signals that occur just by chance when the process is really in control. The standard 3σ control limits are chosen to prevent too many false alarms, because an out-of-control signal calls for an investigation for a special cause. As a result, $\bar{x}$ charts are often slow to respond to a gradual drift in the process center that continues for some time before finally forcing a reading outside the control limits. We can speed the response of a control chart to lack of control—at the cost of also enduring more false alarms—by adding patterns other than "one point out" as signals. The most common step in this direction is to add a *runs signal* to the $\bar{x}$ chart.

Out-of-Control Signals

$\bar{x}$ and s or $\bar{x}$ and R control charts produce an out-of-control signal if:

(a) One point out: A single point lies outside the 3σ control limits of either chart.

(b) Run: The $\bar{x}$ chart shows 9 consecutive points above the center line or 9 consecutive points below the center line. The signal occurs when we see the 9th point of the run.

EXAMPLE 12.7 Using the Runs Signal

Figure 12.14 reproduces the $\bar{x}$ chart from Figure 12.7. The process center began a gradual upward drift at sample 11. The chart shows the effect of the drift—the sample means plotted on the chart move gradually upward, with some random variation. The one-point-out signal does not call for action until sample 18 finally produces an $\bar{x}$ above the UCL. The runs signal reacts more quickly: sample 17 is the ninth consecutive point above the center line.

It is a mathematical fact that the runs signal responds to a gradual drift more quickly (on the average) than the one-point-out signal. The motivation for a runs signal is that when a process is in control, half the points on an $\bar{x}$ chart should lie above the center line and half below. That's true on the average in the long term. In the short term, we will see runs of points above or below, just as we see runs of heads or tails in tossing a coin. How long must a run be to suggest that the process center has moved, so that points are now more likely to fall on one side of the center line? We must once more worry about the cost of false alarms, so we choose a signal for which these are about as frequent as for the familiar one-point-out signal. The 99.7 part of the 68–95–99.7 rule says that we will get a point outside the 3σ control limits about 3 times for every 1000 points plotted

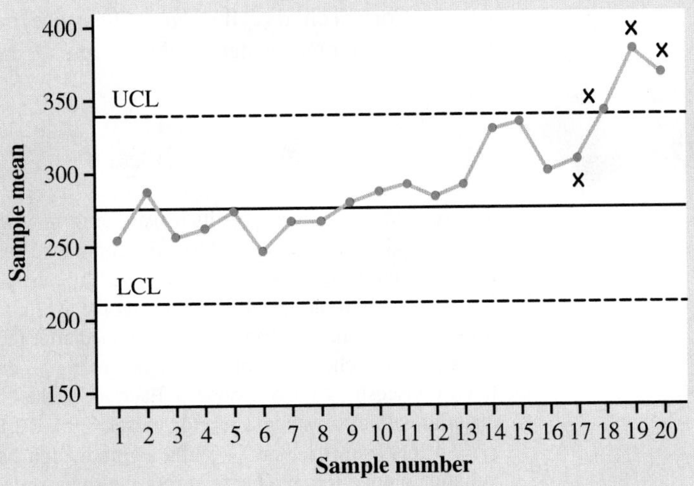

FIGURE 12.14 $\bar{x}$ chart for mesh tension data when the process center drifts upward. The "run of 9" signal gives an out-of-control warning at sample 17.

when the process is in control. The chance of 9 straight points above the center line when the process is in control is $(1/2)^9 = 1/512$, or about 2 per 1000. The chance for a run of 9 below the center line is the same. That's about 4 false alarms per 1000 plotted points overall, close to the false-alarm rate for one-point-out.

There are many other signals that can be added to the rules for responding to $\bar{x}$ and s or $\bar{x}$ and R charts. In our enthusiasm to detect various special kinds of loss of control, it is easy to forget that adding signals always increases the frequency of false alarms. Frequent false alarms are so annoying that the people responsible for responding soon begin to ignore out-of-control signals. It is better to use only a few signals and to reserve signals other than one-point-out and runs for processes that are known to be prone to specific special causes for which there is a tailor-made signal.[9]

APPLY YOUR KNOWLEDGE

12.22 Special causes. Is each of the following examples of a special cause most likely to first result in (i) one point out on the s or R chart; (ii) one point out on the $\bar{x}$ chart; or (iii) a run on the $\bar{x}$ chart? In each case, briefly explain your reasoning.

(a) An etching solution deteriorates as more items are etched.

(b) Buildup of dirt reduces the precision with which parts are placed for machining.

(c) A new customer service representative for a Spanish-language help line is not a native speaker and has difficulty understanding customers.

(d) A data entry employee grows less attentive as her shift continues.

12.23 Mixtures. Here is an artificial situation that illustrates an unusual control chart pattern. Invoices are processed and paid by two clerks, one very experienced and the other newly hired. The experienced clerk processes invoices quickly. The new hire must often refer to a handbook and is much slower. Both are quite consistent, so that their times vary little from invoice to invoice. It happens that each sample of invoices comes from one of the clerks, some samples from one and some from the other. Sketch the $\bar{x}$ chart pattern that will result.

Setting up control charts

When you first encounter a process that has not been carefully studied, it is quite likely that the process is not in control. Your first goal is to discover and respond to special causes with the goal of bringing the process into control. Control charts are an important tool. Control charts for *process monitoring* follow the process forward in time to keep it in control. Control charts at the *chart setup* stage, on the other hand, look back in an attempt to discover the present state of the process. A case study will illustrate the method.

CASE 12.3

VISCOSITY OF AN ELASTOMER

The viscosity of a material is its resistance to flow when under stress. Viscosity is a critical characteristic of rubber and rubber-like compounds called elastomers that have many uses in consumer products. Viscosity is measured by placing specimens of the material above and below a slowly rotating roller, squeezing the assembly, and recording the drag on the roller. Measurements are in "Mooney units," named after the inventor of the instrument.

A specialty chemical company is beginning production of an elastomer that is supposed to have viscosity 45 ± 5 Mooneys. Each lot of the elastomer is produced by "cooking" raw material with catalysts in a reactor vessel. Table 12.5 records $\bar{x}$ and s from samples of size $n = 4$ lots from the first 24 shifts as production begins.[10] An s chart therefore monitors variation among lots produced during the same shift. If the s chart is in control, an $\bar{x}$ chart looks for shift-to-shift variation.

Estimating μ. We do not know the process mean μ and standard deviation σ. What shall we do? Sometimes we can easily adjust the center of a process by setting some control, such as the depth of a cutting tool in a machining operation or the temperature of a reactor vessel in a pharmaceutical plant. In such cases it is common to simply take the process mean μ to be the target value, the depth or temperature that the design of the process specifies as correct. The $\bar{x}$ chart then helps us keep the process mean at this target value.

There is less likely to be a "correct value" for the process mean μ if we are monitoring response times to customer calls or data entry errors. In Case 12.3, we have the target value 45 Mooneys, but there is no simple way to set viscosity at the desired level. In such cases, we want the μ we use in our $\bar{x}$ chart to describe the center of the process as it has actually been operating. To do this, just take the mean of all the individual measurements in the past samples. Because the samples are all the same size, this is just the mean of the sample $\bar{x}$'s. The overall "mean of the sample means" is therefore usually called $\bar{\bar{x}}$. For the 24 samples in Table 12.5,

$$\bar{\bar{x}} = \frac{1}{24}(49.750 + 49.375 + \cdots + 48.625)$$

$$= \frac{1161.125}{24} = 48.380$$

Estimating σ. It is almost never safe to use a "target value" for the process standard deviation σ because it is almost never possible to directly adjust process variation. We must estimate σ from past data. We want to combine the sample standard deviations s from past samples, rather than use the standard deviation of all the individual observations in those samples. That is, in Case 12.3, we want to combine the 24 sample standard deviations in Table 12.5 rather than calculate the standard deviation of the 96 observations in these samples. The reason is that it is the *within-sample* variation that is the benchmark against which we compare the longer-term process variation. Even if the process has been in control, we want only the variation over the short time period of a single sample to influence our value for σ.

TABLE 12.5 $\bar{x}$ **and** s **for 24 samples of elastomer viscosity**

Sample	$\bar{x}$	s	Sample	$\bar{x}$	s
1	49.750	2.684	13	47.875	1.118
2	49.375	0.895	14	48.250	0.895
3	50.250	0.895	15	47.625	0.671
4	49.875	1.118	16	47.375	0.671
5	47.250	0.671	17	50.250	1.566
6	45.000	2.684	18	47.000	0.895
7	48.375	0.671	19	47.000	0.447
8	48.500	0.447	20	49.625	1.118
9	48.500	0.447	21	49.875	0.447
10	46.250	1.566	22	47.625	1.118
11	49.000	0.895	23	49.750	0.671
12	48.125	0.671	24	48.625	0.895

There are several ways to estimate σ from the sample standard deviations. In practice, software may use a somewhat sophisticated method and then calculate the control limits for you. We use a simple method that is traditional in quality control because it goes back to the era before software. If we are basing chart setup on k past samples, we have k sample standard deviations $s_1, s_2, \ldots, s_k$. Just average these to get

$$\bar{s} = \frac{1}{k}(s_1 + s_2 + \cdots + s_k)$$

For the viscosity example, we average the s-values for the 24 samples in Table 12.5,

$$\bar{s} = \frac{1}{24}(2.684 + 0.895 + \cdots + 0.895)$$
$$= \frac{24.156}{24} = 1.0065$$

Combining the sample s-values to estimate σ introduces a complication: the samples are often small (size $n = 4$ in the viscosity example), so s has some bias as an estimator of σ. Recall that $\mu_s = c_4\sigma$. The mean $\bar{s}$ inherits this bias: its mean is also not σ but $c_4\sigma$. The proper estimate of σ corrects this bias. It is

$$\hat{\sigma} = \frac{\bar{s}}{c_4}$$

We get control limits from past data by using the estimates $\bar{\bar{x}}$ and $\hat{\sigma}$ in place of the μ and σ used in charts at the process-monitoring stage. Here are the results.[11]

$\bar{x}$ and s Control Charts using Past Data

Take regular samples of size n from a process. Estimate the process mean μ and the process standard deviation σ from past samples by

$$\hat{\mu} = \bar{\bar{x}} \qquad \text{(or use a target value)}$$
$$\hat{\sigma} = \frac{\bar{s}}{c_4}$$

The center line and control limits for an $\bar{x}$ **chart** are

$$\text{UCL} = \hat{\mu} + 3\frac{\hat{\sigma}}{\sqrt{n}}$$
$$\text{CL} = \hat{\mu}$$
$$\text{LCL} = \hat{\mu} - 3\frac{\hat{\sigma}}{\sqrt{n}}$$

The center line and control limits for an s **chart** are

$$\text{UCL} = B_6\hat{\sigma}$$
$$\text{CL} = c_4\hat{\sigma} = \bar{s}$$
$$\text{LCL} = B_5\hat{\sigma}$$

If the process was not in control when the samples were taken, these should be regarded as trial control limits.

We are now ready to outline the chart setup procedure for elastomer viscosity.

Step 1. As usual, we look first at an s chart. For chart setup, control limits are based on the same past data that we will plot on the chart. Calculate from Table 12.5 that

$$\bar{s} = 1.0065$$

$$\hat{\sigma} = \frac{\bar{s}}{c_4} = \frac{1.0065}{0.9213} = 1.0925$$

The center line and control limits for an s chart based on past data are

$$\text{UCL} = B_6\hat{\sigma} = (2.088)(1.0925) = 2.281$$
$$\text{CL} = \bar{s} = 1.0065$$
$$\text{LCL} = B_5\hat{\sigma} = (0)(1.0925) = 0$$

Figure 12.15 is the s chart. The points for shifts 1 and 6 lie above the UCL. Both are near the beginning of production. Investigation finds that the reactor operator made an error on one lot in each of these samples. The error changed the viscosity of that lot and increased s for that one sample. The error will not be repeated now that the operators have gained experience. That is, this special cause has already been removed.

Step 2. Remove the two values of s that were out of control. This is proper because the special cause responsible for these readings is no longer present. Recalculate from the remaining 22 shifts that $\bar{s} = 0.854$ and $\hat{\sigma} = 0.854/0.9213 = 0.927$. Make a new s chart with

$$\text{UCL} = B_6\hat{\sigma} = (2.088)(0.927) = 1.936$$
$$\text{CL} = \bar{s} = 0.854$$
$$\text{LCL} = B_5\hat{\sigma} = (0)(0.927) = 0$$

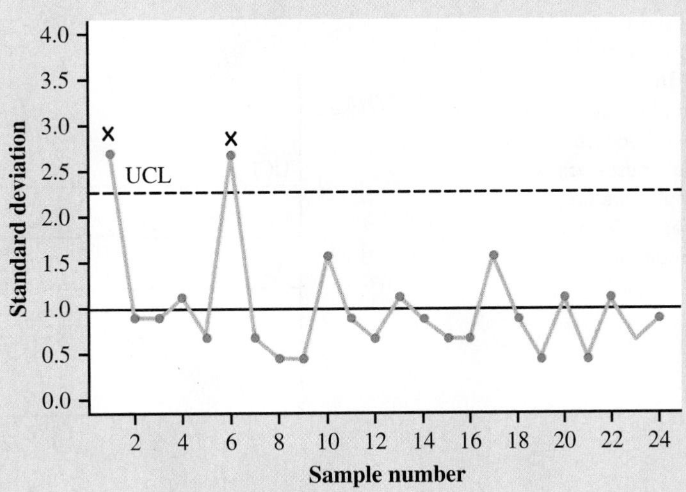

FIGURE 12.15 s chart based on past data for the viscosity data of Table 12.5. The control limits are based on the same $\bar{s}$-values that are plotted on the chart. Points 1 and 6 are out of control.

We don't show the chart, but you can see from Table 12.5 that none of the remaining s values lies above the new, lower, UCL; the largest remaining s is 1.566. If additional points were now out of control, we would repeat the process of finding and eliminating s-type causes until the s chart for the remaining shifts is in control. In practice, of course, this is often a challenging task.

Step 3. Once s-type causes have been eliminated, make an $\bar{x}$ chart *using only the samples that remain* after dropping those that had out-of-control s-values. For the 22 remaining samples, we know that $\hat{\sigma} = 0.927$ and we calculate that $\bar{\bar{x}} = 48.4716$. The center line and control limits for the $\bar{x}$ chart are

$$\text{UCL} = \bar{\bar{x}} + 3\frac{\hat{\sigma}}{\sqrt{n}} = 48.4716 + 3\frac{0.927}{\sqrt{4}} = 49.862$$

$$\text{CL} = \bar{\bar{x}} = 48.4716$$

$$\text{LCL} = \bar{\bar{x}} - 3\frac{\hat{\sigma}}{\sqrt{n}} = 48.4716 - 3\frac{0.927}{\sqrt{4}} = 47.081$$

Figure 12.16 is the $\bar{x}$ chart. Shifts 1 and 6 have been dropped. Six of the 22 points are beyond the 3σ limits, three high and three low. Although within-shift variation is now stable, there is excessive variation from shift to shift. To find the cause, we must understand the details of the process, but knowing that the special cause or causes operate between shifts is a big help. If the reactor is set up anew at the beginning of each shift, that's one place to look more closely.

Step 4. Once the $\bar{x}$ and s charts are both in control (looking backward), use the estimates $\hat{\mu}$ and $\hat{\sigma}$ from the points in control to set tentative control limits to monitor the process going forward. If it remains in control, we can update the charts and move to the process-monitoring stage.

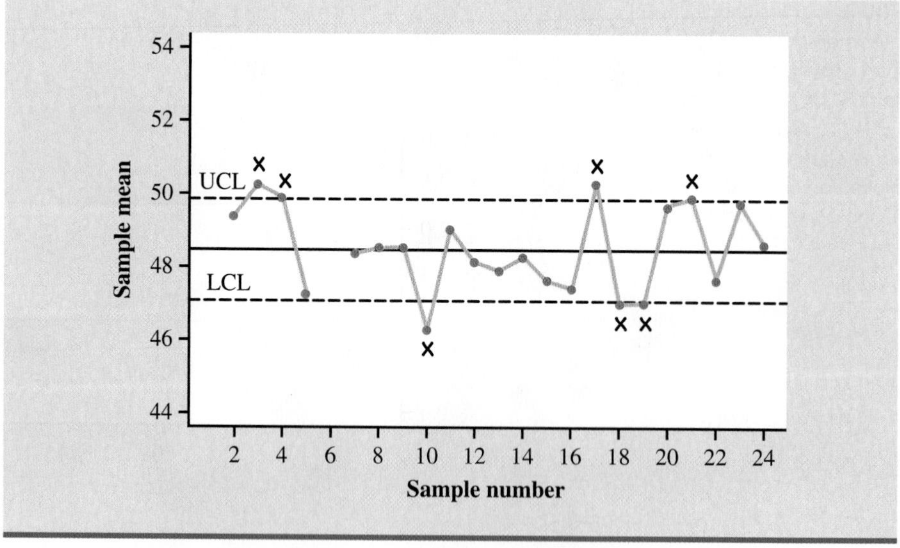

FIGURE 12.16 $\bar{x}$ chart based on past data for the viscosity data of Table 12.5. The samples for shifts 1 and 6 have been removed because s-type special causes active in those samples are no longer active. The $\bar{x}$ chart shows poor control.

APPLY YOUR KNOWLEDGE

12.24 From improvement to monitoring. Suppose that when the process improvement project of Case 12.3 is complete, the points remaining after removing special causes have $\bar{\bar{x}} = 48.7$ and $\bar{s} = 0.92$. What are the center line and control limits for the $\bar{x}$ and s charts you would use to monitor the process going forward?

CASE 12.3

12.25 Estimating process parameters. The $\bar{x}$ and s control charts for the mesh-tensioning example (Figures 12.5 and 12.9) were based on $\mu = 275$ mV and $\sigma = 43$ mV. Table 12.1 gives the 20 most recent samples from this process.

(a) Estimate the process μ and σ based on these 20 samples.

(b) Your calculations suggest that the process σ may now be less than 43 mV. Explain why the s chart in Figure 12.9 (page 703) suggests the same conclusion. (If this pattern continues, we would eventually update the value of σ used for control limits.)

12.26 Hospital losses. Table 12.6 gives data on the losses (in dollars) incurred by a hospital in treating DRG 209 (major joint replacement) patients.[12] The hospital has taken from its records a random sample of 8 such patients each month for 15 months.

(a) Make an s control chart using center lines and limits calculated from these past data. There are no points out of control.

(b) Because the s chart is in control, base the $\bar{x}$ chart on all 15 samples. Make this chart. Is it also in control?

Comments on statistical control

Having seen how $\bar{x}$ and s (or $\bar{x}$ and R) charts work, we can turn to some important comments and cautions about statistical control in practice.

TABLE 12.6 **Hospital losses for 15 samples of DRG 209 patients**

Sample	Loss(dollars)								Sample mean	Standard deviation
1	6835	5843	6019	6731	6362	5696	7193	6206	6360.6	521.7
2	6452	6764	7083	7352	5239	6911	7479	5549	6603.6	817.1
3	7205	6374	6198	6170	6482	4763	7125	6241	6319.8	749.1
4	6021	6347	7210	6384	6807	5711	7952	6023	6556.9	736.5
5	7000	6495	6893	6127	7417	7044	6159	6091	6653.2	503.7
6	7783	6224	5051	7288	6584	7521	6146	5129	6465.3	1034.3
7	8794	6279	6877	5807	6076	6392	7429	5220	6609.2	1104.0
8	4727	8117	6586	6225	6150	7386	5674	6740	6450.6	1033.0
9	5408	7452	6686	6428	6425	7380	5789	6264	6479.0	704.7
10	5598	7489	6186	5837	6769	5471	5658	6393	6175.1	690.5
11	6559	5855	4928	5897	7532	5663	4746	7879	6132.4	1128.6
12	6824	7320	5331	6204	6027	5987	6033	6177	6237.9	596.6
13	6503	8213	5417	6360	6711	6907	6625	7888	6828.0	879.8
14	5622	6321	6325	6634	5075	6209	4832	6386	5925.5	667.8
15	6269	6756	7653	6065	5835	7337	6615	8181	6838.9	819.5

Focus on the process rather than on the products. This is perhaps the fundamental idea in statistical process control. We might attempt to attain high quality by careful inspection of the finished product, measuring every completed forging and reviewing every outgoing invoice and expense account payment. Inspection of finished products can ensure good quality, but it is expensive. Perhaps more important, final inspection comes too late: when something goes wrong early in a process, much bad product may be produced before final inspection discovers the problem. This adds to the expense, because the bad product must then be scrapped or reworked.

The small samples that are the basis of control charts are intended to monitor the process at key points, not to ensure the quality of the particular items in the samples. If the process is kept in control, we know what to expect in the finished product. We want to do it right the first time, not inspect and fix finished product. Choosing the "key points" at which we will measure and monitor the process is important. The choice requires that you understand the process well enough to know where problems are likely to arise. Flowcharts and cause-and-effect diagrams can help. It should be clear that control charts that monitor only the final output are often *not* the best choice.

Rational subgroups. The interpretation of control charts depends on the distinction between $\bar{x}$-type special causes and s-type special causes. This distinction in turn depends on how we choose the samples from which we calculate s (or R). We want the variation *within* a sample to reflect only the item-to-item chance variation that (when in control) results from many small common causes. Walter Shewhart, the founder of statistical process control, used the term **rational subgroup** to emphasize that we should think about the process when deciding how to choose samples.

rational subgroup

EXAMPLE 12.8 Random Sampling versus Rational Subgroups

A pharmaceutical manufacturer forms tablets by compressing a granular material that contains the active ingredient and various fillers. To monitor the compression process, we will measure the hardness of a sample from each 10 minutes' production of tablets. Should we choose a random sample of tablets from the several thousand produced in a 10-minute period?

A random sample would contain tablets spread across the entire 10 minutes. It fairly represents the 10-minute period, but that isn't what we want for process control. If the setting of the press drifts or a new lot of filler arrives during the 10 minutes, the spread of the sample will be increased. That is, a random sample contains both the short-term variation among tablets produced in quick succession and the longer-term variation among tablets produced minutes apart. We prefer to measure a rational subgroup of 5 consecutive tablets every 10 minutes. We expect the process to be stable during this very short time period, so that variation within the subgroups is a benchmark against which we can see special cause variation.

Samples of consecutive items are rational subgroups when we are monitoring the output of a single activity that does the same thing over and over again. Several consecutive items is the most common type of sample for process control. When the stream of product contains output from several machines or several people, however, the choice of samples is more complicated. Do you want to include variation due to different machines or different people within your samples? If you decide that this variation is common cause variation that is acceptable for this process, be sure that the sample items are spread across machines or people. If all the items in each sample have a common origin, $\bar{s}$ will be small and the control limits for the $\bar{x}$ chart will be narrow. Points on the $\bar{x}$ chart from samples representing different machines or different people will often be out of control, some high and some low.

There is no formula for choosing samples that are rational subgroups. You must think about causes of variation in your process and decide which you are willing to think of as common causes that you will not try to eliminate. Rational subgroups are samples chosen to express variation due to these causes and no others. Because the choice requires detailed process knowledge, we will usually accept samples of consecutive items as being rational subgroups. Just remember that real processes are messier than textbooks suggest.

Why statistical control is desirable. To repeat, if the process is kept in control, we know what to expect in the finished product. The process mean μ and standard deviation σ remain stable over time, so (assuming Normal variation) the 99.7 part of the 68–95–99.7 rule tells us that almost all measurements on individual products will lie in the range $\mu \pm 3\sigma$. These are sometimes called the **natural tolerances** for the product. Be careful to distinguish $\mu \pm 3\sigma$, the range we expect for *individual measurements,* from the $\bar{x}$ chart control limits $\mu \pm 3\sigma/\sqrt{n}$, which mark off the expected range of *sample means.*

natural tolerances

EXAMPLE 12.9 Natural Tolerances for Mesh Tension

CASE 12.2

The process of setting the mesh tension on computer monitors has been operating in control. The $\bar{x}$ and s charts were based on $\mu = 275$ mV and $\sigma = 43$ mV. The s chart in Figure 12.9 and your calculation in Exercise 12.25 suggest that the process σ is now less than 43 mV. We may prefer to calculate the natural tolerances from the recent data on 20 samples (80 monitors) in Table 12.1 (page 696). The estimate of the mean is $\bar{\bar{x}} = 275.065$, very close to the target value.

Now a subtle point arises. The estimate $\hat{\sigma} = \bar{s}/c_4$ used for past-data control charts is based entirely on variation *within the samples.* That's what we want for control charts, because within-sample variation is likely to be "pure common cause" variation. Even when the process is in control, there is some additional variation from sample to sample, just by chance. So the variation in the process output will be greater than the variation within samples. *To estimate the natural tolerances, we should estimate σ from all 80 individual monitors, not by averaging the 20 within-sample standard deviations.* The standard deviation for all 80 mesh tensions is

$$s = 38.38$$

(For a sample of size 80, c_4 is very close to 1, so we can ignore it.)

We are therefore confident that almost all individual monitors will have mesh tension between

$$\bar{\bar{x}} \pm 3s = 275.065 \pm (3)(38.38) \doteq 275 \pm 115$$

We expect mesh tension measurements to vary between 160 and 390 mV. You see that the spread of individual measurements is wider than the spread of sample means used for the control limits of the $\bar{x}$ chart.

The natural tolerances in Example 12.9 depend on the fact that the mesh tensions of individual monitors follow a Normal distribution. We know that the process was in control when the 80 measurements in Table 12.1 were made, so we can use them to assess Normality. Figure 12.17 is a Normal quantile plot of these measurements. There are no strong deviations from Normality. All 80 observations, including the one point that may

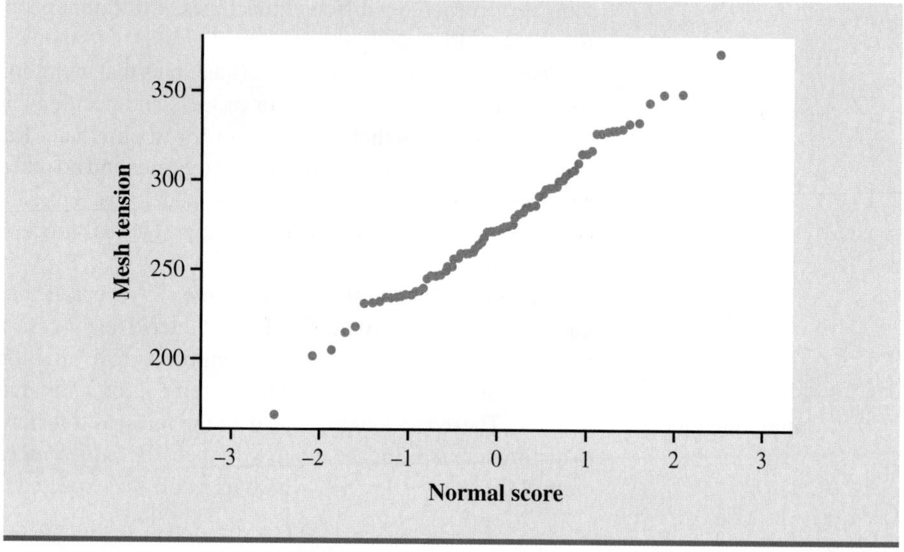

FIGURE 12.17 Normal quantile plot for the 80 mesh tension measurements of Table 12.1. Calculations about individual measurements, such as natural tolerances, depend on approximate Normality.

appear suspiciously low in Figure 12.17, lie within the natural tolerances. Examining the data strengthens our confidence in the natural tolerances.

Because we can predict the performance of the mesh-tensioning process, we can tell the computer makers who buy our monitors what to expect. These customers, in fact, require us to maintain statistical control of our processes so that they need not inspect the monitors we ship to them. What is more, if a process is in control, we can see the effect of any changes we make. A process operating out of control is erratic. We can't do reliable statistical studies on such a process, and if we make a change in the process we can't clearly see the results of the change—they are hidden by erratic special cause variation. If we want to improve a process, we must first bring it into control so that we have a stable starting point from which to improve.

APPLY YOUR KNOWLEDGE

12.27 No incoming inspection. The computer makers who buy monitors require that the monitor manufacturer practice statistical process control and submit control charts for verification. This allows the computer makers to eliminate inspection of monitors as they arrive, a considerable cost saving. Explain carefully why incoming inspection can safely be eliminated.

12.28 Natural tolerances. Table 12.6 (page 717) gives data on hospital losses for samples of DRG 209 patients. The distribution of losses has been stable over time. What are the natural tolerances within which you expect losses on nearly all such patients to fall?

12.29 Normality? Do the losses on the 120 individual patients in Table 12.6 appear to come from a single Normal distribution? Make a Normal quantile plot and discuss what it shows. Are the natural tolerances you found in the previous exercise trustworthy?

Don't confuse control with capability!

A process in control is stable over time. We know how much variation the finished product will show. Control charts are, so to speak, the voice of the process telling us what state it is in. *There is no guarantee that a process in control produces products of satisfactory quality.* "Satisfactory quality" is measured by comparing the product to some standard outside the process, set by technical specifications, customer expectations, or the goals of the organization. These external standards are unrelated to the internal state of the process, which is all that statistical control pays attention to.

Capability

Capability refers to the ability of a process to meet or exceed the requirements placed on it.

Capability has nothing to do with control—except for the very important point that, if a process is not in control, it is hard to tell if it is capable or not.

EXAMPLE 12.10 Capability

CASE 12.2 

The primary customer for our monitors is a large maker of computers. The customer informed us that adequate image quality requires that the mesh tension lie between 100 and 400 mV. Because the mesh-tensioning process is in control, we know (Example 12.9) that almost all monitors will have mesh tension between 160 and 390 mV. The process is capable of meeting the customer's requirement.

Figure 12.18 compares the distribution of mesh tension for individual monitors with the customer's specifications. The distribution of tension is approximately Normal, and we estimate its mean to be very close to 275 mV and the standard deviation to be about 38.4 mV. The distribution is safely within the specifications.

Times change, however. As computer buyers demand better screen quality, the computer maker restudies the effect of mesh tension and decides to require that tension lie between 150 and 350 mV. These new specification limits also appear in Figure 12.18. The process is not capable of meeting the new requirements. The process remains in control. The change in its capability is entirely due to a change in external requirements.

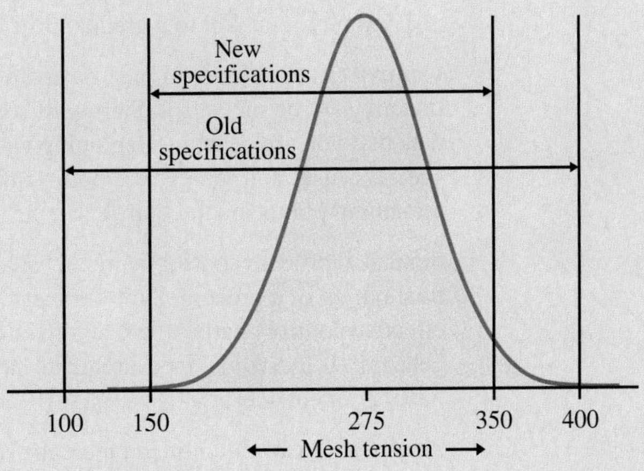

FIGURE 12.18 Comparison of the distribution of mesh tension (Normal curve) with original and tightened specifications. The process in its current state is not capable of meeting the new specifications.

Because the mesh-tensioning process is in control, we know that it is not capable of meeting the new specifications. That's an advantage of control, but the fact remains that control does not guarantee capability. We will discuss numerical measures of capability in Section 12.3.

Managers must understand that, *if a process that is in control does not have adequate capability, fundamental changes in the process are needed.* The process is doing as well as it can and displays only the chance variation that is natural to its present state. Slogans to encourage the workers or disciplining the workers for poor performance will not change the state of the process. Better training for workers is a change in the process that may improve capability. New equipment or more uniform material may also help, depending on the findings of a careful investigation.

APPLY YOUR KNOWLEDGE

12.30 Describing capability. CASE 12.2 If the mesh tension of individual monitors follows a Normal distribution, we can describe capability by giving the percent of monitors that meet specifications. The old specifications for mesh tension are 100 to 400 mV. The new specifications are 150 to 350 mV. Because the process is in control, we can estimate that tension has mean 275 mV and standard deviation 38.4 mV.

(a) What percent of monitors meet the old specifications?

(b) What percent meet the new specifications?

12.31 Improving capability. CASE 12.2 The center of the specifications for mesh tension is 250 mV, but the center of our process is 275 mV. We can improve capability by adjusting the process to have center 250 mV. This is an easy adjustment that does not change the process variation. What percent of monitors now meet the new specifications?

SECTION 12.2 SUMMARY

- An ***R* chart** based on the **range** of observations in a sample is often used in place of an s chart. Interpret $\bar{x}$ and R charts exactly as you would interpret $\bar{x}$ and s charts.
- It is common to use **out-of-control signals** in addition to "one point outside the control limits." In particular, a **runs signal** for the $\bar{x}$ chart allows the chart to respond more quickly to a gradual drift in the process center.
- **Control charts based on past data** are used at the **chart setup** stage for a process that may not be in control. Start with control limits calculated from the same past data that you are plotting. Beginning with the s chart, narrow the limits as you find special causes and remove the points influenced by these causes. When the remaining points are in control, use the resulting limits to monitor the process.
- Statistical process control maintains quality more economically than inspecting the final output of a process. Samples that are **rational subgroups** are important to effective control charts. A process in control is stable, so that we can predict its behavior. If individual measurements have a Normal distribution, we can give the **natural tolerances.**
- A process is **capable** if it can meet the requirements placed on it. Control (stability over time) does not in itself improve capability. Remember that control describes the internal state of the process, whereas capability relates the state of the process to external specifications.

SECTION 12.2 Exercises

For Exercises 12.22 and 12.23, see page 712; for 12.24 to 12.26, see page 717; for 12.27 to 12.29, see page 720; and for 12.30 and 12.31, see page 722.

12.32 Measuring bone density. Loss of bone density is a serious health problem for many people, especially older women. Conventional X-rays often fail to detect loss of bone density until the loss reaches 25% or more. New equipment such as the Lunar bone densitometer is much more sensitive. A health clinic installs one of these machines. The manufacturer supplies a "phantom," an aluminum piece of known density that can be used to keep the machine calibrated. Each morning, the clinic makes two measurements on the phantom before measuring the first patient. Control charts based on these measurements alert the operators if the machine has lost calibration. Table 12.7 contains data for the first 30 days of operation.[13] The units are grams per square centimeter (for technical reasons, area rather than volume is measured).

TABLE 12.7 Daily calibration samples for a Lunar bone densitometer

Day	Measurements		$\bar{x}$	s
1	1.261	1.260	1.2605	0.000707
2	1.261	1.268	1.2645	0.004950
3	1.258	1.261	1.2595	0.002121
4	1.261	1.262	1.2615	0.000707
5	1.259	1.262	1.2605	0.002121
6	1.269	1.260	1.2645	0.006364
7	1.262	1.263	1.2625	0.000707
8	1.264	1.268	1.2660	0.002828
9	1.258	1.260	1.2590	0.001414
10	1.264	1.265	1.2645	0.000707
11	1.264	1.259	1.2615	0.003536
12	1.260	1.266	1.2630	0.004243
13	1.267	1.266	1.2665	0.000707
14	1.264	1.260	1.2620	0.002828
15	1.266	1.259	1.2625	0.004950
16	1.257	1.266	1.2615	0.006364
17	1.257	1.266	1.2615	0.006364
18	1.260	1.265	1.2625	0.003536
19	1.262	1.266	1.2640	0.002828
20	1.265	1.266	1.2655	0.000707
21	1.264	1.257	1.2605	0.004950
22	1.260	1.257	1.2585	0.002121
23	1.255	1.260	1.2575	0.003536
24	1.257	1.259	1.2580	0.001414
25	1.265	1.260	1.2625	0.003536
26	1.261	1.264	1.2625	0.002121
27	1.261	1.264	1.2625	0.002121
28	1.260	1.262	1.2610	0.001414
29	1.260	1.256	1.2580	0.002828
30	1.260	1.262	1.2610	0.001414

(a) Calculate $\overline{x}$ and s for the first 2 days to verify the table entries for those quantities.

(b) What kind of variation does the s chart monitor in this setting? Make an s chart and comment on control. If any points are out of control, remove them and recompute the chart limits until all remaining points are in control. (That is, assume that special causes are found and removed.)

(c) Make an $\overline{x}$ chart using the samples that remain after (b). What kind of variation will be visible on this chart? Comment on the stability of the machine over these 30 days based on both charts.

12.33 Mounting-hole distances. Figure 12.12 (page 708) displays a record sheet for 18 samples of distances between mounting holes in an electrical meter. The data file *ex12_17* adds $\overline{x}$ and s for each sample. In Exercise 12.17, you found that sample 5 was out of control on the process-monitoring s chart. The special cause responsible was found and removed. Based on the 17 samples that were in control, what are the natural tolerances for the distance between the holes?

12.34 Measuring bone density, continued. Remove any samples in Table 12.7 that your work in Exercise 12.32 showed to be out of control on either chart. Estimate the mean and standard deviation of individual measurements on the phantom. What are the natural tolerances for these measurements?

12.35 Mounting-hole distances, continued. The record sheet in Figure 12.12 gives the specifications as 0.6054 ± 0.0010 inch. That's 54 ± 10 as the data are coded on the record. Assuming that the distance varies Normally from meter to meter, about what percent of meters meet the specifications?

12.36 Are bone density measurements Normal? Are the 60 individual measurements in Table 12.7 at least approximately Normal, so that the natural tolerances you calculated in Exercise 12.34 can be trusted? Make a Normal quantile plot (or another graph if your software is limited) and discuss what you see.

12.37 Are mounting-hole distances Normal? Make a Normal quantile plot of the 85 distances in data file *ex12_17* that remain after removing sample 5. How does the plot reflect the limited precision of the measurements (all of which end in 4)? Is there any departure from Normality that would lead you to discard your conclusions from the previous exercise? (If your software will not make Normal quantile plots, use a histogram to assess Normality.)

12.38 A cutting operation. A machine tool in your plant is cutting an outside diameter. A sample of 4 pieces is taken near the end of each hour of production. Table 12.8 gives $\overline{x}$ and s for the first 21 samples, coded in units of 0.0001 inch from the center of the specifications. The specifications allow a range of ± 0.0002 inch about the center (a range of -2 to $+2$ as coded).

(a) Make an s chart based on past data and comment on control of short-term process variation.

(b) Because the data are coded about the center of the specs, we have a given target $\mu = 0$ (as coded) for the process mean. Make an $\overline{x}$ chart and comment on control of long-term process variation. What special $\overline{x}$-type cause probably explains the lack of control of $\overline{x}$?

12.39 Special causes. Is each of the following examples of a special cause most likely to first result in

TABLE 12.8 $\overline{x}$ **and** s **for samples of outside diameter**

Sample	$\overline{x}$	s	Sample	$\overline{x}$	s
1	−0.14	0.48	12	0.55	0.10
2	0.09	0.26	13	0.50	0.25
3	0.17	0.24	14	0.37	0.45
4	0.08	0.38	15	0.69	0.21
5	−0.17	0.50	16	0.47	0.34
6	0.36	0.26	17	0.56	0.42
7	0.30	0.39	18	0.78	0.08
8	0.19	0.31	19	0.75	0.32
9	0.48	0.13	20	0.49	0.23
10	0.29	0.13	21	0.79	0.12
11	0.48	0.25			

(i) a sudden change in level on the s or R chart; (ii) a sudden change in level on the $\bar{x}$ chart; or (iii) a gradual drift up or down on the $\bar{x}$ chart? In each case, briefly explain your reasoning.

(a) An airline pilots' union puts pressure on management during labor negotiations by asking its members to "work to rule" in doing the detailed checks required before a plane can leave the gate.

(b) Measurements of part dimensions that were formerly made by hand are now made by a very accurate laser system. (The process producing the parts does not change—measurement methods can also affect control charts.)

(c) Inadequate air conditioning on a hot day allows the temperature to rise during the afternoon in an office that prepares a company's invoices.

12.40 **Deming speaks.** The quality guru W. Edwards Deming (1900–1993) taught (among much else) that[14]

(a) "People work in the system. Management creates the system."

(b) "Putting out fires is not improvement. Finding a point out of control, finding the special cause and removing it, is only putting the process back to where it was in the first place. It is not improvement of the process."

(c) "Eliminate slogans, exhortations and targets for the workforce asking for zero defects and new levels of productivity."

Choose one of these sayings. Explain carefully what facts about improving quality the saying attempts to summarize.

12.41 **The Boston Marathon.** The Boston Marathon has been run each year since 1897. Winning times were highly variable in the early years, but control improved as the best runners became more professional. A clear downward trend continued until the 1980s. Rick plans to make a control chart for the winning times from 1950 to the present. The first few times are 153 148 152 139 141 138.... Calculation from the winning times from 1950 to 2002 gives

$$\bar{x} = 134.906 \text{ minutes} \quad \text{and} \quad s = 6.523 \text{ minutes}$$

Rick draws a center line at $\bar{x}$ and control limits at $\bar{x} \pm 3s$ for a plot of individual winning times. Explain carefully why these control limits are too wide to effectively signal unusually fast or slow times.

12.42 **Is Joe's weight stable?** Joe has recorded his weight, measured at the gym after a workout, for several years. The mean is 162 pounds and the standard deviation 1.5 pounds, with no signs of lack of control. An injury keeps Joe away from the gym for several months. The data below give his weight, measured once each week for the first 16 weeks after he returns from the injury:

Week	1	2	3	4	5	6
Weight	168.7	167.6	165.8	167.5	165.3	163.4
Week	7	8	9	10	11	12
Weight	163.0	165.5	162.6	160.8	162.3	162.7
Week	13	14	15	16		
Weight	160.9	161.3	162.1	161.0		

Joe wants to plot these individual measurements on a control chart. When each "sample" is just one measurement, short-term variation is estimated by advanced techniques.[15] The short-term variation in Joe's weight is estimated to be about $\sigma = 1.3$ pounds. Joe has a target of $\mu = 162$ pounds for his weight. Make a control chart for his measurements, using control limits $\mu \pm 2\sigma$. It is common to use these narrower limits on an "individuals chart." Comment on individual points out of control and on runs. Is Joe's weight stable or does it change systematically over this period?

12.3 Process Capability Indexes*

Capability describes the quality of the output of a process relative to the needs or requirements of the users of that output. To be more precise, capability relates the *actual performance* of a process in control, after special causes have been removed, to the *desired* performance.

*This material is important in practice but is not needed to understand statistical process control.

Suppose, to take a simple but common setting, that there are *specifications* set for some characteristic of the process output. The viscosity of the elastomer in Case 12.3 (page 712) is supposed to be 45 ± 5 Mooneys. The speed with which calls are answered at a corporate customer service call center is supposed to be no more than 30 seconds. We can then measure capability by the *percent of output that meets the specifications.* When the variable we measure has a Normal distribution, we can estimate this percent using the mean and standard deviation estimated from past control chart samples. When the variable is not Normal, we can use the actual percent of the measurements in the samples that meet the specifications.

EXAMPLE 12.11 Percent Meeting Specifications

CASE 12.3

(a) At the conclusion of the process improvement study in Case 12.3, we have found and fixed special causes and eliminated from our data the samples on which those causes operated. The remaining viscosity measurements have $\overline{\overline{x}} = 48.7$ and $s = 0.85$. Note once again that to draw conclusions about viscosity for individual lots we estimate the standard deviation σ from all individual lots, not from the average $\bar{s}$ of sample standard deviations.

The specifications call for the viscosity of the elastomer to lie in the range 45 ± 5. A Normal quantile plot shows the viscosities to be quite Normal. Figure 12.19(a) shows the Normal distribution of lot viscosities with the specification limits 45 ± 5. These are marked **LSL** for *lower specification limit* and **USL** for *upper specification limit.* The percent of lots that meet the specifications is about

LSL
USL

$$P(40 \le \text{viscosity} \le 50) = P\left(\frac{40 - 48.7}{0.85} \le Z \le \frac{50 - 48.7}{0.85}\right)$$

$$= P(-10.2 \le Z \le 1.53) = 0.937$$

About 94% of the lots meet the specifications. If we can adjust the process center to the center of the specifications, $\mu = 45$, it is clear from Figure 12.19(a) that essentially 100% of lots will meet the specifications.

(b) Times to answer calls to a corporate customer service center are usually right-skewed. Figure 12.19(b) is a histogram of the times for 300 calls to the call center of a large bank.[16] The specification limit 30 seconds is marked USL. The median is 20 seconds, but the mean is 32 seconds. Of the 300 calls, 203 were answered in no more than 30 seconds. That is, $203/300 =$ 68% of the times meet the specifications.

In fact, *percent meeting specifications is a poor measure of capability.* Figure 12.20 shows why. This figure compares the distributions of the diameter of the same part manufactured by two processes. The target diameter and the specification limits are marked. All the parts produced by Process A meet the specifications, but about 1.5% of those from Process B fail to do so. Nonetheless, Process B is superior to Process A because it is less variable: much more of Process B's output is close to the target. Process A produces many parts close to LSL and USL. These parts meet the specifications, but they will fit and perform more poorly than parts with diameters close to the center of the specifications. A distribution like that for Process A might result from inspecting all the parts and discarding those whose diameters fall outside the specifications. That's not an efficient way to achieve quality.

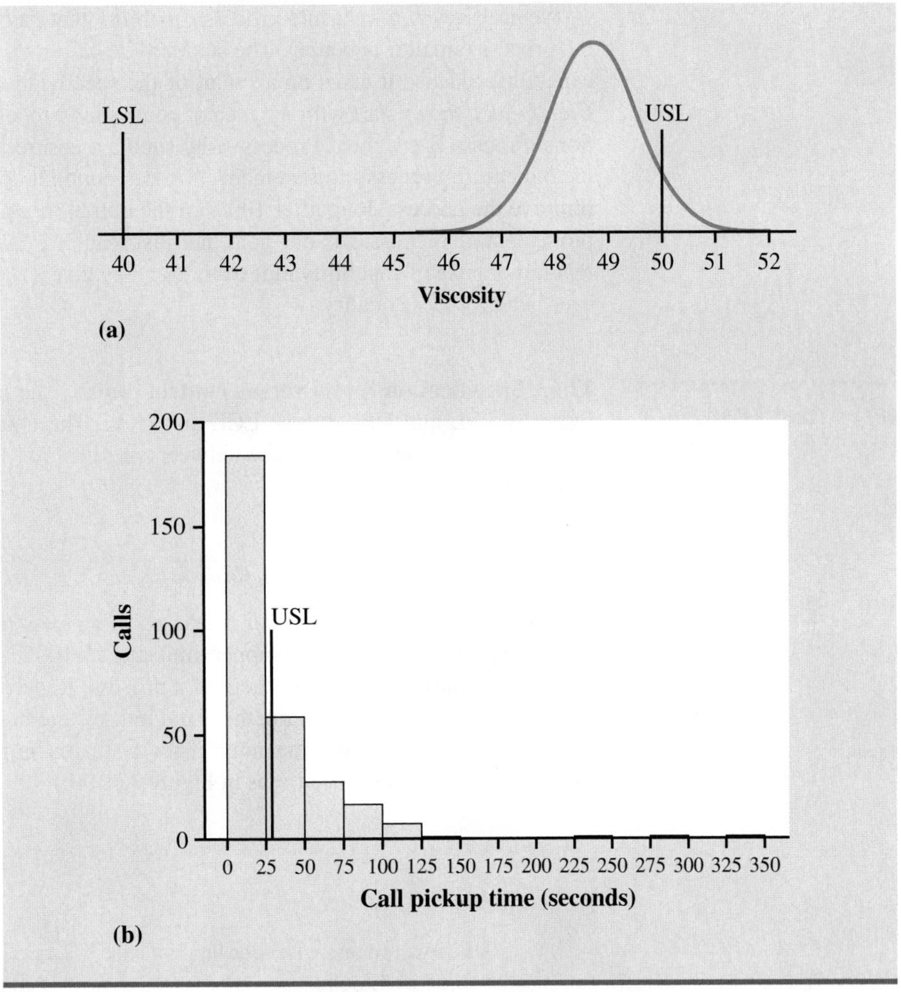

FIGURE 12.19 Comparing distributions of individual measurements with specifications, for Example 12.11. (a) Viscosity has a Normal distribution. The capability is poor, but if we can properly center the process, it will become good. (b) Response times to customer calls have a right-skewed distribution and only an upper specification limit. Capability is again poor.

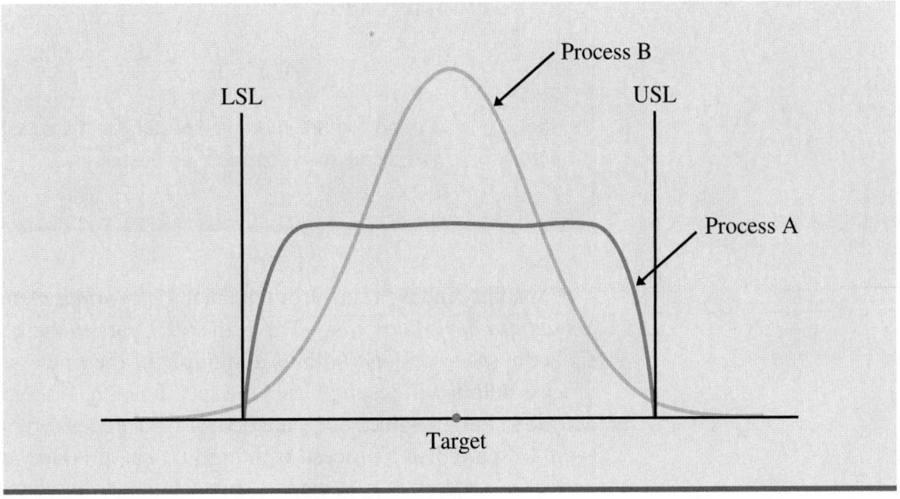

FIGURE 12.20 Two distributions for part diameters. All of the parts from Process A meet the specifications, but a higher proportion of parts from Process B have diameters close to the target.

We need a way to measure process capability that pays attention to the variability of the process (smaller is better). The standard deviation does that, but it doesn't measure capability because it takes no account of the specifications that the output must meet. *Capability indexes* start with the idea of comparing process variation with the specifications. Process B will beat Process A by such a measure. Capability indexes also allow us to measure process improvement—we can continue to drive down variation, and so improve the process, long after 100% of the output meets specifications. Continual improvement of processes is our goal, not just reaching "satisfactory" performance. The real importance of capability indexes is that they give us numerical measures to describe ever-better process quality.

APPLY YOUR KNOWLEDGE

12.43 Specification limits versus control limits. The manager you report to is confused by LSL and USL versus LCL and UCL. The notations look similar. Carefully explain the conceptual difference between specification limits for individual measurements and control limits for $\bar{x}$.

The capability indexes C_p and C_{pk}

Capability indexes are numerical measures of process capability that, unlike percent meeting specifications, have no upper limit such as 100%. We can use capability indexes to measure continuing improvement of a process. Reporting just one number has limitations, of course. What is more, the usual indexes are based on thinking about Normal distributions. They are not meaningful for distinctly non-Normal output distributions like the call center response times in Figure 12.19(b).

Capability Indexes

Consider a process with specification limits LSL and USL for some measured characteristic of its output. The process mean for this characteristic is μ and the standard deviation is σ. The **capability index C_p** is

$$C_p = \frac{\text{USL} - \text{LSL}}{6\sigma}$$

The **capability index C_{pk}** is

$$C_{pk} = \frac{|\mu - \text{nearer spec limit}|}{3\sigma}$$

Set $C_{pk} = 0$ if the process mean μ lies outside the specification limits. Large values of C_p or C_{pk} indicate more capable processes.

Capability indexes start from the fact that *Normal distributions are in practice about 6 standard deviations wide.* That's the 99.7 part of the 68–95–99.7 rule. Conceptually, C_p is the specification width as a multiple of the process width 6σ. When $C_p = 1$, the process output will just fit within the specifications if the center is midway between LSL and USL. Larger values of C_p are better—the process output can fit within the specs with room to spare. But a process with high C_p can produce poor-quality product if it is not correctly centered. C_{pk} remedies this deficiency by considering both the center μ and the variability σ of the measurements. The denominator 3σ in C_{pk} is half the process width. It is the space needed on either side of the mean if essentially all the output is to lie between LSL and USL. When $C_{pk} = 1$, the process has just this much space between the mean and the nearer of LSL and USL. Again, higher values are better. C_{pk} is the most common capability index, but starting with C_p helps us see how the indexes work.

EXAMPLE 12.12 Interpreting Capability Indexes

Consider the series of pictures in Figure 12.21. We might think of a process that machines a metal part. Measure a dimension of the part that has LSL and USL as its specification limits. There is of course variation from part to part. The dimensions vary Normally with mean μ and standard deviation σ.

Figure 12.21(a) shows process width equal to the specification width. That is, $C_p = 1$. Almost all the parts will meet specifications *if,* as in this figure, the process mean μ is at the center of the specs. Because the mean is centered, it is 3σ from both LSL and USL, so $C_{pk} = 1$ also. In Figure 12.21(b), the mean has moved down to LSL. Only half the parts will meet the specifications. C_p is unchanged because the process width has not changed. But C_{pk} sees that the center μ is right on the edge of the specifications, $C_{pk} = 0$. The value remains 0 if μ moves outside the specifications.

In Figures 12.21(c) and (d) the process σ has been reduced to half the value it had in (a) and (b). The process width 6σ is now half the specification width, so $C_p = 2$. In Figure 12.21(c) the center is just 3 of the new σ's above LSL, so that $C_{pk} = 1$. Figure 12.21(d) shows the same smaller

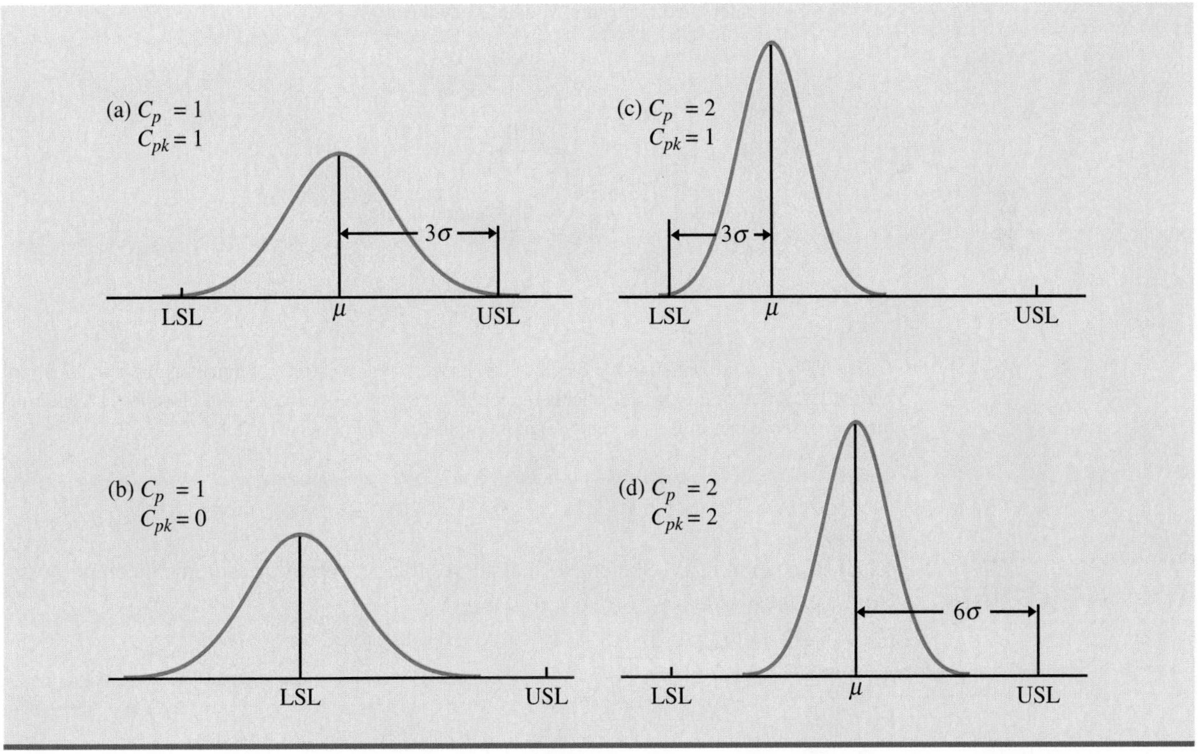

FIGURE 12.21 How capability indexes work. (a) Process centered, process width equal to specification width. (b) Process off-center, process width equal to specification width. (c) Process off-center, process width equal to half the specification width. (d) Process centered, process width equal to half the specification width.

σ accompanied by mean μ correctly centered between LSL and USL. C_{pk} rewards the process for moving the center from 3σ to 6σ away from the nearer limit by increasing from 1 to 2. You see that C_p and C_{pk} are equal if the process is properly centered. If not, C_{pk} is smaller than C_p.

EXAMPLE 12.13 Elastomer Viscosity Process Capability

CASE 12.3

Figure 12.19(a) compares the distribution of the viscosities of lots of elastomers with the specifications LSL = 40 and USL = 50. The distribution here, as is always true in practice, is *estimated* from past observations on the process. The estimates are

$$\hat{\mu} = \overline{\overline{x}} = 48.7$$

$$\hat{\sigma} = s = 0.85$$

Because capability describes the distribution of individual measurements, we once more estimate σ from individual measurements rather than using the estimate $\overline{s}/c_4$ that we employ for control charts.

These estimates may be quite accurate if we have data on many past lots. Estimates based on only a few observations may, however, be inaccurate because statistics from small samples can have large sampling variability. This important point is often not appreciated when capability indexes are used in practice. To emphasize that we can only estimate the indexes, we write $\hat{C}_p$ and $\hat{C}_{pk}$ for values calculated from sample data. They are

$$\hat{C}_p = \frac{\text{USL} - \text{LSL}}{6\hat{\sigma}}$$

$$= \frac{50 - 40}{(6)(0.85)} = \frac{10}{5.1} = 1.96$$

$$\hat{C}_{pk} = \frac{|\hat{\mu} - \text{nearer limit}|}{3\hat{\sigma}}$$

$$= \frac{50 - 48.7}{(3)(0.85)} = \frac{1.3}{2.55} = 0.51$$

$\hat{C}_p = 1.96$ is quite satisfactory because the process width is only about half the specification width. The small value of $\hat{C}_{pk}$ reflects the fact that the process center is not close to the center of the specs. If we can move the center μ to 45, then $\hat{C}_{pk}$ will also be 1.96.

APPLY YOUR KNOWLEDGE

12.44 C_p versus C_{pk}. Sketch Normal curves that represent measurements on products from a process with

(a) $C_p = 3$ and $C_{pk} = 1$.

(b) $C_p = 3$ and $C_{pk} = 2$.

(c) $C_p = 3$ and $C_{pk} = 3$.

12.45 Mesh-tensioning process capability. Table 12.1 (page 696) gives 20 process control samples of the mesh tension of computer monitors. In Example 12.9, we estimated from these samples that $\hat{\mu} = \overline{\overline{x}} = 275.065$ mV and $\hat{\sigma} = s = 38.38$ mV.

CASE 12.2

School absenteeism. An urban school system records the percent of its eighth-grade students who are absent three or more days each month. Because students with high absenteeism in eighth grade often fail to complete high school, the school system has launched programs to reduce absenteeism. These programs include calls to parents of absent students, public-service messages to change community expectations, and measures to ensure that the schools are safe and attractive. A p chart will show if the programs are having an effect.

The manufacturing example illustrates an advantage of p charts: they can combine several specifications in a single chart. Nonetheless, p charts have been rendered outdated in many manufacturing applications by improvements in typical levels of quality. For example, Delphi, the largest North American auto electronics manufacturer, says that it reduced its proportion of problem parts from 200 per million in 1997 to 20 per million in 2001.[17] At either of these levels, even large samples of parts will rarely contain any bad parts. The sample proportions will almost all be 0, so that plotting them is uninformative. It is better to choose important measured characteristics—voltage at a critical circuit point, for example—and keep $\bar{x}$ and s charts. Even if the voltage is satisfactory, quality can be improved by moving it yet closer to the exact voltage specified in the design of the part.

The school absenteeism example is a management application of p charts. More than 20% of all American eighth-graders miss three or more days of school per month, and this proportion is higher in large cities. A p chart will be useful. Proportions of "things going wrong" are often higher in business processes than in manufacturing, so that p charts are an important tool in business.

Control limits for *p* charts

We studied the sampling distribution of a sample proportion $\hat{p}$ in Chapter 8. The center line and control limits for a 3σ control chart follow directly from the facts stated there, in the box on page 495. We ought to call such charts "$\hat{p}$ charts" because they plot sample proportions. Unfortunately, they have always been called p charts in quality control circles. We will keep the traditional name but also keep our usual notation: p is a *process* proportion and $\hat{p}$ is a *sample* proportion.

p Chart Using Past Data

Take regular samples from a process that has been in control. The samples need not all be the same size. Estimate the process proportion p of "successes" by

$$\bar{p} = \frac{\text{total number of successes in past samples}}{\text{total number of opportunities in these samples}}$$

The center line and control limits for a ***p* chart** for future samples of size n are

$$\text{UCL} = \bar{p} + 3\sqrt{\frac{\bar{p}(1-\bar{p})}{n}}$$

$$\text{CL} = \bar{p}$$

$$\text{LCL} = \bar{p} - 3\sqrt{\frac{\bar{p}(1-\bar{p})}{n}}$$

Common **out-of-control signals** are one sample proportion $\hat{p}$ outside the control limits or a run of 9 sample proportions on the same side of the center line.

If we have k past samples of the *same* size n, then $\overline{p}$ is just the average of the k sample proportions. In some settings, you may meet samples of unequal size—differing numbers of students enrolled in a month or differing numbers of parts inspected in a shift. The average $\overline{p}$ estimates the process proportion p even when the sample sizes vary. Note that the control limits use the actual size n of a sample.

CASE 12.4 REDUCING ABSENTEEISM

Unscheduled absences by clerical and production workers are an important cost in many companies. Reducing the rate of absenteeism is therefore an important goal for a company's human relations department. A rate of absenteeism above 5% is a serious concern. Many companies set 3% absent as a desirable target. You have been asked to improve absenteeism in a production facility where 12% of the workers are now absent on a typical day.

You first do some background study—in greater depth than this very brief summary. Companies try to avoid hiring workers who are likely to miss work often, such as substance abusers. They may have policies that reward good attendance or penalize frequent absences by individual workers. Changing those policies in this facility will have to wait until the union contract is renegotiated. What might you do with the current workers under current policies? Studies of absenteeism by clerical and production workers who do repetitive, routine work under close supervision point to unpleasant work environment and harsh or unfair treatment by supervisors as factors that increase absenteeism. It's now up to you to apply this general knowledge to your specific problem.

First, collect data. Daily absenteeism data are already available. You carry out a sample survey that asks workers about their absences and the reasons for them (responses are anonymous, of course). Workers who are more often absent complain about their supervisor and about the lighting at their work station. Female workers complain that the restrooms are dirty and unpleasant. You do more data analysis:

- A Pareto chart of average absenteeism rate for the past month broken down by supervisor (Figure 12.24) shows important differences among supervisors. Only

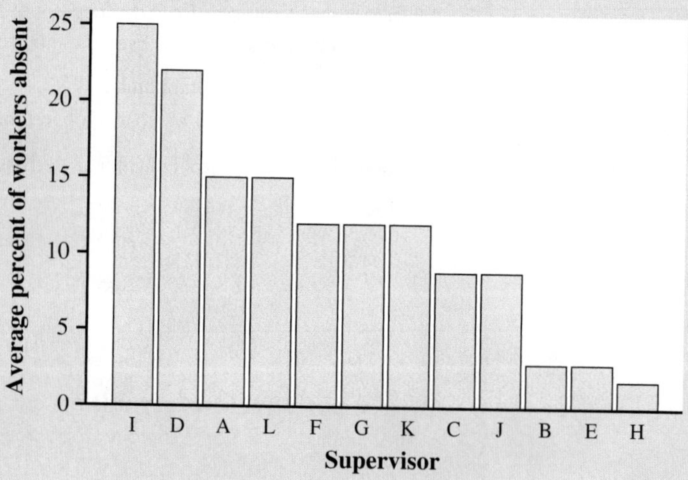

FIGURE 12.24 Pareto chart of the average percent of days absent for workers reporting to each of 12 supervisors.

supervisors B, E, and H meet your goal of 5% or less absenteeism. Workers supervised by I and D have particularly high rates.

- Another Pareto chart (not shown) by type of work station shows that a few types of work have high rates.

Now you take action. You retrain all the supervisors in human relations skills, using B, E, and H as discussion leaders. In addition, a trainer works individually with supervisors I and D. You ask supervisors to talk with any absent worker when he or she returns to work. Working with the engineering department, you study the work stations with high absenteeism rates and make changes such as better lighting. You refurbish the restrooms (for both genders even though only women complained) and schedule more frequent cleaning.

EXAMPLE 12.16 Absenteeism Rate *p* Chart

CASE 12.4 Are your actions effective? You hope to see a reduction in absenteeism. To view progress (or lack of progress), you will keep a p chart of the proportion of absentees. The plant has 987 production workers. For simplicity, you just record the number who are absent from work each day. Only unscheduled absences count, not planned time off such as vacations. Each day you will plot

$$\hat{p} = \frac{\text{number of workers absent}}{987}$$

You first look back at data for the past three months. There were 64 work days in these months. The total workdays available for the workers was

$$(64)(987) = 63{,}168 \text{ person-days}$$

Absences among all workers totaled 7580 person-days. The average daily proportion absent was therefore

$$\begin{aligned}\overline{p} &= \frac{\text{total days absent}}{\text{total days available for work}}\\ &= \frac{7580}{63{,}168} = 0.120\end{aligned}$$

The daily rate has been in control at this level.

These past data allow you to set up a p chart to monitor future proportions absent:

$$\begin{aligned}\text{UCL} &= \overline{p} + 3\sqrt{\frac{\overline{p}(1-\overline{p})}{n}} = 0.120 + 3\sqrt{\frac{(0.120)(0.880)}{987}}\\ &= 0.120 + 0.031 = 0.151\end{aligned}$$

$$\text{CL} = \overline{p} = 0.120$$

$$\begin{aligned}\text{LCL} &= \overline{p} - 3\sqrt{\frac{\overline{p}(1-\overline{p})}{n}} = 0.120 - 3\sqrt{\frac{(0.120)(0.880)}{987}}\\ &= 0.120 - 0.031 = 0.089\end{aligned}$$

Table 12.10 gives the data for the next four weeks. Figure 12.25 is the p chart.

TABLE 12.10 Proportions of workers absent during four weeks

Day	M	T	W	Th	F	M	T	W	Th	F
Workers absent	129	121	117	109	122	119	103	103	89	105
Proportion $\hat{p}$	0.131	0.123	0.119	0.110	0.124	0.121	0.104	0.104	0.090	0.106
Workers absent	99	92	83	92	92	115	101	106	83	98
Proportion $\hat{p}$	0.100	0.093	0.084	0.093	0.093	0.117	0.102	0.107	0.084	0.099

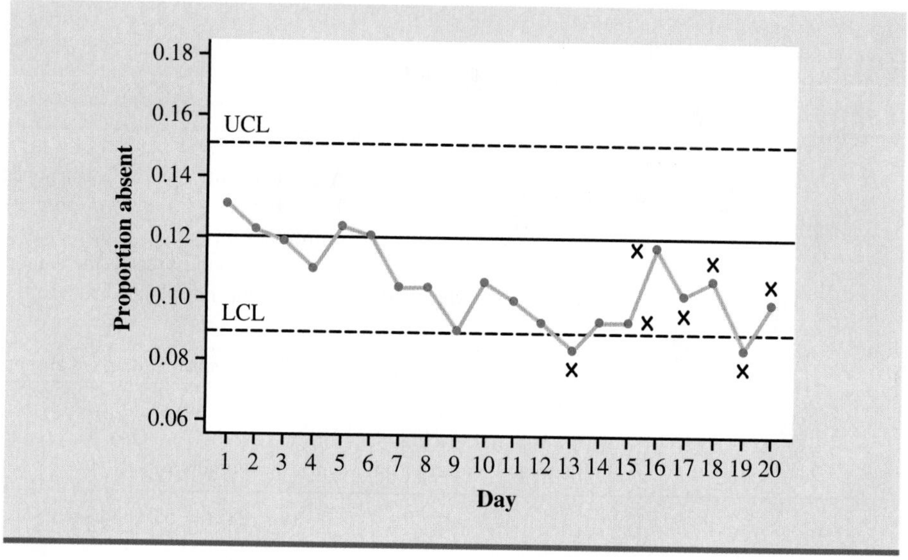

FIGURE 12.25 Process-monitoring p chart for daily proportion of workers absent over a four-week period. The lack of control shows an improvement (decrease) in absenteeism. Update the chart to continue monitoring the process.

Figure 12.25 shows a clear downward trend in the daily proportion of workers who are absent. Days 13 and 19 lie below LCL, and a run of 9 days below the center line is achieved at Day 15 and continues. The points marked "x" are therefore all out of control. It appears that a special cause (the various actions you took) has reduced the absenteeism rate from around 12% to around 10%. The last two weeks' data suggest that the rate has stabilized at this level. You will update the chart based on the new data. If the rate does not decline further (or even rises again as the effect of your actions wears off), you will consider further changes.

Example 12.16 is a bit oversimplified. The number of workers available did not remain fixed at 987 each day. Hirings, resignations, and planned vacations change the number a bit from day to day. The control limits for a day's $\hat{p}$ depend on n, the number of workers that day. If n varies, the control limits will move in and out from day to day. Software will do the extra arithmetic needed for a different n each day, but as long as the count of workers remains close to 987, the greater detail will not change your conclusion.

A single p chart for all workers is not the only, or even the best, choice in this setting. Because of the important role of supervisors in absenteeism, it would be wise to also keep separate p charts for the workers under each supervisor. These charts may show that you must reassign some supervisors.

SECTION 12.4 SUMMARY

- There are control charts for several different types of process measurements. One important type is the **p chart** for sample proportions $\hat{p}$.
- The interpretation of p charts is very similar to that of $\bar{x}$ charts. The out-of-control signals used are also the same.

SECTION 12.4 Exercises

12.60 CASE 12.4 **Setting up a p chart.** After inspecting Figure 12.25, you decide to monitor the next four weeks' absenteeism rates using a center line and control limits calculated from the second two weeks' data recorded in Table 12.10. Find $\bar{p}$ for these 10 days and give the new values of CL, LCL, and UCL. (Until you have more data, these are trial control limits. As long as you are taking steps to improve absenteeism, you have not reached the process-monitoring stage.)

12.61 **Unpaid invoices.** The controller's office of a corporation is concerned that invoices that remain unpaid after 30 days are damaging relations with vendors. To assess the magnitude of the problem, a manager searches payment records for invoices that arrived in the past 10 months. The average number of invoices is 2875 per month, with relatively little month-to month variation. Of all these invoices, 960 remained unpaid after 30 days.

(a) What is the total number of opportunities for unpaid invoices? What is $\bar{p}$?

(b) Give the center line and control limits for a p chart on which to plot the future monthly proportions of unpaid invoices.

12.62 **Lost baggage.** The Department of Transportation reports that about 1 of every 200 passengers on domestic flights of the 10 largest U.S. airlines files a report of mishandled baggage. Starting with this information, you plan to sample records for 1000 passengers per day at a large airport to monitor the effects of efforts to reduce mishandled baggage. What are the initial center line and control limits for a chart of the daily proportion of mishandled baggage reports? (You will find that LCL < 0. Because proportions $\hat{p}$ are always 0 or positive, take LCL $= 0$.)

12.63 **Aircraft rivets.** After completion of an aircraft wing assembly, inspectors count the number of missing or deformed rivets. There are hundreds of rivets in each wing, but the total number varies depending on the aircraft type. Recent data for wings with a total of 34,700 rivets show 208 missing or deformed. The next wing contains 1070 rivets. What are the appropriate center line and control limits for plotting the $\hat{p}$ from this wing on a p chart?

12.64 **Doctors' prescriptions.** A regional chain of retail pharmacies finds that about 1% of prescriptions it receives from doctors are incorrect or illegible. The chain puts in place a secure online system that doctors' offices can use to enter prescriptions directly. It hopes that fewer prescriptions entered online will be incorrect or illegible. A p chart will monitor progress. Use information about past prescriptions to set initial center line and control limits for the proportion of incorrect or illegible prescriptions on a day when the chain fills 75,000 online prescriptions. What are the center line and control limits for a day when only 50,000 online prescriptions are filled?

12.65 **School absenteeism.** Here are data from an urban school district on the number of eighth-grade students with 3 or more unexcused absences from school during each month of a school year. Because the total number of eighth-graders changes a bit from month to month, these totals are also given for each month.

(a) Find $\bar{p}$. Because the number of students varies from month to month, also find $\bar{n}$, the average per month.

(b) Make a p chart using control limits based on $\bar{n}$ students each month. Comment on control.

(c) The exact control limits are different each month because the number of students n is different each month. This situation is common in using p charts. What are the exact limits for October and June, the months with the largest and smallest n? Add these limits to your p chart, using short lines spanning a single month. Do exact limits affect your conclusions?

Month	Sept.	Oct.	Nov.	Dec.	Jan.	Feb.	Mar.	Apr.	May	June
Students	911	947	939	942	918	920	931	925	902	883
Absent	291	349	364	335	301	322	344	324	303	344

12.66 ***p* charts are out of date.** A manufacturer of consumer electronic equipment makes full use not only of statistical process control but of automated testing equipment that efficiently tests all completed products. Data from the testing equipment show that finished products have only 3.5 defects per million opportunities.

(a) What is $\overline{p}$ for the manufacturing process? If the process turns out 5000 pieces per day, how many defects do you expect to see at this rate? In a typical month of 24 working days, how many defects do you expect to see?

(b) What are the center line and control limits for a p chart for plotting daily defect proportions?

(c) Explain why a p chart is of no use at such high levels of quality.

12.67 **Manufacturing isn't everything.** Because the manufacturing quality in the previous exercise is so high, the process of writing up orders is the major source of quality problems: the defect rate there is 8000 per million opportunities. The manufacturer processes about 500 orders per month.

(a) What is $\overline{p}$ for the order-writing process? How many defective orders do you expect to see in a month?

(b) What are the center line and control limits for a p chart for plotting monthly proportions of defective orders? What is the smallest number of bad orders in a month that will result in a point above the upper control limit?

STATISTICS IN SUMMARY

Statistical process control uses a combination of graphical and numerical description to decide when a process has become unstable and requires intervention. Control charts combine time plots with limits based on the sampling distributions of the statistic being charted. This chapter presents only the most common control charts, $\overline{x}$ and s charts and p charts. Other types are also in common use, but in all cases the details are simple and the ideas and interpretation are similar. This chapter emphasizes some aspects of practical use of control charts and places them in context by also giving attention to process capability. Here are the specific skills you should now possess.

A. Processes

1. Describe the process leading to some desired output using flowcharts and cause-and-effect diagrams.
2. Choose promising targets for process improvement, combining the process description with data collection and tools such as Pareto charts.
3. Demonstrate understanding of statistical control, common causes, and special causes by applying these ideas to specific processes.
4. Choose rational subgroups for control charting based on an understanding of the process.

B. Control Charts

1. Make $\overline{x}$ and s charts using given values of the process μ and σ (usually from large amounts of past data) for monitoring a process that has been in control.
2. Demonstrate understanding of the distinction between short-term (within sample) and longer-term (across samples) variation by identifying possible $\overline{x}$-type and s-type special causes for a specific process.
3. Interpret $\overline{x}$ and s charts, starting with the s chart. Use both one-point-out and runs signals.
4. Estimate the process μ and σ from recent samples.

5. Set up initial control charts using recent process data, removing special causes, and basing an initial chart on the remaining data.
6. Decide when a p chart is appropriate. Make a p chart based on past data.

C. Process Capability

1. Know the distinction between control and capability and apply this distinction in discussing specific processes.
2. Give the natural tolerances for a process in control, after verifying Normality of individual measurements on the process.
3. (Optional) Calculate the capability indexes C_p and C_{pk} from a process in control. Describe the meaning of these indexes with sketches of Normal curves.
4. (Optional) Detect practical pitfalls in using capability indexes, especially lack of attention to sampling variability in small samples.

CHAPTER 12 Review Exercises

12.68 Enlighten management. A manager who knows no statistics asks you, "What does it mean to say that a process is in control? Is being in control a guarantee that the quality of the product is good?" Answer these questions in plain language that the manager can understand.

12.69 Pareto charts. You manage the customer service operation for a maker of electronic equipment sold to business customers. Traditionally, the most common complaint is that equipment does not operate properly when installed, but attention to manufacturing and installation quality will reduce these complaints. You hire an outside firm to conduct a sample survey of your customers. Here are the percent of customers with each of several kinds of complaints:

Category	Percent
Accuracy of invoices	25%
Clarity of operating manual	8%
Complete invoice	24%
Complete shipment	16%
Correct equipment shipped	15%
Ease of obtaining invoice adjustments/credits	33%
Equipment operates when installed	6%
Meeting promised delivery date	11%
Sales rep returns calls	4%
Technical competence of sales rep	12%

(a) Why do the percents not add to 100%?

(b) Make a Pareto chart. What area would you choose as a target for improvement?

12.70 What type of chart? What type of control chart or charts would you use as part of efforts to improve each of the following performance measures in a corporate personnel office? Explain your choices.

(a) Time to get security clearance.

(b) Percent of job offers accepted.

(c) Employee participation in voluntary health screening.

12.71 What type of chart? What type of control chart or charts would you use as part of efforts to improve each of the following performance measures in a corporate information systems department? Explain your choices.

(a) Computer system availability.

(b) Time to respond to requests for help.

(c) Percent of programming changes not properly documented.

12.72 Purchased material. At the present time, about 5 lots out of every 1000 lots of material arriving at a plant site from outside vendors are rejected because they are incorrect. The plant receives about 300 lots per week. As part of an effort to reduce errors in the system of placing and filling orders, you will monitor the proportion of rejected lots each week. What type of control chart will you use? What are the initial center line and control limits?

You have just installed a new system that uses an interferometer to measure the thickness of polystyrene film. To control the thickness, you plan to measure 3 film specimens every 10 minutes and keep $\bar{x}$ and s charts. To establish control you measure 22 samples of 3 films each at 10-minute intervals. Table 12.11 gives $\bar{x}$ and s for these samples. The units are

TABLE 12.11 $\bar{x}$ **and** s **for samples of film thickness**

Sample	$\bar{x}$	s	Sample	$\bar{x}$	s
1	848	20.1	12	823	12.6
2	832	1.1	13	835	4.4
3	826	11.0	14	843	3.6
4	833	7.5	15	841	5.9
5	837	12.5	16	840	3.6
6	834	1.8	17	833	4.9
7	834	1.3	18	840	8.0
8	838	7.4	19	826	6.1
9	835	2.1	20	839	10.2
10	852	18.9	21	836	14.8
11	836	3.8	22	829	6.7

millimeters $\times 10^{-4}$. *Exercises 12.73 to 12.77 are based on this process improvement setting.*

12.73 s **chart.** Calculate control limits for s, make an s chart, and comment on control of short-term process variation.

12.74 $\bar{x}$ **chart.** Interviews with the operators reveal that in samples 1 and 10 mistakes in operating the interferometer resulted in one high-outlier thickness reading that was clearly incorrect. Recalculate $\bar{x}$ and s after removing samples 1 and 10. Recalculate UCL for the s chart and add the new UCL to your s chart from the previous exercise. Control for the remaining samples is excellent. Now find the appropriate center line and control limits for an $\bar{x}$ chart, make the $\bar{x}$ chart, and comment on control.

12.75 **Capability.** The specifications call for film thickness 830 ± 25 mm $\times$ 10^{-4}.

(a) What is the estimate $\hat{\sigma}$ of the process standard deviation based on the sample standard deviations (after removing samples 1 and 10)? Estimate the capability ratio C_p and comment on what it says about this process.

(b) Because the process mean can easily be adjusted, C_p is more informative than C_{pk}. Explain why this is true.

(c) The estimate of C_p from (a) is probably too optimistic as a description of the film produced. Explain why.

12.76 **Capability.** Examination of individual measurements shows that they are close to Normal. If the process mean is set to the target value, about what percent of films will meet the specifications?

12.77 **Categorizing the output.** Previously, control of the process was based on categorizing the thickness of each film inspected as satisfactory or not. Steady improvement in process quality has occurred, so that just 15 of the last 5000 films inspected were unsatisfactory.

(a) What type of control chart would be used in this setting, and what would be the control limits for a sample of 100 films?

(b) The chart in (a) is of little practical value at current quality levels. Explain why.

12.78 **More signals.** There are other out-of-control signals that are sometimes used with $\bar{x}$ charts. One is "15 points in a row within the 1σ level." That is, 15 consecutive points fall between $\mu - \sigma/\sqrt{n}$ and $\mu + \sigma/\sqrt{n}$. This signal suggests either that the value of σ used for the chart is too large or that careless measurement is producing results that are suspiciously close to the target. Find the probability that the next 15 points will give this signal when the process remains in control with the given μ and σ.

12.79 **It's all in the wrist.** Consider the saga of a professional basketball player plagued with poor free-throw shooting performance. Below are the number of free throws he made out of 50 attempts on 20 consecutive practice days:

25	27	31	28	22	21	27	20	25	27
23	22	29	34	30	27	26	25	28	25

(a) Construct a p chart for the data. Does the process appear to be in control?

(b) Recognizing that the player needed insight into his free-throw shooting problems, the coach hired an outside consultant to work with the player. The consultant noticed a subtle flaw in the player's technique. Namely, the player was bending back his wrist only 85° when, ideally, the wrist needs to be bent back 90° for proper flick motion. Part of the problem was because the player had a stiff wrist. Over the course of the next week or so, the player was given techniques to loosen his wrist. After implementing a modification to wrist movement, he got the following results on 10 new samples (again out of 50 attempts):

34 38 35 43 31 35 32 36 28 39

Plot the new sample proportions along with the control limits determined in part (a). What are your conclusions? What should be the values of the control limits for future samples?

CHAPTER 12 Appendix

Using Minitab for Statistics for Quality

Automated procedures for constructing control charts of any sort or calculating process capability indexes are not available in standard Excel, but a number of standard control charts are available in the enhanced add-on version of Excel. We focus in this Appendix on using Minitab.

$\bar{x}$ Chart

Stat ➤ Control Charts ➤ Variables Charts for Subgroups ➤ Xbar

The data can be placed either in one column or in separate columns. For example, if the data from Table 12.1 were placed all in one column, they would be inputted from left to right, top to bottom; that is, we would input in a column the values 234.5, 272.3, 234.5, 272.3, 311.1, 305.8, and so on. Alternatively, the data values can be placed in four separate columns in the same manner as shown in Table 12.1. Depending on how you have the data in the worksheet, choose the appropriate option from the pull-down menu found at the top of the box. If you selected the option of all the data in one column, then click the data column into the box found below. You will then need to enter the sample size in the **Subgroups sizes** box. If you chose the option of data in more than one column, click all the data columns into the box found below. You will notice that the **Subgroups sizes** box will disappear.

If you know the mean parameter (μ) and the process standard deviation (σ), you should click the **Xbar Options** button and then select the **Parameters** tab. You can then enter the values of μ and σ in the appropriate boxes. If these boxes are left blank, Minitab will estimate the parameters based on the data. In default mode, Minitab estimates the standard deviation using a "pooled estimate" much like the pooled estimate used with the two-sample t procedure (Section 7.2). To have Minitab use the standard deviation estimate discussed in this chapter, click the **Xbar Options** button and then the **Estimate** tab. Now select the **Sbar** option. Make sure to leave the checkmark in the **Using unbiasing constant** checkbox; with this option, c_4 and c_5 are used. If you want to have the limits of the means chart based on the range (R) statistic, then select the **Rbar** option. While you have the **Xbar Options** pop-up box open, you can select the **Tests** tab. Under this tab you can select the out-of-control signal based on 9 consecutive points above or below the center line. If you want to set aside certain samples because they are found to be associated with special causes, click the **Data Options** button and then choose the option to indicate either which samples to include or which samples to exclude. Subsequently, indicate the rows corresponding to the option chosen (that is, inclusion and exclusion). Once all pop-up option boxes are closed, click **OK** to produce the $\bar{x}$ chart.

s Chart

Stat ➤ Control Charts ➤ Variables Charts for Subgroups ➤ S

Refer to the data entry discussion for the $\bar{x}$ chart, as it applies similarly to the s chart. If you know the process standard deviation (σ), you should click the **S Options** button and then select the **Parameters** tab and enter the value of σ in the **Standard deviation** box. If you wish for Minitab to estimate the standard deviation and use the estimate discussed in this chapter, click the **S Options** button and then the **Estimate** tab. Now select the **Sbar** option. Make sure to leave the checkmark in the **Using unbiasing constant** checkbox; with this option, B_5 and B_6 are used. While you have the **S Options** pop-up box open, you can select the **Tests** tab. Under this tab you can select the out-of-control signal based on 9 consecutive points above or below the center line. As with the $\bar{x}$ chart, you can click that **Data Options** button to set aside specified samples. Once all pop-up option boxes are closed, click **OK** to produce the s chart.

R Chart

Stat ➤ Control Charts ➤ Variables Charts for Subgroups ➤ R

Refer to the data entry discussion for the $\bar{x}$ chart, as it applies similarly to the R chart. If you know the process standard deviation (σ), you should click the **R Options** button and then select the **Parameters** tab and enter the value of σ in the **Standard deviation** box. If you don't provide a value for σ, then Minitab will use a pooled estimate based on the sample standard deviations. The use of an estimate based on the sample standard deviations for the construction of R chart limits is a bit unconventional. Typically, when dealing with ranges, the process standard deviation is estimated using the ranges themselves. To base the estimate of the process standard deviation on the ranges, click the **R Options** button and then the **Estimate** tab and finally select the **Rbar** option. While you have the **R Options** pop-up box open, you can select the **Tests** tab. Under this tab you can select the out-of-control signal based on 9 consecutive points above or below the center line. As with other control chart routines, you can click the **Data Options** button to set aside specified samples. Once all pop-up option boxes are closed, click **OK** to produce the R chart.

Process Capability Indexes

Stat ➤ Quality Tools ➤ Capability Analysis ➤ Normal

In the latest release of the Student Edition of Minitab (Version 14), process capability analysis is not available. If you have an earlier version, the data can be placed either in one column or in separate columns. If the data are in one column, select the **Single column** option and then enter the value of "1" into the **Subgroups sizes** box. If you have control data in separate columns (as in Table 12.1), select the **Subgroups across rows of** option and then click the data columns into the box found below. Now enter the lower and upper specifications in the **Lower spec** and **Upper spec** boxes. Do not place checkmarks in the **Boundary** checkboxes. If you know the mean parameter (μ) and the process standard deviation (σ), enter their values in the **Historical mean** and **Historical standard deviation** boxes. In our discussions about the cautions about capability indexes, we noted that it is preferable to use the standard deviation s of all measurements as opposed to control-chart-based estimates. In default mode, Minitab reports two sets of capability indexes: based on s and based on a control chart. To report only the capability indexes computed based on s, click the **Options** button and remove the checkmark in the **Within subgroup analysis** checkbox. With the **options** pop-up box open, you will notice an **Include confidence intervals** option. Recall that we noted in the chapter that capability indexes are statistics subject to sampling variation. The confidence interval option works on that premise in that it will take sampling variation into account and report interval estimates for the process capability indexes. For more details on the construction of these confidence intervals, click the **Help** button, click the **see also** link, and then click the **Methods and formulas** topic option to find the section "Confidence Intervals and bounds." Click **OK** to close the **Options** pop-up box, and click **OK** to produce a histogram of the data with superimposed specification limits along with the capability indexes. You will notice that Minitab labels the capability indexes as P_p and P_{pk} as opposed to C_p and C_{pk}. The labels C_p and C_{pk} are used to represent the indexes that use the control-chart-based estimate of σ. It should be pointed out that if the process mean is outside, Minitab will report a negative value for P_{pk} and C_{pk} as opposed to "0" as noted in the chapter. The more negative the index, the worse the process is performing relative to specifications.

p Chart

Stat ➤ Control Charts ➤ Attributes Charts ➤ P

This routine works on the basis that there is a worksheet column having the "success" values. For example, for the data of Table 12.10, the column would have the values 129, 121, and so on. Click the data column into the **Variables** box. If the sample size (n) is the same for all samples, enter its value in the **Subgroups sizes** box. If the sample sizes are different, place the sample sizes for each sample in a worksheet column and click this column into the **Subgroups sizes** box. If you want to specify the value of p, click the **P Chart Options** button, select the **Parameters** tab, and then enter the value of p in the **Proportion** box. If you don't specify p, Minitab will estimate the proportion in the manner discussed in Section 12.4. While you have the **P Chart Options** pop-up box open, you can select the **Tests** tab. Under this tab you can select the out-of-control signal based on 9 consecutive points above or below the center line. As with other control chart routines, you can click the **Data Options** button to set aside specified samples. Once all pop-up option boxes are closed, click **OK** to produce the p chart.

CHAPTER 13

Time Series Forecasting

PRELUDE: THE HOLIDAY *SHIPPING* SEASON

Retail stores traditionally see a surge in sales beginning the day after the Thanksgiving holiday and continuing through December 24. This is called the "holiday shopping season" and is a very busy time for retail stores. Related to all this holiday shopping is a surge in the mailing of packages. Online shoppers have their purchases shipped. Many people mail gifts across the country or around the world. Package delivery companies refer to this as the "holiday *shipping* season." The surge in the number of packages to be delivered is huge—more than can be covered by employees working overtime.

One package delivery company, United Parcel Service (UPS), posted details of how the company handles the holiday shipping season on its Web site.[1] UPS estimates it will deliver 18 million packages during the "Peak Day" of the holiday shipping season. (For 2002, Peak Day is Thursday, December 19.) UPS's average number of packages delivered per day is 13.6 million. The extra 4.4 million packages of Peak Day are a 32% surge in UPS deliveries, and that is just one day of the holiday shipping season!

To handle the increase in business in 2002, UPS added about 60,000 seasonal employees to its usual workforce of 360,000 employees. (In past years, UPS has hired as many as 90,000 seasonal employees!) Without enough extra help, the holiday shipping season would be a disaster for UPS and its customers. How does UPS know how much extra help it will need? How does it estimate how many extra packages it will be asked to ship? UPS tracks the number of packages shipped over time. The regular ups and downs during the year are predictable, including the surge of the holiday shipping season. Time series methods identify such patterns and aid in forecasting future values.

Introduction

Business decisions often involve data tracked over time. Quarterly sales figures, annual health benefits costs, monthly product demand, daily stock prices, and changes in market share are all examples of *time series* data.

Time Series

Measurements of a variable taken at regular intervals over time form a **time series.**

We've already encountered time series data in earlier chapters. For example, in Chapter 1, Figure 1.7 (page 19) displays a plot of monthly orange prices from January 1991 to December 2000, and Figure 1.8 (page 20) displays a plot of national unemployment rates from January 1990 to October 2005. In Chapter 10, Exercise 10.5 (page 579) considers a small time series of research and development spending, and in Chapter 11, annual corn and soybean yields are analyzed in Exercises 11.114 through 11.120 (page 679).

The most basic tool for studying time series data is the *time plot.* Figures 1.7 and 1.8 are examples of time plots.

Time Plot

A **time plot** of a variable plots each observation against the time at which it was measured. Time is marked on the horizontal scale of the plot, and the variable you are studying is marked on the vertical scale. Connecting sequential data points by lines helps emphasize any change over time.

Plotting our data against time can reveal the main features of the time series. As with distributions, look first for overall patterns and then for striking deviations from those patterns. Here are some types of overall patterns to look for in a time series.

Trend and Seasonal Variation

A **trend** in a time series is a persistent, long-term rise or fall.

A pattern in a time series that repeats itself at known regular intervals of time is called **seasonal variation.**

Look back to Example 1.7 (page 19). The monthly orange prices exhibit both an upward trend as well as a seasonal pattern. Both are described in Example 1.7 and illustrated in Figure 1.7.

We handle time series data with the same approach used in earlier chapters:

- Plot the data, then add numerical summaries.

- Identify overall patterns and deviations from those patterns.
- When the overall pattern is quite regular, use a compact mathematical model to describe it.

In this chapter, we will focus on the plots and calculations that are most helpful when describing time series data. We will learn to identify patterns common to time series data as well as the models that are commonly used to describe those patterns. Let us begin by considering monthly sales data in the following example. Sales data often exhibit strong seasonal patterns as well as trends over time.

EXAMPLE 13.1 Monthly Retail Sales

The Census Bureau tracks retail sales using the Monthly Retail Trade Survey.[2] Retail establishments are categorized and tracked by their North American Industry Classification System (NAICS) code. NAICS code 452 corresponds to general merchandise stores (like Wal-Mart). Comparing sales data for a specific retail company with national sales data lets us see how the company is performing compared to its industry as a whole.

Figure 13.1 plots monthly retail sales of general merchandise stores beginning in January 1992 and ending in May 2002 (125 months). The plot reveals interesting characteristics of retail sales for these stores:

- Since January 1992, overall sales have gradually increased.
- A distinct pattern repeats itself approximately every 12 months: January sales are lower than the rest of the year; sales then increase but level off until October, when sales dramatically increase to a peak in December.

The gradual increase in overall sales is an example of a ***trend*** in a time series. Embedded in the monthly ups and downs of sales figures, we also see a persistent pattern describing the general, long-run behavior of sales over the time period from January 1992 to May 2002.

The repeating pattern evident in Figure 13.1 is an example of ***seasonal variation*** in a time series. Seasonal variation must be taken into account when making a short-run ***forecast*** of future sales. It would be unwise to ignore the peaks in December and the troughs in January when forecasting sales for specific months.

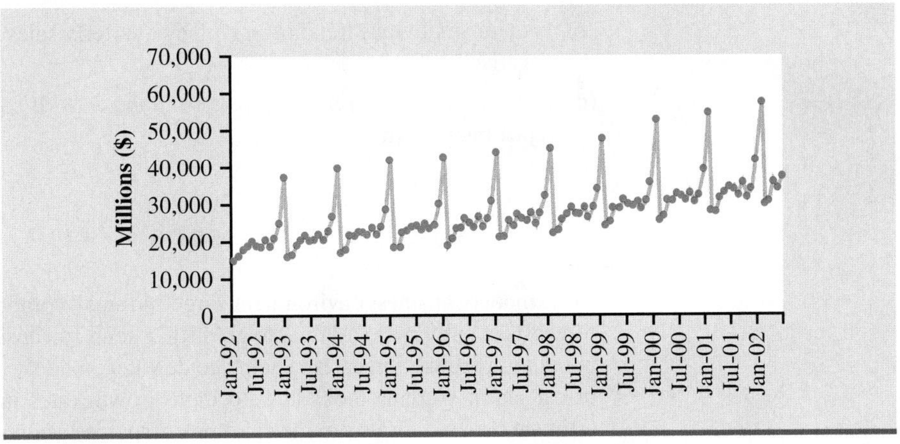

FIGURE 13.1 Time plot of U.S. retail sales of general merchandise stores for each month from January 1992 to May 2002, for Example 13.1.

TABLE 13.1 Quarterly retail sales for JCPenney, 1996–2001 (millions of dollars)

Year-quarter	Sales	Year-quarter	Sales
1996-1st	4452	1999-1st	7339
1996-2nd	4507	1999-2nd	7104
1996-3rd	5537	1999-3rd	7639
1996-4th	8157	1999-4th	9661
1997-1st	6481	2000-1st	7528
1997-2nd	6420	2000-2nd	7207
1997-3rd	7208	2000-3rd	7538
1997-4th	9509	2000-4th	9573
1998-1st	6755	2001-1st	7522
1998-2nd	6483	2001-2nd	7211
1998-3rd	7129	2001-3rd	7729
1998-4th	9072	2001-4th	9542

Forecast

A prediction of a future value of a time series is called a **forecast.**

APPLY YOUR KNOWLEDGE

13.1 JCPenney sales. Table 13.1 contains retail sales for JCPenney in millions of dollars. The data are quarterly, beginning with the first quarter of 1996 and ending with the fourth quarter of 2001.[3]

(a) Before plotting these data, inspect the values in the table. Do you see any interesting features of JCPenney quarterly sales?

(b) Now, make a time plot of the data. Be sure to connect the points in your plot to highlight patterns.

(c) Is there an obvious trend in JCPenney quarterly sales? If so, is the trend positive or negative?

(d) Is there an obvious repeating pattern in the data? If so, clearly describe the repeating pattern.

13.1 Trends and Seasons

In the modern business environment, large and small companies alike depend on long-run forecasts of numerous variables to guide their long-run business plans. A retail chain uses population growth forecasts to help decide where to locate future stores. A manufacturer of car alarm systems looks at auto theft growth rates in key areas of the country to estimate demand for its products. Some companies provide one-year-ahead forecasts of key quantities in their annual reports, so that a 2008 annual report will contain forecasts for how the company will perform in 2009.

Identifying trends

Our first step toward a reliable forecast is to identify any trend in the time series of interest. If a long-term rise or fall is detected, then we will model the trend using the methods of Chapter 10 and 11.

EXAMPLE 13.2 Monthly Retail Sales

Consider the monthly retail sales data from Example 13.1. Since January 1992, overall sales have gradually increased. We can use the ideas of simple linear regression (Chapter 10) and software to estimate this upward trend. From the Excel regression output below, we estimate the linear trend to be

$$\widehat{\text{SALES}} = 18{,}736 + 145.5x$$

where x is the number of months elapsed beginning with the first month of the time series; that is, $x = 1$ corresponds to January 1992, $x = 2$ corresponds to February 1992, etc. Sales are measured in millions of dollars.

SUMMARY OUTPUT

Regression Statistics	
Multiple R	0.655338351
R Square	0.429468354
Adjusted R Square	0.424829885
Standard Error	6101.522201
Observations	125

	Coefficients	*Standard Error*	*t Stat*	*P-value*
Intercept	18736.49742	1098.055282	17.0633462	3.1962E-34
X	145.5311521	15.12438406	9.6222862	1.11261E-16

Figure 13.2 displays the time series plot of Figure 13.1 with the trend line superimposed. The equation of the line provides a mathematical model for the observed trend in sales. The estimated slope of 145.5 indicates that retail sales at general merchandise stores increased an average of $145.5 million per month from January 1992 to May 2002.

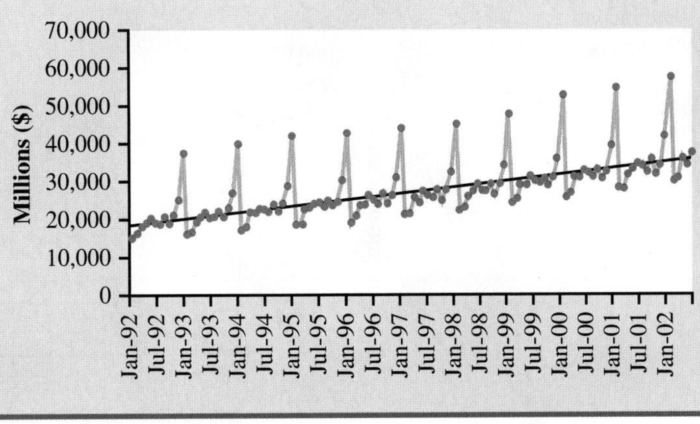

FIGURE 13.2 Trend line (black) fitted to U.S. retail sales of general merchandise stores, for Example 13.2.

Notice how the trend line in Figure 13.2 ignores the seasonal variation in the retail sales time series. Because of this, using the equation above to forecast sales for, say, December 2002 will likely result in a gross underestimate since the line underestimates sales for all the Decembers in the data set. We will need to take the month-to-month pattern into account if we wish to accurately forecast sales in a specific month.

In Chapter 11, we used regression techniques to fit a variety of models to data. For example, we used a polynomial model to predict the prices of houses in Example 11.14 (page 632). Trends in time series data may also be best described by a curved model like a polynomial. The techniques of Chapter 11 help us fit such trend curves to time series data. Case 13.1 illustrates another type of curved relationship—**exponential trend.**

exponential trend

CASE 13.1 SELLING DVD PLAYERS

The popularity of the DVD format has exploded in the relatively short period of time since its introduction in March 1997. At the end of June 2002, nearly 33 million DVD players had been sold in the United States, with over 18,000 titles available in the DVD format. The Consumer Electronics Association (CEA) tracks monthly sales of DVD players. The data are provided in the file *ca13_001*.[4] Figure 13.3 plots the number of units sold over time. The plot includes sales data from April 1997 to June 2002 (63 months).

Let your eye follow the sales numbers from April to April. DVD player sales increased very little from April 1997 to April 1998. Notice how the April-to-April sales increases have grown in magnitude over the years with April 2001 to April 2002 showing the largest increase. This pattern of increasing growth is an example of an *exponential trend.* Figure 13.4 shows the DVD player sales data with an exponential trend superimposed. Statistical software estimates the exponential trend to be

$$\widehat{\text{UNITS}} = 29{,}523.65e^{0.068941x}$$

where x is the number of months elapsed beginning with the first month of the time series; that is, $x = 1$ corresponds to April 1997, $x = 2$ corresponds to May 1997, etc. (The mathematical constant e was introduced in Chapter 5 on page 336.)

We can use our trend model to forecast the number of DVD players to be sold in a future month. July 2002 corresponds to $x = 64$, and we get

$$\widehat{\text{UNITS}} = 29{,}523.65e^{0.068941\times 64} = 2{,}434{,}303$$

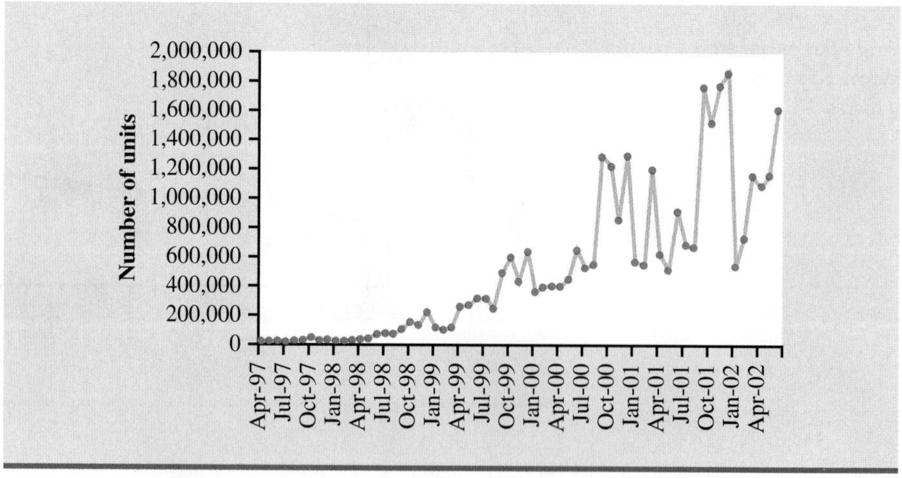

FIGURE 13.3 Time plot of number of DVD players sold for each month from April 1997 to June 2002, for Case 13.1.

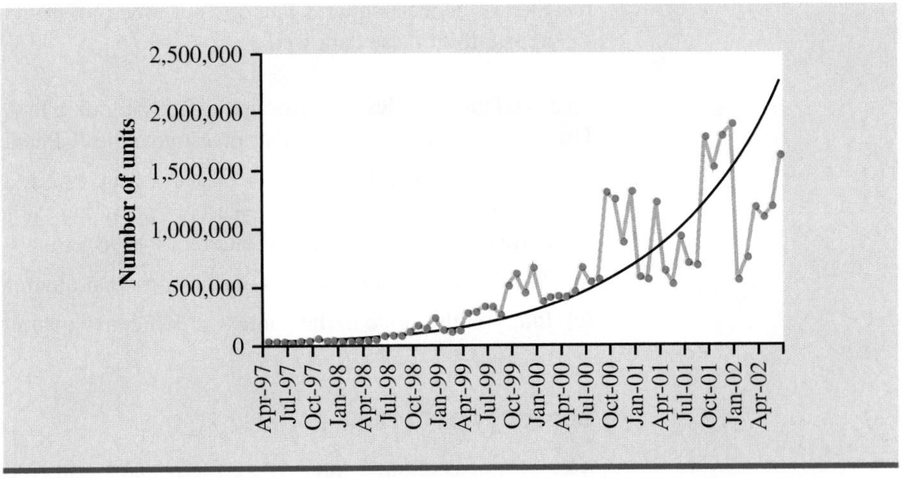

FIGURE 13.4 Exponential trend (black) fitted to the number of DVD players sold, for Case 13.1.

CASE 13.1 SELLING DVD PLAYERS *(Continued)*

Our forecasted value ignores the monthly ups and downs in the time series. In fact, if you look closely at the data, you will see that July sales have always been more than June sales (except in 1998). Our trend model ignores such information about the time series. Our forecast of over 2.4 million DVD players to be sold in July 2002 is greater than the 1.6 million DVD players sold in June 2002.

Remember, a trend equation may be a good description of the long-run behavior of the data, but we need to account for short-run phenomena (like seasonal variation) to improve the accuracy of our forecasts.

APPLY YOUR KNOWLEDGE

13.2 Number of Macs shipped. Table 13.2 displays the time series of the number of Macintosh computers shipped in each of eight consecutive fiscal quarters.[5] We usually want a time series longer than just eight time periods, but this short series will give you a chance to do some calculations by hand. Hand calculations take the mystery out of what computers do so quickly and efficiently for us.

(a) Make a time plot of these data.

(b) Using the following summary information, calculate the least-squares regression line for predicting the number of Macs shipped (in thousands of units). The variable Time simply takes on the values 1, 2, 3, . . . , 8 in time order.

Variable	Mean	Std. dev.	Correlation
Time	4.5	2.44949	0.3095
Macs shipped	773.5	62.56197	

TABLE 13.2 Macintosh computers shipped per fiscal quarter (thousands of units)

Fiscal year-quarter	Units shipped	Fiscal year-quarter	Units shipped
2001-1st	659	2002-1st	746
2001-2nd	751	2002-2nd	813
2001-3rd	827	2002-3rd	808
2001-4th	850	2002-4th	734

(c) Sketch the least-squares line on your time plot from part (a). Does the linear model appear to fit these data well?

13.3 JCPenney sales. In Exercise 13.1, you took a first look at the data in Table 13.1. Use statistical software to further investigate the JCPenney sales data.

(a) Find the least-squares line for the sales data. Use 1, 2, 3, ... as the values for the explanatory variable, with $x = 1$ corresponding to the first quarter of 1996, $x = 2$ corresponding to the second quarter of 1996, etc.

(b) The intercept is a prediction of sales for what quarter?

(c) Interpret the slope in the context of JCPenney quarterly sales.

Seasonal patterns

Variables of economic interest are often tied to other events that repeat with regular frequency over time. Agriculture-related variables will vary with the growing and harvesting seasons. In Example 1.7 (page 19), we saw that the prices of oranges tend to be lowest in January and February and highest in August and September. Sales data may be linked to events like regular changes in the weather, the start of the school year, and the celebration of certain holidays. The monthly retail sales data of Example 13.1 (page 751) exhibit a strong pattern that repeats every twelve months, with sales peaking in December. To improve the accuracy of our forecasts we need to account for seasonal variation in our time series.

Using indicator variables

Indicator variables were introduced in Chapter 11 (page 660). We can use indicator variables to add the seasonal pattern in a time series to a trend model. Let's look at the details for the monthly retail sales data of Examples 13.1 and 13.2.

EXAMPLE 13.3 Monthly Retail Sales

The seasonal pattern in the sales data seems to repeat every 12 months, so we begin by creating $12 - 1 = 11$ indicator variables.

$$X1 = \begin{cases} 1 \text{ if the month is January} \\ 0 \text{ otherwise} \end{cases}$$

$$X2 = \begin{cases} 1 \text{ if the month is February} \\ 0 \text{ otherwise} \end{cases}$$

$$\vdots$$

$$X11 = \begin{cases} 1 \text{ if the month is November} \\ 0 \text{ otherwise} \end{cases}$$

December data are indicated when all 11 indicator variables are 0.

We can extend the trend model estimated in Example 13.2 with these indicator variables. The new model will capture the seasonal pattern in the time series.

$$\text{SALES} = \beta_0 + \beta_1 x + \beta_2 X1 + \cdots + \beta_{12} X11 + \epsilon$$

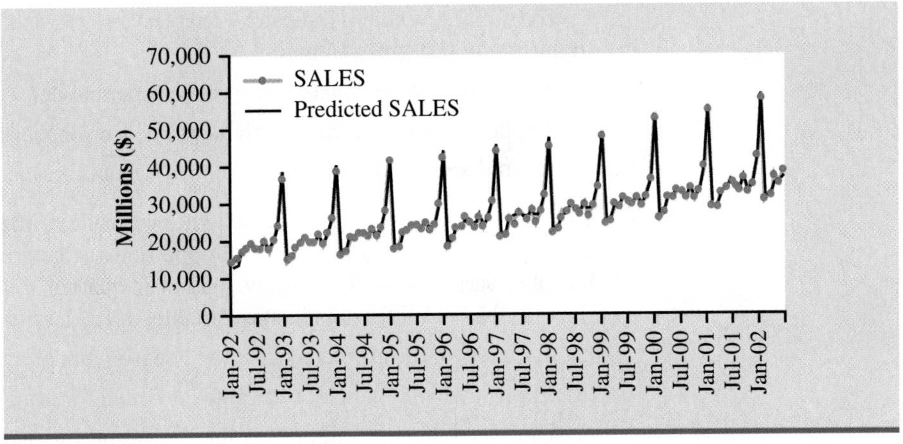

FIGURE 13.5 Trend-and-season model (black) fitted to U.S. retail sales of general merchandise stores, for Example 13.3.

Fitting this multiple regression model to our data, we get the following output:

SUMMARY OUTPUT

Regression Statistics	
Multiple R	0.993493346
R Square	0.987029029
Adjusted R Square	0.985639282
Standard Error	964.1133873
Observations	125

ANOVA

	df	*SS*	*MS*	*F*	*Significance F*
Regression	12	7921942577	660161881.4	710.2221576	1.1832E-99
Residual	112	104105637.8	929514.6235		
Total	124	8026048215			

	Coefficients	*Standard Error*	*t Stat*	*P-value*	*Lower 95%*	*Upper 95%*
Intercept	37472.690244	343.350636	109.138258	1.4241E-115	36792.38499	38152.99550
X	140.130451	2.392702	58.565779	7.61806E-86	135.38962	144.87128
X1	−24276.193200	421.421306	−57.605519	4.57481E-85	−25111.18547	−23441.20093
X2	−23748.687288	421.360169	−56.361965	4.86201E-84	−24583.55842	−22913.81615
X3	−20271.181375	421.312612	−48.114347	1.19904E-76	−21105.95828	−19436.40447
X4	−20250.493644	421.278639	−48.069120	1.32582E-76	−21085.20324	−19415.78405
X5	−18517.987731	421.258254	−43.958753	1.79155E-72	−19352.65694	−17683.31853
X6	−19574.517295	431.403553	−45.374029	6.21054E-74	−20429.28811	−18719.74648
X7	−20323.647746	431.330558	−47.118497	1.1186E-75	−21178.27393	−19469.02156
X8	−18626.878197	431.270826	−43.190675	1.15687E-71	−19481.38603	−17772.37036
X9	−20878.108647	431.224361	−48.415884	6.14847E-77	−21732.52442	−20023.69288
X10	−18933.039098	431.191170	−43.908689	2.02136E-72	−19787.38910	−18078.68909
X11	−13842.169549	431.171253	−32.103647	2.57955E-58	−14696.48009	−12987.85901

Figure 13.5 displays the time series plot of Figure 13.1 with the trend-and-season model superimposed. You can see the dramatic improvement over the trend-only model by comparing Figure 13.2 with Figure 13.5. The improved model fit is reflected in the R^2-values for the two models: $R^2 = 0.987$ for the trend-and-season model and $R^2 = 0.429$ for the trend-only model.

APPLY YOUR KNOWLEDGE

13.4 Number of Macs shipped. In Exercise 13.2, you made a time plot of the data in Table 13.2. With only eight quarters, a strong quarterly pattern is hard to detect. Add indicator variables for first, second, and third quarters to the linear trend model fitted in

Exercise 13.2. Call these indicator variables $X1$, $X2$, and $X3$. Use statistical software to fit this multiple regression model.

(a) Write down the estimated trend-and-season model.

(b) Explain why no indicator variable is needed for fourth quarters.

(c) What does the ANOVA F test indicate about this model?

13.5 JCPenney sales. In Exercise 13.1, you made a time plot of the data in Table 13.1. Sales seem to follow a pattern of ups and downs that repeats every four quarters. Add indicator variables for first, second, and third quarters to the linear trend model fitted in Exercise 13.3. Call these indicator variables $X1$, $X2$, and $X3$, respectively.

(a) Write down the estimated trend-and-season model.

(b) Explain why no indicator variable is needed for fourth quarters.

(c) Does the intercept still predict sales for a specific quarter? If so, what quarter? Compare the estimated intercept of this model with that of the trend-only model (see Exercise 13.3(b)). Given the pattern of seasonal variation, which appears to be the better estimate?

Using seasonality factors

Using indicator variables to incorporate seasonality into a trend model views the model as a trend component plus a seasonal component:

$$y = \text{TREND} + \text{SEASON}$$

You can see this in Example 13.3, where we *added* the indicator variables to the trend model. A second approach to accounting for seasonal variation is to calculate an "adjustment" factor for each season. The trend is adjusted each particular season by *multiplying* it by the appropriate **seasonality factor.** One seasonality factor is calculated for each season observed in the data. Using seasonality factors views the model as a trend component times a seasonal component:

seasonality factor

$$y = \text{TREND} \times \text{SEASON}$$

This view of our model suggests that we can identify the seasonal component by calculating

$$\frac{y}{\text{TREND}} = \text{SEASON}$$

Let's see how this works in practice using the monthly retail sales data of Example 13.1.

EXAMPLE 13.4 Monthly Retail Sales

We have been treating each month as a season for the monthly retail sales data, so we will need to calculate 12 seasonality factors. In Example 13.2 (page 753), the trend component was estimated to be

$$\widehat{\text{SALES}} = 18{,}736 + 145.5x$$

For each of the 125 months in our time series, we calculate the ratio of actual sales divided by predicted sales, $\widehat{\text{SALES}}$. We then average these ratios by month. That is, we compute the average for all the January ratios, then the average for all the February ratios, and so on. These averages become our 12 seasonality factors. The arithmetic needed is straightforward but tedious given that we have 125 months of data. The table below displays the seasonality factors that result.

Month	Seasonality factor	Month	Seasonality factor
January	0.784	July	0.931
February	0.805	August	0.994
March	0.931	September	0.913
April	0.935	October	0.985
May	0.995	November	1.166
June	0.958	December	1.662

Our trend-and-season model is then

$$\widehat{\text{SALES}} = (18{,}736 + 145.5x) \times \text{SF}$$

where SF is the seasonality factor for the appropriate month corresponding to the value of x.

The seasonality factors are a snapshot of the typical ups and downs over the course of a year. The factors are used to adjust the trend model to account for the differences from season to season (month to month in this example). The factors themselves have an interpretation if their average is 1—our factors have an average of 1.005, which is very close to 1.* If you think of the factors as percents, then the factors show how each month's sales compare to average monthly sales for all 12 months. For example, December's seasonality factor is 1.662, or 166.2%, indicating that December sales are typically 66.2% above the average for all twelve months. January's seasonality factor is 0.784, or 78.4%, indicating that January sales are typically 21.6% (100 − 78.4) below the annual average. Figure 13.6 plots the seasonality factors in order from January to December. The reference line marked at 1.0 (100%) is a visual aid for interpreting the factors compared to the overall average monthly sales. Notice how the seasonality factors mimic the pattern that is repeated every 12 months in Figure 13.1—dividing the sales data by the estimated trend has isolated the seasonal pattern in the time series.

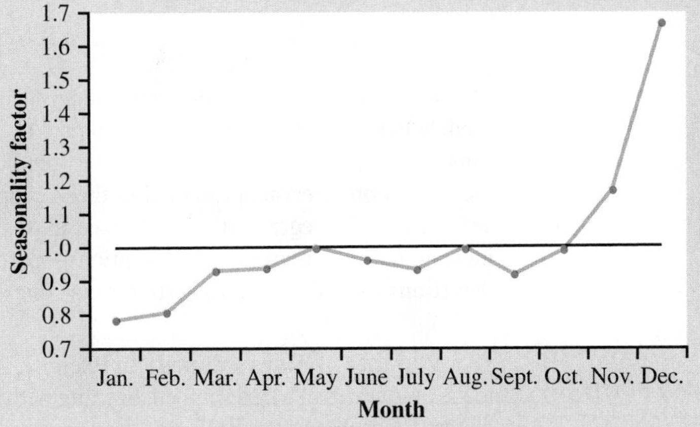

FIGURE 13.6 Seasonality factors for the U.S. retail sales of general merchandise stores plotted against month, for Example 13.4.

*If the factors did not have an average close to 1, we could adjust them so that they did average to 1 by dividing each factor by the average of the 12 factors.

EXAMPLE 13.5 Next Month's DVD Player Sales

CASE 13.1

Identifying an appropriate model to capture trend and, if present, seasonal variation is an important first step in forecasting future values of a time series. In Case 13.1 (page 754), we forecasted the number of DVD players that would sell in July 2002 based on data ending in June 2002. Our forecast used a trend-only model. Let's forecast July 2002 DVD player sales using a trend-and-season model.

The trend-only forecast for DVD player sales in July 2002 ($x = 64$) was calculated as

$$\widehat{\text{UNITS}} = 29{,}523.65e^{0.068941 \times 64} = 2{,}434{,}303$$

If we calculate the seasonality factors for the DVD player sales data using each month as a season, we get the factors displayed in the following table.

Month	Seasonality factor	Month	Seasonality factor
January	0.693	July	0.871
February	0.661	August	0.820
March	0.836	September	1.418
April	0.848	October	1.506
May	0.781	November	1.123
June	0.989	December	1.454

Our July trend-only prediction must be multiplied by the July seasonality factor 0.871 to take seasonal variation into account in our forecast:

$$\widehat{\text{UNITS}} = (29{,}523.65e^{0.068941 \times 64}) \times 0.871 = 2{,}120{,}278$$

Taking seasonal variation into account, we forecast July DVD player sales to be 12.9% below what is forecasted by the exponential trend alone. This forecast is less than the trend-only forecast, but it may still be too high given our observation that July sales are always below June sales (except in 1998), and June 2002 sales were only 1,617,098 units. The seasonal pattern is not as strong as that for the monthly retail sales data of Example 13.1, so we may need more than a trend-and-season model to accurately forecast monthly DVD player sales.

Trend-only and trend-and-season models using indicator variables are both regression models like those used in Chapters 10 and 11. Forecasting with these models uses the same techniques as the regression-based predictions in Chapters 10 and 11. However, the prediction intervals presented in those chapters cannot typically be used with time series data. The regression models used in this section will usually have residuals that indicate that our regression assumptions—particularly the assumption of independent deviations ϵ—are not appropriate for our time series data.

APPLY YOUR KNOWLEDGE

13.6 Number of Macs shipped. In Exercise 13.2, you fitted a linear trend-only model to the time series of Macs shipped. Starting with this trend model, incorporate seasonality factors for each quarter. With only eight quarters of data, these calculations can be done by hand (or computer).

(a) Calculate the seasonality factor for each quarter.

(b) Average the four seasonality factors. Is this average close to 1? If so, interpret the seasonality factor for first quarters.

(c) Make a scatterplot of seasonality factor versus quarter with the seasonality factors on the vertical axis and the quarters on the horizontal axis. Connect the points to see the general pattern of seasonal variation. Also, draw a horizontal line at the average of the four seasonality factors.

13.7 JCPenney sales. In Exercise 13.3, you fitted a linear trend-only model to the JCPenney sales data. Starting with this trend model, we want to incorporate seasonality factors to account for the pattern that repeats every four quarters.

(a) Calculate the seasonality factor for each quarter.

(b) Average the four seasonality factors. Is this average close to 1? If so, interpret the seasonality factor for fourth quarters.

(c) Make a scatterplot of seasonality factor versus quarter with the seasonality factors on the vertical axis and the quarters on the horizontal axis. Connect the points to see the general pattern of seasonal variation. Also, draw a horizontal line at the average of the four seasonality factors.

Seasonally adjusted data

Many economic time series are seasonally adjusted to make the overall trend in the numbers more apparent. Government agencies will often release both versions of a time series, so be careful to notice whether you are analyzing seasonally adjusted data or not when using government sources. A seasonally adjusted time series has had each value divided by the seasonality factor corresponding to the appropriate month.

EXAMPLE 13.6 Seasonally Adjusted Monthly Retail Sales

To calculate seasonally adjusted monthly retail sales, we simply divide each actual sales value by the appropriate seasonality factor calculated in Example 13.4. Figure 13.7 displays the original time series and the seasonally adjusted time series. The seasonally adjusted time series, SALES (SA), does not show the regular ups and downs of the data that are not seasonally adjusted, SALES (NSA). The seasonally adjusted time series shows the overall trend and some random variation. Seasonally adjusted data are easier to interpret because the technique flattens the regular peaks and valleys that we should expect in our data and makes it easier to identify unusual peaks and/or valleys in the data.

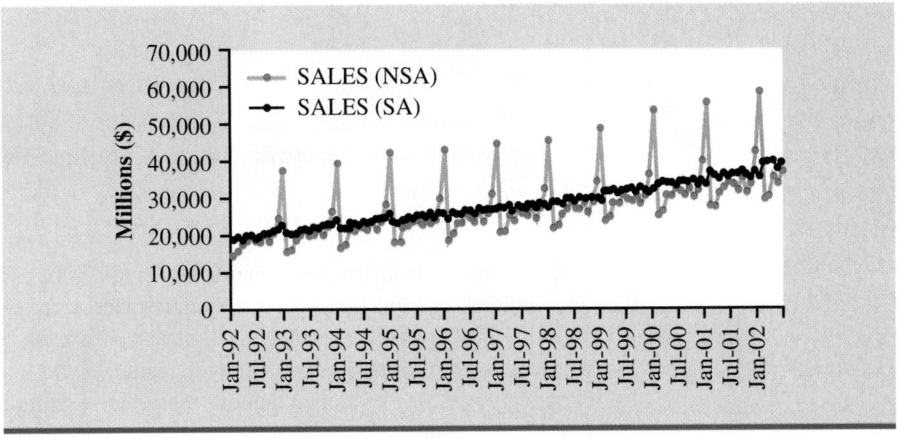

FIGURE 13.7 SALES (NSA) is the original U.S. retail sales of general merchandise stores (green). SALES (SA) is the seasonally adjusted sales data (black), for Example 13.6.

There are many different approaches to seasonal adjustment. The indicator variable model of Example 13.3 can be used, although we won't go through the details. We could also use a trend model that is more complicated than a line. Specialized time series models can also be used to seasonally adjust a time series. Different approaches will lead to different estimates and forecasts; however, for many time series the differences will not be great.

APPLY YOUR KNOWLEDGE

13.8 Seasonally adjusted DVD player data.

(a) CASE 13.1 Make a scatterplot of the seasonality factors in Example 13.5 with the seasonality factors on the vertical axis and the months (in time order) on the horizontal axis. Connect the points and describe the overall pattern of seasonal variation in the DVD player sales data.

(b) Calculate the seasonally adjusted value of the time series for June 2002. Do the calculation by hand.

13.9 Seasonally adjusted DVD player data.

(a) CASE 13.1 Using statistical software, calculate the seasonally adjusted time series of the DVD player sales data. Make a time plot of the original DVD player time series with the seasonally adjusted time series superimposed (see Figure 13.7 for an example).

(b) Did seasonally adjusting the DVD player sales data smooth the time series to the degree that seasonally adjusting the sales data in Figure 13.7 did? What does this imply about the strength of the seasonal pattern in these two time series?

Looking for autocorrelation

Using a regression model with time series data as we've done in this section will often result in residuals that indicate that our regression assumption of independent deviations is not appropriate. The current value of a time series may be heavily influenced by past values of the same series. A simple form of this dependence on past values is known as *autocorrelation.* In Chapter 2, we defined correlation as a measure of the strength of the linear relationship between two variables x and y (page 111). Similarly, autocorrelation measures the strength of the linear relationship between successive values of the same variable.

Autocorrelation

The correlation between successive values y_{t-1} and y_t of a time series is called **first-order autocorrelation** or, simply, **autocorrelation.**

The residuals from a regression model that uses time as an explanatory variable should be examined for signs of autocorrelation. If successive residuals tend to be both negative or both positive, then the residuals will have positive autocorrelation. If successive residuals tend to be of opposite sign, then the residuals will have negative autocorrelation. In either case, we have evidence that our regression assumption of independent deviations ϵ is inappropriate.

Let's examine the residuals that resulted from fitting an exponential trend to the DVD player sales data from Case 13.1.

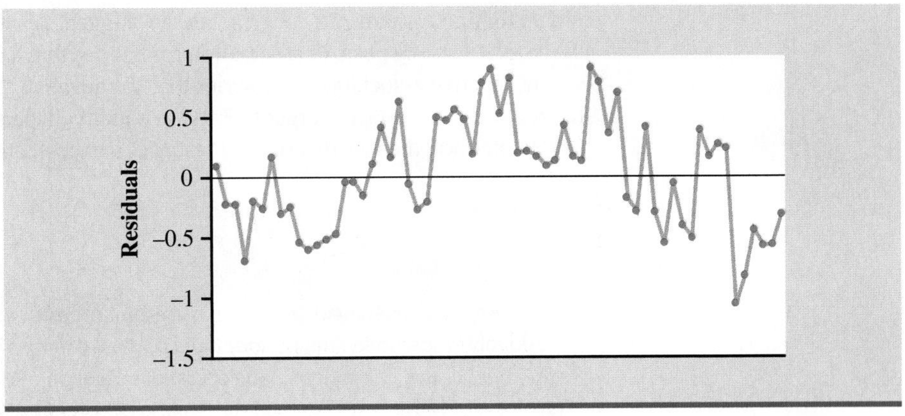

FIGURE 13.8 Time plot of residuals from the exponential trend model for DVD player sales, for Example 13.7.

EXAMPLE 13.7 DVD Player Sales

Figure 13.8 plots the residuals from our exponential trend-only model for DVD player sales. Notice the pattern:

- Starting on the left side of the plot, negative residuals tend to be followed by another negative residual.
- In the middle of the plot, positive residuals tend to be followed by another positive residual.
- On the right side of the plot, negative residuals tend to be followed by another negative residual.

This pattern indicates positive autocorrelation among the residuals.

An alternative plot for detecting autocorrelation is given in Figure 13.9. Because autocorrelation measures the strength of the linear relationship between successive values in a series, plotting pairs of successive values will show a strong linear pattern when significant autocorrelation exists. Figure 13.9 plots points of the form (e_{t-1}, e_t) where e_t is the

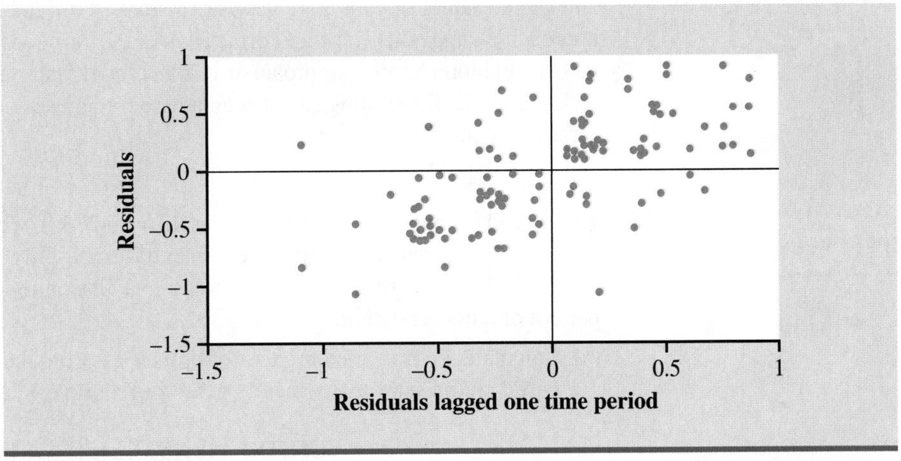

FIGURE 13.9 Lagged residual plot of residuals from the exponential trend model for DVD player sales, for Example 13.8.

residual for time period t. A scatterplot of the "lagged" residuals e_{t-1} against the residuals e_t will show a strong positive association for a series that has positive autocorrelation and a strong negative association for a series that has negative autocorrelation. If the points in a *lagged residual plot* (like Figure 13.9) are equally dispersed among the four quadrants of the scatterplot, then we do not have visual evidence of autocorrelation in our residuals.

Lagged Residual Plot

A **lagged residual plot** is a scatterplot of residuals e_t against the same residuals lagged one time period; that is, we plot the points $(e_1, e_2), (e_2, e_3), \ldots, (e_{n-1}, e_n)$. The plot is used to detect autocorrelation in residuals from a time series. A positive association in the points (e_{t-1}, e_t) indicates positive autocorrelation, while a negative association indicates negative autocorrelation.

EXAMPLE 13.8 DVD Player Sales

CASE 13.1

The linear pattern with positive slope in Figure 13.9 indicates that our residuals may have positive autocorrelation. The correlation for Figure 13.9 is 0.6165. This is approximately the autocorrelation for the residuals lagged one time period. Statistical software calculates the autocorrelation to be 0.6135 using a modified version of our correlation formula from Chapter 2.

Durbin-Watson test

The positive autocorrelation of 0.6135 is another bit of evidence that our residuals are dependent, but is 0.6135 a large enough autocorrelation to give us confidence in our conclusion of dependence? To answer this question conclusively, we would use a statistical test for autocorrelation—the **Durbin-Watson test.** The Durbin-Watson test statistic is provided with the multiple regression output of many statistical software packages. You can consult a multiple regression text for the details of this test.[6]

Several methods are proposed for handling autocorrelation in a time series. You might add lagged values of your residuals as explanatory variables to a trend-only model. Other approaches suggest clever transformations of the variables in the model to adjust for the autocorrelation. Another approach is to fit a model that uses only past values of the time series itself for forecasting rather than a model that uses other explanatory variables for forecasting the time series variable.

APPLY YOUR KNOWLEDGE

13.10 DVD player sales. In Examples 13.7 and 13.8, we found autocorrelation in the residuals from the exponential trend-only model for DVD player sales. The residuals from a trend-and-season model may not exhibit the same pattern of autocorrelation.

CASE 13.1

(a) Calculate the predicted number of units sold using the trend-and-season model based on the seasonality factors given in Example 13.5. That is, calculate

$$\widehat{\text{UNITS}} = (29{,}523.65e^{0.068941x}) \times \text{SF}$$

for each month in the time series. Be sure to use the appropriate seasonality factor (SF) for each month.

(b) Calculate the residuals for the model in part (a). That is, calculate

$$e = \text{UNITS} - \widehat{\text{UNITS}}$$

for each month in the time series.

(c) Make a time plot of the residuals. Do we have visual evidence of autocorrelation in this plot? Describe the evidence.

(d) Make a lagged residual plot and calculate the correlation between successive residuals e_{t-1} and e_t. Do we have evidence of autocorrelation? Describe the evidence.

SECTION 13.1 SUMMARY

- Data collected at regular time intervals are called a **time series.** Time series often display a long-run **trend.** Some time series also display a strong, repeating **seasonal pattern.**
- Regression methods can be used to model the trend and seasonal variation in a time series. Indicator variables can be used to model the seasons in a time series. Alternatively, **seasonality factors** can be used to adjust trend-only models for seasonal effects.
- **Seasonally adjusted** data have been divided by seasonality factors to remove the effect of seasonal variation on the time series. Government agencies typically release seasonally adjusted data for economic time series.
- Successive residuals may be linearly related. A **lagged residual plot** is a scatterplot of residuals plotted against the residuals lagged by one time period. If residuals exhibit **autocorrelation,** then our usual regression assumptions are not appropriate; in particular, the deviations cannot be assumed to be independent. In this case, a model based on past values of the time series should be considered.

SECTION 13.1 Exercises

For Exercise 13.1, see page 752; for 13.2 and 13.3, see pages 755–756; for 13.4 and 13.5, see pages 757–758; for 13.6 and 13.7, see pages 760–761; for 13.8 and 13.9, see pages 762; and for 13.10, see page 764.

13.11 Consumer loans at commercial banks. The data file *ex13_011* records the amount of money (in billions of dollars) held in consumer loans at all commercial banks in the United States. The data are monthly, beginning July 1985 and ending June 2005.[7]

(a) Use statistical software to make a time plot of these data.

(b) Describe the overall trend present in these data.

(c) Do these data exhibit a regular, repeating pattern (seasonal variation)? If so, describe the repeating pattern.

(d) Some time series exhibit *cycles.* Cycles are clear but irregular up-and-down movements that are not part of the overall trend or seasonal variation present in the time series. Does this time series contain any cycles? If so, describe the cycles by noting when each began and ended and if the cycle was a temporary peak or trough in the series.

13.12 Consumer loans at commercial banks. Use statistical software to fit a linear trend model to the consumer loans time series in the data file *ex13_011*. Use 1, 2, 3, ... as the values for the explanatory variable with $x = 1$ corresponding to July 1985, etc.

(a) Record the equation of the fitted linear trend model.

(b) Interpret the slope in the context of the amount of money held in consumer loans.

(c) Indicate stretches of time where the linear trend model consistently underestimates the amount of money in consumer loans. Do the same for stretches of time where the linear trend model consistently overestimates the amount of money in consumer loans.

(d) Forecast the amount of money in consumer loans for July 2005 using the linear trend model. Do you expect this forecast to be less than or more than the actual amount of consumer loans for this month? Explain your reasoning.

13.13 Passenger car production in the United Kingdom. Motor vehicle production in the United Kingdom is tracked monthly. The file *ex13_013* contains 60 months of production data for the number of passenger cars produced. The data begin with May 2000 and end with April 2005.[8]

(a) Use statistical software to make a time plot of these data.

(b) Does this time series exhibit a clear trend? If so, describe the trend.

(c) This time series does have clear lows—months when passenger car production was distinctly less than in other months in the series. Identify the month and year of the points that are clearly lower than the rest of the time series. Do you notice a pattern in these lows? Describe the pattern. How does production in August 2002 relate to this pattern?

13.14 Autocorrelation in passenger car production. Continue the previous exercise.

(a) Fit a linear trend-only model to the passenger car production time series. Record the fitted equation for the model.

(b) Make a time plot of the residuals as well as a lagged residual plot. What do these plots indicate about autocorrelation in this time series?

(c) What is the correlation between successive residuals? What does this correlation indicate about the presence of autocorrelation?

13.15 JCPenney sales. A linear trend-only model was fitted to the JCPenney sales data in Exercise 13.3. Use this model to answer the following:

(a) On a time plot of the sales data, draw the least-squares line. Comment on any pattern of over- or underprediction if we were to use this trend-only model for predicting sales.

(b) Using the equation of the least-squares line, forecast sales for the first quarter of 2002 and for the fourth quarter of 2002.

(c) Which forecast in part (b) do you believe will be more accurate when compared to actual JCPenney sales? Why?

13.16 JCPenney sales. A trend-and-season model with indicator variables was fitted to the JCPenney sales data in Exercise 13.5.

(a) Using the equation of the trend-and-season model, forecast sales for the first quarter of 2002 and for the fourth quarter of 2002.

(b) Compare your forecasts with the same forecasts based on the trend-only model of Exercise 13.15.

13.17 JCPenney sales. A trend-and-season model using seasonality factors was calculated in Exercise 13.7.

(a) Using the linear trend-only model and the seasonality factors, forecast sales for the first quarter of 2002 and for the fourth quarter of 2002.

(b) Compare your forecasts with the same forecasts based on the trend-only model of Exercise 13.15.

(c) Compare your forecasts with the same forecasts based on the trend-and-season model of Exercise 13.16.

13.18 JCPenney sales. The model in part (a) of Exercise 13.5 can be viewed as four models—one for each quarter—by setting the indicator variables to 0 or 1 for each of the four quarters (our seasons for this data set).

(a) Write down the four models (one for each quarter) that are derived from the trend-and-season model in Exercise 13.5.

(b) Each of the models in part (a) is linear. What do you notice about the four slopes?

(c) On a time plot of the sales data, sketch each of the four lines. What geometric property do the lines possess?

13.19 Comparing models for JCPenney sales. Compare the trend-only model of Exercise 13.3 with the trend-and-season model of Exercise 13.5.

(a) Report the value of R^2 for each model and comment on the difference.

(b) Report the value of s for each model and comment on the difference.

(c) Make a time plot of the original JCPenney sales figures. On this plot, overlay both the trend-only predictions and the trend-and-season predictions.

(d) Taking into account parts (a), (b), and (c), is the trend-and-season model a big improvement over the trend-only model?

13.20 Seasonally adjusted consumer loans. The consumer loans data used in Exercises 13.11 and 13.12 are not seasonally adjusted (NSA). The data file *ex13_020* contains the seasonally adjusted consumer loans data as well as the unadjusted data. If we assume that the Federal Reserve used seasonality factors to seasonally adjust the time series, then we can recover approximate seasonality factors.

(a) Using software, create a new variable called "Approximate SF" by dividing the unadjusted data values by the adjusted data values for each of the 240 months in the time series.

(b) Make a time plot of the Approximate SF series. Do you observe a regular, repeating pattern? It may be easier to inspect the time plot if you do not plot the entire series of 240 values. Try plotting just the last 48 values (4 years). If you observe a seasonal pattern, clearly describe the pattern.

13.21 Autocorrelation in consumer loans. In Exercise 13.12, a linear trend-only model was fitted to the consumer loans data. Using the residuals from this model, look for evidence of autocorrelation.

(a) Make a time plot of the residuals. Describe any pattern you see in this plot.

(b) Does the time plot of residuals suggest positive or negative autocorrelation? Explain your response.

(c) Make a lagged residual plot and calculate the correlation between successive residuals e_{t-1} and e_t. Do we have evidence of autocorrelation?

13.22 Seasonally adjusted JCPenney sales. In Exercise 13.7, you calculated seasonality factors for the JCPenney quarterly sales data. Using these factors, complete the following:

(a) Calculate the seasonally adjusted value of the time series for the fourth quarter of 2001. Do the calculation by hand.

(b) Using statistical software, calculate the seasonally adjusted JCPenney sales time series. Make a time plot of the original sales data with the seasonally adjusted sales data superimposed (see Figure 13.7, on page 761, for an example).

(c) Did seasonally adjusting the JCPenney sales data smooth the time series to the degree that seasonally adjusting the sales data in Figure 13.7 did? What does this imply about the strength of the seasonal pattern in these two time series?

13.23 Autocorrelation in the JCPenney time series. In Exercise 13.3, a linear trend-only model was fitted to the JCPenney sales data. Using the residuals from this model, look for evidence of autocorrelation.

(a) Make a time plot of the residuals. Describe any pattern you see in this plot.

(b) Make a lagged residual plot and calculate the correlation between successive residuals e_{t-1} and e_t. Do we have evidence of autocorrelation?

13.24 Autocorrelation in the JCPenney time series. Repeat the previous exercise using the residuals from the trend-and-season model of Exercise 13.5.

13.25 Lagged time series plot. Similar to the lagged residual plot, a ***lagged time series plot*** is a scatterplot with y_t on the vertical axis and y_{t-1} on the horizontal axis. Figure 13.10 is a lagged time series plot of the monthly retail sales data introduced in Example 13.1.

(a) Figure 13.10 consists of three distinct groups of points. One large group contains most of the points,

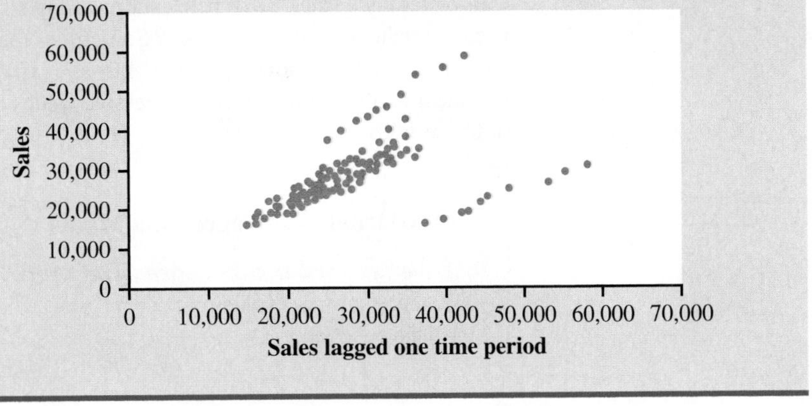

FIGURE 13.10 Lagged time series plot of U.S. retail sales of general merchandise stores, for Exercise 13.25.

and two smaller groups consist of 10 points each. Given what we know about when the ups and downs occur with this time series, we can identify the two smaller groups of points. The group of 10 points crossing the lower-right corner are the points with January sales as the y coordinate. The other group of 10 points has which month as the y coordinate?

(b) The correlation between successive months' sales is 0.4573. If we exclude the two groups of 10 points identified in part (a), the correlation is 0.9206. Does this suggest strong autocorrelation in the time series?

(c) If you looked at the correlation between successive values of the seasonally adjusted time series, would you expect the correlation to be closer to 0.4573 or 0.9206? Explain your response.

13.2 Time Series Models

The previous section applied regression methods from Chapters 10 and 11 to time series data. A time period variable was used as the explanatory variable, and the time series was the response variable. Models like these may not satisfy our usual regression assumptions—particularly the independence assumption. Specific models have been developed to aid in the analysis of time series data when usual regression methods are not appropriate.

Time Series Models

Time series models use past values of the time series to predict future values of the time series.

In the language of regression, a future time period's value is our "response" while one or more past time periods' values (of the same variable) are the explanatory variable(s). This approach is different from using the values of one variable x to predict the values of a second variable y. A time series model makes forecasts based on past values of the time series itself. For example, we might forecast next month's DVD player sales to be some multiple of this month's DVD player sales. Instead, we might use average DVD player sales for the last 3 months to predict DVD player sales this month. A wide variety of time series models exist to implement forecasting strategies like these as well as more elaborate forecasting strategies. This section will introduce a few of the most common time series models and illustrate how to use them for forecasting future values of a time series.

Autoregressive models

Can yesterday's stock price help predict today's stock price? Can last quarter's sales be used to predict this quarter's sales? Sometimes the best explanatory variables are simply past values of the response variable. *Autoregressive time series models* take advantage of the linear relationship between successive values of a time series to predict future values of the series.

First-Order Autoregression Model

The **first-order autoregression model** specifies a linear relationship between successive values of the time series. The shorthand for this model is AR(1), and the equation is

$$y_t = \beta_0 + \beta_1 y_{t-1} + \epsilon_t$$

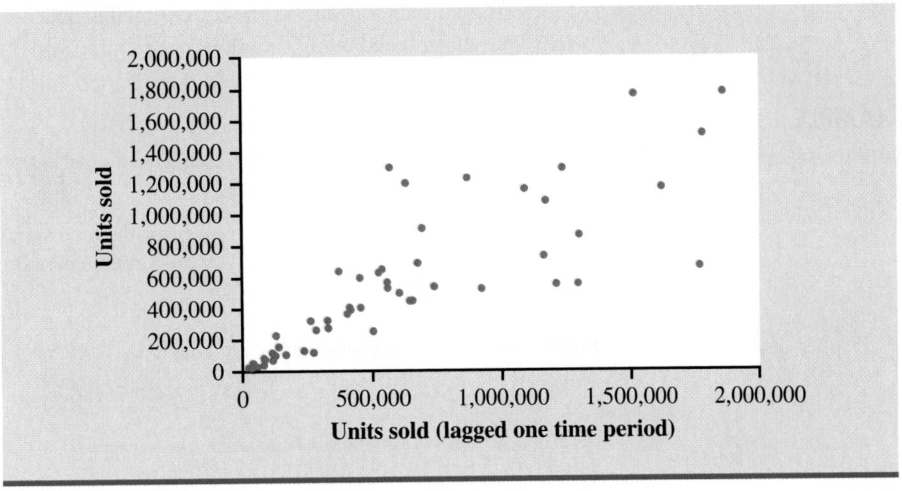

FIGURE 13.11 Lagged time series plot of the DVD player sales time series ($r = 0.80$).

In Figure 13.9 (page 763), we observed a positive, linear relationship between successive residuals from the exponential trend model fitted to the DVD player sales data. Autocorrelation in the residuals from a regression model involving time-related variables indicates that an AR(1) model might fit the data well.

We have two options for specifying an AR(1) model for the DVD player sales data. We can take the number of units sold per month to be the time series, or since the positive correlation in Figure 13.9 is for the residuals from the exponential trend model, we may want to take the logarithm of the number of units sold per month as the time series. In general, fitting an exponential model $y = ae^{bx}$ is the same as fitting a simple linear regression model with $\log(y)$ as the response variable instead of just y. Taking logarithms of both sides reveals a linear model based on $\log(y)$:

$$\log(y) = \log(ae^{bx}) = \log(a) + \log(e^{bx}) = \log(a) + bx$$

Figure 13.11 plots the number of units sold against the number of units sold lagged one period. Figure 13.12 plots the same points after taking logarithms. Figure 13.12 ($r = 0.95$) shows a stronger linear pattern than Figure 13.11 ($r = 0.80$), suggesting

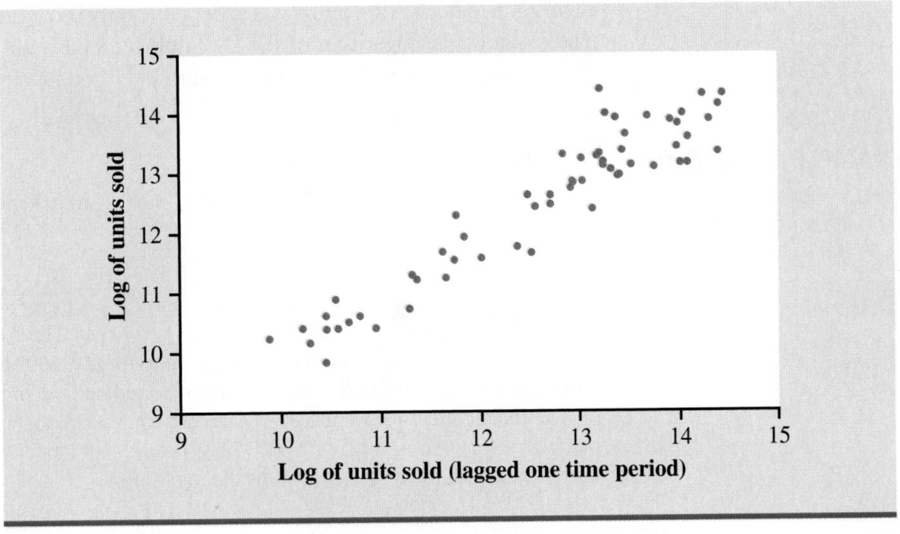

FIGURE 13.12 Lagged time series plot of the log of the DVD player sales time series ($r = 0.95$).

that an AR(1) model will fit the DVD player sales data better after logarithms have been taken. We will proceed using the transformed time series in an AR(1) model.

EXAMPLE 13.9 DVD Player Sales

CASE 13.1

The AR(1) model for the time series $\log(y_t)$ where y_t is the number of DVD players sold in time period t is

$$\log(y_t) = \beta_0 + \beta_1 \log(y_{t-1}) + \epsilon_t$$

Statistical software calculates the fitted model to be

$$\widehat{\log(y_t)} = 0.43717 + 0.96486 \times \log(y_{t-1})$$

The model for DVD player sales in Example 13.9 looks like the simple linear regression models found in Chapter 10 with the exception that the explanatory variable is the same as the response variable but lagged one time period. Despite the similarity in the form of the models, the details that made the least-squares line the best line in the setting of Chapter 10 are no longer valid with the autoregression model in Example 13.9. Most statistical software will estimate β_0 and β_1 in an autoregressive model using a method other than least squares. The most common alternative to least-squares estimation is called **maximum likelihood estimation** or, simply, MLE. The details of maximum likelihood estimation need not concern us. The general principle of MLE is to use the parameter estimates that are most in agreement with our data. The agreement between parameter estimates and our data is measured in terms of "likelihood." Maximum likelihood estimates are the answer to the question "For what values of β_0 and β_1 are my data most likely to appear in a random sample?"

maximum likelihood estimation

For the AR(1) model of Example 13.9, the MLE for β_1 is not too different from the least-squares estimate we would obtain by fitting a simple linear regression model to the time series. The least-squares estimate of β_1 is 0.94963, and the maximum likelihood estimate is 0.96486. However, the intercept estimates differ more. The least-squares intercept estimate is 0.69, versus 0.43717 estimated via maximum likelihood. A difference of this magnitude will affect predictions you make with your model, so be sure to use software that was designed to estimate time series models correctly. Using simple linear regression to fit an AR(1) model is acceptable only if the time series has a mean near zero. The mean of the logarithm of the DVD player sales data is 12.5, so we need software that fits the AR(1) model using maximum likelihood estimation.

EXAMPLE 13.10 Forecasting July DVD Player Sales

CASE 13.1

Our DVD player sales time series ends with June 2002 sales of 1,617,098 units. June 2002 is the 63rd month of our time series, so our notation is $y_{63} = 1{,}617{,}098$. The AR(1) model of Example 13.9 relates DVD player sales for July 2002 to DVD player sales in June 2002, so we can forecast July's sales based on the reported number of units sold in June.

The model fitted in Example 13.9 is for the time series $\log(y_t)$. This creates one extra step in our task of forecasting July 2002 DVD player sales. Our model will forecast $\log(y_{64})$ and we will need to calculate the forecast of y_{64} as the final step.

First, we use the model to forecast the logarithm of July 2002 DVD player sales:

$$\begin{aligned}\widehat{\log(y_{64})} &= 0.43717 + 0.96486 \times \log(y_{63})\\ &= 0.43717 + 0.96486 \times \log(1,617,098)\\ &= 0.43717 + 0.96486 \times 14.2961437\\ &= 14.23095\end{aligned}$$

Second, use your calculator's e^x button (or use software) to calculate the forecast of July 2002 DVD player sales:

$$\begin{aligned}\widehat{\log(y_{64})} &= 14.23095\\ e^{\widehat{\log(y_{64})}} &= e^{14.23095}\\ \widehat{y}_{64} &= 1,515,036\end{aligned}$$

Our AR(1) model for DVD player sales predicts sales of over 1.5 million units for July 2002.

In Case 13.1 (page 754), the exponential trend model predicted sales of 2.4 million units, and in Example 13.5 (page 760), the exponential trend-and-season model predicted sales of 2.1 million units. We noted that July sales are always below June sales (except in 1998), but that both these forecasts are greater than the June 2002 sales of 1.6 million. Our AR(1) model's forecast is an improvement in this respect because the forecast of 1.5 million units is below June 2002 sales of 1.6 million units.

Our forecast of July 2002 DVD player sales was based on an *observed* data value—June 2002 sales is a known value in our time series. If we wish to forecast August 2002 DVD player sales, we will have to base our forecast on an *estimated* value because July 2002 sales is not a known value in our time series.

EXAMPLE 13.11 Forecasting August DVD Player Sales

CASE 13.1

Following Example 13.10, we use the model to forecast the logarithm of August 2002 DVD player sales. Because our time series ends with y_{63}, the value of y_{64} is not known. In its place, we will use the value of $\widehat{y}_{64}$ calculated in Example 13.10:

$$\begin{aligned}\widehat{\log(y_{65})} &= 0.43717 + 0.96486 \times \log(\widehat{y}_{64})\\ &= 0.43717 + 0.96486 \times \log(1,515,036)\\ &= 0.43717 + 0.96486 \times 14.23095\\ &= 14.16804\end{aligned}$$

Finally, use your calculator's e^x button or software to calculate the forecast of August 2002 DVD player sales:

$$\begin{aligned}\widehat{\log(y_{65})} &= 14.16804\\ e^{\widehat{\log(y_{65})}} &= e^{14.16804}\\ \widehat{y}_{65} &= 1,422,662\end{aligned}$$

We can continue in this manner to forecast DVD player sales for other future months.

In Chapters 10 and 11, we calculated prediction intervals for the response in our model. Associated with time series forecasts, your software may provide prediction intervals for future time periods. These intervals can be used and interpreted like the prediction intervals we saw in Chapters 10 and 11, although we will not present the details of their calculation.

The widths of time series prediction intervals generally increase as the time period of the prediction moves further beyond the end of the known time series. Predictions far into the future are subject to more uncertainty than predictions close to the end of the time series. Examples 13.10 and 13.11 demonstrate why this is true. Our forecast for July 2002 DVD player sales (y_{64}) depends on our estimated values of β_0 and β_1 and the *known* value of y_{63}. However, our forecast of y_{65} depends on estimated values of β_0, β_1, *and* y_{64}. The additional uncertainty involved in estimating y_{64} will make our prediction interval for y_{65} wider than our prediction interval for y_{64}. Statistical software provides the prediction intervals in the following table. The widths have been calculated—notice how the widths increase as we predict further into the future.

Time period	Lower 95% PI	Upper 95% PI	Width
July 2002	678,324	3,383,804	2,705,480
August 2002	465,754	4,345,553	3,879,799
September 2002	349,161	5,133,999	4,784,838
October 2002	274,628	5,805,884	5,531,256
November 2002	223,067	6,384,087	6,161,020
December 2002	185,553	6,881,936	6,696,383
January 2003	157,263	7,309,011	7,151,748
February 2003	135,342	7,673,072	7,537,730
March 2003	117,982	7,980,825	7,862,843
April 2003	103,989	8,238,248	8,134,259
May 2003	92,539	8,450,757	8,358,218
June 2003	83,050	8,623,283	8,540,233

Autoregression models are useful when future values of a time series depend linearly on past values of the same time series. With software handling the calculation details, the concepts introduced in Chapters 10 and 11 for regression models apply equally well for autoregression models.

APPLY YOUR KNOWLEDGE

13.26 Existing-home sales. The National Association of Realtors tracks monthly sales of existing homes in the United States. The file *ex13_026* has the existing-home sales time series beginning in January 1968 and ending in July 2001. Use statistical software to analyze this time series.

(a) Make a time plot of the existing-home sales time series.

(b) Describe any important features of the time series. Is there a strong, clear trend? If so, describe it. What about seasonal variation?

(c) Make a lagged time series plot (see Exercise 13.25 for an example) of the existing-home sales time series. Does this plot suggest that an AR(1) model is appropriate for this time series? Why or why not?

13.27 A model for existing-home sales. For this exercise, let y_t denote the number of existing homes sold (in thousands of units) during time period t. Use statistical software and the *ex13_026* data file.

(a) Fit a simple linear regression model using y_t as the response variable and y_{t-1} as the explanatory variable. Record the estimated regression equation. Use this model to forecast August 2001 existing-home sales.

(b) Fit an AR(1) model to the existing-home sales time series. Record the estimated autoregression equation. Use this model to forecast August 2001 existing-home sales.

(c) Compare the two estimated equations as well as the August 2001 forecasts from parts (a) and (b). Briefly explain which of the two estimated models is preferred and why.

Moving average models

The autoregression model AR(1) looks back *one* time period and uses that value of the time series in the forecast for the current time period. This works well when consecutive values of the time series are linearly related, but not all time series fit this pattern. With some time series, our forecasts can be improved by using the *average of many* past time periods. *Moving average* models use the average of the last several values of the time series to forecast the next value.

Moving Average Forecast Model

The **moving average forecast model** uses the average of the last k values of the time series as the forecast for time period t. The equation is

$$\widehat{y}_t = \frac{y_{t-1} + y_{t-2} + \cdots + y_{t-k}}{k}$$

The number of preceding values included in the moving average is called the **span** of the moving average.

Some care should be taken in choosing the span k for a moving average forecast model. As a general rule, larger spans "smooth" the time series more than smaller spans by averaging many ups and downs in each calculation. Smaller spans tend to follow the ups and downs of the time series. With seasonal data, the length of the season is often used for the value of k.

EXAMPLE 13.12 Moving Averages for JCPenney Sales

Exercise 13.1 (page 752) asked you to plot and comment on quarterly JCPenney sales data. Figure 13.13 displays the JCPenney sales time series with the moving average forecast model based on a span of $k = 4$ overlaid. Notice that the seasonal pattern in the time series is not present in the moving averages. Our moving averages are a smoothed version of our original time series. The moving averages follow the general movements of the time series but not every up and down.

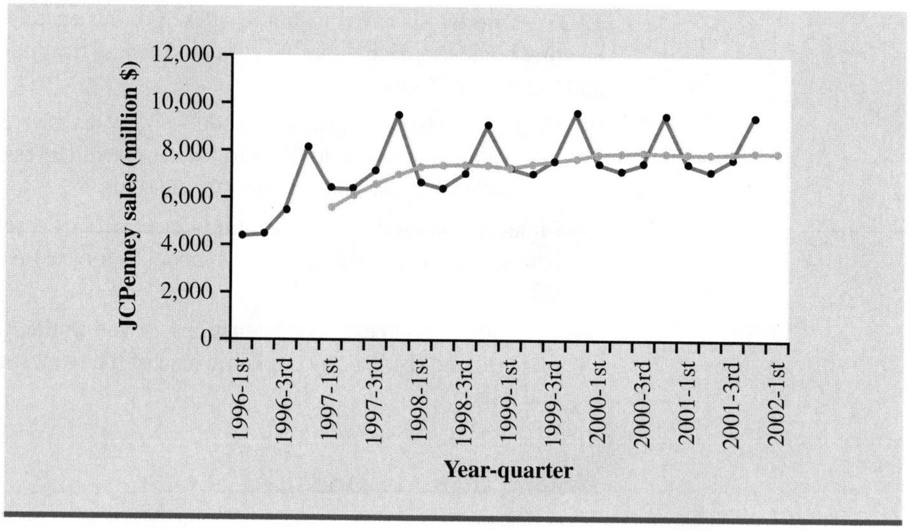

FIGURE 13.13 Moving averages based on a span of $k = 4$ (green) overlaying the JCPenney quarterly sales data (red), for Example 13.12.

The JCPenney sales time series begins with the first quarter of 1996 and ends with the fourth quarter of 2001, for a total of 24 quarters. Figure 13.13 includes the forecasted value for the first quarter of 2002. The forecast is calculated as

$$\widehat{y}_{25} = \frac{y_{24} + y_{23} + y_{22} + y_{21}}{4} = \frac{32{,}004}{4} = 8001$$

When a strong seasonal pattern is present, moving average models with the span set equal to the length of the season are similar to the trend-only models presented in Section 13.1. The moving averages will follow the long-run trend of the time series, but the ups and downs of the seasons are ignored. We would not expect the moving average model of Example 13.12 to forecast fourth-quarter JCPenney sales well.

EXAMPLE 13.13 Chicago Cubs Attendance per Game

Major League Baseball's Chicago Cubs have been playing their home games at Wrigley Field since 1916. The file *eg13_013* has the "attendance per home game" time series beginning in 1916 and ending in 2001.

Figure 13.14 displays the time series, moving averages based on a span of 5 years, and moving averages based on a span of 20 years. The moving averages based on a span of 20 years highlight the general upward trend in attendance per home game at Wrigley Field without following the ups and downs in the data. The 5-year moving averages are not as smooth as the 20-year moving averages. The 5-year moving averages follow the larger ups and downs while smoothing the smaller changes in the time series.

The attendance time series has 86 observations ending with attendance per home game in 2001. Our interest is in forecasting attendance per home game for 2002. We will do this using both the 5-year moving averages and the 20-year moving averages.

$$\widehat{y}_{87} = \frac{y_{86} + y_{85} + \cdots + y_{82}}{5} = \frac{162{,}522}{5} = 32{,}504$$

$$\widehat{y}_{87} = \frac{y_{86} + y_{85} + \cdots + y_{67}}{20} = \frac{553{,}681}{20} = 27{,}684$$

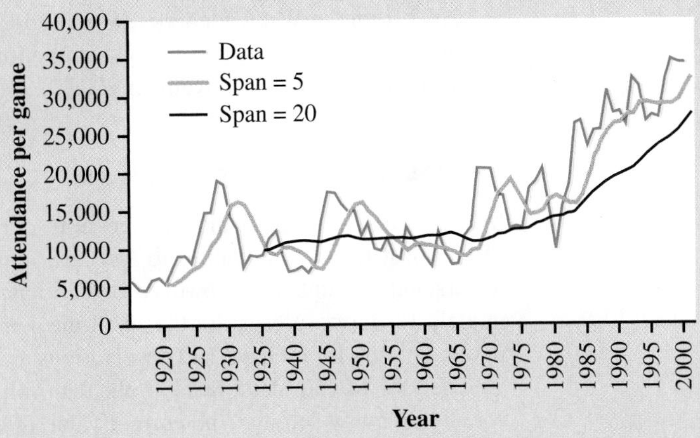

FIGURE 13.14 Chicago Cubs annual attendance per game time series (red) with 5-year (green) and 20-year (black) moving averages overlaid, for Example 13.13.

The forecast based on the 20-year moving average is less than the forecast based on the 5-year moving average because the 20-year average includes the lower attendance figures of the 1980s. We might guess from looking at Figure 13.14 that the 5-year moving average forecast will be more accurate than the 20-year moving average forecast. Actual 2002 attendance figures for Wrigley Field are now available. Total attendance was 2,693,096 for 81 home games, so the average attendance per home game was 2,693,096/81, or 33,248. The 5-year moving average forecast was more accurate.

Once a new value becomes available (like 2002 attendance figures in Example 13.13), we update our time series to include the new observation. We can then calculate a forecast for the next time period (2003 attendance per home game in Example 13.13).

APPLY YOUR KNOWLEDGE

13.28 Winter wheat prices. The U.S. Department of Agriculture (USDA) tracks prices received by Montana farmers for winter wheat crops. The prices are tracked monthly in dollars per bushel. The file *ex13_028* has the wheat prices time series beginning in July 1929 and ending in October 2002 (880 months). Use statistical software to analyze this time series.

(a) Make a time plot of the wheat prices time series.

(b) Describe any important features of the time series. Be sure to comment on trend, seasonal patterns, and significant shifts in the series.

(c) Calculate 12-month moving averages and plot them on your time series plot from part (a).

(d) Calculate 120-month moving averages and plot them together with the time series from part (a) and the 12-month moving averages from part (c).

(e) Compare the 12-month and 120-month moving averages. Which features of the wheat prices time series does each capture? Which features does each smooth?

13.29 Forecasting winter wheat prices.

(a) Using the winter wheat prices from the previous exercise, calculate and compare the 12-month and 120-month moving average forecasts for November 2002.

(b) Record the actual winter wheat price received by Montana farmers for November 2002 from the Web page `www.nass.usda.gov/mt/economic/prices/wwheatpr.htm`. Which moving average forecast model provided the more accurate forecast for November 2002?

Exponential smoothing models

Moving average forecast models appeal to our intuition. Using the average of several of the most recent data values to forecast the next value of the time series is easy to understand conceptually. However, two criticisms can be made against moving average models. First, our forecast for the next time period ignores all but the last k observations in our data set. If you have 100 observations and use a span of $k = 5$, your forecast will not use 95% of your data! Second, the data values used in our forecast are all weighted equally. In many settings, the current value of a time series depends more on the most recent value and less on past values. We may improve our forecasts if we give the most recent values greater "weight" in our forecast calculation. *Exponential smoothing* models address both of these criticisms.

Several variations exist on the basic exponential smoothing model. We will look at the details of the *simple exponential smoothing model,* which we will refer to as, simply, the *exponential smoothing model*. More complex variations exist to handle time series with specific features, but the details of these models are beyond the scope of this chapter. We will only mention the scenarios for which these more complex models are appropriate.

Exponential Smoothing Model

The **exponential smoothing model** uses a weighted average of the observed value y_{t-1} and the forecasted value $\widehat{y}_{t-1}$ as the forecast for time period t. The forecasting equation is

$$\widehat{y}_t = wy_{t-1} + (1 - w)\widehat{y}_{t-1}$$

The weight w is called the **smoothing constant** for the exponential smoothing model. The smoothing constant is a value between 0 and 1. Choosing w close to 1 puts more weight on the most recent value.

Choosing the smoothing constant w in the exponential smoothing model is similar to choosing the span k in the moving average model—both relate directly to the smoothness of the model. Smaller values of w correspond to greater smoothing of the ups and downs in the time series. Larger values of w put most of the weight on the most recent observed value, so the forecasts tend to follow the ups and downs of the series more closely.

EXAMPLE 13.14 Philip Morris Returns

Table 1.12 (page 49) gives the monthly returns on Philip Morris stock for the period from June 1990 to July 2001 (134 months). Figure 13.15 displays the returns, the exponential smoothing model with $w = 0.5$, and the exponential smoothing model with $w = 0.1$.

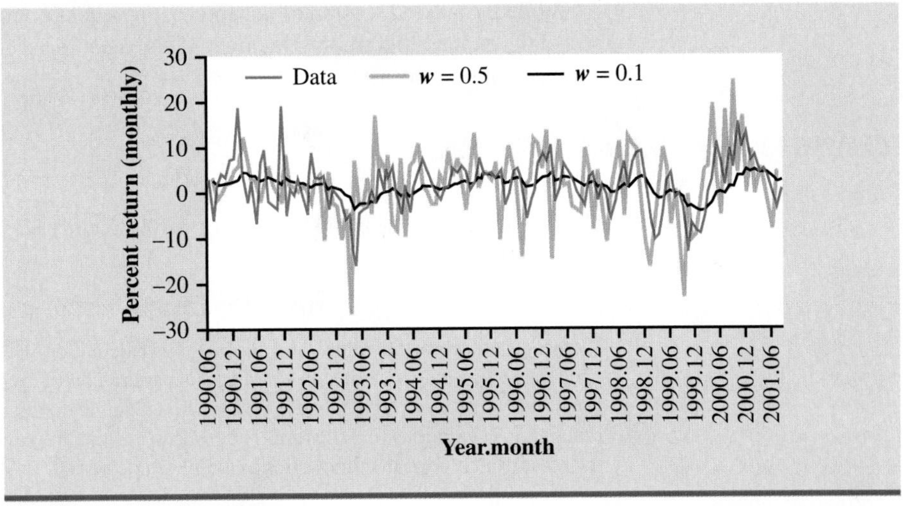

FIGURE 13.15 Philip Morris monthly stock returns (red) with two overlays: exponential smoothing model with $w = 0.5$ (green) and exponential smoothing model with $w = 0.1$ (black), for Example 13.14.

Using a smoothing constant of 0.5 puts more weight on the most recent values of the time series than using a smoothing constant of 0.1 does. As a result, that curve tends to follow the ups and downs of the time series more closely than the smoother curve for $w = 0.1$ does. With a smoothing constant close to 0, the model will follow only the major changes in the time series.

A little algebra is needed to see that exponential smoothing models address the criticisms of moving average models. We will start with the forecasting equation for the exponential smoothing model and imagine forecasting the value of the time series for the time period $n + 1$ where n is the number of observed values in the time series. A specific example would be forecasting the August 2001 Philip Morris return y_{135} using the observed returns for the preceding $n = 134$ months.

$$\begin{aligned}
\widehat{y}_{n+1} &= wy_n + (1-w)\widehat{y}_n \\
&= wy_n + (1-w)[wy_{n-1} + (1-w)\widehat{y}_{n-1}] \\
&= wy_n + (1-w)wy_{n-1} + (1-w)^2\widehat{y}_{n-1} \\
&= wy_n + (1-w)wy_{n-1} + (1-w)^2[wy_{n-2} + (1-w)\widehat{y}_{n-2}] \\
&= wy_n + (1-w)wy_{n-1} + (1-w)^2wy_{n-2} + (1-w)^3\widehat{y}_{n-2} \\
&\ \vdots \\
&= wy_n + (1-w)wy_{n-1} + (1-w)^2wy_{n-2} + \cdots + (1-w)^{n-2}wy_2 + (1-w)^{n-1}y_1
\end{aligned}$$

Careful substitution and multiplication reveal a version of the forecast equation showing exactly how our forecast depends on the values of the time series. First, notice that the calculation of the forecast for y_{n+1} uses *all* available values of the time series $y_1, y_2, \ldots, y_n$, not just the most recent k-values like a moving average model would. Second, the values are not equally weighted. Using a value of w close to 1 puts greater weight on the most recent observation. In this version of the forecast equation, we also see how the model gets its name. The coefficients in the forecast model decrease exponentially in value as you read the equation from left to right (with the exception of the last coefficient, $(1 - w)^{n-1}$). Exercise 13.31 has you explore what happens to the coefficients as you change the value of the smoothing constant w.

While the second version of our forecasting equation reveals some important properties of the exponential smoothing model, it is easier to use the first version of the equation for calculating forecasts.

EXAMPLE 13.15 Forecasting Philip Morris Returns

Consider forecasting the Philip Morris August 2001 return using an exponential smoothing model with $w = 0.5$.

$$\widehat{y}_{135} = 0.5 \times y_{134} + (1 - 0.5) \times \widehat{y}_{134}$$

We need the forecasted value $\widehat{y}_{134}$ to finish our calculation. However, to calculate $\widehat{y}_{134}$ we will need the forecasted value of $\widehat{y}_{133}$! In fact, this pattern continues, and we need to calculate all past forecasts before we can calculate $\widehat{y}_{135}$. We will calculate the first few forecasts here and leave the remaining calculations for software. The forecast for the first time period $\widehat{y}_1$ is always taken to be the actual value y_1 of the time series in the first time period.

$$\begin{aligned} \widehat{y}_2 &= 0.5 \times y_1 + (1 - 0.5) \times \widehat{y}_1 \\ &= (0.5)(3) + (0.5)(3) \\ &= 3 \end{aligned}$$

$$\begin{aligned} \widehat{y}_3 &= 0.5 \times y_2 + (1 - 0.5) \times \widehat{y}_2 \\ &= (0.5)(-5.7) + (0.5)(3) \\ &= -1.35 \end{aligned}$$

$$\begin{aligned} \widehat{y}_4 &= 0.5 \times y_3 + (1 - 0.5) \times \widehat{y}_3 \\ &= (0.5)(1.2) + (0.5)(-1.35) \\ &= -0.075 \end{aligned}$$

Software continues our calculations to arrive at a forecast for y_{134} of -3.812. We use this value to complete our forecast calculation for y_{135}:

$$\begin{aligned} \widehat{y}_{135} &= 0.5 \times y_{134} + (1 - 0.5) \times \widehat{y}_{134} \\ &= (0.5)(4.2) + (0.5)(-3.812) \\ &= 0.194 \end{aligned}$$

Our model forecasts a 0.194% return for Philip Morris stock in August 2001.

With the forecasted value for August 2001 from Example 13.15, calculating the forecast for September 2001 requires only one calculation:

$$\widehat{y}_{136} = (0.5)(y_{135}) + (0.5)(0.194)$$

Once we observe the actual Philip Morris return for August 2001 y_{135}, we can enter that value into the forecast equation above. Updating forecasts from exponential smoothing models only requires that we keep track of last period's forecast and last period's observed value. In contrast, moving average models require that we keep track of the last k observed values of the time series. For this reason, exponential smoothing models are often preferred over moving average models, especially if data storage is an issue.

The simple exponential smoothing model is best suited for forecasting time series with no strong trend or seasonal variation. Variations on the simple exponential smoothing model have been developed to handle time series with a trend (double exponential smoothing and Holt's exponential smoothing), with seasonality (seasonal exponential smoothing), and with both trend and seasonality (Winters' exponential smoothing). Your software may offer one or more of these smoothing models.

APPLY YOUR KNOWLEDGE

13.30 Philip Morris returns.

(a) Using the Philip Morris returns in Table 1.12 (page 49), calculate the first 4 forecasts $\widehat{y}_1, \ldots, \widehat{y}_4$ using an exponential smoothing model with $w = 0.1$. Do not use statistical software for these calculations.

(b) Now, use software to fit a simple exponential smoothing model with $w = 0.1$. Use the forecasts provided by the software to verify your hand calculations in part (a). Are your forecasts the same as those provided by your software?

(c) Provide a forecast for the August 2001 Philip Morris return based on your exponential smoothing model with $w = 0.1$ and compare this to the forecast calculated in Example 13.15.

(d) Write down the forecast equation for the September 2001 Philip Morris return based on the exponential smoothing model with $w = 0.1$.

13.31 It's exponential. Exponential smoothing models are so named because the coefficients

$$w, (1-w)w, (1-w)^2w, \ldots, (1-w)^{n-2}w$$

decrease in value exponentially. For this exercise, take $n = 11$. Use software to do the calculations.

(a) Calculate the coefficients for a smoothing constant of $w = 0.1$.

(b) Calculate the coefficients for a smoothing constant of $w = 0.5$.

(c) Calculate the coefficients for a smoothing constant of $w = 0.9$.

(d) Plot each set of coefficients from parts (a), (b), and (c). The coefficient values should be measured on the vertical axis while the horizontal axis can simply be numbered $1, 2, \ldots, 9, 10$ for the 10 coefficients from each part. Be sure to use a different plotting symbol and/or color to distinguish the 3 sets of coefficients and connect the points for each set. Also, label the plot so that it is clear which curve corresponds to each value of w used.

(e) Describe each curve in part (d). Which curve puts more weight on the most recent value of the time series when calculating a forecast?

(f) The coefficient of y_1 in the exponential smoothing model is $(1-w)^{n-1}$. Calculate the coefficient of y_1 for each of the values of w in parts (a), (b), and (c). How do these values compare to the first 10 coefficients you calculated for each value of w? Which value of w puts the greatest weight on y_1 when calculating a forecast?

BEYOND THE BASICS: SPLINE FITS

smoothing spline

Modern computing capabilities have made possible many statistical tools that would otherwise be impossible or impractical. One such tool is the general-purpose **smoothing spline.** A spline curve can be fitted to any (x, y) data set. For a time series, we take x to be the time variable and y to be the time series values. A spline curve is a single curve consisting of a large number of polynomial curves pieced together in an optimal manner. The more polynomials used, the more flexible and less smooth the spline curve is.

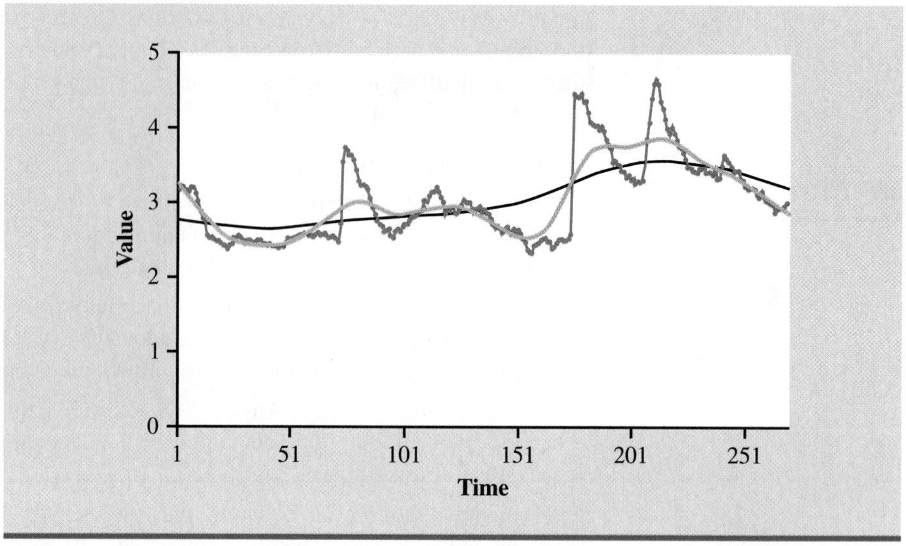

FIGURE 13.16 Spline curve models for three values of the smoothing constant λ: $\lambda = 0.000001$ (red), $\lambda = 10{,}000$ (green), and $\lambda = 1{,}000{,}000$ (black).

The smoothness of a spline fit is determined by the choice of a positive-valued smoothing constant, similar to the choice of w in the exponential smoothing model. The spline smoothing constant is often denoted by the lowercase Greek letter lambda λ. Choosing a value of λ close to zero results in a very flexible and not very smooth spline curve. As greater values of λ are used, the spline curve becomes less flexible and more smooth.

Figure 13.16 displays three spline curves. The red spline curve offers the least amount of smoothing for the data ($\lambda = 0.000001$). With λ nearly zero, the spline curve passes through every point. The green spline curve is based on $\lambda = 10{,}000$. This spline curve follows the ups and downs of the time series without trying to pass through each point. The black spline curve offers the highest degree of smoothing, with $\lambda = 1{,}000{,}000$. The black spline curve reveals the overall pattern in the time series without following the smaller ups and downs.

Spline fits can help you quickly identify overall trends and seasonal variation, as well as less regular patterns, in your time series data. They are a powerful, modern exploratory data analysis tool.

SECTION 13.2 SUMMARY

- Regression models relating a time series to a time variable are not always appropriate. Specifically, the residuals from such a model may exhibit high correlation. **Time series models** use past values of the time series to forecast future values of the time series.
- The **first-order autoregression model** AR(1) is appropriate when successive values of a time series are linearly related. The parameters of the model are often estimated using **maximum likelihood estimation** rather than least-squares estimation.
- **Moving average forecast models** use the average of the last k observed values to forecast next period's value. The number k is called the **span** of the moving average. Larger values of k result in a smoother model.
- The forecast equation for the **simple exponential smoothing model** is a weighted average of last period's observed value and last period's forecasted value. The

degree of smoothing is determined by the choice of a smoothing constant w between 0 and 1. Values of w close to 0 result in a smoother model.

SECTION 13.2 Exercises

For Exercises 13.26 and 13.27, see pages 772–773; for 13.28 and 13.29, see pages 775–776; and for 13.30 and 13.31, see page 779.

13.32 Autocorrelation in consumer loans. Consider the unadjusted (NSA) consumer loan data in the data set *ex13_011*.

(a) Fit a simple linear regression model using y_t as the response variable and y_{t-1} as the explanatory variable. Record the estimated regression equation. Use this model to forecast the amount of consumer loans held by commercial banks for July 2005.

(b) Fit an AR(1) model to the consumer loans time series. Record the estimated autoregression equation. Use this model to forecast the amount of consumer loans held by commercial banks for July 2005.

(c) Compare the two estimated equations as well as the July 2005 forecasts from parts (a) and (b). Briefly explain which of the two estimated models is preferred and why.

13.33 NSA and SA consumer loans. Compare the use of seasonally adjusted (SA) consumer loans data to the use of not seasonally adjusted (NSA) consumer loans data in AR(1) models. Use the time series as provided in *ex13_020* to answer the following:

(a) Fit an AR(1) model to the SA consumer loans time series. Record the estimated autoregression equation. Use this model to forecast the amount of consumer loans held by commercial banks for July 2005.

(b) Compare the estimated equation and forecast from part (a) to the results of using the NSA values (Exercise 13.32, part (b)). Does seasonally adjusting the data before fitting the AR(1) model dramatically change the results of the analysis? Explain your response.

13.34 Last month's production as predictor. Consider the passenger car production data from Exercise 13.13 (page 766). The data are in *ex13_013*.

(a) Make a lagged time series plot (for an example, see Exercise 13.25, page 767) of the passenger car production time series.

(b) What is the correlation between y_t and y_{t-1} (successive values of passenger car production data)?

(c) Does last month's production appear to be a good predictor of this month's production? Explain your response.

13.35 Production 12 months ago as predictor. Continue with the passenger car production data used in the previous exercise.

(a) Make a lagged time series plot of the passenger car production data using y_t on the vertical axis and y_{t-12} on the horizontal axis (a lag of 12 periods).

(b) What is the correlation between y_t and y_{t-12}?

(c) Does the production 12 months ago appear to be a good predictor of this month's production? Explain your response.

13.36 A closer look at oranges. Example 1.7 (page 19) looked at the trend and seasonal variation in the average monthly price of oranges. Figure 1.7 (page 19) is a time series plot of the data. The data are found in the file *fg01_007*.

(a) Make a lagged time series plot (see Exercise 13.25 for an example).

(b) Does the plot in part (a) suggest that an AR(1) model might be appropriate for the orange prices time series?

(c) Calculate the correlation between successive values of orange prices. Does the value of this correlation support your conclusion in part (b)? Why or why not?

13.37 Least-squares or maximum likelihood? Continue analyzing the orange prices data from the previous exercise. Let y_t denote the average price of oranges in time period t.

(a) Fit a simple linear regression model using y_t as the response variable and y_{t-1} as the explanatory variable. Record the estimated regression equation, the value of R^2, and the regression standard error s.

(b) Fit an AR(1) model to the orange prices time series. Record the estimated autoregression equation. Your software should also report a model R^2 and a model standard deviation (or model standard error)—record these values also.

(c) Compare the two estimated slopes and intercepts.

(d) Compare the model R^2-values and the model standard errors s. Do these values give any clear indication as to which fitting method (least squares or maximum likelihood) is preferred?

13.38 Moving averages for consumer loans. Using the consumer loans data in the data file *ex13_011*, answer the following:

(a) Calculate and plot (on a single time series plot) moving averages for spans of $k = 5$, 12, and 20.

(b) Which of the moving average forecast models in part (a) is preferable given the seasonal pattern observed in Exercise 13.20, part (b)?

(c) Calculate and compare forecasts for the amount of consumer loans for June 2005 for each of the models in part (a). Which model's forecast is closest to the actual amount of consumer loans for June 2005?

13.39 Moving averages and linear trend.

(a) A moving average forecast model with a sufficiently large span k will sometimes appear linear. Calculate and plot moving averages for the consumer loans data in *ex13_011* using a span of $k = 120$. Do the moving averages appear to be linear?

(b) Fit a linear trend to the same data and save the predicted values ($\widehat{y}$-values).

(c) Plot the moving averages from part (a) and the predicted values from part (b) on a single time series plot. Are the moving averages obviously different from the linear trend predicted values? If so, how? Explain your responses.

13.40 Moving averages for orange prices.

(a) Calculate and plot (on a single time series plot) moving averages for spans of $k = 5$, 10, and 20 for the orange prices data in *fg01_007*.

(b) Comment on the smoothness of each moving average model in part (a). Which model would be best for forecasting monthly ups and downs in orange prices?

(c) Calculate and compare forecasts for January 2001 orange prices for each of the models in part (a). Which model provides the most accurate forecast? (The actual value of the orange prices time series for January 2001 is 224.2.)

13.41 Exponential smoothing for orange prices. Continue analyzing the orange prices data from the previous exercise.

(a) Calculate and plot (on a single time series plot) exponential smoothing models using smoothing constants of $w = 0.1, 0.5$, and 0.9.

(b) Comment on the smoothness of each exponential smoothing model in part (a). Which model would be best for forecasting monthly ups and downs in orange prices?

(c) Calculate and compare forecasts for January 2001 orange prices for each of the models in part (a). Which model provides the most accurate forecast? (The actual value of the orange prices time series for January 2001 is 224.2.)

(d) Update your data by appending the January 2001 observed value of 224.2. Now forecast the February 2001 orange price with each of the models from part (a). Which model provides the most accurate forecast? (The actual value of the orange prices time series for February 2001 is 229.6.)

13.42 A special AR(1) model. ***Random walk*** models for various financial time series are often mentioned in business literature. A simple random walk model specifies that one-period *differences* in the time series can be modeled as a constant term plus a random error term. The equation for this random walk model is

$$y_t - y_{t-1} = \beta_0 + \epsilon$$

If we rewrite this equation solving for y_t, we get

$$y_t = \beta_0 + y_{t-1} + \epsilon$$

which is our AR(1) model with $\beta_1 = 1$. If we fit an AR(1) model and find that the β_1 estimate is close to 1, then a simple random walk model for the time series is another modeling option.

The CD that accompanies this book contains a data file named *ex13_042*. Daily "USD to EUR" exchange rates beginning July 24, 2001, and ending July 23, 2002, are contained in the data file. The first exchange rate is 1.1509. This means that on July 24, 2001, a single U.S. dollar (USD) was worth 1.1509 euros (EUR).

(a) Fit an AR(1) model to the exchange rate time series. Record the estimated forecast equation, the R^2-value, and the model standard error estimate. What evidence do you have that a simple random walk model for these exchange rates is appropriate?

(b) Use the AR(1) forecast equation to predict the exchange rate for July 24, 2002.

(c) For a simple random walk model, the estimate of β_0 is simply the average of all one-period differences $y_t - y_{t-1}$ (call this average $\overline{y}_{\text{diff}}$), and the forecast equation is $\widehat{y}_t = y_{t-1} + \overline{y}_{\text{diff}}$. Calculate the one-period differences and their average and use this to provide a "random walk forecast" for the exchange rate on July 24, 2002. Compare the random walk forecast to the AR(1) forecast.

(d) You can get the actual exchange rate for July 24, 2002, at the Web site `www.oanda.com/convert/fxhistory`. Compare both forecasts to the actual exchange rate. Which model was more accurate?

13.43 Moving averages for exchange rates. Use statistical software to fit moving average models to the exchange rate data in the file *ex13_042*.

(a) What would the moving average forecast equation be if we used a span of $k = 1$? (Your response to this part is not specific to the exchange rate data.)

(b) Choose a value for k that is larger than 1 and less than 6 and calculate the corresponding moving averages. Be sure to report what value of k you chose.

(c) Choose a value of k that is larger than 35 and less than 365 and calculate the corresponding moving averages. Be sure to report what value of k you chose.

(d) Plot both sets of moving averages on a time series plot of the exchange rates. Be sure to label the plot clearly. Comment on the smoothness of both sets of moving averages.

13.44 Exchange rate moving averages, continued. Use the data in the file *ex13_042*.

(a) Using a span of $k = 1$, forecast the USD to euro exchange rate on July 24, 2002.

(b) Use your model from part (b) of the previous exercise to forecast the USD to euro exchange rate on July 24, 2002.

(c) Use your model from part (c) of the previous exercise to forecast the USD to euro exchange rate on July 24, 2002.

(d) What would our moving average forecast equation be if we used a span of $k = 365$? What would this model forecast for July 24, 2002?

(e) You can get the actual exchange rate for July 24, 2002, at the Web site `www.oanda.com/convert/fxhistory`. Compare these four forecasts to the actual exchange rate. Which model was closest to the actual exchange rate? Which model performed the worst on this forecast?

13.45 Exponential smoothing of exchange rates. Use statistical software to fit exponential smoothing models to the exchange rate data in the file *ex13_042*.

(a) What would the exponential smoothing forecast equation be if we used a smoothing constant of $w = 1$? What about $w = 0$? (Your response to this part is not specific to the exchange rate data.)

(b) Choose a value for w such that $0 < w < 0.3$ and fit the corresponding exponential smoothing model. Be sure to report what value of w you chose.

(c) Choose a value of w such that $0.7 < w < 1$ and fit the corresponding exponential smoothing model. Be sure to report what value of w you chose.

(d) Plot both exponential smoothing models on a time series plot of the exchange rates. Be sure to label the plot clearly. Comment on the smoothness of each model.

(e) Using the models from parts (b) and (c), forecast the July 24, 2002, exchange rate and compare both these forecasts to the actual exchange rate on that day. (You can get the actual exchange rate for July 24, 2002, at the Web site `www.oanda.com/convert/fxhistory`.)

STATISTICS IN SUMMARY

Standard regression methods like those described in Chapters 10 and 11 can be used with time series data with "time" as the explanatory variable and the time series as the response variable. These methods can help model both trend and seasonality in a time series, although the models will generally not satisfy the regression assumptions needed for inference. Special time series models relate the current period's value to past values of the time series. These models are often referred to as "smoothing models." We rely on statistical software for fitting time series models and for forecasting future values using these models. Here is a review list of the most important skills you should have acquired from your study of this chapter.

A. Trends

1. Identify a long-run trend in a time series plot.
2. Use software to fit a regression model to the long-run trend.

3. Use a regression model to forecast future values of a time series based on a trend-only model.

B. Seasons

1. Identify seasonal variation in a time series plot.
2. Model seasonal variation using indicator variables in a regression model.
3. Model seasonal variation using seasonality factors.
4. Forecast future values of a time series taking into account trend and seasonality.
5. Recognize seasonally adjusted data in a time series plot.

C. Time Series Models

1. Identify autocorrelation in a lagged residual plot or a lagged time series plot.
2. Use software to calculate the autocorrelation of a time series.
3. Use software to fit a first-order autoregression model to a time series.
4. Forecast one or more time periods ahead using the software output from an autoregression model.
5. Use software to calculate the moving averages for a time series.
6. Understand how the choice of the span k of a moving average forecast model relates to the smoothness of the model.
7. Forecast next period's value using a moving average forecast model.
8. Use software to fit an exponential smoothing model to a time series.
9. Understand how the choice of the smoothing constant value w in an exponential smoothing model relates to the smoothness of the model.
10. Forecast next period's value using an exponential smoothing model.

CHAPTER 13 Review Exercises

13.46 Just use last month's figures! Working with the financial analysts at your company, you discover that, when it comes to forecasting various time series, they often just use last period's value as the forecast for the current period. This strikes you as a very naive approach to forecasting.

(a) If you could pick the estimates of β_0 and β_1 in the AR(1) model, could you pick values such that the AR(1) forecast equation would provide the same forecasts your company's analysts use? If so, specify the values that accomplish this.

(b) What span k in a moving average forecast model would provide the same forecasts your company's analysts use?

(c) What smoothing constant w in a simple exponential smoothing model would provide the same forecasts your company's analysts use?

(d) Given your responses to parts (a), (b), and (c), are your company's analysts doing the best they can do for forecasting? Explain your response.

13.47 Chicago Cubs attendance trend. The file *eg13_013* on the CD that accompanies this book contains the average attendance per home game beginning in 1916 and ending in 2001 (86 years). Use statistical software to fit trend models to this time series.

(a) Make a time series plot of the attendance per home game data. Is there a clear seasonal pattern in the time series?

(b) Fit a line to the data. Be sure to use attendance per home game as the response variable and year as the explanatory variable. Report the equation of the least-squares line, the R^2-value, and the regression standard error s.

(c) Now, fit a second-degree polynomial to the data. Report the equation of the quadratic model, the R^2-value, and the regression standard error s.

(d) Finally, fit a third-degree polynomial to the data. Report the equation of the cubic model, the R^2-value, and the regression standard error s.

(e) Based on the R^2-values and the regression standard errors, which of your models from parts (b), (c), and (d) would you use as the trend equation for the Chicago Cubs average attendance per home game time series?

13.48 **Forecasting the attendance trend.** Refer to the previous exercise on Chicago Cubs attendance.

(a) Using the models from parts (b), (c), and (d) of the previous exercise, forecast average attendance per home game for the year 2002.

(b) The actual 2002 attendance per home game for the Chicago Cubs was 33,248. Which of the three models provided the most accurate forecast? Is this the same model you chose in part (e) of the previous exercise?

13.49 CASE 13.1 **A seasonal model for DVD player sales.** Following the method of Example 13.3 (page 756), fit a seasonal model for DVD player sales using indicator variables for the months. For the trend portion of the model, express the exponential trend fitted in Case 13.1 (page 754) as a linear trend with the logarithm of UNITS as the response variable. That is, use $\log(\text{UNITS}) = \beta_0 + \beta_1 x$ as the trend portion of the model.

(a) Write down the estimated trend-and-season model.

(b) Explain why no indicator variable is needed for December.

(c) Use this trend-and-season model to forecast July 2002 DVD player sales. Notice that your equation forecasts the *logarithm* of July 2002 DVD player sales, so you will need to use the e^x key on your calculator to complete the forecast. See Example 13.10 (page 770) for an example of such a calculation.

(d) Compare your forecast in part (c) to the forecast using seasonality factors in a trend-and-season model from Example 13.5 (page 760).

(e) Compare your forecast in part (c) to the AR(1) forecast from Example 13.10 (page 770).

The file fg13_016 *on the CD that accompanies this book contains the time series plotted in Figure 13.16 (page 780). The variable measured is the monthly average price for a pound of ground coffee in the United States. The time series begins on January 1980 and ends on May 2002 (269 months). The next five exercises refer to this data set.*

13.50 **Not regression.** Use a time series plot of the coffee price data to help you explain why a trend-only or a trend-and-season model will not fit this time series well.

13.51 **Moving average?** Experiment with several different spans k and choose a value for k that results in a moving average model that smooths the minor ups and downs in the data but captures the major jump in the series that occurs about two-thirds of the way through the values. Use your chosen model to forecast the June 2002 average price for a pound of coffee. Provide a time series plot of the data with your model overlaid.

13.52 **Exponential smoothing?** Experiment with several different smoothing constants w and choose a value for w that results in an exponential smoothing model that smooths the minor ups and downs in the data but captures the major jump in the series that occurs about two-thirds of the way through the values. Use your chosen model to forecast the June 2002 average price for a pound of coffee. Provide a time series plot of the data with your model overlaid.

13.53 **Why not autoregression?** Fit an AR(1) model and plot it with the coffee price data. Can an AR(1) model smooth the minor ups and downs in the data but capture the major jump in the series that occurs about two-thirds of the way through the values? Use the AR(1) model to forecast the June 2002 average price for a pound of coffee.

13.54 **Check the forecasts.** The June 2002 average price for a pound of coffee is available now. Go to the Web site `stats.bls.gov/cpi` and click on "Average Price Data" under the heading "Create Customized Tables (one screen)." On the window that opens next, choose "U.S. city average" and scroll down the list of items to select "Coffee, 100%, ground roast, all sizes, per lb. (453.6 gm)" and then click the "Get Data" button. A new window will open containing coffee price data. Verify you have the correct data by checking that the May 2002 price matches the last value in the file *fg13_016*. Record the June 2002 average coffee price and compare it with your forecasts from the three previous exercises. Which model provides the most accurate forecast for June 2002?

CHAPTER 13 Appendix

Using Minitab and Excel for Time Series Forecasting

Trend Models

Minitab:

Stat ➤ Time Series ➤ Trend Analysis

With this routine, Minitab can fit different types of trend lines. Click in the column for the time series variable in the **Series** box. If you wish to fit a linear trend model as done in Example 13.2, then choose the **Linear** option. If you wish to fit an exponential trend model as done in Case 13.1, then choose the **Exponential Growth** option. The exponential model fitted by this procedure is identical to what has been discussed in the chapter; however, the model is reported in a slightly different form. In particular, if we were to fit the DVD data series, we would find that Minitab would report an estimated model of

$$\widehat{\text{UNITS}} = 29{,}523.6(1.07137^x)$$

This is actually the same prediction equation as given in Case 13.1 when we recognize that $e^{0.068941} = 1.07137$, which implies

$$\widehat{\text{UNITS}} = 29{,}523.6(1.07137^x) = 29{,}523.6(e^{0.068941})^x = 29{,}523.6e^{0.068941x}$$

Whatever type of trend you wish to fit, there are several options. For example, if you wish to change the time scale (for example, to months or years), then click the **Time** button. By clicking the **Graphs** button, you can produce a variety of residual plots. If you wish to obtain the actual residuals or predictions ("Fits"), then click the **Storage** button. Once you have completed your option selections, click **OK** and the estimated trend model will be outputted in the **Session** window. Minitab will also produce a time series plot of the original data with the trend model superimposed.

An alternative to using Minitab's trend analysis routine for fitting linear and exponential trends is to create a time-index variable ($x = 1$, $x = 2$, and so on) and then implement the regression routine in Minitab. To create a time-index variable, you can either type its values into the worksheet or you can do the following pull-down sequence:

Calc ➤ Make Patterned Data ➤ Simple Set of Numbers

Type the column name in the **Store pattern data in** box to indicate where you want to place the values of the time-index variable. Type the value of "1" in the **From first value** box and type the number of total periods in the **To last value** box. Click **OK.** If you wish to take a logarithm (base e) of the data series so that you can use least-squares regression to estimate an exponential trend model as explained on page 754, then you would want to do the following pull-down sequence:

Calc ➤ Calculator

Type the column name in the **Store result in variable** box to indicate where you want to place the logged values. Now, scroll down the function list and select "Natural log (log base e)." Once done, you will find in the **Expression** box the expression "LN(number)." Replace "number" with the column name of the data series you wish to have logged. Click **OK.**

Excel:

Automated trend fitting (linear or exponential) is available in neither standard Excel nor the enhanced add-on version of Excel. You can, however, create a time-index variable ($x = 1$, $x = 2$, and so on) and then implement the regression routine in Excel. These values can be manually typed into a column of Excel. Alternatively, you can set the first cell to the value of "1" and then define the cell below as being equal to the previous cell plus 1 and then copy the formula down the column to a desired ending value. For exponential trend model fitting, you need to take the logarithm (base e) of the data series (see discussion on page 754). To do so, first click on an empty cell in the same row as the first value of the original data series. Now click the **Formulas** tab and then click the **Math & Trig** option found in the **Function Library** group. Scroll down the function list and select the "LN" function. You will then see a **Function Arguments** pop-up box. Click in the cell location of the first value of the original data series in the **Number** box and then click **OK.** Now copy the formula in the first cell down the column to the row of the last value of the original data series. You can now proceed to the regression routine.

Season Models

Minitab:

Stat ➤ Time Series ➤ Decomposition

With this routine, you can ask Minitab to compute the multiplicative seasonal factors with or without a trend component. Click in the column for the time series variable in the **Variable** box. In the **Seasonal length** box, type in the number of seasonal periods (for example, type in "12" for monthly data). Select the **Multiplicative** option to obtain seasonal factors that are used as multiplying factors. If you also want to fit a trend as was done in Example 13.4, then select the **Trend plus seasonal** option. It should be noted that Minitab first estimates the seasonal factors and then estimates the trend line after the data have been deseasonalized. For Example 13.4, we estimated the trend line first and then estimated the seasonal factors. The two different approaches result in slightly different estimates, but overall the differences in predictions are inconsequential for practical purposes. If you wish to obtain the actual residuals or predictions ("Fits"), then click the **Storage** button. Click **OK** when finished making selections, and then the estimated seasonal model will be outputted in the **Session** window. Minitab will also produce a number of graphs, including a time series plot of the original data with the seasonal model superimposed.

In our discussions of seasonal models, we illustrated (Example 13.3) how indicator variables can be used to estimate seasonal factors that are added to the prediction model. The creation of these indicator variables can be done manually by typing 0s and 1s in the worksheet. In the case of Example 13.3, this would mean typing $11 \times 125 = 1375$ values in the worksheet. There is a convenient alternative for creating indicator variables. To begin, we create a coded variable in the worksheet called "Month" which takes on the numbers $1, 2, 3, \ldots, 12$ for the twelve months of the year. These numbers are placed in the "Month" column so that we know on what month any value of the data series has occurred. To create this coded variable, you would want to do the following pull-down sequence:

Calc ➤ Make Patterned Data ➤ Arbitrary Set of Numbers

Type the column name in the **Store patterned data in** box to indicate where you want to place the coded variable. In the **Arbitrary set of numbers** box, if the time series starts in January, then type in the values "1," "2," "3," "4," "5," "6," "7," "8," "9," "10," "11," and "12." If the time series starts in another month, then cycle through the same values but with a different starting point: for example, for a time series starting in August type in "8," "9," "10," "11," "12," "1," "2," "3," "4," "5," "6," and "7." Now enter the number of times the sequence of coded values needs to be repeated to cover the entire data series in the **Number of times to list the sequence** box. In the case of Example 13.3, we have 125 data values, so we would enter "11," which would result in 132 coded values. Click **OK.** If there are any excess values in the coded column, simply go to the worksheet and delete them. You can now proceed to making indicator variables by doing the following pull-down sequence:

Calc ➤ Make Patterned Data ➤ Arbitrary Set of Numbers

In the **Indicator variable for** box, click in the column for the coded variable you just created. Minitab will list the distinct values of the coded variable, and it will give column names for the indicator variables. You can either accept the generic names or you can type in your own names: for example, "Jan," "Feb," "Mar," and so on. Click **OK** and then Minitab will create 12 indicator variables in the worksheet. At this point, as explained in Example 13.3, you would only use at most 11 of these indicator variables in the regression analysis.

Excel:

Automated seasonal model fitting is available in neither standard Excel nor the enhanced add-on version of Excel. Other than typing in all the 0s and 1s, there are a few shortcut ways to make indicator variables. For monthly data, you could type in a cell the value of "1" and then "0" into each of the 11 cells beneath it. Thereafter, you can repetitively copy and paste the stack of 12 values in the column and into other columns to create all the necessary indicator variables. Another approach is to create a column with 12 distinct coded values so that we know on what month any value of the data series has occurred. Then you can use the "IF" function (found within **Logical** functions) to place 0 or 1 values in other columns depending on the value of the code in a given row (for more information on the "IF" function, click on the **Help on this function** link). Once your indicator variables are created, you can proceed to use them with Excel's regression routine.

Autocorrelation

Minitab:

Stat ➤ Time Series ➤ Autocorrelation

Based on a slightly modified formula for computing correlations, the autocorrelation routine in Minitab can be used to report the autocorrelations for a time series variable at various lags. Upon doing the above pull-down sequence, you can then click in the column for the time series variable in the **Series** box. You can allow Minitab to determine how many lags it will report, or you can choose the number of lags by inputting a value in the **Number of lags** box. Click **OK.** You will find that Minitab will produce a bar graph of the autocorrelations, and it will also report the autcorrelation values in the **Session** window, along with other test statistics. An alternative for finding autocorrelations is to create a lag variable in the worksheet and then use the standard correlation formula given in Chapter 2. To create a lag variable, you can do the following pull-down sequence:

Stat ➤ Time Series ➤ Lag

Click in the column for the time series variable that you wish to lag in the **Series** box. Now type the column name (other than the column of the original variable) in the **Store lags in** box to indicate where you want Minitab to place the lagged values. Finally, indicate how far back you want to lag by typing an integer greater than 0 in the **Lag** box (default lag is "1"). Click **OK**. At this stage, you can use Minitab to compute the correlation between the variable and its lag using the standard correlation formula (refer to Appendix of Chapter 2).

Excel:

Excel does not have a routine to compute autocorrelations. However, you can create the lagged variable and then use the standard correlation formula. To create the lagged variable, simply highlight the cell range of the column containing the sequence of time series observations and then paste the values into shifted-down cells of an adjacent column. For example, to create a lag of one variable, paste the values into cells shifted down by one row. You can now use Excel to compute the correlation between the variable and its lag using the standard correlation formula (refer to the Appendix of Chapter 2).

AR(1) Model Estimation

Minitab:

Stat ➤ Time Series ➤ ARIMA

This pull-down sequence leads you to a routine for estimating the model coefficients of an AR(1) or a more complicated time series model based on maximum likelihood estimation. Click in the column for the time series variable in the **Series** box. In the **Autoregressive** box, which is cross-referenced by the **Nonseasonal** label, enter the value of "1." Click **OK.** The AR(1) estimated model will then be outputted in the **Session** window.

Excel:

Maximum likelihood estimation of time series models is available in neither standard Excel nor the enhanced add-on version of Excel.

Moving Average Models

Minitab:

Click in the column for the time series variable in the **Variable** box. Type in the span of the moving average in the **MA length** box. If you wish to change the time scale (for example, to months or years), then click the **Time** button. By clicking the **Graphs** button, you can produce a variety of residual plots. If you wish to obtain the actual residuals or predictions ("Fits"), then click the **Storage** button. You also have the option of generating forecasts into the future. To do so, place a checkmark next to the **Generate forecasts** option. Then type the number of periods into the future you want to forecast into the **Number of forecasts** box and finally type the period of origin from which forecasts are made in the **Starting from origin** box (note: this is typically taken to be the last period of the data series). Once you have completed your option selections, click **OK** and then Minitab will produce a time series plot of the original data with the moving average forecasts overlaid. Additionally, if you requested forecasts, Minitab will project out forecasts on the plot along with 95% prediction limits.

Excel:

Select "Moving Average" in the **Data Analysis** menu box and click **OK.** Enter the cell range of the time series data into the **Input Range** box and type in the span of the moving average in the **Interval** box. If you want to plot the moving average forecasts, place a checkmark next to the **Chart Output** option. Click **OK** to have the moving averages outputted to the spreadsheet. If you requested a plot of the moving averages, you will find it to be a bar graph, which you can change to a time plot by right-clicking on the graph and selecting the **Change Chart Type** option.

Exponential Smoothing Models

Minitab:

Stat ➤ Time Series ➤ Single Exp Smoothing

Click in the column for the time series variable in the **Variable** box. To use your own smoothing constant (w), choose the **Use** option and type the smoothing constant in the adjacent box. Alternatively, you can let Minitab determine the best choice for the smoothing constant by choosing the **Optimal ARIMA** option. It is important to note that Minitab by default uses the average of the first 6 observations as the forecast for the first time period. If you wish to use the actual value of the first period as the forecast for the first time period, as in Example 13.15, click the **Options** button and then type "1" in the **K** = box. You can change the "K"-value only if you are using your own smoothing constant. If you wish to change the time scale (for example, to months or years), then click the **Time** button. By clicking the **Graphs** button, you can produce a variety of residual plots. If you wish to obtain the actual residuals or predictions ("Fits"), then click the **Storage** button. You also have the option of generating forecasts into the future. To do so, place a checkmark next to the **Generate forecasts** option. Then type the number of periods into the future you want to forecast into the **Number of forecasts** box and finally type in the period of origin from which forecasts are made in the **Starting from origin** box (note: this is typically taken to be the last period of the data series). Once you have completed your option selections, click **OK** and then Minitab will produce a time series plot of the original data with the exponential smoothing forecasts overlaid, and it will report the smoothing constant used (either your choice or what Minitab has selected). Additionally, if you requested forecasts, Minitab will project out forecasts on the plot along with 95% prediction limits.

Excel:

Select "Exponential Smoothing" in the **Data Analysis** menu box and click **OK.** Enter the cell range of the time series data into the **Input Range** box. In the **Damping factor** box, you should type in 1 minus the smoothing constant, that is, $1 - w$. If you want to plot the exponential smoothing forecasts, place a checkmark next to the **Chart Output** option. Click **OK** to have the exponential smoothing outputted to the spreadsheet. If you requested a plot of the exponential smoothing forecasts, you will find it to be a bar graph, which you can change to a time plot by right-clicking on the graph and selecting the **Change Chart Type** option.

CHAPTER 14

One-Way Analysis of Variance

PRELUDE: HOW SHOULD WE IMPROVE THE FORMS?

A university requires its faculty to complete a form three times a year that describes the amount of time spent in various activities. For many years there were complaints that the form was difficult to fill out and that many of the questions were not clearly explained.

A new administration decided to revise the form. Several small groups of faculty members studied the old form and made recommendations for how it should be changed. From these groups, three possible versions of a new form were developed. To determine which of the new versions should be adopted, a randomized experiment was performed. From the list of faculty, 150 names were randomly selected. These were then randomly assigned to receive one of the three proposed forms. Thus, there were 50 faculty who received each form. The faculty were asked to review the proposed form and to rate it on a scale of 1 to 10.

The evaluations for the three proposed forms were compared using the analysis of variance methods described in this chapter. The results gave a clear indication that one of the forms was preferred to the other two. This form is now being used.

Introduction

Many of the most effective statistical studies are comparative, whether we compare the salaries of women and men in a sample of firms or the responses to two treatments in a clinical trial. We display comparisons with back-to-back stemplots or side-by-side boxplots, and we measure them with five-number summaries or with means and standard deviations. Now we ask: "Is the difference between groups statistically significant?"

When only two groups are compared, Chapter 7 provides the tools we need. Two-sample t procedures compare the means of two Normal populations, and we saw that these procedures, unlike comparisons of spread, are sufficiently robust to be widely useful. Now we will compare any number of means by techniques that generalize the two-sample t and share its robustness and usefulness.

14.1 One-Way Analysis of Variance

Which of four advertising offers mailed to sample households produces the highest sales in dollars? Which of ten brands of automobile tires wears longest? How long do cancer patients live under each of three therapies for their cancer? In each of these settings we wish to compare several treatments. In each case the data are subject to sampling variability—if we mailed the advertising offers to another set of households, we would get different data. We therefore pose the question for inference in terms of the *mean* response. We compare, for example, the mean tread lifetime of different brands of tires. In Chapter 7 we met procedures for comparing the means of two populations. We are now ready to extend those methods to problems involving more than two populations. The statistical methodology for comparing several means is called **analysis of variance,** or simply **ANOVA.**

ANOVA

one-way ANOVA

We will consider two variations of the ANOVA idea. In **one-way ANOVA** we classify the populations of interest according to a single categorical explanatory variable that we call a **factor.** For example, to compare the tread lifetimes of 10 specific brands of tires we use one-way ANOVA. This chapter presents the details for one-way ANOVA.

factor

In many practical situations we classify populations in more than one way. A mail-order firm might want to compare mailings that offer different discounts and also have different layouts. Will a lower price offered in a plain format draw more sales on the average than a higher price offered in a fancy brochure? Analyzing the effect of price and layout together requires **two-way ANOVA,** and adding yet more factors necessitates higher-way ANOVA techniques. Most of the new ideas in ANOVA with more than two factors already appear in two-way ANOVA, which we discuss in Chapter 15.

two-way ANOVA

The ANOVA setting: comparing means

Do two population means differ? If we have random samples from the two populations, we compute a two-sample t statistic and its P-value to assess the statistical significance of the difference in the sample means. We compare several means in much the same way. Instead of a t statistic, ANOVA uses an F statistic and its P-value to evaluate the null hypothesis that all of several population means are equal.

In the sections that follow, we will examine the basic ideas of analysis of variance and the conditions under which we can use this tool. Although the details differ, many of the concepts are similar to those discussed in the two-sample case.

One-way analysis of variance is a statistical method for comparing several population means. We draw a simple random sample (SRS) from each population and use the data to test the null hypothesis that the population means are all equal.

EXAMPLE 14.1 Comparing Magazine Covers

A magazine publisher wants to compare three different styles of covers for a magazine that will be offered for sale at supermarket checkout lines. She assigns 60 stores at random to the three styles of covers and records the number of magazines that are sold in a one-week period.

EXAMPLE 14.2 Who Shops Where?

How do five bookstores in the same city differ in the demographics of their customers? A market researcher asks 50 customers of each store to respond to a questionnaire. One variable of interest is the customer's age.

These two examples have several similarities. In both there is a single quantitative response variable measured on several individuals. The response variables are magazines sold in the first example and age of the customer in the second. The individuals are stores in the first example and customers in the second. We expect the data to be approximately Normal and will consider a transformation if they are not. We wish to compare several populations, stores displaying three cover styles in the first example and customers of five bookstores in the second. We will often use the term *groups* for the populations to be compared in a one-way ANOVA.

experiment
observational study

There is also an important difference between the examples. Example 14.1 describes an **experiment** in which stores are randomly assigned to cover styles. Example 14.2 is an **observational study** in which customers are selected during a particular time period and not all agree to provide data. We will treat our samples of customers as random samples even though this is only approximately true. In both examples, we will use ANOVA to compare the mean responses. The same ANOVA methods apply to data from random samples and to data from randomized experiments. Do keep the data-production method in mind when interpreting the results, however. A strong case for causation is best made by a randomized experiment.

To assess whether several populations all have the same mean, we compare the means of samples drawn from each population. Figure 14.1 displays the sample means for Example 14.1. Design 2 had the highest average sales. But is the observed difference among the designs just the result of chance variation? We do not expect sample means to be equal even if the population means are all identical. The purpose of ANOVA is to assess whether the observed differences among sample means are *statistically significant.* In other words, could a variation this large be plausibly due to chance, or is it good evidence for a difference among the population means? This question can't be answered from the sample means alone. Because the standard deviation of a sample mean $\bar{x}$ is the population standard deviation σ divided by $\sqrt{n}$, the answer depends upon both the variation within the groups of observations and the sizes of the samples.

Side-by-side boxplots help us see the within-group variation. Compare Figures 14.2(a) and 14.2(b). The sample medians are the same in both figures, but the variation within the

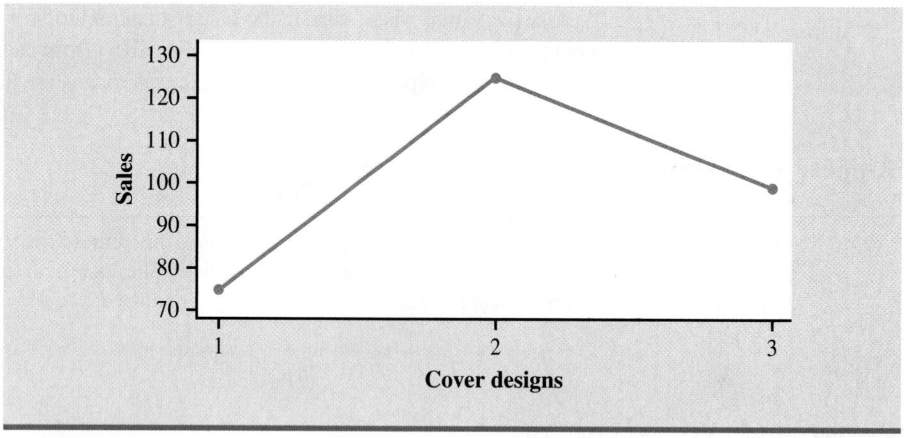

FIGURE 14.1 Mean sales of magazines for three cover designs.

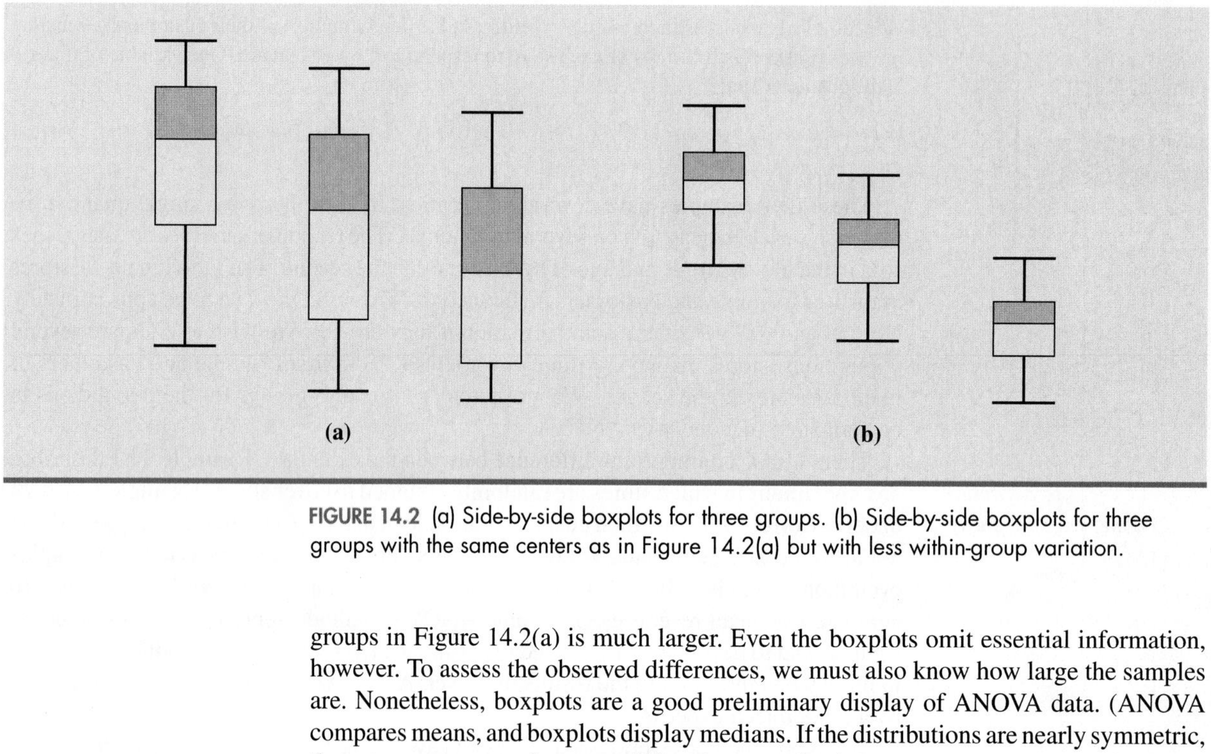

FIGURE 14.2 (a) Side-by-side boxplots for three groups. (b) Side-by-side boxplots for three groups with the same centers as in Figure 14.2(a) but with less within-group variation.

groups in Figure 14.2(a) is much larger. Even the boxplots omit essential information, however. To assess the observed differences, we must also know how large the samples are. Nonetheless, boxplots are a good preliminary display of ANOVA data. (ANOVA compares means, and boxplots display medians. If the distributions are nearly symmetric, these two measures of center will be close together.)

The two-sample *t* statistic

Two-sample t statistics compare the means of two populations. If the two populations are assumed to have equal but unknown standard deviations and the sample sizes are both equal to n, the t statistic is (page 451)

$$t = \frac{\overline{x} - \overline{y}}{s_p\sqrt{\dfrac{1}{n} + \dfrac{1}{n}}} = \frac{\sqrt{\dfrac{n}{2}}(\overline{x} - \overline{y})}{s_p}$$

The square of this t statistic is

$$t^2 = \frac{\frac{n}{2}(\overline{x} - \overline{y})^2}{s_p^2}$$

If we use ANOVA to compare two populations, the ANOVA F statistic is exactly equal to this t^2. We can therefore learn something about how ANOVA works by looking carefully at the statistic in this form.

between-group variation

The numerator in the t^2 statistic measures the variation **between** the groups in terms of the difference between their sample means $\overline{x}$ and $\overline{y}$. It includes a factor for the common sample size n. The numerator can be large because of a large difference between the sample means or because the sample sizes are large. The denominator measures the variation **within** groups by s_p^2, the pooled estimator of the common variance. If the within-group variation is small, the same variation between the groups produces a larger statistic and a more significant result.

within-group variation

Although the general form of the F statistic is more complicated, the idea is the same. To assess whether several populations all have the same mean, we compare the variation *among* the means of several groups with the variation *within* groups. Because we are comparing variation, the method is called *analysis of variance*.

An overview of ANOVA

ANOVA tests the null hypothesis that the population means are *all equal*. The alternative is that they are not all equal. This alternative could be true because all of the means are different or simply because one of them differs from the rest. This is a more complex situation than comparing just two populations. If we reject the null hypothesis, we need to perform some further analysis to draw conclusions about which population means differ from which others.

The computations needed for ANOVA are more lengthy than those for the t test. For this reason we generally use software to perform the calculations. Automating the calculations frees us from the burden of arithmetic and allows us to concentrate on interpretation. The following example illustrates the practical use of ANOVA in analyzing data. Later we will explore the technical details.

EXAMPLE 14.3 Changing Majors

In the computer science department of a large university, many students change their major after the first year. A detailed study of the 256 students enrolled as first-year computer science majors in one year was undertaken to help understand this phenomenon.[1] Students were classified on the basis of their major at the beginning of their second year, and several variables measured at the time of their entrance to the university were obtained. Here are summary statistics for the SAT Mathematics scores:

Second-year major	n	$\overline{x}$	s
Computer science	103	619	86
Engineering and other sciences	31	629	67
Other	122	575	83

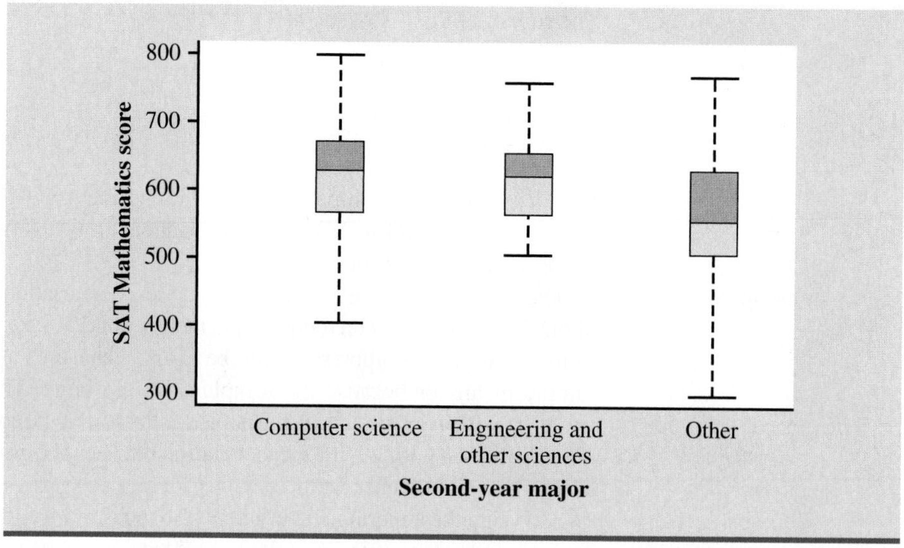

FIGURE 14.3 Side-by-side boxplots of SAT Mathematics scores, for the change-of-majors study.

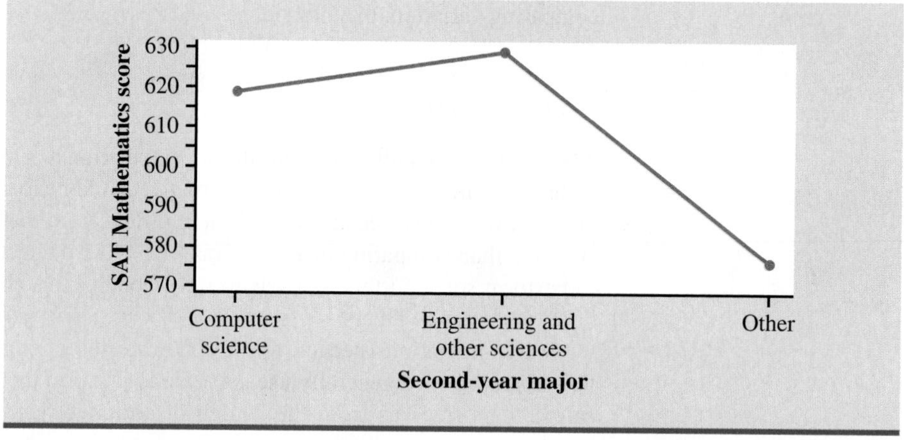

FIGURE 14.4 SAT Mathematics score means for the change-of-majors study.

Figure 14.3 gives side-by-side boxplots of the SAT data. Compare Figure 14.3 with the plot of the mean scores in Figure 14.4. The means appear to be different, but there is a large amount of overlap in the three distributions. When we perform an ANOVA on these data, we ask a question about the group means. The null hypothesis is that the population mean SAT Math scores for the three groups are equal, and the alternative is that they are not all equal. The report on the study states that the ANOVA F statistic is 10.35 with $P < 0.001$. There is very strong evidence that the three groups of students do not all have the same mean SAT Math scores.

Although we rejected the null hypothesis, we cannot conclude that all three population means are different, only that they are not all the same. Inspection of Figures 14.3 and 14.4 suggests that the means of the first two groups are nearly equal and that the third group differs from these two. We need to do some additional analysis to compare the three means. The researchers expected the mathematics scores of the engineering and other sciences group to be similar to those of the computer science group. They suspected that the students in the third (other major) group would have lower mathematics scores, because these students chose to transfer to programs of study that require less mathematics. The researchers had this specific comparison in mind before seeing the data, so they used **contrasts** to assess the significance of this specific relation among the means. If we have no specific relations among the means in mind before looking at the data, we instead use a **multiple-comparisons** procedure to determine which pairs of population means differ significantly. Section 14.2 explores both contrasts and multiple comparisons in detail.

contrasts

multiple comparisons

A purist might argue that ANOVA is inappropriate in Example 14.3. *All* first-year computer science majors in this university for the year studied were included in the analysis. There was no random sampling from larger populations. On the other hand, we can think of these three groups of students as samples from three populations of students in similar circumstances. They may be representative of students in the next few years at the same university or other universities with similar programs. Judgments such as this are very important and must be made, not by statisticians, but by people who are knowledgeable about the subject of the study.

The ANOVA model

When analyzing data, we think in terms of an overall pattern and deviations from it. In shorthand form,

$$\text{DATA} = \text{FIT} + \text{RESIDUAL}$$

In the regression model of Chapter 10, the FIT was the population regression line, and the RESIDUAL represented the deviations of the data from this line. We now apply this framework to describe the statistical models used in ANOVA. These models provide a convenient way to summarize the conditions that are the foundation for our analysis. They also give us the necessary notation to describe the calculations needed.

First, recall the statistical model for a random sample of observations from a single Normal population with mean μ and standard deviation σ. If the observations are

$$x_1, x_2, \ldots, x_n$$

we can describe this model by saying that the x_j are an SRS from the $N(\mu, \sigma)$ distribution. Another way to describe the same model is to think of the x's varying about their population mean. To do this, write each observation x_j as

$$x_j = \mu + \epsilon_j$$

The ϵ_j are then an SRS from the $N(0, \sigma)$ distribution. Because μ is unknown, the ϵ's cannot actually be observed. This form more closely corresponds to our

$$\text{DATA} = \text{FIT} + \text{RESIDUAL}$$

way of thinking. The FIT part of the model is represented by μ. It is the systematic part of the model, like the line in a regression. The RESIDUAL part is represented by ϵ_j. It represents the deviations of the data from the fit and is due to random, or chance, variation.

There are two unknown parameters in this statistical model: μ and σ. We estimate μ by $\overline{x}$, the sample mean, and σ by s, the sample standard deviation. The differences $e_j = x_j - \overline{x}$ are the sample residuals. They correspond to the ϵ_j in the statistical model.

The model for one-way ANOVA is very similar. We take random samples from each of I different populations. The sample size is n_i for the ith population. Let x_{ij} represent

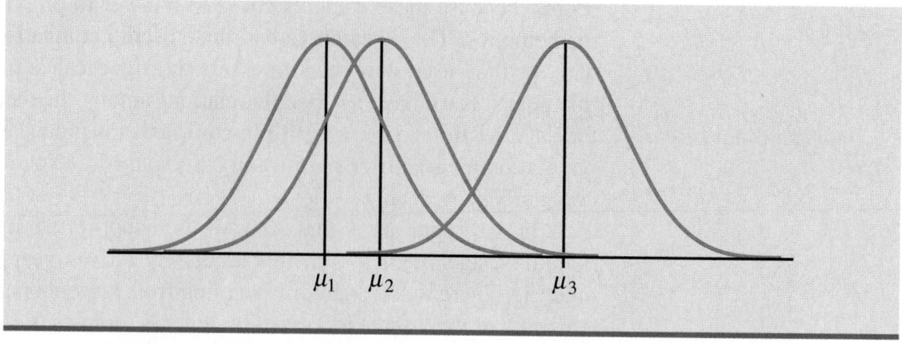

FIGURE 14.5 Model for one-way ANOVA with three groups. The three populations have Normal distributions with the same standard deviation.

the jth observation from the ith population. The I population means are the FIT part of the model and are represented by μ_i. The random variation, or RESIDUAL, part of the model is represented by the deviations ϵ_{ij} of the observations from the means.

The One-Way ANOVA Model

The data for one-way ANOVA are SRSs from each of I populations. The sample from the ith population has n_i observations, $x_{i1}, x_{i2}, \ldots, x_{in_i}$. The **one-way ANOVA model** is

$$x_{ij} = \mu_i + \epsilon_{ij}$$

for $i = 1, \ldots, I$ and $j = 1, \ldots, n_i$. The ϵ_{ij} are assumed to be from an $N(0, \sigma)$ distribution. The **parameters of the model** are the I population means $\mu_1, \mu_2, \ldots, \mu_I$ and the common standard deviation σ.

The sample sizes n_i may differ, but the standard deviation σ is assumed to be the same in all of the populations. Figure 14.5 pictures this model for $I = 3$. The three population means μ_i are different, but the shapes of the three Normal distributions are the same, reflecting the condition that all three populations have the same standard deviation.

EXAMPLE 14.4 How Much Do Students Spend on Textbooks?

A survey of college students attempted to determine how much money they spend per year on textbooks and to compare students by year of study. From lists of students provided by the registrar, SRSs of size 50 were chosen from each of the four classes (freshmen, sophomores, juniors, and seniors). The students selected were asked how much they had spent on textbooks during the current semester.

There are $I = 4$ populations. The population means μ_1, μ_2, μ_3, and μ_4 are the average amounts spent on textbooks by *all* freshmen, sophomores, juniors, and seniors at this college for this semester. The sample sizes n_i are 50, 50, 50, and 50.

Suppose the first freshman sampled is Eve Brogden. The observation x_{11} is the amount spent by Eve. The data for the other freshmen sampled are denoted by x_{12}, x_{13}, and so on. Similarly, the data for the other groups have a first subscript indicating the group and a second subscript indicating the student in the group.

According to our model, Eve's spending is $x_{11} = \mu_1 + \epsilon_{11}$, where μ_1 is the average for *all* of the students in the freshman class and ϵ_{11} is the chance variation due to Eve's specific needs. We are assuming that the ϵ_{ij} are independent and Normally distributed (at least approximately) with mean 0 and standard deviation σ.

APPLY YOUR KNOWLEDGE

14.1 Magazine covers. Example 14.1 (page 793) describes a study designed to compare sales based on different magazine covers. Write out the ANOVA model for this study. Be sure to give specific values for I and the n_i. List all of the parameters of the model.

14.2 Ages of customers at different stores. In Example 14.2 (page 793) the ages of customers at different bookstores are compared. Write out the ANOVA model for this study. Be sure to give specific values for I and the n_i. List all of the parameters of the model.

Estimates of population parameters

The unknown parameters in the statistical model for ANOVA are the I population means μ_i and the common population standard deviation σ. To estimate μ_i we use the sample mean for the ith group:

$$\overline{x}_i = \frac{1}{n_i} \sum_{j=1}^{n_i} x_{ij}$$

residuals

The **residuals** $e_{ij} = x_{ij} - \overline{x}_i$ reflect the variation about the sample means that we see in the data.

The ANOVA model states that the population standard deviations are all equal. The ANOVA test of equality of means requires this condition. If we have unequal standard deviations, we generally try to transform the data so that they are approximately equal. We might, for example, work with $\sqrt{x_{ij}}$ or $\log x_{ij}$. Fortunately, we can often find a transformation that *both* makes the group standard deviations more nearly equal and also makes the distributions of observations in each group more nearly Normal. If the standard deviations are markedly different and cannot be made similar by a transformation, inference requires different methods.

Unfortunately, formal tests for the equality of standard deviations in several groups share the lack of robustness against non-Normality that we noted in Chapter 7 for the case of two groups. Because ANOVA procedures are not extremely sensitive to unequal standard deviations, we do *not* recommend a formal test of equality of standard deviations as a preliminary to the ANOVA. Instead, we will use the following rule of thumb.

Rule for Examining Standard Deviations in ANOVA

If the largest sample standard deviation is less than twice the smallest sample standard deviation, we can use methods based on the condition that the population standard deviations are equal and our results will still be approximately correct.[2]

When we assume that the population standard deviations are equal, each sample standard deviation is an estimate of σ. To combine these into a single estimate, we use a generalization of the pooling method introduced in Chapter 7.

Pooled Estimator of σ

Suppose we have sample variances $s_1^2, s_2^2, \ldots, s_I^2$ from I independent SRSs of sizes $n_1, n_2, \ldots, n_I$ from populations with common variance σ^2. The **pooled sample variance**

$$s_p^2 = \frac{(n_1 - 1)s_1^2 + (n_2 - 1)s_2^2 + \cdots + (n_I - 1)s_I^2}{(n_1 - 1) + (n_2 - 1) + \cdots + (n_I - 1)}$$

is an unbiased estimator of σ^2. The **pooled standard error**

$$s_p = \sqrt{s_p^2}$$

is the estimate of σ.

Pooling gives more weight to groups with larger sample sizes. If the sample sizes are equal, s_p^2 is just the average of the I sample variances. Note that s_p is *not* the average of the I sample standard deviations.

EXAMPLE 14.5 Estimates of Parameters for the Change-of-Majors Study

In the change-of-majors study of Example 14.3 there are $I = 3$ groups and the sample sizes are $n_1 = 103$, $n_2 = 31$, and $n_3 = 122$. The sample means for the SAT Mathematics scores are $\overline{x}_1 = 619$, $\overline{x}_2 = 629$, and $\overline{x}_3 = 575$. These statistics estimate the three unknown population means.

The sample standard deviations are $s_1 = 86$, $s_2 = 67$, and $s_3 = 83$. Because the largest standard deviation (86) is less than twice the smallest ($2 \times 67 = 134$), our rule of thumb allows us to act as if the population standard deviations are equal.

The pooled variance estimate is

$$\begin{aligned} s_p^2 &= \frac{(n_1 - 1)s_1^2 + (n_2 - 1)s_2^2 + (n_3 - 1)s_3^2}{(n_1 - 1) + (n_2 - 1) + (n_3 - 1)} \\ &= \frac{(102)(86)^2 + (30)(67)^2 + (121)(83)^2}{102 + 30 + 121} \\ &= \frac{1{,}722{,}631}{253} = 6809 \end{aligned}$$

The pooled standard error is

$$s_p = \sqrt{6809} = 82.5$$

This is our estimate of the common standard deviation σ of the SAT Mathematics scores in the three populations of students.

APPLY YOUR KNOWLEDGE

14.3 Magazine covers. Example 14.1 (page 793) describes a study designed to compare sales based on different magazine covers, and in Exercise 14.1 you described the ANOVA model for this study. The three covers are designated 1, 2, and 3. The following table summarizes the sales data.

Cover	Mean	Standard deviation	Sample size
1	75	80	20
2	125	100	20
3	100	120	20

(a) Is it reasonable to pool the standard deviations for these data?

(b) For each parameter in your model from Exercise 14.2, give the estimate.

14.4 Ages of customers at different stores. In Example 14.2 (page 793) the ages of customers at different bookstores are compared, and you described the ANOVA model for this study in Exercise 14.2. Here is a summary of the ages of the customers:

Store	Mean	Standard deviation	Sample size
A	35	9	50
B	42	12	50
C	20	7	50
D	22	8	50
E	46	14	50

(a) Is it reasonable to pool the standard deviations for these data?

(b) For each parameter in your model from Exercise 14.2, give the estimate.

Testing hypotheses in one-way ANOVA

ANOVA table

Comparison of several means is accomplished by using an F statistic to compare the variation among groups with the variation within groups. We now show how the F statistic expresses this comparison. Calculations are organized in an **ANOVA table,** which contains numerical measures of the variation among groups and within groups.

First we must specify our hypotheses for one-way ANOVA. As usual, I represents the number of populations to be compared.

Hypotheses for One-Way ANOVA

The **null and alternative hypotheses** for one-way ANOVA are

$$H_0: \mu_1 = \mu_2 = \ldots = \mu_I$$

$$H_a: \text{not all of the } \mu_i \text{ are equal}$$

The following discussion illustrates how to do a one-way ANOVA for the setting of Case 14.1. The calculations are generally performed using statistical software on a computer, so we focus on interpretation of the output.

CASE 14.1  A NEW EDUCATIONAL PRODUCT

Your company markets educational materials aimed at parents of young children. You are planning a new product that is designed to improve children's reading comprehension. Your product is based on new ideas from educational research, and you would like to claim that children will acquire better reading comprehension skills with the new methods than with the traditional approach. Your marketing material will include the results of a study conducted to compare two versions of the new approach with the traditional method.[3] The standard method is called Basal, and the two variations of the new method are called DRTA and Strat (for strategies).

Education researchers randomly divided 66 children into three groups of 22. Each group was taught by one of the three methods. As is common in such studies, the children were given a "pretest" that measured their reading comprehension before receiving any instruction. One purpose of the pretest was to see if the three groups of children were similar in their comprehension skills at the start of the study. One of the pretest variables was an "intruded sentences" measure, which measures one type of reading comprehension skill. The data for the 22 subjects in each group are given in Table 14.1. The three groups are named Basal, DRTA, and Strat.

TABLE 14.1 Pretest reading comprehension scores

Group	Subject	Score	Group	Subject	Score	Group	Subject	Score
Basal	1	4	DRTA	23	7	Strat	45	11
Basal	2	6	DRTA	24	7	Strat	46	7
Basal	3	9	DRTA	25	12	Strat	47	4
Basal	4	12	DRTA	26	10	Strat	48	7
Basal	5	16	DRTA	27	16	Strat	49	7
Basal	6	15	DRTA	28	15	Strat	50	6
Basal	7	14	DRTA	29	9	Strat	51	11
Basal	8	12	DRTA	30	8	Strat	52	14
Basal	9	12	DRTA	31	13	Strat	53	13
Basal	10	8	DRTA	32	12	Strat	54	9
Basal	11	13	DRTA	33	7	Strat	55	12
Basal	12	9	DRTA	34	6	Strat	56	13
Basal	13	12	DRTA	35	8	Strat	57	4
Basal	14	12	DRTA	36	9	Strat	58	13
Basal	15	12	DRTA	37	9	Strat	59	6
Basal	16	10	DRTA	38	8	Strat	60	12
Basal	17	8	DRTA	39	9	Strat	61	6
Basal	18	12	DRTA	40	13	Strat	62	11
Basal	19	11	DRTA	41	10	Strat	63	14
Basal	20	8	DRTA	42	8	Strat	64	8
Basal	21	7	DRTA	43	8	Strat	65	5
Basal	22	9	DRTA	44	10	Strat	66	8

We want to test the null hypothesis that the three groups represent three populations that all have the same mean score on the pretest. First, look at the data. Side-by-side boxplots do not give a good picture of these data. This is a consequence of the relatively small number of observations in each group (22) combined with the fact that the variable has only a few possible values (the values are all integers between 4 and 17). Side-by-side stemplots give a better picture. After inspecting the stemplots, decide whether the ANOVA model should be used to analyze the data.

APPLY YOUR KNOWLEDGE

14.5 Stemplots. CASE 14.1 Display the data in Table 14.1 for the three reading groups using three stemplots. Make the stems the same for the groups and put them side by side so that the data can be compared. Are any systematic differences among the groups apparent? Do any groups show strong skewness or clear outliers?

EXAMPLE 14.6 Verifying the Conditions for ANOVA

CASE 14.1

If ANOVA is to be trusted, three conditions must hold.

SRSs. Can we regard the three samples as SRSs from three populations? An ideal study would start with an SRS of all children of the same age and randomly assign children to the three teaching methods. This isn't practical. The researchers randomly assigned children from one school district. They argue that for comparing reading methods we can act as if these children were randomly chosen. Critics may disagree.

Normality. Are pretest scores Normally distributed in each group? Figure 14.6 displays Normal quantile plots for the three groups. The data do look reasonably Normal. There are only a small number of possible values for the score (the values are all integers between 4 and 17), but this should not cause difficulties in using ANOVA.

Common standard deviation. Figure 14.7 gives the summary statistics generated by Minitab. Because the largest standard deviation (3.342) is less than twice the smallest ($2 \times 2.694 = 5.388$), our rule of thumb tells us that we need not be concerned about violating the condition that the three populations have the same standard deviation.

Because the data look reasonably Normal and meet the condition of equal standard deviations, we proceed with the analysis of variance.

EXAMPLE 14.7 Are the Differences Significant?

CASE 14.1

The ANOVA results produced by Minitab are shown in Figure 14.8. The pooled standard deviation s_p is reported as 3.014. The calculated value of the F statistic appears under the heading F, and its P-value is under the heading P. The value of F is 1.13, with a P-value of 0.329. That is, an F of 1.13 or larger would occur about 33% of the time by chance when the population means are equal. We have no evidence to reject the null hypothesis that the three populations have equal means. This is the conclusion the researchers hoped for—the three groups are on the same level before instruction begins.

FIGURE 14.6 (a) Normal quantile plots of the pretest scores for the (a) Basal, (b) DRTA, and (c) Strat groups in the new-product evaluation study.

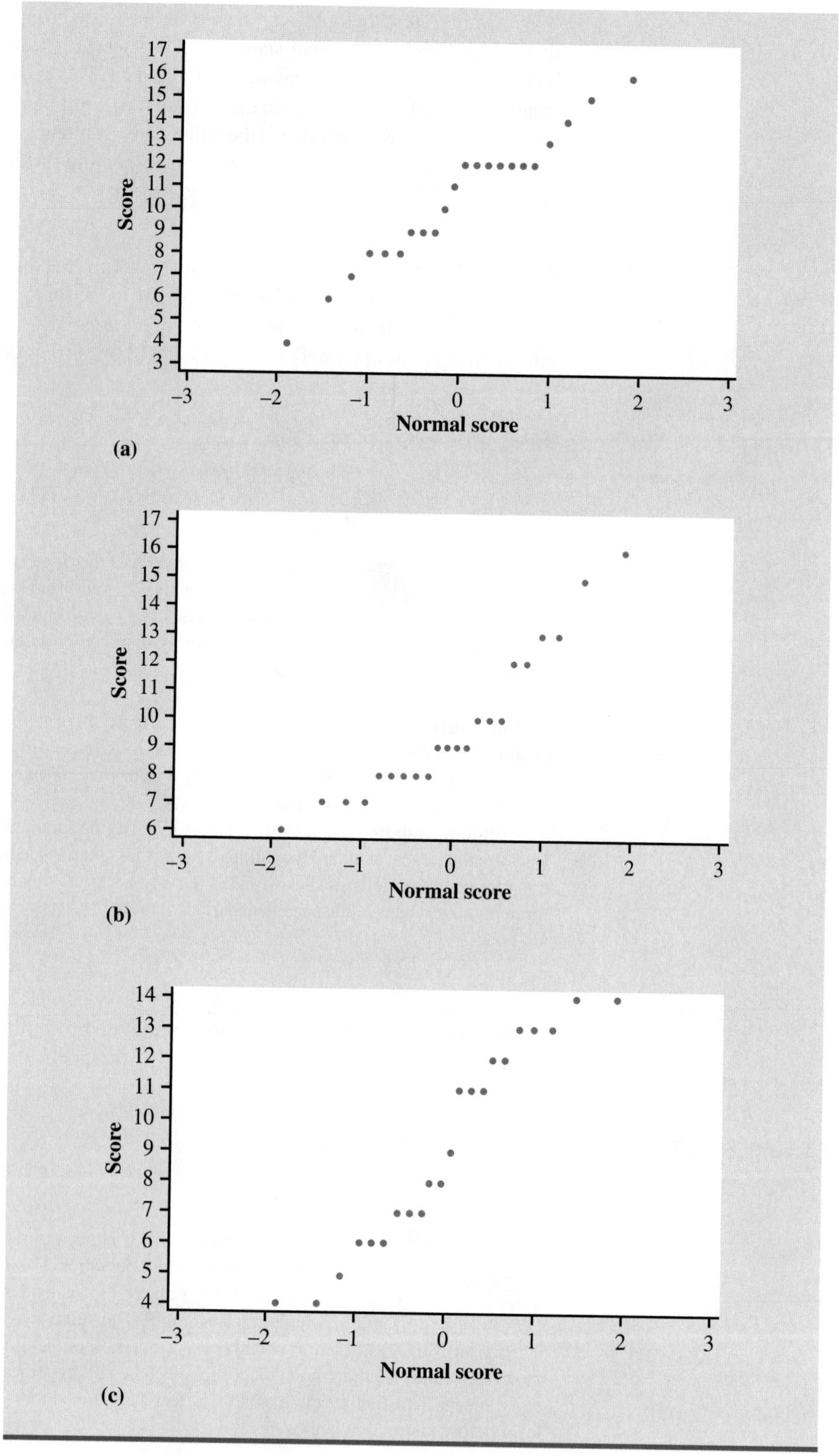

FIGURE 14.7 Summary statistics for the pretest scores of the three groups in the new-product evaluation study.

Descriptive Statistics

Variable	Group	N	Mean	Median	StDev
Score	Basal	22	10.500	11.500	2.972
	DRTA	22	9.727	9.000	2.694
	Strat	22	9.136	8.500	3.342

FIGURE 14.8 Analysis of variance output for the pretest scores in the new-product evaluation study.

One-way ANOVA: Score versus Group

Source	DF	SS	MS	F	P
Group	2	20.58	10.29	1.13	0.329
Error	63	572.45	9.09		
Total	65	593.03			

S = 3.014   R-Sq = 3.47%   R-Sq(adj) = 0.41%

Examples 14.6 and 14.7 illustrate the basics of ANOVA: state the hypotheses, verify that the conditions for ANOVA are met, look at the F statistic and its P-value, and state a conclusion.

APPLY YOUR KNOWLEDGE

14.6 An alternative Normal quantile plot. CASE 14.1 Figure 14.6 displays separate Normal quantile plots for the three groups. An alternative procedure is to make one Normal quantile plot using the *residuals* $e_{ij} = \overline{x}_{ij} - \overline{x}_i$ for all three groups together. Make this plot and summarize what it shows.

The ANOVA table

Software ANOVA output contains more than simply the test statistic. The additional information shows, among other things, where the test statistic comes from.

ANOVA table

The information in an analysis of variance is organized in an **ANOVA table.** In the software output in Figure 14.8, the columns of this table are labeled Source, DF, SS, MS, F, and P. The rows are labeled Group, Error, and Total. These are the three sources of variation in the one-way ANOVA. ("Group" was the name used in entering the data to distinguish the three treatment groups.)

variation among groups

variation within groups

The Group row in the table corresponds to the FIT term in our DATA = FIT + RESIDUAL way of thinking. It gives information related to the variation **among** group means. The ANOVA model allows the groups to have different means. The Error row in the table corresponds to the RESIDUAL term in DATA = FIT + RESIDUAL. It gives information related to the variation **within** groups. The term "error" is most appropriate for experiments in the physical sciences, where the observations within a group differ because of measurement error. In business and the biological and social sciences, on the other hand, the within-group variation is often due to the fact that not all firms or plants or people are the same. This sort of variation is not due to errors and is better described as "residual." Finally, the Total row in the table corresponds to the DATA term in our DATA = FIT + RESIDUAL framework.

For analysis of variance, the idea that

$$\text{DATA} = \text{FIT} + \text{RESIDUAL}$$

translates into an actual equation:

$$\text{total variation} = \text{variation among groups} + \text{variation within groups}$$

sums of squares

The ANOVA idea is to break the total variation in the responses into two parts: the variation due to differences among the group means and that due to differences within groups. Variation is expressed by **sums of squares.** We use SSG, SSE, and SST for the sums of squares for groups, error, and total. Each sum of squares is the sum of the squares of a set of deviations that expresses a source of variation. SST is the sum of squares of $x_{ij} - \overline{x}$, which measure variation of the responses around their overall mean. Variation of the group means around the overall mean $\overline{x}_i - \overline{x}$ is measured by SSG. Finally, SSE is the sum of squares of the deviations $x_{ij} - \overline{x}_i$ of each observation from its group mean. It is always true that SST = SSG + SSE. This is the algebraic version of the ANOVA idea: total variation is the sum of among-group variation and within-group variation.

EXAMPLE 14.8 Sums of Squares for the Three Sources of Variation

CASE 14.1

The SS column in Figure 14.8 gives the values for the three sums of squares. The output gives many more digits than we need. Rounded-off values are SSG $= 21$, SSE $= 572$, and SST $= 593$. In this example it appears that most of the variation is coming from Error, that is, from within groups.

degrees of freedom

Associated with each sum of squares is a quantity called the **degrees of freedom.** Because SST measures the variation of all N observations around the overall mean, its degrees of freedom are DFT $= N - 1$, the degrees of freedom for the sample variance of the N responses. Similarly, because SSG measures the variation of the I sample means around the overall mean, its degrees of freedom are DFG $= I - 1$. Finally, SSE is the sum of squares of the deviations $x_{ij} - \overline{x}_i$. Here we have N observations being compared with I sample means and DFE $= N - I$.

EXAMPLE 14.9 Degrees of Freedom for the Three Sources

CASE 14.1

The DF column in Figure 14.8 gives the values for the three degrees of freedom. These values are DFT $= 65$, DFG $= 2$, and DFE $= 63$.

mean square

For each source of variation, the **mean square** is the sum of squares divided by the degrees of freedom. Generally, the ANOVA table includes mean squares only for the first two sources of variation.

EXAMPLE 14.10 Mean Squares for the Three Sources

CASE 14.1

The MS column in Figure 14.8 gives values for two of the mean squares. These values are MSG = 10.29 and MSE = 9.09.

The mean square corresponding to the total source is the sample variance that we would calculate assuming that we have one sample from a single population—that is, assuming that the means of the three groups are the same.

Sums of Squares, Degrees of Freedom, and Mean Squares

Sums of squares represent variation present in the data. They are calculated by summing squared deviations. In one-way ANOVA there are three **sources of variation:** groups, error, and total. The sums of squares are related by the formula

$$\text{SST} = \text{SSG} + \text{SSE}$$

Thus, the total variation is composed of two parts, one due to groups and one due to "error" (variation within groups).

Degrees of freedom are related to the deviations that are used in the sums of squares. The degrees of freedom are related in the same way as the sums of squares:

$$\text{DFT} = \text{DFG} + \text{DFE}$$

To calculate each **mean square,** divide the corresponding sum of squares by its degrees of freedom.

APPLY YOUR KNOWLEDGE

CASE 14.1 *All of these exercises use the output in Figure 14.8 or the data in Table 14.1.*

14.7 Verify that the SS add. Verify that the sums of squares add, SST = SSG + SSE.

14.8 Check the DF. What are I and N for these data? Verify that the DF entries in the output are DFG $= I - 1$, DFE $= N - I$, and DFT $= N - 1$.

14.9 Do the DF add? Verify that degrees of freedom add in the same way that the sums of squares add. That is, DFT = DFG + DFE.

14.10 Check the MS. Verify that each mean square in the output is the corresponding sum of squares divided by its degrees of freedom.

14.11 Total mean square. The output does not give the total mean square MST = SST/DFT. Calculate this quantity. Then find the mean and variance of all 66 observations in Table 14.1 and verify that MST is the variance of all the responses.

The F test

The ANOVA table also reports the pooled standard error s_p. It is always true that

$$s_p^2 = \text{MSE} = \frac{\text{SSE}}{\text{DFE}}$$

This fact reinforces the idea that MSE measures variation within groups. From the output in Figure 14.8, we can calculate the variance $s_p^2 = 3.014^2 = 9.08$. This is the same as MSE up to roundoff error.

The F statistic is the final entry in the ANOVA table. If H_0 is true, there are no differences among the group means. Then MSG will reflect only chance variation and we expect MSG to be about the same as MSE. The F statistic simply compares these two mean squares, $F = \text{MSG}/\text{MSE}$. This statistic is near 1 if H_0 is true and tends to be larger if H_a is true. In our example, MSG = 10.29 and MSE = 9.09, so the ANOVA F statistic is

$$F = \frac{\text{MSG}}{\text{MSE}} = \frac{10.29}{9.09} = 1.13$$

When H_0 is true, the F statistic has an F distribution that depends upon two numbers: the *degrees of freedom for the numerator* and the *degrees of freedom for the denominator*. These degrees of freedom are those associated with the mean squares in the numerator and denominator of the F statistic. For one-way ANOVA, the degrees of freedom for the numerator are $\text{DFG} = I - 1$ and the degrees of freedom for the denominator are $\text{DFE} = N - I$. We use the notation $F(I - 1, N - I)$ for this distribution.

The ANOVA F Test

To test the null hypothesis in a one-way ANOVA, calculate the F **statistic**

$$F = \frac{\text{MSG}}{\text{MSE}}$$

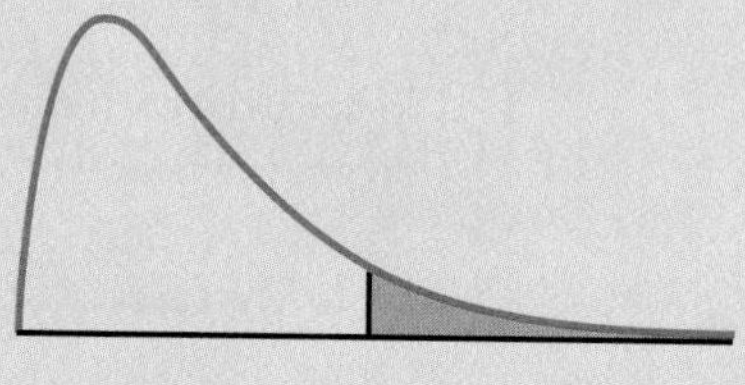

When H_0 is true, the F statistic has the $F(I - 1, N - I)$ distribution. When H_a is true, the F statistic tends to be large. We reject H_0 in favor of H_a if the F statistic is sufficiently large.

The ***P*-value** of the F test is the probability that a random variable having the $F(I - 1, N - I)$ distribution is greater than or equal to the calculated value of the F statistic.

Tables of F critical values are available for use when software does not give the P-value. Table E in the back of the book contains the F critical values for probabilities $p = 0.100, 0.050, 0.025, 0.010$, and 0.001. For one-way ANOVA we use critical values from the table corresponding to $I - 1$ degrees of freedom in the numerator and $N - I$ degrees of freedom in the denominator. We have already seen several examples where the F statistic and its P-value were used to choose between H_0 and H_a.

EXAMPLE 14.11 The Mean GPAs Are Not Identical

p	Critical value
0.100	2.33
0.050	3.04
0.025	3.76
0.010	4.71
0.001	7.15

In the study of computer science students in Example 14.3, $F = 10.35$. There are three populations, so the degrees of freedom in the numerator are DFG $= I - 1 = 2$. The degrees of freedom in the denominator are DFE $= N - I = 256 - 3 = 253$. In Table E first find the column corresponding to 2 degrees of freedom in the numerator. For the degrees of freedom in the denominator, there are entries for 200 and 1000. These entries are very close. To be conservative we use critical values corresponding to 200 degrees of freedom in the denominator since these are slightly larger. Because 10.35 is larger than all of the tabulated values, we reject H_0 and conclude that the differences in means are statistically significant, with $P < 0.001$.

EXAMPLE 14.12 Mean Pretest Scores Do Not Differ Significantly

p	Critical value
0.100	2.39
0.050	3.15
0.025	3.93
0.010	4.98
0.001	7.77

CASE 14.1

For comparing the three teaching methods in Case 14.1, $F = 1.13$. Because there are three populations being compared, the degrees of freedom in the numerator are DFG $= I - 1 = 2$, and the degrees of freedom in the denominator are DFE $= N - I = 66 - 3 = 63$. Table E has entries for 2 degrees of freedom in the numerator. There is no entry for 63 degrees of freedom in the denominator, so we use the slightly larger values corresponding to 60. Because 1.13 is less than any of the tabulated values, we do not have strong evidence in the data against the hypothesis of equal means. We conclude that the differences in sample means are not significant at the 10% level, $P > 0.1$. Statistical software (Figure 14.8) gives the exact value $P = 0.329$.

Remember that the F test is always one-sided because any differences among the group means tend to make F large. The ANOVA F test shares the robustness of the two-sample t test. It is relatively insensitive to moderate non-Normality and unequal variances, especially when the sample sizes are similar.

APPLY YOUR KNOWLEDGE

14.12 Pool the variances. CASE 14.1 Find the variances for the three samples by squaring the standard deviations given in the output in Figure 14.7. Then pool the variances using the formula given on page 800. Verify that this calculation gives the MSE entry in Figure 14.8.

14.13 Use Table E. An ANOVA is run to compare 4 groups. There are 6 observations in each group.

(a) Give the degrees of freedom for the ANOVA F statistic.

(b) How large would this statistic need to be to have a P-value less than 0.05?

14.14 Suppose we had more data. Refer to the previous exercise. Suppose that we are still interested in comparing the 4 groups, but we obtain data on 26 subjects per group. Answer parts (a) and (b) of the previous exercise. Can you explain why the answer to part (b) is smaller than what you found for part (b) of the previous exercise?

Using software

The following display shows the general form of a one-way ANOVA table with the F statistic. The formulas in the sum of squares column can be used for calculations in small problems. There are other formulas that are more efficient for hand or calculator use, but ANOVA calculations are usually done by computer software.

Source	Degrees of freedom	Sum of squares	Mean square	F
Groups	$I - 1$	$\sum_{\text{groups}} n_i(\bar{x}_i - \bar{x})^2$	SSG/DFG	MSG/MSE
Error	$N - I$	$\sum_{\text{groups}} (n_i - 1)s_i^2$	SSE/DFE	
Total	$N - 1$	$\sum_{\text{obs}} (x_{ij} - \bar{x})^2$	SST/DFT	

You should now be able to extract all the ANOVA information we have discussed from output from almost any statistical software. Here is a final example on which to practice this skill.

EXAMPLE 14.13 Advertising and the Quality of a Product

Research suggests that customers think that a product is of high quality if it is heavily advertised. An experiment designed to explore this idea collected quality ratings (on a 1 to 7 scale) of a new line of take-home refrigerated entrées based on reading a magazine ad. Three groups were compared. The first group's ad included information that would undermine (U) the expected positive association between quality and advertising; the second group's ad contained information that would affirm (A) the association; and the third group was a control (C).[4] The data are given in Table 14.2. Outputs from SAS, Excel, and Minitab appear in Figure 14.9.

applet

We recommend the *One-Way ANOVA* applet available on the Web site www.whfreeman.com/pbs as an excellent way to see how the value of the F statistic and its P-value depend on both the variability of the data within the groups and the differences among the group means. Exercises 14.16 and 14.17 make use of this applet.

TABLE 14.2 Quality ratings in three groups

Group	Quality ratings																			
Undermine	6	5	5	5	4	5	4	6	5	5	5	5	3	3	5	4	5	5	5	4
($n = 55$)	5	4	4	5	4	4	4	5	5	5	4	5	5	5	4	4	5	5	4	5
	5	4	4	5	4	3	4	5	5	5	3	4	4	4	4					
Affirm	4	6	4	6	5	5	5	6	4	5	5	5	4	6	6	5	5	7	4	6
($n = 36$)	6	4	5	4	5	5	6	4	5	5	4	6	4	6	5	5				
Control	5	4	5	6	5	7	5	6	7	5	7	5	4	5	4	4	6	6	5	6
($n = 36$)	5	5	4	5	5	6	6	6	5	6	6	7	6	6	5	5				

SAS

```
General Linear Models Procedure

Dependent Variable: QUALITY
                                   Sum of            Mean
Source                DF          Squares          Square  F Value    Pr > F
Model                  2        18.828255        9.414127    15,28    0.0001
Error                124        76.384343        0.616003
Corrected Total      126        95.212598

             R-Square            C.V.        Root MSE        QUALITY Mean
             0.197750        15.94832          0.7849              4.9213

Level of      -----------QUALITY-----------
      GROUP         N        Mean                 SD

      affirm       36      5.05555556         0.82615960
      control      36      5.41666667         0.87423436
      under        55      4.50909091         0.69048365
```

Excel

Anova: Single Factor

SUMMARY

Groups	*Count*	*Sum*	*Average*	*Variance*
affirm	36	182	5.055555556	0.682539683
control	36	195	5.416666667	0.764285714
undermine	55	248	4.509090909	0.476767677

ANOVA

Source of Variation	*SS*	*df*	*MS*	*F*	*P-value*	*F crit*
Between Groups	18.82825499	2	9.414127495	15.28260579	1.16739E-06	3.069286447
Within Groups	76.38434343	124	0.61600277			
Total	95.21259843	126				

(a)

Minitab

One-way ANOVA: Quality versus Group

```
Source      DF      SS      MS      F      P
Group        2  18.828   9.414  15.28  0.000
Error      124  76.384   0.616
Total      126  95.123

S = 0.7849   R-Sq = 19.77%   R-Sq(adj) = 18.48%

                                 Individual 95% CIs For Mean Based on
                                 Pooled StDev
Level       N    Mean   StDev  -------+---------+---------+---------+--
affirm     36  5.0556  0.8262                 (------*-------)
control    36  5.4167  0.8742                           (-------*------)
undermine  55  4.5091  0.6905  (-----*-----)
                               -------+---------+---------+---------+--
                                   4.55      4.90      5.25      5.60

Pooled StDev = 0.7849
```

(b)

FIGURE 14.9 SAS, Excel, and Minitab output for the advertising study of Example 14.13.

APPLY YOUR KNOWLEDGE

14.15 Compare software. The pooled standard error for the data in Table 14.2 is $s_p =$ 0.7849. Look at the software output in Figure 14.9.

(a) Explain to someone new to ANOVA why SAS labels this quantity as "Root MSE."

(b) Excel does not report s_p. How can you find its value from Excel output?

14.16 The effect of within-group variation. Go to the *One-Way ANOVA* applet. In the applet display, the black dots are the mean responses in three treatment groups. Move these up and down until you get a configuration with P-value about 0.01. Note the value of the F statistic. Now increase the variation within the groups without changing their means by dragging the mark on the pooled standard error scale to the right. Describe what happens to the F statistic and the P-value. Explain why this happens.

14.17 The effect of among-group variation. Go to the *One-Way ANOVA* applet. Set the pooled standard error near the middle of its scale and drag the black dots so that the three group means are approximately equal. Note the value of the F statistic and its P-value. Now increase the variation among the group means: drag the mean of the second group up and the mean of the third group down. Describe the effect on the F statistic and its P-value. Explain why they change in this way.

SECTION 14.1 SUMMARY

- **One-way analysis of variance (ANOVA)** is used to compare several population means based on independent SRSs from each population. We assume that the populations are Normal and that, although they may have different means, they have the same standard deviation.
- To do an analysis of variance, first examine the data. Side-by-side boxplots give an overview. Examine Normal quantile plots (either for each group separately or for the residuals) to detect outliers or extreme deviations from Normality. Compute the ratio of the largest to the smallest sample standard deviation. If this ratio is less than 2 and the Normal quantile plots are satisfactory, ANOVA can be performed.
- The **null hypothesis** is that the population means are *all equal*. The **alternative hypothesis** is true if there are *any* differences among the population means.
- ANOVA is based on separating the total variation observed in the data into two parts: variation **among group means** and variation **within groups.** If the variation among groups is large relative to the variation within groups, we have evidence against the null hypothesis.
- An **analysis of variance table** organizes the ANOVA calculations. **Degrees of freedom, sums of squares, and mean squares** appear in the table. The F **statistic** and its P**-value** are used to test the null hypothesis.

14.2 Comparing Group Means

The ANOVA F test gives a general answer to a general question: Are the differences among observed group means significant? Unfortunately, a small P-value simply tells us that the group means are not all the same. It does not tell us specifically which means differ from each other. Plotting and inspecting the means give us some indication of where the differences lie, but we would like to supplement inspection with formal inference. This section presents two approaches to the task of comparing group means.

Contrasts

The preferred approach is to pose specific questions regarding comparisons among the means before the data are collected. We can answer specific questions of this kind and attach a level of confidence to the answers we give. We now explore these ideas through an example.

CASE 14.2 EVALUATION OF THE NEW PRODUCT

Case 14.1 introduces a randomized comparative experiment to compare three methods for teaching reading. We analyzed the pretest scores and found no reason to reject H_0 that the three groups had similar population means on this measure. This was the desired outcome. We now turn to the response variable, a measure of reading comprehension called COMP that was measured by a test taken after the instruction was completed.

The Basal method is the standard method commonly used in schools. Your company will market materials based on two innovative methods, called DRTA and Strat. The DRTA and Strat methods are not identical, but both involve teaching the students to use similar comprehension strategies in their reading. Can you claim that the new methods are superior to Basal?

We can compare new with standard by posing and answering specific questions about the mean responses. First, here is the basic ANOVA.

EXAMPLE 14.14 Are the Comprehension Scores Different?

CASE 14.2

Figure 14.10 gives the summary statistics for COMP computed by SPSS. This software uses only numeric values for the factor, so we coded the groups as 1 for Basal, 2 for DRTA, and 3 for Strat. Side-by-side boxplots appear in Figure 14.11, and Figure 14.12 plots the group means. The ANOVA results generated by SPSS are given in Figure 14.13, and a Normal quantile plot of the residuals appears in Figure 14.14.

FIGURE 14.10 Summary statistics for the comprehension scores in the three groups for the new-product evaluation study.

Descriptives

COMP

	N	Mean	Std. Deviation
1.00	22	41.0455	5.63558
2.00	22	46.7273	7.38842
3.00	22	44.2727	5.76675
Total	66	44.0152	6.64366

FIGURE 14.11 Side-by-side boxplots of the comprehension scores in the new-product evaluation study.

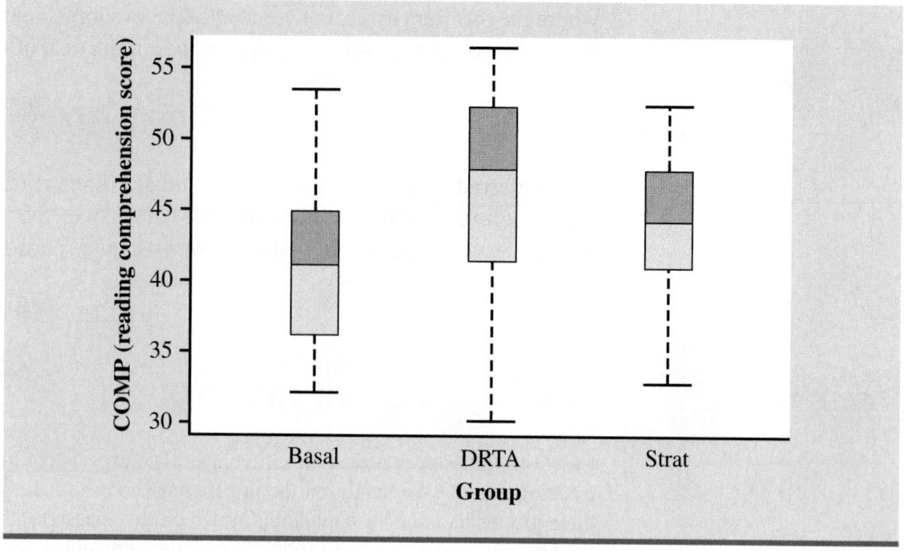

FIGURE 14.12 Comprehension score group means in the new-product evaluation study.

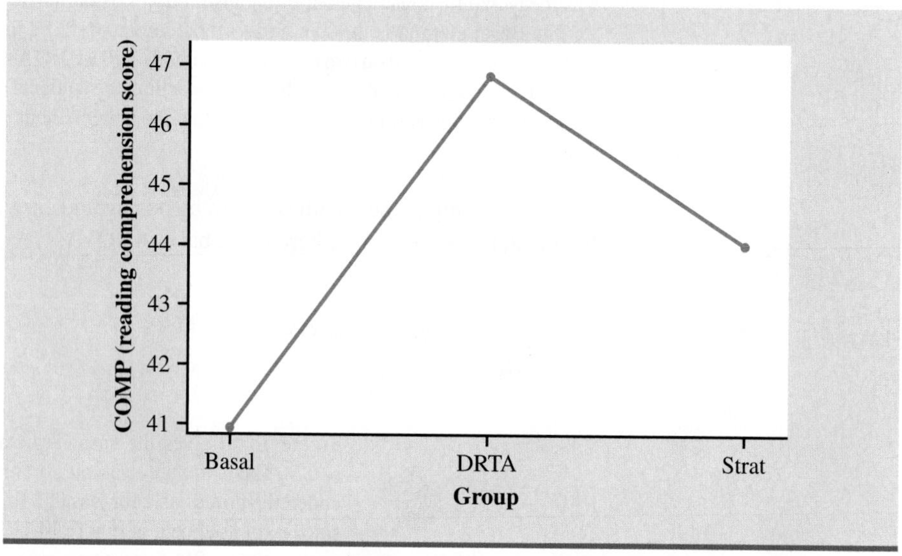

FIGURE 14.13 Analysis of variance output for the comprehension scores in the new-product evaluation study.

ANOVA
COMP

	Sum of Squares	df	Mean Square	F	Sig.
Between Groups	357.303	2	178.652	4.481	0.015
Within Groups	2511.682	63	39.868		
Total	2868.985	65			

The ANOVA null hypothesis is

$$H_0: \mu_B = \mu_D = \mu_S$$

where the subscripts correspond to the group labels Basal, DRTA, and Strat. Figure 14.13 shows that $F = 4.48$ with degrees of freedom 2 and 63. The P-value is 0.015. We have good evidence against H_0.

FIGURE 14.14 Normal quantile plot of the residuals for the comprehension scores in the new-product evaluation study.

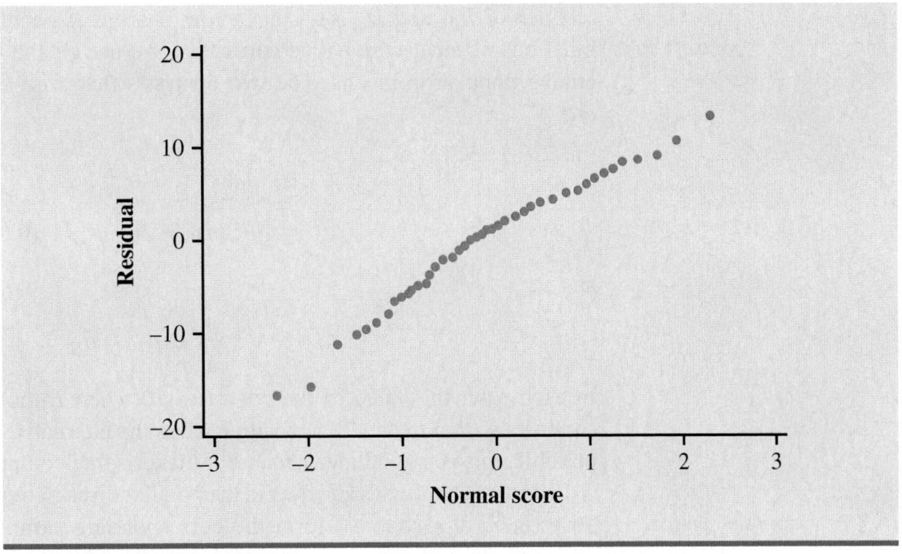

What can the researchers conclude from this analysis? The alternative hypothesis is true if $\mu_B \neq \mu_D$ or if $\mu_B \neq \mu_S$ or if $\mu_D \neq \mu_S$ or if any combination of these statements is true. We would like to be more specific.

EXAMPLE 14.15 The Major Question

CASE 14.2

The two new methods are based on the same idea. Are they superior to the standard method? We can formulate this question as the null hypothesis

$$H_{01}: \frac{1}{2}(\mu_D + \mu_S) = \mu_B$$

with the alternative

$$H_{a1}: \frac{1}{2}(\mu_D + \mu_S) > \mu_B$$

The hypothesis H_{01} compares the average of the two innovative methods (DRTA and Strat) with the standard method (Basal). The alternative is one-sided because the researchers are interested in demonstrating that the new methods are better than the old. We use the subscripts 1 and 2 to distinguish two sets of hypotheses that correspond to two specific questions about the means.

EXAMPLE 14.16 A Secondary Question

CASE 14.2

A secondary question involves a comparison of the two new methods. We formulate this as the hypothesis that the methods DRTA and Strat are equally effective,

$$H_{02}: \mu_D = \mu_S$$

versus the alternative

$$H_{a2}: \mu_D \neq \mu_S$$

contrast ψ

Each of H_{01} and H_{02} says that a combination of population means is 0. These combinations of means are called **contrasts.** We use ψ, the Greek letter psi, for contrasts among population means. The two contrasts that arise from our two null hypotheses are

$$\psi_1 = -\mu_B + \frac{1}{2}(\mu_D + \mu_S)$$
$$= (-1)\mu_B + (0.5)\mu_D + (0.5)\mu_S$$

and

$$\psi_2 = \mu_D - \mu_S$$

In each case, the value of the contrast is 0 when H_0 is true. We chose to define the contrasts so that they will be positive when the alternative hypothesis is true. Whenever possible, this is a good idea because it makes some computations easier.

sample contrast

A contrast expresses an effect in the population as a combination of population means. To estimate the contrast, form the corresponding **sample contrast** by using sample means in place of population means. Under the ANOVA assumptions, a sample contrast is a linear combination of independent Normal variables and therefore has a Normal distribution. We can obtain the standard error of a contrast by using the rules for variances given in Section 4.3. Inference is based on t statistics. Here are the details.

Contrasts

A **contrast** is a combination of population means of the form

$$\psi = \sum a_i \mu_i$$

where the coefficients a_i have sum 0. The corresponding **sample contrast** is the same combination of sample means,

$$c = \sum a_i \bar{x}_i$$

The **standard error of c** is

$$\text{SE}_c = s_p \sqrt{\sum \frac{a_i^2}{n_i}}$$

To test the null hypothesis H_0: $\psi = 0$, use the **t statistic**

$$t = \frac{c}{\text{SE}_c}$$

with degrees of freedom DFE that are associated with s_p. The alternative hypothesis can be one-sided or two-sided.

A **level C confidence interval for ψ** is

$$c \pm t^* \text{SE}_c$$

where t^* is the value for the $t(\text{DFE})$ density curve with area C between $-t^*$ and t^*.

Because each $\overline{x}_i$ estimates the corresponding μ_i, the addition rule for means tells us that the mean μ_c of the sample contrast c is ψ. In other words, c is an unbiased estimator of ψ. Testing the hypothesis that a contrast is 0 assesses the significance of the effect measured by the contrast. It is often more informative to estimate the size of the effect using a confidence interval for the population contrast.

EXAMPLE 14.17 The Coefficients for the Contrasts

CASE 14.2

In our example the coefficients in the contrasts are $a_1 = -1, a_2 = 0.5, a_3 = 0.5$ for ψ_1 and $a_1 = 0, a_2 = 1, a_3 = -1$ for ψ_2, where the subscripts 1, 2, and 3 correspond to B, D, and S. In each case the sum of the a_i is 0.

We look at inference for each of these contrasts in turn.

EXAMPLE 14.18 Are the New Methods Better?

CASE 14.2

The sample contrast that estimates ψ_1 is

$$\begin{aligned} c_1 &= \overline{x}_B + \frac{1}{2}(\overline{x}_D + \overline{x}_S) \\ &= -41.05 + \frac{1}{2}(46.73 + 44.27) = 4.45 \end{aligned}$$

with standard error

$$\begin{aligned} SE_{c_1} &= 6.314\sqrt{\frac{(-1)^2}{22} + \frac{(0.5)^2}{22} + \frac{(0.5)^2}{22}} \\ &= 1.65 \end{aligned}$$

The t statistic for testing H_{01}: $\psi_1 = 0$ versus H_{a1}: $\psi_1 > 0$ is

$$\begin{aligned} t &= \frac{c_1}{SE_{c_1}} \\ &= \frac{4.45}{1.65} = 2.70 \end{aligned}$$

Because s_p has 63 degrees of freedom, software using the $t(63)$ distribution gives the one-sided P-value as 0.0044. If we used Table D, we would conclude that $P < 0.005$. The P-value is small, so there is strong evidence against H_{01}. The researchers have shown that the new methods produce higher mean scores than the old. The size of the improvement can be described by a confidence interval. To find the 95% confidence interval for ψ_1, we combine the estimate with its margin of error:

$$\begin{aligned} c_1 \pm t^* \text{SE}_{c_1} &= 4.45 \pm (2.00)(1.65) \\ &= 4.45 \pm 3.30 \end{aligned}$$

The interval is $(1.15,\ 7.75)$. We are 95% confident that the mean improvement obtained by using one of the innovative methods rather than the old method is between 1.15 and 7.75 points.

EXAMPLE 14.19 Comparing the Two New Methods

CASE 14.2

The second sample contrast, which compares the two new methods, is

$$\begin{aligned} c_2 &= 46.73 - 44.27 \\ &= 2.46 \end{aligned}$$

with standard error

$$\begin{aligned} \text{SE}_{c_2} &= 6.314\sqrt{\frac{(1)^2}{22} + \frac{(-1)^2}{22}} \\ &= 1.90 \end{aligned}$$

The t statistic for assessing the significance of this contrast is

$$t = \frac{2.46}{1.90} = 1.29$$

The P-value for the two-sided alternative is 0.2020. We conclude that either the two new methods have the same population means or the sample sizes are not sufficiently large to distinguish them. A confidence interval helps clarify this statement. To find the 95% confidence interval for ψ_2, we combine the estimate with its margin of error:

$$\begin{aligned} c_2 \pm t^* \text{SE}_{c_2} &= 2.46 \pm (2.00)(1.90) \\ &= 2.46 \pm 3.80 \end{aligned}$$

The interval is $(-1.34,\ 6.26)$. With 95% confidence we state that the difference between the population means for the two new methods is between -1.34 and 6.26.

EXAMPLE 14.20 Using Software

CASE 14.2

Figure 14.15 displays the SPSS output for the analysis of these contrasts. The column labeled "t" gives the t statistics 2.702 and 1.289 for our two contrasts. The degrees of freedom appear in the column labeled "df" and are 63 for each t. The P-values are given in the column with the label "Sig. (2-tailed)." These are correct for two-sided alternative hypotheses. The values are

FIGURE 14.15 Output for contrasts for the comprehension scores in the new-product evaluation study.

Contrast Coefficients

	GROUPN		
Contrast	1.00	2.00	3.00
1	−1	0.5	0.5
2	0	1	−1

Contrast Tests

	Contrast	Value of Contrast	Std. Error	t	df	Sig. (2-tailed)
COMP	1	4.4545	1.64872	2.702	63	0.009
	2	2.4545	1.90378	1.289	63	0.202

0.009 and 0.202. To convert the computer-generated results to apply to our one-sided alternative concerning ψ_1, simply divide the reported P-value by 2 after checking that the value of c is in the direction of H_a (that is, that c is positive).

Some statistical software packages report the test statistics associated with contrasts as F statistics rather than t statistics. These F statistics are the squares of the t statistics described above. The associated P-values are for the two-sided alternatives.

Questions about population means are expressed as hypotheses about contrasts. A contrast should express a specific question that we have in mind when designing the study. When contrasts are formulated before seeing the data, *inference about contrasts is valid whether or not the ANOVA H_0 of equality of means is rejected.* Because the F test answers a very general question, it is less powerful than tests for contrasts designed to answer specific questions. Specifying the important questions before the analysis is undertaken enables us to use this powerful statistical technique.

APPLY YOUR KNOWLEDGE

14.18 Define a contrast. An ANOVA was run with five groups. Give the coefficients for the contrast that compares the average of the means of the first two groups with the average of the means of the last two groups.

14.19 Find the standard error. Refer to the previous exercise. Suppose that there are 25 observations in each group and that $s_p = 10$. Find the standard error for the contrast.

14.20 Is the contrast significant? Refer to the previous exercise. Suppose that the average of the first two groups minus the average of the last two groups is 15. State an appropriate null hypothesis for this comparison, find the test statistic with its degrees of freedom, and report the result.

14.21 Give the confidence interval. Refer to the previous exercises. Give a 95% confidence interval for the difference between the average of the means of the first two groups and the average of the means of the last two groups.

Multiple comparisons

In many studies, specific questions cannot be formulated in advance of the analysis. If H_0 is not rejected, we conclude that the population means are indistinguishable on the

multiple comparisons

basis of the data given. On the other hand, if H_0 is rejected, we would like to know which pairs of means differ. **Multiple-comparisons** methods address this issue. *It is important to keep in mind that multiple-comparisons methods are used only after rejecting the ANOVA* H_0.

Return once more to the reading comprehension study described in Case 14.2. We found in Example 14.14 that the means were not all the same ($F = 4.48$, df $= 2$ and 63, $P = 0.015$).

EXAMPLE 14.21 A *t* Statistic to Compare Two Means

CASE 14.2

There are three pairs of population means. We can compare Groups 1 and 2, Groups 1 and 3, and Groups 2 and 3. For each of these pairs, we can write a t statistic for the difference in means. To compare Basal with DRTA (1 with 2), we compute

$$t_{12} = \frac{\bar{x}_1 - \bar{x}_2}{s_p\sqrt{\dfrac{1}{n_1} + \dfrac{1}{n_2}}}$$

$$= \frac{41.05 - 46.73}{6.31\sqrt{\dfrac{1}{22} + \dfrac{1}{22}}}$$

$$= -2.99$$

The subscripts on t specify which groups are compared.

APPLY YOUR KNOWLEDGE

14.22 Compare Basal with Strat. Verify that $t_{13} = -1.69$.

CASE 14.2

14.23 Compare DRTA with Strat. Verify that $t_{23} = 1.29$. (This is the same t that we used for the contrast $\psi_2 = \mu_2 - \mu_3$ in Example 14.19.)

These t statistics are very similar to the pooled two-sample t statistic for comparing two population means, described in Chapter 7 (page 462). The difference is that we now have more than two populations, so each statistic uses the pooled estimator s_p from all groups rather than the pooled estimator from just the two groups being compared. This additional information about the common σ increases the power of the tests. The degrees of freedom for all of these statistics are DFE $= 63$, those associated with s_p.

Because we do not have any specific ordering of the means in mind as an alternative to equality, we must use a two-sided approach to the problem of deciding which pairs of means are significantly different.

Multiple Comparisons

To perform a **multiple-comparisons procedure,** compute ***t* statistics** for all pairs of means using the formula

$$t_{ij} = \frac{\overline{x}_i - \overline{x}_j}{s_p\sqrt{\dfrac{1}{n_i} + \dfrac{1}{n_j}}}$$

If

$$|t_{ij}| \geq t^{**}$$

we declare that the population means μ_i and μ_j are different. Otherwise, we conclude that the data do not distinguish between them. The value of t^{**} depends upon which multiple-comparisons procedure we choose.

One obvious choice for t^{**} is the upper $\alpha/2$ critical value for the $t(\text{DFE})$ distribution. This choice simply carries out as many separate significance tests of fixed level α as there are pairs of means to be compared. The procedure based on this choice is called the **least-significant differences method,** or simply LSD. LSD has some undesirable properties, particularly if the number of means being compared is large. Suppose, for example, that there are $I = 20$ groups and we use LSD with $\alpha = 0.05$. There are 190 different pairs of means. If we perform 190 t tests, each with an error rate of 5%, our overall error rate will be unacceptably large. We expect about 5% of the 190 to be significant even if the corresponding population means are the same. Since 5% of 190 is 9.5, we expect 9 or 10 false rejections.

LSD method

The LSD procedure fixes the probability of a false rejection for each single pair of means being compared. It does not control the overall probability of *some* false rejection among all pairs. Other choices of t^{**} control possible errors in other ways. The choice of t^{**} is therefore a complex problem, and a detailed discussion of it is beyond the scope of this text. Many choices for t^{**} are used in practice. One major statistical package allows selection from a list of over a dozen choices.

Bonferroni method

We will discuss only one of these, called the **Bonferroni method.** Use of this procedure with $\alpha = 0.05$, for example, guarantees that the probability of *any* false rejection among all comparisons made is no greater than 0.05. This is much stronger protection than controlling the probability of a false rejection at 0.05 for *each separate* comparison.

EXAMPLE 14.22 Which Means Differ?

CASE 14.2

We apply the Bonferroni multiple-comparisons procedure with $\alpha = 0.05$ to the data from the new-product evaluation study in Example 14.14. The value of t^{**} for this procedure (from software or special tables) is 2.46. The t statistic for comparing Basal with DRTA is $t_{12} = -2.99$. Because $|-2.99|$ is greater than 2.46, the value of t^{**}, we conclude that the DRTA method produces higher reading comprehension scores than Basal.

APPLY YOUR KNOWLEDGE

CASE 14.2

14.24 Compare Basal with Strat. The test statistic for comparing Basal with Strat is $t_{13} = -1.69$. For the Bonferroni multiple-comparisons procedure with $\alpha = 0.05$, do you reject the null hypothesis that the population means for these two groups are different?

CASE 14.2

14.25 Compare DRTA with Strat. Answer the same question for the comparison of DRTA with Strat using the calculated value $t_{23} = 1.29$.

Usually we use software to perform the multiple-comparisons procedure. The formats differ from package to package but they all give the same basic information.

EXAMPLE 14.23 Computer Output for Multiple Comparisons

CASE 14.2

The output from SPSS for Bonferroni comparisons appears in Figure 14.16. The first line of numbers gives the results for comparing Basal with DRTA, Groups 1 and 2. The difference between the means is given as -5.6818 with a standard error of 1.90378. The P-value for the comparison is given under the heading "Sig." The value is 0.012. Therefore, we could declare the means for Basal and DRTA to be different according to the Bonferroni procedure as long as we are using a value of α that is less than or equal to 0.012. In particular, these groups are significantly different at the *overall* $\alpha = 0.05$ level. The last two entries in the row give the Bonferroni 95% confidence interval. We will discuss this later.

SPSS does not give the values of the t statistics for multiple comparisons. To compute them, simply divide the difference in the means by the standard error. For comparing Basal with DRTA, we have as before

$$t_{12} = \frac{-5.681}{1.90} = -2.99$$

APPLY YOUR KNOWLEDGE

CASE 14.2

14.26 Compare Basal with Strat. Use the difference in means and the standard error reported in the output of Figure 14.16 to verify that $t_{13} = -1.69$.

Post Hoc Tests

Multiple Comparisons
Dependent Variable: COMP
Bonferroni

(I) GROUP	(J) GROUP	Mean Difference (I-J)	Std. Error	Sig.	95% Confidence Interval Lower Bound	95% Confidence Interval Upper Bound
1.00	2.00	−5.6818	1.90378	0.012	−10.3643	−0.9993
	3.00	−3.2273	1.90378	0.285	−7.9098	1.4552
2.00	1.00	5.6818	1.90378	0.012	0.9993	10.3643
	3.00	2.4545	1.90378	0.606	−2.2280	7.1370
3.00	1.00	3.2273	1.90378	0.285	−1.4552	7.9098
	2.00	−2.4545	1.90378	0.606	−7.1370	2.2280

* The mean difference is significant at the 0.05 level.

FIGURE 14.16 Bonferroni multiple-comparisons output for the comprehension scores in the new-product evaluation study.

14.27 Compare DRTA with Strat. Use the difference in means and the standard error reported in the output of Figure 14.16 to verify that $t_{23} = 1.29$.

CASE 14.2

When there are many groups, the many results of multiple comparisons are difficult to describe. Here is one common format.

EXAMPLE 14.24 Displaying Multiple-Comparisons Results

CASE 14.2

Here is a table of the means and standard deviations for the three treatment groups. To report the results of multiple comparisons, use letters to label the means of pairs of groups that do *not* differ at the overall 0.05 significance level.

Group	Mean	SD	n
Basal	41.05^{A}	2.97	22
DRTA	46.73^{B}	2.65	22
Strat	$44.27^{A,B}$	3.34	22

Label "*A*" shows that Basal and Strat do not differ. Label "*B*" shows that DRTA and Strat do not differ. Because Basal and DRTA do not have a common label, they do differ.

The display in Example 14.24 shows that at the overall 0.05 significance level Basal does not differ from Strat and Strat does not differ from DRTA, yet Basal does differ from DRTA. These conclusions appear to be illogical. If μ_1 is the same as μ_3, and μ_3 is the same as μ_2, doesn't it follow that μ_1 is the same as μ_2? Logically, the answer must be Yes.

This apparent contradiction points out dramatically the nature of the conclusions of tests of significance. A careful statement would say that we found significant evidence that Basal differs from DRTA and failed to find evidence that Basal differs from Strat or that Strat differs from DRTA. Failing to find strong enough evidence that two means differ doesn't say that they are equal. It is very unlikely that any two methods of teaching reading comprehension would give *exactly* the same population means, but the data can fail to provide good evidence of a difference. This is particularly true in multiple-comparisons methods such as Bonferroni that use a single α for an entire set of comparisons.

APPLY YOUR KNOWLEDGE

14.28 Which means differ significantly? Here is a table of means for a one-way ANOVA with five groups:

Group	Mean	SD	n
Group 1	146.4	22.3	30
Group 2	152.1	20.8	30
Group 3	155.8	19.8	30
Group 4	123.5	22.3	30
Group 5	127.0	22.5	30

According to the Bonferroni multiple-comparisons procedure with $\alpha = 0.05$, the means for the following pairs of groups do not differ significantly: 1 and 2, 1 and 3, 2 and 3, 4 and 5. Mark the means of each pair of groups that do *not* differ significantly with the same letter. Summarize the results.

14.29 The groups can overlap. Refer to the previous exercise. Here is a similar table of means:

Group	Mean	SD	n
Group 1	150.2	19.1	30
Group 2	121.9	18.3	30
Group 3	129.2	18.4	30
Group 4	140.8	22.1	30
Group 5	117.2	20.6	30

According to the Bonferroni multiple-comparisons procedure with $\alpha = 0.05$, the means for the following pairs of groups do not differ significantly: 1 and 4, 2 and 3, 2 and 5, 3 and 4, 3 and 5. Mark the means of each pair of groups that do *not* differ significantly with the same letter. Summarize the results.

Simultaneous confidence intervals

simultaneous confidence intervals

One way to deal with these difficulties of interpretation is to give confidence intervals for the differences. The intervals remind us that the differences are not known exactly. We want to give **simultaneous confidence intervals,** that is, intervals for all the differences among the population means with confidence (say) 95% that *all the intervals at once* cover the true population differences. Again, there are many competing procedures—in this case, many methods of obtaining simultaneous intervals.

Simultaneous Confidence Intervals for Differences between Means

Simultaneous confidence intervals for all differences $\mu_i - \mu_j$ between population means have the form

$$(\overline{x}_i - \overline{x}_j) \pm t^{**} s_p \sqrt{\frac{1}{n_i} + \frac{1}{n_j}}$$

The critical values t^{**} are the same as those used for the multiple-comparisons procedure chosen.

The confidence intervals generated by a particular choice of t^{**} are closely related to the multiple-comparisons results for that same method. If one of the confidence intervals includes the value 0, then that pair of means will not be declared significantly different, and vice versa.

EXAMPLE 14.25 Software Output for Confidence Intervals

CASE 14.2

For simultaneous 95% Bonferroni confidence intervals, SPSS gives the output in Figure 14.16 for the data in Case 14.2. We are 95% confident that *all three* intervals simultaneously contain the true values of the population mean differences. After rounding the output, the confidence interval for the difference between the mean of the Basal group and the mean of the DRTA group is (−10.4, −1.0). This interval does not include zero, so we conclude that the DRTA method results in higher mean comprehension scores than the Basal method. This is the same conclusion that we obtained from the significance test, but the confidence interval provides us with additional information about the size of the difference.

APPLY YOUR KNOWLEDGE

14.30 Confidence interval for Basal versus Strat. Refer to the output in Figure 14.16. CASE 14.2 Give the Bonferroni 95% confidence interval for the difference between the mean comprehension score for the Basal method and the mean comprehension score for the Strat method. Be sure to round the numbers from the output in an appropriate way. Does the interval include 0?

14.31 Confidence interval for DRTA versus Strat. Refer to the previous exercise. CASE 14.2 Give the interval for comparing DRTA with Strat. Does the interval include 0?

SECTION 14.2 SUMMARY

- The ANOVA F test does not say which of the group means differ. It is therefore usual to add comparisons among the means to basic ANOVA.
- Specific questions formulated before examination of the data can be expressed as **contrasts.** Tests and confidence intervals for contrasts provide answers to these questions.
- If no specific questions are formulated before examination of the data and the null hypothesis of equality of population means is rejected, **multiple-comparisons** methods are used to assess the statistical significance of the differences between pairs of means. These methods are less powerful than contrasts, so use contrasts whenever a study is designed to answer specific questions.

14.3 The Power of the ANOVA Test*

The power of a test is the probability of rejecting H_0 when H_a is in fact true. Power measures how likely a test is to detect a specific alternative. When planning a study in which ANOVA will be used for the analysis, it is important to perform power calculations to check that the sample sizes are adequate to detect differences among means that are judged to be important. Power calculations also help evaluate and interpret the results of studies in which H_0 was not rejected. We sometimes find that the power of the test was so low against reasonable alternatives that there was little chance of obtaining a significant F.

In Chapter 7 we found the power for the two-sample t test. One-way ANOVA is a generalization of the two-sample t test, so it is not surprising that the procedure for calculating power is quite similar. Here are the steps that are needed:

1. Specify

   (a) an alternative (H_a) that you consider important; that is, values for the true population means $\mu_1, \mu_2, \ldots, \mu_I$;

*This section is optional.

(b) sample sizes $n_1, n_2, \ldots, n_I$; in a preliminary study, these are usually all set equal to a common value n;

(c) a level of significance α, usually equal to 0.05; and

(d) a guess at the standard deviation σ.

2. Find the degrees of freedom DFG $= I - 1$ and DFE $= N - I$ and the critical value that will lead to rejection of H_0. This value, which we denote by F^*, is the upper α critical value for the F(DFG, DFE) distribution.

noncentrality parameter

3. Calculate the **noncentrality parameter**[5]

$$\lambda = \frac{\sum n_i(\mu_i - \overline{\mu})^2}{\sigma^2}$$

where $\overline{\mu}$ is a weighted average of the group means,

$$\overline{\mu} = \sum w_i \mu_i$$

and the weights are proportional to the sample sizes,

$$w_i = \frac{n_i}{\sum n_i} = \frac{n_i}{N}$$

noncentral F distribution

4. Find the power, which is the probability of rejecting H_0 when the alternative hypothesis is true, that is, the probability that the observed F is greater than F^*. Under H_a, the F statistic has a distribution known as the **noncentral F distribution.** This requires special software. SAS, for example, has a function for the noncentral F distribution. Using this function, the power is

$$\text{Power} = 1 - \text{PROBF}(F^*, \text{DFG}, \text{DFE}, \lambda)$$

The noncentrality parameter λ measures how far apart the means μ_i are. If the n_i are all equal to a common value n, $\overline{\mu}$ is the ordinary average of the μ_i and

$$\lambda = \frac{n\sum(\mu_i - \overline{\mu})^2}{\sigma^2}$$

If the means are all equal (the ANOVA H_0), then $\lambda = 0$. Large λ points to an alternative far from H_0, and we expect the ANOVA F test to have high power. Software makes calculation of the power quite easy, but tables and charts are also available.

EXAMPLE 14.26 The Effect of Fewer Subjects

CASE 14.2

The reading comprehension study described in Cases 14.1 and 14.2 had 22 subjects in each group. Suppose that a similar study has only 10 subjects per group. How likely is this study to detect differences in the mean responses that are similar in size to those observed in the actual study?

Based on the results of the actual study, we will calculate the power for the alternative $\mu_1 = 41$, $\mu_2 = 47$, $\mu_3 = 44$, with $\sigma = 7$. The n_i are equal, so $\overline{\mu}$ is simply the average of the μ_i:

$$\overline{\mu} = \frac{41 + 47 + 44}{3} = 44$$

The noncentrality parameter is therefore

$$\lambda = \frac{n\sum(\mu_i - \overline{\mu})^2}{\sigma^2}$$

$$= \frac{(10)[(41 - 44)^2 + (47 - 44)^2 + (44 - 44)^2]}{49}$$

$$= \frac{(10)(18)}{49} = 3.67$$

Because there are three groups with 10 observations per group, DFG = 2 and DFE = 27. The critical value for $\alpha = 0.05$ is $F^* = 3.35$. The power is therefore

$$1 - \text{PROBF}(3.35, 2, 27, 3.67) = 0.3486$$

The chance that we reject the ANOVA H_0 at the 5% significance level is only about 35%.

If the assumed values of the μ_i in this example describe differences among the groups that the experimenter wants to detect, then we would want to use more than 10 subjects per group. Although H_0 is false for these μ_i, the chance of rejecting it at the 5% level is only about 35%. This chance can be increased to acceptable levels by increasing the sample sizes.

EXAMPLE 14.27 Choosing the Sample Size for a Future Study

CASE 14.2

To decide on an appropriate sample size for the experiment described in the previous example, we repeat the power calculation for different values of n, the number of subjects in each group. Here are the results:

n	DFG	DFE	F^*	λ	Power
20	2	57	3.16	7.35	0.65
30	2	87	3.10	11.02	0.84
40	2	117	3.07	14.69	0.93
50	2	147	3.06	18.37	0.97
100	2	297	3.03	36.73	≈ 1

With $n = 40$ the experimenters have a 93% chance of rejecting H_0 with $\alpha = 0.05$ and thereby demonstrating that the groups have different means. In the long run, 93 out of every 100 such experiments would reject H_0 at the $\alpha = 0.05$ level of significance. Using 50 subjects per group increases the chance of finding significance to 97%. With 100 subjects per group, the experimenters are virtually certain to reject H_0. The exact power for $n = 100$ is 0.99989. In most real-life situations the additional cost of increasing the sample size from 50 to 100 subjects per group would not be justified by the relatively small increase in the chance of obtaining statistically significant results.

APPLY YOUR KNOWLEDGE

14.32 Power calculations for planning a study. You are planning a study of the SAT Mathematics scores of four groups of students. From Example 14.3, we know that the standard deviations for the three groups considered in that study were 86, 67, and 83. In Example 14.5, we found the pooled standard error to be 82.5. Since the power of the F test decreases as the standard deviation increases, use $\sigma = 86$ for the calculations in this exercise. This choice will lead to sample sizes that are perhaps a little larger than we need but will prevent us from choosing sample sizes that are too small to detect the effects of interest. You would like to conclude that the population means are different when $\mu_1 = 625$, $\mu_2 = 600$, $\mu_3 = 580$, and $\mu_4 = 560$.

(a) Pick several values for n (the number of students that you will select from each group) and calculate the power of the ANOVA F test for each of your choices.

(b) Plot the power versus the sample size. Describe the general shape of the plot.

(c) What choice of n would you choose for your study? Give reasons for your answer.

14.33 Power against a different alternative. Refer to the previous exercise. Repeat all parts for the alternative $\mu_1 = 615$, $\mu_2 = 600$, $\mu_3 = 590$, and $\mu_4 = 580$.

SECTION 14.3 SUMMARY

- The **power** of the F test depends upon the sample sizes, the variation among population means, and the within-group standard deviations. Some software allows easy calculation of power.

STATISTICS IN SUMMARY

Advanced statistical inference often concerns relationships among several parameters. This chapter introduces the ANOVA F test for one such relationship: equality of the means of any number of populations. The alternative to this hypothesis is "many-sided," because it allows any relationship other than "all equal." The ANOVA F test is an overall test that tells us whether the data give good reason to reject the hypothesis that all the population means are equal. Contrasts are used to answer specific questions about group means that can be formulated before the data are collected. When this is not possible, we use a multiple-comparisons procedure to determine which groups differ significantly whenever the overall F test rejects the null hypothesis that all groups have the same mean. You should always accompany the ANOVA by data analysis to see what kind of inequality is present. Plotting the data in all groups side by side is particularly helpful. After studying this chapter, you should be able to do the following.

A. Recognition

1. Recognize when testing the equality of several means is helpful in understanding data.
2. Recognize that the statistical significance of differences among sample means depends on the sizes of the samples and on how much variation there is within the samples.
3. Recognize when you can safely use ANOVA to compare means. Check the data production, the presence of outliers, and the sample standard deviations for the groups you want to compare.

4. Recognize when to use contrasts and multiple comparisons.
5. Recognize when it is appropriate to compute power for a one-way ANOVA.

B. Interpreting ANOVA

1. Explain what null hypothesis F tests in a specific setting.
2. Locate the F statistic and its P-value on the output of a computer ANOVA program.
3. Find the degrees of freedom for the F statistic from the number and sizes of the samples. Use Table E of F critical values to approximate the P-value when software does not give it.
4. If the F test is significant, use graphs and descriptive statistics to see what differences among the means are most important.
5. Formulate contrasts and analyze them using software.
6. Use multiple comparisons to determine pairs of group means that differ significantly.

CHAPTER 14 Review Exercises

For Exercises 14.1 and 14.2, see page 799; for 14.3 and 14.4, see pages 800–801; for 14.5, see page 803; for 14.6, see page 805; for 14.7 to 14.11, see page 807; for 14.12 to 14.14, see page 809; for 14.15 to 14.17, see page 812; for 14.18 to 14.21, see page 819; for 14.22 and 14.23, see page 820; for 14.24 and 14.25, see page 822; for 14.26 and 14.27, see pages 822–823; for 14.28 and 14.29, see pages 823–824; for 14.30 and 14.31, see page 825; and for 14.32 and 14.33, see page 828.

14.34 What's wrong? For each of the following, explain what is wrong and why.

(a) The ANOVA F statistic tests the null hypothesis that three sample means are equal.

(b) The mean squares in an ANOVA table will add, that is, MST = MSG + MSE.

(c) Within-group variation is the variation in the data due to the differences in the sample means.

14.35 What's wrong? For each of the following, explain what is wrong and why.

(a) Use one-way ANOVA when the response variable has only two possible values.

(b) You cannot use one-way ANOVA when there are more than three means to be compared.

(c) The pooled estimate s_p is a parameter of the ANOVA model.

14.36 How large does the F statistic need to be? For each of the following situations, state how large the F statistic needs to be for rejection of the null hypothesis at the 0.05 level.

(a) Compare 6 groups with 2 observations per group.

(b) Compare 6 groups with 4 observations per group.

(c) Compare 6 groups with 11 observations per group.

(d) Summarize what you have learned about F distributions from this exercise.

14.37 Use the F statistic. A study compared 4 groups with 11 observations per group. An F statistic of 3.52 was reported.

(a) Give the degrees of freedom for this statistic and the entries from Table E that correspond to this distribution.

(b) Sketch a picture of this F distribution with the information from the table included.

(c) Based on the table information, how would you report the P-value?

(d) Can you conclude that all pairs of means are different? Explain your answer.

14.38 Sketch the ANOVA model. For each of the following situations, draw a picture of the ANOVA model similar to Figure 14.5 (page 798). Use numerical values for the μ_i. To sketch the Normal curves, you may want to review the 68–95–99.7 rule on page 56.

(a) $\mu_1 = 10$, $\mu_2 = 25$, $\mu_3 = 24$, and $\sigma = 5$.

(b) $\mu_1 = 10$, $\mu_2 = 20$, $\mu_3 = 30$, $\mu_4 = 30.1$, and $\sigma = 5$.

(c) $\mu_1 = 10$, $\mu_2 = 25$, $\mu_3 = 24$, and $\sigma = 2$.

14.39 Use the F statistic. For each of the following situations, find the F statistic and the degrees of freedom. Then draw a sketch of the distribution under the null hypothesis and shade in the portion corresponding to the P-value. State how you would report the P-value.

(a) Compare 5 groups with 8 observations per group, MSE = 50, and MSG = 57.

(b) Compare 3 groups with 7 observations per group, SSG = 40, and SSE = 90.

14.40 The ANOVA framework. For each of the following situations, identify the response variable and the populations to be compared, and give I, the n_i, and N.

(a) The effects of six different treatments designed to make fabrics stronger were compared. A batch of 120 samples of cloth was available for the experiment, and an equal number were randomly assigned to each of the treatments. The breaking strength of each cloth sample was measured.

(b) A waiter designed a study to see the effects of his behaviors on the tip amounts that he received. For some customers, he would tell a joke; for others, he would describe two of the food items as being particularly good that night; and for others he would behave normally. Using a table of random numbers, he assigned equal numbers of his next 30 customers to his different behaviors.

(c) A supermarket wants to compare the effects of providing free samples of cheddar cheese on sales. An experiment will be conducted from 5:00 P.M. to 6:00 P.M. for the next 20 weekdays. On each day, customers will be offered one of the following: a small cube of cheese pierced by a toothpick, a small slice of cheese on a cracker, a cracker with no cheese, or nothing.

14.41 The ANOVA framework. For each of the following situations, identify the response variable and the populations to be compared, and give I, the n_i, and N.

(a) Last semester, an alcohol awareness program was conducted for three groups of students at an eastern university. Follow-up questionnaires were sent to the participants two months after each presentation. There were 220 responses from students in an elementary statistics course, 145 from a health and safety course, and 76 from a cooperative housing unit. One of the questions was "Did you discuss the presentation with any of your friends?" The answers were rated on a five-point scale with 1 corresponding to "not at all" and 5 corresponding to "a great deal."

(b) A study examined the effects of consuming three different varieties of onions on blood cholesterol levels. Five crossbred (Large White by Landrace) pigs were randomly assigned to each treatment.

(c) A researcher for a video game developer wanted to evaluate a prototype of a new game. Free copies were given to 25 eighth-graders, 25 third-year high school students, and 25 second-year college students who were regular video game players. Two weeks later they were asked to report how much they liked the game on a 1 to 10 scale.

14.42 Provide some details. Refer to Exercise 14.40. For each situation, give the following:

(a) Degrees of freedom for the model, for error, and for the total.

(b) Null and alternative hypotheses.

(c) Numerator and denominator degrees of freedom for the F statistic.

14.43 Provide some details. Refer to Exercise 14.41. For each situation, give the following:

(a) Degrees of freedom for the model, for error, and for the total.

(b) Null and alternative hypotheses.

(c) Numerator and denominator degrees of freedom for the F statistic.

14.44 How much can you generalize? Refer to Exercise 14.40. For each situation, discuss the method of obtaining the data and how this would affect the extent to which the results could be generalized.

14.45 How much can you generalize? Refer to Exercise 14.41. For each situation, discuss the method of obtaining the data and how this would affect the extent to which the results could be generalized.

14.46 Pooling variances. An experiment was run to compare four groups. The sample sizes were 30, 22, 180, and 25, and the corresponding estimated standard deviations were 20, 21, 10, and 19.

(a) Is it reasonable to use the assumption of equal standard deviations when we analyze these data? Give a reason for your answer.

(b) Give the values of the variances for the four groups.

(c) Find the pooled variance.

(d) What is the value of the pooled standard deviation?

(e) Explain why your answer in part (c) is much closer to the standard deviation for the third group than to any of the other standard deviations.

14.47 Pooling variances. An experiment was run to compare three groups. The sample sizes were 20, 18, and 15, and the corresponding estimated standard deviations were 220, 190, and 200.

(a) Is it reasonable to use the assumption of equal standard deviations when we analyze these data? Give a reason for your answer.

(b) Give the values of the variances for the three groups.

(c) Find the pooled variance.

(d) What is the value of the pooled standard deviation?

14.48 Does sleep deprivation affect your work? Sleep deprivation experienced by physicians during residency training and the possible negative consequences are of concern to many in the health care community. One study of 33 resident anesthesiologists compared their changes from baseline in reaction times on four tasks.[6] Under baseline conditions, the physicians reported getting an average of 7.04 hours of sleep. While on duty, however, the average was 1.66 hours. For each of the tasks the researchers reported a statistically significant increase in the reaction time when the residents were working in a state of sleep deprivation.

(a) If each task is analyzed separately as the researchers did in their report, what is the appropriate statistical method to use? Explain your answer.

(b) Is it appropriate to use a one-way ANOVA with $I = 4$ to analyze these data? Explain why or why not.

14.49 ADA and exams. The Americans with Disabilities Act (ADA) requires that students with learning disabilities (LD) and/or attention deficit disorder (ADD) be given certain accommodations when taking examinations. One study designed to assess the effects of these accommodations examined the relationship between end-of-term grades and the number of accommodations given.[7] The researchers reported the mean grades with sample sizes and standard deviations versus the number of accommodations in a table similar to this.

Accommodations	Mean grade	n	s
0	2.7894	160	0.85035
1	2.8605	38	0.83068
2	2.5757	37	0.82745
3	2.6286	7	1.03072
4	2.4667	3	1.66233
Total	2.7596	245	0.85701

(a) Plot the means versus the number of accommodations. Is there a pattern evident?

(b) A large number of digits are reported for the means and the standard deviations. Do you think that all of these are necessary? Give reasons for your answer and describe how you would report these results.

(c) Should we pool to obtain an estimate of an assumed standard deviation for these data? Explain your answer and give the pooled estimate if your answer is Yes.

(d) The small numbers of observations with 3 or 4 accommodations lead to estimates that are highly variable in these groups compared with the other groups. Inclusion of groups with relatively few observations in an ANOVA can also lead to low power. We could eliminate these two levels from the analysis or we could combine them with the 37 observations in the group above to form a new group with 2 or more accommodations. Which of these options would you prefer? Give reasons for your answer.

(e) The 245 grades reported in the table were from a sample of 61 students who completed three, four, or five courses during a spring term at one college and who were qualified to receive accommodations. Students in the sample were self-identified, in the sense that they had to request qualification. Even when qualified, some students choose not to request accommodations for some or all of their courses. Based on these facts, would you advise that ANOVA methods be used for these data? Explain your answer. (The authors did not present the results of an ANOVA in their publication.)

(f) To what extent do you think the results of this study can be generalized to other settings? Give reasons for your answer.

(g) Most reasonable approaches to the analysis of these data would conclude that the data fail to provide evidence that the number of accommodations is related to the mean grades. Does this imply that the accommodations are not needed or does it suggest that they are ineffective? Discuss your answer.

14.50 Emotions and cultures of college students. Do people from different cultures experience emotions differently? One study designed to examine this question collected data from 416 college students from five different cultures.[8] The participants were asked to record, on a 1 (never) to 7 (always) scale, how much of the time they typically felt eight specific emotions. These were averaged to produce the global emotion score for each participant. Here is a summary of this measure:

Culture	n	Mean (s)
European American	46	4.39 (1.03)
Asian American	33	4.35 (1.18)
Japanese	91	4.72 (1.13)
Indian	160	4.34 (1.26)
Hispanic American	80	5.04 (1.16)

Note that the convention of giving the standard deviations in parentheses after the means saves a great deal of space in a table such as this.

(a) From the information given, do you think that we need to be concerned that a possible lack of Normality in the data will invalidate the conclusions that we might draw using ANOVA to analyze the data? Give reasons for your answer.

(b) Is it reasonable to used a pooled standard deviation for these data? Why or why not?

(c) The ANOVA F statistic was reported as 5.69. Give the degrees of freedom and either an approximate (from a table) or an exact (from software) P-value. Sketch a picture of the F distribution that illustrates the P-value. What do you conclude?

(d) Without doing any additional formal analysis, describe the pattern in the means that appears to be responsible for your conclusion in part (c). Are there pairs of means that are quite similar?

14.51 **A different measure of emotions.** Refer to the previous exercise. The experimenters also measured emotions in some different ways. For a period of a week, each participant carried a device that sounded an alarm at random times during a 3-hour interval 5 times a day. When the alarm sounded, participants recorded several mood ratings indicating their emotions for the time immediately preceding the alarm. These responses were combined to form two variables: frequency, the number of emotions recorded, expressed as a percent; and intensity, an average of the intensity scores measured on a scale of 0 to 6. At the end of the 1-week experimental period, the subjects were asked to recall the percent of time that they experienced different emotions. This variable was called "recall." Here is a summary of the results:

Culture	n	Frequency mean (s)	Intensity mean (s)	Recall mean (s)
European American	46	82.87 (18.26)	2.79 (0.72)	49.12 (22.33)
Asian American	33	72.68 (25.15)	2.37 (0.60)	39.77 (23.24)
Japanese	91	73.36 (22.78)	2.53 (0.64)	43.98 (22.02)
Indian	160	82.71 (17.97)	2.87 (0.74)	49.86 (21.60)
Hispanic American	80	92.25 (8.85)	3.21 (0.64)	59.99 (24.64)
F statistic		11.89	13.10	7.06

(a) For each response variable state whether or not it is reasonable to use a pooled standard deviation to analyze these data. Give reasons for your answer.

(b) Give the degrees of freedom for the F statistics and find the associated P-values. Summarize what you can conclude from these ANOVA analyses.

(c) Summarize the means, paying particular attention to similarities and differences across cultures and across variables. Include the means from the previous exercise in your summary.

(d) The European American and Asian American subjects were from the University of Illinois, the Japanese subjects were from two universities in Tokyo, the Indian subjects were from eight universities in or near Calcutta, and the Hispanic American subjects were from California State University at Fresno. Participants were paid \$25 or an equivalent monetary incentive for the Japanese and Indians. Ads were posted on or near the campuses to recruit volunteers for the study. Discuss how these facts influence your conclusions and the extent to which you would generalize the results.

(e) The percents of female students in the samples were as follows: European American, 83%; Asian American, 67%; Japanese, 63%; Indian, 64%; and Hispanic American, 79%. Use a chi-square test to compare these proportions (see Section 9.2) and discuss how this information influences your interpretation of the results that you have found in this exercise.

14.52 **Do poets die young?** According to William Butler Yeats, "She is the Gaelic muse, for she gives inspiration to those she persecutes. The Gaelic poets die young, for she is restless, and will not let them remain long on earth." One study designed to investigate this issue examined the age at death for writers from different cultures and genders.[9] Three

TABLE 14.3 Age at death for women writers

Type	Age at death									
Novels	57	90	67	56	90	72	56	90	80	74
($n = 67$)	73	86	53	72	86	82	74	60	79	80
	79	77	64	72	88	75	79	74	85	71
	78	57	54	50	59	72	60	77	50	49
	73	39	73	61	90	77	57	72	82	54
	62	74	65	83	86	73	79	63	72	85
	91	77	66	75	90	35	86			
Poems	88	69	78	68	72	60	50	47	74	36
($n = 32$)	87	55	68	75	78	85	69	38	58	51
	72	58	84	30	79	90	66	45	70	48
	31	43								
Nonfiction	74	86	87	68	76	73	63	78	83	86
($n = 24$)	40	75	90	47	91	94	61	83	75	89
	77	86	66	97						

categories of writers examined were novelists, poets, and nonfiction writers. The ages at death for female writers in these categories from North America are given in Table 14.3. Most of the writers are from the United States, but Canadian and Mexican writers are also included.

(a) Use graphical and numerical methods to describe the data.

(b) Examine the assumptions necessary for ANOVA. Summarize your findings.

(c) Run the ANOVA and report the results.

(d) Use a contrast to compare the poets with the two other types of writers. Do you think that the quote from Yeats justifies the use of a one-sided alternative for examining this contrast? Explain your answer.

(e) Use another contrast to compare the novelists with the nonfiction writers. Explain your choice for an alternative hypothesis for this contrast.

(f) Use a multiple-comparisons procedure to compare the three means. How do the conclusions from this approach compare with those using the contrasts?

14.53 A natural product can help bones. Kudzu is a plant that was imported to the United States from Japan and now covers over seven million acres in the South. The plant contains chemicals called isoflavones that have been shown to have beneficial effects on bones. One study used three groups of rats to compare a control group with rats that were fed either a low dose or a high dose of isoflavones from kudzu.[10] One of the outcomes examined was the bone mineral density in the femur (in grams per square centimeter). Below are the data.

(a) Use graphical and numerical methods to describe the data.

(b) Examine the assumptions necessary for ANOVA. Summarize your findings.

(c) Run the ANOVA and report the results.

Treatment	Bone mineral density (g/cm^2)							
Control	0.228	0.207	0.234	0.220	0.217	0.228	0.209	0.221
	0.204	0.220	0.203	0.219	0.218	0.245	0.210	
Low dose	0.211	0.220	0.211	0.233	0.219	0.233	0.226	0.228
	0.216	0.225	0.200	0.208	0.198	0.208	0.203	
High dose	0.250	0.237	0.217	0.206	0.247	0.228	0.245	0.232
	0.267	0.261	0.221	0.219	0.232	0.209	0.255	

(d) Use a multiple-comparisons method to compare the three groups.

(e) Write a short report explaining the effect of kudzu isoflavones on the femur of the rat.

14.54 Does a product lose value when stored? Does bread lose its vitamins when stored? Small loaves of bread were prepared with flour that was fortified with a fixed amount of vitamins. After baking, the vitamin C content of two loaves was measured. Another two loaves were baked at the same time, stored for one day, and then the vitamin C content was measured. In a similar manner, two loaves were stored for three, five, and seven days before measurements were taken. The units are milligrams per hundred grams of flour (mg/100 g).[11] Here are the data:

Condition	Vitamin C (mg/100 g)	
Immediately after baking	47.62	49.79
One day after baking	40.45	43.46
Three days after baking	21.25	22.34
Five days after baking	13.18	11.65
Seven days after baking	8.51	8.13

(a) Give a table of the sample sizes, means, and standard deviations for the five conditions.

(b) Perform a one-way ANOVA for these data. State hypotheses and give the test statistic, its degrees of freedom, and the P-value.

(c) Summarize the data and the means with a plot. Use the plot and the ANOVA results to write a short summary of your conclusions.

14.55 Compare the means. Refer to the previous exercise. Use the Bonferroni or another multiple-comparisons procedure to compare the group means. Summarize the results.

14.56 Two other vitamins in the product. Refer to Exercise 14.54. Measurements of the amounts of vitamin A (beta-carotene) and vitamin E in each loaf are given below. Use an analysis of variance to study the data for each of these vitamins.

Condition	Vitamin A (mg/100 g)		Vitamin E (mg/100 g)	
Immediately after baking	3.36	3.34	94.6	96.0
One day after baking	3.28	3.20	95.7	93.2
Three days after baking	3.26	3.16	97.4	94.3
Five days after baking	3.25	3.36	95.0	97.7
Seven days after baking	3.01	2.92	92.3	95.1

14.57 Multiple comparisons. Refer to the previous exercise.

(a) Explain why it is inappropriate to perform a multiple-comparisons analysis for the vitamin E data.

(b) Perform the Bonferroni or another multiple-comparisons procedure for the vitamin A data and summarize the results.

14.58 Write a report. In Exercises 14.54 to 14.57 you have studied vitamin loss in bread stored after baking. Write a report summarizing the overall findings. Include appropriate statistical inference results and graphs.

14.59 Promotions and the expected price of a product. If a supermarket product is frequently offered at a reduced price, do customers expect the price of the product to be lower in the future? This question was examined by researchers in a study conducted on students enrolled in an introductory management course at a large midwestern university. For 10 weeks, 160 subjects read weekly ads for the same product. Students were randomly assigned to read 1, 3, 5, or 7 ads featuring price promotions during the 10-week period. They were then asked to estimate what the product's price would be the following week.[12] Table 14.4 gives the data.

(a) Make a Normal quantile plot for the data in each of the four treatment groups. Summarize the information in the plots and draw a conclusion regarding the Normality of these data.

(b) Summarize the data with a table containing the sample size, mean, and standard deviation for each group.

(c) Is the assumption of equal standard deviations reasonable here? Explain why or why not.

(d) Carry out a one-way ANOVA. Give the hypotheses, the test statistic with its degrees of freedom, and the P-value. Summarize your conclusion.

14.60 Compare the means. Refer to the previous exercise. Use the Bonferroni or another multiple-comparisons procedure to compare the group means. Summarize the results and support your conclusions with a graph of the means.

14.61 Piano lessons and spatial-temporal reasoning. Do piano lessons improve the spatial-temporal reasoning of preschool children? In Exercise 7.84 (page 470) we examined this question by comparing the change scores (after treatment minus before treatment) of 34 children who took piano lessons with the scores

TABLE 14.4 Price promotion data

Number of promotions	Expected price (dollars)									
1	3.78	3.82	4.18	4.46	4.31	4.56	4.36	4.54	3.89	4.13
	3.97	4.38	3.98	3.91	4.34	4.24	4.22	4.32	3.96	4.73
	3.62	4.27	4.79	4.58	4.46	4.18	4.40	4.36	4.37	4.23
	4.06	3.86	4.26	4.33	4.10	3.94	3.97	4.60	4.50	4.00
3	4.12	3.91	3.96	4.22	3.88	4.14	4.17	4.07	4.16	4.12
	3.84	4.01	4.42	4.01	3.84	3.95	4.26	3.95	4.30	4.33
	4.17	3.97	4.32	3.87	3.91	4.21	3.86	4.14	3.93	4.08
	4.07	4.08	3.95	3.92	4.36	4.05	3.96	4.29	3.60	4.11
5	3.32	3.86	4.15	3.65	3.71	3.78	3.93	3.73	3.71	4.10
	3.69	3.83	3.58	4.08	3.99	3.72	4.41	4.12	3.73	3.56
	3.25	3.76	3.56	3.48	3.47	3.58	3.76	3.57	3.87	3.92
	3.39	3.54	3.86	3.77	4.37	3.77	3.81	3.71	3.58	3.69
7	3.45	3.64	3.37	3.27	3.58	4.01	3.67	3.74	3.50	3.60
	3.97	3.57	3.50	3.81	3.55	3.08	3.78	3.86	3.29	3.77
	3.25	3.07	3.21	3.55	3.23	2.97	3.86	3.14	3.43	3.84
	3.65	3.45	3.73	3.12	3.82	3.70	3.46	3.73	3.79	3.94

of 44 children who did not. The latter group actually contained three groups of children: 10 were given singing lessons, 20 had some computer instruction, and 14 received no extra lessons. The data appear in Table 14.5.

(a) Make a table giving the sample size, mean, and standard deviation for each group.

(b) Analyze the data using one-way analysis of variance. State the null and alternative hypotheses, the test statistic with degrees of freedom, the P-value, and your conclusion.

14.62 Compare the means. Refer to the previous exercise. Use the Bonferroni or another multiple-comparisons procedure to compare the group means. Summarize the results and support your conclusions with a graph of the means.

14.63 A contrast. The researchers in Exercise 14.61 based their research on a biological argument for a causal

TABLE 14.5 Piano lesson data

Lessons	Scores									
Piano	2	5	7	−2	2	7	4	1	0	7
	3	4	3	4	9	4	5	2	9	6
	0	3	6	−1	3	4	6	7	−2	7
	−3	3	4	4						
Singing	1	−1	0	1	−4	0	0	1	0	−1
Computer	0	1	1	−3	−2	4	−1	2	4	2
	2	2	−3	−3	0	2	0	−1	3	−1
None	5	−1	7	0	4	0	2	1	−6	0
	2	−1	0	−2						

link between music and spatial-temporal reasoning. It is therefore natural to test the contrast that compares the mean of the piano lesson group with the average of the three other means. Construct this contrast, perform the significance test, and summarize the results. Note that this is not the test that we performed in Exercise 7.84 (page 470), where we did not differentiate among the three groups who did not receive piano instruction.

14.64 Exercise and healthy bones. Many studies have suggested that there is a link between exercise and healthy bones. Exercise stresses the bones and this causes them to get stronger. One study examined the effect of jumping on the bone density of growing rats.[13] There were three treatments: a control with no jumping, a low-jump condition (the jump height was 30 centimeters), and a high-jump condition (60 centimeters). After 8 weeks of 10 jumps per day, 5 days per week, the bone density of the rats (expressed in mg/cm^3) was measured. Here are the data:

Group	Bone density (mg/cm^3)									
Control	611	621	614	593	593	653	600	554	603	569
Low jump	635	605	638	594	599	632	631	588	607	596
High jump	650	622	626	626	631	622	643	674	643	650

(a) Make a table giving the sample size, mean, and standard deviation for each group of rats. Is it reasonable to pool the variances?

(b) Carry out an analysis of variance. Report the F statistic with its degrees of freedom and P-value. What do you conclude?

14.65 Residuals and multiple comparisons. Refer to the previous exercise.

(a) Examine the residuals. Is the Normality assumption reasonable for these data?

(b) Use the Bonferroni or another multiple-comparisons procedure to determine which pairs of means differ significantly. Summarize your results in a short report. Be sure to include a graph.

14.66 Cooking pots and dietary iron. Iron-deficiency anemia is the most common form of malnutrition in developing countries, affecting about 50% of children and women and 25% of men. Iron pots for cooking foods had traditionally been used in many of these countries, but they have been largely replaced by aluminum pots, which are cheaper and lighter. Some research has suggested that food cooked in iron pots will contain more iron than food cooked in other types of pots. One study designed to investigate this issue compared the iron content of some Ethiopian foods cooked in aluminum, clay, and iron pots.[14] One of the foods was *yesiga wet'*, beef cut into small pieces and prepared with several Ethiopian spices. The iron content of four samples of *yesiga wet'* cooked in each of the three types of pots is given below. The units are milligrams of iron per 100 grams of cooked food.

Type of pot	Iron (mg/100 g food)			
Aluminum	1.77	2.36	1.96	2.14
Clay	2.27	1.28	2.48	2.68
Iron	5.27	5.17	4.06	4.22

(a) Make a table giving the sample size, mean, and standard deviation for each type of pot. Is it reasonable to pool the variances? Note that with the small sample sizes in this experiment, we expect a large amount of variability in the sample standard deviations.

(b) Carry out the analysis of variance. Report the F statistic with its degrees of freedom and P-value. What do you conclude?

14.67 Residuals and multiple comparisons. Refer to the previous exercise.

(a) Examine the residuals. Is the Normality assumption reasonable for these data?

(b) Use the Bonferroni or another multiple-comparisons procedure to determine which pairs of means differ significantly. Summarize your results in a short report. Be sure to include a graph.

14.68 A new material to repair wounds. One way to repair serious wounds is to insert some material as a scaffold for the body's repair cells to use as a template for new tissue. Scaffolds made from extracellular material (ECM) are particularly promising for this purpose. Because ECMs are biological material, they serve as an effective scaffold and are then absorbed. Unlike biological material that includes cells, ECMs do not trigger tissue rejection reactions in the body. One study compared 6 types of scaffold material.[15] Three of these were ECMs and the other three were made of inert materials. The subjects were three mice per scaffold type. The response measure was the percent of glucose phosphated isomerase (Gpi) cells in the region of the wound. A large value is good, indicating the presence of many bone marrow cells sent by the body to repair the tissue. Here are the data:

Material	Gpi (%)		
ECM1	55	70	70
ECM2	60	65	65
ECM3	75	70	75
MAT1	20	25	25
MAT2	5	10	5
MAT3	10	15	10

(a) Make a table giving the sample size, mean, and standard deviation for each of the six types of material. Is it reasonable to pool the variances? Note that the sample sizes are small and the data are rounded.

(b) Run the analysis of variance. Report the F statistic with its degrees of freedom and P-value. What do you conclude?

14.69 Residuals and multiple comparisons. Refer to the previous exercise.

(a) Examine the residuals. Is the Normality assumption reasonable for these data?

(b) Use the Bonferroni or another multiple-comparisons procedure to determine which pairs of means differ significantly. Summarize your results in a short report. Be sure to include a graph.

14.70 A contrast. Refer to the previous two exercises. Use a contrast to compare the three ECM materials with the three other materials. Summarize your conclusions. How do these results compare with those that you obtained from the multiple-comparisons procedure in the previous exercise?

14.71 What colors attract beetles? The presence of harmful insects in farm fields is detected by erecting boards covered with a sticky material and then examining the insects trapped on the board. To investigate which colors are most attractive to cereal leaf beetles, researchers placed six boards of each of four colors in a field of oats in July.[16] The table below gives data on the number of cereal leaf beetles trapped:

Color	Insects trapped					
Lemon yellow	45	59	48	46	38	47
White	21	12	14	17	13	17
Green	37	32	15	25	39	41
Blue	16	11	20	21	14	7

(a) Make a table of means and standard deviations for the four colors, and plot the means.

(b) State H_0 and H_a for an ANOVA on these data, and explain in words what ANOVA tests in this setting.

(c) Using computer software, run the ANOVA. What is the value of s_p? What are the F statistic and its P-value? What do you conclude?

14.72 Multiple comparisons. Return to the previous exercise. For the Bonferroni procedure with $\alpha = 0.05$, the value of t^{**} is 2.61. Use this multiple-comparisons procedure to decide which pairs of colors are significantly different. Summarize your results. Which color would you recommend for attracting cereal leaf beetles?

14.73 Exercise and fitness. A study of the effects of exercise on physiological and psychological variables compared four groups of male subjects. The treatment group (T) consisted of 10 participants in an exercise program. A control group (C) of 5 subjects volunteered for the program but were unable to attend for various reasons. Subjects in the other two groups were selected to be similar to those in the first two groups in age and other characteristics. These were 11 joggers (J) and 10 sedentary people (S) who did not regularly exercise.[17] One of the variables measured at the end of the program was a physical fitness score. Here is part of the ANOVA table for these data:

Source	Degrees of freedom	Sum of squares	Mean square	F
Groups	3	104,855.87		
Error	32	70,500.59		
Total				

(a) Fill in the missing entries in the ANOVA table.

(b) State H_0 and H_a for this experiment.

(c) What is the distribution of the F statistic under the assumption that H_0 is true? Using Table E, give an approximate P-value for the ANOVA test. Write a brief conclusion.

(d) What is s_p^2, the estimate of the within-group variance? What is the pooled standard error s_p?

14.74 Exercise and depression. Another variable measured in the experiment described in the previous exercise was a depression score. Higher values of this score indicate more depression. Here is part of the ANOVA table for these data:

Source	Degrees of freedom	Sum of squares	Mean square	F
Groups	3		158.96	
Error	32		62.81	
Total				

(a) Fill in the missing entries in the ANOVA table.

(b) State H_0 and H_a for this experiment.

(c) What is the distribution of the F statistic under the assumption that H_0 is true? Using Table E, give an approximate P-value for the ANOVA test. What do you conclude?

(d) What is s_p^2, the estimate of the within-group variance? What is s_p?

14.75 Weight gain during pregnancy. The weight gain of women during pregnancy has an important effect on the birth weight of their children. If the weight gain is not adequate, the infant is more likely to be small and will tend to be less healthy. In a study conducted in three countries, weight gains (in kilograms) of women during the third trimester of pregnancy were measured.[18] The results are summarized in the following table:

Country	n	$\bar{x}$	s
Egypt	46	3.7	2.5
Kenya	111	3.1	1.8
Mexico	52	2.9	1.8

(a) Find the pooled estimate of the within-country variance s_p^2. What entry in an ANOVA table gives this quantity?

(b) The sum of squares for countries (groups) is 17.22. Use this information and that given above to construct an ANOVA table.

(c) State H_0 and H_a for this study.

(d) What is the distribution of the F statistic under the assumption that H_0 is true? Use Table E to find an approximate P-value for the significance test. Report your conclusion.

14.76 Food intake. In another part of the study described in the previous exercise, measurements of food intake in kilocalories were taken on many individuals several times during the period of a year. From these data, average daily food intake values were computed for each individual. The results for toddlers aged 18 to 30 months are summarized in the following table:

Country	n	$\bar{x}$	s
Egypt	88	1217	327
Kenya	91	844	184
Mexico	54	1119	285

(a) Find the pooled estimate of the within-country variance s_p^2. What entry in an ANOVA table gives this quantity?

(b) The sum of squares for countries (groups) is 6,572,551. Use this information and that given above to construct an ANOVA table.

(c) State H_0 and H_a for this study.

(d) What is the distribution of the F statistic under the assumption that H_0 is true? Use Table E to find an approximate P-value for the significance test. Report your conclusion.

14.77 Writing contrasts. Refer to the change-of-majors study described in Example 14.3 (page 795). Let μ_1, μ_2, and μ_3 represent the population mean SAT Mathematics scores for the three groups.

(a) Because the first two groups (computer science, engineering and other sciences) are majoring in areas that require mathematics skills, it is natural to compare the average of these two with the third group. Write an expression in terms of the μ_i for a contrast ψ_1 that represents this comparison.

(b) Let ψ_2 be a contrast that compares the first two groups. Write an expression in terms of the μ_i for ψ_2 that represents this comparison.

14.78 Writing contrasts. Return to the survey of college students described in Example 14.4 (page 798). Let μ_1, μ_2, μ_3, and μ_4 represent the population mean expenditures on textbooks for the freshmen, sophomores, juniors, and seniors.

(a) Because juniors and seniors take higher-level courses, which might use more expensive textbooks, we want to compare the average of the freshmen and sophomores with the average of the juniors and seniors. Write a contrast that expresses this comparison.

(b) Write a contrast for comparing the freshmen with the sophomores.

(c) Write a contrast for comparing the juniors with the seniors.

14.79 Analyzing contrasts. Return to the SAT Mathematics scores for the change-of-majors study in Example 14.3 (page 795). Answer the following questions for the two contrasts that you defined in Exercise 14.77.

(a) For each contrast give H_0 and an appropriate H_a. In choosing the alternatives you should use information given in the description of the problem, but you may not consider any impressions obtained by inspection of the sample means.

(b) Find the values of the corresponding sample contrasts c_1 and c_2.

(c) Using the value $s_p = 82.5$, calculate the standard errors s_{c_1} and s_{c_2} for the sample contrasts.

(d) Give the test statistics and approximate P-values for the two significance tests. What do you conclude?

(e) Compute 95% confidence intervals for the two contrasts.

14.80 High school grades and changing majors. The following table presents data on the high school mathematics grades of the students in the change-of-majors study described in Example 14.3 (page 795). The sample sizes in this exercise are different from those in Example 14.3 because complete information was not available on all students. The grades have been coded so that 10 = A, 9 = A−, and so on.

Second-year major	n	$\bar{x}$	s
Computer science	90	8.77	1.41
Engineering and other sciences	28	8.75	1.46
Other	106	7.83	1.74

The two contrasts that you defined in Exercise 14.77 naturally lead to questions about high school mathematics grades.

(a) For each contrast state H_0 and an appropriate H_a. In choosing the alternatives you should use information given in the description of the problem, but you may not consider any impressions obtained by inspection of the sample means.

(b) Find the values of the corresponding sample contrasts c_1 and c_2.

(c) Using the value $s_p = 1.581$, calculate the standard errors s_{c_1} and s_{c_2} for the sample contrasts.

(d) Give the test statistics and approximate P-values for the two significance tests. What do you conclude?

(e) Compute 95% confidence intervals for the two contrasts.

14.81 Contrasts for exercise and fitness. In the exercise program study described in Exercise 14.73, the summary statistics for physical fitness scores are as follows:

Group	n	$\bar{x}$	s
Treatment (T)	10	291.91	38.17
Control (C)	5	308.97	32.07
Joggers (J)	11	366.87	41.19
Sedentary (S)	10	226.07	63.53

The researchers wanted to address the following questions for the physical fitness scores. In these questions "better" means a higher fitness score. (1) Is T better than C? (2) Is T better than the average of C and S? (3) Is J better than the average of the other three groups?

(a) For each of the three questions, define an appropriate contrast. Translate the questions into null and alternative hypotheses about these contrasts.

(b) Test your hypotheses and give approximate P-values. Summarize your conclusions. Do you think that the use of contrasts in this way gives an adequate summary of the results?

(c) You found that the groups differ significantly in the physical fitness scores. Does this study allow conclusions about causation—for example, that a sedentary lifestyle causes people to be less physically fit? Explain your answer.

14.82 Contrasts for exercise and depression. Exercise 14.74 gives the ANOVA table for depression scores from the exercise program study described in Exercise 14.73. Here are the summary statistics for the depression scores:

Group	n	$\bar{x}$	s
Treatment (T)	10	51.90	6.42
Control (C)	5	57.40	10.46
Joggers (J)	11	49.73	6.27
Sedentary (S)	10	58.20	9.49

In planning the experiment, the researchers wanted to address the following questions for the depression scores. In these questions "better" means a lower depression score. (1) Is T better than C? (2) Is T better than the average of C and S? (3) Is J better than the average of the other three groups?

(a) For each of the three questions, define an appropriate contrast. Translate the questions into null and alternative hypotheses about these contrasts.

(b) Test your hypotheses and give approximate P-values. Summarize your conclusions. Do you think that the use of contrasts in this way gives an adequate summary of the results?

(c) You found that the groups differ significantly in the depression scores. Does this study allow conclusions about causation—for example, that a sedentary lifestyle causes people to be more depressed? Explain your answer.

14.83 Multiple comparisons for exercise and fitness. Refer to the physical fitness scores for the four groups in the exercise program study discussed in Exercises 14.73 and 14.81. Computer software gives the critical value for the Bonferroni multiple-comparisons procedure with $\alpha = 0.05$ as $t^{**} = 2.81$. Use this procedure to compare the mean fitness scores for the four groups. Summarize your conclusions.

14.84 Multiple comparisons for exercise and depression. Refer to the depression scores for the four groups in the exercise program study discussed in Exercises 14.74 and 14.82. Computer software gives the critical value for the Bonferroni multiple-comparisons procedure with $\alpha = 0.05$ as $t^{**} = 2.81$. Use this procedure to compare the mean depression scores for the four groups. Summarize your conclusions.

14.85 Power for weight gain during pregnancy (optional). You are planning a study of the weight gains of women during the third trimester of pregnancy similar to that described in Exercise 14.75. The standard deviations given in that exercise range from 1.8 to 2.5. To perform power calculations, assume that the standard deviation is $\sigma = 2.4$. You have three groups, each with n subjects, and you would like to reject the ANOVA H_0 when the alternative $\mu_1 = 2.6$, $\mu_2 = 3.0$, and $\mu_3 = 3.4$ is true. Use software to make a table of powers against this alternative (similar to the table in Example 14.27, page 827) for the following numbers of women in each group: $n = 50$, 100, 150, 175, and 200. What sample size would you choose for your study?

14.86 More power (optional). Repeat the previous exercise for the alternative $\mu_1 = 2.7$, $\mu_2 = 3.1$, and $\mu_3 = 3.5$. Why are the results the same?

14.87 Transform amounts to percents. Refer to Exercise 14.54 (page 834), where we studied the effects of storage on the vitamin C content of bread. In this experiment 64 mg/100 g of vitamin C was added to the flour that was used to make each loaf.

(a) Convert the vitamin C amounts (mg/100 g) to percents of the amounts originally in the loaves by dividing the amounts in Exercise 14.54 by 64 and multiplying by 100. Calculate the transformed means, standard deviations, and standard errors and summarize them with the sample sizes in a table.

(b) Explain how you could have calculated the table entries directly from the table you gave in part (a) of Exercise 14.54.

(c) Analyze the percents using analysis of variance. Compare the test statistic, degrees of freedom, P-value, and conclusion you obtain here with the corresponding values that you found in Exercise 14.54.

14.88 Changing units and ANOVA. Refer to the previous exercise. Suggest a general conclusion about what happens to the F test statistic, degrees of freedom, P-value, and conclusion when you perform analysis of variance on data after changing the units of measurement. (A change of units is a linear transformation that multiplies each observation by the same positive constant and perhaps adds another constant.)

14.89 The effect of an outlier. Refer to the color attractiveness experiment described in Exercise 14.71 (page 837). Suppose that when entering the data into the computer, you accidentally entered the first observation as 450 rather than 45.

(a) Run the ANOVA with the incorrect observation. Summarize the results.

(b) Compare this run with the results obtained with the correct data set. What does this illustrate about the effect of outliers in an ANOVA?

(c) Compute a table of means and standard deviations for each of the four treatments using the incorrect data. How does this table help you to detect the incorrect observation?

14.90 Try a transformation. Refer to the color attractiveness experiment described in Exercise 14.71 (page 837). The square root transformation is often used for variables that are counts, such as the number of insects trapped in this example. In many cases data transformed in this way will conform more closely to the assumptions of Normality and equal standard deviations.

(a) Make a table of the new data after taking square roots. Find the group means and standard deviations. Are the standard deviations of the transformed data more nearly equal than those of the original data?

(b) Carry out the ANOVA for the transformed data. Compare your conclusions with the original ANOVA in Exercise 14.71.

14.91 Regression or ANOVA? Refer to the price promotion study that we examined in Exercise 14.59 (page 834). The explanatory variable in this study is the number of price promotions in a 10-week period, with possible values of 1, 3, 5, and 7. ANOVA treats the explanatory variable as categorical—it just labels the groups to be compared. In this study the explanatory variable is in fact quantitative, so we could use simple linear regression rather than one-way ANOVA if there is a linear pattern.

(a) Make a scatterplot of the responses against the explanatory variable. Is the pattern roughly linear?

(b) In ANOVA, the F test null hypothesis states that groups have no effect on the mean response. What test in regression tests the null hypothesis that the explanatory variable has no linear relationship with the response?

(c) Carry out the regression. Compare your results with those from the ANOVA in Exercise 14.59. Are there any reasons—perhaps from part (a)—to prefer one or the other analysis?

CHAPTER 14 Case Study Exercises

CASE STUDY 1: Compare three products for treating dandruff. Analysis of variance methods are often used to compare different products. In medical settings, studies to assess the effectiveness of one or more treatments for a particular medical condition are often called *clinical trials*. A clinical trial compared the effectiveness of three products and a placebo in reducing dandruff. The products were 1% pyrithione zinc shampoo (PyrI), the same shampoo but with instructions to shampoo two times (PyrII), 2% ketoconazole shampoo (Keto), and a placebo shampoo (Placebo). After six weeks of treatment, eight sections of the scalp were examined and given a score that measured the amount of scalp flaking on a 0 to 10 scale. The response variable was the sum of these eight scores.

An analysis of the baseline flaking measure indicated that randomization of patients to treatments was successful in that no differences were found among the groups. At baseline there were 112 subjects in each of the three treatment groups and 28 subjects in the Placebo group. During the clinical trial, 3 dropped out from the PyrII group and 6 from the Keto group. No patients dropped out of the other two groups. The data are given in the DANDRUFF data set described in the Data Appendix. Analyze the data using the methods you learned in this chapter. Be sure to include numerical and graphical summaries, a detailed explanation of the statistical model used, and a summary of all results. Include an analysis of the residuals to examine the assumptions of your model. Include an analysis of the following contrasts: (1) Placebo versus the average of the three treatments; (2) Keto versus the average of the two Pyr treatments; and (3) PyrI versus PyrII.

CASE STUDY 2: Compare the three educational products. Cases 14.1 (page 802) and 14.2 (page 813) compare pretest and posttest reading comprehension scores for three different products designed to teach reading to young children. In the actual study there were 2 pretest measures and 3 posttest measures. The data are given in the READING data set described in the Data Appendix. The pretest variable analyzed in Case 14.1 is Pre1 and the posttest variable analyzed in Case 14.2 is Post3. Analyze the other pretest variable and the other 2 posttest variables. Use the exercises in the text to guide your analyses. Summarize the results for all 5 variables in a report. In particular, do the pretests show that the three groups of subjects were similar at the start of the study? Do the posttests point to one or more of the teaching methods as more effective than the others?

CHAPTER 14 Appendix

Using Minitab and Excel for One-Way Analysis of Variance

One-Way ANOVA Analysis

Minitab:

Stat ➤ ANOVA ➤ One-Way

With this pull-down sequence, you should have two worksheet columns. One column should contain all the response data from all the groups. The other column should contain distinct labels (numerical or text) for each group that indicate for a given row which group the corresponding data observation comes from. Given this setup, click the data column into the **Response** box, and click the column of labels into the **Factor** box. Residuals and fitted values from the ANOVA analysis can be stored in the worksheet by selecting the **Store residuals** and **Store fits** options. To make multiple comparisons, click the **Comparisons** button. By means of computing simultaneous confidence intervals, Minitab offers four different methods (Tukey's, Fisher's, Dunnett's, and Hsu's) for making multiple comparisons. Fisher's method is the least-significant differences (LSD) method noted in this chapter. Minitab, however, does not offer the Bonferroni method also discussed in this chapter. For making simultaneous confidence intervals for all the differences among the population means, Tukey's method is typically recommended as the best choice among the methods offered by Minitab. You will notice that Tukey's method is the default selection. In the adjacent box, notice that the overall α ("family error rate") is set to 5%. If you wish to change this overall rate, input the rate in percentage units (for example, input "10" for overall $\alpha = 0.10$). Click **OK** to close the pop-up box and then click **OK** to find one-way ANOVA output in the Session window.

Minitab offers another means to obtain one-way ANOVA results with the following pull-down sequence:

Stat ➤ ANOVA ➤ One-Way (Unstacked)

This routine is used if the data for each group are stored in separate columns, as opposed to the data all being in one column. Click all the data columns into the **Responses (in separate columns)** box. All other aspects of this routine are similar to the just-described one-way ANOVA routine.

Excel:

Data from a given group can be either grouped in a column (that is, observations inputted in one column going down the rows) or grouped in a row (that is, observations inputted in one row going across columns). In either case, the data from one group to the next group must be adjacent (that is, in adjacent columns or adjacent rows). To perform one-way ANOVA, select "Anova: Single Factor" in the **Data Analysis** menu box and click **OK.** Enter the cell range of the data into the **Input Range** box. Click **OK.** Multiple-comparisons methods are not available in standard Excel but they are available in the enhanced add-on version of Excel.

Power (ANOVA Test)

Minitab:

Stat ➤ Power and Sample Size ➤ One-Way ANOVA

Once you have invoked this routine, you can specify values for any two of the following three dialog boxes: **Sample sizes, Values of the maximum difference between means,** or **Power values.** Minitab, in turn, will compute the item not specified. For example, if we wish to compute the power for the ANOVA test, then we would input the group sample sizes and the maximum difference between the smallest and largest means found in the particular alternative of interest. In the case of Example 14.26, we only need to input the value "10" in the **Sample sizes** box (since sample sizes are equal) and input the value of "6" (= 47 − 41) in the **Values of the maximum difference between means** box. This routine can also be used to determine what minimal sample size is required to have a desired power in relation to a particular alternative. In addition to providing values for two of the three dialog boxes, you must input the number of groups in the **Number of levels** box and the estimate for population standard deviation (σ) in the **Standard deviation** box. If you wish to change the value of α from the default value of 0.05, then click the **Options** button and input your desired significance level in the **Significance level** box. Click **OK** to close the pop-up box and then click **OK** to find results reported in the Session window. Additionally, Minitab will produce a "Power Curve," which is simply a graph of the different power values against a range of maximum-difference values.

Excel:

Automated power calculations for ANOVA are not available in standard Excel or the enhanced add-on version of Excel. Furthermore, since the noncentral F distribution is not available in Excel, computing the power by that means is not an option.

NOTES AND DATA SOURCES

Preface

1. This consensus is expressed in a report of the joint curriculum committee of the American Statistical Association and the Mathematical Association of America, a summary of which was unanimously endorsed by the ASA Board of Directors. The full report is George Cobb, "Teaching statistics," in L. A. Steen (ed.), *Heeding the Call for Change: Suggestions for Curricular Action,* Mathematical Association of America, 1990, pp. 3–43. Another broad discussion of the current state of the first course in statistics, with discussion by leading statisticians from industry as well as academia, is David S. Moore and discussants, "New pedagogy and new content: the case of statistics," *International Statistical Review,* 65 (1997), pp. 123–165.

2. See, for example, Joan Garfield and Andrew Ahlgren, "Difficulties in learning basic concepts in probability and statistics: implications for research," *Journal for Research in Mathematics Education*, 19 (1988), pp. 44–63.

3. L. Knuesel, "On the accuracy of statistical distributions in Microsoft Excel 97," *Computational Statistics and Data Analysis,* 26 (1998), pp. 375–377. B. D. McCullough and Berry Wilson, "On the accuracy of statistical procedures in Microsoft Excel 97," *Computational Statistics and Data Analysis,* 31 (1999), pp. 27–31.

Introduction

1. The rise of statistics from the physical, life, and behavioral sciences is described in detail by S. M. Stigler, *The History of Statistics: The Measurement of Uncertainty before 1900,* Harvard-Belknap, 1986. Much of the information in the brief historical notes appearing throughout the text is drawn from this book.

Chapter 1

1. Based on news articles in the *New York Times* of April 18, 1992, and September 10, 1992.

2. The Firestone data are derived from information posted on the National Highway Traffic Safety Administration (NHTSA) Web site, `www.nhtsa.dot.gov/`.

3. Pareto charts are named for the Italian economist Vilfredo Pareto (1848–1923). Pareto was one of the first to analyze economic problems with mathematical tools. The Pareto Principle (sometimes called the 80/20 rule) takes various forms, such as "80% of the work is done by 20% of the people." Pareto charts are a graphical version of the principle—the chart identifies the few important categories (the 20%) that account for most of the responses (the 80%). Of course, in any given setting, the actual percents will vary.

4. Data from the Iowa State University Fact Book based on fall semester enrollment for 1999. Found online at `www.public.iastate.edu/~inst_res_info/factbk.html`.

5. Occupational fatalities data from the Bureau of Labor Statistics Web site, `www.bls.gov`.

6. Our eyes do respond to area, but not quite linearly. It appears that we perceive the ratio of two bars to be about the 0.7 power of the ratio of their actual areas. See W. S. Cleveland, *The Elements of Graphing Data,* Wadsworth, 1985, pp. 278–284.

7. Data from the U.S. Department of Energy, *Model Year 2001 Fuel Economy Guide,* `www.epa.gov/OMSWWW/`.

8. From a table entitled "Largest Indianapolis-Area Architectural Firms," *Indianapolis Business Journal,* September 20–26, 1999.

9. Data from the Web site of Professor Kenneth French of Dartmouth, `mba.tuck.dartmouth.edu/pages/faculty/ken.french/data_library.html`.

10. From the Web site of the Bureau of Labor Statistics, `www.bls.gov/cpi`. Detailed data such as these can be found under "Customized Tables."

11. From the Web site of Professor Kenneth French of Dartmouth; see Note 9.

12. Press release for the 2003 DuPont Automotive Color Survey, at `www.automotive.dupont.com`.

13. Robyn Greenspan, "The deadly duo: spam and viruses, October 2003," at `cyberatlas.internet.com`.

14. National Climatic Data Center, storm events database. Found at `sciencepolicy.colorado.edu/sourcebook/tornadoes.html`.

15. Found online at `earthtrends.wri.org`.

16. From the Bureau of Labor Statistics Web site, `www.bls.gov/data`.

17. Centers for Disease Control and Prevention, *Births and Deaths: Preliminary Data for 1997,* Monthly Vital Statistics Reports, 47, No. 4, 1998.

18. Hurricane data from H. C. S. Thom, *Some Methods of Climatological Analysis,* World Meteorological Organization, 1966.

19. Data from the August 2000 supplement to the Current Population Survey, from the Census Bureau Web site, `www.census.gov`.

20. Wage data for Table 1.11 are from the Bureau of Labor Statistics, `stat.bls.gov/oes/` under November 2004 Occupational Employment and Wage Estimates.

21. See Note 20.

22. *Extreme Weather Sourcebook 2001,* at `sciencepolicy.colorado.edu/sourcebook`.

23. Douglas Fore, "Do we have a retirement crisis in America?" TIAA-CREF Institute *Research Dialogue* No. 77, 2003. The data are for the year 2001.

24. Data from the March 2002 annual demographic supplement to the Current Population Survey, downloaded from `www.bls.census.gov/cps`.

25. Scott DeCarlo, Michael Schubach, and Vladimir Naumovski, "A decade of new issues," *Forbes,* March 5, 2001.

26. Data from the U.S. Department of Energy; see Note 7.

27. From *GMAT Examinee Score Interpretation Guide,* Graduate Management Admissions Council, 2000. Found online at `www.gmac.com`.

28. Data provided by Charles Hicks, Purdue University.

29. Data provided by the city of Ames, Iowa, `www.city.ames.ia.us/assessorweb/assessorpages/CommercialSales.htm`.

30. A subset of data posted at Damodaran Online, `http://pages.stern.nyu.edu/~adamodar/`.

31. Data tracked by The Conference Board, `www.conference-board.org`.

32. Based on Antoni Basinski, "Almost never on Sunday: implications of the patterns of admission and discharge for common conditions," Institute for Clinical Evaluative Sciences in Ontario, October 18, 1993.

33. New York Yankees salaries found online at `espn.go.com/mlb/`.

34. Based on data summaries in G. L. Cromwell et al., "A comparison of the nutritive value of *opaque-2, floury-2* and normal corn for the chick," *Poultry Science,* 57 (1968), pp. 840–847.

35. Data from the U.S. Department of Energy; see Note 7.

36. Data from J. Marcus Jobe and Hutch Jobe, "A statistical approach for additional infill development," *Energy Exploration and Exploitation,* 18 (2000), 89–103.

37. From the Census Bureau Web site, `www.census.gov`.

38. See B. D. McCullough, "Assessing the reliability of statistical software: Part II," *The American Statistician,* 53, No. 2 (1999), pp. 149–159. Also, B. D. McCullough and B. Wilson, "On the accuracy of statistical procedures in Microsoft Excel 2000 and Excel XP," *Computational Statistics and Data Analysis,* 40, No. 4 (2002), pp. 713–721. Many other articles can be found on the topic of Excel's poor performance in (statistical) calculations.

Chapter 2

1. The data in Table 2.1 were provided by the owners of Duck Worth Wearing, Ames, Iowa.

2. Data provided by Robert Dale, Purdue University.

3. Based on T. N. Lam, "Estimating fuel consumption from engine size," *Journal of Transportation Engineering,* 111 (1985), pp. 339–357. The data for 10 to 50 km/hr are measured; those for 60 and higher are calculated from a model given in the paper and are therefore smoothed.

4. A sophisticated treatment of improvements and additions to scatterplots is W. S. Cleveland and R. McGill, "The many faces of a scatterplot," *Journal of the American Statistical Association,* 79 (1984), pp. 807–822.

5. Compiled from Fidelity data by the *Fidelity Insight* newsletter, 20 (2004), No. 1.

6. Data from the March 2002 annual demographic supplement to the Current Population Survey, downloaded from `www.bls.census.gov/cps`.

7. Data from the World Bank's *1999 World Development Indicators*. Life expectancy is estimated for 1997, and GDP per capita (purchasing-power parity basis) for 1998.

8. Net cash flow data from Sean Collins, *Mutual Fund Assets and Flows in 2000,* Investment Company Institute, 2001. Found online at `www.ici.org`. The raw data were converted to real dollars using annual average values of the consumer price index.

9. Data from *Consumer Reports,* June 1986, pp. 366–367.

10. W. L. Colville and D. P. McGill, "Effect of rate and method of planting on several plant characters and yield of irrigated corn," *Agronomy Journal,* 54 (1962), pp. 235–238.

11. Data from Table 885 of the *1999 Statistical Abstract of the United States.*

12. Data from the Energy Information Administration, recorded in Robert H. Romer, *Energy: An Introduction to Physics,* W. H. Freeman, 1976, for 1880 to 1970, and in the *Statistical Abstract of the United States* for more recent years.

13. Compiled from Fidelity data by the *Fidelity Insight* newsletter, found online at `fidelity.kobren.com`.

14. A careful study of this phenomenon is W. S. Cleveland, P. Diaconis, and R. McGill, "Variables on scatterplots look more highly correlated when the scales are increased," *Science,* 216 (1982), pp. 1138–1141.

15. Data from a plot in Timothy G. O'Brien and Margaret F. Kinnaird, "Caffeine and conservation," *Science,* 300 (2003), p. 587.

16. From the performance data for the fund presented at the Vanguard Group Web site, `personal.vanguard.com`. The EAFE returns differ from those given in Table 2.6. For reasons unknown to us, we often find minor variations in EAFE returns reported by different sources. We have elected to use Vanguard's reported values in this exercise.

17. Data from a survey by the Wheat Industry Council reported in *USA Today,* October 20, 1983.

18. *T. Rowe Price Report,* Winter 1997, p. 4.

19. From the Web site of the Sarasota County Property Appraiser, `www.sarasotaproperty.net`.

20. "Dancing in step," *Economist,* March 22, 2001.

21. From a presentation by Charles Knauf, Monroe County (New York) Environmental Health Laboratory.

22. The U.S. returns are for the Standard & Poor's 500-stock index. The overseas returns are for the Morgan Stanley Europe, Australasia, Far East (EAFE) index.

23. Frank J. Anscombe, "Graphs in statistical analysis," *The American Statistician,* 27 (1973), pp. 17–21.

24. Gary Smith, "Do statistics test scores regress toward the mean?" *Chance,* 10, No. 4 (1997), pp. 42–45.

25. Target store counts for 1990–1993 obtained from *USA Today,* January 14, 2000. Target store count for 2000 obtained from `www.targetcorp.com/investor-relations`.

26. The quotation is from Dr. Daniel Mark of Duke University, in the article "Age, not bias, may explain differences in treatment," *New York Times,* April 26, 1994.

27. M. Goldstein, "Preliminary inspection of multivariate data," *The American Statistician,* 36 (1982), pp. 358–362.

28. *The Health Consequences of Smoking: 1983,* U.S. Public Health Service, 1983.

29. From a Gannett News Service article appearing in the *Lafayette (Indiana) Journal and Courier,* April 23, 1994.

30. See Gary Taubes, "Magnetic field–cancer link—will it rest in peace?" *Science,* 277 (1997), p. 29.

31. Sanders Korenman and David Neumark, "Does marriage really make men more productive?" *Journal of Human Resources,* 26 (1991), pp. 282–307.

32. S. V. Zagona (ed.), *Studies and Issues in Smoking Behavior,* University of Arizona Press, 1967, pp. 157–180.

33. F. D. Blau and M. A. Ferber, "Career plans and expectations of young women and men," *Journal of Human Resources,* 26 (1991), pp. 581–607.

34. These data, from reports submitted by airlines to the Department of Transportation, appear in A. Barnett, "How numbers can trick you," *Technology Review,* October 1994, pp. 38–45.

35. Based on Melisa L. Collinsworth, "The analysis and review of the scuba diver market segment who has the propensity to utilize resorts in the Florida keys," M.S. thesis, Purdue University, 1991.

36. Karen M. Herbert, "Does impulse buying vary by mode of payment?" M.S. thesis, Purdue University, 1994.

37. *Digest of Education Statistics 2000,* accessed on the National Center for Education Statistics Web site, `nces.ed.gov`.

38. D. M. Barnes, "Breaking the cycle of addiction," *Science,* 241 (1988), pp. 1029–1030.

39. Data provided by Duck Worth Wearing of Ames, Iowa.

40. From Table 55 of the *2000 Statistical Abstract of the United States.*

41. See P. J. Bickel and J. W. O'Connell, "Is there a sex bias in graduate admissions?" *Science,* 187 (1975), pp. 398–404.

42. The data behind Figure 2.25 are from the Web site of Professor Kenneth French of Dartmouth. See Note 9 for Chapter 1. The stock returns are for all common stocks listed on any of the AMEX, NASDAQ, and NYSE exchanges.

43. P. Velleman, *ActivStats 2.0,* Addison-Wesley Interactive, 1997.

44. Data provided by Robert Dale, Purdue University.

45. Data provided by the Ames City Assessor, Ames, Iowa.

46. Search for "When the market sneezes" at `blackfriarsinc.com/blog/` for a short explanation of how to think about a company's beta in the context of AAPL stock.

47. Reported in the *New York Times,* July 20, 1989, from an article appearing that day in the *New England Journal of Medicine.*

48. Condensed from D. R. Appleton, J. M. French, and M. P. J. Vanderpump, "Ignoring a covariate: an example of Simpson's paradox," *The American Statistician,* 50 (1996), pp. 340–341.

49. Lien-Ti Bei, "Consumers' purchase behavior toward recycled products: an acquisition-transaction utility theory perspective," M.S. thesis, Purdue University, 1993.

Chapter 3

1. Based on Pamela Sherrid, "Big brother in Springfield," *Forbes,* December 2, 1985, pp. 210–212. See also Magid M. Abraham and Leonard M. Lodish, "Getting the most out of advertising and promotion," *Harvard Business Review,* May–June 1990, pp. 50–60.

2. A good review paper (already a bit out of date) is J. E. Moulder et al., "Cell phones and cancer: what is the evidence for a connection?" *Radiation Research,* 151 (1999), pp. 513–531.

3. Reported by D. Horvitz in his contribution to "Pseudo-opinion polls: SLOP or useful data?" *Chance,* 8, No. 2 (1995), pp. 16–25.

4. Based in part on Randall Rothenberger, "The trouble with mall interviewing," *New York Times,* August 16, 1989.

5. The information in this example is taken from *The ASCAP Survey and Your Royalties,* ASCAP, undated.

6. The most recent account of the design of the Current Population Survey appears in the "Technical Notes" to the Bureau of Labor Statistics report *Employment and Earnings,* available online at `www.bls.gov`. The account here omits many complications, such as the need to separately sample "group quarters" like college dormitories.

7. For more detail on the material of this section, along with references, see P. E. Converse and M. W. Traugott, "Assessing the accuracy of polls and surveys," *Science,* 234 (1986), pp. 1094–1098.

8. The nonresponse rate for the CPS comes from "Technical notes to household survey data published in *Employment and Earnings,*" found on the Bureau of Labor Statistics Web site, `www.bls.gov`. The General Social Survey reports its response rate on its Web site, `www.norc.org/projects/gensoc.asp`. The Pew study is described in Gregory Flemming and Kimberly Parker, "Race and reluctant respondents: possible consequences of non-response for pre-election surveys," Pew Research Center for the People and the Press, 1997, found at `www.people-press.org`.

9. For more detail on the limits of memory in surveys, see N. M. Bradburn, L. J. Rips, and S. K. Shevell, "Answering autobiographical questions: the impact of memory and inference on surveys," *Science,* 236 (1987), pp. 157–161.

10. Cynthia Crossen, "Margin of error: studies galore support products and positions, but are they reliable?" *Wall Street Journal,* November 14, 1991.

11. The responses on welfare are from a *New York Times*/CBS News poll reported in the *New York Times,* July 5, 1992. Those for Scotland are from "All set for independence?" *Economist,* September 12, 1998.

12. Giuliana Coccia, "An overview of non-response in Italian telephone surveys," *Proceedings of the 99th Session of the International Statistical Institute, 1993,* Book 3, pp. 271–272.

13. W. Mitofsky, "Mr. Perot, you're no pollster," *New York Times,* March 27, 1993.

14. This example is very loosely based on C. J. Schwarz, R. E. Bailey, J. R. Irvine, and F. C. Dalziel, "Estimating salmon spawning escapement using capture-recapture methods," *Canadian Journal of Fisheries and Aquatic Sciences,* 50 (1993), pp. 1181–1197.

15. Simplified from Arno J. Rethans, John L. Swasy, and Lawrence J. Marks, "Effects of television commercial repetition, receiver knowledge, and commercial length: a test of the two-factor model," *Journal of Marketing Research,* 23 (1986), pp. 50–61.

16. L. L. Miao, "Gastric freezing: an example of the evaluation of medical therapy by randomized clinical trials," in J. P. Bunker, B. A. Barnes, and F. Mosteller (eds.), *Costs, Risks, and Benefits of Surgery,* Oxford University Press, 1977, pp. 198–211.

17. Taken from "Advertising: the cola war," *Newsweek,* August 30, 1976, p. 67.

18. Joel Brockner et al., "Layoffs, equity theory, and work performance: further evidence of the impact of survivor guilt," *Academy of Management Journal,* 29 (1986), pp. 373–384.

19. John H. Kagel, Raymond C. Battalio, and C. G. Miles, "Marijuana and work performance: results from an experiment," *Journal of Human Resources,* 15 (1980), pp. 373–395. A general discussion of failures of blinding is Dean Ferguson et al., "Turning a blind eye: the success of blinding reported in a random sample of randomised, placebo controlled trials," *British Medical Journal,* 328 (2004), p. 432.

20. Simplified from Sanjay K. Dhar, Claudia González-Vallejo, and Dilip Soman, "Modeling the effects of advertised price claims: tensile versus precise pricing," *Marketing Science,* 18 (1999), pp. 154–177.

21. Based on Stephen A. Woodbury and Robert G. Spiegelman, "Bonuses to workers and employers to reduce unemployment: randomized trials in Illinois," *American Economic Review,* 77 (1987), pp. 513–530.

22. Michael W. Peugh, "Field Investigation of ventilation and air quality in duck and turkey slaughter plants," M.S. thesis, Purdue University, 1996.

23. Based on Christopher Anderson, "Measuring what works in health care," *Science,* 263 (1994), pp. 1080–1082.

24. See `www.yankelovich.com`. The survey question and result are reported in Trish Hall, "Shop? Many say 'Only if I must,'" *New York Times,* November 28, 1990.

25. The gross domestic sales of all U.S.-released movies for the 1990s were obtained from `www.worldwideboxoffice.com`.

26. Warren McIsaac and Vivek Goel, "Is access to physician services in Ontario equitable?" Institute for Clinical Evaluative Sciences in Ontario, October 18, 1993.

27. From the *New York Times,* August 21, 1989.

28. John C. Bailar III, "The real threats to the integrity of science," *The Chronicle of Higher Education,* April 21, 1995, pp. B1–B2.

29. See the details on the Web site of the Office for Human Research Protections of the Department of Health and Human Services, `www.hhs.goc/ohrp`.

30. The difficulties of interpreting guidelines for informed consent and for the work of institutional review boards in medical research are a main theme of Beverly Woodward, "Challenges to human subject protections in U.S. medical research," *Journal*

of the American Medical Association, 282 (1999), pp. 1947–1952. The references in this paper point to other discussions. Updated regulations and guidelines appear on the OHRP Web site (see Note 2).

31. Quotation from the *Report of the Tuskegee Syphilis Study Legacy Committee,* May 20, 1996. A detailed history is James H. Jones, *Bad Blood: The Tuskegee Syphilis Experiment,* Free Press, 1993.

32. Dr. Hennekens's words are from an interview in the Annenberg/Corporation for Public Broadcasting video series *Against All Odds: Inside Statistics.*

33. R. D. Middlemist, E. S. Knowles, and C. F. Matter, "Personal space invasions in the lavatory: suggestive evidence for arousal," *Journal of Personality and Social Psychology,* 33 (1976), pp. 541–546.

34. For a review of domestic violence experiments, see C. D. Maxwell et al., *The Effects of Arrest on Intimate Partner Violence: New Evidence from the Spouse Assault Replication Program,* U.S. Department of Justice, NCH188199, 2001. Available online at `www.ojp.usdoj.gov/nij/pubs-sum/188199.htm`.

35. From *CIS Boletín 9, Spaniards' Economic Awareness,* found online at `www.cis.es/ingles/opinion/economia.htm`.

36. Javier Gimeno et al., "Survival of the fittest? Entrepreneurial human capital and the persistence of under-performing firms," *Administrative Science Quarterly,* 42, No. 4 (1997).

37. The study is described in G. Kolata, "New study finds vitamins are not cancer preventers," *New York Times,* July 21, 1994. Look in the *Journal of the American Medical Association* of the same date for the details.

38. Ko Wang, Yuming Li, and John Erickson, "A new look at the Monday effect," *Journal of Finance,* 52 (1997), pp. 2171–2186.

39. From the Dupont Automotive North America Color Popularity Survey, reported at `www.dupont.com/automotive/`.

Chapter 4

1. U.S. Bureau of the Census, Current Population Reports, P60-213, *Money Income in the United States, 2000,* Government Printing Office, 2001. Available online at `www.census.gov`.

2. The Gallup Organization, *Justice Department vs. Microsoft: The Public's Opinion,* June 7, 2000. Found at `www.gallup.com/poll/releases`.

3. You can find a mathematical explanation of Benford's Law in Ted Hill, "The first-digit phenomenon," *American Scientist,* 86 (1996), pp. 358–363, and Ted Hill, "The difficulty of faking data," *Chance,* 12, No. 3 (1999), pp. 27–31. Applications in fraud detection are discussed in the second paper by Hill and in Mark A. Nigrini, "I've got your number," *Journal of Accountancy,* May 1999, available online at `www.aicpa.org/pubs/jofa/joaiss.htm`.

4. U.S. Census Bureau, *Statistical Abstract of the United States 1999,* p. 420.

5. The Gallup Organization, *American Workers Generally Satisfied, but Indicate Their Jobs Leave Much to Be Desired,* September 3, 1999. Found at `www.gallup.com/poll`.

6. From the Web site of Statistics Canada, `www.statcan.ca`.

7. Robyn Greenspan, "The deadly duo: spam and viruses, October 2003," at `cyberatlas.internet.com`.

8. From the Dupont Automotive North America Color Popularity Survey, reported at `www.dupont.com/automotive`.

9. We use $\bar{x}$ both for the random variable, which takes different values in repeated sampling, and for the numerical value of the random variable in a particular sample. Similarly, s stands both for a random variable and for a specific value. This notation is mathematically imprecise but statistically convenient.

10. In this chapter we consider only the case in which X takes a finite number of possible values. The same ideas, implemented with more advanced mathematics, apply to random variables with an infinite but still countable collection of values.

11. The mean of a continuous random variable X with density function $f(x)$ can be found by integration:

$$\mu_X = \int x f(x) dx$$

This integral is a kind of weighted average, analogous to the discrete-case mean

$$\mu_X = \sum x P(X = x)$$

The variance of a continuous random variable X is the average squared deviation of the values of X from their mean, found by the integral

$$\sigma_X^2 = \int (x - \mu)^2 f(x) dx$$

12. From the Web site of Professor Kenneth French of Dartmouth; see Note 9 for Chapter 1.

13. Returns data are from several sources, especially the *Fidelity Insight* newsletter, `fidelity.kobren.com`.

14. From the Census Bureau's 1998 American Housing Survey.

15. See Note 11.

16. Pfeiffer Consulting, *The Design and Publishing Workflow Benchmark Report*. This report can be found at `www.pfeifferreport.com`.

17. See A. Tversky and D. Kahneman, "Belief in the law of small numbers," *Psychological Bulletin,* 76 (1971), pp. 105–110, and other writings of these authors for a full account of our misperception of randomness.

18. Probabilities involving runs can be quite difficult to compute. That the probability of a run of three or more heads in 10 independent tosses of a fair coin is $(1/2) + (1/128) = 0.508$ can be found by clever counting, as can the other results given in the text. A general treatment using advanced methods appears in Section XIII.7 of William Feller, *An Introduction to Probability Theory and Its Applications,* Vol. 1, 3rd ed., Wiley, 1968.

19. R. Vallone and A. Tversky, "The hot hand in basketball: on the misperception of random sequences," *Cognitive Psychology,* 17 (1985), pp. 295–314. A later series of articles that debate the independence question is A. Tversky and T. Gilovich, "The

cold facts about the 'hot hand' in basketball," *Chance,* 2, No. 1 (1989), pp. 16–21; P. D. Larkey, R. A. Smith, and J. B. Kadane, "It's OK to believe in the 'hot hand,'" *Chance,* 2, No. 4 (1989), pp. 22–30; and A. Tversky and T. Gilovich, "The 'hot hand': statistical reality or cognitive illusion?" *Chance,* 2, no. 4 (1989), pp. 31–34.

20. Strictly speaking, the recipe $\sigma/\sqrt{n}$ for the standard deviation of $\bar{x}$ assumes that we draw an SRS of size n from an *infinite* population. If the population has finite size N, the standard deviation in the recipe is multiplied by $\sqrt{1-(n-1)/(N-1)}$. This "finite population correction" approaches 1 as N increases. When the population is at least 10 times as large as the sample, the correction factor is between about 0.95 and 1. It is reasonable to use the simpler form $\sigma/\sqrt{n}$ in these settings.

21. Values based on Sherri A. Buzinski, "The effect of position of methylation on the performance properties of durable press treated fabrics," CSR490 honors paper, Purdue University, 1985.

22. Data from `www.ncsu.edu/class/grades/`.

23. The distinction between the two types of infinity in Exercises 4.120 and 4.121 is subtle. The sample space in Exercise 4.120 is *countable*. That is, we can at least begin to count the possible values of Y: 0 days, 1 day, 2 days, and so on. However, in Exercise 4.121, one cannot even begin to count the possible values of W. The sample space can only be described as an interval of values.

Chapter 5

1. A collection of documents related to the FDIV bug can be found at `www.mathworks.com/company/pentium/index.shtml`.

2. Corey Kilgannon, "When New York is on the end of the line," *New York Times,* November 7, 1999.

3. J. Gollehon, *Pay the Line!* Putnam, 1988.

4. Some demonstrations of these methods can be found at `mitsloan.mit.edu/vc/Pages/demo.html`.

5. The survey question is reported in Trish Hall, "Shop? Many say 'Only if I must,'" *New York Times,* November 28, 1990. In fact, 66% (1650 of 2500) in the sample said "Agree."

6. Office of Technology Assessment, *Scientific Validity of Polygraph Testing: A Research Review and Evaluation,* Government Printing Office, 1983.

7. These probabilities come from studies by the sociologist Harry Edwards, reported in the *New York Times,* February 25, 1986.

8. Projections by the National Center for Education Statistics, from the *Digest of Education Statistics, 2000,* available at `nces.ed.gov`.

9. Probabilities are from trials with 2897 people known to be free of HIV antibodies and 673 people known to be infected, reported in J. Richard George, "Alternative specimen sources: methods for confirming positives," 1998 Conference on the Laboratory Science of HIV, found online at the Centers for Disease Control and Prevention, `www.cdc.gov`.

10. From `www.apple.com/hotnews/features/mwsf99keynote3.html`.

Chapter 6

1. See Noel Cressie, *Statistics for Spatial Data,* Wiley, 1993. The significance test result that we report is one of several that could be used to address this question. See pp. 607–609 of the Cressie book for more details.

2. The Community Bank Earnings Survey that is the basis for this example appears in the *ABA Banking Journal,* September 1999, pp. 18–28.

3. P. H. Lewis, "Technology" column, *New York Times,* May 29, 1995.

4. A standard reference is Bradley Efron and Robert J. Tibshirani, *An Introduction to the Bootstrap,* Chapman Hall, 1993. A less technical overview is in Bradley Efron and Robert J. Tibshirani, "Statistical data analysis in the computer age," *Science,* 253 (1991), pp. 390–395.

5. The vehicle is a 1997 Pontiac Transport Van owned by the second author.

6. Chris Chambers, "Americans skeptical about mergers of big companies," Gallup News Service, November 1, 2000. Found at `www.gallup.com`.

7. Seung-Ok Kim, "Burials, pigs, and political prestige in neolithic China," *Current Anthropology,* 35 (1994), pp. 119–141.

8. From R. M. Lyle et al.,"Blood pressure and metabolic effects of calcium supplementation in normotensive white and black men," *Journal of the American Medical Association,* 257 (1987), pp. 1772–1776.

9. Based on information reported in Sandy Baum and Marie O'Malley, "College on credit: how borrowers perceive their education debt," Nellie Mae Corporation (2003), found online at `www.nelliemae.com/library/research_10.html`.

10. Jon E. Keeley, C. J. Fotheringham, and Marco Morais, "Reexamining fire suppression impacts on brushland fire regimes," *Science,* 284 (1999), pp. 1829–1831.

11. From a study by M. R. Schlatter et al., Division of Financial Aid, Purdue University.

12. Data provided by Diana Schellenberg, Purdue University School of Health Sciences

13. Based on D. L. Shankland et al., "The effect of 5-thio-D-glucose on insect development and its absorption by insects," *Journal of Insect Physiology,* 14 (1968), pp. 63–72.

14. From William T. Robinson, "Sources of market pioneer advantages: the case of industrial goods industries," *Journal of Marketing Research,* 25 (1988), pp. 87–94.

15. Warren E. Leary, "Cell phones: questions but no answers," *New York Times,* October 26, 1999.

16. Robert J. Schiller, "The volatility of stock market prices," *Science,* 235 (1987), pp. 33–36.

17. Sabrina Oesterle et al., "Volunteerism during the transition to adulthood: a life course perspective," *Social Forces,* 83 (2004), pp. 1123–1149.

18. Based on A. M. Garcia et al., "Why do workers behave unsafely at work? Determinants of safe work practices in industrial workers," *Occupational and Environmental Medicine,* 61 (2004), pp. 239–246.

19. Paula R. Worthington, "Investment, cash flow, and sunk costs," *Journal of Industrial Economics* 63 (1995), pp. 49–61.

20. Kathryn L. Dewenter, "Do exchange rate changes drive foreign direct investment?" *Journal of Business,* 68 (1995), pp. 405–433.

21. Data provided by Mugdha Gore and Joseph Thomas, Purdue University School of Pharmacy.

22. Barbara A. Almanza, Richard Ghiselli, and William Jaffe, "Foodservice design and aging baby boomers: importance and perception of physical amenities in restaurants," *Foodservice Research International,* 12 (2000), pp. 25–40.

Chapter 7

1. From C. Don Wiggins, "The legal perils of 'underdiversification'—a case study," *Personal Financial Planning,* 1, No. 6 (1999), pp. 16–18.

2. These data are from "Results report on the vitamin C pilot program," prepared by SUSTAIN (Sharing United States Technology to Aid in the Improvement of Nutrition) for the U.S. Agency for International Development. The report was used by the Committee on International Nutrition of the National Academy of Sciences and Institute of Medicine (NAS/IOM) to make recommendations on whether or not the vitamin C content of food commodities used in U.S. food aid programs should be increased. The program was directed by Peter Ranum and Françoise Chomé.

3. Based on the source in Note 1.

4. Data provided by Joseph A. Wipf, Department of Foreign Languages and Literatures, Purdue University.

5. These recommendations are based on extensive computer work. See, for example, Harry O. Posten, "The robustness of the one-sample t-test over the Pearson system," *Journal of Statistical Computation and Simulation,* 9 (1979), pp. 133–149, and E. S. Pearson and N. W. Please, "Relation between the shape of population distribution and the robustness of four simple test statistics," *Biometrika,* 62 (1975), pp. 223–241.

6. Data from J. Marcus Jobe and Hutch Jobe, "A statistical approach for additional infill development," *Energy Exploration and Exploitation,* 18 (2000), 89–103.

7. The vehicle is a 1997 Pontiac Transport van owned by the second author.

8. Based on Dan Dauwakter's master's thesis in the Department of Forestry and Natural Resources at Purdue University. More information is available in Daniel C. Dauwalter et al., "An index of biotic integrity for fish assemblages in Ozark Highland streams of Arkansas," *Southeastern Naturalist,* 2 (2003), pp. 447–468. These data were provided by Emmanuel Frimpong.

9. Based on R. G. Hood, "Results of the prices received by farmers for grain—quality assurance project," USDA Report SRB-95-07, 1995.

10. Based on A. N. Dey, "Characteristics of elderly home health care users," National Center for Health Statistics, 1996.

11. Data from F. H. Rauscher et al., "Music training causes long-term enhancement of preschool children's spatial-temporal reasoning," *Neurological Research,* 19 (1997), pp. 2–8.

12. Based on D. L. Shankland et al., "The effect of 5-thio-D-glucose on insect development and its absorption by insects," *Journal of Insect Physiology,* 14 (1968), pp. 63–72.

13. Data provided by Diana Schellenberg, Purdue University School of Health Sciences.

14. Data provided by Timothy Sturm.

15. Data provided by Joseph A. Wipf, Department of Foreign Languages and Literatures, Purdue University.

16. Detailed information about the conservative t procedures can be found in Paul Leaverton and John J. Birch, "Small sample power curves for the two sample location problem," *Technometrics,* 11 (1969), pp. 299–307; in Henry Scheffé, "Practical solutions of the Behrens-Fisher problem," *Journal of the American Statistical Association,* 65 (1970), pp. 1501–1508; and in D. J. Best and J. C. W. Rayner, "Welch's approximate solution for the Behrens-Fisher problem," *Technometrics,* 29 (1987), pp. 205–210.

17. This example is adapted from Maribeth C. Schmitt, "The effects of an elaborated directed reading activity on the metacomprehension skills of third graders," Ph.D. dissertation, Purdue University, 1987.

18. Extensive simulation studies are reported in Harry O. Posten, "The robustness of the two-sample t test over the Pearson system," *Journal of Statistical Computation and Simulation,* 6 (1978), pp. 295–311; Harry O. Posten, H. Yeh, and D. B. Owen, "Robustness of the two-sample t-test under violations of the homogeneity assumption," *Communications in Statistics,* 11 (1982), pp. 109–126; and Harry O. Posten, "Robustness of the two-sample t-test under violations of the homogeneity assumption, part II," *Journal of Statistical Computation and Simulation,* 8 (1992), pp. 2169-2184.

19. See Note 8.

20. Based on C. Papoulias and P. Theodossiou, "Analysis and modeling of recent business failures in Greece," *Managerial and Decision Economics,* 13 (1992), pp. 163–169.

21. M. K. Campbell et al., "A tailored multimedia nutrition education pilot program for low-income women receiving food assistance," *Health Education Research,* 14 (1999), pp. 257–267.

22. B. Bakke et al., "Cumulative exposure to dust and gases as determinants of lung function decline in tunnel construction workers," *Occupational Environmental Medicine,* 61 (2004), pp. 262–269.

23. Samara Joy Nielsen and Barry M. Popkin, "Patterns and trends in food portion sizes, 1977–1998," *Journal of the American Medical Association,* 289 (2003), pp. 450–453.

24. Gordana Mrdjenovic and David A. Levitsky, "Nutritional and energetic consequences of sweetened drink consumption in 6- to 13-year old children," *Journal of Pediatrics,* 142 (2003), pp. 604–610.

25. Data provided by Helen Park; see Helen Park, et al., "Fortifying bread with each of three antioxidants," *Cereal Chemistry,* 74 (1997), pp. 202–206.

26. See Note 10.

27. Based on A. H. Ismail and R. J. Young,"The effect of chronic exercise on the personality of middle-aged men,"*Journal of Human Ergology,* 2 (1973), pp. 47–57.

28. Based on M. C. Wilson et al., "Impact of cereal leaf beetle larvae on yields of oats," *Journal of Economic Entomology,* 62 (1969), pp. 699–702.

29. Data from a study conducted at the Medical University of South Carolina in 1989.

30. Based on a sudy conducted Marvin Schlatter, Division of Financial Aid, Purdue University.

31. See the paper of Pearson and Please cited in Note 4 for one example of simulations that demonstrate the lack of robustness of the F test for comparing standard deviations.

32. The problem of comparing spreads is difficult even with advanced methods. Common distribution-free procedures do not offer a satisfactory alternative to the F test, because they are sensitive to unequal shapes when comparing two distributions. A good introduction to the available methods is W. J. Conover, M. E. Johnson, and M. M. Johnson, "A comparative study of tests for homogeneity of variances, with applications to outer continental shelf bidding data," *Technometrics,* 23 (1981), pp. 351–361. Modern resampling procedures often work well. See Dennis D. Boos and Colin Brownie, "Bootstrap methods for testing homogeneity of variances," *Technometrics,* 31 (1989), pp. 69–82.

33. G. E. P. Box, "Non-Normality and tests on variances," *Biometrika,* 40 (1953), pp. 318–335. The quote appears on page 333.

34. P. Glick et al., "Evaluations of sexy women in low- and high-status jobs," *Psychology of Women Quarterly,* 29 (2005), pp. 389–395.

35. W. G. Kim and H.-B. Kim, "Measuring customer-based restaurant brand equity," *Cornell Hotel and Restaurnat Administration Quarterly,* 45 (2004), pp. 115–131.

36. Michael W. Peugh, "Field Investigation of ventilation and air quality in duck and turkey slaughter plants," M.S. thesis, Purdue University, 1996.

37. Ajay Ghei, "An empirical analysis of psychological androgeny in the personality profile of the successful hotel manager," M.S. thesis, Purdue University, 1992.

38. Data from the "wine" database in the archive of machine learning data bases at the University of California, Irvine, `ftp.ics.uci.edu/pub/machine-learning-databases`.

39. See Note 35.

40. Yvan R. Germain, "The dyeing of ramie with fiber reactive dyes using the cold pad-batch method," M.S. thesis, Purdue University, 1988.

41. Refer to the previous note.

42. Data from Wayne Nelson, *Applied Life Data Analysis,* Wiley, 1982, p. 471.

43. This exercise is based on events that are real. The data and details have been altered to protect the privacy of the individuals involved.

44. Data taken from the Web site `www.assist-2-sell.com` on July 9, 2001.

45. Data provided by Professor Sebastian Heath, School of Veterinary Medicine, Purdue University.

46. Based loosely on D. R. Black et al., "Minimal interventions for weight control: a cost-effective alternative," *Addictive Behaviors,* 9 (1984), pp. 279–285.)

47. Based on G. Salvendy, "Selection of industrial operators: the one-hole test," *International Journal of Production Research,* 13 (1973), pp. 303–321.

48. From J. W. Marr and J. A. Heady, "Within- and between-person variation in dietary surveys: number of days needed to classify individuals," *Human Nutrition: Applied Nutrition,* 40A (1986), pp. 347–364.

49. Data taken from the Web site `www.assist-2-sell.com`.

Chapter 8

1. This case is discussed in D. H. Kaye and M. Aickin (eds.), *Statistical Methods in Discrimination Litigation,* Marcel Dekker, 1986, and D. C. Baldus and J. W. L. Cole, *Statistical Proof of Discrimination,* McGraw-Hill, 1980.

2. National Institute for Occupational Safety and Health, *Stress at Work,* 2000, `www.cdc.gov/niosh/stresswk.html`.

3. Results of this survey were reported in *Restaurant Business,* September 15, 1999, pp. 45–49.

4. Details of procedures based on the binomial distributions can be found in Myles Hollander and Douglas Wolfe, *Nonparametric Statistical Inference,* 2nd ed., Wiley, 1999.

5. The poll is part of the "American Express Retail Index Project" and is reported in *Stores,* December 2000, pp. 38–40.

6. See A. Agresti and B. A. Coull, "Approximate is better than 'exact' for interval estimation of binomial proportions," *The American Statistician,* 52 (1998), pp. 119–126. A detailed theoretical study is Lawrence D. Brown, Tony Cai, and Anirban DasGupta, "Confidence intervals for a binomial proportion and asymptotic expansions," *Annals of Statistics,* 30 (2002), pp. 160–201.

7. This example is adapted from a survey directed by Professor Joseph N. Uhl of the Department of Agricultural Economics, Purdue University. The survey was sponsored by the Indiana Christmas Tree Growers Association.

8. Based on information in "NCAA 2003 national study of collegiate sports wagering and associated health risks," which can be found at the NCAA Web site, `http://www.ncaa.org`.

9. From the "National Survey of Student Engagement, the college student report," 2003, available online at `http://www.indiana.edu˜nsse/`.

10. James Otto et al., "Training rats to search and alert on contraband odors," *Applied Animal Behaviour Science,* 77 (2002), pp. 271–232.

11. Information about the survey can be found online at `http://saint-denis.library.arizona.edu/natcong/`.

12. Based on information reported in Sandy Baum and Marie O'Malley, "College on credit: how borrowers perceive their education debt," Nellie Mae Corporation, 2003, found online at `www.nelliemae.com/library/research_10.html`.

13. From Heeseung Roh Ryu, Roseann M. Lyle, and George P. McCabe, "Factors associated with weight concerns and unhealthy eating patterns among young Korean females," *Eating Disorders,* 11 (2003), pp. 129–141.

14. Data from Roland J. Thorpe, Jr., and based on his analysis of "Health ABC," a 10-year longitudinal study of older adults supported by the Laboratory of Epidemiology, Demography, and Biometry of the National Institute on Aging. Additional analyses are given in his Ph.D. dissertation, "Relationship between pet ownership, physical activity, and human health in an elderly population," Purdue University, 2004.

15. From Teenage Research Unlimited reported on November 22, 2004. See `www.teenresearch.com`.

16. Data provided by Jude M. Werra & Associates, Brookfield, Wisconsin.

17. Results of this survey are reported in Henry Wechsler et al., "Health and behavioral consequences of binge drinking in college," *Journal of the American Medical Association,* 272 (1994), pp. 1672–1677.

18. Data from Guohua Li and Susan P. Baker, "Alcohol in fatally injured bicyclists," *Accident Analysis and Prevention,* 26 (1994), pp. 543–548.

19. Marsha A. Dickson, "Utility of no sweat labels for apparel customers: profiling label users and predicting their purchases," *The Journal of Consumer Affairs,* 35 (2001), pp. 96–119.

20. Based on Greg Clinch, "Employee compensation and firms' research and development activity," *Journal of Accounting Research,* 29 (1991), pp. 59–78.

21. Sara J. Solnick and David Hemenway, "Complaints and disenrollment at a health maintenance organization," *The Journal of Consumer Affairs,* 26 (1992), pp. 90–103.

22. See Alan Agresti and Brian Caffo, "Simple and effective confidence intervals for proportions and differences of proportions result from adding two successes and two failures," *The American Statistician,* 45 (2000), pp. 280–288. The Wilson interval is a bit conservative (true coverage probability is higher than the confidence level) when p_1 and p_2 are equal and close to 0 or 1, but the traditional interval is much less accurate and has the fatal flaw that the true coverage probability is *less* than the confidence level.

23. The study and data are described in J. Stamler, "The mass treatment of hypertensive disease: defining the problem," *Mild Hypertension: To Treat or Not to Treat,* New York Academy of Sciences (1978), pp. 333–358.

24. Karen M. Herbert, "Does impulse buying vary by mode of payment?" M.S. thesis, Purdue University, 1994.

25. Data produced by Ries and Smith, found in William D. Johnson and Gary G. Koch, "A note on the weighted least squares analysis of the Ries-Smith contingency table data," *Technometrics,* 13 (1971), pp. 438–447. These are the counts for people who have soft water and wash at high temperature; the source has data on other settings as well.

26. See S. W. Lagakos, B. J. Wessen, and M. Zelen, "An analysis of contaminated well water and health effects in Woburn, Massachusetts," *Journal of the American Statistical Association,* 81 (1986), pp. 583–596, and the following discussion. This case is the basis for the movie *A Civil Action.*

27. Data from W. E. Sell and W. E. Field, "Evaluation of PTO master shield usage on John Deere tractors," paper presented at the American Society of Agricultural Engineers 1984 Summer Meeting.

28. From Monica Macaulay and Colleen Brice, "Don't touch my projectile: gender bias and stereotyping in syntactic examples," *Language,* 73 (1997), pp. 798–825. The first part of the title is a direct quote from one of the texts.

29. From William S. Fields et al., "Controlled trial of aspirin in cerebral ischemia," *Stroke,* 8 (1977), pp. 301–315.

30. Data from H. A. Witkin et al., "Criminality in XYY and XXY men," *Science,* 193 (1976), pp. 547–555.

31. Based on Elray M. Roper and Charles G. Wright, "German cockroach (Orthoptera: Blattellidae) mortality on various surfaces following application of diazinon," *Journal of Economic Entomology,* 78 (1985), pp. 733–737.

32. From M. L. Burr et al., "Effects on respiratory health of a reduction in air pollution from vehicle exhaust emissions," *Occupational and Environmental Medicine,* 61 (2004), pp. 212–218.

33. Lee Rainie et al., "The state of music downloading and file-sharing online," Pew Internet Project and Comscore Media Metrix Data Memo, 2004. This memo is available online at `http://www.pewinternet.org/`.

34. From Karin Weber and Weley S. Roehl, "Profiling people searching for and purchasing travel products on the World Wide Web," *Journal of Travel Research,* 37 (1999), pp. 291–298.

35. Based on Robert T. Driescher, "A quality swing with Ping," *Quality Progress,* August 2001, pp. 37–41.

36. From Rick B. van Baaren, "The parrot effect: how to increase tip size," *Cornell Hotel and Restaurant Administration Quarterly,* 46 (2005), pp. 79–84.

37. From Dennis N. Bristow and Richard J. Sebastian, "Holy cow! Wait 'til next year! A closer look at the brand loyalty of Chicago Cubs baseball fans," *Journal of Consumer Marketing,* 18 (2001), pp. 256–275.

38. Based on a Gallup poll conducted April 6–8, 2001.

39. From Charles T. Clotfelter et al., "State lotteries at the turn of the century: report to the National Gambling Impact Study Commission" (1999).

40. Based on Deborah Roedder John and Ramnath Lakshmi-Ratan, "Age differences in children's choice behavior: the impact of available alternatives," *Journal of Marketing Research,* 29 (1992), pp. 216–226.

41. Based on an article on the study reported in the *New York Times* on January 30, 1988.

42. Some details are given in D. H. Kaye and M. Aickin (eds.), *Statistical Methods in Discrimination Litigation,* Marcel Dekker, 1986.

Chapter 9

1. C. M. Ryan, C. A. Northrup-Clewes, B. Knox, and D. I. Thurnham, "The effect of in-store music on consumer choice of wine," *Proceedings of the Nutrition Society,* 57 (1998), p. 1069A.

2. From P. Azoulay and S. Shane, "Entrepreneurs, contracts, and the failure of young firms," *Management Science,* 47 (2001), pp. 337–358.

3. When the expected cell counts are small, it is best to use a test based on the exact distribution rather than the chi-square approximation, particularly for 2×2 tables. Many statistical software systems offer an "exact" test as well as the chi-square test for 2×2 tables.

4. The full report of the study appeared in George H. Beaton et al., "Effectiveness of vitamin A supplementation in the control of young child morbidity and mortality in developing countries," United Nations ACC/SCN State-of-the-Art Series, Nutrition Policy Discussion Paper no. 13, 1993.

5. See Note 1.

6. An alternative formula that can be used for hand or calculator computations is

$$X^2 = \sum \frac{(\text{observed})^2}{\text{expected}} - n$$

7. See, for example, Alan Agresti, *Categorical Data Analysis,* Wiley, 1990.

8. Although these data are fictitious, similar though less simple situations occur. See P. J. Bickel and J. W. O'Connell, "Is there a sex bias in graduate admissions?" *Science,* 187 (1975), pp. 398–404.

9. Tom Reichert, "The prevalence of sexual imagery in ads targeted to young adults," *Journal of Consumer Affairs,* 37 (2003), pp. 403–412.

10. See George R. Milne, "How well do consumers protect themselves from identity theft?" *Journal of Consumer Affairs,* 37 (2003), pp. 388–402.

11. Based on information in "NCAA 2003 national study of collegiate sports wagering and associated health risks," which can be found at the NCAA Web site, `http://www.ncaa.org`.

12. Christopher Somers et al., "Air pollution induces heritable DNA mutations," *Proceedings of the National Academy of Sciences,* 99 (2002), pp. 15,904–15,907.

13. Ethan J. Temeles and W. John Kress, "Adaption in a plant-hummingbird association," *Science,* 300 (2003), pp. 630–633.

14. Dellavalle et al., "Going, going, gone: lost Internet references," *Science,* 302 (2003), pp. 787–788.

15. These data are from an Undergraduate Task Force study of student retention in the Purdue University College of Science.

16. Francine D. Blau and Marianne A. Ferber, "Career plans and expectations of young women and men," *Journal of Human Resources,* 26 (1991), pp. 581–607.

17. Erdener Kaynak and Wellington Kang-yen Kuan, "Environment, strategy, structure, and performance in the context of export activity: an empirical study of Taiwanese manufacturing firms," *Journal of Business Research,* 27 (1993), pp. 33–49.

18. William D. Darley, "Store-choice behavior for pre-owned merchandise," *Journal of Business Research,* 27 (1993), pp. 17–31.

19. David M. Blau, "The child care labor market," *Journal of Human Resources,* 27 (1992), pp. 9–39.

20. James E. Stafford, "Influence of preliminary contact on mail returns," *Journal of Marketing Research,* 3 (1966), pp. 410–411.

21. Patricia H. Shiono and Mark A. Klebanoff, "The effect of two mailing strategies on the response to a survey of physicians," *American Journal of Epidemiology,* 134 (1991), pp. 539–542.

22. Burton G. Malkeil, "Returns from investing in equity mutual funds, 1971 to 1991," *Journal of Finance,* 50 (1995), pp. 549–572.

23. Data provided by Susan Prohofsky, from her Ph.D. dissertation, "Selection of undergraduate major: the influence of expected costs and expected benefits," Purdue University, 1991.

24. Data are from *Seventh Report to the President and Congress on the Status of Health Personnel in the United States,* U. S. Public Health Service, 1990.

25. Data provided by Dr. Susan Meyer, Senior Vice President of the American Association of Colleges of Pharmacy.

26. Gary J. Patronek et al., "Risk factors for relinquishment of cats to an animal shelter," *Journal of the American Veterinary Medical Association,* 209 (1996), pp. 582–588.

27. Gary J. Patronek et al., "Risk factors for relinquishment of dogs to an animal shelter," *Journal of the American Veterinary Medical Association,* 209 (1996), pp. 572–581.

28. From Robert J. M. Dawson, "The 'unusual episode' data revisited," *Journal of Statistics Education,* 3, No. 3 (1995). Electronic journal available at the American Statistical Association Web site, `www.amstat.org`.

29. This study is reported in Joan L. Duda, "The relationship between goal perspectives, persistence and behavioral intensity among male and female recreational sport participants," *Leisure Sciences,* 10 (1988), pp. 95–106.

30. From an article by David W. Moore, "Only one in five Americans without a credit card," describing the results of a poll conducted April 6–8, 2001. The article was found on the Gallup Web site, `www.gallup.com`.

31. From K. Weber and W. S. Roehl, "Profiling people searching for and purchasing travel products on the World Wide Web," *Journal of Travel Research,* 37 (1999), pp. 291–298. The Web site `www.gvu.gatech.edu/user_surveys` has more information about this and similar surveys.

32. From Sang Suk Lee and Jerome S. Osteryoung, "A comparison of determinants for business start-up in the U.S. and Korea," *Journal of Small Business Management,* 39, No. 2 (2001), pp. 193–200.

Chapter 10

1. In practice, x may also be a random quantity. Inferences can then be interpreted as *conditional* on a given value of x. If the error in measuring x is large, more advanced inference methods are needed.

2. These data were collected for a study of relationships between work-family tension and work conditions in small and large workplaces. Results are reported in S. M. MacDermid, M. Williams, S. Marks, and G. Heilbrun, "Is small beautiful? Work-family tension, work conditions and organization size," *Family Relations,* 44 (1994), pp. 159–167. We have transformed the WAGES variable to maintain confidentiality.

3. National Science Foundation, Division of Science Resources Statistics, *Academic Research and Development Expenditures: Fiscal Year 2001,* NSF 03-316, Project Officer, M. Marge Machen (Arlington, VA 2003). Available from `http://www.nsf.gov/sbe/srs/stats.htm`.

4. As the text notes, the residuals are not independent observations. They also have somewhat different standard deviations. For practical purposes of examining a regression model, we can nonetheless interpret the normal quantile plot as if the residuals were data from a single distribution.

5. Inflation is measured by the December-to-December change in the Consumer Price Index. See the Web site of Professor Kenneth French of Dartmouth University, `mba.tuck.dartmouth.edu/pages/faculty/ken.french`.

6. See the essay "Regression toward the mean" in Stephen M. Stigler, *Statistics on the Table,* Harvard University Press, 1999. The quotation from Milton Friedman appears in this essay.

7. In fact, the Excel regression output does not report the sign of the correlation r. The scatterplot in Figure 10.3 shows that r is positive. To get the correlation with the correct sign in Excel, you must use the "Correlation" function.

8. Based on Dan Dauwakter's master's thesis in the Department of Forestry and Natural Resources at Purdue University. More information is available in Daniel C. Dauwalter et al., "An index of biotic integrity for fish assemblages in Ozark Highland streams of Arkansas," *Southeastern Naturalist,* 2 (2003), pp. 447–468. These data were provided by Emmanuel Frimpong.

9. Data were provided by the Ames City Assessor, Ames, Iowa.

10. Net cash flow data from Sean Collins, *Mutual Fund Assets and Flows in 2000,* Investment Company Institute, 2001. Found online at `www.ici.org`. The raw data were converted to real dollars using annual average values of the CPI.

11. These are part of the data from the EESEE story "Blood Alcohol Content," found on the text Web site.

12. Data for the first four years from Manuel Castells, *The Rise of the Network Society,* 2nd edition, Blackwell, 2000, p. 41.

13. Based on summaries in Charles Fombrun and Mark Shanley, "What's in a name? Reputation building and corporate strategy," *Academy of Management Journal,* 33 (1990), pp. 233–258.

14. M. J. Braid, K. F. Forbes, and D. W. Moran, "Pharmaceutical 'Charge Compression' under the Medicare Outpatient Prospective Payment System," *Journal of Health Care Finance,* 30, No. 3 (2004), pp. 21–33.

15. S. E. Kimes and S. K. A. Robson, "The impact of restuarant table characteristics on meal duration and spending," *Cornell Hotel and Restuarant Administration Quarterly,* 45, No. 4 (2004), pp. 333–346.

16. W. G. Kim and H.-B. Kim, "Measuring customer-based restaurant brand equity," *Cornell Hotel and Restuarant Administration Quarterly,* 45, No. 2 (2004), pp. 115–131.

17. S. Groschl, "Persons with disabilities, a source of nontraditional labor for Canada's hotel industry," *Cornell Hotel and Restuarant Administration Quarterly,* 46, No. 2 (2005), pp. 258–274.

18. From the Facts and Figures Web pages of the Food Marketing Institute, `http://www.fmi.org`.

19. From the Web pages of the Indiana Department of Education, `http://www.doe.state.in.us/`.

20. G. Geri and B. Palla, "Considerazioni sulle più recenti osservazioni ottiche alla Torre Pendente di Pisa," *Estratto dal Bollettino della Società Italiana di Topografia e Fotogrammetria,* 2 (1988), pp. 121–135. Professor Julia Mortera of the University of Rome provided valuable assistance with the translation.

21. Marty Ahearn, Jet Yee, Eldon Ball, and Rich Nehring, *Agricultural Productivity in the United States,* U.S. Department of Agriculture Information Bulletin No. 740, 1998.

Chapter 11

1. Based on the Space Management Model for Purdue University implemented by Keith Murray, Director of Space Managment and Academic Scheduling.

2. Of the thirty companies that are components of the DJIA, Home Depot, Intel, Microsoft, and SBC Communications were new components as of November 1, 1999.

3. Source: Bloomberg News Bureau. Sales (total revenue) and profits (net income) are from the Annual Income Statement. Assets are total assets from the Balance Sheet at the end of the year.

4. U.S. Federal Deposit Insurance Corp., *Statistics on Banking,* issued annually. Also see *Statistical Abstract of the United States,* 1998, Table 811.

5. From *Consumer Reports,* August 2005, pp. 44–45.

6. From Alan Levinsohn, "Online brokerage, the new core account?" *ABA Banking Journal,* September 1999, pp. 34–42.

7. Results of the study are reported in Patricia F. Campbell and George P. McCabe, "Predicting the success of freshmen in a computer science major," *Communications of the ACM,* 27 (1984), pp. 1108–1113.

8. From Stephanie Aaronson and Julie Coronado, "Are firms or workers behind the shift away from DB pension plans?" Federal Reserve Board (2005), available at `http://www.federalreserve.gov/pubs/feds`.

9. From Michael E. Staten et al., "Information costs and the organization of credit markets: a theory of indirect lending," *Economic Inquiry,* 28 (1990), pp. 508–529.

10. From Susan Stites-Doe and James J. Cordeiro, "An empirical assessment of the determinants of bank branch manager compensation," *The Journal of Applied Business Research,* 15 (1999), pp. 55–66.

11. The data were collected from the Web site `http://www.realtor.com` on October 8, 2001.

12. This example describes an analysis done by Christine Smiley of Kestnbaum Consulting Company, Chicago, Illinois.

13. For more information on logistic regression see Chapter 17.

14. Based on M. U. Kalwani and C. K. Yim, "Consumer price and promotion expectations: an experimental study," *Journal of Marketing Research,* 29 (1992), pp. 90–100.

15. Based on Dan Dauwakter's master's thesis in the Department of Forestry and Natural Resources at Purdue University. More information is available in Daniel C. Dauwalter et al., "An index of biotic integrity for fish assemblages in Ozark Highland streams of Arkansas," *Southeastern Naturalist,* 2 (2003), pp. 447–468. These data were provided by Emmanuel Frimpong.

16. A description of this case, as well as other examples of the use of statistics in legal settings, is given in Michael O. Finkelstein, *Quantitative Methods in Law,* Free Press, 1978.

17. Data provided by Helen Park; see H. Park et al., "Fortifying bread with each of three antioxidants," *Cereal Chemistry,* 74 (1997), pp. 202–206.

18. See G. P. McCabe, "Regression analysis in discrimination cases," in D. H. Kaye and M. Aickin (eds.), *Statistical Methods in Discrimination Litigation,* Marcel Dekker, 1986, for an explanation of how multiple regression is used in this setting.

Chapter 12

1. Based on Arvind Salvekar, "Application of Six Sigma to DRG 209," found at the Smarter Solutions Web site, `www.smartersolutions.com`.

2. As of 2007, The American Society for Quality (ASQ) has honored twenty three individuals by conferring on them the status of Honorary Member. A detailed summary of the background and contributions of the individuals noted here, along with other pioneers, can be found from an ASQ Web site `www.asq.org/about-asq/who-we-are/honorary-members.html`.

3. Texts on quality management give more detail about basic quality tools including the ones noted in this section. The classic reference for the basic tools is Kaoru Ishikawa, *Guide to Quality Control,* Asian Productivity Organization, 1986. For expanded presentation of tools often used in conjunction with the DMAIC improvement model, an excellent resource is *The Black Belt Memory Jogger*™ (2002), Salem, NH: GOAL/QPC.

4. The flow chart and a more elaborate version of the cause-and-effect diagram for Case 12.1 were prepared by S. K. Bhat of the General Motors Technical Center as part of a course assignment at Purdue University.

5. We have adopted the terms "chart setup" and "process monitoring" from Andrew C. Palm's discussion of William H. Woodall, "Controversies and contradictions in statistical process control," *Journal of Quality Technology,* 32 (2000), pp. 341–350. Palm's discussion appears in the same issue, pp. 356–360. We have combined Palm's stages B ("process improvement") and C ("process monitoring") in writing for beginners because the distinction between them is one of degree.

6. It is common to call these "standards given" $\overline{x}$ and s charts. We avoid this term because it easily leads to the common and serious error of confusing control limits (based on the process itself) with standards or specifications imposed from outside.

7. Provided by Charles Hicks, Purdue University.

8. See, for example, Chapter 3 of Stephen B. Vardeman and J. Marcus Jobe, *Statistical Quality Assurance Methods for Engineers,* Wiley, 1999.

9. The classic discussion of out-of-control signals and the types of special causes that may lie behind special control chart patterns is the *AT&T Statistical Quality Control Handbook,* Western Electric, 1956.

10. The data in Table 12.7 are adapted from data on viscosity of rubber samples appearing in Table P3.3 of Irving W. Burr, *Statistical Quality Control Methods,* Marcel Dekker, 1976.

11. The control limits for the s chart based on past data are commonly given as $B_4\bar{s}$ and $B_3\bar{s}$. That is, $B_4 = B_6/c_4$ and $B_3 = B_5/c_4$. This is convenient for users, but we choose to minimize the number of control chart constants students must keep straight and to emphasize that process monitoring and past data charts are exactly the same except for the source of μ and σ.

12. Simulated data based on information appearing in the article cited in Note 1.

13. Data provided by Linda McCabe, Purdue University.

14. The first two Deming quotes are from *Public Sector Quality Report,* December 1993, p. 5. They were found online at `deming.eng.clemson.edu/pub/den/files/demqtes.txt`. The third quote is part of the 10th of Deming's "14 points of quality management," from his book *Out of the Crisis,* MIT Press, 1986.

15. Control charts for *individual measurements* cannot use within-sample standard deviations to estimate short-term process variability. The spread between successive observations is the next best thing. Texts such as that cited in Note 8 give the details.

16. The data in Figure 12.17(b) are simulated from a probability model for call pickup times. That pickup times for large financial institutions have median 20 seconds and mean 32 seconds is reported by Jon Anton, "A case study in benchmarking call centers," Purdue University Center for Customer-Driven Quality, no date.

17. Micheline Maynard, "Building success from parts," *New York Times,* March 17, 2002.

Chapter 13

1. The UPS press release regarding the holiday shipping season was posted at `www.ups.com/content/corp/about/news/art_4230.html`.

2. The home page for the Monthly Retail Trade Survey is found at `www.census.gov/mrts/www/mrtshist.html`.

3. JCPenney quarterly net sales data were extracted from annual reports found at `www.jcpenney.net/company/finance/finarch.htm`.

4. Consumer Electronics Association (CEA), `www.ce.org`. Data used by permission.

5. The number of Macintoshes shipped per fiscal quarter can be found in Apple's quarterly earnings press release. Follow the "Financial Releases" link at `www.apple.com/find/sitemap.html` to find the documents.

6. For example, details of the Durbin-Watson test for autocorrelation can be found in M. H. Kutner, C. J. Nachtschiem, W. Wasserman, and J. Neter, *Applied Linear Statistical Models,* 4th edition, McGraw-Hill, 1996.

7. The consumer loans data is maintained at the Federal Reserve Web site. The Web address for monthly consumer loans data is `www.federalreserve.gov/releases/h8/data/m/b1029a.txt`. Values in this series are sometimes revised after their initial posting to the site.

8. The motor vehicle production data are provided at the National Statistics Web site for the UK at `www.statistics.gov.uk`. The passenger car production time series is coded JCYM.

Chapter 14

1. Results of the study are reported in P. F. Campbell and G. P. McCabe, "Predicting the success of freshmen in a computer science major," *Communications of the ACM,* 27 (1984), pp. 1108–1113.

2. This rule is intended to provide a general guideline for deciding when serious errors may result by applying ANOVA procedures. When the sample sizes in each group are very small, the sample variances will tend to vary much more than when the sample sizes are large. In this case, the rule may be a little too conservative. For unequal sample sizes, particular difficulties can arise when a relatively small sample size is associated with a population having a relatively large standard deviation. Careful judgment is needed in all cases. By considering P-values rather than fixed level α testing, judgments in ambiguous cases can more easily be made; for example, if the P-value is very small, say 0.001, then it is probably safe to reject H_0 even if there is a fair amount of variation in the sample standard deviations.

3. This example is based on data from a study conducted by Jim Baumann and Leah Jones of the Purdue University School of Education.

4. This example is based on Amna Kirmani and Peter Wright, "Money talks: perceived advertising expense and expected product quality," *Journal of Consumer Research,* 16 (1989), pp. 344–353.

5. Several different definitions for the noncentrality parameter of the noncentral F distribution are in use. When $I = 2$, the λ defined here is equal to the square of the noncentrality parameter δ that we used for the two-sample t test in Chapter 7. Many authors prefer $\phi = \sqrt{\lambda/I}$. We have chosen to use λ because it is the form needed for the SAS function PROBF.

6. These data were provided by Helen Park; see H. Park et al., "Fortifying bread with each of three antioxidants," *Cereal Chemistry,* 74 (1997), pp. 202–206.

7. Based on M. U. Kalwani and C. K. Yim, "Consumer price and promotion expectations: an experimental study," *Journal of Marketing Research,* 29 (1992), pp. 90–100.

8. Data provided by Jo Welch of the Purdue University Department of Foods and Nutrition.

9. Based on A. A. Adish et al., "Effect of consumption of food cooked in iron pots on iron status and growth of young children: a randomised trial," *The Lancet,* 353 (1999), pp. 712–716.

10. See S. Badylak et al., "Marrow-derived cells populate scaffolds composed of xenogeneic extracellular matrix," *Experimental Hematology,* 29 (2001), pp. 1310–1318.

11. Modified from M. C. Wilson and R. E. Shade, "Relative attractiveness of various luminescent colors to the cereal leaf beetle and the meadow spittlebug," *Journal of Economic Entomology,* 60 (1967), pp. 578–580.

12. Data provided by Dennis Lobstein, from his Ph.D. dissertation, "A multivariate study of exercise training effects on beta-endorphin and emotionality in psychologically normal, medically healthy men," Purdue University, 1983.

13. These data were taken from Collaborative Research Support Program in Food Intake and Human Function, *Management Entity Final Report,* University of California, Berkeley, 1988.

DATA APPENDIX

Some of the exercises in the text refer to fourteen relatively large data sets that are on the CD that accompanies this text. The CD also contains data from many other exercises and examples.

Background information for each of the fourteen data sets is presented below. For each, the first five observations are given here.

1 ARCH

Text Reference: Case Study Exercise 7.1

Characteristics of 24 large Indianapolis-area architectural firms are given in this data set. The variables are OBS, a numerical identifier for each firm; FIRM, the name of the firm; BILL98, billings in 1998 in millions of dollars; BILL97, billings in 1997 in millions of dollars; ARCH, the number of architects in the firm; ENG, the number of engineers in the firm; STAFF, the number of staff members in the firm; and FOUNDYR, the year that the firm was founded. Here are the data for the first five firms:

OBS	FIRM	BILL98	BILL97	ARCH	ENG	STAFF	FOUNDYR
1	Schmidt	11.5	5.0	19	7	111	1976
2	CSO	9.3	8.8	29	12	126	1961
3	BSA	9.0	7.5	31	21	155	1975
4	InterDes	6.4	4.7	19	3	57	1975
5	Browning	6.2	3.9	24	0	70	1967

2 CHEESE

Text References: Exercise 11.88; Examples 17.5, 17.9, 17.10; Case Study Exercises 11.1, 17.1

As cheddar cheese matures, a variety of chemical processes take place. The taste of matured cheese is related to the concentration of several chemicals in the final product. In a study of cheddar cheese from the LaTrobe Valley of Victoria, Australia, samples of cheese were analyzed for their chemical composition and were subjected to taste tests.

Data for one type of cheese-manufacturing process appear below. The variable "Case" is used to number the observations from 1 to 30. "Taste" is the response variable of interest. The taste scores were obtained by combining the scores from several tasters.

Three of the chemicals whose concentrations were measured were acetic acid, hydrogen sulfide, and lactic acid. For acetic acid and hydrogen sulfide (natural) log transformations were taken. Thus the explanatory variables are the transformed concentrations of acetic acid ("Acetic") and hydrogen sulfide ("H2S") and the untransformed concentration of lactic acid ("Lactic"). These data are based on experiments performed by G. T. Lloyd and E. H. Ramshaw of the CSIRO Division of Food Research, Victoria, Australia. Some results of the statistical analyses of these data are given in G. P. McCabe, L. McCabe, and A. Miller, "Analysis of taste and chemical composition of cheddar cheese, 1982–83 experiments," CSIRO Division of Mathematics and Statistics Consulting Report VT85/6; and in I. Barlow et al., "Correlations and changes in flavour and chemical parameters of cheddar cheeses during maturation," *Australian Journal of Dairy Technology*, 44 (1989), pp. 7–18. The table gives the data for the first five samples of cheese.

Case	Taste	Acetic	H2S	Lactic
01	12.3	4.543	3.135	0.86
02	20.9	5.159	5.043	1.53
03	39.0	5.366	5.438	1.57
04	47.9	5.759	7.496	1.81
05	5.6	4.663	3.807	0.99

3 COFFEEEXPORTS

Text Reference: Case Study Exercise 2.3

Coffee is one of the world's largest traded commodities. Coffee is a universally popular drink, with over 50 billion dollars (U.S. dollars) in worldwide retail sales a year. The International Coffee Organization (ICO) is an intergovernmental body whose members are coffee exporting and importing countries. ICO exporting members account for over 97% of world coffee production and its importing members are responsible for 66% of world coffee consumption.

One stated objective of the ICO is "ensuring transparency in the coffee market through *statistics,* with around 200,000 records processed each year." To this end, the ICO provides data on coffee exports, imports, and prices at its website, `www.ico.org`.

The data found in the file *coffeexports.dat* show exports for 48 ICO member countries covering four time periods: December 2001, December 2000, January to December 2001, and January to December 2000. Exports are measured in number of 60-kilo bags.

Here are the data for the first five countries:

Country	Dec-2001	Dec-2000	2001	2000
Colombia	1216914	1060661	9943630	9175370
Kenya	47795	97645	982440	1328305
Tanzania	86394	102358	866162	755744
Bolivia	9000	7000	124625	111558
Burundi	31200	41056	303183	444242

4 CONCEPT

Text Reference: Case Study Exercise 11.2

Darlene Gordon of the Purdue University School of Education provided the data in the CONCEPT data set. The data were collected on 78 seventh-grade students in a rural midwestern school. The research concerned the relationship between the students' "self-concept" and their academic performance. The variables are OBS, a subject identification number; GPA, grade point average; IQ, score on an IQ test; AGE, age in years; SEX, female (1) or male (2); SC, overall score on the Piers-Harris Children's Self-Concept Scale; and C1 to C6, "cluster scores" for specific aspects of self-concept: C1 = behavior, C2 = school status, C3 = physical appearance, C4 = anxiety, C5 = popularity, and C6 = happiness. Here are data for the first five students:

OBS	GPA	IQ	AGE	SEX	SC	C1	C2	C3	C4	C5	C6
001	7.940	111	13	2	67	15	17	13	13	11	9
002	8.292	107	12	2	43	12	12	7	7	6	6
003	4.643	100	13	2	52	11	10	5	8	9	7
004	7.470	107	12	2	66	14	15	11	11	9	9
005	8.882	114	12	1	58	14	15	10	12	11	6

5 CSDATA

Text References: Case 11.2; Exercises 11.121–11.129; Case Study Exercises 2.2, 17.2

The computer science department of a large university was interested in understanding why a large proportion of their first-year students failed to graduate as computer science majors. An examination of records from the registrar indicated that most of the attrition occurred during the first three semesters. Therefore, they decided to study all first-year students entering their program in a particular year and to follow their progress for the first three semesters.

The variables studied included the grade point average after three semesters and a collection of variables that would be available as students entered the program. These variables included scores on standardized tests such as the SATs and high school grades in various subjects. The researchers who conducted the study were also interested in examining differences between men and women in this program. Therefore, sex was included as a variable.

Data on 224 students who began study as computer science majors in a particular year were analyzed. A few exceptional cases were excluded, such as students whose data on the variables of interest was incomplete (a few students were admitted who did not take the SATs). Data for the first five students appear in the table. There are eight variables for each student. OBS is a variable used to identify the student. The data files kept by the registrar identified students by social security number, but for this study they were simply given a number from 1 to 224. The grade point average after three semesters is the variable GPA. This university uses a four-point scale, with A corresponding to 4, B to 3, C to 2, etc. A straight-A student has a 4.00 GPA.

The high school grades included in the data set are the variables HSM, HSS, and HSE—average high school grades in math, science, and English. High schools use different grading systems (some high schools have a grade higher than A for honors courses), so the university's task in constructing these variables is not easy. The researchers were willing to accept the university's judgment and used its values. High school grades were recorded on a scale from 1 to 10, with 10 corresponding to A, 9 to A−, 8 to B+, and so on.

The SAT scores are SATM and SATV, corresponding to the mathematics and verbal parts of the SAT. Gender was recorded as 1 for men and 2 for women. This is an arbitrary code. For software packages that can use alphanumeric variables (values do not have to be numbers), it is more convenient to use M and F or Men and Women as values for the sex variable. With this kind of user-friendly capability, you do not have to remember who are the 1's and who are the 2's.

Results of the study are reported in P. F. Campbell and G. P. McCabe, "Predicting the success of freshmen in a computer science major," *Communications of the ACM*, 27 (1984), pp. 1108–1113. The table below gives data for the first five students.

OBS	GPA	HSM	HSS	HSE	SATM	SATV	SEX
001	3.32	10	10	10	670	600	1
002	2.26	6	8	5	700	640	1
003	2.35	8	6	8	640	530	1
004	2.08	9	10	7	670	600	1
005	3.38	8	9	8	540	580	1

6 DANDRUFF

Text Reference: Case Study Exercise 14.1

The DANDRUFF data set is based on W. L. Billhimer et al., "Results of a clinical trial comparing 1% pyrithione zinc and 2% ketoconazole shampoos," *Cosmetic Dermatology*, 9 (1996), pp. 34–39. The study reported in this paper is a clinical trial that compared three treatments for dandruff and a placebo. The treatments were 1% pyrithione zinc shampoo (PyrI), the same shampoo but with instructions to shampoo two times (PyrII), 2% ketoconazole shampoo (Keto), and a placebo shampoo (Placebo). After six weeks of treatment, eight sections of the scalp were examined and given a score that measured the amount of scalp flaking on a 0 to 10 scale. The response variable was the sum of these eight scores. An analysis of the baseline flaking measure indicated that randomization of patients to treatments was successful in that no differences were found between the groups. At baseline there were 112 subjects in each of the three treatment groups and 28 subjects in the Placebo group. During the clinical trial 3 dropped out from the PyrII group and 6 from the Keto group. No patients dropped out of the other two groups. Summary statistics given in the paper were used to generate random data that give the same conclusions. Here are the data for the first five subjects:

OBS	Treatment	Flaking
001	PyrI	17
002	PyrI	16
003	PyrI	18
004	PyrI	17
005	PyrI	18

7 HOMES

Text Reference: Case 11.3; Case Study Exercises 11.5, 17.4

People wanting to buy a home can find information on the Internet about homes for sale in their community. We will work with online data for all homes for sale in Lafayette and West Lafayette, Indiana. The data were collected from the Web site `http://www.realtor.com` on October 8, 2001.

The variables are Obs, a numerical home identifier; Price, the asking price of the home; SqFt, the number of square feet for the home; BedRooms, the number of bedrooms; Baths, the number of bathrooms; Garage, the number of cars that can fit in the garage; and Zip, the last digit of postal zip code for the address. (The first four digits are 4790.) There are 504 homes in the data set. Here are the data for the first five homes:

Obs	Price	SqFt	BedRooms	Baths	Garage	Zip
1	52900	932	1	1.0	0	4
2	61500	780	3	1.0	0	5
3	62000	1500	3	1.0	0	9
4	62900	760	2	1.0	0	4
5	64900	900	2	1.0	0	4

8 HOURLY

Text References: Case 1.2; Case Study Exercises 1.2, 11.3

Executive Order 11246, signed by President Lyndon B. Johnson in 1965, prohibits discrimination in hiring and employment decisions on the basis of race, color, gender, religion, and national origin. It applies to contractors doing business in excess of $10,000 with the U.S. government. The Office of Federal Contract Compliance Programs (OFCCP) is responsible for monitoring compliance with this Executive Order. Setting employees' pay is an important employment decision, and the OFCCP frequently examines the salary data of government contractors.

Many banks are subject to the OFCCP guidelines and they periodically review their salary data to verify that they are in compliance with the regulations. This data set contains records for 1745 hourly workers at one such bank. The data are based on real records, but to preserve confidentiality, we simply call the bank National Bank. We have also made minor modifications to the numbers. The variables are ID, an employee identifier; gender coded as "F" for female and "M" for male; race, coded as "Black," "White," and "Other"; earnings; and status, with values "PT" for a part time worker and "FT" for a full time worker. Here are the data for the first five employees:

Id	Gender	Race	Earnings	Status
1	F	Black	14682	FT
2	F	Black	12655	PT
3	F	Black	12641	FT
4	F	Black	14678	PT
5	F	Black	14714	FT

9 INDIVIDUALS

Text References: Case Study Exercises 1.1, 3.2

Each March, the Bureau of Labor Statistics carries out an Annual Demographic Supplement to its monthly Current Population Survey. The BLS collects detailed data about the 50,000 randomly selected households in its sample. The data file *individuals.dat* contains data about 55,899 people from the March 2000 survey. We included all people between the ages of 25 and 65 who have worked but whose main work experience is not in agriculture. Moreover, we combined the 16 levels of education in the BLS survey to form 6 levels.

There are five variables in the data set. Age is age in years. Education is the highest level of education a person has reached, with the following values: 1 = did not reach high school; 2 = some high school, but no high school diploma; 3 = high school diploma; 4 = some college but no bachelor's degree (this includes people with an associate degree); 5 = bachelor's degree; 6 = postgraduate degree (master's, professional, or doctorate). Sex is gender coded as 1 = male and 2 = female. Total income is income from all sources. Note that income can be less than zero in some cases. Job class is a categorization of the person's main work experience, with 5 = private sector (outside households); 6 = government; 7 = self-employed. Here are the first five cases:

Age	Education	Sex	Total income	Job Class
25	2	2	7234	5
25	5	1	37413	5
25	4	2	29500	5
25	3	2	13500	5
25	4	1	17660	6

The first individual in the file is a 25-year-old female who did not graduate from high school, works in the private sector, and had $7234 of income.

10 MAJORS

Text Reference: Case Study Exercise 15.1

See the description of the CSDATA data set for background information on the study for this data set. In this data file, the variables described for CSDATA are given with an additional variable "Maj" that specifies the student's major field of study at the end of three semesters. The codes 1, 2, and 3 correspond to Computer Science, Engineering and Other Sciences, and Other. All available data were used in the analyses performed, which resulted in sample sizes that were unequal in the six sex-by-major groups.

For a one-way ANOVA this causes no particular problems. However, for a two-way ANOVA several complications arise when the sample sizes are unequal. A detailed discussion of these complications is beyond the scope of this text. To avoid these difficulties and still use these interesting data, simulated data based on the results of this study are given on the data disk. ANOVA based on these simulated data gives the same qualitative conclusions as those obtained with the original data. Here are the first five cases:

OBS	SEX	Maj	SATM	SATV	HSM	HSS	HSE	GPA
001	1	1	640	530	8	6	8	2.35
002	1	1	670	600	9	10	7	2.08
003	1	1	600	400	8	8	7	3.21
004	1	1	570	480	7	7	6	2.34
005	1	1	510	530	6	8	8	1.40

11 PLANTS1

Text Reference: Case Study Exercise 15.2

These data were collected by Maher Tadros from the Purdue University Department of Forestry and Natural Resources under the direction of his major professor, Andrew Gillespie. Maher is from Jordan, a Middle Eastern country where there is very little rainfall in many areas. His research concerns four species of plants that may be suitable for commercial development in his country. Products produced by these species can be used as feed for animals and in some cases for humans. The four species of plants are *Leucaena leucocephala, Acacia saligna, Prosopis juliflora,* and *Eucalyptus citriodora.* A major research question concerns how well these species can tolerate drought stress.

PLANTS1 gives data for a laboratory experiment performed by Maher at Purdue University. Seven different amounts of water were given daily to plants of each species. For each of the species-by-water combinations, there were nine plants. The response variable is the percent of the plant that consists of nitrogen. A high nitrogen content is desirable for plant products that are used for food.

The actual experiment performed to collect these data had an additional factor that is not given in the data set. The 4 × 7, species-by-water combinations were actually run with three plants per combination. This design was then repeated three times. The repeat factor is often called a replicate, or rep, and is a standard part of most well-designed experiments of this type. For our purposes we ignore this additional factor and analyze the design as a 4×7 two-way ANOVA with 9 observations per treatment combination. The first five cases are listed below. The four species, *Leucaena leucocephala, Acacia saligna, Prosopis juliflora,* and *Eucalyptus citriodora,* are coded 1 to 4. The water levels, 50 mm, 150 mm, 250 mm, 350 mm, 450 mm, 550 mm, and 650 mm, are coded 1 to 7.

OBS	Species	Water	pctnit
001	1	1	3.644
002	1	1	3.500
003	1	1	3.509
004	1	1	3.137
005	1	1	3.100

12 PLANTS2

Text Reference: Case Study Exercise 15.3

PLANTS2 gives data for a second experiment conducted by Maher Tadros in a lab at Purdue University. As in PLANTS1, there are the same four species of plants and the same seven levels of water. Here, however, there are four plants per species-by-water combination. The two response variables in the data set are fresh biomass and dry biomass. High values for these response variables indicate that the plants of the given species are resistant to drought at the given water level. Here are the first five cases:

OBS	Species	Water	fbiomass	dbiomass
001	1	1	105.13	37.65
002	1	1	138.95	48.85
003	1	1	90.05	38.85
004	1	1	102.25	36.91
005	1	1	207.90	74.35

13 READING

Text Reference: Case Study Exercise 14.2

Jim Baumann and Leah Jones of the Purdue University School of Education conducted a study to compare three methods of teaching reading comprehension. The 66 students who participated in the study were randomly assigned to the methods (22 to each). The standard practice of comparing new methods with a traditional one was used in this study. The traditional method is called Basal and the two innovative methods are called DRTA and Strat.

In the data set the variable Subject is used to identify the individual students. The values are 1 to 66. The method of instruction is indicated by the variable Group, with values B, D, and S, corresponding to Basal, DRTA, and Strat. Two pretests and three posttests were given to all students. These are the variables Pre1, Pre2, Post1, Post2, and Post3. Data for the first five subjects are given below.

Subject	Group	Pre1	Pre2	Post1	Post2	Post3
01	B	4	3	5	4	41
02	B	6	5	9	5	41
03	B	9	4	5	3	43
04	B	12	6	8	5	46
05	B	16	5	10	9	46

14 RUNNERS

Text Reference: Exercise 15.51

A study of cardiovascular risk factors compared runners who averaged at least 15 miles per week with a control group described as "generally sedentary." Both men and women were included in the study. The data set was constructed based on information provided in P. D. Wood et al., "Plasma lipoprotein distributions in male and female runners," in P. Milvey (ed.), *The Marathon: Physiological, Medical, Epidemiological, and Psychological Studies,* New York Academy of Sciences, 1977.

The study design is a 2 × 2 ANOVA with the factors group and gender. There were 200 subjects in each of the four combinations. The variables are Id, a numeric subject identifier; Group, with values "Control" and "Runners"; Gender, with values Female and Male; and HeartRate, heart rate after the subject ran for 6 minutes on a treadmill. Here are the data for the first five subjects:

Id	Group	Gender	HeartRate
001	Control	Female	159
002	Control	Female	183
003	Control	Female	140
004	Control	Female	140
005	Control	Female	125

15 SALARY

Text Reference: Case Study Exercise 11.4

Refer to the HOURLY data set described above. Data for salaried employees were also examined. The SALARY data set contains the following variables: Id, a numeric employee identifier; Gender, coded as "M" for males and "F" for females; Salary, annual salary; and JobLevel, a numerical variable that classifies the job description of each employee. Here are the data for the first five employees:

Id	Gender	Salary	JobLevel
1	M	34843.00	7
2	M	27520.00	7
3	F	30779.00	7
4	F	33076.00	7
5	M	27097.00	7

TABLES

Table entry for z is the area under the standard normal curve to the left of z.

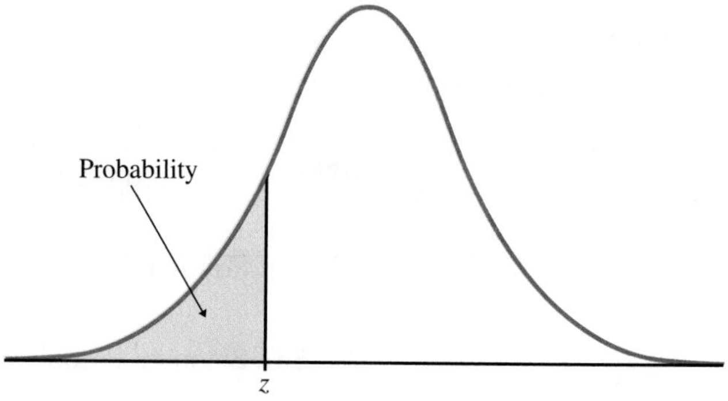

TABLE A Standard normal probabilities

z	.00	.01	.02	.03	.04	.05	.06	.07	.08	.09
−3.4	.0003	.0003	.0003	.0003	.0003	.0003	.0003	.0003	.0003	.0002
−3.3	.0005	.0005	.0005	.0004	.0004	.0004	.0004	.0004	.0004	.0003
−3.2	.0007	.0007	.0006	.0006	.0006	.0006	.0006	.0005	.0005	.0005
−3.1	.0010	.0009	.0009	.0009	.0008	.0008	.0008	.0008	.0007	.0007
−3.0	.0013	.0013	.0013	.0012	.0012	.0011	.0011	.0011	.0010	.0010
−2.9	.0019	.0018	.0018	.0017	.0016	.0016	.0015	.0015	.0014	.0014
−2.8	.0026	.0025	.0024	.0023	.0023	.0022	.0021	.0021	.0020	.0019
−2.7	.0035	.0034	.0033	.0032	.0031	.0030	.0029	.0028	.0027	.0026
−2.6	.0047	.0045	.0044	.0043	.0041	.0040	.0039	.0038	.0037	.0036
−2.5	.0062	.0060	.0059	.0057	.0055	.0054	.0052	.0051	.0049	.0048
−2.4	.0082	.0080	.0078	.0075	.0073	.0071	.0069	.0068	.0066	.0064
−2.3	.0107	.0104	.0102	.0099	.0096	.0094	.0091	.0089	.0087	.0084
−2.2	.0139	.0136	.0132	.0129	.0125	.0122	.0119	.0116	.0113	.0110
−2.1	.0179	.0174	.0170	.0166	.0162	.0158	.0154	.0150	.0146	.0143
−2.0	.0228	.0222	.0217	.0212	.0207	.0202	.0197	.0192	.0188	.0183
−1.9	.0287	.0281	.0274	.0268	.0262	.0256	.0250	.0244	.0239	.0233
−1.8	.0359	.0351	.0344	.0336	.0329	.0322	.0314	.0307	.0301	.0294
−1.7	.0446	.0436	.0427	.0418	.0409	.0401	.0392	.0384	.0375	.0367
−1.6	.0548	.0537	.0526	.0516	.0505	.0495	.0485	.0475	.0465	.0455
−1.5	.0668	.0655	.0643	.0630	.0618	.0606	.0594	.0582	.0571	.0559
−1.4	.0808	.0793	.0778	.0764	.0749	.0735	.0721	.0708	.0694	.0681
−1.3	.0968	.0951	.0934	.0918	.0901	.0885	.0869	.0853	.0838	.0823
−1.2	.1151	.1131	.1112	.1093	.1075	.1056	.1038	.1020	.1003	.0985
−1.1	.1357	.1335	.1314	.1292	.1271	.1251	.1230	.1210	.1190	.1170
−1.0	.1587	.1562	.1539	.1515	.1492	.1469	.1446	.1423	.1401	.1379
−0.9	.1841	.1814	.1788	.1762	.1736	.1711	.1685	.1660	.1635	.1611
−0.8	.2119	.2090	.2061	.2033	.2005	.1977	.1949	.1922	.1894	.1867
−0.7	.2420	.2389	.2358	.2327	.2296	.2266	.2236	.2206	.2177	.2148
−0.6	.2743	.2709	.2676	.2643	.2611	.2578	.2546	.2514	.2483	.2451
−0.5	.3085	.3050	.3015	.2981	.2946	.2912	.2877	.2843	.2810	.2776
−0.4	.3446	.3409	.3372	.3336	.3300	.3264	.3228	.3192	.3156	.3121
−0.3	.3821	.3783	.3745	.3707	.3669	.3632	.3594	.3557	.3520	.3483
−0.2	.4207	.4168	.4129	.4090	.4052	.4013	.3974	.3936	.3897	.3859
−0.1	.4602	.4562	.4522	.4483	.4443	.4404	.4364	.4325	.4286	.4247
−0.0	.5000	.4960	.4920	.4880	.4840	.4801	.4761	.4721	.4681	.4641

Table entry for z is the area under the standard normal curve to the left of z.

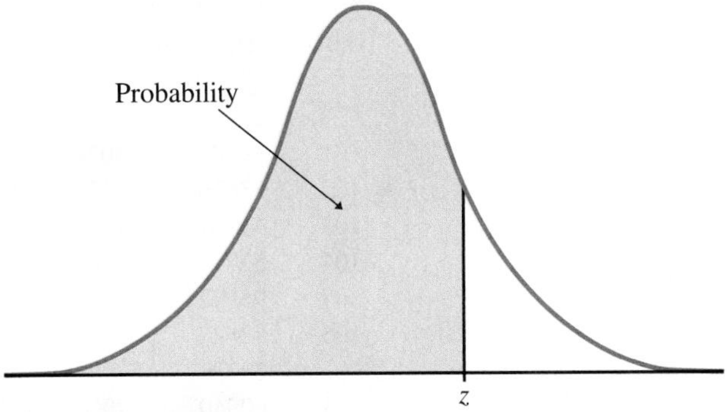

TABLE A **Standard normal probabilities** ***(continued)***

z	.00	.01	.02	.03	.04	.05	.06	.07	.08	.09
0.0	.5000	.5040	.5080	.5120	.5160	.5199	.5239	.5279	.5319	.5359
0.1	.5398	.5438	.5478	.5517	.5557	.5596	.5636	.5675	.5714	.5753
0.2	.5793	.5832	.5871	.5910	.5948	.5987	.6026	.6064	.6103	.6141
0.3	.6179	.6217	.6255	.6293	.6331	.6368	.6406	.6443	.6480	.6517
0.4	.6554	.6591	.6628	.6664	.6700	.6736	.6772	.6808	.6844	.6879
0.5	.6915	.6950	.6985	.7019	.7054	.7088	.7123	.7157	.7190	.7224
0.6	.7257	.7291	.7324	.7357	.7389	.7422	.7454	.7486	.7517	.7549
0.7	.7580	.7611	.7642	.7673	.7704	.7734	.7764	.7794	.7823	.7852
0.8	.7881	.7910	.7939	.7967	.7995	.8023	.8051	.8078	.8106	.8133
0.9	.8159	.8186	.8212	.8238	.8264	.8289	.8315	.8340	.8365	.8389
1.0	.8413	.8438	.8461	.8485	.8508	.8531	.8554	.8577	.8599	.8621
1.1	.8643	.8665	.8686	.8708	.8729	.8749	.8770	.8790	.8810	.8830
1.2	.8849	.8869	.8888	.8907	.8925	.8944	.8962	.8980	.8997	.9015
1.3	.9032	.9049	.9066	.9082	.9099	.9115	.9131	.9147	.9162	.9177
1.4	.9192	.9207	.9222	.9236	.9251	.9265	.9279	.9292	.9306	.9319
1.5	.9332	.9345	.9357	.9370	.9382	.9394	.9406	.9418	.9429	.9441
1.6	.9452	.9463	.9474	.9484	.9495	.9505	.9515	.9525	.9535	.9545
1.7	.9554	.9564	.9573	.9582	.9591	.9599	.9608	.9616	.9625	.9633
1.8	.9641	.9649	.9656	.9664	.9671	.9678	.9686	.9693	.9699	.9706
1.9	.9713	.9719	.9726	.9732	.9738	.9744	.9750	.9756	.9761	.9767
2.0	.9772	.9778	.9783	.9788	.9793	.9798	.9803	.9808	.9812	.9817
2.1	.9821	.9826	.9830	.9834	.9838	.9842	.9846	.9850	.9854	.9857
2.2	.9861	.9864	.9868	.9871	.9875	.9878	.9881	.9884	.9887	.9890
2.3	.9893	.9896	.9898	.9901	.9904	.9906	.9909	.9911	.9913	.9916
2.4	.9918	.9920	.9922	.9925	.9927	.9929	.9931	.9932	.9934	.9936
2.5	.9938	.9940	.9941	.9943	.9945	.9946	.9948	.9949	.9951	.9952
2.6	.9953	.9955	.9956	.9957	.9959	.9960	.9961	.9962	.9963	.9964
2.7	.9965	.9966	.9967	.9968	.9969	.9970	.9971	.9972	.9973	.9974
2.8	.9974	.9975	.9976	.9977	.9977	.9978	.9979	.9979	.9980	.9981
2.9	.9981	.9982	.9982	.9983	.9984	.9984	.9985	.9985	.9986	.9986
3.0	.9987	.9987	.9987	.9988	.9988	.9989	.9989	.9989	.9990	.9990
3.1	.9990	.9991	.9991	.9991	.9992	.9992	.9992	.9992	.9993	.9993
3.2	.9993	.9993	.9994	.9994	.9994	.9994	.9994	.9995	.9995	.9995
3.3	.9995	.9995	.9995	.9996	.9996	.9996	.9996	.9996	.9996	.9997
3.4	.9997	.9997	.9997	.9997	.9997	.9997	.9997	.9997	.9997	.9998

TABLE B **Random digits**

Line								
101	19223	95034	05756	28713	96409	12531	42544	82853
102	73676	47150	99400	01927	27754	42648	82425	36290
103	45467	71709	77558	00095	32863	29485	82226	90056
104	52711	38889	93074	60227	40011	85848	48767	52573
105	95592	94007	69971	91481	60779	53791	17297	59335
106	68417	35013	15529	72765	85089	57067	50211	47487
107	82739	57890	20807	47511	81676	55300	94383	14893
108	60940	72024	17868	24943	61790	90656	87964	18883
109	36009	19365	15412	39638	85453	46816	83485	41979
110	38448	48789	18338	24697	39364	42006	76688	08708
111	81486	69487	60513	09297	00412	71238	27649	39950
112	59636	88804	04634	71197	19352	73089	84898	45785
113	62568	70206	40325	03699	71080	22553	11486	11776
114	45149	32992	75730	66280	03819	56202	02938	70915
115	61041	77684	94322	24709	73698	14526	31893	32592
116	14459	26056	31424	80371	65103	62253	50490	61181
117	38167	98532	62183	70632	23417	26185	41448	75532
118	73190	32533	04470	29669	84407	90785	65956	86382
119	95857	07118	87664	92099	58806	66979	98624	84826
120	35476	55972	39421	65850	04266	35435	43742	11937
121	71487	09984	29077	14863	61683	47052	62224	51025
122	13873	81598	95052	90908	73592	75186	87136	95761
123	54580	81507	27102	56027	55892	33063	41842	81868
124	71035	09001	43367	49497	72719	96758	27611	91596
125	96746	12149	37823	71868	18442	35119	62103	39244
126	96927	19931	36089	74192	77567	88741	48409	41903
127	43909	99477	25330	64359	40085	16925	85117	36071
128	15689	14227	06565	14374	13352	49367	81982	87209
129	36759	58984	68288	22913	18638	54303	00795	08727
130	69051	64817	87174	09517	84534	06489	87201	97245
131	05007	16632	81194	14873	04197	85576	45195	96565
132	68732	55259	84292	08796	43165	93739	31685	97150
133	45740	41807	65561	33302	07051	93623	18132	09547
134	27816	78416	18329	21337	35213	37741	04312	68508
135	66925	55658	39100	78458	11206	19876	87151	31260
136	08421	44753	77377	28744	75592	08563	79140	92454
137	53645	66812	61421	47836	12609	15373	98481	14592
138	66831	68908	40772	21558	47781	33586	79177	06928
139	55588	99404	70708	41098	43563	56934	48394	51719
140	12975	13258	13048	45144	72321	81940	00360	02428
141	96767	35964	23822	96012	94591	65194	50842	53372
142	72829	50232	97892	63408	77919	44575	24870	04178
143	88565	42628	17797	49376	61762	16953	88604	12724
144	62964	88145	83083	69453	46109	59505	69680	00900
145	19687	12633	57857	95806	09931	02150	43163	58636
146	37609	59057	66967	83401	60705	02384	90597	93600
147	54973	86278	88737	74351	47500	84552	19909	67181
148	00694	05977	19664	65441	20903	62371	22725	53340
149	71546	05233	53946	68743	72460	27601	45403	88692
150	07511	88915	41267	16853	84569	79367	32337	03316

TABLE B **Random digits *(continued)***

Line								
151	03802	29341	29264	80198	12371	13121	54969	43912
152	77320	35030	77519	41109	98296	18984	60869	12349
153	07886	56866	39648	69290	03600	05376	58958	22720
154	87065	74133	21117	70595	22791	67306	28420	52067
155	42090	09628	54035	93879	98441	04606	27381	82637
156	55494	67690	88131	81800	11188	28552	25752	21953
157	16698	30406	96587	65985	07165	50148	16201	86792
158	16297	07626	68683	45335	34377	72941	41764	77038
159	22897	17467	17638	70043	36243	13008	83993	22869
160	98163	45944	34210	64158	76971	27689	82926	75957
161	43400	25831	06283	22138	16043	15706	73345	26238
162	97341	46254	88153	62336	21112	35574	99271	45297
163	64578	67197	28310	90341	37531	63890	52630	76315
164	11022	79124	49525	63078	17229	32165	01343	21394
165	81232	43939	23840	05995	84589	06788	76358	26622
166	36843	84798	51167	44728	20554	55538	27647	32708
167	84329	80081	69516	78934	14293	92478	16479	26974
168	27788	85789	41592	74472	96773	27090	24954	41474
169	99224	00850	43737	75202	44753	63236	14260	73686
170	38075	73239	52555	46342	13365	02182	30443	53229
171	87368	49451	55771	48343	51236	18522	73670	23212
172	40512	00681	44282	47178	08139	78693	34715	75606
173	81636	57578	54286	27216	58758	80358	84115	84568
174	26411	94292	06340	97762	37033	85968	94165	46514
175	80011	09937	57195	33906	94831	10056	42211	65491
176	92813	87503	63494	71379	76550	45984	05481	50830
177	70348	72871	63419	57363	29685	43090	18763	31714
178	24005	52114	26224	39078	80798	15220	43186	00976
179	85063	55810	10470	08029	30025	29734	61181	72090
180	11532	73186	92541	06915	72954	10167	12142	26492
181	59618	03914	05208	84088	20426	39004	84582	87317
182	92965	50837	39921	84661	82514	81899	24565	60874
183	85116	27684	14597	85747	01596	25889	41998	15635
184	15106	10411	90221	49377	44369	28185	80959	76355
185	03638	31589	07871	25792	85823	55400	56026	12193
186	97971	48932	45792	63993	95635	28753	46069	84635
187	49345	18305	76213	82390	77412	97401	50650	71755
188	87370	88099	89695	87633	76987	85503	26257	51736
189	88296	95670	74932	65317	93848	43988	47597	83044
190	79485	92200	99401	54473	34336	82786	05457	60343
191	40830	24979	23333	37619	56227	95941	59494	86539
192	32006	76302	81221	00693	95197	75044	46596	11628
193	37569	85187	44692	50706	53161	69027	88389	60313
194	56680	79003	23361	67094	15019	63261	24543	52884
195	05172	08100	22316	54495	60005	29532	18433	18057
196	74782	27005	03894	98038	20627	40307	47317	92759
197	85288	93264	61409	03404	09649	55937	60843	66167
198	68309	12060	14762	58002	03716	81968	57934	32624
199	26461	88346	52430	60906	74216	96263	69296	90107
200	42672	67680	42376	95023	82744	03971	96560	55148

TABLE C Binomial probabilities

Entry is $P(X = k) = \binom{n}{k} p^k (1-p)^{n-k}$

		p								
n	*k*	.01	.02	.03	.04	.05	.06	.07	.08	.09
2	0	.9801	.9604	.9409	.9216	.9025	.8836	.8649	.8464	.8281
	1	.0198	.0392	.0582	.0768	.0950	.1128	.1302	.1472	.1638
	2	.0001	.0004	.0009	.0016	.0025	.0036	.0049	.0064	.0081
3	0	.9703	.9412	.9127	.8847	.8574	.8306	.8044	.7787	.7536
	1	.0294	.0576	.0847	.1106	.1354	.1590	.1816	.2031	.2236
	2	.0003	.0012	.0026	.0046	.0071	.0102	.0137	.0177	.0221
	3				.0001	.0001	.0002	.0003	.0005	.0007
4	0	.9606	.9224	.8853	.8493	.8145	.7807	.7481	.7164	.6857
	1	.0388	.0753	.1095	.1416	.1715	.1993	.2252	.2492	.2713
	2	.0006	.0023	.0051	.0088	.0135	.0191	.0254	.0325	.0402
	3			.0001	.0002	.0005	.0008	.0013	.0019	.0027
	4									.0001
5	0	.9510	.9039	.8587	.8154	.7738	.7339	.6957	.6591	.6240
	1	.0480	.0922	.1328	.1699	.2036	.2342	.2618	.2866	.3086
	2	.0010	.0038	.0082	.0142	.0214	.0299	.0394	.0498	.0610
	3		.0001	.0003	.0006	.0011	.0019	.0030	.0043	.0060
	4						.0001	.0001	.0002	.0003
	5									
6	0	.9415	.8858	.8330	.7828	.7351	.6899	.6470	.6064	.5679
	1	.0571	.1085	.1546	.1957	.2321	.2642	.2922	.3164	.3370
	2	.0014	.0055	.0120	.0204	.0305	.0422	.0550	.0688	.0833
	3		.0002	.0005	.0011	.0021	.0036	.0055	.0080	.0110
	4					.0001	.0002	.0003	.0005	.0008
	5									
	6									
7	0	.9321	.8681	.8080	.7514	.6983	.6485	.6017	.5578	.5168
	1	.0659	.1240	.1749	.2192	.2573	.2897	.3170	.3396	.3578
	2	.0020	.0076	.0162	.0274	.0406	.0555	.0716	.0886	.1061
	3		.0003	.0008	.0019	.0036	.0059	.0090	.0128	.0175
	4				.0001	.0002	.0004	.0007	.0011	.0017
	5								.0001	.0001
	6									
	7									
8	0	.9227	.8508	.7837	.7214	.6634	.6096	.5596	.5132	.4703
	1	.0746	.1389	.1939	.2405	.2793	.3113	.3370	.3570	.3721
	2	.0026	.0099	.0210	.0351	.0515	.0695	.0888	.1087	.1288
	3	.0001	.0004	.0013	.0029	.0054	.0089	.0134	.0189	.0255
	4			.0001	.0002	.0004	.0007	.0013	.0021	.0031
	5							.0001	.0001	.0002
	6									
	7									
	8									

TABLE C Binomial probabilities *(continued)*

Entry is $P(X = k) = \binom{n}{k} p^k (1-p)^{n-k}$

		p								
n	*k*	.10	.15	.20	.25	.30	.35	.40	.45	.50
2	0	.8100	.7225	.6400	.5625	.4900	.4225	.3600	.3025	.2500
	1	.1800	.2550	.3200	.3750	.4200	.4550	.4800	.4950	.5000
	2	.0100	.0225	.0400	.0625	.0900	.1225	.1600	.2025	.2500
3	0	.7290	.6141	.5120	.4219	.3430	.2746	.2160	.1664	.1250
	1	.2430	.3251	.3840	.4219	.4410	.4436	.4320	.4084	.3750
	2	.0270	.0574	.0960	.1406	.1890	.2389	.2880	.3341	.3750
	3	.0010	.0034	.0080	.0156	.0270	.0429	.0640	.0911	.1250
4	0	.6561	.5220	.4096	.3164	.2401	.1785	.1296	.0915	.0625
	1	.2916	.3685	.4096	.4219	.4116	.3845	.3456	.2995	.2500
	2	.0486	.0975	.1536	.2109	.2646	.3105	.3456	.3675	.3750
	3	.0036	.0115	.0256	.0469	.0756	.1115	.1536	.2005	.2500
	4	.0001	.0005	.0016	.0039	.0081	.0150	.0256	.0410	.0625
5	0	.5905	.4437	.3277	.2373	.1681	.1160	.0778	.0503	.0313
	1	.3280	.3915	.4096	.3955	.3602	.3124	.2592	.2059	.1563
	2	.0729	.1382	.2048	.2637	.3087	.3364	.3456	.3369	.3125
	3	.0081	.0244	.0512	.0879	.1323	.1811	.2304	.2757	.3125
	4	.0004	.0022	.0064	.0146	.0284	.0488	.0768	.1128	.1562
	5		.0001	.0003	.0010	.0024	.0053	.0102	.0185	.0312
6	0	.5314	.3771	.2621	.1780	.1176	.0754	.0467	.0277	.0156
	1	.3543	.3993	.3932	.3560	.3025	.2437	.1866	.1359	.0938
	2	.0984	.1762	.2458	.2966	.3241	.3280	.3110	.2780	.2344
	3	.0146	.0415	.0819	.1318	.1852	.2355	.2765	.3032	.3125
	4	.0012	.0055	.0154	.0330	.0595	.0951	.1382	.1861	.2344
	5	.0001	.0004	.0015	.0044	.0102	.0205	.0369	.0609	.0937
	6			.0001	.0002	.0007	.0018	.0041	.0083	.0156
7	0	.4783	.3206	.2097	.1335	.0824	.0490	.0280	.0152	.0078
	1	.3720	.3960	.3670	.3115	.2471	.1848	.1306	.0872	.0547
	2	.1240	.2097	.2753	.3115	.3177	.2985	.2613	.2140	.1641
	3	.0230	.0617	.1147	.1730	.2269	.2679	.2903	.2918	.2734
	4	.0026	.0109	.0287	.0577	.0972	.1442	.1935	.2388	.2734
	5	.0002	.0012	.0043	.0115	.0250	.0466	.0774	.1172	.1641
	6		.0001	.0004	.0013	.0036	.0084	.0172	.0320	.0547
	7				.0001	.0002	.0006	.0016	.0037	.0078
8	0	.4305	.2725	.1678	.1001	.0576	.0319	.0168	.0084	.0039
	1	.3826	.3847	.3355	.2670	.1977	.1373	.0896	.0548	.0313
	2	.1488	.2376	.2936	.3115	.2965	.2587	.2090	.1569	.1094
	3	.0331	.0839	.1468	.2076	.2541	.2786	.2787	.2568	.2188
	4	.0046	.0185	.0459	.0865	.1361	.1875	.2322	.2627	.2734
	5	.0004	.0026	.0092	.0231	.0467	.0808	.1239	.1719	.2188
	6		.0002	.0011	.0038	.0100	.0217	.0413	.0703	.1094
	7			.0001	.0004	.0012	.0033	.0079	.0164	.0312
	8					.0001	.0002	.0007	.0017	.0039

TABLE C Binomial probabilities *(continued)*

Entry is $P(X = k) = \binom{n}{k} p^k (1-p)^{n-k}$

		p								
n	*k*	.01	.02	.03	.04	.05	.06	.07	.08	.09
9	0	.9135	.8337	.7602	.6925	.6302	.5730	.5204	.4722	.4279
	1	.0830	.1531	.2116	.2597	.2985	.3292	.3525	.3695	.3809
	2	.0034	.0125	.0262	.0433	.0629	.0840	.1061	.1285	.1507
	3	.0001	.0006	.0019	.0042	.0077	.0125	.0186	.0261	.0348
	4			.0001	.0003	.0006	.0012	.0021	.0034	.0052
	5						.0001	.0002	.0003	.0005
	6									
	7									
	8									
	9									
10	0	.9044	.8171	.7374	.6648	.5987	.5386	.4840	.4344	.3894
	1	.0914	.1667	.2281	.2770	.3151	.3438	.3643	.3777	.3851
	2	.0042	.0153	.0317	.0519	.0746	.0988	.1234	.1478	.1714
	3	.0001	.0008	.0026	.0058	.0105	.0168	.0248	.0343	.0452
	4			.0001	.0004	.0010	.0019	.0033	.0052	.0078
	5					.0001	.0001	.0003	.0005	.0009
	6									.0001
	7									
	8									
	9									
	10									
12	0	.8864	.7847	.6938	.6127	.5404	.4759	.4186	.3677	.3225
	1	.1074	.1922	.2575	.3064	.3413	.3645	.3781	.3837	.3827
	2	.0060	.0216	.0438	.0702	.0988	.1280	.1565	.1835	.2082
	3	.0002	.0015	.0045	.0098	.0173	.0272	.0393	.0532	.0686
	4		.0001	.0003	.0009	.0021	.0039	.0067	.0104	.0153
	5				.0001	.0002	.0004	.0008	.0014	.0024
	6							.0001	.0001	.0003
	7									
	8									
	9									
	10									
	11									
	12									
15	0	.8601	.7386	.6333	.5421	.4633	.3953	.3367	.2863	.2430
	1	.1303	.2261	.2938	.3388	.3658	.3785	.3801	.3734	.3605
	2	.0092	.0323	.0636	.0988	.1348	.1691	.2003	.2273	.2496
	3	.0004	.0029	.0085	.0178	.0307	.0468	.0653	.0857	.1070
	4		.0002	.0008	.0022	.0049	.0090	.0148	.0223	.0317
	5			.0001	.0002	.0006	.0013	.0024	.0043	.0069
	6						.0001	.0003	.0006	.0011
	7								.0001	.0001
	8									
	9									
	10									
	11									
	12									
	13									
	14									
	15									

TABLE C Binomial probabilities (*continued*)

		p								
n	*k*	.10	.15	.20	.25	.30	.35	.40	.45	.50
9	0	.3874	.2316	.1342	.0751	.0404	.0207	.0101	.0046	.0020
	1	.3874	.3679	.3020	.2253	.1556	.1004	.0605	.0339	.0176
	2	.1722	.2597	.3020	.3003	.2668	.2162	.1612	.1110	.0703
	3	.0446	.1069	.1762	.2336	.2668	.2716	.2508	.2119	.1641
	4	.0074	.0283	.0661	.1168	.1715	.2194	.2508	.2600	.2461
	5	.0008	.0050	.0165	.0389	.0735	.1181	.1672	.2128	.2461
	6	.0001	.0006	.0028	.0087	.0210	.0424	.0743	.1160	.1641
	7			.0003	.0012	.0039	.0098	.0212	.0407	.0703
	8				.0001	.0004	.0013	.0035	.0083	.0176
	9						.0001	.0003	.0008	.0020
10	0	.3487	.1969	.1074	.0563	.0282	.0135	.0060	.0025	.0010
	1	.3874	.3474	.2684	.1877	.1211	.0725	.0403	.0207	.0098
	2	.1937	.2759	.3020	.2816	.2335	.1757	.1209	.0763	.0439
	3	.0574	.1298	.2013	.2503	.2668	.2522	.2150	.1665	.1172
	4	.0112	.0401	.0881	.1460	.2001	.2377	.2508	.2384	.2051
	5	.0015	.0085	.0264	.0584	.1029	.1536	.2007	.2340	.2461
	6	.0001	.0012	.0055	.0162	.0368	.0689	.1115	.1596	.2051
	7		.0001	.0008	.0031	.0090	.0212	.0425	.0746	.1172
	8			.0001	.0004	.0014	.0043	.0106	.0229	.0439
	9					.0001	.0005	.0016	.0042	.0098
	10							.0001	.0003	.0010
12	0	.2824	.1422	.0687	.0317	.0138	.0057	.0022	.0008	.0002
	1	.3766	.3012	.2062	.1267	.0712	.0368	.0174	.0075	.0029
	2	.2301	.2924	.2835	.2323	.1678	.1088	.0639	.0339	.0161
	3	.0852	.1720	.2362	.2581	.2397	.1954	.1419	.0923	.0537
	4	.0213	.0683	.1329	.1936	.2311	.2367	.2128	.1700	.1208
	5	.0038	.0193	.0532	.1032	.1585	.2039	.2270	.2225	.1934
	6	.0005	.0040	.0155	.0401	.0792	.1281	.1766	.2124	.2256
	7		.0006	.0033	.0115	.0291	.0591	.1009	.1489	.1934
	8		.0001	.0005	.0024	.0078	.0199	.0420	.0762	.1208
	9			.0001	.0004	.0015	.0048	.0125	.0277	.0537
	10					.0002	.0008	.0025	.0068	.0161
	11						.0001	.0003	.0010	.0029
	12								.0001	.0002
15	0	.2059	.0874	.0352	.0134	.0047	.0016	.0005	.0001	.0000
	1	.3432	.2312	.1319	.0668	.0305	.0126	.0047	.0016	.0005
	2	.2669	.2856	.2309	.1559	.0916	.0476	.0219	.0090	.0032
	3	.1285	.2184	.2501	.2252	.1700	.1110	.0634	.0318	.0139
	4	.0428	.1156	.1876	.2252	.2186	.1792	.1268	.0780	.0417
	5	.0105	.0449	.1032	.1651	.2061	.2123	.1859	.1404	.0916
	6	.0019	.0132	.0430	.0917	.1472	.1906	.2066	.1914	.1527
	7	.0003	.0030	.0138	.0393	.0811	.1319	.1771	.2013	.1964
	8		.0005	.0035	.0131	.0348	.0710	.1181	.1647	.1964
	9		.0001	.0007	.0034	.0116	.0298	.0612	.1048	.1527
	10			.0001	.0007	.0030	.0096	.0245	.0515	.0916
	11				.0001	.0006	.0024	.0074	.0191	.0417
	12					.0001	.0004	.0016	.0052	.0139
	13						.0001	.0003	.0010	.0032
	14								.0001	.0005
	15									

TABLE C Binomial probabilities *(continued)*

n	*k*	*p* = .01	.02	.03	.04	.05	.06	.07	.08	.09
20	0	.8179	.6676	.5438	.4420	.3585	.2901	.2342	.1887	.1516
	1	.1652	.2725	.3364	.3683	.3774	.3703	.3526	.3282	.3000
	2	.0159	.0528	.0988	.1458	.1887	.2246	.2521	.2711	.2818
	3	.0010	.0065	.0183	.0364	.0596	.0860	.1139	.1414	.1672
	4		.0006	.0024	.0065	.0133	.0233	.0364	.0523	.0703
	5			.0002	.0009	.0022	.0048	.0088	.0145	.0222
	6				.0001	.0003	.0008	.0017	.0032	.0055
	7						.0001	.0002	.0005	.0011
	8								.0001	.0002
	9									
	10									
	11									
	12									
	13									
	14									
	15									
	16									
	17									
	18									
	19									
	20									

n	*k*	*p* = .10	.15	.20	.25	.30	.35	.40	.45	.50
20	0	.1216	.0388	.0115	.0032	.0008	.0002	.0000	.0000	.0000
	1	.2702	.1368	.0576	.0211	.0068	.0020	.0005	.0001	.0000
	2	.2852	.2293	.1369	.0669	.0278	.0100	.0031	.0008	.0002
	3	.1901	.2428	.2054	.1339	.0716	.0323	.0123	.0040	.0011
	4	.0898	.1821	.2182	.1897	.1304	.0738	.0350	.0139	.0046
	5	.0319	.1028	.1746	.2023	.1789	.1272	.0746	.0365	.0148
	6	.0089	.0454	.1091	.1686	.1916	.1712	.1244	.0746	.0370
	7	.0020	.0160	.0545	.1124	.1643	.1844	.1659	.1221	.0739
	8	.0004	.0046	.0222	.0609	.1144	.1614	.1797	.1623	.1201
	9	.0001	.0011	.0074	.0271	.0654	.1158	.1597	.1771	.1602
	10		.0002	.0020	.0099	.0308	.0686	.1171	.1593	.1762
	11			.0005	.0030	.0120	.0336	.0710	.1185	.1602
	12			.0001	.0008	.0039	.0136	.0355	.0727	.1201
	13				.0002	.0010	.0045	.0146	.0366	.0739
	14					.0002	.0012	.0049	.0150	.0370
	15						.0003	.0013	.0049	.0148
	16							.0003	.0013	.0046
	17								.0002	.0011
	18									.0002
	19									
	20									

Table entry for p and C is the critical value t^* with probability p lying to its right and probability C lying between $-t^*$ and t^*.

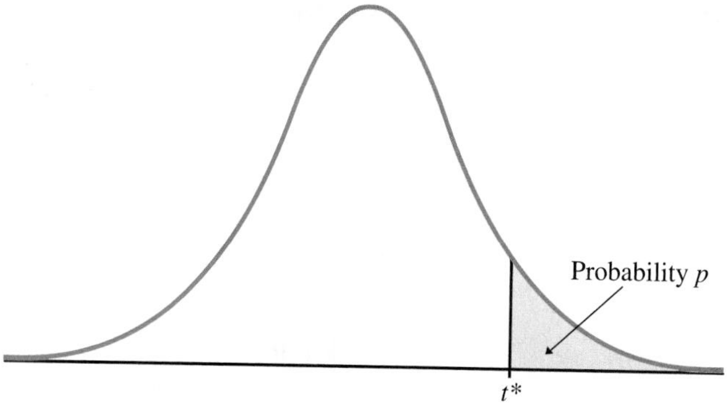

TABLE D ***t* distribution critical values**

	Upper tail probability p											
df	**.25**	**.20**	**.15**	**.10**	**.05**	**.025**	**.02**	**.01**	**.005**	**.0025**	**.001**	**.0005**
1	1.000	1.376	1.963	3.078	6.314	12.71	15.89	31.82	63.66	127.3	318.3	636.6
2	0.816	1.061	1.386	1.886	2.920	4.303	4.849	6.965	9.925	14.09	22.33	31.60
3	0.765	0.978	1.250	1.638	2.353	3.182	3.482	4.541	5.841	7.453	10.21	12.92
4	0.741	0.941	1.190	1.533	2.132	2.776	2.999	3.747	4.604	5.598	7.173	8.610
5	0.727	0.920	1.156	1.476	2.015	2.571	2.757	3.365	4.032	4.773	5.893	6.869
6	0.718	0.906	1.134	1.440	1.943	2.447	2.612	3.143	3.707	4.317	5.208	5.959
7	0.711	0.896	1.119	1.415	1.895	2.365	2.517	2.998	3.499	4.029	4.785	5.408
8	0.706	0.889	1.108	1.397	1.860	2.306	2.449	2.896	3.355	3.833	4.501	5.041
9	0.703	0.883	1.100	1.383	1.833	2.262	2.398	2.821	3.250	3.690	4.297	4.781
10	0.700	0.879	1.093	1.372	1.812	2.228	2.359	2.764	3.169	3.581	4.144	4.587
11	0.697	0.876	1.088	1.363	1.796	2.201	2.328	2.718	3.106	3.497	4.025	4.437
12	0.695	0.873	1.083	1.356	1.782	2.179	2.303	2.681	3.055	3.428	3.930	4.318
13	0.694	0.870	1.079	1.350	1.771	2.160	2.282	2.650	3.012	3.372	3.852	4.221
14	0.692	0.868	1.076	1.345	1.761	2.145	2.264	2.624	2.977	3.326	3.787	4.140
15	0.691	0.866	1.074	1.341	1.753	2.131	2.249	2.602	2.947	3.286	3.733	4.073
16	0.690	0.865	1.071	1.337	1.746	2.120	2.235	2.583	2.921	3.252	3.686	4.015
17	0.689	0.863	1.069	1.333	1.740	2.110	2.224	2.567	2.898	3.222	3.646	3.965
18	0.688	0.862	1.067	1.330	1.734	2.101	2.214	2.552	2.878	3.197	3.611	3.922
19	0.688	0.861	1.066	1.328	1.729	2.093	2.205	2.539	2.861	3.174	3.579	3.883
20	0.687	0.860	1.064	1.325	1.725	2.086	2.197	2.528	2.845	3.153	3.552	3.850
21	0.686	0.859	1.063	1.323	1.721	2.080	2.189	2.518	2.831	3.135	3.527	3.819
22	0.686	0.858	1.061	1.321	1.717	2.074	2.183	2.508	2.819	3.119	3.505	3.792
23	0.685	0.858	1.060	1.319	1.714	2.069	2.177	2.500	2.807	3.104	3.485	3.768
24	0.685	0.857	1.059	1.318	1.711	2.064	2.172	2.492	2.797	3.091	3.467	3.745
25	0.684	0.856	1.058	1.316	1.708	2.060	2.167	2.485	2.787	3.078	3.450	3.725
26	0.684	0.856	1.058	1.315	1.706	2.056	2.162	2.479	2.779	3.067	3.435	3.707
27	0.684	0.855	1.057	1.314	1.703	2.052	2.158	2.473	2.771	3.057	3.421	3.690
28	0.683	0.855	1.056	1.313	1.701	2.048	2.154	2.467	2.763	3.047	3.408	3.674
29	0.683	0.854	1.055	1.311	1.699	2.045	2.150	2.462	2.756	3.038	3.396	3.659
30	0.683	0.854	1.055	1.310	1.697	2.042	2.147	2.457	2.750	3.030	3.385	3.646
40	0.681	0.851	1.050	1.303	1.684	2.021	2.123	2.423	2.704	2.971	3.307	3.551
50	0.679	0.849	1.047	1.299	1.676	2.009	2.109	2.403	2.678	2.937	3.261	3.496
60	0.679	0.848	1.045	1.296	1.671	2.000	2.099	2.390	2.660	2.915	3.232	3.460
80	0.678	0.846	1.043	1.292	1.664	1.990	2.088	2.374	2.639	2.887	3.195	3.416
100	0.677	0.845	1.042	1.290	1.660	1.984	2.081	2.364	2.626	2.871	3.174	3.390
1000	0.675	0.842	1.037	1.282	1.646	1.962	2.056	2.330	2.581	2.813	3.098	3.300
z^*	0.674	0.841	1.036	1.282	1.645	1.960	2.054	2.326	2.576	2.807	3.091	3.291
	50%	**60%**	**70%**	**80%**	**90%**	**95%**	**96%**	**98%**	**99%**	**99.5%**	**99.8%**	**99.9%**
	Confidence level C											

Table entry for p is the critical value F^* with probability p lying to its right.

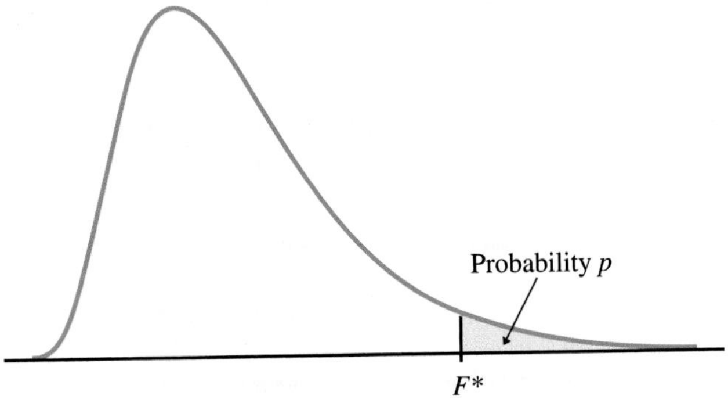

TABLE E ***F* critical values**

Degrees of freedom in the denominator	p	Degrees of freedom in the numerator: 1	2	3	4	5	6	7	8	9
1	.100	39.86	49.50	53.59	55.83	57.24	58.20	58.91	59.44	59.86
	.050	161.45	199.50	215.71	224.58	230.16	233.99	236.77	238.88	240.54
	.025	647.79	799.50	864.16	899.58	921.85	937.11	948.22	956.66	963.28
	.010	4052.2	4999.5	5403.4	5624.6	5763.6	5859.0	5928.4	5981.1	6022.5
	.001	405284	500000	540379	562500	576405	585937	592873	598144	602284
2	.100	8.53	9.00	9.16	9.24	9.29	9.33	9.35	9.37	9.38
	.050	18.51	19.00	19.16	19.25	19.30	19.33	19.35	19.37	19.38
	.025	38.51	39.00	39.17	39.25	39.30	39.33	39.36	39.37	39.39
	.010	98.50	99.00	99.17	99.25	99.30	99.33	99.36	99.37	99.39
	.001	998.50	999.00	999.17	999.25	999.30	999.33	999.36	999.37	999.39
3	.100	5.54	5.46	5.39	5.34	5.31	5.28	5.27	5.25	5.24
	.050	10.13	9.55	9.28	9.12	9.01	8.94	8.89	8.85	8.81
	.025	17.44	16.04	15.44	15.10	14.88	14.73	14.62	14.54	14.47
	.010	34.12	30.82	29.46	28.71	28.24	27.91	27.67	27.49	27.35
	.001	167.03	148.50	141.11	137.10	134.58	132.85	131.58	130.62	129.86
4	.100	4.54	4.32	4.19	4.11	4.05	4.01	3.98	3.95	3.94
	.050	7.71	6.94	6.59	6.39	6.26	6.16	6.09	6.04	6.00
	.025	12.22	10.65	9.98	9.60	9.36	9.20	9.07	8.98	8.90
	.010	21.20	18.00	16.69	15.98	15.52	15.21	14.98	14.80	14.66
	.001	74.14	61.25	56.18	53.44	51.71	50.53	49.66	49.00	48.47
5	.100	4.06	3.78	3.62	3.52	3.45	3.40	3.37	3.34	3.32
	.050	6.61	5.79	5.41	5.19	5.05	4.95	4.88	4.82	4.77
	.025	10.01	8.43	7.76	7.39	7.15	6.98	6.85	6.76	6.68
	.010	16.26	13.27	12.06	11.39	10.97	10.67	10.46	10.29	10.16
	.001	47.18	37.12	33.20	31.09	29.75	28.83	28.16	27.65	27.24
6	.100	3.78	3.46	3.29	3.18	3.11	3.05	3.01	2.98	2.96
	.050	5.99	5.14	4.76	4.53	4.39	4.28	4.21	4.15	4.10
	.025	8.81	7.26	6.60	6.23	5.99	5.82	5.70	5.60	5.52
	.010	13.75	10.92	9.78	9.15	8.75	8.47	8.26	8.10	7.98
	.001	35.51	27.00	23.70	21.92	20.80	20.03	19.46	19.03	18.69
7	.100	3.59	3.26	3.07	2.96	2.88	2.83	2.78	2.75	2.72
	.050	5.59	4.74	4.35	4.12	3.97	3.87	3.79	3.73	3.68
	.025	8.07	6.54	5.89	5.52	5.29	5.12	4.99	4.90	4.82
	.010	12.25	9.55	8.45	7.85	7.46	7.19	6.99	6.84	6.72
	.001	29.25	21.69	18.77	17.20	16.21	15.52	15.02	14.63	14.33

Table entry for p is the critical value F^* with probability p lying to its right.

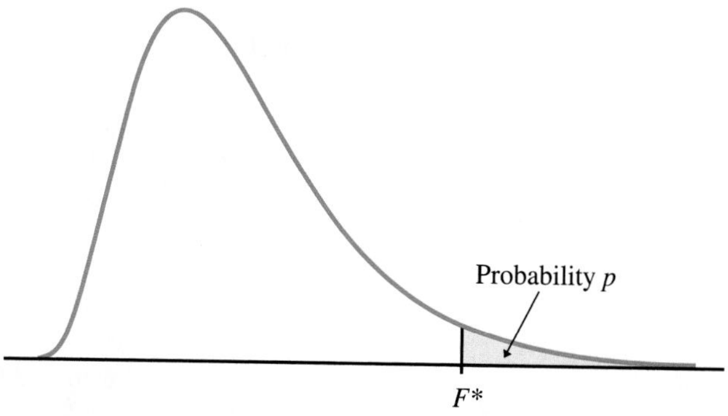

TABLE E ***F* critical values *(continued)***

Degrees of freedom in the numerator										
10	12	15	20	25	30	40	50	60	120	1000
60.19	60.71	61.22	61.74	62.05	62.26	62.53	62.69	62.79	63.06	63.30
241.88	243.91	245.95	248.01	249.26	250.10	251.14	251.77	252.20	253.25	254.19
968.63	976.71	984.87	993.10	998.08	1001.4	1005.6	1008.1	1009.8	1014.0	1017.7
6055.8	6106.3	6157.3	6208.7	6239.8	6260.6	6286.8	6302.5	6313.0	6339.4	6362.7
605621	610668	615764	620908	624017	626099	628712	630285	631337	633972	636301
9.39	9.41	9.42	9.44	9.45	9.46	9.47	9.47	9.47	9.48	9.49
19.40	19.41	19.43	19.45	19.46	19.46	19.47	19.48	19.48	19.49	19.49
39.40	39.41	39.43	39.45	39.46	39.46	39.47	39.48	39.48	39.49	39.50
99.40	99.42	99.43	99.45	99.46	99.47	99.47	99.48	99.48	99.49	99.50
999.40	999.42	999.43	999.45	999.46	999.47	999.47	999.48	999.48	999.49	999.50
5.23	5.22	5.20	5.18	5.17	5.17	5.16	5.15	5.15	5.14	5.13
8.79	8.74	8.70	8.66	8.63	8.62	8.59	8.58	8.57	8.55	8.53
14.42	14.34	14.25	14.17	14.12	14.08	14.04	14.01	13.99	13.95	13.91
27.23	27.05	26.87	26.69	26.58	26.50	26.41	26.35	26.32	26.22	26.14
129.25	128.32	127.37	126.42	125.84	125.45	124.96	124.66	124.47	123.97	123.53
3.92	3.90	3.87	3.84	3.83	3.82	3.80	3.80	3.79	3.78	3.76
5.96	5.91	5.86	5.80	5.77	5.75	5.72	5.70	5.69	5.66	5.63
8.84	8.75	8.66	8.56	8.50	8.46	8.41	8.38	8.36	8.31	8.26
14.55	14.37	14.20	14.02	13.91	13.84	13.75	13.69	13.65	13.56	13.47
48.05	47.41	46.76	46.10	45.70	45.43	45.09	44.88	44.75	44.40	44.09
3.30	3.27	3.24	3.21	3.19	3.17	3.16	3.15	3.14	3.12	3.11
4.74	4.68	4.62	4.56	4.52	4.50	4.46	4.44	4.43	4.40	4.37
6.62	6.52	6.43	6.33	6.27	6.23	6.18	6.14	6.12	6.07	6.02
10.05	9.89	9.72	9.55	9.45	9.38	9.29	9.24	9.20	9.11	9.03
26.92	26.42	25.91	25.39	25.08	24.87	24.60	24.44	24.33	24.06	23.82
2.94	2.90	2.87	2.84	2.81	2.80	2.78	2.77	2.76	2.74	2.72
4.06	4.00	3.94	3.87	3.83	3.81	3.77	3.75	3.74	3.70	3.67
5.46	5.37	5.27	5.17	5.11	5.07	5.01	4.98	4.96	4.90	4.86
7.87	7.72	7.56	7.40	7.30	7.23	7.14	7.09	7.06	6.97	6.89
18.41	17.99	17.56	17.12	16.85	16.67	16.44	16.31	16.21	15.98	15.77
2.70	2.67	2.63	2.59	2.57	2.56	2.54	2.52	2.51	2.49	2.47
3.64	3.57	3.51	3.44	3.40	3.38	3.34	3.32	3.30	3.27	3.23
4.76	4.67	4.57	4.47	4.40	4.36	4.31	4.28	4.25	4.20	4.15
6.62	6.47	6.31	6.16	6.06	5.99	5.91	5.86	5.82	5.74	5.66
14.08	13.71	13.32	12.93	12.69	12.53	12.33	12.20	12.12	11.91	11.72

TABLE E ***F* critical values *(continued)***

Degrees of freedom in the denominator	*p*	Degrees of freedom in the numerator 1	2	3	4	5	6	7	8	9
8	.100	3.46	3.11	2.92	2.81	2.73	2.67	2.62	2.59	2.56
	.050	5.32	4.46	4.07	3.84	3.69	3.58	3.50	3.44	3.39
	.025	7.57	6.06	5.42	5.05	4.82	4.65	4.53	4.43	4.36
	.010	11.26	8.65	7.59	7.01	6.63	6.37	6.18	6.03	5.91
	.001	25.41	18.49	15.83	14.39	13.48	12.86	12.40	12.05	11.77
9	.100	3.36	3.01	2.81	2.69	2.61	2.55	2.51	2.47	2.44
	.050	5.12	4.26	3.86	3.63	3.48	3.37	3.29	3.23	3.18
	.025	7.21	5.71	5.08	4.72	4.48	4.32	4.20	4.10	4.03
	.010	10.56	8.02	6.99	6.42	6.06	5.80	5.61	5.47	5.35
	.001	22.86	16.39	13.90	12.56	11.71	11.13	10.70	10.37	10.11
10	.100	3.29	2.92	2.73	2.61	2.52	2.46	2.41	2.38	2.35
	.050	4.96	4.10	3.71	3.48	3.33	3.22	3.14	3.07	3.02
	.025	6.94	5.46	4.83	4.47	4.24	4.07	3.95	3.85	3.78
	.010	10.04	7.56	6.55	5.99	5.64	5.39	5.20	5.06	4.94
	.001	21.04	14.91	12.55	11.28	10.48	9.93	9.52	9.20	8.96
11	.100	3.23	2.86	2.66	2.54	2.45	2.39	2.34	2.30	2.27
	.050	4.84	3.98	3.59	3.36	3.20	3.09	3.01	2.95	2.90
	.025	6.72	5.26	4.63	4.28	4.04	3.88	3.76	3.66	3.59
	.010	9.65	7.21	6.22	5.67	5.32	5.07	4.89	4.74	4.63
	.001	19.69	13.81	11.56	10.35	9.58	9.05	8.66	8.35	8.12
12	.100	3.18	2.81	2.61	2.48	2.39	2.33	2.28	2.24	2.21
	.050	4.75	3.89	3.49	3.26	3.11	3.00	2.91	2.85	2.80
	.025	6.55	5.10	4.47	4.12	3.89	3.73	3.61	3.51	3.44
	.010	9.33	6.93	5.95	5.41	5.06	4.82	4.64	4.50	4.39
	.001	18.64	12.97	10.80	9.63	8.89	8.38	8.00	7.71	7.48
13	.100	3.14	2.76	2.56	2.43	2.35	2.28	2.23	2.20	2.16
	.050	4.67	3.81	3.41	3.18	3.03	2.92	2.83	2.77	2.71
	.025	6.41	4.97	4.35	4.00	3.77	3.60	3.48	3.39	3.31
	.010	9.07	6.70	5.74	5.21	4.86	4.62	4.44	4.30	4.19
	.001	17.82	12.31	10.21	9.07	8.35	7.86	7.49	7.21	6.98
14	.100	3.10	2.73	2.52	2.39	2.31	2.24	2.19	2.15	2.12
	.050	4.60	3.74	3.34	3.11	2.96	2.85	2.76	2.70	2.65
	.025	6.30	4.86	4.24	3.89	3.66	3.50	3.38	3.29	3.21
	.010	8.86	6.51	5.56	5.04	4.69	4.46	4.28	4.14	4.03
	.001	17.14	11.78	9.73	8.62	7.92	7.44	7.08	6.80	6.58
15	.100	3.07	2.70	2.49	2.36	2.27	2.21	2.16	2.12	2.09
	.050	4.54	3.68	3.29	3.06	2.90	2.79	2.71	2.64	2.59
	.025	6.20	4.77	4.15	3.80	3.58	3.41	3.29	3.20	3.12
	.010	8.68	6.36	5.42	4.89	4.56	4.32	4.14	4.00	3.89
	.001	16.59	11.34	9.34	8.25	7.57	7.09	6.74	6.47	6.26
16	.100	3.05	2.67	2.46	2.33	2.24	2.18	2.13	2.09	2.06
	.050	4.49	3.63	3.24	3.01	2.85	2.74	2.66	2.59	2.54
	.025	6.12	4.69	4.08	3.73	3.50	3.34	3.22	3.12	3.05
	.010	8.53	6.23	5.29	4.77	4.44	4.20	4.03	3.89	3.78
	.001	16.12	10.97	9.01	7.94	7.27	6.80	6.46	6.19	5.98
17	.100	3.03	2.64	2.44	2.31	2.22	2.15	2.10	2.06	2.03
	.050	4.45	3.59	3.20	2.96	2.81	2.70	2.61	2.55	2.49
	.025	6.04	4.62	4.01	3.66	3.44	3.28	3.16	3.06	2.98
	.010	8.40	6.11	5.19	4.67	4.34	4.10	3.93	3.79	3.68
	.001	15.72	10.66	8.73	7.68	7.02	6.56	6.22	5.96	5.75

TABLE E *F* critical values *(continued)*

Degrees of freedom in the numerator										
10	12	15	20	25	30	40	50	60	120	1000
2.54	2.50	2.46	2.42	2.40	2.38	2.36	2.35	2.34	2.32	2.30
3.35	3.28	3.22	3.15	3.11	3.08	3.04	3.02	3.01	2.97	2.93
4.30	4.20	4.10	4.00	3.94	3.89	3.84	3.81	3.78	3.73	3.68
5.81	5.67	5.52	5.36	5.26	5.20	5.12	5.07	5.03	4.95	4.87
11.54	11.19	10.84	10.48	10.26	10.11	9.92	9.80	9.73	9.53	9.36
2.42	2.38	2.34	2.30	2.27	2.25	2.23	2.22	2.21	2.18	2.16
3.14	3.07	3.01	2.94	2.89	2.86	2.83	2.80	2.79	2.75	2.71
3.96	3.87	3.77	3.67	3.60	3.56	3.51	3.47	3.45	3.39	3.34
5.26	5.11	4.96	4.81	4.71	4.65	4.57	4.52	4.48	4.40	4.32
9.89	9.57	9.24	8.90	8.69	8.55	8.37	8.26	8.19	8.00	7.84
2.32	2.28	2.24	2.20	2.17	2.16	2.13	2.12	2.11	2.08	2.06
2.98	2.91	2.85	2.77	2.73	2.70	2.66	2.64	2.62	2.58	2.54
3.72	3.62	3.52	3.42	3.35	3.31	3.26	3.22	3.20	3.14	3.09
4.85	4.71	4.56	4.41	4.31	4.25	4.17	4.12	4.08	4.00	3.92
8.75	8.45	8.13	7.80	7.60	7.47	7.30	7.19	7.12	6.94	6.78
2.25	2.21	2.17	2.12	2.10	2.08	2.05	2.04	2.03	2.00	1.98
2.85	2.79	2.72	2.65	2.60	2.57	2.53	2.51	2.49	2.45	2.41
3.53	3.43	3.33	3.23	3.16	3.12	3.06	3.03	3.00	2.94	2.89
4.54	4.40	4.25	4.10	4.01	3.94	3.86	3.81	3.78	3.69	3.61
7.92	7.63	7.32	7.01	6.81	6.68	6.52	6.42	6.35	6.18	6.02
2.19	2.15	2.10	2.06	2.03	2.01	1.99	1.97	1.96	1.93	1.91
2.75	2.69	2.62	2.54	2.50	2.47	2.43	2.40	2.38	2.34	2.30
3.37	3.28	3.18	3.07	3.01	2.96	2.91	2.87	2.85	2.79	2.73
4.30	4.16	4.01	3.86	3.76	3.70	3.62	3.57	3.54	3.45	3.37
7.29	7.00	6.71	6.40	6.22	6.09	5.93	5.83	5.76	5.59	5.44
2.14	2.10	2.05	2.01	1.98	1.96	1.93	1.92	1.90	1.88	1.85
2.67	2.60	2.53	2.46	2.41	2.38	2.34	2.31	2.30	2.25	2.21
3.25	3.15	3.05	2.95	2.88	2.84	2.78	2.74	2.72	2.66	2.60
4.10	3.96	3.82	3.66	3.57	3.51	3.43	3.38	3.34	3.25	3.18
6.80	6.52	6.23	5.93	5.75	5.63	5.47	5.37	5.30	5.14	4.99
2.10	2.05	2.01	1.96	1.93	1.91	1.89	1.87	1.86	1.83	1.80
2.60	2.53	2.46	2.39	2.34	2.31	2.27	2.24	2.22	2.18	2.14
3.15	3.05	2.95	2.84	2.78	2.73	2.67	2.64	2.61	2.55	2.50
3.94	3.80	3.66	3.51	3.41	3.35	3.27	3.22	3.18	3.09	3.02
6.40	6.13	5.85	5.56	5.38	5.25	5.10	5.00	4.94	4.77	4.62
2.06	2.02	1.97	1.92	1.89	1.87	1.85	1.83	1.82	1.79	1.76
2.54	2.48	2.40	2.33	2.28	2.25	2.20	2.18	2.16	2.11	2.07
3.06	2.96	2.86	2.76	2.69	2.64	2.59	2.55	2.52	2.46	2.40
3.80	3.67	3.52	3.37	3.28	3.21	3.13	3.08	3.05	2.96	2.88
6.08	5.81	5.54	5.25	5.07	4.95	4.80	4.70	4.64	4.47	4.33
2.03	1.99	1.94	1.89	1.86	1.84	1.81	1.79	1.78	1.75	1.72
2.49	2.42	2.35	2.28	2.23	2.19	2.15	2.12	2.11	2.06	2.02
2.99	2.89	2.79	2.68	2.61	2.57	2.51	2.47	2.45	2.38	2.32
3.69	3.55	3.41	3.26	3.16	3.10	3.02	2.97	2.93	2.84	2.76
5.81	5.55	5.27	4.99	4.82	4.70	4.54	4.45	4.39	4.23	4.08
2.00	1.96	1.91	1.86	1.83	1.81	1.78	1.76	1.75	1.72	1.69
2.45	2.38	2.31	2.23	2.18	2.15	2.10	2.08	2.06	2.01	1.97
2.92	2.82	2.72	2.62	2.55	2.50	2.44	2.41	2.38	2.32	2.26
3.59	3.46	3.31	3.16	3.07	3.00	2.92	2.87	2.83	2.75	2.66
5.58	5.32	5.05	4.78	4.60	4.48	4.33	4.24	4.18	4.02	3.87

TABLE E ***F*** **critical values *(continued)***

Degrees of freedom in the denominator	p	Degrees of freedom in the numerator 1	2	3	4	5	6	7	8	9
18	.100	3.01	2.62	2.42	2.29	2.20	2.13	2.08	2.04	2.00
	.050	4.41	3.55	3.16	2.93	2.77	2.66	2.58	2.51	2.46
	.025	5.98	4.56	3.95	3.61	3.38	3.22	3.10	3.01	2.93
	.010	8.29	6.01	5.09	4.58	4.25	4.01	3.84	3.71	3.60
	.001	15.38	10.39	8.49	7.46	6.81	6.35	6.02	5.76	5.56
19	.100	2.99	2.61	2.40	2.27	2.18	2.11	2.06	2.02	1.98
	.050	4.38	3.52	3.13	2.90	2.74	2.63	2.54	2.48	2.42
	.025	5.92	4.51	3.90	3.56	3.33	3.17	3.05	2.96	2.88
	.010	8.18	5.93	5.01	4.50	4.17	3.94	3.77	3.63	3.52
	.001	15.08	10.16	8.28	7.27	6.62	6.18	5.85	5.59	5.39
20	.100	2.97	2.59	2.38	2.25	2.16	2.09	2.04	2.00	1.96
	.050	4.35	3.49	3.10	2.87	2.71	2.60	2.51	2.45	2.39
	.025	5.87	4.46	3.86	3.51	3.29	3.13	3.01	2.91	2.84
	.010	8.10	5.85	4.94	4.43	4.10	3.87	3.70	3.56	3.46
	.001	14.82	9.95	8.10	7.10	6.46	6.02	5.69	5.44	5.24
21	.100	2.96	2.57	2.36	2.23	2.14	2.08	2.02	1.98	1.95
	.050	4.32	3.47	3.07	2.84	2.68	2.57	2.49	2.42	2.37
	.025	5.83	4.42	3.82	3.48	3.25	3.09	2.97	2.87	2.80
	.010	8.02	5.78	4.87	4.37	4.04	3.81	3.64	3.51	3.40
	.001	14.59	9.77	7.94	6.95	6.32	5.88	5.56	5.31	5.11
22	.100	2.95	2.56	2.35	2.22	2.13	2.06	2.01	1.97	1.93
	.050	4.30	3.44	3.05	2.82	2.66	2.55	2.46	2.40	2.34
	.025	5.79	4.38	3.78	3.44	3.22	3.05	2.93	2.84	2.76
	.010	7.95	5.72	4.82	4.31	3.99	3.76	3.59	3.45	3.35
	.001	14.38	9.61	7.80	6.81	6.19	5.76	5.44	5.19	4.99
23	.100	2.94	2.55	2.34	2.21	2.11	2.05	1.99	1.95	1.92
	.050	4.28	3.42	3.03	2.80	2.64	2.53	2.44	2.37	2.32
	.025	5.75	4.35	3.75	3.41	3.18	3.02	2.90	2.81	2.73
	.010	7.88	5.66	4.76	4.26	3.94	3.71	3.54	3.41	3.30
	.001	14.20	9.47	7.67	6.70	6.08	5.65	5.33	5.09	4.89
24	.100	2.93	2.54	2.33	2.19	2.10	2.04	1.98	1.94	1.91
	.050	4.26	3.40	3.01	2.78	2.62	2.51	2.42	2.36	2.30
	.025	5.72	4.32	3.72	3.38	3.15	2.99	2.87	2.78	2.70
	.010	7.82	5.61	4.72	4.22	3.90	3.67	3.50	3.36	3.26
	.001	14.03	9.34	7.55	6.59	5.98	5.55	5.23	4.99	4.80
25	.100	2.92	2.53	2.32	2.18	2.09	2.02	1.97	1.93	1.89
	.050	4.24	3.39	2.99	2.76	2.60	2.49	2.40	2.34	2.28
	.025	5.69	4.29	3.69	3.35	3.13	2.97	2.85	2.75	2.68
	.010	7.77	5.57	4.68	4.18	3.85	3.63	3.46	3.32	3.22
	.001	13.88	9.22	7.45	6.49	5.89	5.46	5.15	4.91	4.71
26	.100	2.91	2.52	2.31	2.17	2.08	2.01	1.96	1.92	1.88
	.050	4.23	3.37	2.98	2.74	2.59	2.47	2.39	2.32	2.27
	.025	5.66	4.27	3.67	3.33	3.10	2.94	2.82	2.73	2.65
	.010	7.72	5.53	4.64	4.14	3.82	3.59	3.42	3.29	3.18
	.001	13.74	9.12	7.36	6.41	5.80	5.38	5.07	4.83	4.64
27	.100	2.90	2.51	2.30	2.17	2.07	2.00	1.95	1.91	1.87
	.050	4.21	3.35	2.96	2.73	2.57	2.46	2.37	2.31	2.25
	.025	5.63	4.24	3.65	3.31	3.08	2.92	2.80	2.71	2.63
	.010	7.68	5.49	4.60	4.11	3.78	3.56	3.39	3.26	3.15
	.001	13.61	9.02	7.27	6.33	5.73	5.31	5.00	4.76	4.57

TABLE E ***F*** **critical values *(continued)***

Degrees of freedom in the numerator

10	12	15	20	25	30	40	50	60	120	1000
1.98	1.93	1.89	1.84	1.80	1.78	1.75	1.74	1.72	1.69	1.66
2.41	2.34	2.27	2.19	2.14	2.11	2.06	2.04	2.02	1.97	1.92
2.87	2.77	2.67	2.56	2.49	2.44	2.38	2.35	2.32	2.26	2.20
3.51	3.37	3.23	3.08	2.98	2.92	2.84	2.78	2.75	2.66	2.58
5.39	5.13	4.87	4.59	4.42	4.30	4.15	4.06	4.00	3.84	3.69
1.96	1.91	1.86	1.81	1.78	1.76	1.73	1.71	1.70	1.67	1.64
2.38	2.31	2.23	2.16	2.11	2.07	2.03	2.00	1.98	1.93	1.88
2.82	2.72	2.62	2.51	2.44	2.39	2.33	2.30	2.27	2.20	2.14
3.43	3.30	3.15	3.00	2.91	2.84	2.76	2.71	2.67	2.58	2.50
5.22	4.97	4.70	4.43	4.26	4.14	3.99	3.90	3.84	3.68	3.53
1.94	1.89	1.84	1.79	1.76	1.74	1.71	1.69	1.68	1.64	1.61
2.35	2.28	2.20	2.12	2.07	2.04	1.99	1.97	1.95	1.90	1.85
2.77	2.68	2.57	2.46	2.40	2.35	2.29	2.25	2.22	2.16	2.09
3.37	3.23	3.09	2.94	2.84	2.78	2.69	2.64	2.61	2.52	2.43
5.08	4.82	4.56	4.29	4.12	4.00	3.86	3.77	3.70	3.54	3.40
1.92	1.87	1.83	1.78	1.74	1.72	1.69	1.67	1.66	1.62	1.59
2.32	2.25	2.18	2.10	2.05	2.01	1.96	1.94	1.92	1.87	1.82
2.73	2.64	2.53	2.42	2.36	2.31	2.25	2.21	2.18	2.11	2.05
3.31	3.17	3.03	2.88	2.79	2.72	2.64	2.58	2.55	2.46	2.37
4.95	4.70	4.44	4.17	4.00	3.88	3.74	3.64	3.58	3.42	3.28
1.90	1.86	1.81	1.76	1.73	1.70	1.67	1.65	1.64	1.60	1.57
2.30	2.23	2.15	2.07	2.02	1.98	1.94	1.91	1.89	1.84	1.79
2.70	2.60	2.50	2.39	2.32	2.27	2.21	2.17	2.14	2.08	2.01
3.26	3.12	2.98	2.83	2.73	2.67	2.58	2.53	2.50	2.40	2.32
4.83	4.58	4.33	4.06	3.89	3.78	3.63	3.54	3.48	3.32	3.17
1.89	1.84	1.80	1.74	1.71	1.69	1.66	1.64	1.62	1.59	1.55
2.27	2.20	2.13	2.05	2.00	1.96	1.91	1.88	1.86	1.81	1.76
2.67	2.57	2.47	2.36	2.29	2.24	2.18	2.14	2.11	2.04	1.98
3.21	3.07	2.93	2.78	2.69	2.62	2.54	2.48	2.45	2.35	2.27
4.73	4.48	4.23	3.96	3.79	3.68	3.53	3.44	3.38	3.22	3.08
1.88	1.83	1.78	1.73	1.70	1.67	1.64	1.62	1.61	1.57	1.54
2.25	2.18	2.11	2.03	1.97	1.94	1.89	1.86	1.84	1.79	1.74
2.64	2.54	2.44	2.33	2.26	2.21	2.15	2.11	2.08	2.01	1.94
3.17	3.03	2.89	2.74	2.64	2.58	2.49	2.44	2.40	2.31	2.22
4.64	4.39	4.14	3.87	3.71	3.59	3.45	3.36	3.29	3.14	2.99
1.87	1.82	1.77	1.72	1.68	1.66	1.63	1.61	1.59	1.56	1.52
2.24	2.16	2.09	2.01	1.96	1.92	1.87	1.84	1.82	1.77	1.72
2.61	2.51	2.41	2.30	2.23	2.18	2.12	2.08	2.05	1.98	1.91
3.13	2.99	2.85	2.70	2.60	2.54	2.45	2.40	2.36	2.27	2.18
4.56	4.31	4.06	3.79	3.63	3.52	3.37	3.28	3.22	3.06	2.91
1.86	1.81	1.76	1.71	1.67	1.65	1.61	1.59	1.58	1.54	1.51
2.22	2.15	2.07	1.99	1.94	1.90	1.85	1.82	1.80	1.75	1.70
2.59	2.49	2.39	2.28	2.21	2.16	2.09	2.05	2.03	1.95	1.89
3.09	2.96	2.81	2.66	2.57	2.50	2.42	2.36	2.33	2.23	2.14
4.48	4.24	3.99	3.72	3.56	3.44	3.30	3.21	3.15	2.99	2.84
1.85	1.80	1.75	1.70	1.66	1.64	1.60	1.58	1.57	1.53	1.50
2.20	2.13	2.06	1.97	1.92	1.88	1.84	1.81	1.79	1.73	1.68
2.57	2.47	2.36	2.25	2.18	2.13	2.07	2.03	2.00	1.93	1.86
3.06	2.93	2.78	2.63	2.54	2.47	2.38	2.33	2.29	2.20	2.11
4.41	4.17	3.92	3.66	3.49	3.38	3.23	3.14	3.08	2.92	2.78

TABLE E ***F*** **critical values *(continued)***

Degrees of freedom in the denominator	*p*	Degrees of freedom in the numerator 1	2	3	4	5	6	7	8	9
28	.100	2.89	2.50	2.29	2.16	2.06	2.00	1.94	1.90	1.87
	.050	4.20	3.34	2.95	2.71	2.56	2.45	2.36	2.29	2.24
	.025	5.61	4.22	3.63	3.29	3.06	2.90	2.78	2.69	2.61
	.010	7.64	5.45	4.57	4.07	3.75	3.53	3.36	3.23	3.12
	.001	13.50	8.93	7.19	6.25	5.66	5.24	4.93	4.69	4.50
29	.100	2.89	2.50	2.28	2.15	2.06	1.99	1.93	1.89	1.86
	.050	4.18	3.33	2.93	2.70	2.55	2.43	2.35	2.28	2.22
	.025	5.59	4.20	3.61	3.27	3.04	2.88	2.76	2.67	2.59
	.010	7.60	5.42	4.54	4.04	3.73	3.50	3.33	3.20	3.09
	.001	13.39	8.85	7.12	6.19	5.59	5.18	4.87	4.64	4.45
30	.100	2.88	2.49	2.28	2.14	2.05	1.98	1.93	1.88	1.85
	.050	4.17	3.32	2.92	2.69	2.53	2.42	2.33	2.27	2.21
	.025	5.57	4.18	3.59	3.25	3.03	2.87	2.75	2.65	2.57
	.010	7.56	5.39	4.51	4.02	3.70	3.47	3.30	3.17	3.07
	.001	13.29	8.77	7.05	6.12	5.53	5.12	4.82	4.58	4.39
40	.100	2.84	2.44	2.23	2.09	2.00	1.93	1.87	1.83	1.79
	.050	4.08	3.23	2.84	2.61	2.45	2.34	2.25	2.18	2.12
	.025	5.42	4.05	3.46	3.13	2.90	2.74	2.62	2.53	2.45
	.010	7.31	5.18	4.31	3.83	3.51	3.29	3.12	2.99	2.89
	.001	12.61	8.25	6.59	5.70	5.13	4.73	4.44	4.21	4.02
50	.100	2.81	2.41	2.20	2.06	1.97	1.90	1.84	1.80	1.76
	.050	4.03	3.18	2.79	2.56	2.40	2.29	2.20	2.13	2.07
	.025	5.34	3.97	3.39	3.05	2.83	2.67	2.55	2.46	2.38
	.010	7.17	5.06	4.20	3.72	3.41	3.19	3.02	2.89	2.78
	.001	12.22	7.96	6.34	5.46	4.90	4.51	4.22	4.00	3.82
60	.100	2.79	2.39	2.18	2.04	1.95	1.87	1.82	1.77	1.74
	.050	4.00	3.15	2.76	2.53	2.37	2.25	2.17	2.10	2.04
	.025	5.29	3.93	3.34	3.01	2.79	2.63	2.51	2.41	2.33
	.010	7.08	4.98	4.13	3.65	3.34	3.12	2.95	2.82	2.72
	.001	11.97	7.77	6.17	5.31	4.76	4.37	4.09	3.86	3.69
100	.100	2.76	2.36	2.14	2.00	1.91	1.83	1.78	1.73	1.69
	.050	3.94	3.09	2.70	2.46	2.31	2.19	2.10	2.03	1.97
	.025	5.18	3.83	3.25	2.92	2.70	2.54	2.42	2.32	2.24
	.010	6.90	4.82	3.98	3.51	3.21	2.99	2.82	2.69	2.59
	.001	11.50	7.41	5.86	5.02	4.48	4.11	3.83	3.61	3.44
200	.100	2.73	2.33	2.11	1.97	1.88	1.80	1.75	1.70	1.66
	.050	3.89	3.04	2.65	2.42	2.26	2.14	2.06	1.98	1.93
	.025	5.10	3.76	3.18	2.85	2.63	2.47	2.35	2.26	2.18
	.010	6.76	4.71	3.88	3.41	3.11	2.89	2.73	2.60	2.50
	.001	11.15	7.15	5.63	4.81	4.29	3.92	3.65	3.43	3.26
1000	.100	2.71	2.31	2.09	1.95	1.85	1.78	1.72	1.68	1.64
	.050	3.85	3.00	2.61	2.38	2.22	2.11	2.02	1.95	1.89
	.025	5.04	3.70	3.13	2.80	2.58	2.42	2.30	2.20	2.13
	.010	6.66	4.63	3.80	3.34	3.04	2.82	2.66	2.53	2.43
	.001	10.89	6.96	5.46	4.65	4.14	3.78	3.51	3.30	3.13

TABLE E *F* critical values *(continued)*

					Degrees of freedom in the numerator					
10	12	15	20	25	30	40	50	60	120	1000
1.84	1.79	1.74	1.69	1.65	1.63	1.59	1.57	1.56	1.52	1.48
2.19	2.12	2.04	1.96	1.91	1.87	1.82	1.79	1.77	1.71	1.66
2.55	2.45	2.34	2.23	2.16	2.11	2.05	2.01	1.98	1.91	1.84
3.03	2.90	2.75	2.60	2.51	2.44	2.35	2.30	2.26	2.17	2.08
4.35	4.11	3.86	3.60	3.43	3.32	3.18	3.09	3.02	2.86	2.72
1.83	1.78	1.73	1.68	1.64	1.62	1.58	1.56	1.55	1.51	1.47
2.18	2.10	2.03	1.94	1.89	1.85	1.81	1.77	1.75	1.70	1.65
2.53	2.43	2.32	2.21	2.14	2.09	2.03	1.99	1.96	1.89	1.82
3.00	2.87	2.73	2.57	2.48	2.41	2.33	2.27	2.23	2.14	2.05
4.29	4.05	3.80	3.54	3.38	3.27	3.12	3.03	2.97	2.81	2.66
1.82	1.77	1.72	1.67	1.63	1.61	1.57	1.55	1.54	1.50	1.46
2.16	2.09	2.01	1.93	1.88	1.84	1.79	1.76	1.74	1.68	1.63
2.51	2.41	2.31	2.20	2.12	2.07	2.01	1.97	1.94	1.87	1.80
2.98	2.84	2.70	2.55	2.45	2.39	2.30	2.25	2.21	2.11	2.02
4.24	4.00	3.75	3.49	3.33	3.22	3.07	2.98	2.92	2.76	2.61
1.76	1.71	1.66	1.61	1.57	1.54	1.51	1.48	1.47	1.42	1.38
2.08	2.00	1.92	1.84	1.78	1.74	1.69	1.66	1.64	1.58	1.52
2.39	2.29	2.18	2.07	1.99	1.94	1.88	1.83	1.80	1.72	1.65
2.80	2.66	2.52	2.37	2.27	2.20	2.11	2.06	2.02	1.92	1.82
3.87	3.64	3.40	3.14	2.98	2.87	2.73	2.64	2.57	2.41	2.25
1.73	1.68	1.63	1.57	1.53	1.50	1.46	1.44	1.42	1.38	1.33
2.03	1.95	1.87	1.78	1.73	1.69	1.63	1.60	1.58	1.51	1.45
2.32	2.22	2.11	1.99	1.92	1.87	1.80	1.75	1.72	1.64	1.56
2.70	2.56	2.42	2.27	2.17	2.10	2.01	1.95	1.91	1.80	1.70
3.67	3.44	3.20	2.95	2.79	2.68	2.53	2.44	2.38	2.21	2.05
1.71	1.66	1.60	1.54	1.50	1.48	1.44	1.41	1.40	1.35	1.30
1.99	1.92	1.84	1.75	1.69	1.65	1.59	1.56	1.53	1.47	1.40
2.27	2.17	2.06	1.94	1.87	1.82	1.74	1.70	1.67	1.58	1.49
2.63	2.50	2.35	2.20	2.10	2.03	1.94	1.88	1.84	1.73	1.62
3.54	3.32	3.08	2.83	2.67	2.55	2.41	2.32	2.25	2.08	1.92
1.66	1.61	1.56	1.49	1.45	1.42	1.38	1.35	1.34	1.28	1.22
1.93	1.85	1.77	1.68	1.62	1.57	1.52	1.48	1.45	1.38	1.30
2.18	2.08	1.97	1.85	1.77	1.71	1.64	1.59	1.56	1.46	1.36
2.50	2.37	2.22	2.07	1.97	1.89	1.80	1.74	1.69	1.57	1.45
3.30	3.07	2.84	2.59	2.43	2.32	2.17	2.08	2.01	1.83	1.64
1.63	1.58	1.52	1.46	1.41	1.38	1.34	1.31	1.29	1.23	1.16
1.88	1.80	1.72	1.62	1.56	1.52	1.46	1.41	1.39	1.30	1.21
2.11	2.01	1.90	1.78	1.70	1.64	1.56	1.51	1.47	1.37	1.25
2.41	2.27	2.13	1.97	1.87	1.79	1.69	1.63	1.58	1.45	1.30
3.12	2.90	2.67	2.42	2.26	2.15	2.00	1.90	1.83	1.64	1.43
1.61	1.55	1.49	1.43	1.38	1.35	1.30	1.27	1.25	1.18	1.08
1.84	1.76	1.68	1.58	1.52	1.47	1.41	1.36	1.33	1.24	1.11
2.06	1.96	1.85	1.72	1.64	1.58	1.50	1.45	1.41	1.29	1.13
2.34	2.20	2.06	1.90	1.79	1.72	1.61	1.54	1.50	1.35	1.16
2.99	2.77	2.54	2.30	2.14	2.02	1.87	1.77	1.69	1.49	1.22

Table entry for p is the critical value $(\chi^2)^*$ with probability p lying to its right.

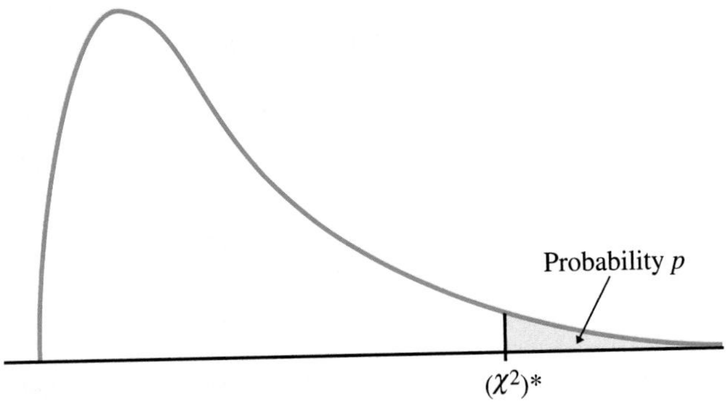

TABLE F χ^2 **distribution critical values**

	Tail probability p											
df	.25	.20	.15	.10	.05	.025	.02	.01	.005	.0025	.001	.0005
1	1.32	1.64	2.07	2.71	3.84	5.02	5.41	6.63	7.88	9.14	10.83	12.12
2	2.77	3.22	3.79	4.61	5.99	7.38	7.82	9.21	10.60	11.98	13.82	15.20
3	4.11	4.64	5.32	6.25	7.81	9.35	9.84	11.34	12.84	14.32	16.27	17.73
4	5.39	5.99	6.74	7.78	9.49	11.14	11.67	13.28	14.86	16.42	18.47	20.00
5	6.63	7.29	8.12	9.24	11.07	12.83	13.39	15.09	16.75	18.39	20.51	22.11
6	7.84	8.56	9.45	10.64	12.59	14.45	15.03	16.81	18.55	20.25	22.46	24.10
7	9.04	9.80	10.75	12.02	14.07	16.01	16.62	18.48	20.28	22.04	24.32	26.02
8	10.22	11.03	12.03	13.36	15.51	17.53	18.17	20.09	21.95	23.77	26.12	27.87
9	11.39	12.24	13.29	14.68	16.92	19.02	19.68	21.67	23.59	25.46	27.88	29.67
10	12.55	13.44	14.53	15.99	18.31	20.48	21.16	23.21	25.19	27.11	29.59	31.42
11	13.70	14.63	15.77	17.28	19.68	21.92	22.62	24.72	26.76	28.73	31.26	33.14
12	14.85	15.81	16.99	18.55	21.03	23.34	24.05	26.22	28.30	30.32	32.91	34.82
13	15.98	16.98	18.20	19.81	22.36	24.74	25.47	27.69	29.82	31.88	34.53	36.48
14	17.12	18.15	19.41	21.06	23.68	26.12	26.87	29.14	31.32	33.43	36.12	38.11
15	18.25	19.31	20.60	22.31	25.00	27.49	28.26	30.58	32.80	34.95	37.70	39.72
16	19.37	20.47	21.79	23.54	26.30	28.85	29.63	32.00	34.27	36.46	39.25	41.31
17	20.49	21.61	22.98	24.77	27.59	30.19	31.00	33.41	35.72	37.95	40.79	42.88
18	21.60	22.76	24.16	25.99	28.87	31.53	32.35	34.81	37.16	39.42	42.31	44.43
19	22.72	23.90	25.33	27.20	30.14	32.85	33.69	36.19	38.58	40.88	43.82	45.97
20	23.83	25.04	26.50	28.41	31.41	34.17	35.02	37.57	40.00	42.34	45.31	47.50
21	24.93	26.17	27.66	29.62	32.67	35.48	36.34	38.93	41.40	43.78	46.80	49.01
22	26.04	27.30	28.82	30.81	33.92	36.78	37.66	40.29	42.80	45.20	48.27	50.51
23	27.14	28.43	29.98	32.01	35.17	38.08	38.97	41.64	44.18	46.62	49.73	52.00
24	28.24	29.55	31.13	33.20	36.42	39.36	40.27	42.98	45.56	48.03	51.18	53.48
25	29.34	30.68	32.28	34.38	37.65	40.65	41.57	44.31	46.93	49.44	52.62	54.95
26	30.43	31.79	33.43	35.56	38.89	41.92	42.86	45.64	48.29	50.83	54.05	56.41
27	31.53	32.91	34.57	36.74	40.11	43.19	44.14	46.96	49.64	52.22	55.48	57.86
28	32.62	34.03	35.71	37.92	41.34	44.46	45.42	48.28	50.99	53.59	56.89	59.30
29	33.71	35.14	36.85	39.09	42.56	45.72	46.69	49.59	52.34	54.97	58.30	60.73
30	34.80	36.25	37.99	40.26	43.77	46.98	47.96	50.89	53.67	56.33	59.70	62.16
40	45.62	47.27	49.24	51.81	55.76	59.34	60.44	63.69	66.77	69.70	73.40	76.09
50	56.33	58.16	60.35	63.17	67.50	71.42	72.61	76.15	79.49	82.66	86.66	89.56
60	66.98	68.97	71.34	74.40	79.08	83.30	84.58	88.38	91.95	95.34	99.61	102.7
80	88.13	90.41	93.11	96.58	101.9	106.6	108.1	112.3	116.3	120.1	124.8	128.3
100	109.1	111.7	114.7	118.5	124.3	129.6	131.1	135.8	140.2	144.3	149.4	153.2

Table entry for p is the value of r with probability p lying above it.

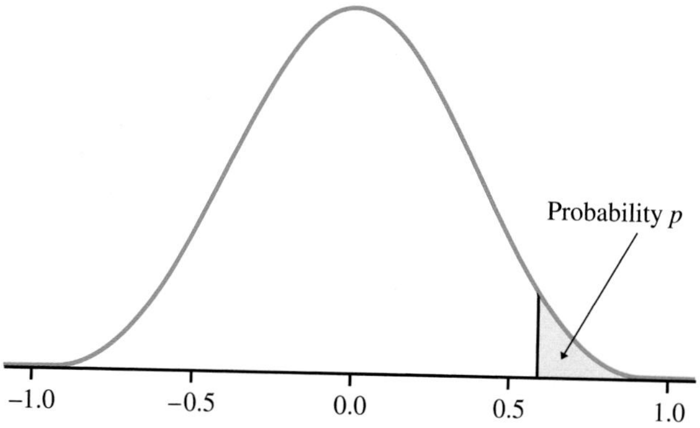

TABLE G Critical values of the correlation r

	Tail probability p									
n	.20	.10	.05	.025	.02	.01	.005	.0025	.001	.0005
3	0.8090	0.9511	0.9877	0.9969	0.9980	0.9995	0.9999	1.0000	1.0000	1.0000
4	0.6000	0.8000	0.9000	0.9500	0.9600	0.9800	0.9900	0.9950	0.9980	0.9990
5	0.4919	0.6870	0.8054	0.8783	0.8953	0.9343	0.9587	0.9740	0.9859	0.9911
6	0.4257	0.6084	0.7293	0.8114	0.8319	0.8822	0.9172	0.9417	0.9633	0.9741
7	0.3803	0.5509	0.6694	0.7545	0.7766	0.8329	0.8745	0.9056	0.9350	0.9509
8	0.3468	0.5067	0.6215	0.7067	0.7295	0.7887	0.8343	0.8697	0.9049	0.9249
9	0.3208	0.4716	0.5822	0.6664	0.6892	0.7498	0.7977	0.8359	0.8751	0.8983
10	0.2998	0.4428	0.5494	0.6319	0.6546	0.7155	0.7646	0.8046	0.8467	0.8721
11	0.2825	0.4187	0.5214	0.6021	0.6244	0.6851	0.7348	0.7759	0.8199	0.8470
12	0.2678	0.3981	0.4973	0.5760	0.5980	0.6581	0.7079	0.7496	0.7950	0.8233
13	0.2552	0.3802	0.4762	0.5529	0.5745	0.6339	0.6835	0.7255	0.7717	0.8010
14	0.2443	0.3646	0.4575	0.5324	0.5536	0.6120	0.6614	0.7034	0.7501	0.7800
15	0.2346	0.3507	0.4409	0.5140	0.5347	0.5923	0.6411	0.6831	0.7301	0.7604
16	0.2260	0.3383	0.4259	0.4973	0.5177	0.5742	0.6226	0.6643	0.7114	0.7419
17	0.2183	0.3271	0.4124	0.4821	0.5021	0.5577	0.6055	0.6470	0.6940	0.7247
18	0.2113	0.3170	0.4000	0.4683	0.4878	0.5425	0.5897	0.6308	0.6777	0.7084
19	0.2049	0.3077	0.3887	0.4555	0.4747	0.5285	0.5751	0.6158	0.6624	0.6932
20	0.1991	0.2992	0.3783	0.4438	0.4626	0.5155	0.5614	0.6018	0.6481	0.6788
21	0.1938	0.2914	0.3687	0.4329	0.4513	0.5034	0.5487	0.5886	0.6346	0.6652
22	0.1888	0.2841	0.3598	0.4227	0.4409	0.4921	0.5368	0.5763	0.6219	0.6524
23	0.1843	0.2774	0.3515	0.4132	0.4311	0.4815	0.5256	0.5647	0.6099	0.6402
24	0.1800	0.2711	0.3438	0.4044	0.4219	0.4716	0.5151	0.5537	0.5986	0.6287
25	0.1760	0.2653	0.3365	0.3961	0.4133	0.4622	0.5052	0.5434	0.5879	0.6178
26	0.1723	0.2598	0.3297	0.3882	0.4052	0.4534	0.4958	0.5336	0.5776	0.6074
27	0.1688	0.2546	0.3233	0.3809	0.3976	0.4451	0.4869	0.5243	0.5679	0.5974
28	0.1655	0.2497	0.3172	0.3739	0.3904	0.4372	0.4785	0.5154	0.5587	0.5880
29	0.1624	0.2451	0.3115	0.3673	0.3835	0.4297	0.4705	0.5070	0.5499	0.5790
30	0.1594	0.2407	0.3061	0.3610	0.3770	0.4226	0.4629	0.4990	0.5415	0.5703
40	0.1368	0.2070	0.2638	0.3120	0.3261	0.3665	0.4026	0.4353	0.4741	0.5007
50	0.1217	0.1843	0.2353	0.2787	0.2915	0.3281	0.3610	0.3909	0.4267	0.4514
60	0.1106	0.1678	0.2144	0.2542	0.2659	0.2997	0.3301	0.3578	0.3912	0.4143
80	0.0954	0.1448	0.1852	0.2199	0.2301	0.2597	0.2864	0.3109	0.3405	0.3611
100	0.0851	0.1292	0.1654	0.1966	0.2058	0.2324	0.2565	0.2786	0.3054	0.3242
1000	0.0266	0.0406	0.0520	0.0620	0.0650	0.0736	0.0814	0.0887	0.0976	0.1039

SOLUTIONS TO ODD-NUMBERED EXERCISES

CHAPTER 1

1.1 Answers will vary.

1.3 **(a)** The bars can be drawn in any order since major is a categorical variable. **(b)** The percents add to 98.5%, so a pie chart would not be appropriate without a category for Other.

1.5 The histogram is unimodal and fairly symmetric except for a high outlier (Toyota Prius at 51). The range of the data without the outlier is 19 to 37 mpg.

1.7 **(a)** See solutions to Exercise 1.5. **(b)** The Rolls-Royce Phantom (19 mpg) and Mercedes-Benz E55 AMG (21 mpg) have the lowest mileage. However, there are no low outliers.

1.9 **(a)** It is fairly symmetric with one low outlier. Excluding the low outlier, the spread is from about −18% to 18%. **(b)** About 1%. **(c)** Smallest is about −18% and the largest is about 18%. **(d)** About 35% to 40%.

1.11 From the stemplot, the center is \$28 and the spread is from \$3 to \$93. There are no obvious outliers. Examination of the stemplot shows the distribution is clearly right-skewed. With or without split stems, the conclusions are the same.

1.13 **(a)** and **(b)** are bar graphs. **(c)** One example of how to do this is by using the "clustered bar graph" on SPSS.

1.15 **(a)** The top five are Texas, Minnesota, Oklahoma, Missouri, and Illinois. The bottom five are Alaska, Puerto Rico, Rhode Island, Nevada, and Vermont. **(b)** The distribution is strongly unimodal and right-skewed with a large peak in the $0 \leq \text{damage} < 10$ group. The range is 0 to 90. The three states with the most damage (Texas, Minnesota, and Oklahoma) may be outliers. **(c)** Answers will vary.

1.17 **(a)** Alaska has 5.7% and Florida has 17.6% older residents. **(b)** The distribution is unimodal and symmetric with a peak around 13%. Without Alaska and Florida, the range is 8.5% to 15.6%.

1.19 GM had more complaints than Toyota each year, but both companies seem to have fewer complaints in general over time.

1.21 **(a)** The individuals are the different cars. **(b)** The variables are vehicle type (categorical), transmission type (categorical), number of cylinders (can be considered categorical because the number of cylinders divides the cars into only a few categories), city MPG (quantitative), and highway MPG (quantitative).

1.23 **(a)** The different public mutual funds are the individuals. **(b)** The variables "category" and "largest holding" are both categorical, while the variables "net assets" and "year-to-date return" are quantitative. **(c)** Net assets are in millions of dollars, and year-to-date return is given as a percent.

1.25 Some possible variables are cost of living, taxes, utility costs, number of similar facilities in the area, and average age of residents in the location.

1.27 The distribution of dates of coins will be skewed to the left because as the dates go further back there are fewer of these coins currently in circulation. Various left-skewed sketches are possible.

1.29 **(a)** Many more readers who completed the survey owned Brand A than Brand B. **(b)** It would be better to consider the proportion of readers owning each brand who required service calls. In this case, 22% of the Brand A owners required a service call, while 40% of the Brand B owners required a service call.

1.31 Some possible variables that could be used to measure the "size" of a company are number of employees, assets, and amount spent on research and development.

1.33 The stemplot shows that the costs per month are skewed slightly to the right, with a center of \$20 and a spread from \$8 to \$50. America Online and its larger competitors were probably charging around \$20, and the members of the sample who were early adopters of fast Internet access probably correspond to the monthly costs of more than \$30.

1.35 When you change the scales, some extreme changes on one scale will be barely noticeable on the other. Addition of white space in the graph also changes visual impressions.

1.37 **(a)** Household income is the total income of all persons in the household, so it will be higher than the income of any individual in the household. **(c)** Both distributions are fairly symmetric, although the distribution of mean personal income has two high outliers. The distribution of median household incomes has a larger spread and a higher center. The center of the distribution of mean personal income is about \$25,000, while the center of the distribution of median household income is about \$37,000.

1.39 The means are \$19,804.17, \$21,484.80, and \$21,283.92 for black men, white females, and white males, respectively. Since we have not taken into account the type of jobs performed by individuals in each category or years employed, we cannot make claims of discrimination without first adjusting for these factors.

1.41 The medians are \$18,383.50, \$19,960, and \$19,977 for black men, white females, and white males, respectively. The medians are smaller, but our general conclusions are similar.

1.43 Because of strong skewness to the right, the median is the lower number of \$330,000 and the mean is \$675,000.

1.45 For Asian countries the five-number summary is 1.3, 3.4, 4.65, 6.05, 8.8; and for Eastern European countries it is -12.1, -1.6, 1.4, 4.3, 7.0. Side-by-side boxplots show that the growth of per capita consumption tends to be much higher for the Asian countries than for the Eastern European countries and that the growth of per capita consumption for the Eastern European countries is much more spread out.

1.47 **(a)** The mean is \$983.5. **(b)** The standard deviation is \$347.23. **(c)** Results should agree except for number of digits retained.

1.49 A rare, catastrophic loss would be considered an outlier, and averages are not resistant to outliers. The five-number summary is more appropriate for describing the distributions of data with outliers.

1.51 **(a)** The five-number summary is 5.7, 11.7, 12.75, 13.5, 17.6. **(b)** The IQR is 1.8. Any low outliers would have to be less than 9, and any high outliers would have to be greater than 16.2. Therefore, Florida and Alaska are definitely outliers, but so is the state with 8.5% older residents.

1.53 **(a)** The five-number summary is 0, 0.75, 3.2, 7.8, 19.9. **(b)** The *IQR* is 7.05. Any low outliers would have to be less than −9.825, and any high outliers would have to be greater than 18.375. The histogram shows that the U.S., Australia, and Canada all have CO_2 emissions much higher than the rest of the countries, but only the U.S. is officially considered an outlier using the $1.5 \times IQR$ rule.

1.55 **(a)** The 5th percentile is approximately at the 748th position. The 95th percentile is approximately at the 14,211th position. **(b)** The 5th percentile value is approximately \$10,000. The 95th percentile value is approximately \$140,000.

1.57 **(a)** The distribution is skewed left with a possible low outlier. **(b)** Use stems from the tens place as −2, −1, −0, 0, 1, 2, 3.

1.59 The median is \$27.855. The mean is \$34.70 and is larger than the median because the distribution is skewed right.

1.61 **(a)** The mean change is $\bar{x} = 28.767\%$ and the standard deviation is $s = 17.766\%$. **(b)** Ignoring the outlier, $\bar{x} = 31.707\%$ and the standard deviation is $s = 14.150\%$. The low outlier has pulled the mean down toward it and increased the variability in the data. **(c)** "Identical" in this case probably means that the 5-liter vehicles were all the same make and model.

1.63 You will learn about the effects of outliers on the mean and median by interactively using the applet.

1.65 From the boxplot, the clear pattern is that as the level of education increases, the incomes tend to increase and also become more spread out.

1.67 Ignoring the District of Columbia, the histogram of violent crimes is fairly symmetric, with a center of about 450 violent crimes per 100,000. The spread is from about 100 to 1000 violent crimes per 100,000 for the 50 states, with the District of Columbia being a high outlier with a rate of slightly over 2000 violent crimes per 100,000.

1.69 Both data sets have a mean of 7.501 and a standard deviation of 2.032. Data A has a distribution that is left-skewed while Data B has a distribution that is fairly symmetric except for one high outlier. Thus, we see two distributions with quite different shapes but with the same mean and standard deviation.

1.71 **(a)** The five-number summary is 0.9%, 3.0%, 4.95%, 6.6%, 14.2%. **(b)** The mean is larger because the distribution is moderately skewed to the right with a high outlier.

1.73 **(a)** A histogram is better because the data set is moderate size. **(b)** The two low outliers are −26.6% and −22.9%. The distribution is fairly symmetric, with a median, or center, of 2.65%. The spread is from −16.5% to 24.4%. **(c)** The mean is 1.551%. At the end of the month, you would have \$101.55. **(d)** At the end of the month, you would have \$74.40. Excluding the two outliers gives a mean of 1.551% and a standard deviation of 8.218%. Both have changed. Quartiles and medians are relatively unaffected.

1.75 \$2.36 million must be the mean since fewer than half of the players' salaries were above it.

1.77 **(a)** 1, 1, 1, 1. **(b)** 0, 0, 10, 10. **(c)** There are several answers for (a) but (b) is unique.

1.79 You can use the Uniform distribution for an example of a symmetric distribution, and there are many choices for a left-skewed distribution.

1.81 **(a)** Mean is C; median is B. **(b)** Mean is A; median is A. **(c)** Mean is A; median is B.

1.83 **(a)** 0.025. **(b)** 64 inches to 74 inches. **(c)** 16%.

1.85 Eleanor's z-score is 1.8, while Gerald's z-score is 1.5, so Eleanor scored relatively higher.

1.87 **(a)** 0.0505. **(b)** 0.0454. **(c)** 0.0505.

1.89 **(a)** 0.5948. **(b)** 452. **(c)** 712.

1.91 The plot suggests no major deviations except for a possible low outlier.

1.93 Answers will vary.

1.95 **(a)** No, this apartment building is no longer an outlier. It's not even one of the top two data points now. It fits in perfectly with the rest of the data. **(b)** The distribution looks fairly normal except for 2 new high outliers (#11 and #13). It looks much better than the distributions in 1.94.

1.97 Answers will vary. For right-skewed data, the normal quantile plot will show the highest and lowest points below the diagonal. For left-skewed data, the normal quantile plot will show the highest and lowest points above the diagonal. For symmetric data, the points will follow the diagonal fairly closely, even at the ends.

1.99 **(a)** Mean $= -0.0224$, standard deviation $= 0.2180$. **(b)** $\bar{x} \pm s = (-0.2404, 0.1956)$; $\bar{x} \pm 2s = (-0.4584, 0.4136)$; $\bar{x} \pm 3s = (-0.6764, 0.6316)$. **(c)** 72.7%, 90.9%, and 100%. The distribution is not exactly normal.

1.101 The stemplot shows a fairly symmetric distribution with a high and low outlier. The normal quantile plot shows a fairly good fit to the diagonal line in the middle, but the two outliers stick out again.

1.103 0.65 to 2.25 grams per mile driven.

1.105 **(a)** 0.0122. **(b)** 0.9878. **(c)** 0.0384. **(d)** 0.9494.

1.107 0.1711 or 17.11%.

1.109 **(a)** Between -21% and 47%. **(b)** 0.2236. **(c)** 0.2389.

1.111 **(a)** The first and third quartiles for the standard Normal distribution are approximately ± 0.67. **(b)** The first quartile is about 255 days, and the third quartile is about 277 days.

1.113 Normal quantile plot looks fairly linear.

1.115 The histogram is fairly rectangular and the Normal quantile plot is S-shaped.

1.117 **(a)** The mean is 64.49. **(b)** The beginning years are all below average until January 1966. **(c)** The values are high (in the 80s) between 1/00 and 7/00, but then the last month to be above average is 4/01. Then there is a severe drop with no recovery. (d) The dot.com economy was still booming in January 2000. As 2001 progressed, the dot.com economy started to crash, and September 11, 2001, did bad things to the economy as well.

1.119 **(a)** Min $= 1$, $Q_1 = 1$, $M = 1$, $Q_3 = 1$. **(b)** The box has a length of 0. This makes sense because Q_1, M, and Q_3 are all the same. **(c)** The box plot indicates very, very right, skewed data. Almost all the data was 1.

1.121 **(a)** $11/22 = 50\%$. **(b)** Negative revenue growth means the previous year's revenue was higher than this year's revenue. **(c)** 0.82%. (d) The top 25% of all telecom companies had revenue growth greater than 0.12475.

1.123 Gender and automobile preference are categorical. Age and household income are quantitative.

1.125 The distribution is right-skewed. The median salary is \$1.6 million and the mean salary is slightly over \$3.5 million, being pulled up by the strong right-skewness of the distribution. The spread goes from \$200 thousand to slightly over \$12 million.

1.127 **(a)** For normal corn, $M = 358$ grams, $Q_1 = 337$ grams, $Q_3 = 400.5$ grams, the minimum is 272 grams, and the maximum is 462 grams. For new corn, $M = 406.5$ grams, $Q_1 = 383.5$ grams, $Q_3 = 428.5$ grams, the minimum is 318 grams, and the maximum is 477 grams. Overall, new corn gives higher weight gains. **(b)** For normal corn, $\bar{x} = 366.30$ and $s = 50.80$, and for the new corn $\bar{x} = 402.95$ and $s = 42.73$. The mean weight gain for the new corn is 36.65 grams larger than for the normal corn.

1.129 **(a)** From the histogram or the boxplot, it is clear that the distribution is skewed to the right, with three high outliers. **(b)** $M = 37.8$ thousand barrels and $\bar{x} = 48.25$ thousand barrels. Since the distribution is skewed right and has three high outliers, we expect the mean to be substantially larger than the median. **(c)** $M = 37.8$ thousand barrels, $Q_1 = 21.5$ thousand barrels, $Q_3 = 60.1$ thousand barrels, the minimum is 2 thousand barrels, and the maximum is 204.9 thousand barrels. The box containing the first quartile, the median, and the third quartile is fairly symmetric, with the third quartile being slightly farther from the median, indicating some right-skewness. The maximum is much farther from the median than the minimum, which could suggest right-skewness or just a high outlier. The boxplot and the histogram clearly show the right-skewness, but it is difficult to be certain of this from only the five-number summary.

1.131 The mean is $\mu = 250$ and the standard deviation is $\sigma = 175.78$.

1.133 The range of values is extreme, making plotting difficult. Because of the right-skewness, the mean of the populations is 583,994 and is clearly quite far from the center of the data. The median is 159,778. Division into three groups is fairly arbitrary. A natural way to proceed is to use cutoffs that correspond to gaps in the data. For example, the group of the most populous counties might consist of the 8 counties with populations over 1 million, and we would sample from all of these counties. The next break is not as clear, but it could be taken at 100,000. There are 27 counties with populations between 100,000 and 1 million, and we could sample households from half of these counties. Finally, there are 23 counties with populations below 100,000, and a smaller fraction of these could be sampled.

1.135 Answers will vary. For the mean, the distribution should look fairly symmetric with a center at about 20. Because of the small number of observations, the Normal quantile plot may not be that smooth, but it shouldn't appear to deviate from a straight line in a systematic way. For the standard deviation, the distribution should look slightly skewed to the right with a center close to 5. The Normal quantile plot should not look nearly as much like a straight line as when plotting the 20 values of $\overline{x}$, suggesting the distribution of s is not Normal.

CHAPTER 2

2.1 **(a)** Time spent studying is the explanatory variable, and grade on the exam is the response. **(b)** Explore the relationship between the two variables. **(c)** Yearly rainfall is the explanatory variable, and the yield of a crop is the response variable. **(d)** Many factors affect salary and the number of sick days one takes. It may be most reasonable to simply explore the relationship between these two variables. **(e)** Economic class of the father is the explanatory variable, and that of the son is the response.

2.3 Hand wipe is the explanatory variable, and whether or not the skin appears abnormally irritated is the response. Both are categorical variables.

2.5 **(a)** The city gas mileage is approximately 62 MPG, and the highway mileage is 68 MPG. **(b)** The pattern is roughly linear. Highway gas mileage tends to be between 5 and 10 MPG greater than city mileage. **(c)** It appears to fall roughly on the line defined by the pattern of the remaining points.

2.7 **(a)** Speed is the explanatory variable and would be plotted on the x axis. **(b)** At first, fuel used decreases, and then, at about 60 km/h, it increases as speed increases. At very slow speeds and at very high speeds, engines are very inefficient and use more fuel. **(c)** In the scatterplot, both low and high speeds correspond to high values of fuel used, so we cannot say that the variables are positively or negatively associated. **(d)** The points lie close to a simple curved form, so the relationship is reasonably strong.

2.9 Explanatory variable: parent income. Response variable: money student borrows. Both variables are quantitative and probably have a negative association because the more money the parents have, the less a student will probably need to borrow to pay for college tuition.

2.11 **(a)** The means for the market sectors are: consumer (30.960), financial services (32.760), natural resources (23.317), and technology (54.314). **(b)** Technology was the best place to invest in 2003. **(c)** No, because market sector is a categorical variable.

2.13 **(a)** Explanatory variable = accounts, response variable = assets. **(c)** Strong, positive, and linear, but two points stand out at the top right corner of the plot. (d) Charles Schwab and Fidelity.

2.15 **(a)** The longer the duration, the greater the decline. The plot shows a positive association. **(b)** A straight line that slopes up from left to right describes the general trend reasonably well. The association is not very strong. **(c)** This bear market appears to have had a decline of 48% and a duration of about 21 months.

2.17 **(a)** If a person has a high income, his or her household income will also be high, so personal and household incomes are positively associated. We therefore expect mean personal income for a state to be positively associated with its median household income. Household incomes will always be greater than or equal to the incomes of the individuals in the household. We therefore expect median household income in a state to be larger than mean personal income in that state. **(b)** If the distribution of incomes in a state is strongly right-skewed, we know that the mean will be larger than the median. Although mean household income must be larger than mean personal income, and median household income must be larger than median personal income, *median* household income could be smaller than *mean* personal income. **(c)** The overall pattern of the plot is roughly linear. The variables are positively associated. The strength of the relationship (ignoring outliers) is moderately strong. **(d)** The two points are the District of Columbia and Connecticut. The District of Columbia is a city with a few very wealthy inhabitants and many poorer inhabitants. Many very wealthy people who work in New York City live in Connecticut, resulting in a high mean income. We expect the distribution of both personal and household incomes to be strongly right-skewed.

2.19 **(a)** The overall pattern is linear, the association is positive, and the strength is moderately strong. Hot dogs that are high in calories are generally high in sodium. **(b)** Brand 13 has the fewest calories, so this probably corresponds to "Eat Slim Veal Hot Dogs."

2.21 **(a)** Business starts is taken as the explanatory variable, so it is represented on the horizontal axis. **(b)** The association is positive. **(c)** Of the four points in the right side of the plot, Florida is the one with the fewest failures. **(d)** The outlier is California. **(e)** The four states outside the cluster are California, Florida, New York, and Texas. These states are scattered throughout the country. They are the most populous states in the country.

2.23 **(a)** The means are: Consumer $= -7.66$, Financial services $= 35.68$, Technology $= -24.03$, Utilities and natural resources $= 25.4$. **(b)** Financial services and Utilities and natural resources were good places to invest. **(c)** Market sector is categorical, so we cannot speak of positive or negative association between market sector and total return.

2.25 **(a)** In this case, neither variable is necessarily the explanatory variable. We arbitrarily put City MPG on the horizontal axis of our plot. **(b)** $\bar{x} = 18.87$, $\bar{y} = 29.07$, $s_x = 0.3055$, $s_y = 0.3215$, and $r = 0.8487$. **(c)** The association is positive and is reasonably strong.

2.27 **(a)** High values of duration go with high values of decline, so the association is positive. The points are not tightly clustered about a line, so the correlation is not near 1. **(b)** The correlation in Figure 2.2 is closer to 1 than the correlation in Figure 2.6. The points in Figure 2.2 appear to lie more closely along a line than do those in Figure 2.6.

2.29 Computation shows $r = 0$. The correlation r measures the strength of a straight-line relationship.

2.31 **(a)** Explanatory variable = price. The pattern is strong, positive, and linear. **(b)** For price, the mean is 50.000 and the standard deviation is 16.325. For deforestation, the mean is 1.738 and the standard deviation is 0.928. The correlation is 0.955.

2.33 **(a)** In 2.31 we found that the scatterplot shows a strong, positive, linear relationship and the correlation is 0.955. **(b)** Answers will vary, but results should look fairly random and without pattern. **(c)** The correlation should be close to 0.

2.35 **(a)** 0.968. **(b)** 0.707. **(c)** These points are apparently not outliers because the correlation dropped quite a bit when they were removed.

2.37 There is a straight-line pattern that is fairly strong. The correlation, computed from statistical software, is $r = 0.898$. There do not appear to be any extreme outliers from the straight-line pattern.

2.39 **(a)** and **(b)** The plots look very different. **(c)** The correlation between x and y is 0.253. The correlation between x^* and y^* is also 0.253. This is not surprising: r does not change when we change the units of measurement of x, y, or both.

2.41 The magazine's report implies that there is a negative correlation between compensation of corporate CEOs and the performance of their company's stock, not that there is no correlation. A more accurate statement might be that in companies that compensate their CEOs highly, the stock is just as likely to perform well as to not perform well—likewise for companies that do not compensate their CEOs highly.

2.43 In Figure 2.8, after removing the outliers, the remaining points appear to be more tightly clustered around a line. In Figure 2.2, the outlier accentuates the linear trend because it appears to lie along the line defined by the other points. After its removal, the linear trend is not as pronounced.

2.45 **(a)** Gender is a categorical variable. **(b)** A correlation of 1.09 is not possible. **(c)** The correlation has no unit of measurement.

2.47 **(a)** $\hat{y} = 1.0892 + 0.188999x$. **(b)** $\bar{x} = 22.31$, $s_x = 17.74$, $\bar{y} = 5.306$, $s_y = 3.368$, $r = 0.995$, $b = r\frac{s_y}{s_x} = 0.1889$, and $a = \bar{y} - b\bar{x} = 1.0916$.

2.49 **(a)** The percent is 35.5% because $r^2 = (0.596)^2 = 0.355$. **(b)** $\hat{y} = 6.08\% + 1.707x$. **(c)** $\hat{y} = 9.08\%$. The least-squares regression line passes through the point $(\bar{x}, \bar{y})$. Thus, we would predict $\hat{y} = \bar{y} = 9.07\%$ when $x = \bar{x} = 1.75\%$.

2.51 **(a)** The scatterplot shows a curved pattern. **(b)** No. The scatterplot suggests that the relation between y and x is a curved relationship, not a straight-line relationship. **(c)** Using a calculator we found the sum to be -0.01. **(d)** The residuals show the same curved pattern.

2.53 **(a)** $\hat{y} = 2.95918 + 6.74776x$. Observation 1 is not very influential. **(b)** r^2 increases from 0.660 to 0.779. Observation 1 is an outlier, and after its removal, the remaining points appear more tightly clustered about the least-squares regression line.

2.55 **(a)** The number y in inventory after x weeks must be $y = 96 - 4x$. **(b)** The graph shows a negatively sloping line. **(c)** No. After 25 weeks the equation predicts that there will be $y = -4$.

2.57 No, you could not make an accurate prediction of stock returns because the R^2 is so low and the scatterplot shows a very weak association between Treasury bills and stock returns.

2.59 **(a)** Slightly parabolic, opening downward, very weak. **(b)** $R^2 = 2.3\%$, which is very low. The regression line with year does not do a good job of explaining the variation in returns.

2.61 **(a)** There is a fairly strong, positive, linear relationship between appraised value and selling price. **(b)** $\hat{y} = 127.270 + 1.047x$. The predicted selling price is 967.6 thousand dollars for a unit appraised for $802,600.

2.63 **(a)** Slope $= b = 0.0832$, and intercept $= a = -17.1275$. **(b)** $\hat{y} = -17.1275 + 0.0832x$. If 793.6 is substituted for x, then y will be 48.9. Therefore, Fact 3 is true for this least-squares line. **(c)** $R^2 = 93.76\%$. R^2 is the percent of the variation in the values of total assets that is explained by the least-squares regression line of total assets on number of accounts.

2.65 **(a)** The predicted assets for DLJ Direct with 590 accounts will be 31.849. **(b)** The actual assets are 11.2, so the prediction is an overestimate. The actual assets − the predicted assets = −20.76946 = the residual. **(c)** The residual is −20.76946. Yes.

2.67 **(a)** $R^2 = 93.4\%$, $a = 1{,}859{,}988$, and $b = 0.879$. **(b)** $R^2 = 93.4\%$, $a = 1.860$, and $b = 0.879$. **(c)** Only the intercept is affected by the change in units.

2.69 **(a)** Yes, there is a fairly strong, positive, linear relationship. **(b)** $R = 0.928$, $R^2 = 86.1\%$. R^2 is the percent of the variation in the selling price that is explained by the least-squares regression line of selling price on appraisal values. **(c)** $\hat{y} = 127.270 + 1.047x$. (d) The predicted selling price will be \$848,391. **(e)** The mean selling price is \$848,130, and the mean appraisal is \$688,750.

2.71 If the correlation has increased to 0.8, then there is a stronger relationship between American and European stocks. When American stocks have gone down, European stocks have tended to go down also, so European stocks have not provided much protection against losses in American stocks.

2.73 **(a)** $\hat{y} = 15.464 + 0.858x$. **(b)** r^2 is 39.5%. **(c)** The predicted value is $\hat{y} = 28.334\%$. The observed decline for this particular bear market is 14%, so the residual is −14.334%.

2.75 **(a)** $r = 0.999993$, so the calibration does not need to be done again. **(b)** $\hat{y} = 1.6571 + 0.113301x$. For $x = 500$, $\hat{y} = 58.3$. We would expect the predicted absorbance to be very accurate based on the plot and the correlation.

2.77 Experiment with the applet on the Web and comment.

2.79 **(a)** Spaghetti and snack cake appear to be outliers. **(b)** For all 10 points, $\hat{y} = 58.5879 + 1.30356x$. Leaving out spaghetti and snack cake, $\hat{y} = 43.8814 + 1.14721x$. **(c)** The points, taken together, are moderately influential.

2.81 **(a)** $b = 0.16$ and $a = 30.2$. **(b)** We would predict Julie's final exam score to be 78.2. **(c)** $r^2 = 0.36$. With 64% of the variation unexplained, the least-squares regression line would not be considered an accurate predictor of final-exam score.

2.83 $r^2 = 0.64$. Smaller raises tended to be given to those who missed more days, and so the variables are negatively associated. Thus, $r = -0.8$.

2.85 We would predict Octavio to score 4.1 points above the class mean on the final exam.

2.87 **(a)** Number of Target stores = −0.525483 + 0.382345 × (number of Wal-Mart stores). **(b)** There are 254 Wal-Mart stores in Texas, so we predict number of Target stores = 96.590147. There are 90 Target stores in Texas, so the residual = −6.590147. **(c)** Number of Wal-Mart stores = 30.3101 + 1.13459 × (number of Target stores). **(d)** There are 90 Target stores in Texas, so we predict number of Wal-Mart stores = 132.4232. There are 254 Wal-Mart stores in Texas, so the residual = 121.5768.

2.89 We would expect the correlation for individual stocks to be lower. Correlations based on averages (such as the stock index) are usually too high when applied to individuals.

2.91 The reasoning assumes that the correlation between the number of firefighters at a fire and the amount of damage done is due to causation. It is more plausible that a lurking variable, namely the size of the fire, is behind the correlation.

2.93 No. Correlation does not imply causation. The most seriously ill patients may be sent to larger hospitals rather than smaller hospitals, and this could account for the observed correlation.

2.95 Answers will vary but may include: age, years of education, years of experience in job, and location.

2.97 **(a)** The story states that these are the "ten kinds of business that employ the MOST people" so it would not be possible to have GREATER x-values than the ones listed in this data. **(b)** Yes, this is an extrapolation because it is very unlikely that a kind of business that has 0 employees in 1997 would have 1.86 million employees only 5 years later.

2.99 Intelligence or support from parents may be a lurking variable. More generally, factors that may lead students to take more math in high school may also lead to more success in college. If lurking variables are present, then requiring students to take algebra and geometry may have little effect on success in college.

2.101 **(a)** If the consumption of an item falls when price rises, we should see a negative association. However, the plot shows a modest positive association. **(b)** $\hat{y} = 44.6954 + 9.59163x$. $r^2 = 0.365$. **(c)** There are periodic fluctuations with two peaks around 1977 and 1986. There also appears to be an overall downward trend over time.

2.103 **(a)** $r^2 = 0.9101$. This is the fraction of the variation in daily sales data that can be attributed to a linear relationship between daily sales and total item count. **(b)** We would expect the correlation to be smaller. Correlations based on averages are usually higher than the correlation one would compute for the individual values from which an average was computed.

2.105 Intelligence or family background may be lurking variables. Families with a tradition of more education and high-paying jobs may encourage children to follow a similar career path.

2.107 **(a)** The residuals are more widely scattered about the horizontal line as the predicted value increases. The regression model will predict low salaries more precisely because lower predicted salaries have smaller residuals and hence are closer to the actual salaries. **(b)** There is a curved pattern in the plot. For very low and very high numbers of years in the majors, the residuals tend to be negative. For intermediate numbers of years the residuals tend to be positive. The model will overestimate the salaries of players that are new to the majors, will underestimate the salaries of players who have been in the major leagues about 8 years, and will overestimate the salaries of players who have been in the majors more than 15 years.

2.109 **(a)** The data describe 5375 students. **(b)** The number who smoke is 1004, so the percent who smoke is 18.68%.

(c)

	Neither parent smokes	One parent smokes	Both parents smoke
Total	1356	2239	1780
Percent	25.23%	41.66%	33.12%

2.111

	Neither parent smokes	One parent smokes	Both parents smoke
% students who smoke	13.86%	18.58%	22.47%

The data support the belief that parents' smoking increases smoking in their children.

2.113 (a)

	Female	Male
Accounting	30.22%	34.78%
Administration	40.44%	24.84%
Economics	2.22%	3.73%
Finance	27.11%	36.65%

The most popular choice for women is administration, while for men accounting and finance are the most popular. **(b)** 46.54% did not respond.

2.115 **(a)** Percent of Hospital A patients who died = 3%. Percent of Hospital B patients who died = 2%. **(b)** Percent of Hospital A patients who died who were classified as "poor" before surgery = 3.8%. Percent of Hospital B patients who died who were classified as "poor" before surgery = 4%. **(c)** Percent of Hospital A patients who died who were classified as "good" before surgery = 1%. Percent of Hospital B patients who died who were classified as "good" before surgery = 1.3%. **(d)** If you are in "good" condition before surgery or if you are in "bad" condition before surgery, your chance of dying is lower in Hospital A, so choose Hospital A. **(e)** The majority of patients in Hospital A are in poor condition before surgery, while the majority of patients in Hospital B are in good condition before surgery. Patients in poor condition are more likely to die, and this makes the overall number of deaths in Hospital A higher than in Hospital B, even though both types of patients fare better in Hospital A.

2.117 The marginal distribution for payment method is: cash (0.351), check (0.155), and credit card (0.495). The conditional distribution of payment method for impulse purchases is: cash (0.452), check (0.129), and credit card (0.419). The conditional distribution of payment method for planned purchases is: cash (0.303), check (0.167), and credit card (0.530). For impulse purchases, cash is most likely. For planned purchases, credit card is most likely. For both types of purchases, check is least likely. Answers will vary for explaining the choice of payment method for impulse purchases.

2.119 **(a)** The percent is 20.40%. **(b)** The percent is 9.85%.

2.121 There are 1716 thousands of older students. The distribution is

	2-year part-time	2-year full-time	4-year part-time	4-year full-time
% older students	7.05%	43.59%	13.75%	35.61%

Older students tend to prefer full-time colleges and universities to part-time colleges and universities, with 79.2% of all older students enrolled in some full-time institution.

2.123 **(a)**

	Hired	Not hired
Applicants < 40	6.44%	93.56%
Applicants ≥ 40	0.61%	99.39%

(b) A graph shows results similar to those in **(a)**. **(c)** Only a small percent of all applicants are hired, but the percent (6.44%) of applicants who are less than 40 who are hired is more than 10 times the percent (0.61%) of applicants who are 40 or older who are hired. **(d)** Lurking variables that might be involved are past employment history (why are older applicants without a job and looking for work?) or health.

2.125 **(a)**

	Desipramine	Lithium	Placebo
Relapse	41.67%	75%	83.33%
No relapse	58.33%	25%	16.67%

(b) The data show that those taking desipramine had fewer relapses than those taking either lithium or a placebo. These results are interesting but association does not imply causation.

2.127 **(a)** The sum is 59,920 thousand. The entry in the Total column is 59,918 thousand. The difference may be due to rounding off to the nearest thousand.
(b)

Never married	Married	Widowed	Divorced
21.05%	57.69%	10.54%	10.73%

2.129 **(a)** A combined two-way table is

	Admit	Deny
Male	490	210
Female	280	220

(b) Converting to percents gives

	Admit	Deny
Male	70%	30%
Female	56%	44%

(c) The percents for each school are as follows:

	Business			Law	
	Admit	Deny		Admit	Deny
Male	80%	20%	Male	10%	90%
Female	90%	10%	Female	33%	67%

(d) If we look at the tables, we see that it is easier to get into the business school than the law school, and more men apply to the business school than the law school, while more women apply to the law school than the business school. Because it is easier to get into the business school, the overall admission rate for men appears relatively high. It is hard to get into the law school, and this makes the overall admission rate for women appear low.

2.131 **(b)** There is a fairly strong, positive, linear association with an outlier from point Professor #9 (102,300, 144,200). **(c)** Professors #3 and #5 have 2002 salary similar to this one. Professor #16 has a 2005 salary similar to this one. Professor #9 does not follow the overall pattern and would be considered an outlier. **(d)** Professor #15 has the highest 2002 and 2005 values, but the data point follows the general trend of the other data. It would not be considered an outlier.

2.133 **(d)** The association looks stronger as the range of axes increases because the points look closer together.

2.135 **(a)** 0.966. **(b)** 0.966. **(c)** 0.966. **(d)** The calculations are the same, which is a general fact. Units of measure don't change the correlation between two variables. **(e)** The rounding didn't have an effect for this data because the part of each data point which was rounded off was a small percentage of the actual data value.

2.137 **(a)** If a professor had a 2002 salary of \$0, his or her 2005 salary would be \$27,459.44. This is not a "practical" interpretation because no professor would have had a 2002 salary of \$0. **(c)** The "zero intercept" line completely misses all the data because it is too low. The estimated intercept raises the least-squares regression line to the right height to pass through the data.

2.139 **(a)** With all data points: $\hat{y} = 27459.441 + 0.896x$, $R^2 = 75.6\%$, $s = 8710.554$. With #15 removed: $\hat{y} = 21681.387 + 0.952x$, $R^2 = 75.6\%$, $s = 8765.396$. **(b)** No, #15 is not an influential observation because R^2, s, and the slope hardly changed at all when it was removed.

2.141 **(a)** 0.676.
(b)

Amps	10	12	13	14	15
Average weight	9.5	10.5	11.5	12.5	11.56

(c) 0.877. The correlation of amps with average weight is greater than the correlation of amps with the individual weights.

2.143 High interest rates are weakly negatively associated with lower stock returns. Because many other factors (lurking variables) affect stock returns, one should not conclude from these data that the observed association is evidence that high interest rates cause low stock returns.

2.145 Removing this point would make the correlation closer to 0. The point is an outlier in the horizontal direction, and its location strongly influences the regression line.

2.147 Suppose the return on Fund A is always twice that of Fund B. Then if Fund B increases by 10%, Fund B increases by 20%, and if Fund B increases by 20%, Fund A increases by 40%. This is a case where there is a perfect straight-line relation between Funds A and B.

2.149 **(a)** and **(b)** The overall pattern shows strength decreasing as length increases until length is 9, then the pattern is relatively flat with strength decreasing only very slightly for lengths greater than 9. **(c)** The least-squares line is Strength = 488.38 − 20.75 × Length. A straight line does not adequately describe these data because it fails to capture the "bend" in the pattern at Length = 9. **(d)** The equation for the lengths of 5 to 9 inches is 283.1 − 3.4 × Length. The equation for the lengths of 9 to 14 inches is 667.5 − 46.9 × Length. The two lines describe the data much better than a single line. I would want to know how the strength of the wood product compares to solid wood of various lengths. For what lengths is it stronger, and are these common lengths that are used in building?

2.151 Let x denote degree-days per day and y gas consumed per day. $\overline{x} = 21.544$, $s_x = 13.419$, $\overline{y} = 558.889$, $s_y = 274.383$, and $r = 0.989$. Thus, $b = r\frac{s_y}{s_x} = 20.222$ and $a = \overline{y} - b\overline{x} = 123.226$. The equation of the regression line is gas use = 123.226 + 20.222 × (degree-days). The slope has units of cubic feet per degree-day. To find the equation of the regression line for predicting degree-days from gas use, we interchange the roles of x and y and compute $b = 0.048$ and $a = -5.283$. The equation of the regression line is degree-days = −5.283 + 0.048 × (gas use). The slope has units of degree-days per cubic feet.

2.153 **(a)** Selling price = 189,226 − 1334.49 × age. **(b)** For a house built in 2000, age is 0 and selling price = 189,226. For a house built in 1999, age is 1 and selling price = \$187,891.51. For a house built in 1998, age is 2 and selling price = \$186,557.02. For a house built in 1997, age is 3 and selling price = \$185,222.53. We see that for each 1-year increase in age the selling price drops by \$1334.49. **(c)** 1900 (age = 100) is within the range of the data used to calculate the least-squares regression line, and 1899 (age = 101) is almost within the range, so we would probably trust the regression line to predict the selling price of a house in these years. 1850 (age = 150) is well outside the range of the data, and we would not trust the regression line to predict the selling price of such a house. The regression line predicts a house that is 150 years old to have a selling price = 189,226 − 1334.49 × 150 = −\$10,947.50; a negative value makes no sense! **(d)** $r = -0.682$. The association is negative, indicating that older houses are associated with lower selling prices and newer houses with higher selling prices.

2.155 We convert the table entries into percents of the column totals to get the conditional distribution of heart attacks and strokes for the aspirin group and for the placebo group.

	Aspirin group	Placebo group
Fatal heart attacks	0.09%	0.24%
Other heart attacks	1.17%	1.93%
Strokes	1.08%	0.89%

The data show that aspirin is associated with reduced rates of heart attacks but a slightly increased rate of strokes.

Association does not imply causation. However, the design of the study is such that it is difficult to identify lurking variables. Doctors were assigned at random to the treatments (aspirin or placebo), so there should be no systematic differences in the groups that received the two treatments.

2.157 **(a)** The marginal distribution of opinion about quality is: higher (0.368), same (0.241), lower (0.391). The proportions for "higher" and "lower" are very close, with the proportion for "lower" slightly bigger. These are the proportions of opinion in general, not separated out for buyers and nonbuyers. **(b)** The conditional distribution of opinion for buyers is: higher (0.556), same (0.194), and lower (0.250). The conditional distribution of opinion for nonbuyers is: higher (0.299), same (0.258), and lower (0.443). For buyers, the majority voted for "higher." For nonbuyers, the largest proportion was for "lower." For both groups, the smallest proportion was for "same." Yes, we can conclude that using recycled filters causes more favorable opinions.

CHAPTER 3

3.1 It is an observational study because information is gathered without imposing a treatment. The explanatory variable is consumer's gender, and the response variables are whether or not the individual considers the particular features essential in a health plan.

3.3 Many variables (lurking variables) could have changed over the five years to increase the unemployment rate, such as a recession or factories leaving the area.

3.5 **(a)** All adult U.S. residents. **(b)** U.S. households. **(c)** All regulators from the supplier, *or* just the regulators in the last shipment.

3.7 We have used two-digit labels, numbering across rows. The selected sample is 04—Bowman, 10—Fleming, 17—Liao, 19—Naber, 12—Gates, and 13—Goel.

3.9 Label the retailers from 001 to 440. The selected sample includes the retailers numbered 400, 077, 172, 417, 350, 131, 211, 273, 208, and 074.

3.11 Label the midsize accounts 001, 002, . . . , 500 and select an SRS of 25 of these. Label the small accounts 0001, 0002, . . . , 4400 and select an SRS of 44 of these. First select 5 midsize accounts and, continuing from where you left off in the table, select 5 small accounts. The first 5 midsize accounts have labels 417, 494, 322, 247, and 097, and the first 5 small accounts have labels 3698, 1452, 2605, 2480, and 3716.

3.13 You would expect that the higher rate of no-answer was probably during the second period, as more families are likely to be gone on vacation.

3.15 **(a)** To make this an experiment, randomly assign 25 members to a control group that just has them visiting a health club and 25 members to a treatment group which has them visiting a health club and working with a trainer. The unseen bias involved in using the study as written in the exercise is that currently individuals have decided on their own to work with the trainer. These individuals may be more health conscious, more actively training for some athletic event, or more seriously trying to lose weight. **(b)** To make this an experiment, start with a sample of tellers, all of the same experience and ability, and randomly select half to participate in the advanced training while the other half get no additional training. An alternate way of doing this is to treat it as a matched pairs experiment where pairs of tellers with similar backgrounds and experience are paired up, with one from each pair completing the training and the other not. The unseen bias in the study as written in the exercise is that since the tellers were allowed to select themselves for advanced training, these are probably the tellers who are more experienced or more interested in advancing their careers.

3.17 **(a)** The site is a true random number generator which uses little variations in amplitude in atmospheric noise picked up by a radio. **(b)** There are testimonials on the Web site. **(c)** and **(d)** Answers will vary.

3.19 **(a)** The committee intends for the population to be all local businesses, but in actuality the population they are using is all local businesses listed in the telephone book. **(b)** The sample is 150 randomly selected businesses. **(c)** 51.33%. **(d)** Answers will vary. Some businesses list only in the yellow pages, and some only in the white pages. Some businesses are listed by a person's name. Some businesses may only use cell phones or Web sites and choose not to be listed in the phone book at all. How did the committee know which names in the phone book were businesses?

3.21 **(a)** The population "eating-and-drinking establishments" in the large city. **(b)** The population is the congressman's constituents. **(c)** The population is all claims filed in a given month.

3.23 This is a voluntary response sample, and persons with strong opinions on the subject are more likely to take the time to write.

3.25 We have used two-digit labels, numbering across rows. The selected sample is 12—B0986, 04—A1101, and 11—A2220.

3.27 Various labels are possible. We labeled tracts numbered in the 1000s one to six, in the 2000s seven to eighteen, and in the 3000s nineteen to forty-four. The labels and blocks selected are 21 (block 3002), 18 (block 2011), 23 (block 3004), 19 (block 3000), and 10 (block 2003).

3.29 **(a)** The selected number is 35, so the systematic sample includes clusters numbered 35, 75, 115, 155, and 195. **(b)** A simple random sample of size n would allow every set of n individuals an equal chance of being selected. A systematic sample doesn't allow every set of n individuals a chance of being selected. The clusters numbered 1, 2, 3, 4, and 5 would have no chance of being selected in a systematic sample.

3.31 Label the alphabetized lists 001 to 500 for the females and 0001 to 2000 for the males. The first 5 females are those with the labels 138, 159, 052, 087, and 359. Continuing in the table, the first 5 males are those with the labels 1369, 0815, 0727, 1025, and 1868.

3.33 **(a)** "A national system of health insurance should be favored because it would provide health insurance for everyone and would reduce administrative costs." **(b)** "The elimination of the tenure system at public institutions should be considered as a means of increasing the accountability of faculty to the public, while at the same time the question of whether such a move would have a deleterious effect on the academic freedom so important to such institutions cannot be ignored."

3.35 Subjects are the 300 sickle cell patients, the factor is the type of medication given, and the treatments are the two levels of medication. The response variable is the number of pain episodes reported.

3.37 **(a)** The individuals are different batches and the response is the yield. **(b)** There are two factors—temperature and stirring rate—and six treatments. Lay them out in a diagram like that in Figure 3.3. **(c)** Twelve batches, or "individuals," are needed.

3.39 To assign the 20 pairs to the four treatments, give each of the pairs a two-digit number from 01 to 20. The first 5 selected are assigned to Group 1, the next 5 to Group 2, and the next 5 to Group 3. The remaining 5 are assigned to Group 4. Group 1 is pairs numbered 16, 04, 19, 07, and 10; Group 2 is 13, 15, 05, 09, and 08; Group 3 is 18, 03, 01, 06, and 11. The remaining 5 pairs are assigned to Group 4. Use a diagram like those in Figures 3.4 and 3.5 to describe the design.

3.41 If charts or indicators are introduced in the second year, and the electric consumption in the first year is compared with the second year, you won't know if the observed differences are due to the introduction of the chart or indicator or due to lurking variables.

3.43 A statistically significant result means that it is unlikely that the salary differences we are observing are just due to chance.

3.45 This experiment suffers from lack of realism and limits the ability to apply the conclusions of the experiment to the situation of interest.

3.47 **(a)** The subjects and their excess weights, rearranged in increasing order of excess weight, are listed with the columns as the 5 blocks and the 4 subjects in each block labeled 1 to 4. With these conventions, Regimen A = Williams, Smith, Obrach, Brown, Birnbaum; Regimen B = Moses, Kendall, Loren, Stall, Wilansky; Regimen C = Hernandez, Santiago, Brunk, Jackson, Nevesky; Regimen D = Deng, Mann, Rodriguez, Cruz, Tran.

3.49 **(a)** This is a completely randomized design with two treatment groups. **(b)** Answers will vary using software, but using line 131 on Table B, Group 1 will contain: Dubois (05), Travers (19), Chen (04), Ullman (20), Quinones (16), Thompson (18), Fluharty (07), Lucero (13), Afifi (02), Gerson (08). Group 2 will then contain the remaining subjects: Abate, Brown, Engel, Gutierrez, Hwang, Iselin, Kaplan, McNiell, Morse, and Rosen.

3.51 **(a)** Randomly assign your subjects to either Group 1 or Group 2. Each group will taste and rate both the regular and the light mocha drink. However, Group 1 will drink them in the regular/light order, and Group 2 will drink them in the light/regular order. For each group, the taste ratings of the regular and light drinks will be compared, and then the results of the two groups will be compared to see if the order of tasting made a difference to the ratings. To properly blind the subjects, both mocha drinks should be in identical opaque (we are only measuring taste, not appearance) cups with no labels on them. **(b)** Using line 141 on Table B, the regular/light group will use subjects with labels: 12, 16, 02, 08, 17, 10, 05, 09, 19, 06. The light/regular group will use the remaining 10 subjects.

3.53 **(a)** This is matched pairs data because each day two related measurements are taken. **(b)** The sample mean for the kill room is 2138.5, and the sample mean for the processing is 314.

3.55 This is a comparative experiment with two treatments: steady price and price cuts. The explanatory variable is the price history that is viewed. The response variable is the price the student would expect to pay for the detergent.

3.57 **(a)** The subjects are the 210 children. **(b)** The factor is the set of choices that are presented to each subject. The levels correspond to the three sets of choices. The response variable is whether they chose a milk drink or a fruit drink. **(c)** Use a diagram like those in Figures 3.4 and 3.5 to describe the design. **(d)** The first

5 children to be assigned to receive Set 1 have labels 119, 033, 199, 192, and 148.

3.59 **(a)** The more seriously ill patients may be assigned to the new method by their doctors. The seriousness of the illness would be a lurking variable that would make the new treatment look worse than it really is. **(b)** Use a diagram like those in Figures 3.4 and 3.5 to describe the design.

3.61 In a controlled scientific study, the effects of factors other than the treatment can be eliminated or accounted for.

3.63 **(a)** Use a diagram like those in Figures 3.4 and 3.5 to describe the design. **(b)** As a practical issue, it may take a long time to carry out the study. Some people might object because some participants will be required to pay for part of their health care, while others will not.

3.65 **(a)** Use a diagram like those in Figures 3.4 and 3.5 to describe the design. **(b)** Each subject will do the task twice, once under each temperature condition in a random order. The difference in the number of correct insertions at the two temperatures is the observed response.

3.67 Use a diagram like those in Figures 3.4 and 3.5 to describe the design.

3.69 Draw a rectangular array with five rows and four columns. Label the plots across rows. The first 10 plots selected are labeled 19, 06, 09, 10, 16, 01, 08, 20, 02, and 07. These are assigned to Method A, and the remaining 10 are assigned to Method B.

3.71 The number 73% is a statistic and the number 68% is a parameter.

3.73 **(a)** 25.234 million dollars, which is smaller. **(b)** 30.788 million dollars, which is smaller. **(c)** 13.3 million dollars, which is close to the other medians.

3.75 **(a)** Approximately 10 million to 70 million dollars. **(b)** Approximately 5 million to 80 million dollars. **(c)** Approximately 18 million to 40 million dollars. **(d)** Sampling variability decreases as the sample size increases.

3.77 **(a)** Population is all people who live in Ontario. Sample is the 61,239 residents interviewed. **(b)** Yes. This is a very large probability sample.

3.79 **(a)** Worst case scenario would be that we have a $\hat{p}$ of 1, which would be 0.8 away from the true proportion. **(b)** If we use a p of 0.5, then $\hat{p}$ would only be 0.5 away from the true proportion at most.

3.81 **(a)** $\hat{p} = 0.8133$. **(b)** Worst case scenario is the true proportion is 0. Then the estimate would be 0.8133 away. **(c)** It is impossible to know how far off this sample proportion is from the true population proportion because we do not know what the true population proportion is.

3.83 **(b)** Approximately 95% of the $\hat{p}$ values are inside the interval (0.8072, 0.9196). **(c)** Approximately 95% of the $\hat{p}$ values from 1200 samples are between 0.8072 and 0.9196, so this is a good indication of where the true proportion is.

3.85 2.503 is a parameter and 2.515 is a statistic.

3.87 The larger sample size suggested by the faculty advisor will decrease the sampling variability of the estimates.

3.89 The number of adults is larger than the number of men.

3.91 **(a)** Answers will vary depending on the random numbers you choose. For a sample of invoice numbers 9, 8, 1, and 6 corresponding to days past due of 6, 7, 12, and 15, the average is $\overline{x} = 10$. **(b)** Answers will vary depending on the random numbers you choose. The center of the histogram of the 10 repetitions should not be far from 8.2.

3.93 **(a)** Starting at line 101, $\hat{p} = 0.6$. **(b)** The 9 additional samples have $\hat{p} = 0.4, 0.6, 0.4, 0.0, 0.6, 0.2, 0.8, 0.8$, and 0.6. **(c)** These 10 samples can be used to draw a histogram. **(d)** The center is close to 0.6. If more samples were taken, the center should be 0.6 since $\hat{p}$ is an unbiased estimator of p.

3.95 **(a)** Many of the subjects will be non-scientists, and their viewpoint is important to consider. Scientists may be so concerned with the experiment itself that they do not fully consider the experience of participating in the experiment from the subject's point of view. **(b)** Answers will vary. Choosing a member of the clergy might be tricky—which religion would be picked? A medical doctor might be considered just another scientist. An activist for patients' rights might be acceptable; however, the activist would have a bias before even reviewing the experiment.

3.97 **(a)** This is acceptable. **(b)** This is acceptable as long as no names will be reported and the social psychologist doesn't interfere in any way. **(c)** This is not acceptable.

3.99 This is not anonymous because it takes place in the person's home. However, it is confidential if the name/address is then separated from the response before the results are publicized.

3.101 **(a)** The pollsters must tell the potential respondents what type of questions will be asked and how long it will take to complete the survey. **(b)** This is required so the respondents can make sure the polling group is legitimate or so the respondent can issue a complaint if necessary.

3.103 Psychology 001 uses dependent subjects, which does not seem ethical. The other two courses have acceptable alternatives which make the use of the students more ethical.

3.105 Answers will vary.

3.107 Answers will vary.

3.109 Answers will vary.

3.111 **(a)** This is an experiment because the students are reacting to the ads they were shown. The ads are the treatment which is applied to the subjects. **(b)** The explanatory variable is the type of ad which is shown to the student, and the response variable is the expected price for the cola which the student states.

3.113 **(a)** All adults. **(b)** 37.17%. **(c)** Most people probably will not be able to accurately remember how many movies they have watched in a movie theater over the past 12 months. That is a very long time period, and they were not warned ahead of time to keep track of their ticket stubs. **(d)** The results would be more accurate if the question concerned just the past month.

3.115 **(a)** This is a completely randomized design with 2 treatment groups (20 women in each group). One group would receive the brochures for Company A and for Company B with child-care. The other group would receive the brochures for Company A and for Company B without child-care. At the end of the experiment, record the each women's choice of company. **(b)** Using Table B, starting at line

161, Group 1 will consist of: Wong (40), Adamson (02), Rivera (31), Chen (06), Morse (28), Roberts (32), Janle (21), Ullmann (38), Gupta (16), Brown (04), Chen (06), Sugiwara (34), Gerson (14), Travers (36), Kim (23), Edwards (11), McNeill (27), Danielson (09), and Afifi (03). The other 20 subjects would be in Group 2.

3.117 This is an observational study because no treatment is applied. The researcher is just measuring the men as they already are.

3.119 This is a matched pairs experiment. The two types of muffin are the treatments.

3.121 The wording of questions has the most important influence on the answers to a survey. Leading questions can introduce strong bias, and both of these questions lead the respondent to answer Yes, which results in contradictory responses.

3.123 **(a)** There may be systematic differences between the recitations attached to the two lectures. **(b)** Randomly assign the 20 recitations to the two groups, 10 in each group. First number the 20 recitations from 01 to 20. To carry out the random assignment, enter Table B and read two-digit groups until 10 recitations have been selected. Answers will vary depending on where in the table you start.

3.125 The nonresponse rate can produce serious bias. For the original questionnaires, there was a 37% response rate. For the firms sent follow-up questionnaires, nonresponse was a serious problem as well.

3.127 Take an SRS from each of the four groups for a stratified sample.

3.129 This is a sensitive question and many people are embarrassed to admit that they do not vote.

3.131 **(a)** The response variable is whether or not the subject gets colon cancer. The explanatory variables are the four different supplement combinations. **(b)** Use a diagram like those in Figures 3.4 and 3.5 to describe the design. **(c)** The first five subjects assigned to the beta carotene group are subjects 731, 253, 304, 470, and 296. **(d)** Neither the subjects nor those evaluating the subjects' response knew which treatments were applied. **(e)** Any observed differences are due to chance. **(f)** People who eat lots of fruits and vegetables tend to have different diets, may exercise more, may smoke less, etc.

3.133 **(a)** The factors are "storage method" at three levels and "when cooked" at two levels. **(b)** One possible design is to take the group of judges and divide them at random into six groups. One group is assigned to each treatment. **(c)** Having each subject taste fries from each of the six treatments in a random order is a block design and eliminates the variability between subjects.

3.135 Subjects should not be told where each burger comes from and in fact shouldn't be told which two burger chains are being compared.

3.137 Answers will vary depending on the random numbers you choose. We would expect that in a long series of random assignments, about half, or 5, of the rats with genetic defects would be in the experimental group.

3.139 For comparison purposes, it is important to draw the histograms using the same scales. Increasing the sample size decreases the sampling variability of $\hat{p}$. The histograms are becoming more concentrated about their center, which is $p = 0.6$, so the chance of getting a value of $\hat{p}$ far from 0.6 becomes smaller as the sample size increases.

CHAPTER 4

4.1 We spun a nickel 50 times and got 22 heads. We estimate the probability of heads to be 0.44.

4.3 Answers will vary.

4.5 The first 200 digits contain 21 0s. The proportion of 0s is 0.105.

4.7 We tossed a thumbtack 100 times and it landed with the point up 39 times. The approximate probability of landing point up is 0.39.

4.9 **(a)** 0. **(b)** 1. **(c)** 0.01. **(d)** 0.6.

4.11 **(a)** The number of "buys" (1s) in our simulation was 50. The percent of simulated customers who bought a new computer is 50%. **(b)** The longest run of "buys" (1s) was 4. The longest run of "not buys" was 5.

4.13 **(a)** In our 100 draws the number in which at least 14 people had a favorable opinion was 37. The approximate probability is 0.37. **(b)** The shape of our histogram was roughly symmetric and bell-shaped, the center appeared to be about 65%, and the values ranged from 40% to 90%. **(c)** The shape of our histogram was roughly symmetric and bell-shaped, the center was about 65% or 66%, and the values ranged from 58% to 74%. **(d)** Both distributions are roughly symmetric with similar centers. The histogram in **(b)** is more spread out.

4.15 **(a)** Answers will vary, but should be close to 6%. **(b)** This simulation represents 100 randomly selected items which have been purchased. A success is an item which is returned. Over the long run, there is a 0.06 probability that an item which is purchased will be returned.

4.17 **(a)** $S = \{$any number (including fractional values) between 0 and 24 hours$\}$. **(b)** $S = \{$any integer value between 0 and 11,000$\}$. **(c)** $S = \{0, 1, 2, 3, 4, 5, 6, 7, 8, 9, 10, 11, 12\}$. **(d)** One possibility is $S = \{$any number 0 or larger$\}$. **(e)** We might take $S = \{$any possible number, either positive or negative$\}$.

4.19 P(death was either agriculture-related or manufacturing-related) $= 0.253$. P(death was related to some other occupation) $= 0.747$.

4.21 Model 1: Not legitimate. The probabilities do not sum to 1. Model 2: Legitimate. Model 3: Not legitimate. The probabilities do not sum to 1. Model 4: Not legitimate. Some of the probabilities are greater than 1.

4.23 **(a)** P(completely satisfied) $= 0.39$ since probabilities sum to 1. **(b)** P(dissatisfied) $= 0.14$.

4.25 **(a)** The area of a triangle is $(1/2) \times$ height $\times$ base $= (1/2) \times 1 \times 2 = 1$. **(b)** The probability that T is less than 1 is 0.5. **(c)** The probability that T is less than 0.5 is 0.1125.

4.27 **(a)** $P(Y > 300) = 0.5$. **(b)** $P(Y > 370) = 0.025$.

4.29 **(a)** 0.19. **(b)** 0.287. **(c)** 0.790.

4.31 **(a)** $P(Y > 1) = 0.69$. **(b)** 0.28. **(c)** 0.65.

4.33 **(a)** Yes, the percentages add up to 100%. **(b)** 0.02. **(c)** 0.919.

4.35 **(a)** P(not farmland) $= 0.08$. **(b)** P(either farmland or forest) $= 0.93$. **(c)** P(something other than farmland or forest) $= 0.07$.

4.37 **(a)** $P(\text{blue}) = 0.1$. **(b)** $P(\text{blue}) = 0.2$. **(c)** P(plain M&M is red, yellow, or orange) $= 0.5$. P(peanut M&M is red, yellow, or orange) $= 0.5$.

4.39 **(a)** Legitimate. **(b)** Not legitimate. The sum of the probabilities is greater than 1. **(c)** Not legitimate. The probabilities of the outcomes do not sum to 1.

4.41 **(a)** $P(A) = 0.29$. $P(B) = 0.18$. **(b)** "A does not occur" means the farm is 50 acres or more. $P(A \text{ does not occur}) = 0.71$. **(c)** "$A$ or B" means the farm is less than 50 acres or 500 or more acres. $P(A \text{ or } B) = 0.47$.

4.43 **(a)** The 8 arrangements of preferences are NNN, NNO, NON, ONN, NOO, ONO, OON, OOO. Each must have probability 0.125. **(b)** $P(X = 2) = 0.375$. **(c)**

X	0	1	2	3
$P(X)$	0.125	0.375	0.375	0.125

4.45 **(a)** All the probabilities given are between 0 and 1 and they sum to 1. **(b)** $P(X \geq 5) = 0.11$. **(c)** $P(X > 5) = 0.04$. **(d)** $P(2 < X \leq 4) = 0.32$. **(e)** $P(X \neq 1) = 0.75$. **(f)** P(a randomly chosen household contains more than two persons) $= P(X > 2) = 0.43$.

4.47 **(a)** Continuous. All times greater than 0 are possible without any separation between values. **(b)** Discrete. It is a count that can take only the values 0, 1, 2, 3, or 4. **(c)** Continuous. Any number 0 or larger is possible without any separation between values. **(d)** Discrete. Household size can take only the values 1, 2, 3, 4, 5, 6, or 7.

4.49 **(a)** All the probabilities given are between 0 and 1 and they sum to 1. **(b)** $\{X \geq 1\}$ means the household owns at least 1 car. $P(X \geq 1) = 0.91$. **(c)** Households that have more cars than the garage can hold have 3 or more cars. 20% of households have more cars than the garage can hold.

4.51 **(a)** The probability that a tire lasts more than 50,000 miles is $P(X > 50{,}000) = 0.5$. **(b)** $P(X > 60{,}000) = 0.0344$. **(c)** The normal distribution is continuous, so $P(X = 60{,}000) = 0$ and $P(X \geq 60{,}000) = P(X > 60{,}000) = 0.0344$.

4.53 $\mu = 18.5$. If we record the size of the hard drive chosen by many, many customers in the 60-day period and compute the average of these sizes, the average will be close to 18.5. Knowing μ is not very helpful, as it is not one of the possible choices and does not indicate which choice is most popular.

4.55 **(a)** $\mu_X = 280$. $\mu_Y = 195$. **(b)** Profit at the mall is $25X$ and $\mu_{25X} = 7000$. Profit downtown is 35 and $\mu_{35Y} = 6825$. **(c)** The combined profit is $25X + 35Y$. $\mu_{25X+35Y} = 13{,}825$.

4.57 $\mu_Y = 445$, $\sigma_Y^2 = 19{,}225.00$, and $\sigma_Y = 138.65$.

4.59 **(a)** $\mu_X = 280$, $\sigma_Y^2 = 5600$, and $\sigma_X = 74.83$. **(b)** $\mu_Y = 195$, $\sigma_Y^2 = 6475.00$, and $\sigma_Y = 80.47$.

4.61 $\mu_{X-Y} = 100$. $\sigma_{X-Y}^2 = 10{,}000$. $\sigma_{X-Y} = 100$. If the correlation between two variables is positive, then large values of one tend to be associated with large values of the other, resulting in a relatively small difference. Also, small values of one tend to be associated with small values of the other, again resulting in a relatively small difference. This suggests that when two variables are positively associated, they vary together and the difference tends to stay relatively small and varies little.

4.63 **(a)** 720.
(b)

No. of transactions	0	1	2	3	4	5
% of clients	0.08	0.17	0.35	0.19	0.18	0.13

(c) Yes, if for 5 transactions the 0.125 is rounded to 0.13, then the probabilities add up to 1. If the 0.125 is rounded down to 0.12, the probabilities add up to 0.99.

4.65 **(a)** 0.0010. **(b)** 0.1131. **(c)** 379.28 bets per second.

4.67 **(a)** −1280.
(b)

X	218,720	−1280
Probability	0.003	0.997

4.69 **(a)** Two important differences between the histograms are (1) the center of the distribution of the number of rooms of owner-occupied units is larger than the center of the distribution of the number of rooms of renter-occupied units and (2) the spread of the distribution of the number of rooms of owner-occupied units is slightly larger than the spread of the distribution of the number of rooms of renter-occupied units. **(b)** $\mu_{\text{owned}} = 6.284$. $\mu_{\text{rented}} = 4.187$. The mean number of rooms for owner-occupied units is larger than the mean number of rooms for renter-occupied units. This reflects the fact that the center of the distribution of the number of rooms of owner-occupied units is larger than the center of the distribution of the number of rooms of renter-occupied units.

4.71 The histogram for renter-occupied units is more peaked and less spread out than the histogram for owner-occupied units. $\sigma^2_{\text{owned}} = 2.69204$, $\sigma^2_{\text{rented}} = 1.71174$, $\sigma_{\text{owned}} = 1.64074$, $\sigma_{\text{rented}} = 1.30833$.

4.73 There are 1000 three-digit numbers (000 to 999). If you pick a number with three different digits, your probability of winning is 6/1000 and your probability of not winning is 994/1000. Your expected payoff is \$0.49998.

4.75 **(a)** We would expect X and Y to be independent because they correspond to events that are widely separated in time. **(b)** Experience suggests that the amount of rainfall on one day is not closely related to the amount of rainfall on the next. We might expect X and Y to be independent or, because they are not widely separated in time, perhaps slightly dependent. **(c)** Orlando and Disney World are close to each other. Rainfall usually covers more than just a very small geographic area. We would not expect X and Y to be independent.

4.77 **(a)** If X is the time to bring the part from the bin to its position on the automobile chassis and Y is the time required to attach the part to the chassis, then the total time for the entire operation is $X + Y$. $\mu_{X+Y} = 31$ seconds. **(b)** It will not affect the mean. **(c)** The answer in **(a)** will remain the same in both cases.

4.79 $\sigma_{X+Y} = 4.47$. If X and Y have correlation 0.3, $\sigma_{X+Y} = 4.98$. If X and Y are positively correlated, then large values of X and Y tend to occur together, resulting in a very large value of $X + Y$. Likewise, small values of X and Y tend to occur together, resulting in a small value of $X + Y$. Thus, $X + Y$ exhibits larger variation when X and Y are positively correlated than if they are not.

4.81 $\mu_X = (\mu + \sigma)(0.5) + (\mu - \sigma)(0.5) = \mu$. $\sigma_X^2 = (\mu + \sigma - \mu_X)^2(0.5) + (\mu - \sigma - \mu_X)^2(0.5) = \sigma^2$. Thus, $\sigma_X = \sigma$.

4.83 **(a)** $\sigma_{X+Y}^2 = 7{,}812{,}763.75$ and $\sigma_{X+Y} = 2795.13$. **(b)** $\sigma_Z^2 = \sigma_{2000X+3500Y}^2 = 3.135635594 \times 10^{13}$. Thus, $\sigma_Z = 5{,}599{,}674$.

4.85 **(a)** The two students are selected at random and we expect their scores to be unrelated or independent. **(b)** $\mu_{\text{female}-\text{male}} = 15$. $\sigma_{\text{female}-\text{male}}^2 = 2009$ and $\sigma_{\text{female}-\text{male}}^2 = 44.82$. **(c)** We cannot find the probability that the woman chosen scores higher than the man chosen because we do not know the probability distribution for the scores of women or men.

4.87 $\sigma_{0.8W+0.2Y}^2 = 15.60$. Thus, $\sigma_{0.8W+0.2Y} = 3.95$. This is smaller than the result in Exercise 4.70 because we no longer include the positive term $2\rho\sigma_{0.8W}\sigma_{0.2Y}$. The mean return remains the same.

4.89 If $\rho_{XY} = 1$, $\sigma_{X+Y}^2 = \sigma_X^2 + \sigma_Y^2 + 2\rho_{XY}\sigma_X\sigma_Y = \sigma_X^2 + \sigma_Y^2 + 2\sigma_X\sigma_Y = (\sigma_X + \sigma_Y)^2$. So $\sigma_{X+Y} = \sigma_X + \sigma_Y$.

4.91 **(a)** $\mu_X = 550$. $\sigma_X = 5.7$. **(b)** $\mu_{X-550} = 0$. $\sigma_{X-550}^2 = 32.5$ and $\sigma_{X-550} = 5.7$. **(c)** $\mu_Y = \mu_{(9X/5)+32} = 1022$. $\sigma_Y^2 = \sigma_{(9X/5)+32}^2 = 105.3$ and $\sigma_Y = 10.26$.

4.93 These are statistics. Pfeiffer undoubtedly tested only a sample of all the models produced by Apple, and these means are computed from these samples.

4.95 The law of large numbers says that in the long run, the average payout to Joe will be 60 cents. However, Joe pays \$1.00 to play each time, so in the long run his average winnings are −\$0.40. Thus, in the long run, if Joe keeps track of his net winnings and computes the average per bet, he will find that he loses an average of 40 cents per bet.

4.97 That is not right. The law of large numbers tells us that the long-run average will be close to 34%. Six of seven at-bats is hardly the "long run." Furthermore, the law of large numbers says nothing about the next event. It only tells us what will happen if we keep track of the long-run average.

4.99 **(a)** Using statistical software we compute the mean of the 10 sizes to be $\mu = 69.4$. **(b)** Using line 120, our SRS is companies 3, 5, 4, 7. $\overline{x} = 67.25$. **(c)** The center of our histogram appears to be at about 69, which is close to the value of $\mu = 69.4$ computed in part **(a)**.

4.101 **(a)** To say that $\overline{x}$ is an unbiased estimator of μ means that $\overline{x}$ will neither systematically overestimate or underestimate μ in repeated use and that if we take many, many samples, calculate $\overline{x}$ for each, and compute the average of these $\overline{x}$-values, this average would be close to μ. **(b)** If we draw a large sample from a population, compute the value of some statistic (such as $\overline{x}$), repeat this many times, and keep track of our results, these results will vary less from sample to sample than the results we would obtain if our samples were small.

4.103 The sampling distribution of $\overline{x}$ should be approximately $N(1.6, 0.085)$. $P(\overline{x} > 2) = P(Z > 4.76)$, which is approximately 0.

4.105 500,000,000 is a parameter, and 5.6 is a statistic.

4.107 19 is a parameter. 14 is a statistic.

4.109 The gambler pays \$1.00 for an expected payout of \$0.947. His expected winnings are −\$0.053 per bet. The law of large numbers tells us that if the gambler makes a large number of bets on red, keeps track of his net winnings, and computes the average of these, this average will be close to −\$0.053. He will find he loses about 5.3 cents per bet on average.

4.111 **(a)** The mean $\overline{x}$ of $n = 3$ weighings will follow an $N(123, 0.0462)$ distribution. **(b)** $P(\overline{x} \geq 124) = P(Z \geq 21.65)$, which is approximately 0.

4.113 $P(\overline{X} > 210.53) = 0.0052$.

4.115 0.0125.

4.117 **(a)** $P(X < 295) = 0.1587$. **(b)** The mean contents $\overline{x}$ will vary according to an $N(298, 1.225)$ distribution. $P(\overline{x} < 295) = P(Z < -2.45) = 0.0071$.

4.119 The range 0.11 to 0.19 will contain approximately 95% of the many $\overline{x}$'s.

4.121 **(a)** $P(\overline{x} > 400) = P(Z > 10.94)$, which is approximately 0. **(b)** We would need to know the distribution of weekly postal expenses to compute the probability that postage for a particular week will exceed \$400. In part (a) we applied the central limit theorem, which does not require that we know the distribution of weekly expenses.

4.123 Sheila's mean glucose level $\overline{x}$ will vary according to an $N(125, 5)$ distribution. L must satisfy $P(\overline{x} > L) = 0.05$. We find $L = 133.25$.

4.125 **(a)** $E(X) = -620$ and $= 12{,}031.808$. **(b)** $E(Y) = 620$ and $= 12{,}031.808$. **(c)** The standard deviation is the same for both.

4.127 **(a)** 0.0866. **(b)** 9. **(c)** There is always sampling variability, but this variability is reduced when an average is used instead of an individual measurement. The larger the sample size, the smaller the variability.

4.129 **(a)** 0.3544. **(b)** 0.8558. **(c)** 0.9990. **(d)** The probabilities using the central limit theorem are more accurate as the sample size increases. The 150-bag probability calculation is probably fairly accurate, but the 3-bag probability calculation is probably not.

4.131 $P(\text{Chavez promoted}) = 0.55$.

4.133 **(a)** All the probabilities listed are between 0 and 1 and they sum to 1. **(b)** $P(\text{worker is female}) = 0.43$. **(c)** $P(\text{not in occupation F}) = 0.96$. **(d)** $P(\text{occupation D or E}) = 0.28$. **(e)** $P(\text{not in occupation D or E}) = 0.72$.

4.135 The probability distribution is

Y	1	2	3	4	5	6	7	8	9	10	11	12
$P(Y)$	1/12	1/12	1/12	1/12	1/12	1/12	1/12	1/12	1/12	1/12	1/12	1/12

4.137 The weight of a carton varies according to an $N(780, 17.32)$ distribution. Letting Y denote the weight of a carton, $P(750 < Y < 825) = P(-1.73 < Z < 2.60) = 0.9535$.

4.139 **(a)** All the probabilities listed are between 0 and 1 and they sum to 1. **(b)** $\mu = 2.45$.

4.141 If a single home is destroyed by fire, the replacement cost could be several hundred thousand dollars. The money received from 12 policies (unless extra charges for costs and profits are huge) would not cover this replacement cost.

Although the chance that a home will be destroyed by fire is small, the risk to the company is too great.

If one sells thousands of policies, one can appeal to the law of large numbers and feel confident that the mean loss per policy will be close to \$250. Thus, the company can be reasonably sure that the amount it charges for extra costs and profits will be available for these costs and profits, and that the company will make money. The more policies the company sells, the better off the company will be.

4.143 $P(\text{age at death} \geq 26) = 0.99058$. $\mu_X = 303.35$.

4.145 $\sigma_X^2 = 94{,}236{,}826.6$. $\sigma_X = 9707.57$.

4.147 **(a)** $S = \{0, 1, 2, 3, \ldots, 100\}$ is one possibility (but assuming a person could be employed for 100 years is extreme). **(b)** Because we are allowing only a finite number of possible values, X is discrete. **(c)** We included 101 possible values (0 to 100).

4.149 **(a)** $S = \{\text{all numbers between 0 and 35 ml with no gaps}\}$. **(b)** S is a continuous sample space. All values between 0 and 35 ml are possible with no gaps. **(c)** We included an infinite number of possible values.

CHAPTER 5

5.1 **(a)** The probability that the rank of the second student falls into the five categories is unaffected by the rank of the first student selected. **(b)** 0.1681. **(c)** 0.0041.

5.3 **(a)** 0.32768. **(b)** 0.65908.

5.5 0.66761.

5.7 **(a)** 15% drink only cola. **(b)** 20% drink none of these beverages.

5.9 **(a)** $W = \{0, 1, 2, 3\}$.

		Part (b)	Part (c)
W	Arrangements	Probability of each arrangement	Probability for W
$W = 0$	DDD	$(0.73)^3 = 0.389$	0.389
	DDF	$(0.27)(0.73)^2 = 0.144$	
$W = 1$	DFD	$(0.27)(0.73)^2 = 0.144$	0.432
	FDD	$(0.27)(0.73)^2 = 0.144$	
	DFF	$(0.27)^2(0.73) = 0.0532$	
$W = 2$	FDF	$(0.27)^2(0.73) = 0.0532$	0.160
	FFD	$(0.27)^2(0.73) = 0.0532$	
$W = 3$	FFF	$(0.27)^3 = 0.0197$	0.197

5.11 **(a)** $(0.09)^6 = 0.0000005$. **(b)** $(0.91)^6 = 0.568$. **(c)** 0.337.

5.13 0.09608.

5.15 **(a)** 0.2746. **(b)** The probability of the price being down in any given year is $1 - 0.65 = 0.35$. Since the years are independent, the probability of the price being down in the third year is 0.35. **(c)** 0.5450.

5.17 0.8.

5.19 Yes. A and B are independent if $P(A \text{ and } B) = P(A)P(B)$ and $0.3 = (0.6)(0.5)$.

5.21 0.3762.

5.23 P(O and Rh-positive) = 0.3780, P(O and Rh-negative) = 0.0720, P(A and Rh-positive) = 0.3360, P(A and Rh-negative) = 0.0640, P(B and Rh-positive) = 0.0924, P(B and Rh-negative) = 0.0176, P(AB and Rh-positive) = 0.0336, and P(AB and Rh-negative) = 0.0064.

5.25 **(a)** The probability of an 11 is 2/36. The probability of three 11s in three independent throws is 0.000171. **(b)** The writer's first statement is correct. The odds against throwing three straight 11s, however, are $\frac{1-P}{P} = \frac{1-(2/36)^3}{(2/36)^3} = 5831$ to 1. When computing the odds for the three tosses, the writer multiplied the odds, which is not the correct way to compute the odds for the three throws.

5.27 The assumption of a fixed number of observations is violated.

5.29 **(a)** X can be 0, 1, 2, 3, 4, 5. **(b)** $P(X = 0) = 0.2373$, $P(X = 1) = 0.3955$, $P(X = 2) = 0.2637$, $P(X = 3) = 0.0879$, $P(X = 4) = 0.0146$, and $P(X = 5) = 0.0010$. These probabilities can be used to draw a histogram.

5.31 $P(X = 11) = 0.0074$.

5.33 $\mu = 8$ and $\sigma = \sqrt{np(1-p)} = \sqrt{20(0.4)(0.6)} = 2.191$.

5.35 **(a)** $\mu = 16$. **(b)** $\sigma = \sqrt{np(1-p)} = \sqrt{20(0.8)(0.2)} = 1.789$. **(c)** When $p = 0.9$, $\sigma = 1.342$; and when $p = 0.99$, $\sigma = 0.455$. As the value of p gets closer to 1, there is less variability in the values of X.

5.37 **(a)** Using the Normal approximation, $P(X \geq 100) = 0.0019$. This probability is extremely small and suggests that p may be greater than 0.4. **(b)** $P(X \geq 10)$ was evaluated for a sample of size 20 and found to be 0.2447. The proportion in the sample will be closer to 40% for larger sample sizes, so the chance of the proportion in the sample being as large as 50% decreases.

5.39 **(a)** $\mu_x = np = 6$, $\mu_{\hat{p}} = p = 0.5$. **(b)** $\mu_x = 60$ if $n = 120$, and $\mu_x = 600$ if $n = 1200$. $\mu_{\hat{p}}$ stays the same regardless of sample size.

5.41 **(a)** X is binomial with $n = 1555$ and $p = 0.20$. **(b)** Using the Normal approximation to the binomial for proportions, $\mu_{\hat{p}} = 0.20$, $\sigma_{\hat{p}} = 0.0101$, and the $P(\hat{p} \leq 0.193) = 0.2451$. Using software for the binomial distribution, $P(X \leq 300) = 0.254$.

5.43 **(a)** The 20 machinists selected are not an SRS from a large population of machinists and could have different success probabilities. **(b)** We know that the count of successes in an SRS from a large population containing a proportion p of successes is well approximated by the binomial distribution. This description fits this setting.

5.45 **(a)** $n = 10$ and $p = 0.25$. **(b)** $P(X = 2) = 0.2816$. **(c)** $P(X \leq 2) = P(X = 0) + P(X = 1) + P(X = 2) = 0.5256$. **(d)** $\mu = 2.5$ and $\sigma = \sqrt{np(1-p)} = \sqrt{10(0.25)(0.75)} = 1.37$.

5.47 **(a)** $n = 5$ and $p = 0.65$. **(b)** The possible values of X are 0, 1, 2, 3, 4, 5. **(c)** $P(X = 0) = 0.0053$, $P(X = 1) = 0.0488$, $P(X = 2) = 0.1811$, $P(X = 3) = 0.3364$, $P(X = 4) = 0.3124$, and $P(X = 5) = 0.1160$. **(d)** $\mu = 3.25$ and $\sigma = \sqrt{np(1-p)} = \sqrt{5(0.65)(0.35)} = 1.067$. The value of 3.25 should be included in the histogram from part **(c)** and should be a good indication of the center of the distribution.

5.49 **(a)** Using the Normal approximation, $P(X \le 70) = 0.1251$. **(b)** $P(X \le 175)$ corresponds to Jodi scoring 70% or lower. Using the Normal approximation, $P(X \le 175) = 0.0344$.

5.51 **(a)** The binomial distribution with $n = 150$ and $p = 0.5$ is reasonable for the count of successes in an SRS of size n from a large population, as in this case. **(b)** We expect 75 businesses to respond. **(c)** Using the Normal approximation, $P(X \le 70) = 0.2061$. **(d)** n must be increased to 200.

5.53 **(a)** $\mu = 180$ and $\sigma = \sqrt{np(1-p)} = \sqrt{1500(0.12)(0.88)} = 12.586$. **(b)** Using the Normal approximation, $P(X \le 170) = 0.2148$.

5.55 **(a)** Poisson distribution with a mean of $12 \times 7 = 84$ accidents. **(b)** $P(X \le 66) = 0.0248$.

5.57 **(a)** The employees are independent and each equally likely to be hospitalized. **(b)** 0.0620. **(c)** 0.938. **(d)** 0.256.

5.59 **(a)** 0.0821. **(b)** 0.2424.

5.61 **(a)** Poisson distribution with a mean of 48.7. $P(X \ge 50) = 1 - P(X \le 49) = 0.4450$. **(b)** For a 15-minute period, $\sigma = \sqrt{\mu} = \sqrt{48.7} = 6.98$. For a 30-minute period, $\sigma = \sqrt{\mu} = \sqrt{97.4} = 9.87$. **(c)** Poisson with mean $2 \times 48.7 = 97.4$. $P(X \ge 100) = 1 - P(X \le 99) = 1 - 0.5905 = 0.4095$.

5.63 **(a)** $\sigma = \sqrt{\mu} = \sqrt{17} = 4.12$. **(b)** $P(X \le 10) = 0.0491$. **(c)** $P(X > 30) = 1 - P(X \le 30) = 1 - 0.9986 = 0.0014$.

5.65 **(a)** $P(X \ge 5) = 1 - P(X \le 4) = 1 - 0.0018 = 0.9982$. **(b)** Poisson with mean $1/2 \times 14 = 7$. $P(X \ge 5) = 1 - P(X \le 4) = 1 - 0.1730 = 0.8270$. **(c)** Poisson with mean $1/4 \times 14 = 3.5$. $P(X \ge 5) = 1 - P(X \le 4) = 1 - 0.7254 = 0.2746$.

5.67 **(a)** $\sigma = \sqrt{\mu} = \sqrt{2.3} = 1.52$. **(b)** $P(X > 5) = 1 - P(X \le 5) = 1 - 0.9700 = 0.0300$. **(c)** $k = 3$.

5.69 0.1472.

5.71 **(a)** 0.4335. **(b)** 0.4776. **(c)** 0.4617. **(d)** 0.0489.

5.73 **(a)** 0.5970. **(b)** 0.3150. **(c)** If the events A and B were independent, then $P(B|A) = P(B)$, which is not the case.

5.75 Using Bayes's rule, the probability is 0.7660.

5.77 0.3090.

5.79 0.8989. Given that the customer defaults on the loan, there is an 89.89% chance that the customer overdraws the account.

5.81 **(a)** 0.25. **(b)** 0.3333.

5.83 $P(Y < 1/2 \text{ and } Y > X) = 1/8$. Drawing a diagram should help.

5.85 **(a)** 0.20. **(b)** 0.62. These answers are simpler to see if you first draw a tree diagram.

5.87 Using Bayes's rule, the probability is 0.323.

5.89 **(a)** Using Bayes's rule, the probability is 0.064. **(b)** Expect 94 not to have defaulted. **(c)** With the credit manager's policy, the vast majority of those whose future credit is denied would not have defaulted.

5.91 Yes. A and B are independent if $P(A \text{ and } B) = P(A)P(B)$ and $0.3 = (0.6)(0.5)$.

5.93 Using Bayes's rule, the probability is 0.1930.

5.95 **(a)** 0.1416. **(b)** 0.1029. **(c)** The people are independent from each other, and each person has a 70% chance of being male.

5.97 0.75.

5.99 **(a)** $\mu = 3.75$. **(b)** $P(X \geq 10) = 1 - P(X \leq 9) = 1 - 0.9992 = 0.0008$. **(c)** Using the Normal approximation, $P(X \geq 275) = 0.0336$.

5.101 **(a)** $\mu = 1250$. **(b)** Using the Normal approximation, $P(X \geq 1245) = 0.5596$.

5.103 **(a)** The probability of a success p should be the same for each observation. To ensure that this is true, it is important to take the observations under similar conditions, such as the same location and time of day. **(b)** The probability of the driver being male for observations made outside a church on Sunday morning may differ from the probability for observations made on campus after a dance. **(c)** $P(X \leq 8) = 0.4557$. **(d)** Using software, $P(X \leq 80) = 0.1065$.

5.105 0.84.

5.107 **(a)** 0.674. **(b)** 0.787. **(c)** If the events "in labor force" and "college graduate" were independent, we should have $P(\text{in labor force}) = P(\text{in labor force} \mid \text{college graduate})$, which is not true by comparing the answers in **(a)** and **(b)**.

5.109 **(a)** Drawing the tree diagram will be helpful in solving the remaining parts. **(b)** 0.01592. **(c)** 0.627.

5.111 **(a)** $(\frac{5}{6})(\frac{1}{6})$. **(b)** $(\frac{5}{6})^2(\frac{1}{6})$. **(c)** $P(\text{first one on } k\text{th toss}) = (\frac{5}{6})^{k-1}(\frac{1}{6})$.

5.113 **(a)** 0.751. **(b)** 0.48.

5.115 **(a)** 0.125. **(b)** 0.024.

5.117 Using Bayes's rule, the probability is 0.0404.

CHAPTER 6

6.1 The standard deviation for $\bar{x}$ is \$22.

6.3 $2 \times$ (standard deviation for $\bar{x}$) = \$44.

6.5 (189.91 million dollars, 250.09 million dollars).

6.7 $n = 1244.68$. Use $n = 1245$.

6.9 **(a)** The response rate is $1468/13{,}000 = 0.1129$. **(b)** If there are systematic patterns in the organizations that did not respond, the survey results may be biased. The small margin of error is probably not a good measure of the accuracy of the survey's results.

6.11

Sample size	10	20	40	100
Margin of error	3.10	2.19	1.55	0.98

As sample size increases, the width of the confidence interval (or the size of the margin of error) decreases.

6.13 The students in your major will have a smaller standard deviation because many of them will be taking the same classes which require the same textbooks. The smaller standard deviation leads to a smaller margin of error.

6.15 30.8 ± 4.51 or (26.29, 35.31).

6.17 5.96 ± 0.41

6.19 **(a)** 115 ± 13.25 minutes, or (101.75 minutes, 128.25 minutes). **(b)** No. The confidence coefficient of 95% is the probability that the method we used will give an interval containing the correct value of the population mean study time. It does not tell us about individual study times.

6.21 **(a)** The mean weight of the runners in kilograms is $\bar{x} = 61.863$. The mean weight of runners in pounds is 136.099. **(b)** The standard deviation of the mean weight in kilograms is 0.9186. The standard deviation of the mean weight in pounds is 2.0208. **(c)** A 95% confidence interval for the mean weight, in kilograms, of the population is (60.062, 63.664). In pounds we get (132.137, 140.061).

6.23 11.8 ± 0.77 years or (11.03 years, 12.57 years).

6.25 \$17,528.90 ± \$961.53, or (\$16,567.37, \$18,490.43).

6.27 $n = 74.37$. Use $n = 75$.

6.29 **(a)** No. We are 95% confident that the true population percent falls in this interval. **(b)** This particular interval was produced by a method that will give an interval that contains the true percent of the population that like their job 95% of the time. When we apply the method once, we do not know if our interval correctly includes the population percent or not. Because the method yields a correct result 95% of the time, we say we are 95% confident that this is one of the correct intervals. **(c)** 1.531. **(d)** No, the margin of error only covers random variation.

6.31 Answers will vary. Some possibilities include blue collar vs. white collar jobs, management vs. entry- and mid-level employees.

6.33 **(a)** 95% confidence means that this particular interval was produced by a method that will give an interval that contains the true percent of the population that will vote for Ringel 95% of the time. When we apply the method once, we do not know if our interval correctly includes the true population percent or not. Thus, 95% refers to the method, not to any particular interval produced by the method. **(b)** The margin of error is 3%, so the 95% confidence interval is $52\% \pm 3\% = (49\%, 55\%)$. The interval includes 50%, so we cannot be "confident" that the true percent is 50% or even slightly less than 50%. Hence, the election is too close to call from the results of the poll.

6.35 The results are not trustworthy. The formula for a confidence interval is relevant if our sample is an SRS (or can plausibly be considered an SRS). Phone-in polls are not SRSs.

6.37 $H_0: \mu = 0$, $H_a: \mu < 0$.

6.39 **(a)** $z = -1.58$. **(b)** P-value $= 0.1142$. This would not be considered strong evidence that Cleveland differs from the national average.

6.41 If the homebuilders have no idea whether Cleveland residents spend more or less than the national average, then they are not sure whether μ is larger or smaller than 31%. The appropriate hypotheses are H_0: $\mu = 31\%$, H_a: $\mu \neq 31\%$.

6.43 z-values that are significant at the $\alpha = 0.005$ level are $z > 2.807$ and $z < -2.807$.

6.45 The significance level corresponding to $z^* = 2$ is 0.0456, and the significance level corresponding to $z^* = 3$ is 0.0026.

6.47 **(a)** P-value = 0.0287. **(b)** P-value = 0.9713. **(c)** P-value = 0.0574.

6.49 **(a)** With a P-value of 0.07 we would not reject H_0: $\mu = 15$, and thus 15 would not fall outside the 95% confidence interval. **(b)** With a P-value of 0.07 we would reject H_0: $\mu = 15$, and thus 15 would fall outside the 90% confidence interval.

6.51 **(a)** Yes. $0.049 < 0.05$. **(b)** No. $0.049 > 0.01$. **(c)** Reject the null hypothesis whenever the P-value is $\leq \alpha$.

6.53 **(a)** The null hypothesis should be $\mu = 0$. The alternative hypothesis could be $\mu > 0$. **(b)** The standard deviation of the sample mean should be $18/\sqrt{30}$. **(c)** The hypothesis test uses the population parameter μ, not the sample statistic $\overline{x}$.

6.55 H_0: $\mu = 100$, H_a: $\mu \neq 100$, $Z = -0.108$, P-value = 2(0.4562) = 0.9124. Do not reject the null hypothesis. There is not enough evidence to say that the average north-south location is significantly different from 100.

6.57 If a significance level of 0.05 is used, do not reject the null hypothesis. There is not enough evidence to say that private four-year students have significantly higher debt than public four-year borrowers.

6.59 **(a)** H_0: $\mu = 31$, H_a: $\mu > 31$. **(b)** H_0: $\mu = 4$, H_a: $\mu \neq 4$. **(c)** H_0: $\mu = 1400$, H_a: $\mu < 1400$.

6.61 **(a)** H_0: $p_M = p_F$, H_a: $p_M > p_F$, where the parameters of interest are the percent of males, p_M, and the percent of females, p_F, in the population who name economics as their favorite subject. **(b)** H_0: $\mu_A = \mu_B$, H_a: $\mu_A > \mu_B$, where μ_A is the mean score on the test of basketball skills for the population of all sixth-grade students if all were treated as those in group A and μ_B is the mean score on the test of basketball skills for the population of all sixth-grade students if all were treated as those in group B. **(c)** H_0: $\rho = 0$, H_a: $\rho > 0$, where the parameter of interest is the correlation ρ between income and the percent of disposable income that is saved by employed young adults.

6.63 The P-value is the probability that we would observe, simply by chance, results that are as strongly or more strongly in support of the calcium supplement if it is really no more effective than the placebo. In this case the P-value is 0.008, which is very small. Because it is unlikely that we would obtain data this strongly in support of the calcium supplement by chance, this is strong evidence against the assumption that the effect of the calcium supplement is the same as that of the placebo.

6.65 **(a)** Answers may vary, but one possibility is a two-sample comparison of means test with H_0: $\mu_A = \mu_B$, H_a: $\mu_A \neq \mu_B$ where group A consists of students who exercise regularly and group B consists of students who do not exercise regularly. **(b)** No, the P-value is large. There is not enough evidence to say that exercise significantly affects how students perform on their final exam in statistics. **(c)** It would be good to know how the sample was selected and if this was an observational study or an experiment.

6.67 $z = 3.56$. The P-value is $P(Z \geq 3.56) < 0.002$. We would conclude that there is strong evidence that these 5 sonnets come from a population with a mean number of new words that is larger than 6.9, and thus we have evidence that the new sonnets are not by our poet.

6.69 The P-value is 0.0164. This is reasonably strong evidence against the null hypothesis that the population mean corn yield is 135. Our results are based on the mean of a sample of 40 observations, and such a mean may vary approximately according to a Normal distribution (by the central limit theorem) even if the population is not Normal, so our conclusions are probably still valid.

6.71 **(a)** The P-value $= 0.2040$ and the result is not significant at the 5% level. **(b)** The P-value is 0.2040 and the result is not significant at the 1% level.

6.73 The approximate P-value is < 0.001.

6.75 **(a)** $z > 1.645$. **(b)** $z > 1.96$ or $z < -1.96$. **(c)** In part (a) we reject H_0 only for large values of z because such values are evidence against H_0 in favor of $H_a\colon \mu > 0$. In part (b) we reject H_0 in favor of $H_a\colon \mu \neq 0$ if either z is too large or z is too small because both extremes are evidence against H_0 in favor of $H_a\colon \mu \neq 0$.

6.77 **(a)** (99.041, 109.225). **(b)** The hypotheses are $H_0\colon \mu = 105$, $H_a\colon \mu \neq 105$. The 95% confidence interval in part (a) contains 105, so we would not reject H_0 at the 5% level.

6.79 **(a)** $H_0\colon \mu = 7$, $H_a\colon \mu \neq 7$. The 95% confidence interval does not contain 7, so we would reject H_0 at the 5% level. **(b)** 5 is in the 95% confidence interval, so we would not reject the hypothesis that $\mu = 5$ at the 5% level.

6.81 **(a)** $z = 1.64$. We reject H_0 at the 5% level if $z > 1.645$. The result is not significant at the 5% level. **(b)** $z = 1.65$. The result is significant at the 5% level.

6.83 Any convenience sample (phone-in or write-in polls, surveys of acquaintances only) will produce data for which statistical inference is not appropriate. Poorly designed experiments also provide examples of data for which statistical inference is not valid.

6.85 Statistical significance and practical significance are not necessarily the same thing. With a significance level this high, we would be willing to reject the null hypothesis even when no practical effect exists. A P-value of 0.5 corresponds to a Z value of 0, which means that our sample statistic would be 0 standard deviations away from the null hypothesis mean, but we would still reject the null hypothesis.

6.87 Answers will vary.

6.89 **(a)** No. **(b)** Yes. **(c)** No.

6.91 **(a)** P-value $= 0.3821$. **(b)** P-value $= 0.1711$. **(c)** P-value $= 0.0013$.

6.93 The conclusion is not justified. Statistical inference is not valid for badly designed surveys or experiments. This is a call-in poll, and such polls are not random samples.

6.95 Using the Bonferroni procedure for $k = 6$ tests with $\alpha = 0.05$, we should require a P-value of $\alpha/k = 0.05/6 = 0.0083$ (or less) for statistical significance for each test. Of the six P-values given, only two, 0.008 and 0.001, are below $0.05/6 = 0.0083$.

6.97 **(a)** X has a binomial distribution with $n = 77$ and $p = 0.05$. **(b)** The probability that 2 or more are significant is 0.90266.

6.99 As sample size increases, power increases.

6.101 Since 80 is farther away from 50 than 70 is, the power will be higher than 0.5.

6.103 **(a)** The power of the test against the alternative $\mu = 298$ is 0.4960. **(b)** The power is higher. The alternative $\mu = 295$ is farther away from $\mu_0 = 300$ than $\mu = 298$ and so is easier to detect.

6.105 The power of the test against the alternative $\mu = 298$ is 0.9099. This is quite a bit larger than the power of 0.4960 that we found in Exercise 6.81.

6.107 The probability of a Type I error is $\alpha = 0.05$. The probability of a Type II error at $\mu = 298$ is 1 minus the power of the test at $\mu = 298$, which is $1 - 0.4960 = 0.5040$.

6.109 **(a)** The hypotheses are H_0: patient does not need to see a doctor and H_a: patient does need to see a doctor. The program can make two types of error: (1) The patient is told to see a doctor when, in fact, the patient does not need to see a doctor. This is a "false-positive." (2) The patient is diagnosed as not needing to see a doctor when, in fact, the patient does need to see one. This is a "false-negative." **(b)** The error probability one chooses to control usually depends on which error is considered more serious. In most cases, a false-negative is considered more serious. If you have an illness and it is not detected, the consequences can be serious.

6.111

Age	18	19	20	21	22	23	24	25	26
Months employed, $\bar{x}$	2.9	4.2	5.0	5.3	6.4	7.4	8.5	8.9	9.3
95% CI, $\bar{x} \pm 0.32$	(2.58, 3.22)	(3.88, 4.52)	(4.68, 5.32)	(4.98, 5.62)	(6.08, 6.72)	(7.08, 7.72)	(8.18, 8.82)	(8.58, 9.22)	(8.98, 9.62)

There is a strong, positive, linear relationship between age and months employed. All the widths of all the confidence intervals are exactly the same.

6.113 Answers will vary.

6.115 Industries with SHRUSED values above the median were found to have cash flow elasticities less than those for industries with lower SHRUSED values. The probability is less than 0.05 that we would observe a difference as large as or larger than this by chance if, in fact, on average the cash flow elasticities for the two types of industries are the same. This probability is quite low, and so it is unlikely that the observed difference is merely accidental.

6.117 **(a)** The stemplot shows that the data are roughly symmetric. **(b)** (26.06 μg/l, 34.74 μg/l). **(c)** Let μ denote the mean DMS odor threshold among all beginning oenology students. We test the hypotheses H_0: $\mu = 25$, H_a: $\mu > 25$. $z = 2.44$.

The P-value is 0.0073. This is strong evidence that the mean odor threshold for beginning oenology students is higher than the published threshold of 25 μg/l.

6.119 \$782.82 $\pm$ \$6.02 = (\$776.80, \$788.84).

6.121 **(a)** The authors probably want to draw conclusions about the population of all adult Americans. The population to which their conclusions most clearly apply is all people listed in the Indianapolis telephone directory.
(b)

Store type	95% confidence interval
Food stores	18.67 ± 3.45
Mass merchandisers	32.38 ± 4.61
Pharmacies	48.60 ± 4.92

(c) None of these intervals overlap, which suggests that the observed differences are likely to be real.

6.123 **(a)** Increasing the size n of a sample will decrease the width of a level C confidence interval. **(b)** Increasing the size n of a sample will decrease the P-value. **(c)** Increasing the sample size n will increase the power.

6.125 No. The null hypothesis is either true or false. Statistical significance at the 0.05 level means that if the null hypothesis is true, the probability that we will obtain data that lead us to incorrectly reject H_0 is 0.05.

6.127 **(a)** Assume that in the population of all mothers with young children, those who would choose to attend the training program and those who would not choose to attend actually remain on welfare at the same rate. The probability is less than 0.01 that we would observe a difference as or more extreme than that actually observed. **(b)** 95% confidence means that the method used to construct the interval 21% $\pm$ 4% will produce an interval that contains the true difference 95% of the time. Because the method is reliable 95% of the time, we say that we are 95% confident that this particular interval is accurate. **(c)** The study is not good evidence that requiring job training of all welfare mothers will greatly reduce the percent who remain on welfare for several years. Mothers chose to participate in the training program. They were not assigned using randomization. Thus, the effect of the program is confounded with the reasons why some women chose to participate and some didn't.

6.129 Only in 5 cases did we reject H_0. Thus, the proportion of times was 0.05. This is consistent with the meaning of a 0.05 significance level. In 100 trials where H_0 was true, we would expect the proportion of times we reject to be about 0.05.

6.131 **(a)** We used statistical software to conduct the simulations. **(b)** The sample size is large, and the central limit theorem suggests that it is probably reasonable to assume that the sampling distribution for the sample means is approximately Normal. **(c)** $m = 10.11$. **(d)** The calculations agree with our simulation result up to roundoff error. **(e)** 15 of the 25, or 60%, of the simulations contained $\mu = 240$. If we repeated the simulations, we would not expect to get exactly the same number of intervals to contain $\mu = 240$. This is because each simulation is random, and so results will vary from one simulation to the next. The probability that any given simulation contains $\mu = 240$ is 0.50, and so in a very large number of simulations we would expect about 50% to contain $\mu = 240$.

CHAPTER 7

7.1 **(a)** $SE_{\bar{x}} = 24.54$. **(b)** There are 11 degrees of freedom.

7.3 The 95% confidence interval for the mean monthly rent is (\$481.19, \$604.81).

7.5 Hypotheses are $H_0: \mu = 500$ and $H_a: \mu > 500$. $t = 1.574$ with 9 df, and using software, we get P-value $= 0.075$. We conclude that there is not much evidence that the mean rent of all advertised apartments exceeds \$500.

7.7 **(a)** Two-sided, since we are interested in whether the average sales are different from last month (no direction of the difference is specified). Hypotheses are $H_0: \mu = 0\%$ and $H_a: \mu \neq 0\%$. **(b)** $t = 2.47$ with 49 df, and using software, $0.005 < P\text{-value} < 0.01$. There is strong evidence that the average sales have increased. **(c)** The mean is 4.8% and the standard deviation is 15%, so there are certainly stores with a percent change that is negative.

7.9 **(a)** The t statistic must exceed 2.5768. **(b)** This result can be found in Table D in the row corresponding to z^*. This illustrates that for large degrees of freedom, there is little difference between critical values for the t and the Normal distribution.

7.11 A 95% confidence interval for the mean loss in vitamin C is (50.11, 59.89).

7.13 **(a)** The stemplot using split stems shows the data are clearly skewed to the right and have several high outliers. **(b)** The 95% confidence interval is (20.00, 27.12), which agrees quite well with the bootstrap intervals. The lesson is that for large sample sizes the t procedures are very robust.

7.15 The power of the t test against the alternative $\mu = 2.2$ is 0.9394.

7.17 **(a)** $t^* = 2.262$ using degrees of freedom $n - 1 = 9$. **(b)** $t^* = 2.064$ using degrees of freedom $n - 1 = 24$. **(c)** $t^* = 2.797$ using degrees of freedom $n - 1 = 24$. **(d)** As sample size increases, the t^* decreases for the same confidence level. As the confidence level increases, t^* increases for the same sample size.

7.19 **(a)** Degrees of freedom = 19. **(b)** 2.093 and 2.205. **(c)** 0.025 and 0.02. **(d)** $0.02 < P\text{-value} < 0.025$. **(e)** Significant at 5%, not significant at 1%. **(f)** Excel gives 0.02145.

7.21 **(a)** Degrees of freedom = 119, but use df = 100 on Table D to be conservative. **(b)** P-value < 0.0005. **(c)** Excel gives 9.7287×10^{-6} using 119 degrees of freedom.

7.23 (17.022, 19.938).

7.25 **(a)** 0.9916. **(b)** (59.811, 63.914). **(c)** No, this is the confidence interval for the population average weight, not for individuals.

7.27 **(a)** There is no obvious skewness and there are no outliers present. **(b)** A 95% confidence interval for the mean annual earnings of hourly-paid white female workers at this bank is (\$22,719.87, \$27,350.63).

7.29 The hypotheses are $H_0: \mu = 20{,}000$ and $H_a: \mu > 20,000$. $t = 4.552$ with 19 df, and using software, P-value ≈ 0. We conclude there is strong evidence that the mean annual earnings exceed \$20,000.

7.31 **(a)** The data are skewed right with 3 points that are particularly high, clearly non-Normal. **(b)** $\bar{x} = 34.156$, $s = 21.36917$, $\sigma_{\bar{x}} = 3.37876$. **(c)** (27.3218, 40.9902).

7.33 **(a)** 6 streams are classified very poor or poor out of 49 total, so the sample proportion is 0.122. **(b)** No, sample proportions use Z^*, not t^*. Sample proportions are for categorical data, sample means are for quantitative data. We have converted quantitative data into categorical data by sorting the streams into very poor, poor, and other.

7.35 A 95% confidence interval for the mean price received by farmers for corn sold in October is (\$1.76, \$2.45).

7.37 A 95% confidence interval for the mean score on the question "Feeling welcomed at Purdue" is (3.734, 3.866).

7.39 The hypotheses are $H_0\colon \mu = 0$ and $H_a\colon \mu > 0$, where μ represents the average improvement in scores over six months for preschool children. $t = 6.90$ with 33 df and P-value < 0.0005. There is extremely strong evidence that the scores improved over six months, which is in agreement with the confidence interval (2.55, 6.88) obtained in Exercise 7.34.

7.41 A 95% confidence interval for the mean amount of D-glucose in cockroach hindguts under these conditions is (18.69 micrograms, 70.19 micrograms).

7.43 **(a)** The hypotheses are $H_0\colon \mu = 0$ and $H_a\colon \mu < 0$, where μ represents the average difference in vitamin C between the measurement five months later in Haiti and the factory measurement. **(b)** $t = -4.95$ with 26 df, and using software, P-value < 0.0005. There is very strong evidence that vitamin C is destroyed as a result of storage and shipment. **(c)** The 95% confidence intervals are (40.96, 44.75) for the mean at the factory, (36.55, 38.48) for the mean after five months, and (−7.54, −3.12) for the mean change.

7.45 The 90% confidence interval for the mean time advantage is (−21.17, −5.47). The ratio of mean time for right-hand threads as a percent of mean time for left-hand threads is $\overline{x}_R/\overline{x}_L = 88.7\%$, so those using the right-hand threads complete the task in about 90% of the time it takes those using the left-hand threads.

7.47 Taking the differences (Variety A – Variety B) to determine if there is evidence that Variety A has the higher yield corresponds to the hypotheses $H_0\colon \mu = 0$ and $H_a\colon \mu > 0$ for the mean of the differences. $t = 1.29$ with 9 df, and $0.10 < P\text{-value} < 0.15$. Do not reject the null hypothesis. There is not enough evidence to support that Variety A tomatoes have a higher mean yield than Variety B tomatoes.

7.49 **(a)** Single sample. **(b)** The best answer is 2 independent samples. Even though we are looking at changes of opinion over time from the same basic group, problems with missing values for one survey due to nonresponse or customers leaving the pool would make the paired sample difficult. However, if the exact same sample was used both years with a stable population of customers, matched pairs would also be an acceptable answer.

7.51 **(a)** $t^* = 2.403$. **(b)** $\overline{x} \geq 34.745$. **(c)** The power is $P(Z \geq -4.513) = 1.000$. There is no need for increasing the sample size beyond 50.

7.53 **(a)** H_0: population median $= 0$ and H_a: population median > 0, or the population of differences (time to complete task with left-hand thread) – (time to complete task with right-hand thread). If p is the probability of completing the task faster with the right-hand thread, the hypotheses would be $H_0\colon p = 1/2$ and $H_a\colon p > 1/2$. **(b)** The number of pairs with a positive difference in our data is 19, and $n = 24$ since the zero difference is dropped. The P-value is $P(X \geq 19) = 0.0021$ using the Normal approximation or 0.0033 using the binomial distribution.

7.55 **(a)** Two-sided significance test, since you just want to know if there is evidence of a difference in the two designs. **(b)** 29 df using the conservative approximation. **(c)** P-value lies between $2 \times 0.0025 = 0.005$ and $2 \times 0.001 = 0.002$. There is strong evidence of a difference in daily sales for the two designs.

7.57 This is a matched pairs experiment with the pairs being the two measurements on each day of the week.

7.59 Randomization makes the two groups similar except for the treatment and is the best way to ensure that no bias is introduced.

7.61 **(a)** All report both means. **(b)** Excel reports the two variances, SPSS and Minitab report both the standard deviation and the standard error of the mean for each group, while SAS reports only the standard error of the mean for each group. **(c)** Excel is doing the pooled two-sample t procedure, SPSS and SAS provide the t with Satterthwaite degrees of freedom as well as the pooled t, and Minitab provides the t with Satterthwaite degrees of freedom. All report degrees of freedom and P-values to various accuracies. **(d)** With the exception of Excel, all report the confidence interval for the mean difference. **(e)** Excel has the least information, while SAS seems to provide the most information because it includes more information about the two groups individually.

7.63 The pooled $t = 17.13$ with 133 df. Results are almost identical to those of Example 7.13.

7.65 First write pooled variance as the average of the individual variances and then use this expression in the pooled t to see that it gives the same result for equal sample sizes.

7.67 **(a)** The data are probably not exactly normally distributed because there are only 5 discrete answer choices. **(b)** Yes, the large sample sizes would compensate for uneven distributions. The two-sample comparison of means t test is fairly robust. **(c)** $H_0\colon \mu_I = \mu_C$ and $H_a\colon \mu_I > \mu_C$. (A "$\neq$" would also be appropriate in the alternative hypothesis, but be sure to double the P-value when checking your answer with this one.) **(d)** $t = 3.57$, P-value < 0.0005. Reject the null hypothesis. There is strong evidence the average self-efficacy score for the intervention group is significantly higher than the average self-efficacy score for the control group. **(e)** $(0.191, 0.669)$.

7.69 **(b)** $(4.374, 5.426)$. **(c)** $H_0\colon \mu_{D/B} = \mu_C$ and $H_a\colon \mu_{D/B} > \mu_C$. $t = 18.49$, P-value is close to 0. Reject the null hypothesis. There is very strong evidence the average exposure to respirable dust is significantly higher for the drill and blast workers than it is for the concrete workers. **(d)** The sample sizes are so large that a little skewness will not affect the results of the two-sample comparison of means test.

7.71 **(a)** No. If we use the 68–95–99.7% rule, then 68% of the younger kids would consume between -2.5 and 18.9 oz. of sweetened drinks every day. The same problem with negative consumption for the older kids (starting with 95%) as well. **(b)** $H_0\colon \mu_{\text{older}} = \mu_{\text{younger}}$ and $H_a\colon \mu_{\text{older}} \neq \mu_{\text{younger}}$. $t = 1.44$, $0.2 < P\text{-value} < 0.3$. Do not reject the null hypothesis. There is not enough evidence to say that there is a significant difference between the average consumption of sugary drinks between the older and younger groups of children. **(c)** (−5.85, 18.45). **(d)** The sample sizes are very uneven and fairly small. The sample data is not normally distributed either. The t procedures are not particularly appropriate here. **(e)** How were these children selected to participate? Where they chosen because they consume such large quantities of sweetened drinks?

7.73 **(a)** Reject the null hypothesis because 0 is not inside the confidence interval. $H_0: \mu_A = \mu_B$ can also be written as $H_0: \mu_A - \mu_B = 0$. **(b)** As sample size increases, the margin of error decreases.

7.75 95% CI = (15.54, 24.46) using 40 degrees of freedom as the conservative estimate from the t-table. A 99% CI will be wider than a 95% CI because the t^* value increases as the confidence level increases.

7.77 The 95% confidence interval for the cost of the extra bedroom is (−0.662, 160.662) using software.

7.79 **(a)** The hypotheses are $H_0: \mu_0 = \mu_3$ and $H_a: \mu_0 > \mu_3$, where 0 corresponds to immediately after baking and 3 corresponds to three days after baking. $t = 22.16$, df $= 1.47$, and P-value $= 0.014$, which indicates there is strong evidence that the vitamin C content has decreased after three days. **(b)** The 90% confidence interval is (19.2, 34.58).

7.81 **(a)** The hypotheses are $H_0: \mu_0 = \mu_3$ and $H_a: \mu_0 > \mu_3$, where 0 corresponds to immediately after baking and 3 corresponds to three days after baking. $t = -0.32$, and P-value > 0.5, which indicates no evidence of a loss of vitamin E. **(b)** The 90% confidence interval is (−11.29, 10.2).

7.83 **(a)** P-value is $1 - 0.07/2 = 0.965$. Do not reject the null hypothesis. Our sample mean difference $(\bar{x}_1 - \bar{x}_2)$ is far below 0, so it is very unlikely that the first mean is greater than the second mean. **(b)** P-value is $0.07/2 = 0.035$. Reject the null hypothesis. Our sample mean difference is well above 0, so it is reasonable to conclude that the first mean is greater than the second mean.

7.85 Using 33 df, the 95% confidence interval is (1.932, 4.532), so the improvement is greater for those who took piano lessons.

7.87 **(a)** The hypotheses are $H_0: \mu_{\text{Low}} = \mu_{\text{High}}$ and $H_a: \mu_{\text{Low}} \neq \mu_{\text{High}}$. $t = -8.23$, df $=$ 21.77, and the P-value is approximately zero. You reject at both the 1% and 5% levels of significance. **(b)** The individuals in the study are not random samples from low-fitness and high-fitness groups of middle-aged men, so the possibility of bias is definitely present. **(c)** These are observational data.

7.89 This would now be a matched pairs design, since we have before and after measurements on the same men. The analysis would proceed by first taking the change in score and then computing the mean and standard deviation of the changes. These values would be used in the t statistic.

7.91 **(a)** Using 50 df to be conservative and using Table D, the 95% confidence interval is (−0.9, 6.9). **(b)** The negative values correspond to a decrease in sales. If the true difference in means was −1, which is included in the confidence interval, then the percent sales would have decreased.

7.93 **(a)** The Normal quantile plots are fairly linear, and the sum of the sample sizes is close to 40, so in spite of the skewness appearing in the histograms, the t procedures can be used. **(b)** The value of the t statistic is 2.223 with a P-value of

0.0165. This gives fairly strong evidence that the mean SSHA score is lower for men than for women at this college. **(c)** The confidence interval for the difference is (4.907, 35.981).

7.95 The approximate degrees of freedom are 37.859.

7.97 **(a)** $t^* = 12.71$. **(b)** $t^* = 4.303$. **(c)** The increase in degrees of freedom means that the value of the t statistic needs to be less extreme for the pooled t statistic in order to find a statistically significant difference.

7.99 **(a)** The upper 5% critical value is $F^* = 2.20$. **(b)** Significant at the 10% level but not at the 5% level.

7.101 The hypotheses are $H_0\colon \sigma_1 = \sigma_2$ and $H_a\colon \sigma_1 \neq \sigma_2$. $F = 1.59$, and using an $F(33, 43)$ distribution and statistical software, P-value $= 2 \times 0.0764 = 0.1528$, so there is little evidence of a difference in variances between the two groups.

7.103 **(a)** The value in the table is 647.79. **(b)** $F = 3.94$, and using an $F(1, 1)$ distribution and statistical software, P-value $= 2 \times 0.2981 = 0.5962$, so there is little evidence of a difference in variances between the two groups.

7.105 **(a)** The hypotheses are $H_0\colon \sigma_M = \sigma_W$ and $H_a\colon \sigma_M > \sigma_W$. **(b)** $F = 1.74$. **(c)** Using an $F(19, 17)$ distribution P-value > 0.10, so there is little evidence that the males have larger variability in their scores.

7.107 The power for $n = 25$ is 0.4855; $n = 50$ is 0.7411; $n = 75$ is 0.8787; $n = 100$ is 0.9460; $n = 125$ is 0.9769. These powers were calculated using SAS. The powers obtained using the Normal approximation are quiter close to these values.

7.109 **(a)** Using SAS, POWER = 1-PROBT(t^*, DF, δ) = 0.3390. **(b)** Using SAS, POWER = 1-PROBT(t^*, DF, δ) = 0.7765, which is greater than the power found in **(a)**.

7.111

Perceived quality	$\overline{x}_H - \overline{x}_L$	$\sqrt{\frac{s_H^2}{170} + \frac{s_L^2}{224}}$	t	P-value	Conclusion
Food served in promised time	0.45	0.139	3.24	Between 0.001 and 0.002	Reject H_0
Quickly corrects mistakes	0.16	0.125	1.28	Between 0.2 and 0.3	Do not reject H_0
Well-dressed staff	0.39	0.136	2.87	≈ 0.005	Reject H_0
Attractive menu	0.21	0.143	1.47	Between 0.1 and 0.2	Do not reject H_0
Serving accurately	0.37	0.123	3.01	Between 0.002 and 0.005	Reject H_0
Well-trained personnel	0.06	0.125	0.48	> 0.5	Do not reject H_0
Clean dining area	0.08	0.127	0.630	> 0.5	Do not reject H_0
Employees adjust to needs	0.14	0.23	0.609	> 0.5	Do not reject H_0
Employees know menu	0.29	0.119	2.44	Between 0.01 and 0.02	Reject H_0
Convenient hours	0.24	0.129	1.86	Between 0.05 and 0.1	Do not reject H_0

There is a significant difference between the high- and low-performing restaurants in regards to food served in promised time, well-dressed staff, serving ordered food accurately, and employees know menu. There is not a significant difference in the other qualities. We need to assume fairly normally distributed data without outliers and that a simple random sample was taken from each group.

7.113 **(a)** Study was done in South Korea; results may not apply to other countries. Only selected QSRs were studied; results may not apply to other QSRs. Response rate is low (394/950); we would trust the results more if the rate were higher. The fact that no differences were found when the demographics of this study were compared with the demographics of similar studies suggests that we do not have a serious problem with bias based on these characteristics. **(b)** Answers will vary.

7.115 $H_0: \mu = 4.88$ and $H_a: \mu > 4.88$. $t = 21.98$, P-value is close to 0 so we can reject the null hypothesis. There is strong evidence that hotel managers have a significantly higher average masculinity score than the general male population.

7.117 **(a)** No outliers, slightly skewed right but fairly symmetric. **(b)** (12.9998, 13.3077).

7.119 $\bar{x}_C = 48.9513$, $s_C = 0.25377$, $\bar{x}_R = 41.6488$, $s_R = 0.39219$. Side-by-side boxplot shows cotton much higher than ramie. $H_0: \mu_C = \mu_R$ and $H_a: \mu_C > \mu_R$. $t = 46.162$, P-value is very close to 0 so reject the null hypothesis. There is strong evidence that cotton has a significantly higher mean lightness than ramie.

7.121 (1.0765, 7.6035).

7.123 2.555 ± 0.139.

7.125 The 95% confidence interval on percentage of lower priced products at the alternate supplier is (64.55, 92.09). This suggests that more than half of the products at the alternate supplier are priced lower than the original supplier.

7.127 **(a)** This study used a matched pairs design; therefore they used a single sample t test. **(b)** The average weight loss in this program was significantly different from zero, and we can conclude that the program was effective. **(c)** The P-value is approximately equal to zero.

7.129 **(a)** $H_0: \mu_1 = \mu_2$ and $H_a: \mu_1 < \mu_2$, $t = -8.954$, P-value ≈ 0. Conclude that the workers were faster than the students. **(b)** The t procedures are robust for large sample sizes even when the distributions are slightly skewed. **(c)** The middle 95% of scores would be from 29.66 to 44.98. **(d)** The scores for the first minute are clearly much lower than the scores for the 15th minute.

7.131 **(a)** (0.207, 0.573). **(b)** (−0.312, 0.012).

7.133 **(a)** No, the t test is robust to skewness. **(b)** Yes, the F test is not robust to skewness.

7.135 The F test result shows that there is no reason to believe the variances of the two sexes are unequal. Results of the t tests show that there is a significant difference in the average SATM scores between the two sexes. The P-values of both are approximately zero.

7.137 As the degrees of freedom increase for small values of n, the value of t rapidly approaches the z score. As sample sizes get larger, the t values are close to $z = 1.96$ but never become greater than 1.96.

CHAPTER 8

8.1 (0.21, 0.47).

8.3 (0.22, 0.48). This plus four interval is shifted slightly to the right of the original interval of (0.21, 0.47).

8.5 Smaller samples sizes will make a bigger difference when the sample proportion is close to 0. An example would be 1/100.

8.7 **(a)** (0.23, 0.41). If we know how many answered "Yes," we automatically know how many answered "No." **(b)** The test statistic is $z = 1.62$ and P-value $=$ 0.1052. Because the proportion who answer "Yes" is 1 minus the proportion who answer "No," testing whether the proportion who answer "Yes" is equal to 0.75 is equivalent to testing whether the proportion who answer "No" is 0.25.

8.9 Need to sample at least 601 people if a p^* of 0.5 is used.

8.11 **(a)** $\hat{p} \pm Z^* SE_{\hat{p}}$ (forgot the Z^*). **(b)** Hypotheses need population parameters, not the sample statistics. H_0: $p = 0.3$ is appropriate.

8.13 **(a)** 0.634 $\pm$ 0.0126. If we were to repeat our sampling many times and compute a confidence interval from each sample, over the long run, approximately 95% of these intervals would contain the population proportion. **(b)** No, a high nonresponse rate would skew the results. Those most likely not to reply are the cheaters.

8.15 **(a)** $m = 0.00132$. **(b)** Students most likely not to respond are the cheaters, and a 15% response rate is very low. What about the schools that can't afford the fee? Just because the sample size is large doesn't mean that good data was collected. The response rate and other issues may be larger sources of error here than pure statistical variation quantified by the margin of error.

8.17 **(a)** (0.300, 0.354). **(b)** (0.301, 0.355). The methods have the same margin of error $=$ 0.027, but the plus four method shifts the interval slightly higher. **(c)** Nonresponse rate is only 3.64%, which is small, so we can trust these results. **(d)** Yes, the person delivering the sermon probably thinks the sermon is shorter than it actually is, and the congregation would probably think the sermons are longer than they actually are.

8.19 (0.324, 0.376).

8.21 99% confidence interval is wider because the Z^* is bigger. (0.316, 0.384).

8.23 (0.635, 0.745).

8.25 (0.218, 0.251).

8.27 **(a)** (0.359, 0.401). **(b)** Teens 16–19 years old may have jobs, 18 and 19 year olds may be living on their own. It would make more sense to group the teens as 12–15 year olds, 16–17 year olds, and 18–19 year olds.

8.29 No. A person could have both lied about having a degree (for example, having an advanced degree such as a master's or Ph.D.) and about their major (for example, their undergraduate major if they lied about having a master's degree but did have a bachelor's degree). Because lying about having a degree and lying about major are not necessarily mutually exclusive events, we cannot automatically conclude that a total of $24 = 15 + 9$ applicants lied about one or the other.

8.31 (0.768, 0.912).

8.33 (0.642, 0.768).

8.35 **(a)** $\hat{p} = 0.3168$, $n = 1711$, and $X = 542$ (the number who tested positive) are basic summary statistics. **(b)** (0.295, 0.339). **(c)** This is an observational study, not a designed experiment. Observational studies generally do not provide a good basis for concluding causality, only association. Also, this is not a random sample from the population of all bicyclists who were fatally injured in a bicycle accident.

8.37 **(a)** Not safe. $np_0 = 4 < 10$ and $n(1 - p_0) = 6 < 10$. **(b)** Safe. $np_0 = 60$ and $n(1 - p_0) = 40$. Both are greater than 10. **(c)** Safe. **(d)** Safe. $np_0 = 150$ and $n(1 - p_0) = 350$. Both are greater than 10.

8.39 **(a)** H_0: $p = 0.64$, H_a: $p \neq 0.64$. **(b)** The test statistic is $z = -0.93$. The P-value $= 0.3524$. This is not strong evidence against the null hypothesis that the sample represents the state in regard to rural versus urban residence in terms of the proportion of urban residents. **(c)** These results are consistent (same P-value) with the previous exercise. We conclude there is not strong evidence against the hypothesis that the sample represents the state in regard to rural versus urban residence in terms either of the proportion of rural residents or in terms of the proportion of urban residents.

8.41 (0.106, 0.294).

8.43 **(a)** The test statistic is $z = 1.34$. The P-value $= 0.1802$, and since this is larger than 0.05, we would not reject the null hypothesis that the probability that Kerrich's coin comes up heads is 0.5. **(b)** (0.4969, 0.5165).

8.45 $n = 450.18$. Round up to get $n = 451$.

8.47 We round up to get $n = 201$. The margin of error for the 90% confidence interval is 0.0691.

8.49

$\hat{p}$:	0.1	0.2	0.3	0.4	0.5	0.6	0.7	0.8	0.9
m:	0.0537	0.0716	0.0820	0.0877	0.0895	0.0877	0.0820	0.0716	0.0537

8.51 **(a)** For $\hat{p}_1$: mean $\mu_{\hat{p}_1} = p_1$, standard deviation $\sigma_{\hat{p}_1} = \sqrt{\frac{p_1(1-p_1)}{n}}$. For $\hat{p}_2$: mean $\mu_{\hat{p}_2} = p_2$, standard deviation $\sigma_{\hat{p}_2} = \sqrt{\frac{p_2(1-p_2)}{n}}$. **(b)** $\mu_D = \mu_{\hat{p}_1 - \hat{p}_2} = \mu_{\hat{p}_1} - \mu_{\hat{p}_2} = p_1 - p_2$. **(c)** $\sigma_D^2 = \sigma_{\hat{p}_1 - \hat{p}_2}^2 = \sigma_{\hat{p}_1}^2 + \sigma_{\hat{p}_2}^2 = \frac{p_1(1-p_1)}{n} + \frac{p_2(1-p_2)}{n}$.

8.53 (0.0301, 0.0788).

8.55 Plus four interval: (−0.125, 0.267), Z interval: (−0.112, 0.272).

8.57 H_0: $p_1 = p_2$, H_a: $p_1 > p_2$. The test statistic $z = 4.46$. The P-value is approximately 0. This is strong evidence that a higher proportion of complainers than noncomplainers leave voluntarily.

8.59 **(a)** $\mu_{\hat{p}_1 - \hat{p}_2} = -0.1$ and $\sigma_{\hat{p}_1 - \hat{p}_2} = 0.0947$. **(c)** (−0.289, 0.089).

8.61 **(a)** H_0: $p_{\text{Impulse}} = p_{\text{Planned}}$ and H_a: $p_{\text{Impulse}} \neq p_{\text{Planned}}$, $Z = -1.02$, P-value $=$ 0.3078. Do not reject the null hypothesis. There is not enough evidence to say the difference in credit card use between impulse and planned purchases is statistically significant.

8.63 H_0: $p_S = p_H$ and H_a: $p_S \neq p_H$, $Z = 1.14$, P-value $= 0.2542$. Do not reject the null hypothesis. There is not enough evidence to say that the detergent preferences are significantly different for people with hard water and people with soft water.

8.65 **(a)** Tippecanoe County: $\hat{p}_1 = 0.511$. Benton County: $\hat{p}_2 = 0.408$. **(b)** $SE_{\hat{D}} = 0.029$. **(c)** (0.0273, 0.1787). The interval does not contain 0, and this is strong evidence that the opinions differed in the two counties.

8.67 **(a)** H_0: $p_1 = p_2$, H_a: $p_1 \neq p_2$. **(b)** $z = 1.23$, P-value $= 0.2186$. This is not strong evidence that there is a difference in preference for natural trees versus artificial trees between urban and rural households. **(c)** $(-0.0209, 0.1389)$.

8.69 **(a)** $z = 5.40$, P-value = approximately 0. This is strong evidence that there is a difference in the proportions of the two types of shields removed. **(b)** (0.2125, 0.4115). Zero is well outside this interval, so that bolt-on shields appear to be removed more often than flip-up shields. We would recommend that flip-up shields be used on new tractors.

8.71 **(a)** $\hat{p}_1 = 0.141$ and $\hat{p}_2 = 0.339$. A 95% confidence interval is $(-0.253, -0.143)$. **(b)** The term $\frac{\hat{p}_1(1-\hat{p}_1)}{n_1}$ contributes more to the standard error of the difference because $n_1 = 191$ is so much smaller than $n_2 = 1520$.

8.73 We test the hypotheses H_0: $p_1 = p_2$, H_a: $p_1 \neq p_2$. $z = -5.5$, P-value = approximately 0. This is strong evidence that there is a difference in the proportions of females and males who were in a fatal bicycle accident, were tested for alcohol, and tested positive.

8.75 H_0: $p_1 = p_2$, H_a: $p_1 \neq p_2$, $Z = -0.34$, P-value $= 0.7333$. There is not enough evidence to say that the applicants are lying in different proportions than they did 6 months ago.

8.77 Let p_1 denote the proportion of all Danish males born in Copenhagen with a normal male chromosome who have had criminal records and p_2 the proportion of all Danish males born in Copenhagen with an abnormal male chromosome who have had criminal records. We test the hypotheses H_0: $p_1 = p_2$, H_a: $p_1 < p_2$. $z = -3.51$, P-value < 0.0003. This is strong evidence that the proportion of males born in Copenhagen with an abnormal male chromosome who have criminal records is larger than that of males born in Copenhagen with a normal male chromosome.

8.79 **(a)** $(-0.038, 0.482)$. **(b)** $z = -1.91$, P-value $= 0.0281$. We could conclude that there is reasonably strong evidence that the proportion of cockroaches that will die on glass is less than the proportion that will die on plasterboard.

8.81 H_0: $p_1 = p_2$, H_a: $p_1 \neq p_2$, $Z = 14.8$, P-value is approximately 0, so reject the null hypothesis. There is evidence of a significant difference between the proportion of male athletes who admit to cheating and the proportion of female athletes who admit to cheating. The 95% confidence interval (male – female) is (0.1963, 0.2377). Someone who gambles will be less likely to respond to the survey. Do you think men or women are more likely to report that they do not gamble when, in fact, they do gamble?

8.83 **(a)** and **(b)**

Category	$\hat{p}$ (in %)	n	m (in %)
Download less	38	247	3.09
Peer-to-peer	33.3	247	3.00
E-mail and IM	24	247	2.72
Web sites	20	247	2.55
iTunes	17	247	2.39
Overall use of new services	7	1371	0.69
Overall use paid services	3	1371	0.46

(c) Argument for (A): Readers should understand that the population percent is not guaranteed to be at the sample percent; there is variability involved in taking a sample. Argument for (B): Listing each individual margin of error does seem excessive, so you could summarize by saying that the margin of error was no greater than 3.09% for each of these questions. You could also separate out the last 2 questions by saying their margin of error was less than 1%.

8.85 **(a)** H_0: $p_1 = p_2$, H_a: $p_1 \neq p_2$, $Z = 6.97$ with a P-value near 0, so reject the null hypothesis. There is strong evidence that the users and nonusers differ significantly in the proportion of college graduates. **(b)** 95% CI (users – nonusers) = $(0.1141, 0.2019)$.

8.87

	Users (total number)	Nonusers (total number)
Analysis of education	1132	852
Analysis of income	871	677

For users, the proportion of "rather not say" is 0.231. For nonusers, the proportion of "rather not say" is 0.205. H_0: $p_1 = p_2$, H_a: $p_1 \neq p_2$, $Z = 1.38$, P-value $= 0.1676$, so do not reject the null hypothesis. There is not much evidence of a significant difference in the proportion of "rather not say" answers between users and nonusers. The 95% CI (users – nonusers) is $(-0.0106, 0.0626)$. Since the nonresponse rate is not significantly different for the two groups, it is not a serious limitation for this study.

8.89 **(a)** $\hat{p}_{\text{repeat}} = 0.783$, $\hat{p}_{\text{norepeat}} = 0.517$, 95% CI (repeat – no repeat) is (0.102, 0.430). **(b)** H_0: $p_1 = p_2$, H_a: $p_1 \neq p_2$, $Z = 3.05$, P-value $= 0.0022$, so reject the null hypothesis. There is strong evidence of a significant difference in the proportion of tips received between servers who repeat the customer's order and those who do not repeat the order. **(c)** Cultural differences, personalities of the servers, and gender differences could all play a role in interpreting these results. Did one server only do the repeating while the other server did no repeating, or did they switch off? **(d)** Answers will vary.

8.91 Let p_1 be the proportion of all die-hard fans who attend a Cubs game at least once a month and p_2 the proportion of less loyal fans who attend a Cubs game at least once a month. We test H_0: $p_1 = p_2$, H_a: $p_1 > p_2$. $z = 9.04$, P-value = approximately 0. This is strong evidence that the proportion of die-hard Cubs fans who attend a game at least once a month is larger than the proportion of less loyal

Cubs fans who attend a game at least once a month. A 95% confidence interval for the difference in the two proportions is (0.3755, 0.5645), so the magnitude of the difference is large.

8.93 The number of people in the survey who said they had at least one credit card is $n = 0.76(1025) = 779$ (after rounding off). The margin of error is $m = 0.0275$.

8.95 The 95% confidence interval is (0.5524, 0.6736). This does not include 0.485, the proportion of U.S. adults who are male, so we would conclude that the proportion of heavy lottery players who are male is different from the proportion of U.S. adults who are male.

8.97 Let p be the proportion of products that will fail to conform to specifications in the modified process. We test the hypotheses $H_0: p = 0.11$, $H_a: p < 0.11$. $z = -3.16$, P-value $= 0.0008$. This is strong evidence that the proportion of non-conforming items is less than 0.11, the former value. This conclusion is justified provided the trial run can be considered a random sample of all (future) runs from the modified process and that items produced by the process are independently conforming or nonconforming.

8.99 Let p_1 denote the proportion of male college students who engage in frequent binge drinking and p_2 the proportion of female college students who engage in frequent binge drinking. We test the hypotheses $H_0: p_1 = p_2$, $H_a: p_1 \neq p_2$. $z = 9.5$, P-value $=$ approximately 0. This is strong evidence that there is a difference in the proportions of male and female college students who engage in frequent binge drinking.

8.101 **(a)** Let p_1 denote the proportion of men with low blood pressure who die from cardiovascular disease and p_2 the proportion of men with high blood pressure who die from cardiovascular disease. A 95% confidence interval for the difference in the two proportions is (−0.01411, −0.00319). This is consistent with the results in Example 8.8. **(b)** $H_0: p_1 = p_2$, $H_a: p_1 < p_2$. $z = -3$, P-value $=$ 0.0013. We would conclude that there is strong evidence that the proportion of men with low blood pressure who die from cardiovascular disease is less than the proportion of men with high blood pressure who die from cardiovascular disease.

8.103

n	10	25	50	100	150	200	400	500
m	0.438	0.277	0.196	0.139	0.113	0.098	0.069	0.062

As sample size increases, the margin of error decreases.

8.105 Starting with a sample size of 25 for the first sample, it is not possible to guarantee a margin of error of 0.15 or less. $m = 1.960\sqrt{\frac{(0.5)(0.5)}{25} + \frac{(0.5)(0.5)}{n_2}}$. This leads to a negative value for n_2, which is not feasible.

8.107 **(a)** $p_0 = 0.791$. **(b)** $\hat{p} = 0.390$, $z = -29.09$, P-value $=$ approximately 0. We would conclude that there is strong evidence that the probability that a randomly selected juror is Mexican American is less than the proportion of eligible voters who are Mexican American. **(c)** $z = -29.20$, P-value $=$ approximately 0. The z statistic and P-value are almost the same as in part **(b)**.

CHAPTER 9

9.1 **(a)** Simplest is two columns, French or not French music playing, and two rows, French wine purchased or other wine purchased. **(b)** The explanatory variable is the type of music because we think this influences the type of wine purchased, so the columns are type of music.

9.3 87.8% of successful firms and 72.3% of unsuccessful firms offer exclusive territories.

9.5 28 firms lack exclusive territories and 27.6% of all firms are unsuccessful. If there is no association between success and exclusive territories, then firms with exclusive territories and those lacking exclusive territories should both have 27.6% unsuccessful firms.

9.7 df = 10.

9.9 **(a)** Minitab calculates $\chi^2 = 10.949$. $z^2 = (3.31)^2 = 10.95$. **(b)** $(3.291)^2 = 10.83$. **(c)** No relation says that whether or not a person is a label user has no relationship to gender, which is the same as H_0: $p_1 = p_2$.

9.11 Answers will vary, but one example would be:

	X	Y	Z	Totals
A	10	10	10	30
B	10	10	10	30
C	10	10	10	30
Totals	30	30	30	90

9.13 **(a)** Two-way table:

	Admit		
Gender	Yes	No	Total
Male	490	310	800
Female	400	300	700
Total	890	610	1500

(b) % of males who are admitted: 490/800 = 61.25%; % of females who are admitted: 400/700 = 57.14%. **(c)** H_0: There is no association between gender and admission, H_a: There is an association between gender and admission. $\chi^2 = 2.610$, P-value = 0.106 from SPSS. Do not reject the null hypothesis. There is not enough evidence to say that there is an association between gender and admission. **(d)** % of males who are admitted to business school: 400/600 = 66.67%; % of females who are admitted to business school: 200/300 = 66.67%. % of males who are admitted to law school: 90/200 = 45%; % of females who are admitted to law school: 200/400 = 50%. **(e)** Business: $\chi^2 = 0$, P-value = 1 from SPSS. Do not reject the null hypothesis. There is not enough evidence to say that there is an association between gender and admission in business school. Law: $\chi^2 = 1.335$, P-value = 0.248 from SPSS. Do not reject the null hypothesis. There is not enough evidence to say that there is an association between gender and admission in law school. (f) Simpson's paradox: Because the business school has so many more students both admitted and rejected (and 600 men apply, more than any gender to any program), it changes the overall results when business and law are combined.

9.15 % of Department A's classes which are small: 32/52 = 61.54%. % of Department B's classes which are small: 42/106 = 39.62%. % of Department A's classes which are for third and fourth year students: 40/52 = 76.92%. % of Department B's classes which are for third and fourth year students: 36/106 = 33.96%. Department A teaches a much larger percentage of small classes, but Department A teaches more than twice the percentage of third and fourth year students as Department B.

9.17 $\chi^2 = 2.591$, P-value $= 0.107$ from SPSS. Do not reject the null hypothesis. There is not enough evidence to say that there is an association between model dress and magazine readership age group. The marginal percentages for model dress were 73.6% of the ads had models dressed not sexually, and 26.4% had models dressed sexually. The marginal percentages for age group were 33.3% in the young adult category and 66.7% in the mature adult category.

9.19 **(a)** $\chi^2 = 76.675$, P-value is close to 0 from SPSS. Reject the null hypothesis. There is very strong evidence that there is an association between collegiate sports division and report of cheating. **(b)** Answers will vary, but here is one possibility: If we change all the sample sizes to 1000 but keep the percentages the same, $\chi^2 = 15.713$ and the P-value remains very close to 0. If we change all the "yes" answer counts to 100 but keep the percentages the same, then $\chi^2 = 7.749$ and the P-value increases to 0.021. **(c)** The people most likely not to respond are those who gamble, so the results may be biased towards "no" answers. **(d)** If one member of a team is cheating, it may be more likely that others are cheating too. The teammates also may have had a discussion about how to fill out the form.

9.21 $\chi^2 = 12$, P-value $= 0.001$ from SPSS. Reject the null hypothesis. There is strong evidence to say that there is an association between gender and visits to the *H. bihai* flowers. The 0 cell count does not invalidate the significance test. It is the expected counts that need to be 5 or greater for a 2×2 table in order for the chi-square test to be appropriate.

	Visits *H. bihai*		
Gender	Yes	No	Total
Female	20	29	49
Male	0	21	21
Total	20	50	70

9.23

Initial major	Transferred to other
Biology	202
Chemistry	64
Mathematics	38
Physics	33

$\chi^2 = 50.527$, P-value is close to 0 from SPSS. Reject the null hypothesis. There is strong evidence to say that there is an association between initial major and transferred area.

9.25 $\chi^2 = 50.81$, df $= 2$, P-value $= 0.000$. The older employees (over 40) are almost twice as likely to fall into the lowest performance category but are only 1/3 as likely to fall into the highest category.

9.27 $\chi^2 = 3.277$, df $= 4$, P-value $= 0.513$. The data show no evidence the response rates vary by industry.

9.29 df $= 4$. Statistical software gives P-value $= 0.4121$. There is no evidence of a difference in the income distribution of the customers at the two stores.

9.31 **(a)** A phone call has a 68.2% response rate, a letter has a 43.7% response rate, and no intervention has a 20.6% response rate. **(b)** H_0: There is no relationship between intervention and response rate. H_a: There is a relationship. **(c)** $\chi^2 = 163.413$, df $= 2$, P-value $= 0.000$. Intervention seems to increase the response rate, with a phone call being more effective than a letter.

9.33 Use the information on nonresponse rate, and take a larger sample size than necessary to make sure that you have enough observations with nonresponse accounted for.

9.35 $z = 6.1977$ and $\chi^2 = 38.411$. It is easily verified that $z^2 = \chi^2$.

9.37 $\chi^2 = 19.683$, df $= 1$, P-value $= 0.000$. There is strong evidence of a relationship between winning or losing this year and winning or losing next year. In Exercise 9.20 good performance continued, while for the data in this exercise the opposite is true.

9.39 **(a)** Combined $\chi^2 = 13.572$ and $P < 0.000$, so the difference in percent on time for the two airlines is highly significant, with America West being the winner. **(b)** Los Angeles: $\chi^2 = 3.241$ and $P = 0.072$. Phoenix: $\chi^2 = 2.346$ and $P = 0.126$. San Diego: $\chi^2 = 4.845$ and $P = 0.028$. San Francisco: $\chi^2 = 21.223$ and $P < 0.001$. Seattle: $\chi^2 = 14.903$ and $P < 0.001$. **(c)** Most of the effects illustrating the paradox are statistically significant.

9.41 $\chi^2 = 43.487$, df $= 12$, P-value $= 0.000$. This is highly significant, indicating a relationship between the PEOPLE score and field of study. Among the major differences, note that science has an unusually large percent of low-scoring students relative to other fields, while liberal arts and education have an unusually large percent of high-scoring students relative to the other fields.

9.43 The graph shows an increasing trend, yet $\chi^2 = 9.969$ with 13 degrees of freedom (P-value $= 0.696$). Although there appears to be a strong increasing trend, the changes in the percents are quite small (from 60% to about 66%). Women represented a very small percent in 1970, but that percent increased quite rapidly until the mid-1980s, when it reached about 60%. The percent continued to increase in the late 1980s but much more slowly, with some leveling off in the early 1990s. The percent started increasing again in the mid-1990s, but very slowly.

9.45 **(a)** Column percents because the "source" of the cat is the explanatory variable. **(b)** $\chi^2 = 6.611$, df $= 2$, P-value $= 0.037$. At the 5% level of significance we would conclude a relationship between the source of the cat and whether or not the cat is brought to an animal shelter.

9.47 $\chi^2 = 24.9$, df $= 2$, and P-value < 0.0005. The source of dogs and cats differs. A much higher percent of dogs than cats come from private sources, while a much higher percent of cats than dogs come from other sources such as born in home, stray, or obtained from a shelter.

9.49 Exercise 9.12 is a test of independence based on a single sample. Exercise 9.13 is a comparison of several populations based on separate samples from each. Exercise 9.14 is a comparison of several populations based on separate samples from each. Exercise 9.16 is a test of independence based on a single sample.

9.51 **(a)** $\chi^2 = 24.9$, df $= 2$, and P-value < 0.0005. Inspection of the data shows that the males have higher percents in the two high social comparison categories, while the females have higher percents in the two low social comparison categories. **(b)** $\chi^2 = 23.45$ and P-value < 0.0005. This agrees with what we found from the full 4×2 table. **(c)** $\chi^2 = 0.03$ and P-value $= 0.863$, which indicates no gender differences for the high versus low mastery categories.

CHAPTER 10

10.1 Predicted wages = \$449.91. Residual = −\$60.91.

10.3 **(a)** $\beta_0 = 4.7$. When U.S. returns are 0%, overseas returns are 4.7%. **(b)** $\beta_1 = 0.66$. A 1% increase in U.S. returns is associated with a 0.66% increase in overseas returns. **(c)** MEAN OVERSEAS RETURN $= 4.7 + 0.66 \times$ U.S. RETURN $+ \varepsilon$. The ε term in this model accounts for the differences in overseas returns in years when the U.S. return is the same.

10.5 **(a)** Yes, there is a strong, positive, linear relationship between year and spending. **(b)** $\hat{y} = -2651.400 + 1.340x$.
(c)

Year	1995	1996	1997	1998	1999
Residual	0.30	−0.24	−0.18	−0.12	0.24

(d) SPENDING $= \beta_0 + \beta_1 \cdot$ YEAR $+ \varepsilon$, with estimates $\beta_0 = -2651.400$, $\beta_1 = 1.340$, $\varepsilon = 0.2898$. **(e)** For 2001, the predicted spending is \$29.94. The residual is \$2.76. This is an extrapolation. The trend might not stay the same beyond 1999.

10.7 $b_1 = 0.6270$. $\text{SE}_{b_1} = 0.0992$. H_0: $\beta_1 = 0$, H_a: $\beta_1 > 0$. $t = 6.32$ with 49 degrees of freedom. P-value < 0.0005.

10.9 The mutual funds that had the highest returns last year did so well partly because they were a good investment and partly because of good luck (chance).

10.11 **(a)** $r = 0.6700$. $t = 6.32$ with 49 degrees of freedom. P-value < 0.0005 and there is strong evidence that the population correlation $\rho > 0$. **(b)** The output gives $t = 6.3177$.

10.13 Area: $\bar{x} = 28.29$, $s = 17.714$, min = 2, max = 70, fairly symmetric and normally distributed except for 2 high outliers. IBI: $\bar{x} = 65.94$, $s = 18.280$, min = 29, max = 9, skewed left but no outliers. **(b)** Scatterplot looks weak, positive, and linear. It's very hard to tell if there are any outliers or unusual patterns because the relationship is so weak. **(c)** IBI $= \beta_0 + \beta_1 \cdot$ AREA $+ \varepsilon$. **(d)** H_0: $\beta_1 = 0$, H_a: $\beta_1 \neq 0$. **(e)** $\hat{y} = 52.923 + 0.460x$. From SPSS, the hypothesis test in part **(d)** has $t = 3.415$ and a P-value of 0.001, so we can reject the null hypothesis. There is strong evidence that Area and IBI have a linear relationship. $R^2 = 19.9\%$, and the regression standard error is $s = 16.535$. **(f)** The residual plot shows that the residuals get slightly less spread out as Area increases, but overall it doesn't look too bad. **(g)** Yes, the normal probability plot looks good. **(h)** The assumptions are reasonable—we are assuming a simple random sample from the population, there is a fairly linear (although weak) relationship between IBI and Area, there is approximately the same spread above and below the regression line on the scatterplot which is fairly uniform for all Area values on the plot, and the Normal probability and residual plots look good.

10.15 Area is the better explanatory variable for regression with IBI. IBI and Forest have a much weaker relationship than IBI and Area.

10.17 $H_0: \rho = 0$, $H_a: \rho \neq 0$, P-value $= 0.061$, so do not reject the null hypothesis. There is not enough evidence to say that the correlation is significantly different from 0 if a significance level of 0.05 is used. This agrees with what we saw in the test using the slope in the 10.14. The correlation is a numerical description of the linear relationship between Area and Forest, which is very weak.

10.19 **(a)** Each of the vertical stacks corresponds to an integer value of age. **(b)** Older men might earn more than younger men because of seniority or experience. Younger men might earn more than older men because they are better trained for certain types of high-paying jobs (technology) or have more education. The correlation is positive, so there is a positive association between age and income in the sample. $r^2 = 0.03525$, so that age explains only about 3% of the variation in income. The relationship is weak. **(c)** Income $= 24{,}874.3745 + 892.1135 \times$ Age. The slope tells us that for each additional year in age, the predicted income increases by $892.1135.

10.21 **(a)** We see the skewness in the plot by looking at the vertical stacks of points. There are many points in the bottom (lower income) portion of each stack. At the upper (higher income) portion of each vertical stack the points are more dispersed, with only a very few at the highest incomes. **(b)** Regression inference is robust against a moderate lack of Normality for larger sample sizes.

10.23 **(a)** The intercept tells us what the T-bill percent will be when inflation is at 0%. No one will purchase T-bills if they do not offer a rate greater than 0. **(b)** $b_0 = 2.6660$ and $SE_{b_0} = 0.5039$. **(c)** $t = 5.29$ with 49 degrees of freedom. P-value < 0.0005. This is strong evidence that $\beta_0 > 0$. **(d)** (1.6476, 3.6844).

10.25 **(a)** $r^2 = 0.696$ and indicates that square footage is helpful for predicting selling price. **(b)** Selling price $= 4786.46 + 92.8209 \times$ Square footage. P-value $<$ 0.0001. There is a statistically significant straight-line relationship between selling price and square footage.

10.27 $H_0: \rho = 0$, $H_a: \rho > 0$, $r = 0.835$, $t = 10.51$ with 48 degrees of freedom, P-value $<$ 0.0005. We conclude that there is strong evidence that $\rho > 0$.

10.29 **(a)** r^2 increases from 69.6% to 71.8%, the intercept and slope for the least-squares regression line change from 4786.46 and 92.8209 to 8039.26 and 89.3029, respectively, and the t statistic for the slope changes from 10.5 to 10.9. The conclusion we reached in Exercise 10.17 is not changed. **(b)** r^2 decreases from 69.6% to 59.1%, the intercept and slope for the least-squares regression line change from 4786.46 and 92.8209 to 27982.8 and 73.3070, respectively, and the t statistic for the slope changes from 10.5 to 7.97. The conclusion we reached in Exercise 10.17 is not changed.

10.31 **(a)** Growth is much faster than linear. **(b)** The plot looks very linear. **(c)** (0.187469, 0.200261).

10.33 **(a)** $\hat{y} \pm t^* SE_{\hat{\mu}} = (391.86, 454.54)$. **(b)** $\hat{y} \pm t^* SE_{\hat{\mu}} = (397.05, 449.35)$.

10.35 **(a)** (62.379, 71.996). **(b)** (33.579, 100.797). **(c)** A 95% confidence interval for mean response is the interval for the average IBI for all areas of 31 km^2. A 95% prediction interval for a future response estimates a single IBI for a 31 km^2 area. **(d)** It would depend on the type of terrain and the location. Mountain regions, latitude, and proximity to industrial areas might make a difference.

10.37 The confidence intervals for mean response and the prediction intervals are both fairly similar. They are not exactly the same because the IBI and Forest did not have as strong a relationship as IBI and Area.

10.39 **(a)** $\hat{y} = 24{,}874.3745 + 892.1135 \times \text{Age} = 51{,}637.78$. **(b)** Under the column labeled 95.0% CI, we see that the desired interval is (49,780, 53,496). **(c)** Under the column labeled 95.0% PI, we see that the desired interval is (−41,735, 145,010). It is too wide to be very useful.

10.41 (58,915, 62,203).

10.43 **(a)** (44,446, 55,314). **(b)** This interval is wider because the regression output uses all 5712 men in the data set, while the one-sample t procedure uses only the 195 men of age 30.

10.45 A 90% prediction interval for the BAC of someone who drinks 5 beers is (0.03996, 0.11428). This interval includes values larger than 0.08, so Steve can't be confident that he won't be arrested if he drives and is stopped.

10.47 $\text{SE}_{b_1} = 0.09944$.

10.49 The hypotheses are $H_0\colon \beta_1 = 0$, $H_a\colon \beta_1 \neq 0$. $F = 39.914$ and $t = 6.3177$. $\sqrt{F} = t$. P-value $= 7.563\text{E} - 08$.

10.51 **(a)** $r^2 = \dfrac{\text{Regression SS}}{\text{Total SS}} = 0.4489$. **(b)** $s = \sqrt{\text{Residual MS}} = 2.1801$.

10.53 $s = 19.0417$. $r^2 = 0.2534$.

10.55 **(a)** $H_0\colon \beta_1 = 0$, $H_a\colon \beta_1 \neq 0$, $t = 6.041$, and P-value $= 0.0001$. There is strong evidence that the slope of the population regression line of profitability on reputation is nonzero. **(b)** 19.36% of the variation in profitability among these companies is explained by regression on reputation. **(c)** Part **(a)** tells us that the test of whether the slope of the regression line of profitability on reputation is 0 is statistically significant, but the value of r^2 in part **(b)** tells us that only 19.36% of the variation in profitability among these companies is explained by regression on reputation.

10.57 (0.111822, 0.140586).

10.59 The F statistic (36.492) is the square of the t statistic (6.041) for the slope. P-value for F statistic $= 0.0001 = P$-value for t statistic for the slope.

10.61 $r^2 = 0.1936$, which equals the value of R-square in the output.

10.63 Answers will vary.

10.65 **(a)** For more expensive items, the pharmacy would be charging less of a markup. **(b)** $\hat{y} = 2.885 - 0.295x$ where $\hat{y}$ is the predicted (log) markup and x is the (log) cost. **(c)** df $= 137$, but using the t table we would use df $= 100$ to be conservative. For testing $H_0\colon \beta_1 = 0$, $H_a\colon \beta_1 < 0$, the P-value is less than 0.005, so we can reject the null hypothesis. There is strong evidence that (log) markup and (log) cost have a negative linear relationship (evidence that charge compression is taking place).

10.67 **(a)** Some questions to consider: Is this a national chain or an independent restaurant? What kind of food is prepared? Do the restaurants have similar staffing and experience? **(b)** Answers will vary.

10.69 **(a)** The relationship looks positive, linear, and moderately strong except for potential outliers for the two largest hotels (1388 and 1590 rooms each). **(b)** The moderately strong linear relationship is good, but the outliers are not. **(c)** $\hat{y} = 101.981 + 0.514x$, where $\hat{y}$ is the predicted number of employees and x is the number of rooms. **(d)** $H_0: \beta_1 = 0$, $H_a: \beta_1 \neq 0$ with $t = 4.287$ and P-value from SPSS of 0.001, so reject the null hypothesis. There is strong evidence that there is a significant linear relationship between the number of rooms and the number of employees working at hotels in Toronto. **(e)** (0.253, 0.775).

10.71 **(a)** Hotel 1 (1388 rooms) and Hotel 11 (1590 rooms) are the two outliers. **(b)** The R^2 drops from 60.5% in the original model to just 26.3% in the model without the outliers. The s drops from 188.774 in the original model to 129.151 in the model without the outliers. The new equation of the line is $\hat{y} = 72.526 + 0.589x$. The new t test statistic is 1.891, and the P-value is now 0.088, so we cannot reject the null hypothesis. There is not enough evidence to say that the slope is significantly different from 0. The 95% confidence interval for the slope is (−0.105, 1.284), which contains 0. The 95% confidence interval for the slope from the original model did not contain 0.

10.73 The scatterplot shows a strong, linear, and positive relationship between the number of students and the total yearly expenditures. The least squares regression line is $\hat{y} = 0.526 + 0.530x$, where $\hat{y}$ is the predicted total yearly expenditure and x is the number of students. R^2 is very good at 98.4%, and the regression standard error is $s = 1.70$. A two-sided test of the slope gives a $t = 41.623$ and a P-value close to 0. These results sound very promising; however, the normal probability plot does not look good, and the residual plot has a distinct funnel shape. The assumptions for regression may not be appropriate here.

10.75 It appears that regressing wages on length of service will do a better job of explaining wages for women who work in small banks than for women who work in large banks.

10.77 For women who work for large banks, the P-value for the test of the hypothesis that the slope is 0 is 0.2134. For women who work in small banks, the P-value for the test of the hypothesis that the slope is 0 is 0.0002. We might use length of service to predict wages for women who work in small banks, but not for women who work in large banks.

10.79 **(a)** $\hat{y} = 106.6$, or 2.91066 meters. **(b)** A plot of the data shows that these data closely follow a straight line. $r^2 = 99.8\%$, which tells us that for the years 1975 to 1987, the least-squares regression line of lean on year explains 99.8% of the variation in lean. The standard error of regression is $s = 4.181$. However, the absolute difference between the observed value in 1918 (coded value of 71) and the value predicted by the least-squares regression line (coded value 106.6) is 35.6. This is a multiple of more than 8 times s and would be considered an extreme outlier from the pattern of the data from 1975 to 1987.

10.81 $t = 2.16$, and $0.02 < P\text{-value} < 0.04$.

CHAPTER 11

11.1 Pred. SPACE = 210 + 160(45.24) + 160(17.00) + 150(38.00) + 65(315.00) + 120(43.25) = 41,533.4 ft^2.

11.3 **(a)** The response variable is bank assets. **(b)** The explanatory variables are the number of banks and deposits. **(c)** $p = 2$. **(d)** $n = 54$.

11.5 The distribution of sales is skewed to the right with two high outliers. The two high outliers are different than the high outliers in sales. It is not surprising that Wal-Mart has high sales relative to its assets because its primary business function is the distribution of products to final users. This would require less in the form of assets and increases the amount of sales.

11.7 The correlation between log(profits) and log(sales) is 0.526 (compared to 0.538 on the original scale). The correlation between log(profits) and log(assets) is 0.569 (compared to 0.533 on the original scale). The correlation between the explanatory variables log(assets) and log(sales) is 0.643 (compared to 0.455 on the original scale). The linear association between log(assets) and log(sales) appears much stronger, and the high outliers were eliminated from the other two plots.

11.9 log(profits) = −1.50 + 0.238 log(assets) + 0.478 log(sales).

11.11 With General Motors and Wal-Mart deleted, profits = 1.55 + 0.00496 assets + 0.0553 sales. The coefficient of sales has more than doubled, and the coefficient of assets is much smaller.

11.13 For Excel, the unrounded values are $s = 2.449581635$ and $s^2 = 6.000450185$. The name given to s in the output is Standard Error. For Minitab, the unrounded values are $s = 2.450$ and $s^2 = 6.000$. The name given to s in the output is S. For SPSS, the unrounded values are $s = 2.44958$ and $s^2 = 6.000$. The name given to s in the output is Std. Error of the Estimate. For SAS, the unrounded values are $s = 2.44958$ and $s^2 = 6.00045$. The name given to s in the output is Root MSE.

11.15 **(a)**

Variable	$\bar{x}$	s	Min	$Q1$	M	$Q3$	Max
Price	91.84	43.308	30	50	90	140	150
Weight	11.21	1.032	9	11	11	12	13
Amps	13.53	1.744	10	12	14	15	15
Depth	2.416	0.0765	2.2	2.4	2.4	2.5	2.5

(b) and **(c)** Price: fairly normally distributed, no outliers. Weight: fairly normally distributed, one low outlier. Amps: very left-skewed, no outliers. Depth: fairly normally distributed, one low outlier.

11.17 **(a)** $\hat{y} = -303.445 - 10.808 \cdot \text{weight} + 25.674 \cdot \text{amps} + 70.030 \cdot \text{depth}$ **(b)** $27.831 = \sqrt{774.574}$.

11.19 **(a)** A histogram shows that the residuals are fairly Normally distributed with no outliers. **(b)** Residuals vs. Weight plot looks good with possibly an outlier at Weight = 9. Residuals vs. Amps looks good with possibly an outlier at Amps = 10. Residuals vs. Depth looks funnel shaped.

11.21 Saw 6 has the most negative residual of all, and Saws 2 and 11 both have negative residuals. However, Saw 8 has a positive residual. Therefore, we cannot say that there is a relationship between rank and the residuals. A scatterplot of Residuals vs. Rank looks completely random.

11.23 **(a)**

Variable	Mean	St.dev.	Median	Min.	Max.	Q_1	Q_3
Share	8.96	7.74	8.85	1.30	27.50	2.80	11.60
Accounts	794	886	509	125	2500	134	909
Assets	48.9	76.2	15.35	1.3	219.0	5.9	38.8

(b) Use split stems. **(c)** All three distributions appear to be skewed to the right, with high outliers.

11.25 **(a)** Share = 5.16 – 0.00031 Accounts + 0.0828 Assets. **(b)** $s = 5.488$.

11.27 All summaries are smaller except minimums. Largest effect is on the mean and standard deviation.

Variable	Mean	St.dev.	Median	Min.	Max.	Q_1	Q_3
Share	6.60	4.63	6.00	1.30	12.90	2.50	10.80
Accounts	392	293	316.5	125	909	132	602.5
Assets	13.76	12.27	9.00	1.30	38.80	5.70	20.30

11.29 Share = 1.85 + 0.00663 Accounts + 0.157 Assets and $s = 3.501$.

11.31 **(a)** Stemplots show that all four distributions are right-skewed and that gross sales, cash items, and credit items have high outliers.

Variable	Mean	Median	St.dev.
Gross	320.3	263.3	180.1
Cash	20.52	19.00	11.80
Credit	20.04	15.00	14.07
Check	7.68	5.00	7.98

(b) There is a strong linear trend between gross sales and both cash and credit card items. The association is less strong with check items but this is due to an outlier.

11.33 Plot the residuals versus the three explanatory variables and give a Normal quantile plot for the residuals. There are no obvious problems in the plots.

11.35 **(a)** TBill98 = 0.883 + 0.138 Arch + 0.160 Eng + 0.0478 Staff. **(b)** $s = 1.162$.

11.37 HSS does not help much in predicting GPA, with math and English grades available for prediction.

Package	Coefficient	Standard error	*t*-statistic	*P*-value
Excel	0.034315568	0.03755888	0.913647251	0.361902429
Minitab	0.03432	0.03756	0.91	0.362
SPSS	3.432E-02	.038	.914	.362
SAS	0.03432	0.03756	0.91	0.3619

11.39 GPA = 0.624 + 0.183 HSM + 0.0607 HSE. HSM is still the most important variable in predicting GPA, although HSE is more helpful without HSS in the model.

11.41 The two models give similar predictions.

	Fit	95.0% C.I.	95.0% P.I.
HSM, HSE	1.84086	(1.6011, 2.0806)	(0.4415, 3.2402)

11.43 **(a)** HSM, HSS, HSE: 20.5%. **(b)** HSM, HSE: 20.2%. **(c)** HSM, HSS: 20.0%. **(d)** HSS, HSE: 12.3%. **(e)** HSM: 19.1%. Almost all of the information for predicting GPA is contained in HSM.

11.45 $R_1^2 = 21.15\%$, and after removing the grade variables, $R_2^2 = 6.34\%$. $F = 13.65$ with degrees of freedom $q = 3$ and $n - p - 1 = 218$. Software gives $P < 0.0001$. High school grades contribute significantly to explaining GPA when SAT scores are already in the model.

11.47 **(a)** $t = -8.917$, $\text{df} = 40 - 30 - 1 = 9$, P-value < 0.001. There is strong evidence that the coefficient of P5 is not 0. **(b)** $(-1.6135, -0.7585)$. Since we rejected the null hypothesis in part **(a)**, we did not expect the confidence interval to include 0.

11.49 The difference in signs makes sense because employees generally sign up for either the DC or the DB plan. The total number of dual-earner couples available to sign up for a plan probably stays about the same from year to year; however, as more dual-earner couples sign up for DB plans, fewer would be signing up for DC plans.

11.51 **(a)** The squared multiple correlation, R^2, gives the proportion of the variation in the response variable that is explained by the explanatory variables. **(b)** The null hypothesis should be $H_0\colon \beta_2 = 0$. **(c)** One of the assumptions for multiple regression is that the deviations ε_i are independent Normal random variables with mean 0 and a common standard deviation σ. Another possible correction would be: in each subpopulation, y varies Normally with a mean given by the population regression equation.

11.53 **(a)** $F = 4$, which has the $F(2, 60)$ distribution. Software gives $P = 0.0234$. **(b)** $R^2 = 11.76\%$. Very little of the variability in the response is explained by this set of 3 explanatory variables.

11.55 **(a)** The hypotheses about the jth explanatory variable are $H_0\colon \beta_j = 0$ and $H_a\colon \beta_j \neq 0$. The degrees of freedom for the t statistics are 2215. At the 5% level, values that are less than -1.96 or greater than 1.96 will lead to rejection of the null hypothesis. **(b)** The significant explanatory variables are loan size, length of loan, percent down payment, cosigner, unsecured loan, total income, bad credit report, young borrower, own home, and years at current address. If a t is not significant, conclude that the explanatory variable is not useful in prediction when all other variables are available to use for prediction. **(c)** The interest rate is lower for larger loans, lower for longer length loans, lower for a higher percent down payment, lower when there is a cosigner, higher for an unsecured loan, lower for those with higher total income, higher when there is a bad credit report, higher when there is a young borrower, lower when the borrower owns a home, and lower when the number of years at current address is higher.

11.57 **(a)** The hypotheses about the jth explanatory variable are H_0: $\beta_j = 0$ and H_a: $\beta_j \neq 0$. The degrees of freedom for the t statistics are 5650. At the 5% level, values that are less than -1.96 or greater than 1.96 will lead to rejection of the null hypothesis. **(b)** The statistically significant explanatory variables are loan size, length of loan, percent down payment, and unsecured loan. **(c)** The interest rate is lower for larger loans, lower for longer length loans, lower for a higher percent down payment, and higher for an unsecured loan.

11.59 **(a)** y varies Normally with a mean $\mu_{\text{GPA}} = \beta_0 + 8\beta_1 + 9\beta_2 + 7\beta_3$. **(b)** The GPA of students with an B$^+$ in math, A$^-$ in science, and B in English has a Normal distribution with an estimated mean of 2.563.

11.61 **(a)** $y_i = \beta_0 + \beta_{2002}x_{2002i} + \beta_{\text{years}}x_{\text{years}i} + \varepsilon_i$. **(b)** β_0, β_{2002}, β_{years}, σ. **(c)** $b_0 =$ 30,236.981, $b_{2002} = 0.865$, $b_{years} = 57.392$, $s = 9035.243$. **(d)** $F = 20.177$ with degrees of freedom 2 and 13, and P-value $= 0.000$ from software. We conclude years in rank and 2002 salary contain information that can be used to predict 2005 salary. **(e)** $R^2 = 75.6\%$. **(f)** For 2002 salary, $t = 2.750$, P-value $=$ 0.017, reject the null hypothesis. For years in rank, $t = 0.109$, P-value $= 0.915$, do not reject the null hypothesis. Both tests use df $= 13$. There is evidence the coefficient for 2002 salary is significantly different from zero, but the coefficient for years in rank is not.

11.63 $\hat{y} = 112{,}518.7 + 1351.837x$. **(b)** $t = 4.725$, P-value is close to 0. Years in rank are useful for predicting 2006 salary. **(c)** Years in rank included with the 2002 salary produced these results: coefficient $= 57.392$, $t = 0.109$, P-value $= 0.915$. When included with the data concerning 2002 salary, years in rank is not very useful in predicting 2005 salary; however, rank in years is useful when performing the same regression analysis without the data from 2002 salary.

11.65 From the stemplot, six of these are the six most expensive homes. Three of these are clearly outliers (the three most expensive) for this location.

11.67 1000-square-foot homes, predicted price $=$ \$79,621.62. For 1500-square-foot homes, predicted price $=$ \$96,783.43.

11.69 For 1000-square-foot homes, predicted price $=$ \$78,253.47. For 1500-square-foot homes, predicted price $=$ \$97,041.71. Overall, the two sets of predictions are fairly similar.

11.71 The pooled t test statistic is $t = 2.875$ with df $= 35$ and $0.005 < P\text{-value} < 0.01$. These results agree (up to roundoff) with the results for the coefficient of Bed3 in Example 11.16.

11.73 The trend is increasing and roughly linear as one goes from 0 to 2 garages and then levels off.

11.75 With an extra half bath, predicted price $=$ \$99,719. Without an extra half bath, predicted price $=$ \$84,585. The difference in price is \$15,134.

11.77 Because we have no data on smaller homes with an extra half bath, our regression equation is probably not trustworthy.

11.79 **(a)** The relationship between μ_y and x is curved and increasing. **(b)** The relationship between μ_y and x is curved, first decreasing and then increasing. **(c)** The relationship between μ_y and x is curved and decreasing.

11.81 For part **(a)**, the difference in means (Group B − Group A) = 3 = the coefficient of x. This can be verified directly for the other parts and shown to be true in general.

11.83 For part **(a)**, the difference in slopes (coefficient x_2 for Group B − coefficient x_2 for Group A) = 19 − 7 = −12 = the coefficient of x_1x_2. The difference in the intercepts (Group B − Group A) = 120 − 80 = 40 = coefficient of x_1. This can be verified directly for the other parts and shown to be true in general.

11.85 **(a)** Assets = 7.61 − 0.0046 Account + 0.000034 Account2. **(b)** 0.000034 ± 0.000021. **(c)** $t = 3.76$, df = 7, and $P = 0.007$. The quadratic term is useful for predicting assets in a model that already contains the linear term. **(d)** The variables Account and the square of Account are highly correlated.

11.87 **(a)** $R_1^2 = 65.38\%$, and after removing the squared term, $R_2^2 = 62.48\%$. **(b)** $F = 1.09$ with 1 and 13 df. Software gives $P = 0.3155$. The squared term does not contribute significantly to explaining salary. **(c)** $t = -1.05$, and $t^2 = 1.10$, which agrees with F up to rounding error.

11.89 **(a)** Price vs. Promotions: negative, moderate, linear. Price vs. Discount: negative, weak, fairly linear. **(b)** The table below shows the mean and standard deviation for expected price for each combination of promotion and discount.

Promotions	10	20	30	40
1	4.920, 0.1520	4.689, 0.2331	4.225, 0.3856	4.423, 0.1848
3	4.756, 0.2429	4.524, 0.2707	4.097, 0.2346	4.284, 0.2040
5	4.393, 0.2685	4.251, 0.2648	3.89, 0.1629	4.058, 0.1760
7	4.269, 0.2699	4.094, 0.2407	3.76, 0.2618	3.780, 0.2144

(b) and **(c)** At every promotion level, the 10% discount yields the highest expected price, then 20%, then 40%, then 30%. For every discount level, the 1 promotion yields the highest expected price, then 3, then 5, then 7.

11.91 In the previous exercise, the residual plot for promotions looks ok but the residual plot for discount seems to have a curved shape. Therefore, try the quadratic term for discount and the interaction of discount and promotion. If the quadratic term for discount is used, the R^2 increases to 61.1%, the s decreases to 0.2511, the F test statistic is 81.809, and the P-value is still very close to 0. All coefficients are significantly different from 0. If the quadratic term is removed and the interaction of discount and promotion is used instead, the coefficient for the interaction term is not significant, and R^2 and s are very close to what they were in the original model. The best model is the one with the quadratic term for discount: $\hat{y} = 5.540 - 0.102$ Promotion − 0.060 Discount+ 0.001 Discount^2.

11.93 **(a)**

	Area	Forest	IBI
Mean	28.29	39.39	65.94
St. dev.	17.714	32.204	18.280
Description of stemplot	Right skewed, 2 high outliers	Right skewed, no outliers	Left skewed, no outliers

(b) All relationships are linear and moderately weak. Area and Forest have a negative relationship, but the others are positive. Data point #40 looks like a potential outlier on the Area/Forest scatterplot, but not anyplace else. **(c)** $y_i = \beta_0 + \beta_{\text{Area}} x_{\text{Area}i} + \beta_{\text{Forest}} x_{\text{Forest}i} + \varepsilon_i$. **(d)** H_0: $\beta_{\text{Area}} = \beta_{\text{Forest}} = 0$, H_a: The coefficients are not both 0. **(e)** $R^2 = 35.7\%$, $s = 14.972$, $F = 12.776$, P-value $=$ 0.000. All coefficients are significant. $\hat{y} = 40.629 + 0.569$ Area $+ 0.234$ Forest. **(f)** Residual plots look good—random and no outliers. **(g)** A histogram of the residuals looks slightly skewed left, but the Normal probability plot looks good. **(h)** Yes. We had general linear relationships between the variables and the residuals look good. However, only 35.7% of the variation in IBI is explained by Area and Forest.

11.95 **(a)**

	Mean	St. dev.	Description of distribution
PCB	68.4674	59.3906	Skewed right, 5 high outliers
PCB52	0.9580	1.5983	Skewed right, 6 high outliers
PCB118	3.2563	3.0191	Skewed right, 5 high outliers
PCB138	6.8268	5.8627	Skewed right, 5 high outliers
PCB180	4.1584	4.9864	Skewed right, 7 high outliers

(b) All the variables are positively correlated with each other. All the explanatory variables are significantly correlated with PCB, although PCB52 is the most weakly correlated with PCB and with the other explanatory variables. Only the correlation between PCB52 and PCB180 is not significant (P-value $= 0.478$).

11.97 **(a)** #50 and #65 are the two potential outliers. #50 (residual $= -22.0864$) is the overestimate. **(b)** $\hat{y} = 1.628 + 14.442$ PCB52 $+ 2.600$ PCB118 $+ 4.054$ PCB138 $+ 4.109$ PCB 180. All coefficients are significant again. $R^2 = 99.4\%$, $s = 4.555$, $F = 2628.685$, P-value $= 0$. The residuals look fairly Normally distributed, and the residual plots look random. There are two new potential outliers though at #44 and #58.

11.99 **(a)** $\beta_0 = 0$, $\beta_1 = \beta_2 = \beta_3 = 1$ because TEQ $=$ TEQPCB $+$ TEQDIOXIN $+$ TEQFURAN. **(b)** The error terms are all 0, so $\sigma = 0$. **(c)** Confirms what we did in **(a)** and **(b)**.

11.101 **(a)** Results will vary with software. **(b)** Most software should ignore these data points, but ignoring data is not a good idea. **(c)** Table below uses Base 10 logs.

Log of variable	Mean	St. dev.	Description of stemplot
PCB138	0.7009	0.3494	Fairly symmetric, 1 low outlier
PCB153	0.7397	0.3914	Fairly symmetric, no outliers
PCB180	0.4235	0.4028	Fairly symmetric, 1 high outlier
PCB28	−0.5793	0.4918	Fairly symmetric, 1 low and 1 high outlier
PCB52	−0.3354	0.5167	Fairly symmetric, 1 low and 2 high outliers
PCB126	−1.504	0.8576	Right skewed, 16 high outliers
PCB118	0.3717	0.3592	Fairly symmetric, 1 low and 1 high outlier
PCB	1.701	0.3483	Fairly symmetric, no outliers
TEQ	0.3495	0.2591	Right skewed, no outliers

11.103 Answers will vary, but if you start with the full model and then drop one variable at a time, one good possibility is leaving out Log PCB126 because all the coefficients are significant at the 5% level. This model has $R^2 = 97.5\%$ and

$s = 0.0581$. The least-squares regression line is: $\hat{y} = 1.287 + 0.400$ Log PCB138+ 0.144 Log PCB153 + 0.132 Log PCB180 + 0.088 Log PCB28 + 0.101 Log PCB52 + 0.151 Log PCB118. If the students choose a lower significance level, a good model with only 4 variables would be: $\hat{y} = 1.212 + 0.668$ Log PCB138 + 0.152 Log PCB153 + 0.108 Log PCB28 + 0.087 Log PCB52. This model has an $R^2 = 97.2\%$ and $s = 0.0600$. A model with 3 variables would be: $\hat{y} = 1.214 + 0.821$ Log PCB138 + 0.091 Log PCB28 + 0.103 Log PCB52. This model has an $R^2 = 96.8\%$ and $s = 0.0638$.

11.105 Answers will vary.

11.107 **(a)** $R^2 = 18.9\%$, $s = 1.1421$, $F = 3.152$, P-value = 0.059. Neither the coefficient for x_1 or for x_2 is significant. **(b)** All correlations are significant. The scatterplots show that both x_1 and x_2 have positive linear relationships with y and with each other. If just x_1 is used, its coefficient is significant. If just x_2 is used, its coefficient is significant. **(c)** This isn't always the best approach either. Multiple regression is complicated.

11.109 **(a)** Vitamin C = 46 − 6.05 Days, $t = -10.62$, df = 8, P-value = 0. It appears there is a significant linear relationship between vitamin C level and the number of days after baking. **(b)** It appears that the relationship may be slightly curved. The residuals show a systematic pattern in that the values go from positive to negative to positive as the number of days increases. **(c)** Vitamin C = 50.1 − 11.3 Days + 0.763 Days^2. The squared term t statistic is 6.08 and df = 7. The P-value = 0.000503. It appears that the squared term is significant in the model. **(d)** R^2 without the squared term is 0.93 and with the squared term is 0.99. A look at the scatterplot of residuals vs. days in the second model shows that there is no systematic pattern. Choose the model with the squared term.

11.111 Wages = 349 + 0.6 LOS, $t = 2.86$, P-value = 0.006. $R^2 = 0.12$. While the t statistic shows that the coefficient on the variable LOS is significantly different from zero, it does not appear that this is a strong linear model. LOS does not explain more than 12% of the variation in wages.

11.113 Wages = 302.5 + 0.67 × LOS + 71.8 × Size, $R^2 = 0.29$, t statistics have small P-values.

11.115 **(a)** Corn yield = −46.2+4.8 × Soybean yield, $R^2 = 0.87$, $t = 16.04$, P-value = 0. **(b)** The residuals appear fairly Normal. **(c)** It appears that there is an increasing and then decreasing effect when looking at the residuals plotted against year. It makes sense to include year in the regression model.

11.117 **(a)** Corn yield = −607.5 + 0.3x Year −0.045 × Year2 + 3.9 × Soybean yield. **(b)** H_0: All coefficients are equal to 0. H_a: At least one coefficient is not equal to zero. $F = 233$, df = 3 and 36, P-value = 0. This indicates that the model provides significant prediction of corn yield. **(c)** $R^2 = 0.95$, compared to 0.90 from the previous model. **(d)** In the order they appear in the model, the t statistics for the coefficients are: $t = -5.82$ with a P-value = 0, $t = 1.73$ with a P-value = 0.09, $t = 9.512$ with a P-value = 0. **(e)** The residuals all appear random when plotted against the explanatory variables.

11.119 For the linear model, predicted yield for 2001 was 136.41 with a 95% prediction interval of (114, 158.61). For the quadratic model, predicted yield for 2001 was 127.14 with a 95% prediction interval of (101.82, 152. 45). The linear model gave a closer prediction to actual.

11.121 The scatterplots do not show strong relationships. The plot of SATM vs. GPA shows two possible outliers on the left side. The plot of SATV vs. GPA does not show any obvious outliers.

11.123 The residuals do not show any obvious patterns or problems.

11.125 GPA = 0.666 + 0.193 HSM + 0.00061 SATM. **(b)** H_0: All coefficients are equal to 0. H_a: At least one coefficient is not equal to zero. This means that we assume the model is not a significant predictor of GPA and let the data provide evidence that the model is a significant predictor. $F = 26.63$ and P-value = 0. This model provides significant prediction of GPA. **(c)** HSM: (0.1295, 0.2565), SATM: (−0.00059, 0.001815). Yes, the interval describing SATM coefficient does contain zero. **(d)** HSM: $t = 5.99$, P-value = 0. SATM: $t = 0.999$, P-value = 0.319. Based on the large P-value associated with the SATM coefficient, one should conclude that SATM does not provide significant prediction of GPA. **(e)** $s = 0.703$. **(f)** $R^2 = 0.1942$.

11.127 Looking at the sample of males only shows the same results when compared to the sample of all students. $R^2 = 0.184$ (compared to 0.20) and while HSM is a significant predictor, HSS and HSE are not.

11.129 **(a)** GPA = 0.582 + 0.155 HSM + 0.050 HSS + 0.044 HSE + 0.067 Gender + 0.05 GHSM − 0.05 GHSS − 0.012 GHSE. The t statistics for each coefficient have P-values greater than 0.10 for all except the explanatory variable HSM. **(b)** Verify. **(c)** Verify. **(d)** $F = 0.143$, P-value = 0.966. This indicates there is no reason to include gender and the interactions.

CHAPTER 12

12.1 A flowchart for making coffee might look like Measure coffee ∅ Grind coffee ∅ Add coffee and water to coffeemaker ∅ Brew coffee ∅ Pour coffee into mug and add milk and sugar if desired. In making a cause-and-effect diagram, consider what factors might affect the final cup of coffee at each stage of the flowchart.

12.3 The 9 DRGs account for 80.5% of total losses. A Pareto chart indicates that the hospital ought to study DRGs 209 and 116 first in attempting to reduce its losses.

12.5 In Exercise 12.1 we described the process of making a good cup of coffee. Some sources of common cause variation are variation in how long the coffee has been stored and the conditions under which it has been stored, variation in the measured amount of coffee used, variation in how finely ground the coffee is, variation in the amount of water added to the coffeemaker, variation in the length of time the coffee sits between when it has finished brewing and when it is drunk, and variation in the amount of milk and/or sugar added.

Some special causes that might at times drive the process out of control would be a bad batch of coffee beans, a serious mismeasurement of the amount of coffee used or the amount of water used, a malfunction of the coffeemaker or a power outage, interruptions that result in the coffee sitting a long time before it is drunk, and the use of milk that has gone bad.

12.7 **(a)** CL = 11.5, UCL = 11.8, LCL = 11.2. **(b)** In the chart for data set A one finds that samples 12 and 20 fall above UCL. In the chart for data set B no samples are outside the control limits. In the chart for data set C, samples 19 and 20 are above UCL. **(c)** Data set B comes from a process that is in control. Data set A comes from a process in which the mean shifted suddenly. Data set C comes from a process in which the mean drifted gradually upward.

12.9 CL = 0.46065, UCL = 1.044, LCL = 0.

12.11 5:45 A.M., alarm rings ∅ 5:45 A.M., get out of bed ∅ 5:46 A.M., start coffeemaker ∅ 5:47 A.M., shower, shave, and dress ∅ 6:15 A.M., breakfast ∅ 6:30 A.M., brush teeth ∅ 6:35 A.M., leave home ∅ 6:50 A.M., park at school ∅ 6:55 A.M., arrive at office.

12.13 My main reasons for late arrivals at work are "don't get out of bed when the alarm rings" (responsible for about 40% of late arrivals), "too long eating breakfast" (responsible for about 25% of late arrivals), "too long showering, shaving, and dressing" (responsible for about 20% of late arrivals), and "slow traffic on the way to work" (responsible for about 15% of late arrivals).

12.15 For the s chart, CL = 0.001128, UCL = 0.0023568, LCL = 0. For the $\overline{x}$ chart, CL = 0.8750, UCL = 0.87662, LCL = 0.87338.

12.17 First sample: $\overline{x} = 48$, $s = 8.94$. Second sample: $\overline{x} = 46$, $s = 13.03$. For the $\overline{x}$ chart UCL = 60.09, CL = 43, LCL = 25.9. For the s chart we note that UCL = 25.02, CL = 11.98, LCL = 0. The s chart shows a lack of control at sample point 5 (8:15 3/8), but otherwise neither chart shows a lack of control. We would want to find out what happened at sample 5 to cause a lack of control in the s chart.

12.19 We want to compute the probability that $\overline{x}$ will be beyond the control limits, that is, that $\overline{x}$ will be either larger than UCL = 713 or smaller than LCL = 687. The desired probability is 0.1591.

12.21 **(a)** 2σ control limits are UCL $= \mu + 2(\sigma/\sqrt{n})$, LCL $= \mu - 2(\sigma/\sqrt{n})$. **(b)** For an s chart, the 2σ control limits are UCL $= (c_4 + 2c_5)\sigma$, LCL $= (c_4 - 2c_5)\sigma$.

12.23 Presumably, a given sample is equally likely to be from the experienced clerk or the inexperienced clerk, and which clerk a sample comes from will be random. Thus, the $\overline{x}$ chart should display two types of points: those that have relatively small values (corresponding to the experienced clerk) and those with relatively large values (corresponding to the inexperienced clerk). Both types should occur about equally often in the chart, and the pattern of large and small values should appear random.

12.25 **(a)** $\hat{\mu} = 275.065$, $\hat{\sigma} = 37.5$. **(b)** In Figure 12.7 we see that most of the points lie below 40 (and more than half of those below 40 lie well below 40). Of the points above 40, all but one (Sample 12) are only slightly larger than 40. The s chart suggests that typical values of s are below 40, which is consistent with the estimate of σ in part **(a)**.

12.27 By practicing statistical process control, the manufacturer is, in essence, inspecting samples of the monitors it produces and fixing any problems that arise. The control charts the manufacturer creates are a record of this inspection process. Incoming inspection is thus redundant and no longer necessary.

12.29 The plot shows no serious departures from Normality. For Normal data the natural tolerances are trustworthy, so based on our Normal quantile plot, the natural tolerances we found in the previous exercise are trustworthy.

12.31 99.06% of monitors will meet the new specifications if the process is centered at 250 mV.

12.33 The natural tolerances for the distance between the holes are $\hat{\mu} \pm 3\hat{\sigma} = 43.41 \pm 37.17$.

12.35 About 43.16% of meters meet specifications.

12.37 The large-scale pattern in the plot looks Normal in that the centers of the horizontal bands of points appear to lie along a straight line. These horizontal bands correspond to observations having the same value, resulting from the limited precision (roundoff). With greater precision, these observations would undoubtedly differ and would probably appear to come from a Normal distribution. However, because of the lack of precision, we should probably view these data as only approximately Normal and thus the calculations in Exercise 12.34 should be considered only approximate.

12.39 **(a)** If all pilots suddenly adopt the policy of "work to rule" (and are now more careful and thorough about doing all the checks), one would expect to see a sudden increase in the time to complete the checks but probably not much of a change in the variability of the time. Thus, we would expect to see a sudden change in level on the $\bar{x}$ chart. **(b)** Presumably samples of measurements made by the laser system will have a much smaller standard deviation than samples of measurements made by hand. We would expect to see this reflected in a sudden change (decrease) in the level of an s or R chart. **(c)** Presumably the measurement of interest is either the temperature in the office or the number of invoices prepared. If it is the temperature of the office, then as time passes, the temperature will gradually increase as outdoor temperature increases. This would be reflected in a gradual shift up on the $\bar{x}$ chart. If the measurement of interest is the number of invoices prepared, as the temperature in the office gradually increases, the workers gradually become less comfortable. They may take more breaks for water or become tired more quickly and thus accomplish less. We might expect to see a gradual decrease in the number of invoices prepared and hence a gradual shift down in the $\bar{x}$ chart.

12.41 The winning time for the Boston Marathon has been gradually decreasing over time. There are thus two sources of variation in the data. One is the process variation that we would observe if times were stable (random variation that we might observe over short periods of time), and the other is variation due to the downward trend in times (the large differences between times from the early 1950s compared to recent times). In using the standard deviation s of all the times between 1950 and 2002, we include both of the sources of variation. However, to determine if times in the next few years are unusual, we should consider only the process variation (variability in recent times, where the process is relatively stable). Using s overestimates the process variation, resulting in control limits that are too wide to effectively signal unusually fast or slow times.

12.43 LSL and USL define the acceptable set of values for *individual* measurements on the output of a process. These limits represent the *desired performance* of the process. LCL and UCL for $\bar{x}$ are the lower and upper control limits for the *means of samples* of several individual measurements on the output of a process. They represent the *actual performance* of the process when it is in control.

12.45 **(a)** $\hat{C}_p = 1.303$, $\hat{C}_{pk} = 1.085$. **(b)** $\hat{C}_p = 0.869$, $\hat{C}_{pk} = 0.651$.

12.47 **(a)** $C_{pk} = 1$, 50% meet specifications. **(b)** 99.74%. **(c)** The capability index formulas make sense for normal distributions, but for distributions that are clearly not normal they will give misleading results.

12.49 C_p is referred to as the potential capability index because it measures process variability against the standard provided by external specifications for the output of the process. It estimates what the process is capable of producing if the process could be centered. C_{pk} is referred to as the actual capability because index because it considers both the center and the variability against the standard provided by external specifications for the output of the process. It estimates what the process is capable of if the process target is centered between the specification limits.

12.51 **(a)** $\hat{\mu} = 43.41$, $\hat{\sigma} = 12.39$. **(b)** $\hat{C}_p = 0.27$, $\hat{C}_{pk} = 0.02$. The capability is poor (both indexes are small). The reasons are that the process is not centered (we estimate the process mean to be 43.41, but the midpoint of the specification limits is 54), and the process variability is large (we saw in Exercise 12.33 that the natural tolerances for the process are 43.41 ± 37.17, a much wider range than the specification limits of 54 ± 10).

12.53 **(a)** 17.78% of clip openings will meet specifications if the process remains in its current state. **(b)** $\hat{C}_{pk} = 0.06$.

12.55 $C_p = \text{USL} - \text{LSL}/6\sigma$, so if $C_p \geq 2$ we must have $\text{USL} - \text{LSL} \geq 22\sigma$. If the process is properly centered, then its mean μ will be halfway between USL and LSL, and hence USL and LSL will be at least 6σ from μ. Thus, this is called six-sigma quality.

12.57 If the same representatives work a given shift, and calls can be expected to arrive at random during a given shift, then it might make sense to choose calls at random from all calls received during the shift. In this case, the process mean and standard deviation should be stable over the entire shift, and random selection should lead to sensible estimates of the process mean and standard deviation.

If different representatives work during a shift, or if the rate of calls varies over a shift, then the process may not be stable over the entire shift. There may be changes in either the process mean or the process standard deviation over the shift. A random sample from all calls received during the shift would overestimate the process variability because it would include variability due to special causes. Stability would more likely be seen only over much shorter time periods, and thus it would be more reasonable to time 6 consecutive calls.

12.59 The three outliers are a response time of 276 seconds (occurring in Sample 28), resulting in a value of $s = 107.20$; a response time of 244 seconds (occurring in Sample 42), resulting in a value of $s = 93.68$; and a response time of 333 seconds (occurring in Sample 46), resulting in a value of $s = 119.53$. When the outliers are omitted, the values of s become $s = 9.28$ (Sample 28), $s = 6.71$ (Sample 42), $s = 31.01$ (Sample 46).

12.61 **(a)** The total number of opportunities for unpaid invoices = 128,750, $\overline{p} = 0.0334$. **(b)** UCL = 0.0435, CL = 0.0334, LCL = 0.0233.

12.63 UCL = 0.01307, CL = 0.00599, LCL = 0.

12.65 **(a)** $\overline{p} = 0.356$, $\overline{n} = 921.8$. **(b)** For the p chart, UCL = 0.4033, CL = 0.356, LCL = 0.3087. The process (proportion of students per month with 3 or more unexcused absences) appears to be in control. That is, there are no months with unusually high or low proportions of absences, and no obvious trends. **(c)** For October, UCL = 0.4027 and LCL = 0.3093. For June, UCL = 0.4043 and LCL = 0.3077. These exact limits do not affect our conclusions in this case.

12.67 **(a)** $\overline{p} = 0.008$ and if the manufacturer processes 500 orders per month, we would expect to see 4 defective orders per month. **(b)** UCL = 0.020, CL = 0.008,

LCL = 0. To be above the UCL, the number of defective orders must be greater than 10.

12.69 **(a)** The percents add up to larger than 100% because customers can have more than one complaint. **(b)** The category with the largest number of complaints is the ease of obtaining invoice adjustments/credits, so we might target this area for improvement.

12.71 **(a)** Presumably we are interested in monitoring and controlling the amount of time the system is unavailable. We might measure the time the system is not available in sample time periods and use an $\overline{x}$ and an s chart to monitor how this length of time the system is unavailable varies. **(b)** To monitor the time to respond to requests for help we might measure the response times in a sample of time periods and use an $\overline{x}$ and an s chart to monitor how the response times vary. **(c)** We might examine samples of programming changes and record the proportion in the sample that are not properly documented. Because we are monitoring a proportion, we would use a p chart.

12.73 CL = 7.65, UCL = 19.642, LCL = 0. The first sample is out of control, perhaps reflecting an initial lack of skill or initial problems in using the new system. After the first sample, the process is in control with respect to short-term variation, although sample 10 is very close to the upper control limit.

12.75 **(a)** $\hat{C}_p = 1.14$. This value tells us that the specification limits will lie just within 3 standard deviations of the process mean if the process mean is in the center of the specification limits. **(b)** C_{pk} depends on the value of the process mean. If the process mean can easily be adjusted, it is easy to change the value of C_{pk}. A better measure of the process capability is to center the process mean within the specification limits and then compute a capability index. If the process is properly centered, C_{pk} and C_p will be the same, so using C_p is ultimately more informative about the process capability. **(c)** We used $\overline{s}/c_4$ to estimate σ, the process variation. A better estimate would be to compute the sample standard deviation s of all $22 \times 3 = 66$ observations in the samples. This gives an estimate of all the variation in the output of the process (including sample-to-sample variation). Using $\overline{s}/c_4$ is likely to give a slightly too small estimate of the process variation and hence a slightly too large (optimistic) estimate of C_p.

12.77 **(a)** We would use a p chart. The control limits would be UCL = 0.019, CL = 0.003, and LCL = 0. **(b)** If the proportion of unsatisfactory films is 0.003, then in a sample of 100 films the expected number of unsatisfactory films is 0.3. Thus, most of our samples will have no unsatisfactory films, and plotting the sample values (most of which will be 0) will not be very informative.

12.79 **(a)** With $\overline{p} = 0.506$, UCL = 0.718, and LCL = 0.294, the process does appear to be in control. **(b)** The new sample proportions are not in control according to the original control limits from part **(a)**. Attempts 2, 4, and 10 are above the UCL. With new $\overline{p} = 0.702$, the new limits for future samples should be UCL = 0.896, and LCL = 0.508.

CHAPTER 13

13.1 **(a)** Each year, sales are lowest for the first two quarters and then increase in the third and fourth quarters. Sales decrease from the fourth quarter of one year to the first quarter of the next. **(b)** The pattern described is obvious in the time plot.

(c) There appears to be a positive trend, although the trend levels off after 1998. **(d)** The pattern described in part **(a)** is repeated year after year.

13.3 **(a)** Sales = 5903.22 + 118.75x with sales in millions of dollars and x takes on values 1, 2, . . . , 24. **(b)** The fourth quarter of 1995. **(c)** The slope is the increase in sales (in millions of dollars) that occurs from one quarter to the next.

13.5 **(a)** Sales = 7858.76 + 99.54x − 2274.21$X1$ − 2564.58$X2$ − 2022.79$X3$. **(b)** If we know that $X1 = X2 = X3 = 0$, then we know that we are not in any of the first three quarters, and hence must be in the fourth quarter. **(c)** The intercept again represents the fourth quarter of 1995.

13.7 **(a)** The seasonality factors are 0.923, 0.885, 0.960, and 1.231 for quarters 1 through 4, respectively. **(b)** The average is 0.999, which is close to 1. The fourth-quarter seasonality factor of 1.231 tells us that fourth-quarter sales are typically 23.1% above the average for all four quarters. **(c)** The plot mimics the pattern of seasonal variation in the original series.

13.9 **(a)** Seasonally adjusted series is a little smoother. **(b)** Seasonally adjusting the DVD player sales data smoothed the time series a little but not to the degree that seasonally adjusting the sales data in Figure 13.7 did. This suggests that the seasonal pattern in the DVD player sales data is not as strong as it is in the monthly retail sales data.

13.11 **(b)** There is a positive, fairly linear trend over time. **(c)** There is usually a peak in January, a drop until April, and then an increase until the next January each year. **(d)** There are two temporary troughs: a big one from January 1991 to November 1994 and a smaller one from January 1998 to January 2003. There could also be considered a temporary peak at the very end of the data set where there is a steep increase.

13.13 **(b)** There is no obvious increase or decrease overall, but there is lots of month-to-month variability. **(c)** The biggest dips come in August each year, and then there is another major (but not quite as big) dip in December each year. There are smaller dips in June each year. In August 2002, there is a dip, but it's just not as dramatic as for all the other years. However, the June 2002 dip was bigger than all the other June dips, so that might help explain why the August dip isn't as big as expected.

13.15 **(a)** The dashed line in the time plot corresponds to the least-squares line. Using the trend-only model, we find that the sales for the first three quarters tend to be overpredicted and those for the fourth quarter are underpredicted. **(b)** The first quarter of 2002 is \$8871.97 million. The fourth quarter of 2002 is \$9228.22 million. **(c)** In the past, predictions in the first three quarters tended to be slightly more accurate than in the fourth quarter, so the first quarter of 2002.

13.17 **(a)** The first quarter of 2002 is \$8188.83 million. The fourth quarter of 2002 is \$11,359.94 million. **(b)** The first-quarter forecast has been multiplied by 0.923 as the trend-only model typically overpredicts the first quarter, while the fourth-quarter forecast has been multiplied by 1.231 to account for the fact that the trend-only model typically underpredicts the fourth quarter. **(c)** The trend-and-season model and the trend-only model with seasonality factors give similar predictions as both are adjusting the trend model for the seasonality effects.

13.19 **(a)** For the trend-only model $R^2 = 35\%$ and for the trend-and-season model $R^2 = 86.8\%$. The trend-and-season model explains much more of the variability in the JCPenney sales. **(b)** For the trend-only model, $s = 1170$, and for the trend-and-season model, $s = 566.7$. **(c)** The trend-and-season model closely follows the original series. **(d)** It is clear from the plot that the trend-and-season model is a substantial improvement over the trend-only model.

13.21 **(a)** There are two very large temporary troughs (approximately) between July 1990 and July 1995 and then between April 1997 and November 2003. At the end of the data, there is a sharp rise. **(b)** A closer look at the time plot suggests a positive autocorrelation. The majority of pairs of successive residuals shows the first residual lower than the second residual in the pair. **(c)** The lagged residual plot shows a beautiful, positive, linear relationship between e_{t-1} and e_t. The correlation between e_{t-1} and e_t is 0.985. Yes, we have strong evidence of autocorrelation.

13.23 **(a)** The residuals for the fourth quarters are positive, and most of the residuals for the first three quarters are negative. **(b)** Autocorrelation is not apparent in the lagged residual plot. The correlation between successive residuals e_t and e_{t-1} is only 0.095.

13.25 **(a)** The other group of 10 points has December as the y coordinate. **(b)** The correlation of 0.9206 suggests a strong autocorrelation in much of the time series. **(c)** If we looked at the seasonally adjusted time series, the correlation would be closer to 0.9206. The outlying groups of points have the December sales as either the x or y coordinate, and this is what is reducing the correlation from 0.9206 to 0.4573. If there were a seasonal adjustment, these two sets of 10 points should no longer stand out from the remaining points.

13.27 **(a)** Fitting the simple linear regression model using y_t as the response variable and y_{t-1} as the predictor gives the equation $y_t = 34.0 + 0.992y_{t-1}$. The sales in July 2001 are 5170 thousands of units, so the forecast of August 2001 sales using this model is 5162.64. **(b)** Fitting the AR(1) model gives the equation $y_t = 13.9 + 0.996y_{t-1}$. The sales in July 2001 are 5170 thousands of units, so the forecast of August 2001 sales using this model is 5163.22. **(c)** The coefficients of y_{t-1} are very similar in parts **(a)** and **(b)**, but the constants differ. The constant for the AR(1) model is much smaller than the constant (intercept) for the simple linear regression model. The August 2001 estimates are very close. The AR(1) model is preferred because it was estimated using maximum likelihood, which is preferred over least-squares for time series models.

13.29 **(a)** The 12-month moving average forecast predicts the November 2002 price by the average of the preceding 12 months. Averaging the last 12 values in the series gives the 12-month moving average forecast as \$3.31. The 120-month moving average forecast predicts the November 2002 price by the average of the preceding 120 months. Averaging the last 120 values in the series gives the 120-month moving average forecast as \$3.39. **(b)** Going to the Web page gives the actual winter wheat price received by Montana farmers for November 2002 as \$4.28. The 120-month moving average forecast is slightly better, but neither captures the sharp rise in price that occurred over the latter part of 2002.

13.31 **(a)** When $w = 0.1$ the coefficients are 0.1, 0.09, 0.081, 0.0729, 0.06561, 0.059049, 0.0531441, 0.0478297, 0.0430467, and 0.0387420. **(b)** When $w = 0.5$ the coefficients are 0.5, 0.25, 0.125, 0.0625, 0.03125, 0.015625, 0.0078125, 0.0039062, 0.0019531, and 0.0009766. **(c)** When $w = 0.9$ the coefficients are 0.9, 0.09, 0.009, 0.0009, 0.00009, 0.000009, 0.0000009, 0.0000001, 0.0000000, and

0.0000000. **(d), (e)** The curves for $w = 0.9$ and $w = 0.5$ show a more rapid exponential decrease than the curve for $w = 0.1$, which decreases more slowly. The curve for $w = 0.9$ puts more weight on the most recent value of the time series in the computation of a forecast. **(f)** The coefficients of y_1 are 0.348678, 0.000977, and 0.0000000 for the values $w = 0.1$, $w = 0.5$, and $w = 0.9$, respectively. The value of $w = 0.1$ puts the greatest weight on y_1 in the calculation of a forecast. Note that as indicated in the text, the values of the coefficients in the forecast model decrease exponentially in value with the exception of this last coefficient.

13.33 **(a)** $\hat{y}_t = -0.021 + 1.004y_{t-1}$, $\hat{y}_{\text{July2005}} = 703.5822$. **(b)** $\hat{y}_t = -2.45385 + 1.00877y_{t-1}$, $\hat{y}_{\text{July2005}} = 704.49217$. **(c)** The slope is very similar for both equations; however, the y-intercept is not the same. The estimates are fairly close. The assumptions necessary for the regression model are no longer valid, so it is better to use the AR(1) model.

13.35 **(a)** There is a moderate positive linear relationship. **(b)** 0.692. **(c)** Yes, the relationship is strong enough to make production 12 months ago a good predictor or this month's production. The correlation is large and the relationship looks strong.

13.37 **(a)** Fitting the simple linear regression model using y_t as the response variable and y_{t-1} as the predictor gives $y_t = 100.4 + 0.572y_{t-1}$. $R^2 = 0.327$ and the regression standard error is 47.89. **(b)** An AR(1) model was fitted and the estimated autoregression equation is $y_t = 100.9 + 0.568y_{t-1}$. $R^2 = 0.327$ and the model standard error is 47.74. **(c)** The equations obtained for least-squares and maximum likelihood are almost identical. **(d)** There is very little difference between the values of R^2 the model standard error s in this example. Thus, there is no clear indication which fitting method is preferred, although in general maximum likelihood is preferred to least-squares in time series models.

13.39 **(a)** The moving averages do appear to be very linear. **(b)** $\hat{y} = 181.372 + 1.481x$. **(c)** The moving average line and predicted value line completely overlap until about 1996. From 1996 on until the end of the data, there is a slight spiraling of the moving averages around the predicted value line, but he lines are still very close.

13.41 **(a), (b)** The smoothness decreases as the value of w increases. The model with $w = 0.9$ would be best for forecasting the monthly ups and downs in orange prices. **(c)** The Minitab output for an exponential smoothing model provides forecasts for each value of the smoothing constant. The results are summarized below.

Smoothing constant w	Prediction
0.1	218.998
0.5	219.329
0.9	216.976

The forecasts are fairly similar, but the model with $w = 0.5$ provided the forecast that was closest to the actual value. **(d)** The January 2001 data point was added to the series and the models with the three weighting constants were fit to the new series. These were then used to forecast the orange price for February 2001. The results are summarized on the next page.

Smoothing constant w	Prediction
0.1	219.518
0.5	221.764
0.9	223.478

The actual value in February was 229.6, so in this case the model with $w = 0.9$ provided the forecast that was closest to the actual value.

13.43 **(a)** If we use a span of $k = 1$, the moving average forecast equation would be $\hat{y}_t = y_{t-1}$. **(b), (c), (d)** We used $k = 4$ and $k = 100$. The moving averages with a span of $k = 4$ are not particularly smooth. The moving averages with a span of $k = 100$ are quite smooth.

13.45 **(a)** If we use an exponential smoothing forecast equation with smoothing constant of $w = 1$, the forecast equation is $\hat{y}_t = y_{t-1}$. If we use an exponential smoothing forecast equation with smoothing constant of $w = 0$, the forecast equation is $\hat{y}_t = y_{t-1}$. **(b), (c), (d)** We used $w = 0.2$ and $w = 0.9$. The exponential smoothing model with $w = 0.2$ is smoother than the exponential smoothing model with $w = 0.9$. **(e)** Using the model from part **(b)**, we find the forecast for the July 24, 2002, exchange rate to be 0.993532. Using the model from part **(c)**, we find the forecast for the July 24, 2002, exchange rate to be 0.991149. The actual exchange rate on July 24, 2002 (from the web site www.oanda.com/convert/fxhistory), is 1.01140. Both forecasts underestimate the actual exchange rate.

13.47 **(a)** There are no clear seasonal patterns in the time series plot. **(b)** We fitted a line to the data using statistical software and obtained $\hat{y} = -487{,}430 + 256.735(\text{year})$, $R^2 = 0.620$, and $s = 5048$. **(c)** We fitted a second degree polynomial to the data using statistical software and obtained $\hat{y} = 20{,}082{,}384 - 20{,}752.3(\text{year}) + 5.36356(\text{year})^2$, $R^2 = 0.753$, and $s = 4091$. **(d)** We fitted a third degree polynomial to the data using statistical software and obtained $\hat{y} = -1{,}101{,}586{,}137 + 1{,}697{,}733(\text{year}) - 872.171(\text{year})^2 + 0.149355(\text{year})^3$, $R^2 = 0.802$, and $s = 3684$. **(e)** Both the quadratic and cubic models appear to fit appreciably better than the straight line model. The cubic model fits a little better (a bit larger R^2 and a bit smaller s) than the quadratic model and might be a slightly better choice for the trend equation.

13.49 **(a)** To fit the trend-and-season model, we must first define 11 indicator variables, as in Example 13.3. We let Jan. = 1 if the month is January, 0 otherwise; Feb. = 1 if the month is February, 0 otherwise; and so on through November. Using software we obtained the estimated trend-and-season model ln(UNITS) = 10.691 + 0.069(Case) − 0.761(Jan.) − 0.786(Feb.) − 0.556(Mar.) − 0.544(Apr.) − 0.632 (May) − 0.371(Jun.) − 0.525(Jul.) − 0.533(Aug.) − 0.041(Sep.) + 0.057(Oct.) − 0.225(Nov.). **(b)** If Jan. = 0, Feb. = 0, Mar. = 0, . . . , Nov. = 0, then we know the month must be December. Adding an indicator variable for December would be redundant. We can determine whether the month is December from the other indicator variables. **(c)** To use the equation in part **(a)** to forecast for July 2002, we notice that this would correspond to case 64. We set all indicators equal to 0 except the indicator for July, which we set to 1. We get ln(UNITS) = 14.582 Thus, we forecast sales for July 2002 to be UNITS = $e^{14.582}$ = 2,152,198. **(d)** The forecast using the seasonality factors in a trend-and-season model from Example 13.5 is UNITS = 2,120,278. The forecast in part **(c)** is slightly larger.

(e) The forecast using the AR(1) model from Example 13.10 is 1,515,036. The forecast in part **(c)** is considerably larger.

13.51 We tried spans of 12, 24, and 36. The plot with span $k = 36$ does the best job of smoothing the minor ups and downs while still capturing the major jump about two-thirds of the way through the data. An even larger value of k might also work well. Using the moving average model with span $k = 36$, Minitab forecasts the June 2002 average price per pound of coffee as 3.25178.

13.53 The AR(1) model does not smooth the minor ups and downs in the data, although it does capture the major jump in the series that occurs two-thirds of the way through the values. Using the AR(1) model, Minitab forecasts the June 2002 average price per pound of coffee as 3.01245.

CHAPTER 14

14.1 $I = 3$, $N = 60$, $n_1 = 20$, $n_2 = 20$, and $n_3 = 20$. The ANOVA model is $x_{ij} = \mu_i + \varepsilon_{ij}$. The ε_{ij} are assumed to be from an $N(0, \sigma)$ distribution where σ is the common standard deviation. The parameters of the model are the I population means μ_1, μ_2, and μ_3, and the common standard deviation σ.

14.3 **(a)** The largest standard deviation is 120 and the smallest is 80. The ratio of these is $120/80 = 1.5$. This ratio is less than 2, so it is reasonable to pool the standard deviations for these data. **(b)** $I = 3, \bar{x}_1 = 150, \bar{x}_2 = 175, \bar{x}_3 = 200$. We estimate σ by $s_p = 101.32$

14.5 Stem plots for the three groups are given below.

Basal		DRTA		Strat	
0	4	0		0	445
0	67	0	6777	0	666777
0	888999	0	888889999	0	889
1	01	1	000	1	111
1	22222223	1	2233	1	22333
1	45	1	5	1	44
1	6	1	6	1	

The distribution for the Basal group appears to be centered at a slightly larger score than that for the DRTA group and perhaps for the Strat group. The distribution of the DRTA scores shows some right-skewness. There are no clear outliers in any of the groups.

14.7 SSG + SSE = 20.58 + 572.45 = 593.03 = SST.

14.9 DFG + DFE = 2 + 63 = 65 = DFT.

14.11 MST = 9.124. Using statistical software (we used Minitab) we find the mean of all 66 observations in Table 14.1 to be 9.788 and the variance of all 66 observations in Table 14.1 to be 9.125.

14.13 **(a)** The ANOVA F statistic has 3 numerator degrees of freedom and 20 denominator degrees of freedom. **(b)** The F statistic would need to be larger than 3.10 to have a P-value less than 0.05.

14.15 **(a)** It is always true that $s_p^2 = \text{MSE}$. Hence, $s_p = \sqrt{\text{MSE}}$. Because of this, SAS calls s_p "Root MSE." **(b)** $s_p = \sqrt{\text{MSE}}$. In Excel, MSE is found in the ANOVA table in the row labeled "Within Groups" and under the column labeled MS. Take the square root of this entry (0.616003 in this case) to get s_p.

14.17 Try the applet. You should find that the F statistic increases and the P-value decreases if the pooled standard error is kept fixed and the variation among the group means increases.

14.19 The standard error for the contrast $\text{SE}_c = 2$.

14.21 The 95% confidence interval is $15 \pm 3.968 = (11.032, 18.968)$.

14.23 $$t_{23} = \frac{46.7273 - 44.2727}{6.31\sqrt{\frac{1}{22} + \frac{1}{22}}} = 1.29.$$

14.25 The value of t^{**} for the Bonferroni procedure when $\alpha = 0.05$ is $t^{**} = 2.46$ (see Example 14.22). $t_{23} = 1.29$. Because $|1.29| < t^{**}$, using the Bonferroni procedure we would not reject the null hypothesis that the population means for groups 2 and 3 are different.

14.27 From the output in Figure 14.16 $\overline{x}_2 - \overline{x}_3 = 2.4545$ and the standard error for this difference is 1.90378. Thus, $t_{23} = 2.4545/1.90378 = 1.29$.

14.29

Group	Mean	SD	n
Group 1	150.2[a]	19.1	30
Group 2	121.9[b,c]	18.3	30
Group 3	129.2[b,d,e]	18.4	30
Group 4	140.8[a,d]	22.1	30
Group 5	117.2[c,e]	20.6	30

We see that Groups 1 and 4 have the largest means. Group 1 differs from Groups 2, 3, and 5. Group 4 differs from Groups 2 and 5.

14.31 The Bonferroni 95% confidence interval is $(-2.2, 7.1)$. This interval includes 0.

14.33 **(a)**

n	F^*	DFG	DFE	λ	PROBF	Power
10	2.866	3	36	0.9042	0.89757	0.10243
20	2.725	3	76	1.8084	0.83012	0.16988
30	2.683	3	116	2.7126	0.75683	0.24317
40	2.663	3	156	3.6168	0.68113	0.31887
50	2.651	3	196	4.521	0.60573	0.39427
100	2.627	3	396	9.042	0.29117	0.70883

(b) As sample size increases, power increases. **(c)** Of the sample sizes selected in the table above, 100 would be best since the power is fairly low at smaller sample sizes.

14.35 **(a)** The response variable needs to be quantitative, not categorical. **(b)** You do want to use one-way ANOVA when there are at least three means to be compared. **(c)** The pooled estimate s_p is an estimate for σ, which is a parameter.

14.37 **(a)** $F(3, 7)$.

p	0.100	0.050	0.025	0.010	0.001
F	3.07	4.35	5.89	8.45	18.77

(b) The P-value would be between 0.050 and 0.100. **(c)** You can never conclude from an F test that all the means are different. The alternative hypothesis is that "not all the means are the same." However, in this case, with a large P-value at the 5% significance level, do not reject the null hypothesis. There is not enough evidence to stay that any of the means are different.

14.39 **(a)** $F(4, 35)$, $F = 1.14$, P-value $= 0.3538$ (from software). **(b)** $F(2, 18)$, $F = 4$, P-value $= 0.0365$ (from software).

14.41 **(a)** $I = 3$, $n_1 = 220$, $n_2 = 145$, $n_3 = 76$, $N = 441$, response variable = 1 to 5 rating of "Did you discuss the presentation with any of your friends?" **(b)** $I = 3$, $n_i = 5$, $N = 15$, response = cholesterol level. **(c)** $I = 3$, $n_i = 25$, $N = 75$, response = 1 to 10 rating of the game.

14.43 For parts **(a)**, **(b)**, and **(c)**: $H_0: \mu_1 = \mu_2 = \mu_3$ and H_a: Not all the means are the same. **(a)** DFG = 2, DFE = 438, DFT = 440, $F(2, 438)$. **(b)** DFG = 2, DFE = 12, DFT = 14, $F(2, 12)$. **(c)** DFG = 2, DFE = 72, DFT = 74, F (2, 72).

14.45 Answers will vary.

14.47 **(a)** Yes, because $20 < 2 \times 15$. **(b)** 48,400; 36,100; and 40,000. **(c)** 41,866. **(d)** 204.61.

14.49 **(a)** In general, as the number of accommodations increased, the mean grade decreased, but it is not a steady decline. **(b)** So many decimal places are not necessary. No additional information is gained by having so many. Using 2 decimal places would be fine. **(c)** The biggest s is not exactly less than 2 times the smallest s (1.66233 vs. 2×0.82745), but it is close. Pooling should not be used (s_p would be 0.86). **(d)** It is never a good idea to eliminate data points without a good reason. Since the mean grade is affected similarly for 2, 3, and 4 accommodations, it is not unreasonable to group these data together. **(e)** These data do not represent 245 independent observations. Some students were measured multiple times. **(f)** Answers will vary. University policies, teacher policies, student backgrounds might not be the same from school to school. **(g)** There is no control group, so it is impossible to comment on the effectiveness of the accommodations.

14.51 **(a)** Checking whether the largest $s < 2 \times$ smallest s for each group indicates that it is appropriate to pool the standard deviations for intensity and recall but not frequency. **(b)** $F(4, 405)$. The P-value for all three one-way ANOVA tests is < 0.001, so for frequency, intensity, and recall there is strong evidence that not all the means are the same.

p	0.100	0.050	0.025	0.010	0.001
F	1.95	2.42	2.85	3.41	4.81

(c) Hispanic Americans were highest in each of the three groups. For Emotion score, the European, Asian, and Indian scores were low but close together. For

Frequency and Intensity and Recall, Asian and Japanese were both low, and European and Indian are close together in the middle. **(d)** Answers will vary. People near a university might not be representative of all citizens of those countries. **(e)** The chi-square test has a test statistic of 11.353 and a P-value of 0.023, so at the 5% significance level there is enough evidence to say that there is a relationship between gender and culture. In other words, there is evidence that the proportion of men and women is not the same for all of the cultural groups. This may affect how broadly the results can be applied.

14.53 **(a)** The histogram of bone density for the control group shows a skewed right distribution. The histograms for low and high groups show fairly symmetric distributions. There are no outliers for any groups. A side-by-side boxplot of the groups shows heavy overlap of control and low but not much overlap of high with the other two groups. A means plot shows that control is slightly higher than low but high is much higher than the other two groups. The following are the (mean, standard deviation) for each group: control (0.219, 0.0116), low (0.216, 0.0115), high (0.235, 0.0188). **(b)** The normal quantile plots for low and high look good, but the plot for control shows some deviation from Normality towards the very low and very high ends. The largest s is $< 2 \times$ smallest s, so it is appropriate to pool the standard deviations. **(c)** $F = 7.718$, P-value $= 0.001$. There is strong evidence that not all the means are the same. **(d)** Bonferroni multiple comparisons shows that high is significantly different from both control and low groups, but control and low groups are not significantly different from each other. **(e)** The high dose of kudzu isoflavones yields a significantly greater mean bone density for the femur of a rat than the control or low dose does. There is no significant difference in mean bone density between the control and low dose.

14.55

	Bonferroni Tests		
Condition $i - j$	Difference	Std. error	P-value
1 − 0	−6.75000	1.321	0.036734
3 − 0	−26.9100	1.321	0.000053
3 − 1	−20.1600	1.321	0.000219
5 − 0	−36.2900	1.321	0.000012
5 − 1	−29.5400	1.321	0.000033
5 − 3	−9.38000	1.321	0.008542
7 − 0	−40.3850	1.321	0.000007
7 − 1	−33.6350	1.321	0.000017
7 − 3	−13.4750	1.321	0.001551
7 − 5	−4.09500	1.321	0.238149

The differences in the group means are all significantly different from 0 at the $\alpha = 0.05$ level except the difference after 5 and 7 days. At the $\alpha = 0.01$ level, all the differences are significantly different from 0 except the difference between 0 and 1 days after baking, and the difference between 5 and 7 days after baking.

14.57 **(a)** The ANOVA in Exercise 14.56 did not reject the hypothesis at the 0.05 level that any of the group means differed. Thus, no further analysis on which group means differed is appropriate.

(b)

Condition $i - j$	Bonferroni Tests Difference	Std. error	P-value
1 − 0	−0.110000	0.0608	0.752553
3 − 0	−0.140000	0.0608	0.514112
3 − 1	−0.030000	0.0608	0.999966
5 − 0	−0.045000	0.0608	0.998871
5 − 1	0.065000	0.0608	0.982858
5 − 3	0.095000	0.0608	0.861026
7 − 0	−0.385000	0.0608	0.014421
7 − 1	−0.275000	0.0608	0.061029
7 − 3	−0.245000	0.0608	0.096013
7 − 5	−0.340000	0.0608	0.025003

The only group means that are significantly different at the $\alpha = 0.05$ level are the difference between 0 and 7 days after baking and between 7 and 5 days after baking.

14.59 **(a)** The plots show that Group 2 has a modest outlier, but otherwise there are no serious departures from Normality. The assumption that the data are (approximately) Normal is not unreasonable.
(b)

Number of promotions	Sample size	Mean	Std. dev.
1	40	4.22400	0.273410
3	40	4.06275	0.174238
5	40	3.75900	0.252645
7	40	3.54875	0.275031

(c) The ratio of the largest to the smallest is $0.275031/0.174238 = 1.58$. This is less than 2, so it is not unreasonable to assume that the population standard deviations are equal. **(d)** The hypotheses for AVOVA are H_0: $\mu_1 = \mu_2 = \mu_3 = \mu_4$, H_a: not all of the μ_i are equal. The ANOVA table is

Source	Degrees of freedom	Sum of squares	Mean square	F	P-value
Groups	3	10.9885	3.66285	59.903	≤ 0.0001
Error	156	9.53875	0.061146		
Total	159	20.5273			

The F statistic has 3 numerator and 156 denominator degrees of freedom. The P-value is ≤ 0.0001, and we would conclude that there is strong evidence that the population mean expected prices associated with the different numbers of promotions are not all equal.

14.61 **(a)**

Group	Sample size	Mean	Std. dev.
Piano	34	3.61765	3.05520
Singing	10	−0.300000	1.49443
Computer	20	0.450000	2.21181
None	14	0.785714	3.19082

(b) The hypotheses for ANOVA are H_0: $\mu_1 = \mu_2 = \mu_3 = \mu_4$, H_a: not all of the μ_i are equal. The ANOVA table is

Source	Degrees of freedom	Sum of squares	Mean square	F	P-value
Groups	3	207.281	69.0938	9.2385	≤ 0.0001
Error	74	553.437	7.47887		
Total	77	760.718			

The F statistic has 3 numerator and 74 denominator degrees of freedom. The P-value is ≤ 0.0001, and we would conclude that there is strong evidence that the population mean changes in scores associated with the different types of instruction are not all equal.

14.63 The contrast is $\psi = \mu_1 - (1/3)\mu_2 - (1/3)\mu_3 - (1/3)\mu_4$. To test the null hypothesis H_0: $\psi = 0$, the t statistic is $t = c/\text{SE}_c = 3.306/0.636 = 5.20$. P-value ≤ 0.001. We conclude that there is strong statistical evidence that the mean of the piano group differs from the average of the means of the other three groups.

14.65 **(a)** Plots show no serious departures from Normality, so the Normality assumption is reasonable.

(b)

Bonferroni Tests

Group $i - j$	Difference	Std. error	P-value
2 − 1	11.4000	9.653	0.574592
3 − 1	37.6000	9.653	0.001750
3 − 2	26.2000	9.653	0.033909

At the $\alpha = 0.05$ level we see that Group 3 (the high-jump group) differs from the other two. The other two groups (the control group and the low-jump group) are not significantly different. It appears that the mean density after 8 weeks is different (higher) for the high-jump group than for the other two.

14.67 **(a)** Plots show no serious departures from Normality, so the Normality assumption is reasonable.

(b)

Bonferroni Tests

Group $i - j$	Difference	Std. error	P-value
2 − 1	0.120000	0.3751	0.985534
3 − 1	2.62250	0.3751	0.000192
3 − 2	2.50250	0.3751	0.000274

At the $\alpha = 0.05$ level we see that Group 3 (the iron pots) differs from the other two. The other two groups (the aluminum and clay pots) are not significantly different. It appears that the mean iron content of *yesiga wet'* when it is cooked in iron pots is different (higher) than when it is cooked in the other two.

14.69 **(a)** Plots show no serious departures from Normality (but note the granularity of the Normal probability plot. It appears that values are rounded to the nearest 5%), so the Normality assumption is not unreasonable.

(b)

Group $i - j$	Bonferroni Tests Difference	Std. error	P-value
ECM2 − ECM1	−1.66667	3.600	1.00000
ECM3 − ECM1	8.33333	3.600	0.450687
ECM3 − ECM2	10.0000	3.600	0.223577
MAT1 − ECM1	−41.6667	3.600	0.000001
MAT1 − ECM2	−40.0000	3.600	0.000002
MAT1 − ECM3	−50.0000	3.600	0.000000
MAT2 − ECM1	−58.3333	3.600	0.000000
MAT2 − ECM2	−56.6667	3.600	0.000000
MAT2 − ECM3	−66.6667	3.600	0.000000
MAT2 − MAT1	−16.6667	3.600	0.008680
MAT3 − ECM1	−53.3333	3.600	0.000000
MAT3 − ECM2	−51.6667	3.600	0.000000
MAT3 − ECM3	−61.6667	3.600	0.000000
MAT3 − MAT1	−11.6667	3.600	0.101119
MAT3 − MAT2	5.00000	3.600	0.957728

At the $\alpha = 0.05$ level we see that none of the ECMs differ from each other, that all the ECMs differ from all the other types of materials (the MATs), and that MAT1 and MAT2 differ from each other. The most striking differences are those between the ECMs and the other materials.

14.71 **(a)**

Group	Sample size	Mean	Std. dev.
Lemon	6	47.1667	6.79461
White	6	15.6667	3.32666
Green	6	31.5000	9.91464
Blue	6	14.8333	5.34478

(b) The hypotheses are H_0: $\mu_1 = \mu_2 = \mu_3 = \mu_4$, H_a: not all of the μ_i are equal. ANOVA tests whether the mean number of insects trapped by the different colors are the same or if they differ. If they differ, ANOVA does not tell us which ones differ.

(c)

Source	Degrees of freedom	Sum of squares	Mean square	F	P-value
Groups	3	4218.46	1406.15	30.552	≤ 0.0001
Error	20	920.500	46.0250		
Total	23	5138.96			

$s_p = 6.78$. We conclude that there is strong evidence of a difference in the mean number of insects trapped by the different colors.

14.73 **(a)**

Source	Degrees of freedom	Sum of squares	Mean square	F
Groups	3	104,855.87	34,951.96	15.86
Error	32	70,500.59	2,203.14	
Total	35	175,356.46	5,010.18	

(b) H_0: $\mu_1 = \mu_2 = \mu_3 = \mu_4$, H_a: not all of the μ_i are equal. **(c)** The F statistic has the $F(3, 32)$ distribution. The P-value is smaller than 0.001. **(d)** $s_p^2 = 2{,}203.14$, $s_p = 46.94$.

14.75 **(a)** $s_p^2 = 3.90$. This quantity corresponds to MSE in the ANOVA table. **(b)**

Source	Degrees of freedom	Sum of squares	Mean square	F
Groups	2	17.22	8.61	2.21
Error	206	803.4	3.90	
Total	208	175,356.46	5010.18	

(c) H_0: $\mu_1 = \mu_2 = \mu_3$, H_a: not all of the μ_i are equal. **(d)** The F statistic has the $F(2, 206)$ distribution. The P-value is greater than 0.100. We conclude that these data do not provide evidence that the mean weight gains of pregnant women in these three countries differ.

14.77 **(a)** A contrast is $\psi_1 = (0.5)\mu_1 + (0.5)\mu_2 - \mu_3$. **(b)** A contrast is $\psi_2 = \mu_1 - \mu_2$.

14.79 **(a)** For the contrast $\psi_1 = (0.5)\mu_1 + (0.5)\mu_2 - \mu_3$, it would be reasonable to test the hypotheses H_0: $\psi_1 = 0$, H_a: $\psi_1 > 0$. For the contrast $\psi_2 = \mu_1 - \mu_2$, it would be reasonable to test the hypotheses H_0: $\psi_2 = 0$, H_a: $\psi_2 \neq 0$. **(b)** Estimate of ψ_1: $c_1 = 49$. Estimate of ψ_2: $c_2 = -10$. **(c)** $SE_{c_1} = 6.32$, $SE_{c_2} = 7.29$. **(d)** The test statistic for H_0: $\psi_1 = 0$, H_a: $\psi_1 > 0$, is $t = 7.75$. P-value < 0.005. We conclude that there is strong evidence that the average of the mean SAT mathematics scores for computer science and engineering and other sciences majors is larger than the mean SAT mathematics scores for all other majors.

For H_0: $\psi_2 = 0$, H_a: $\psi_2 \neq 0$, the test statistic is $t = 1.37$. $0.10 <$ P-value < 0.20. We conclude that there is not strong evidence that the average of the mean SAT mathematics scores for computer science majors differs from that for engineering and other science majors. **(e)** A 95% confidence interval for ψ_1 is $49 \pm 12.54 = (36.46,\ 61.54)$. A 95% confidence interval for ψ_2 is $-10 \pm 14.46 = (-24.46,\ 4.46)$.

14.81 **(a)** Question 1. Contrast: $\psi_1 = \mu_1 - \mu_2$. Hypotheses: H_0: $\psi_1 = 0$, H_a: $\psi_1 > 0$. Question 2. Contrast: $\psi_2 = \mu_1 - (0.5)\mu_2 - (0.5)\mu_4$. Hypotheses: H_0: $\psi_2 = 0$, H_a: $\psi_2 > 0$. Question 3. Contrast: $\psi_3 = \mu_3 - (1/3)\mu_1 - (1/3)\mu_2 - (1/3)\mu_4$. Hypotheses: H_0: $\psi_3 = 0$, H_a: $\psi_3 > 0$. **(b)** Question 1: P-value > 0.25. We do not have evidence that T is better than C. Question 2: $0.10 <$ P-value < 0.15. There is at best weak evidence that T is better than the average of C and S. Question 3: P-value < 0.005. There is strong evidence that J is better than the average of the other three groups. **(c)** This is an observational study. Males were not assigned at random to treatments. Thus, although the researchers tried to match those in the groups with respect to age and other characteristics, there are reasons why people choose to jog or choose to be sedentary that may affect other aspects of their health. It is always risky to draw conclusions of causality from a single (small) observational study, no matter how well designed it is in other respects.

14.83 For each pair of means we get the following: Group 1 (T) vs. Group 2 (C): $t_{12} = -0.66$. $|-.66|$ is not larger than $t^{**} = 2.81$, so we do not have strong evidence that T and C differ. Group 1 (T) vs. Group 3 (J): $t_{13} = -3.65$. $|-3.65|$ is larger than $t^{**} = 2.81$, so we have strong evidence that T and J differ.

Group 1 (T) vs. Group 4 (S): $t_{14} = 3.14$. $|3.14|$ is larger than $t^{**} = 2.81$, so we have strong evidence that T and S differ. Group 2 (C) vs. Group 3 (J): $t_{23} = -2.29$. $|-2.29|$ is not larger than $t^{**} = 2.81$, so we do not have strong evidence that C and J differ. Group 2 (C) vs. Group 4 (S): $t_{24} = 3.22$. $|3.22|$ is larger than $t^{**} = 2.81$, so we have strong evidence that C and S differ. Group 3 (J) vs. Group 4 (S): $t_{34} = 6.86$. $|6.86|$ is larger than $t^{**} = 2.81$, so we have strong evidence that J and S differ.

14.85

n	DFG	DFE	F^*	λ	Power
50	2	147	3.0576	2.78	0.2950
100	2	297	3.0261	5.56	0.5453
150	2	447	3.0158	8.34	0.7336
175	2	522	3.0130	9.73	0.8017
200	2	597	3.0108	11.12	0.8548

A sample size of 175 gives reasonable power. The gain in power by using 200 women per group may not be worthwhile unless it is easy to get women for the study. If it is difficult or expensive to include more women in the study, one might consider a sample size of 150 per group.

14.87 **(a)**

Group	Sample size	Mean	Std. dev.	Std. error
0	2	76.1016	2.39753	1.695
1	2	65.5547	3.32561	2.352
3	2	34.0547	1.20429	0.852
5	2	19.3984	1.69043	1.195
7	2	13	0.419845	0.297

(b) The sample sizes would be the same in both tables. The means, standard deviations, and standard errors above could have been obtained from those in Exercise 14.44 by dividing each by 64 and multiplying the result by 100. Means, standard deviations, and standard errors change the same way as individual values do. **(c)** The ANOVA table is

Source	Degrees of freedom	Sum of squares	Mean square	F	P-value
Groups	4	6263.97	1565.99	367.74	≤ 0.0001
Error	5	21.2920	4.25840		
Total	9	6285.26			

We conclude that there is strong evidence that the group means differ, that is, that the mean % vitamin C content is not the same for all conditions. The degrees of freedom, the F statistic, and P-value are all the same as in Exercise 14.44.

14.89 **(a)** The ANOVA table with the incorrect observation is

Source	Degrees of freedom	Sum of squares	Mean Square	F	P-value
Groups	3	40,820.3	13,606.8	2.0032	0.1460
Error	20	135,853	6,792.65		
Total	23	176,673			

The P-value is larger than 0.10, so we would conclude that we do not have strong evidence that the mean number of insects that will be trapped differs between the different-colored traps. **(b)** The results are very different. In Exercise 14.61, P-value ≤ 0.0001, and we concluded that there was strong evidence that the mean number of insects that will be trapped differs between the different-colored traps. The outlier increased the sum of squares of error considerably, and this results in a much smaller value of F.

(c)

Group	Count	Mean	Std. dev.
Lemon yellow	6	114.667	164.416
White	6	15.6667	3.32666
Green	6	31.5000	9.91464
Blue	6	14.8333	5.34478

The unusually large values of the mean and standard deviation might indicate that there was an error in the data recorded for the lemon yellow trap.

14.91 **(a)** The pattern in the scatterplot is a roughly linear, decreasing trend. **(b)** The test in regression that tests the null hypothesis that the explanatory variable has no linear relationship with the response variable is the t test of whether or not the slope is 0. **(c)** Using software we obtain the following:

Variable	Coefficient	Std. error of coeff.	t ratio	P-value
Constant	4.36453	0.0401	109	≤ 0.0001
Number of promotions	−0.116475	0.0087	−13.3	≤ 0.0001

The t statistic for testing whether the slope is 0 is −133, and we see that P-value is ≤ 0.0001. Thus, there is strong evidence that the slope is not 0. The ANOVA in Exercise 14.49 showed that there is strong evidence that the mean expected price is different for the different numbers of promotions. This is consistent with our regression results here, because if the slope is different from 0, the mean expected price is changing as the number of promotions changes.

In this example the regression is more informative. It not only tells us that the means differ but also gives us information about how they differ.

INDEX